Skills in
Mathematics for
JEE Main &
Advanced

Integral Calculus

Skills in
Mathematics for
**JEE Main &
Advanced**

Integral Calculus

With Sessionwise Theory & Exercises...

Amit M. Agarwal

ARIHANT PRAKASHAN (Series), MEERUT

ARIHANT PRAKASHAN (Series), MEERUT

卐 Administrative & Production Offices

Regd. Office

'Ramchhaya' 4577/15, Agarwal Road, Darya Ganj, New Delhi -110002
Tele: 011- 47630600, 43518550

卐 Head Office

Kalindi, TP Nagar, Meerut (UP) - 250002 Tel: 0121-7156203, 7156204

卐 Sales & Support Offices

Agra, Ahmedabad, Bengaluru, Bareilly, Chennai, Delhi, Guwahati, Hyderabad, Jaipur, Jhansi, Kolkata, Lucknow, Nagpur & Pune.

卐 ISBN : 978-93-26191-63-0

卐 PRICE : ₹275.00

PO No. : TXT-59-T045726-3-22

Published by Arihant Publications (India) Ltd.

For further information about the books published by Arihant, log on to www.arihantbooks.com or e-mail at info@arihantbooks.com

Follow us on   

PREFACE

"YOU CAN DO ANYTHING IF YOU SET YOUR MIND TO IT, I TEACH CALCULUS TO JEE ASPIRANTS BUT BELIEVE THE MOST IMPORTANT FORMULA IS COURAGE + DREAMS = SUCCESS*"*

It is a matter of great pride and honour for me to have received such an overwhelming response to the previous editions of this book from the readers. In a way, this has inspired me to revise this book thoroughly as per the changed pattern of JEE Main & Advanced. I have tried to make the contents more relevant as per the needs of students, many topics have been re-written, a lot of new problems of new types have been added in etcetc. All possible efforts are made to remove all the printing errors that had crept in previous editions. The book is now in such a shape that the students would feel at ease while going through the problems, which will in turn clear their concepts too.

A Summary of changes that have been made in Revised & Enlarged Edition

- Theory has been completely updated so as to accommodate all the changes made in JEE Syllabus & Pattern in recent years.
- The most important point about this new edition is, now the whole text matter of each chapter has been divided into small sessions with exercise in each session. In this way the reader will be able to go through the whole chapter in a systematic way.
- Just after completion of theory, Solved Examples of all JEE types have been given, providing the students a complete understanding of all the formats of JEE questions & the level of difficulty of questions generally asked in JEE.
- Along with exercises given with each session, a complete cumulative exercises have been given at the end of each chapter so as to give the students complete practice for JEE along with the assessment of knowledge that they have gained with the study of the chapter.
- Previous Years questions asked in JEE Main & Adv, IIT-JEE & AIEEE have been covered in all the chapters.

However I have made the best efforts and put my all calculus teaching experience in revising this book. Still I am looking forward to get the valuable suggestions and criticism from my own fraternity i.e. the fraternity of JEE teachers.

I would also like to motivate the students to send their suggestions or the changes that they want to be incorporated in this book.

All the suggestions given by you all will be kept in prime focus at the time of next revision of the book.

Amit M. Agarwal

CONTENTS

SYLLABUS

JEE MAIN

Integral Calculus

Integral as an anti - derivative. Fundamental integrals involving algebraic, trigonometric, exponential and logarithmic functions. Integration by substitution, by parts and by partial fractions. Integration using trigonometric identities.

Evaluation of simple integrals of the type

$$\int \frac{dx}{x^2 \pm a^2}, \quad \int \frac{dx}{\sqrt{x^2 \pm a^2}}, \quad \int \frac{dx}{a^2 - x^2}, \quad \int \frac{dx}{\sqrt{a^2 - x^2}},$$

$$\int \frac{dx}{ax^2 + bx + c}, \quad \int \frac{dx}{\sqrt{ax^2 + bx + c}}, \quad \int \frac{(px + q)\,dx}{ax^2 + bx + c},$$

$$\int \frac{(px + q)\,dx}{\sqrt{ax^2 + bx + c}}, \quad \int \sqrt{a^2 \pm x^2}\,dx \quad \text{and} \quad \int \sqrt{x^2 - a^2}\,dx$$

Integral as limit of a sum. Fundamental Theorem of Calculus. Properties of definite integrals. Evaluation of definite integrals, determining areas of the regions bounded by simple curves in standard form.

Differential Equations

Ordinary differential equations, their order and degree. Formation of differential equations. Solution of differential equations by the method of separation of variables, solution of homogeneous and linear differential equations of the type $\frac{dy}{dx} + p(x)y = q(x)$

JEE ADVANCED

Integral Calculus

Integration as the inverse process of differentiation, indefinite integrals of standard functions, definite integrals as the limit of sums, definite integral and their properties, fundamental theorem of integral calculus.

Integration by parts, integration by the methods of substitution and partial fractions, application of definite integrals to the determination of areas bounded by simple curves. Formation of ordinary differential equations, solution of homogeneous differential equations of first order and first degree, separation of variables method, linear first order differential equations.

CHAPTER

01

Indefinite Integral

Learning Part

Session 1

- Fundamental of Indefinite Integral

Session 2

- Methods of Integration

Session 3

- Some Special Integrals

Session 4

- Integration by Parts

Session 5

- Integration Using Partial Fractions

Session 6

- Indirect and Derived Substitutions

Session 7

- Euler's Substitution, Reduction Formula and Integration Using Differentiation

Practice Part

- JEE Type Examples
- Chapter Exercises

Arihant on Your Mobile !

Exercises with the symbol can be practised on your mobile. See inside cover page to activate for free.

It was in this aspect that the process of integration was treated by Leibnitz, the symbol of $\int$ being regarded as the initial letter of the word sum, in the same way as the symbol of differentiation d is the initial letter in the word difference.

Definition

If f and g are functions of x such that $g'(x) = f(x)$, then the function g is called a anti-derivative (or primitive function or simply integral) of f w.r.t. x. It is written symbolically, $\int f(x)\,dx = g(x)$, where, $\frac{d}{dx} g(x) = f(x)$

Remarks

1. In other words, $\int f(x)\,dx = g(x)$ iff $g'(x) = f(x)$
2. $\int f(x)\,dx = g(x) + c$, where c is constant, $[\because (g(x) + C)' = g'(x) = f(x)]$ and C is called constant of integration.

Example 1 If $\frac{d}{dx}[x^{n+1} + c] = (n+1)\,x^n$, then find $\int x^n\,dx$.

Sol. As, $\frac{d}{dx}[x^{n+1} + C] = (n+1)\,x^n$

$\Rightarrow$ $(x^{n+1} + C)$ is anti-derivative or integral of $(n+1)\,x^n$.

$$\therefore \quad \int x^n\,dx = \frac{x^{n+1}}{n+1} + C$$

Example 2 If $\frac{d}{dx}(\sin x + c) = \cos x$, then find $\int \cos x\,dx$.

Sol. As, $\frac{d}{dx}(\sin x + C) = \cos x$

$\Rightarrow$ $\sin x + C$ is anti-derivative or integral of $\cos x$.

$$\therefore \quad \int \cos x\,dx = (\sin x) + C$$

Session 1

Fundamental of Indefinite Integral

Fundamental of Indefinite Integral

Since, $\quad \frac{d}{dx}\{g(x)\} = f(x)$

$\Leftrightarrow \quad \int f(x)\,dx = g(x) + C$

Therefore, based upon this definition and various standard differentiation formulas, we obtain the following integration formulae

(i) $\frac{d}{dx}\left(\frac{x^{n+1}}{n+1}\right) = x^n, n \neq -1 \Rightarrow \int x^n\,dx = \frac{x^{n+1}}{n+1} + C, n \neq -1$

(ii) $\frac{d}{dx}(\log|x|) = \frac{1}{x} \Rightarrow \int \frac{1}{x}\,dx = \log|x| + C$, when $x \neq 0$

(iii) $\frac{d}{dx}(e^x) = e^x \Rightarrow \int e^x\,dx = e^x + C$

(iv) $\frac{d}{dx}\left(\frac{a^x}{\log_e a}\right) = a^x, a > 0, a \neq 1$

$\Rightarrow \int a^x\,dx = \frac{a^x}{\log_e a} + C$

(v) $\frac{d}{dx}(-\cos x) = \sin x \Rightarrow \int \sin x\,dx = -\cos x + C$

(vi) $\frac{d}{dx}(\sin x) = \cos x \Rightarrow \int \cos x\,dx = \sin x + C$

(vii) $\frac{d}{dx}(\tan x) = \sec^2 x \Rightarrow \int \sec^2 x\,dx = \tan x + C$

(viii) $\frac{d}{dx}(-\cot x) = \operatorname{cosec}^2 x \Rightarrow \int \operatorname{cosec}^2 x\,dx = -\cot x + C$

(ix) $\frac{d}{dx}(\sec x) = \sec x \tan x$

$\Rightarrow \int \sec x \tan x\,dx = \sec x + C$

(x) $\frac{d}{dx}(-\operatorname{cosec} x) = \operatorname{cosec} x \cot x$

$\Rightarrow \int \operatorname{cosec} x \cot x\,dx = -\operatorname{cosec} x + C$

(xi) $\frac{d}{dx}(\log|\sin x|) = \cot x$

$\Rightarrow \int \cot x\,dx = \log|\sin x| + C$

(xii) $\frac{d}{dx}(-\log|\cos x|) = \tan x$

$\Rightarrow \int \tan x \, dx = -\log|\cos x| + C$

(xiii) $\frac{d}{dx}(\log|\sec x + \tan x|) = \sec x$

$\Rightarrow \int \sec x \, dx = \log|\sec x + \tan x| + C$

(xiv) $\frac{d}{dx}(\log|\operatorname{cosec} x - \cot x|) = \operatorname{cosec} x$

$\Rightarrow \int \operatorname{cosec} x \, dx = \log|\operatorname{cosec} x - \cot x| + C$

(xv) $\frac{d}{dx}\left(\sin^{-1}\frac{x}{a}\right) = \frac{1}{\sqrt{a^2 - x^2}}$

$\Rightarrow \int \frac{dx}{\sqrt{a^2 - x^2}} = \sin^{-1}\left(\frac{x}{a}\right) + C$

(xvi) $\frac{d}{dx}\left(\cos^{-1}\frac{x}{a}\right) = \frac{-1}{\sqrt{a^2 - x^2}}$

$\Rightarrow \int \frac{-1}{\sqrt{a^2 - x^2}} dx = \cos^{-1}\left(\frac{x}{a}\right) + C$

(xvii) $\frac{d}{dx}\left(\frac{1}{a}\tan^{-1}\frac{x}{a}\right) = \frac{1}{a^2 + x^2}$

$\Rightarrow \int \frac{dx}{a^2 + x^2} = \frac{1}{a}\tan^{-1}\left(\frac{x}{a}\right) + C$

(xviii) $\frac{d}{dx}\left(\frac{1}{a}\cot^{-1}\frac{x}{a}\right) = \frac{-1}{a^2 + x^2}$

$\Rightarrow \int \frac{-1}{a^2 + x^2} dx = \frac{1}{a}\cot^{-1}\left(\frac{x}{a}\right) + C$

(xix) $\frac{d}{dx}\left(\frac{1}{a}\sec^{-1}\frac{x}{a}\right) = \frac{1}{x\sqrt{x^2 - a^2}}$

$\Rightarrow \int \frac{dx}{x\sqrt{x^2 - a^2}} = \frac{1}{a}\sec^{-1}\left(\frac{x}{a}\right) + C$

(xx) $\frac{d}{dx}\left(\frac{1}{a}\operatorname{cosec}^{-1}\frac{x}{a}\right) = \frac{-1}{x\sqrt{x^2 - a^2}}$

$\Rightarrow \int \frac{-dx}{x\sqrt{x^2 - a^2}} = \frac{1}{a}\operatorname{cosec}^{-1}\left(\frac{x}{a}\right) + C$

| Example 3 Evaluate

(i) $\int \frac{x^2 + 5x - 1}{\sqrt{x}} dx$ (ii) $\int (x^2 + 5)^3 dx$

Sol. (i) $I = \int \frac{x^2 + 5x - 1}{\sqrt{x}} dx = \int \left(\frac{x^2}{x^{1/2}} + \frac{5x^1}{x^{1/2}} - \frac{1}{x^{1/2}}\right) dx$

$= \int (x^{3/2} + 5x^{1/2} - x^{-1/2}) \, dx$

$\left[\text{using } \int x^n \, dx = \frac{x^{n+1}}{n+1} + C\right]$

$= \frac{x^{3/2+1}}{3/2+1} + \frac{5x^{1/2+1}}{1/2+1} - \frac{x^{-1/2+1}}{-1/2+1} + C$

$\Rightarrow I = \frac{2}{5}x^{5/2} + \frac{2}{3}\cdot 5x^{3/2} - 2x^{1/2} + C$

(ii) $I = \int (x^2 + 5)^3 \, dx$ [using $(a+b)^3 = a^3 + 3a^2b + 3ab^2 + b^3$]

$I = \int (x^6 + 15x^4 + 75x^2 + 125) \, dx$

$I = \frac{x^7}{7} + \frac{15x^5}{5} + \frac{75x^3}{3} + 125x + C$

$I = \frac{x^7}{7} + 3x^5 + 25x^3 + 125x + C$

| Example 4 Evaluate

(i) $\int \tan^2 x \, dx$ (ii) $\int \frac{dx}{\sin^2 x \cos^2 x}$

(iii) $\int \frac{\sin^6 x + \cos^6 x}{\sin^2 x \cos^2 x} dx$ (iv) $\int \frac{\cos x - \cos 2x}{1 - \cos x} dx$

Sol. (i) $I = \int \tan^2 x \, dx \Rightarrow I = \int (\sec^2 x - 1) \, dx$

$I = \int \sec^2 x \, dx - \int 1 \, dx$ [using $\int \sec^2 x dx = \tan x + C$]

$\Rightarrow I = \tan x - x + C$

(ii) $I = \int \frac{1}{\sin^2 x \cos^2 x} dx$

$I = \int \frac{\sin^2 x + \cos^2 x}{\sin^2 x \cos^2 x} dx$ [Using $\sin^2 x + \cos^2 x = 1$]

$I = \int \frac{\sin^2 x}{\sin^2 x \cos^2 x} dx + \int \frac{\cos^2 x}{\sin^2 x \cos^2 x} dx$

$I = \int \sec^2 x \, dx + \int \operatorname{cosec}^2 x \, dx$

$I = \tan x - \cot x + C$

(iii) $I = \int \frac{\sin^6 x + \cos^6 x}{\sin^2 x \cos^2 x} dx$

$I = \int \frac{(\sin^2 x)^3 + (\cos^2 x)^3}{\sin^2 x \cos^2 x} dx$

[using $(a+b)^3 = a^3 + b^3 + 3ab(a+b)$]

$I = \int \frac{(\sin^2 x + \cos^2 x)^3 - 3\sin^2 x \cos^2 x(\sin^2 x + \cos^2 x)}{\sin^2 x \cos^2 x} dx$

$I = \int \frac{1 - 3\sin^2 x \cos^2 x}{\sin^2 x \cos^2 x} dx$

$$I=\int\frac{1}{\sin^2 x\cos^2 x}dx-\int 3\,dx$$

$$I=\int\frac{(\sin^2 x+\cos^2 x)}{\sin^2 x\cos^2 x}dx-3x+C$$

$$I=\int\sec^2 x\,dx+\int\operatorname{cosec}^2 x\,dx-3x+C$$

$$I=\tan x-\cot x-3x+C$$

(iv) $I=\int\frac{\cos x-\cos 2x}{1-\cos x}dx$ [using $\cos 2x=2\cos^2 x-1$.]

$$I=\int\frac{\cos x-(2\cos^2 x-1)}{1-\cos x}dx$$

$$=\int\frac{-2\cos^2 x+\cos x+1}{1-\cos x}dx$$

$$\Rightarrow I=\int\frac{-(2\cos x+1)(\cos x-1)}{-(\cos x-1)}dx$$

[as $-2\cos^2 x+\cos x-1=-(2\cos x+1)\cdot(\cos x-1)$]

$$\Rightarrow\quad I=\int(2\cos x+1)\,dx$$

$$\therefore\quad I=2\sin x+x+C$$

Remark

In rational algebraic functions if the degree of numerator is greater than or equal to degree of denominator, then always divide the numerator by denominator and use the result of integration.

| Example 5 Evaluate

(i) $\int\frac{x^3}{x+2}dx$ (ii) $\int\frac{x^2}{x^2+5}dx$

Sol. (i) $I=\int\frac{x^3}{x+2}dx=\int\frac{x^3+8-8}{x+2}dx$

$$I=\int\left(\frac{(x^3+2^3)}{x+2}-\frac{8}{x+2}\right)dx$$

$$\Rightarrow\quad I=\int\left(\frac{(x+2)(x^2-2x+4)}{x+2}-\frac{8}{x+2}\right)dx$$

$$I=\int\left(x^2-2x+4-\frac{8}{x+2}\right)dx$$

$$\therefore\quad I=\frac{x^3}{3}-x^2+4x-8\log|x+2|+C$$

(ii) $I=\int\frac{x^2}{x^2+5}dx=\int\frac{x^2+5-5}{x^2+5}dx=\int\left(\frac{x^2+5}{x^2+5}-\frac{5}{x^2+5}\right)dx$

$$I=\int\left(1-\frac{5}{x^2+5}\right)dx=x-5\int\frac{dx}{x^2+(\sqrt{5})^2}$$

$$I=x-\frac{5}{\sqrt{5}}\tan^{-1}\left(\frac{x}{\sqrt{5}}\right)+C$$

$$I=x-\sqrt{5}\tan^{-1}\left(\frac{x}{\sqrt{5}}\right)+C$$

| Example 6 Evaluate

(i) $\int 5^{\log_e x}dx$ (ii) $\int 2^{\log_4 x}dx$

Sol. (i) $I=\int 5^{\log_e x}dx=\int x^{\log_e 5}dx$ [Using $a^{\log_c b}=b^{\log_c a}$]

$$=\frac{x^{\log_e 5+1}}{(\log_e 5+1)}+C$$

$$\therefore\quad\int 5^{\log_e x}dx=\frac{x^{\log_e 5+1}}{\log_e 5+1}+C$$

(ii) $I=\int 2^{\log_4 x}dx=\int 2^{\log_{2^2} x}dx=\int 2^{1/2\log_2 x}dx$

$\left[\text{using }\log_{b^n}x=\frac{1}{n}\log_b x\right]$

$$=\int 2^{\log_2\sqrt{x}}dx=\int\sqrt{x}\,dx$$ [using $a^{\log_a b}=b$]

$$=\frac{x^{3/2}}{3/2}+C$$

$$\therefore\quad\int 2^{\log_4 x}dx=\frac{2}{3}x^{3/2}+C$$

| Example 7 Evaluate $\int\frac{(\sqrt{x}+1)(x^2-\sqrt{x})}{x\sqrt{x}+x+\sqrt{x}}dx$.

Sol. Here, $I=\int\frac{(\sqrt{x}+1)\cdot\sqrt{x}(x^{3/2}-1)}{\sqrt{x}(x+\sqrt{x}+1)}dx$

$$\therefore\quad I=\int\frac{(\sqrt{x}+1)[(\sqrt{x})^3-1^3]}{(x+\sqrt{x}+1)}dx$$

$$=\int\frac{(\sqrt{x}+1)(\sqrt{x}-1)(x+\sqrt{x}+1)}{(x+\sqrt{x}+1)}dx$$

[Using, $a^3-b^3=(a-b)(a^2+ab+b^2)$]

$$=\int(x-1)\,dx=\frac{x^2}{2}-x+C$$

| Example 8 Evaluate

(i) $\int\frac{1+2x^2}{x^2(1+x^2)}dx$ (ii) $\int\frac{x^6-1}{(x^2+1)}dx$

Sol. (i) Here, $I=\int\frac{1+2x^2}{x^2(1+x^2)}dx=\int\frac{1+x^2+x^2}{x^2(1+x^2)}dx$

$$=\int\frac{1+x^2}{x^2(1+x^2)}dx+\int\frac{x^2}{x^2(1+x^2)}dx$$

$$=\int\frac{1}{x^2}dx+\int\frac{1}{1+x^2}dx=-\frac{1}{x}+\tan^{-1}x+C$$

(ii) Here, $I=\int\frac{x^6-1}{x^2+1}dx=\int\frac{x^6+1-2}{x^2+1}dx$

$$=\int\frac{(x^2)^3+1^3}{x^2+1}dx-\int\frac{2}{x^2+1}dx$$

$$I = \int \frac{(x^2+1)(x^4-x^2+1)}{(x^2+1)}\,dx - 2\int \frac{dx}{x^2+1}$$

[Using, $a^3+b^3=(a+b)(a^2-ab+b^2)$]

$$= \int (x^4-x^2+1)\,dx - 2\int \frac{1}{x^2+1}\,dx$$

$$= \frac{x^5}{5} - \frac{x^3}{3} + x - 2\tan^{-1}x + C$$

| Example 9 Evaluate

(i) $\displaystyle\int \left(\frac{1-x^{-2}}{x^{1/2}-x^{-1/2}} - \frac{2}{x^{3/2}} + \frac{x^{-2}-x}{x^{1/2}-x^{-1/2}} \right) dx$

(ii) $\displaystyle\int \left(\frac{x^{-6}-64}{4+2x^{-1}+x^{-2}} \cdot \frac{x^2}{4-4x^{-1}+x^{-2}} - \frac{4x^2(2x+1)}{1-2x} \right) dx$

Sol. (i) Here, $I = \displaystyle\int \left(\frac{1-x^{-2}}{x^{1/2}-x^{-1/2}} - \frac{2}{x^{3/2}} + \frac{x^{-2}-x}{x^{1/2}-x^{-1/2}} \right) dx$

$$= \int \left(\frac{(1-x^{-2})+(x^{-2}-x)}{x^{1/2}-x^{-1/2}} - \frac{2}{x^{3/2}} \right) dx$$

$$= \int \left(\frac{1-x}{\sqrt{x}-\frac{1}{\sqrt{x}}} - \frac{2}{x^{3/2}} \right) dx = \int \left(\frac{1-x}{\frac{x-1}{\sqrt{x}}} - \frac{2}{x^{3/2}} \right) dx$$

$$= \int (-\sqrt{x} - 2x^{-3/2})\,dx$$

$$= \left(-\frac{x^{3/2}}{3/2} - 2\cdot\frac{x^{-1/2}}{-1/2} \right) + C = -\frac{2}{3}x^{3/2} + \frac{4}{\sqrt{x}} + C$$

(ii) Here

$$I = \int \left(\frac{x^{-6}-64}{4+2x^{-1}+x^{-2}} \cdot \frac{x^2}{4-4x^{-1}+x^{-2}} - \frac{4x^2(2x+1)}{1-2x} \right) dx$$

$$= \int \left(\frac{\frac{1-64x^6}{x^6}}{\frac{4x^2+2x+1}{x^2}} \cdot \frac{x^2}{\frac{4x^2-4x+1}{x^2}} - \frac{4x^2(2x+1)}{(1-2x)} \right) dx$$

$$= \int \left(\frac{1-(4x^2)^3}{x^6\cdot(4x^2+2x+1)} \cdot \frac{x^6}{(4x^2-4x+1)} - \frac{4x^2(2x+1)}{(1-2x)} \right) dx$$

$$= \int \left(\frac{(1-4x^2)(1+4x^2+16x^4)}{(4x^2+2x+1)(4x^2-4x+1)} - \frac{4x^2(2x+1)}{(1-2x)} \right) dx$$

$$= \int \left(\frac{(1-4x^2)\cdot(4x^2+2x+1)(4x^2-2x+1)}{(4x^2+2x+1)(2x-1)^2} - \frac{4x^2(2x+1)}{(1-2x)} \right) dx$$

[using, $16x^4+4x^2+1 = 16x^4+8x^2+1-4x^2$
$= (4x^2+1)^2-(2x)^2 = (4x^2+1+2x)$]

$$= \int \left(\frac{(1-2x)(1+2x)(4x^2-2x+1)}{(1-2x)^2} - \frac{4x^2(2x+1)}{(1-2x)} \right) dx$$

$$= \int \left(\frac{(1+2x)\cdot(4x^2-2x+1)}{(1-2x)} - \frac{4x^2(2x+1)}{(1-2x)} \right) dx$$

$$= \int \frac{(2x+1)\{4x^2-2x+1-4x^2\}\,dx}{1-2x}$$

$$= \int \frac{(2x+1)(1-2x)}{(1-2x)}\,dx$$

$$= \int (2x+1)\,dx = x^2 + x + C$$

| Example 10 Evaluate

(i) $\displaystyle\int \frac{1}{\sin(x-a)\cos(x-b)}\,dx$

(ii) $\displaystyle\int \frac{1}{\cos(x-a)\cos(x-b)}\,dx$

Sol. (i) $I = \displaystyle\int \frac{1}{\sin(x-a)\cos(x-b)}\,dx$

$$I = \frac{\cos(a-b)}{\cos(a-b)} \int \frac{dx}{\sin(x-a)\cos(x-b)}$$

$$= \frac{1}{\cos(a-b)} \cdot \int \frac{\cos\{(x-b)-(x-a)\}}{\sin(x-a)\cos(x-b)}\,dx$$

$$= \frac{1}{\cos(a-b)} \cdot \int \left\{ \frac{\cos(x-b)\cdot\cos(x-a)}{\sin(x-a)\cos(x-b)} + \frac{\sin(x-b)\cdot\sin(x-a)}{\sin(x-a)\cos(x-b)} \right\} dx$$

$$= \frac{1}{\cos(a-b)} \int \{\cot(x-a) + \tan(x-b)\}\,dx$$

$$= \frac{1}{\cos(a-b)} \{\log|\sin(x-a)| - \log|\cos(x-b)|\} + C$$

$$= \frac{1}{\cos(a-b)} \log_e \left| \frac{\sin(x-a)}{\cos(x-b)} \right| + C$$

(ii) $I = \displaystyle\int \frac{1}{\cos(x-a)\cos(x-b)}\,dx$

$$= \frac{1}{\sin(a-b)} \int \frac{\sin(a-b)}{\cos(x-a)\cos(x-b)}\,dx$$

$$= \frac{1}{\sin(a-b)} \int \frac{\sin\{(x-b)-(x-a)\}}{\cos(x-a)\cos(x-b)}\,dx$$

$$= \frac{1}{\sin(a-b)} \int \left\{ \frac{\sin(x-b)\cos(x-a)}{\cos(x-a)\cos(x-b)} - \frac{\cos(x-b)\sin(x-a)}{\cos(x-a)\cos(x-b)} \right\} dx$$

$$= \frac{1}{\sin(a-b)} \int \{\tan(x-b) - \tan(x-a)\}\,dx$$

$$= \frac{1}{\sin(a-b)} [-\log|\cos(x-b)| + \log|\cos(x-a)|] + C$$

$$= \frac{1}{\sin(a-b)} \left[\log \left| \frac{\cos(x-a)}{\cos(x-b)} \right| \right] + C$$

| Example 11 Evaluate $\int \frac{\sin(x+a)}{\sin(x+b)}dx.$

Sol. Let $I = \int \frac{\sin(x+a)}{\sin(x+b)}dx$. Put $x + b = t \Rightarrow dx = dt$

$$\therefore \quad I = \int \frac{\sin(t-b+a)}{\sin t}dt$$

$$= \int \left\{ \frac{\sin t \cos(a-b)}{\sin t} + \frac{\cos t \sin(a-b)}{\sin t} \right\} dt$$

$$= \cos(a-b)\int 1\,dt + \sin(a-b)\int \cot(t)\,dt$$

$$= t\cos(a-b) + \sin(a-b)\log|\sin t| + C$$

$$= (x+b)\cos(a-b) + \sin(a-b)\log|\sin(x+b)| + C$$

| Example 12

(i) If $f'(x) = \frac{x}{2} + \frac{2}{x}$ and $f(1) = \frac{5}{4}$, then find $f(x)$.

(ii) The gradient of the curve is given by $\frac{dy}{dx} = 2x - \frac{3}{x^2}$.

The curve passes through (1, 2) find its equation.

Sol. (i) Given, $f'(x) = \frac{x}{2} + \frac{2}{x}$,

On integrating both sides w.r.t. x,

we get $\int f'(x)\,dx = \int \left(\frac{x}{2} + \frac{2}{x}\right) dx$

$$\Rightarrow \quad f(x) = \frac{1}{2}\cdot\frac{x^2}{2} + 2\log|x| + c \quad \text{...(i)}$$

Now, as $f(1) = \frac{5}{4}$ (called as initial value problem

i.e. when $x = 1, y = \frac{5}{4}$ or $f(1) = \frac{5}{4}$)

Putting, $x = 1$ in Eq. (i),

$$f(1) = \frac{1}{4} + 2\log|1| + C, \text{ but } f(1) = \frac{5}{4}$$

$$\therefore \quad \frac{5}{4} = \frac{1}{4} + C \Rightarrow C = 1$$

$$\Rightarrow \quad f(x) = \frac{x^2}{4} + 2\log|x| + 1$$

(ii) Given, $\frac{dy}{dx} = 2x - \frac{3}{x^2}$ or $dy = \left(2x - \frac{3}{x^2}\right)dx$,

On integrating both sides w.r.t. x, we get

$$\int dy = \int \left(2x - \frac{3}{x^2}\right)dx$$

$$\Rightarrow \quad y = \frac{2x^2}{2} + \frac{3}{x} + C$$

Since, curve passes through (1, 1).

$$\Rightarrow \quad 1 = 1 + 3 + C \Rightarrow C = -3$$

$$\therefore \quad f(x) = x^2 + \frac{3}{x} - 3$$

Important Points Related to Integration

1. $\int k\,f(x)\,dx = k\int f(x)\,dx$, where k is constant. i.e. the integral of the product of a constant and a function = the constant × integral of the function

2. $\int \{f_1(x) \pm f_2(x) \pm \ldots \pm f_n(x)\}\,dx$
$$= \int f_1(x)\,dx \pm \int f_2(x)\,dx \pm \ldots \pm \int f_n(x)\,dx.$$
i.e. the integral of the sum or difference of a finite number of functions is equal to the sum or difference of the integrals of the various functions.

3. **Geometrical interpretation of constant of integration** By adding C means the graph of function would shift in upward or downward direction along y-axis as C is +ve or − ve respectively.

e.g. $\quad y = \int x\,dx = \frac{x^2}{2} + C$

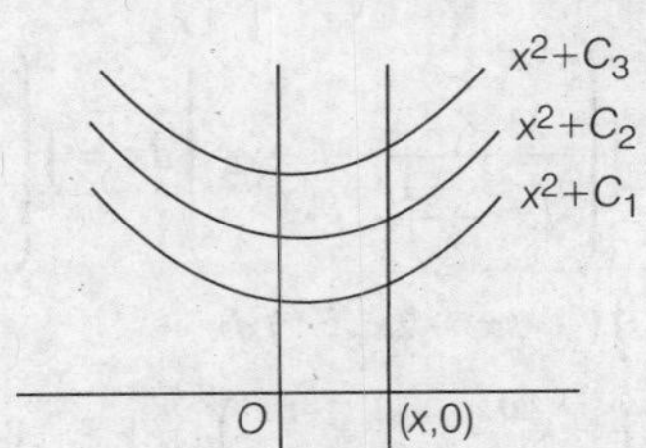

Figure. 1.1

$$\therefore \quad y = \int f(x)\,dx = F(x) + C$$

$$\Rightarrow \quad F'(x) = f(x);\ F'(x_1) = f(x_1)$$

Hence, $y = \int f(x)\,dx$ denotes a family of curves such that the slope of the tangent at $x = x_1$ on every member is same i.e. $F'(x_1) = f(x)$ [when x_1 lies in the domain of $f(x)$]

Hence, anti-derivative of a function is not unique. If $g_1(x)$ and $g_2(x)$ are two anti-derivatives of a function $f(x)$ on $[a, b]$, then they differ only by a constant.

i.e. $\quad g_1(x) - g_2(x) = C$

Anti-derivative of a continuous function is differentiable.

4. If $f(x)$ is continuous, then
$$\int f(x)\,dx = F(x) + C$$
$$\Rightarrow \quad F'(x) = f(x)$$
⇒ always exists and is continuous.
$$\Rightarrow \quad F'(x)$$

5. If integral is discontinuous at $x = x_1$, then its anti-derivative at $x = x_1$ need not be discontinuous.

e.g. $\int x^{-1/3} dx$. Here, $x^{-1/3}$ is discontinuous at $x = 0$. But $\int x^{-1/3} dx = \frac{3}{2} x^{2/3} + C$ is continuous at $x = 0$.

6. Anti-derivative of a periodic function need not be a periodic function. e.g. $f(x) = \cos x + 1$ is periodic but $\int (\cos x + 1)\, dx = \sin x + x + C$ is a periodic.

Daily Life Applications

Function	The Derivative Its derivative function	In symbols	Function	The Integral It's Anti-derivative Function	In symbols
Distance (s)	Velocity (v)	$v = \frac{ds}{dt}$	Velocity	Distance	$s = \int v(t)\, dt$
Velocity (v)	Acceleration (a)	$a = \frac{dv}{dt}$	Acceleration	Velocity	$v = \int a(t)\, dt$
Mass (μ)	Liner Density (ρ)	$\rho = \frac{d\mu}{dx}$	Linear Density	Mass	$\mu = \int \rho(x)\, dx$
Population (P)	Instantaneous growth	$\frac{dP}{dt}$	Instantaneous Growth	Population	$\rho = \int \left(\frac{dP}{dt}\right) dt$
Cost (C)	Marginal cost (MC)	$\text{MC} = \frac{dC}{dq}$	Marginal Cost	Cost	$C(q) = \int \left(\frac{dC}{dq}\right) dq$
Revenue (R)	Marginal Revenue (MR)	$\text{MR} = \frac{dR}{dq}$	Marginal Revenue	Revenue	$R(q) = \int \left(\frac{dR}{dq}\right) dq$

Here, q is quantity of products.

Exercise for Session 1

- **Evaluate the following integration**

1. $\int \frac{dx}{\sqrt{x+1} - \sqrt{x}}$

2. $\int \frac{x^2 + 3}{x^6(x^2 + 1)} dx$

3. $\int \frac{(1+x)^2}{x(1+x^2)} dx$

4. $\int \frac{x^4}{1+x^2} dx$

5. $\int \frac{x^4 + x^2 + 1}{2(1+x^2)} dx$

6. $\int \frac{(x^2 + \sin^2 x)\sec^2 x}{(1+x^2)} dx$

7. $\int \frac{x^2}{(a+bx)^2} dx$

8. $\int 2^x \cdot e^x \cdot dx$

9. $\int \frac{e^{3x} + e^{5x}}{e^x + e^{-x}} dx$

10. $\int (e^{a \log x} + e^{x \log a})\, dx$

11. $\int \frac{1 + \cos 4x}{\cot x - \tan x} dx$

12. $\int \tan x \tan 2x \tan 3x\, dx$

13. $\int \frac{\sin 4x}{\sin x} dx$

14. $\int \cos^3 x\, dx$

15. $\int \sin^3 x \cos^3 x\, dx$

Session 2

Methods of Integration

Methods of Integration

If the integral is not a derivative of a simple function, then the corresponding integrals cannot be found directly. In order to find the integral of complex problems.

e.g. $\int \frac{\sin x}{x} dx, \int \frac{\cos x}{x} dx, \int \frac{1}{\log x} dx$

Some Integrals which Cannot be Found

Any function continuous on an interval (a, b) has an anti-derivative in that interval. In other words, there exists a function $F(x)$ such that $F'(x) = f(x)$.

However, not every anti-derivative $F(x)$, even when it exists, is expressible in closed form in terms of elementary functions such as polynomials, trigonometric, logarithmic, exponential functions etc. Then, we say that such anti-derivatives or integrals "cannot be found".

Some typical examples are

(i) $\int \frac{\sin x}{x} dx$ (ii) $\int \frac{\cos x}{x} dx$

(iii) $\int \frac{1}{\log x} dx$ (iv) $\int \sqrt{1-k^2 \sin^2 x}\, dx$

(v) $\int \sqrt{\sin x}\, dx$ (vi) $\int \sin(x^2)\, dx$

(vii) $\int \cos(x^2)\, dx$ (viii) $\int x \tan x\, dx$

(ix) $\int e^{-x^2} dx$ (x) $\int e^{x^2} dx$

(xi) $\int \frac{x^2}{1+x^5} dx$ (xii) $\int \sqrt[3]{1+x^2}\, dx$

(xiii) $\int \sqrt{1+x^3}\, dx$ etc.

Integration by Substitution

(or by change of the independent variable)

If $g(x)$ is a continuously differentiable function, then to evaluate integrals of the form,

$$I = \int f(g(x)) \cdot g'(x)\, dx,$$

we substitute $g(x) = t$ and $g'(x)\, dx = dt$

The substitution reduces the integral to $\int f(t)\, dt$. After evaluating this integral we substitute back the value of t.

| Example 13 Prove that

$$\int (ax+b)^n dx = \frac{(ax+b)^{n+1}}{(n+1)a} + C, n \neq 1.$$

Sol. Putting, $ax + b = t$, we get

$$a dx = dt \text{ or } dx = \frac{1}{a} dt$$

$$\therefore \quad I = \int (ax+b)^n dx = \int t^n \cdot \frac{dt}{a} = \frac{1}{a} \cdot \frac{t^{n+1}}{n+1} + C$$

$$= \frac{1\,(ax+b)^{n+1} dx}{a(n+1)} + C.$$

Remarks

1. If $\int f(x)\, dx = g(x) + C$, then $\int f(ax+b)\, dx = \frac{1}{a} g(ax+b) + C$

2. If $\int \frac{1}{x} dx = \log|x| + C$, then $\int \frac{1}{ax+b} dx = \frac{1}{a} \log|ax+b| + C$

Thus, in any fundamental integral formulae given in article fundamental integration formulae if in place of x we have $(ax + b)$, then same formula is applicable but we must divide by coefficient of x or derivative of $(ax + b)$ i.e. a.

Here is the list of some of frequently used formulae

(i) $\int (ax+b)^n\, dx = \frac{(ax+b)^{n+1}}{a(n+1)} + C, n \neq -1$

(ii) $\int \frac{1}{ax+b} dx = \frac{1}{a} \log|ax+b| + C$

(iii) $\int e^{ax+b}\, dx = \frac{1}{a} e^{ax+b} + C$

(iv) $\int a^{bx+c}\, dx = \frac{1}{b} \cdot \frac{a^{bx+c}}{\log a} + C$

(v) $\int \sin(ax+b)\, dx = -\frac{1}{a} \cos(ax+b) + C$

(vi) $\int \cos(ax+b)\, dx = \frac{1}{a} \sin(ax+b) + C$

(vii) $\int \sec^2(ax+b)\, dx = \frac{1}{a} \tan(ax+b) + C$

(viii) $\int \text{cosec}^2 (ax+b)\, dx = -\frac{1}{a} \cot (ax+b) + C$

(ix) $\int \sec (ax+b) \tan (ax+b)\, dx = \frac{1}{a} \sec (ax+b) + C$

(x) $\int \text{cosec} (ax+b) \cot (ax+b)\, dx = -\frac{1}{a} \text{cosec} (ax+b) + C$

(xi) $\int \tan (ax+b)\, dx = -\frac{1}{a} \log |\cos (ax+b)| + C$

(xii) $\int \cot (ax+b)\, dx = \frac{1}{a} \log |\sin (ax+b)| + C$

(xiii) $\int \sec (ax+b) dx = \frac{1}{a} \log |\sec (ax+b) + \tan (ax+b)| + C$

(xiv) $\int \text{cosec} (ax+b) dx = \frac{1}{a} \log |\text{cosec} (ax+b) - \cot (ax+b)| + C$

| Example 14 Evaluate

(i) $\int \frac{1}{\sqrt{3x+4} - \sqrt{3x+1}} dx$ (ii) $\int \frac{8x+13}{\sqrt{4x+7}} dx$.

(iii) $\int (7x-2) \sqrt{3x+2}\, dx$. (iv) $\int \frac{2+3x^2}{x^2 (1+x^2)} dx$.

Sol. (i) Here, $I = \int \frac{dx}{\sqrt{3x+4} - \sqrt{3x+1}}$

$$= \int \frac{(\sqrt{3x+4} + \sqrt{3x+1})}{(\sqrt{3x+4} - \sqrt{3x+1})(\sqrt{3x+4} + \sqrt{3x+1})} dx$$

$$= \int \frac{(\sqrt{3x+4} + \sqrt{3x+1})}{(3x+4) - (3x+1)} dx$$

$$= \frac{1}{3} \int \sqrt{3x+4}\, dx + \frac{1}{3} \int \sqrt{3x+1}\, dx$$

$$= \frac{1}{3} \left\{ \frac{(3x+4)^{3/2}}{3/2 \times 3} \right\} + \frac{1}{3} \left\{ \frac{(3x+1)^{3/2}}{3/2 \times 3} \right\} + C$$

Using, $\int (ax+b)^n\, dx = \frac{(ax+b)^{n+1}}{(n+1)\, a} + C$

$$= \frac{2}{27} [(3x+4)^{3/2} + (3x+1)^{3/2}] + C$$

(ii) Here, $I = \int \frac{8x+13}{\sqrt{4x+7}} dx = \int \frac{8x+14-1}{\sqrt{4x+7}} dx$

$$= \int \frac{2(4x+7) - 1}{\sqrt{4x+7}} dx$$

$$= 2 \int \frac{4x+7}{\sqrt{4x+7}} dx - \int \frac{dx}{\sqrt{4x+7}}$$

$$= 2 \int (\sqrt{4x+7}) dx - \int (4x+7)^{-1/2} dx$$

$$= 2 \left(\frac{(4x+7)^{3/2}}{3/2 \times 4} \right) - \left(\frac{(4x+7)^{1/2}}{1/2 \times 4} \right) + C$$

$$= \frac{1}{3} (4x+7)^{3/2} - \frac{1}{2} (4x+7)^{1/2} + C$$

(iii) Here, $I = \int (7x-2) \sqrt{3x+2}\, dx = 7 \int \left(x - \frac{2}{7} \right) \sqrt{3x+2}\, dx$

$$= \frac{7}{3} \int \left(3x - \frac{6}{7} \right) \sqrt{3x+2}\, dx$$

$$= \frac{7}{3} \int \left(3x + 2 - 2 - \frac{6}{7} \right) \sqrt{3x+2}\, dx$$

$$= \frac{7}{3} \int (3x+2) \sqrt{3x+2}\, dx - \frac{20}{3} \int \sqrt{3x+2}\, dx$$

$$= \frac{7}{3} \int (3x+2)^{3/2}\, dx - \frac{20}{3} \int \sqrt{3x+2}\, dx$$

$$= \frac{7}{3} \left(\frac{(3x+2)^{5/2}}{\frac{5}{2} \times 3} \right) - \frac{20}{3} \left(\frac{(3x+2)^{3/2}}{\frac{3}{2} \times 3} \right) + C$$

$$= \frac{14}{45} (3x+2)^{5/2} - \frac{40}{27} (3x+2)^{3/2} + C$$

(iv) Here, $I = \int \frac{(2+3x^2)\, dx}{x^2(1+x^2)} = \int \frac{2+2x^2+x^2}{x^2(1+x^2)} dx$

$$= \int \left(\frac{2(1+x^2)}{x^2(1+x^2)} + \frac{x^2}{x^2(1+x^2)} \right) dx$$

$$= \int \left(\frac{2}{x^2} + \frac{1}{1+x^2} \right) dx = 2 \int x^{-2} dx + \int \frac{1}{1+x^2} dx$$

$$= 2 \cdot \frac{x^{-1}}{-1} + \tan^{-1} x + C = -\frac{2}{x} + \tan^{-1} x + C$$

| Example 15 Evaluate

(i) $\int \frac{\sin (\log x)}{x} dx$ (ii) $\int \left(\frac{3 \sin x + 4 \cos x}{4 \sin x - 3 \cos x} \right) dx$

(iii) $\int \frac{e^{m \tan^{-1} x}}{1+x^2} dx$ (iv) $\int x \sin (4x^2+7)\, dx$

Sol. (i) $I = \int \frac{\sin (\log x)}{x} dx$

We know that, $\frac{d}{dx} (\log x) = \frac{1}{x}$

Thus, let $\log x = t$

$\Rightarrow \quad \frac{1}{x} dx = dt$ ...(i)

$\therefore \quad I = \int \sin (t)\, dt = -\cos (t) + C$

$= -\cos (\log x) + C$ [using Eq. (i)]

(ii) $I = \int \frac{3 \sin x + 4 \cos x}{4 \sin x - 3 \cos x} dx$

We know, $\frac{d}{dx} (4 \sin x - 3 \cos x) = (4 \cos x + 3 \sin x)$

Thus, let $4 \sin x - 3 \cos x = t$ ...(i)

$\Rightarrow \quad (4 \cos x + 3 \sin x)\, dx = dt$

$\therefore \quad I = \int \frac{dt}{t} = \log|t| + C$

$= \log|4\sin x - 3\cos x| + C \quad$ [using Eq. (i)]

(iii) $I = \int \frac{e^{m\tan^{-1}x}}{1+x^2}\,dx$ Let $\quad m\tan^{-1}x = t$

$\Rightarrow \quad \frac{m}{1+x^2}\,dx = dt \Rightarrow \frac{1}{1+x^2}\,dx = \frac{1}{m}\,dt$

$\therefore \quad I = \int e^t \cdot \frac{dt}{m} \Rightarrow I = \frac{1}{m}\int e^t\,dt$

$I = \frac{1}{m}e^t + C = \frac{1}{m}e^{m\tan^{-1}x} + C$

(iv) $I = \int x\sin(4x^2+7)\,dx$

Let $\quad 4x^2+7 = t \Rightarrow 8x\,dx = dt \Rightarrow x\,dx = \frac{1}{8}\,dt$

$\therefore \quad I = \int \sin(t)\frac{dt}{8} = -\frac{1}{8}\cos(t) + C$

$= -\frac{1}{8}\cos(4x^2+7) + C$

Remarks

While solving product of trignometric, it is expedient to use the following trigonometric identities

1. $\sin mx\cos nx = \frac{1}{2}\{\sin(m-n)x + \sin(m+n)x\}$
2. $\cos mx\sin nx = \frac{1}{2}\{\sin(m+n)x - \sin(m-n)x\}$
3. $\sin mx\sin nx = \frac{1}{2}\{\cos(m-n)x - \cos(m+n)x\}$
4. $\cos mx\cos nx = \frac{1}{2}\{\cos(m-n)x + \cos(m+n)x\}$

Example 16 Evaluate

(i) $\int \cos 4x\cos 7x\,dx$ (ii) $\int \cos x\cos 2x\cos 5x\,dx$

Sol. When calculating such integrals it is advisable to use the trigonometric product formulae.

(i) $\int \cos 4x\cos 7x\,dx$

Here, $\cos 4x\cos 7x = \frac{1}{2}(\cos 3x + \cos 11x)$,

[using $\cos mx\cdot\cos nx = \frac{1}{2}\{\cos(m-n)x + \cos(m+n)x\}$]

$\therefore I = \int \cos 4x\cos 7x\,dx = \frac{1}{2}\int(\cos 3x + \cos 11x)\,dx$

$= \frac{1}{2}\int \cos 3x\,dx + \frac{1}{2}\int \cos 11x\,dx$

$= \frac{\sin 3x}{6} + \frac{\sin 11x}{22} + C$

(ii) $\int \cos x\cos 2x\cos 5x\,dx$,

We have $(\cos x\cos 2x)\cos 5x = \frac{1}{2}(\cos x + \cos 3x)\cos 5x$,

[using $\cos mx.\cos nx = \frac{1}{2}\{\cos(m-n)x + \cos(m+n)x\}$]

$= \frac{1}{4}\{2\cos x\cos 5x + 2\cos 3x\cos 5x\}$

$= \frac{1}{4}\{(\cos 4x + \cos 6x) + (\cos 2x + \cos 8x)\}$

$\therefore \cos x\cos 2x\cos 5x = \frac{1}{4}\{\cos 2x + \cos 4x + \cos 6x + \cos 8x\}$

$\therefore \quad I = \int(\cos x\cos 2x\cos 5x)\,dx$

$= \frac{1}{4}\int(\cos 2x + \cos 4x + \cos 6x + \cos 8x)\,dx$

$= \frac{\sin 2x}{8} + \frac{\sin 4x}{16} + \frac{\sin 6x}{24} + \frac{\sin 8x}{32} + C$

Example 17 Evaluate

(i) $\int \sin x\cos x\cdot\cos 2x\cdot\cos 4x\,dx$

(ii) $\int \frac{1-\tan^2 x}{1+\tan^2 x}\,dx$ (iii) $\int \frac{1+\cos^2 x}{1+\cos 2x}\,dx$

(iv) $\int \frac{\cos 2x}{\cos^2 x\sin^2 x}\,dx$ (v) $\int \frac{\sec 2x - 1}{\sec 2x + 1}\,dx$

Sol. (i) Here, $I = \int \sin x\cos x\cdot\cos 2x\cos 4x\,dx$

$= \frac{1}{2}\int 2\sin x\cdot\cos x\cdot\cos 2x\cdot\cos 4x\,dx$

[using, $\sin 2x = 2\sin x\cdot\cos x$]

$= \frac{1}{2\times 2}\int 2\sin 2x\cdot\cos 2x\cdot\cos 4x\cdot dx$

$= \frac{1}{4}\int \sin 4x\cdot\cos 4x\,dx = \frac{1}{2\times 4}\int 2\sin 4x\cos 4x\,dx$

$= \frac{1}{8}\int \sin 8x\,dx = \frac{-\cos 8x}{64} + C$

(ii) Here, $I = \int \frac{1-\tan^2 x}{1+\tan^2 x}\,dx$

$\therefore \quad I = \int \cos 2x\,dx \qquad$ Using, $\cos 2x = \frac{1-\tan^2 x}{1+\tan^2 x}$

$= \frac{\sin 2x}{2} + c$

(iii) Here, $I = \int \frac{1+\cos^2 x}{1+\cos 2x}\,dx$,

$= \int \frac{1+\cos^2 x}{1+2\cos^2 x - 1}\,dx = \int \frac{1+\cos^2 x}{2\cos^2 x}\,dx$

[Using, $\cos 2x = 2\cos^2 x - 1$]

$= \frac{1}{2}\int(\sec^2 x + 1)\,dx = \frac{1}{2}(\tan x + x) + C$

(iv) Here, $I = \int \frac{\cos 2x}{\cos^2 x\cdot\sin^2 x}\,dx$

$I = \int \frac{(\cos^2 x - \sin^2 x)\,dx}{\cos^2 x\cdot\sin^2 x}$

[Using, $\cos 2x = \cos^2 x - \sin^2 x$]

$$= \int \left(\frac{1}{\sin^2 x} - \frac{1}{\cos^2 x} \right) dx$$

$$= \int (\text{cosec}^2 x - \sec^2 x)\, dx = -\cot x - \tan x + C$$

(v) Here, $I = \int \frac{\sec 2x - 1}{\sec 2x + 1} \cdot dx = \int \frac{1 - \cos 2x}{1 + \cos 2x}\, dx,$

We get, $I = \int \frac{2\sin^2 x}{2\cos^2 x}\, dx$

[using, $1 - \cos 2x = 2\sin^2 x$ and $1 + \cos 2x = 2\cos^2 x$]

$$= \int \tan^2 x \cdot dx$$

As, $\tan^2 x = \sec^2 x - 1$

$\therefore \quad I = \int (\sec^2 x - 1)\, dx = \tan x - x + C$

Example 18 Evaluate

$$I = \int \left(\frac{\cot^2 2x - 1}{2\cot 2x} - \cos 8x \cdot \cot 4x \right) dx.$$

Sol. Here, $I = \int \left(\frac{\cot^2 2x - 1}{2\cot 2x} - \cos 8x \cdot \cot 4x \right) dx$

$$I = \int (\cot 4x - \cos 8x \cdot \cot 4x)\, dx$$

$\left[\text{using } \cot 2A = \frac{\cot^2 A - 1}{2\cot A} \right]$

$$= \int \cot 4x (1 - \cos 8x)\, dx$$

[using $1 - \cos 2A = 2\sin^2 A$]

$$= \int \cot 4x \cdot 2\sin^2 (4x)\, dx$$

$$= \int \frac{\cos 4x}{\sin 4x} \cdot 2\sin^2 4x\, dx$$

$$= \int 2\sin 4x \cdot \cos 4x dx,$$

using $\quad \sin 2A = 2\sin A \cos A$

$$= \int \sin 8x\, dx = \frac{-\cos 8x}{8} + C$$

Exercise for Session 2

- Solve the following integration

1. $\int \frac{dx}{1 + \sin x}$

2. $\int \frac{\cos x - \sin x}{\cos x + \sin x} \cdot (2 + 2\sin 2x)\, dx$

3. $\int (3\sin x \cos^2 x - \sin^3 x)\, dx$

4. $\int \cos x^\circ\, dx$

5. $\int \frac{\sin x + \cos x}{\sqrt{1 + \sin 2x}} \cdot dx$, here $(\sin x + \cos x) > 0$

6. $\int \frac{\cos 2x - \cos 2\alpha}{\cos x - \cos \alpha} \cdot dx$

7. $\int \frac{\sin^3 x + \cos^3 x}{\sin^2 x \cdot \cos^2 x}\, dx$

8. $\int \sec^2 x \cdot \text{cosec}^2 x\, dx$

9. $\int \sqrt{1 - \sin 2x}\, dx$

10. $\int \frac{\sin^6 x + \cos^6 x}{\sin^2 x \cdot \cos^2 x}\, dx$

11. $\int \left(\sin^2 \left(\frac{9\pi}{8} + \frac{x}{4} \right) - \sin^2 \left(\frac{7\pi}{8} + \frac{x}{4} \right) \right) dx$

12. $\int \frac{\cos 4x + 1}{\cot x - \tan x}\, dx$

13. $\int \left(\sin \alpha \cdot \sin (x - \alpha) + \sin^2 \left(\frac{x}{2} - \alpha \right) \right) dx$

14. $\int \frac{\sin 2x + \sin 5x - \sin 3x}{\cos x + 1 - 2\sin^2 2x}\, dx$

15. $\int \frac{\cos^4 x + \sin^4 x}{\sqrt{1 + \cos 4x}}\, dx$, here $\cos 2x > 0$

Session 3

Some Special Integrals

Some Special Integrals

(i) $\int \frac{dx}{x^2+a^2} = \frac{1}{a}\tan^{-1}\left(\frac{x}{a}\right)+C$

(ii) $\int \frac{dx}{x^2-a^2} = \frac{1}{2a}\log\left|\frac{x-a}{x+a}\right|+C$

(iii) $\int \frac{dx}{a^2-x^2} = \frac{1}{2a}\log\left|\frac{a+x}{a-x}\right|+C$

(iv) $\int \frac{dx}{\sqrt{a^2-x^2}} = \sin^{-1}\left(\frac{x}{a}\right)+C$

(v) $\int \frac{dx}{\sqrt{a^2+x^2}} = \log|x+\sqrt{x^2+a^2}|+C$

(vi) $\int \frac{dx}{\sqrt{x^2-a^2}} = \log|x+\sqrt{x^2-a^2}|+C$

(vii) $\int \sqrt{a^2-x^2}\,dx = \frac{1}{2}x\sqrt{a^2-x^2}+\frac{1}{2}a^2\sin^{-1}\left(\frac{x}{a}\right)+C$

(viii) $\int \sqrt{a^2+x^2}\,dx$

$= \frac{1}{2}x\sqrt{a^2+x^2}+\frac{1}{2}a^2\log|x+\sqrt{a^2+x^2}|+C$

(ix) $\int \sqrt{x^2-a^2}\,dx$

$= \frac{1}{2}x\sqrt{x^2-a^2}-\frac{1}{2}a^2\log|x+\sqrt{x^2-a^2}|+C$

Some Important Substitutions

Expression	Substitution
a^2+x^2	$x=a\tan\theta$ or $a\cot\theta$
a^2-x^2	$x=a\sin\theta$ or $a\cos\theta$
x^2-a^2	$x=a\sec\theta$ or $a\,\mathrm{cosec}\,\theta$
$\sqrt{\frac{a-x}{a+x}}$ or $\sqrt{\frac{a+x}{a-x}}$	$x=a\cos 2\theta$
$\sqrt{\frac{x-\alpha}{\beta-x}}$ or $\sqrt{(x-\alpha)(x-\beta)}$	$x=\alpha\cos^2\theta+\beta\sin^2\theta$

Application of these Formulae

The above standard integrals are very important. Given below are integrals which are applications of these.

Type I

(i) $\int \frac{dx}{ax^2+bx+c}$ (ii) $\int \frac{dx}{\sqrt{ax^2+bx+c}}$

(iii) $\int \sqrt{ax^2+bx+c}\,dx$

If ax^2+bx+c can be factorised, then the integration is easily done by the method of partial fractions (explained later). If the denominator cannot be factorised, then express it as the sum or difference of two squares by the method of completing the square

$$ax^2+bx+c = a\left(x^2+\frac{b}{a}x+\frac{c}{a}\right) = a\left\{\left(x+\frac{b}{2a}\right)^2+\left(\frac{c}{a}\right)-\frac{b^2}{4a^2}\right\}$$

make the substitution $x+\frac{b}{2a}=t$.

Example 19 Evaluate

(i) $\int \frac{1}{x^2-x+1}dx$ (ii) $\int \frac{1}{2x^2+x-1}dx$

(iii) $\int \frac{1}{\sqrt{x^2-2x+3}}dx$ (iv) $\int \sqrt{2x^2-3x+1}\,dx$

Sol. (i) $I = \int \frac{dx}{x^2-x+1}$,

completing x^2-x+1 into perfect square.

$$= \int \frac{dx}{x^2-x+1/4-1/4+1} = \int \frac{dx}{(x-1/2)^2+3/4}$$

$$\therefore I = \int \frac{dx}{(x-1/2)^2+(\sqrt{3}/2)^2}$$

$$= \frac{1}{\sqrt{3}/2}\tan^{-1}\left(\frac{x-1/2}{\sqrt{3}/2}\right)+C$$

$$\therefore I = \frac{2}{\sqrt{3}}\tan^{-1}\left(\frac{2x-1}{\sqrt{3}}\right)+C$$

$$\left[\text{using } \int \frac{1}{x^2+a^2}dx = \frac{1}{a}\tan^{-1}\left(\frac{x}{a}\right)+C\right]$$

(ii) $I = \int \frac{1}{2x^2+x-1}dx = \frac{1}{2}\int \frac{1}{x^2+x/2-1/2}dx$

$$= \frac{1}{2}\int \frac{1}{x^2+x/2+1/16-1/16-1/2}dx$$

$$= \frac{1}{2}\int \frac{dx}{(x+1/4)^2 - 9/16} = \frac{1}{2}\int \frac{dx}{(x+1/4)^2 - (3/4)^2}$$

$$= \frac{1}{2}\cdot\frac{1}{2(3/4)} \log\left|\frac{x+1/4-3/4}{x+1/4+3/4}\right| + C$$

$$\left[\text{using } \int \frac{dx}{x^2-a^2} = \frac{1}{2a}\log\left|\frac{x-a}{x+a}\right| + C\right]$$

$$= \frac{1}{3}\log\left|\frac{x-1/2}{x+1}\right| + C$$

$$\therefore \quad I = \frac{1}{3}\log\left|\frac{2x-1}{2(x+1)}\right| + C$$

(iii) $I = \int \frac{dx}{\sqrt{x^2-2x+3}} = \int \frac{dx}{\sqrt{x^2-2x+1-1+3}}$

$$= \int \frac{dx}{\sqrt{(x-1)^2 + (\sqrt{2})^2}}$$

$$= \log|(x-1) + \sqrt{(x-1)^2 + (\sqrt{2})^2}|$$

$$\left[\text{using } \int \frac{dx}{\sqrt{x^2+a^2}} = \log|x + \sqrt{x^2+a^2}| + C\right]$$

$$\therefore \quad I = \log|(x-1) + \sqrt{x^2-2x+3}| + C$$

(iv) $I = \int (\sqrt{2x^2-3x+1})\,dx = \sqrt{2}\int(\sqrt{x^2-3x/2+1/2})\,dx$

$$= \sqrt{2}\int(\sqrt{x^2-3x/2+9/16-9/16+1/2})\,dx$$

$$= \sqrt{2}\int(\sqrt{(x-3/4)^2 - 1/16})\,dx$$

$$= \sqrt{2}\left\{\begin{array}{l}\frac{1}{2}(x-3/4)\sqrt{(x-3/4)^2 - 1/16} \\ -\frac{1}{16\times 2}\log|(x-3/4) + \sqrt{(x-3/4)^2 - 1/16}\end{array}\right\} + C$$

$$= \sqrt{2}\left\{\begin{array}{l}\frac{1}{8}(4x-3)\sqrt{x^2-3x/2+1/2} \\ -\frac{1}{32}\log|(x-3/4) + \sqrt{x^2-3x/2+1/2}\end{array}\right\} + C$$

Example 20 Evaluate

(i) $\int \frac{1}{\sqrt{1-e^{2x}}}\,dx$ (ii) $\int \frac{2x}{\sqrt{1-x^2-x^4}}\,dx$

(iii) $\int \frac{a^x}{\sqrt{1-a^{2x}}}\,dx$ (iv) $\int \sqrt{\frac{x}{a^3-x^3}}\,dx$

Sol. (i) Here, $I = \int \frac{dx}{\sqrt{1-e^{2x}}}$

Let, $1 - e^{2x} = t^2$

Then, $-2e^{2x}dx = 2t\,dt$

$$\Rightarrow \quad dx = -\frac{-t\,dt}{e^{2x}},$$

$$dx = \frac{t\,dt}{t^2-1} = \int \frac{1}{\sqrt{t^2}}\cdot\frac{t}{t^2-1}\,dt$$

$$I = \int \frac{dt}{t^2-1} = \frac{1}{2\cdot 1}\log\left|\frac{t-1}{t+1}\right| + C$$

$$= \frac{1}{2}\log\left|\frac{\sqrt{1-e^{2x}}-1}{\sqrt{1-e^{2x}}+1}\right| + C$$

(ii) Here, $I = \int \frac{2x}{\sqrt{1-x^2-x^4}}\,dx$

Let, $x^2 = t, 2x\,dx = dt$

$$\therefore \quad I = \int \frac{dt}{\sqrt{1-t-t^2}} = \int \frac{dt}{\sqrt{1+\frac{1}{4}-\frac{1}{4}-t-t^2}}$$

$$I = \int \frac{dt}{\sqrt{5/4-(t+1/2)^2}} = \int \frac{dt}{\sqrt{(\sqrt{5}/2)^2-(t+1/2)^2}}$$

$$= \sin^{-1}\left(\frac{t+1/2}{\sqrt{5}/2}\right) + C = \sin^{-1}\left(\frac{2x^2+1}{\sqrt{5}}\right) + C$$

(iii) Here, $I = \int \frac{a^x}{\sqrt{1-a^{2x}}}\,dx$. Let, $a^x = t$

$$\therefore \quad a^x \log a\,dx = dt, \; a^x\,dx = \frac{dt}{\log a}$$

$$\therefore \quad I = \int \frac{1}{\sqrt{1-t^2}}\cdot\frac{dt}{\log a} = \frac{1}{\log a}\cdot\sin^{-1}(t) + C$$

$$I = \frac{1}{\log a}\sin^{-1}(a^x) + C$$

(iv) Here, $I = \int \sqrt{\frac{x}{a^3-x^3}}\,dx = \int \frac{x^{1/2}\,dx}{\sqrt{(a^{3/2})^2-(x^{3/2})^2}}$

Let, $x^{3/2} = t, \frac{3}{2}x^{1/2}\,dx = dt, x^{1/2}\,dx = \frac{2}{3}\,dt$

$$= \int \frac{\frac{2}{3}\,dt}{\sqrt{(a^{3/2})^2-(t)^2}}$$

$$= \frac{2}{3}\cdot\sin^{-1}\left(\frac{t}{a^{3/2}}\right) + C = \frac{2}{3}\sin^{-1}\left(\frac{x^{3/2}}{a^{3/2}}\right) + C$$

Example 21 Evaluate

(i) $\int \frac{\cos x}{\sqrt{\sin^2 x - 2\sin x - 3}}\,dx$. (ii) $\int \sqrt{\frac{\sin(x-\alpha)}{\sin(x+\alpha)}}\,dx$.

(iii) $\int \frac{2\sin 2x - \cos x}{6-\cos^2 x - 4\sin x}\,dx$.

Sol. (i) Let $I = \int \frac{\cos x \, dx}{\sqrt{\sin^2 x - 2\sin x - 3}}$

Put $\sin x = t \quad \therefore \cos x \, dx = dt$

$$\Rightarrow I = \int \frac{dt}{\sqrt{t^2 - 2t - 3}} = \int \frac{dt}{\sqrt{t^2 - 2t + 1 - 1 - 3}}$$

$$I = \int \frac{dt}{\sqrt{(t-1)^2 - (2)^2}}$$

$$= \log |(t-1) + \sqrt{(t-1)^2 - (2)^2}| + C$$

$$\therefore \quad I = \log |(\sin x - 1) + \sqrt{\sin^2 x - 2\sin x - 3}| + C$$

(ii) Let $I = \int \sqrt{\frac{\sin(x-\alpha)}{\sin(x+\alpha)}} \, dx$

$$I = \int \sqrt{\frac{\sin(x-\alpha)}{\sin(x+\alpha)} \times \frac{\sin(x-\alpha)}{\sin(x-\alpha)}} \, dx$$

$$= \int \frac{\sin(x-\alpha)}{\sqrt{\sin^2 x - \sin^2 \alpha}} \, dx$$

$$I = \int \frac{\sin x \cos \alpha - \cos x \sin \alpha}{\sqrt{\sin^2 x - \sin^2 \alpha}} \, dx$$

$$= \cos\alpha \int \frac{\sin x \, dx}{\sqrt{\sin^2 x - \sin^2 \alpha}} - \sin\alpha \int \frac{\cos x \, dx}{\sqrt{\sin^2 x - \sin^2 \alpha}}$$

$$= \cos \alpha \int \frac{\sin x \, dx}{\sqrt{1 - \cos^2 x - \sin^2 \alpha}} - \sin \alpha \int \frac{\cos x \, dx}{\sqrt{\sin^2 x - \sin^2 \alpha}}$$

$$= \cos\alpha \int \frac{\sin x \, dx}{\sqrt{\cos^2 \alpha - \cos^2 x}} - \sin\alpha \int \frac{\cos x \, dx}{\sqrt{\sin^2 x - \sin^2 \alpha}}$$

In the first part, put $\cos x = t$, so that $-\sin x \, dx = dt$ and in second part, put $\sin x = u$, so that $\cos x \, dx = du$

$$\therefore I = -\cos \alpha \int \frac{dt}{\sqrt{\cos^2 \alpha - t^2}} - \sin \alpha \int \frac{du}{\sqrt{u^2 - \sin^2 \alpha}}$$

$$= -\cos \alpha \cdot \sin^{-1}\left(\frac{t}{\cos \alpha}\right) - \sin \alpha \cdot \log |u - \sqrt{(u^2 - \sin^2 \alpha)}| + C$$

$$= -\cos \alpha \cdot \sin^{-1}\left(\frac{\cos x}{\cos \alpha}\right) - \sin \alpha \cdot \log |\sin x - \sqrt{\sin^2 x - \sin^2 \alpha}\ | + C$$

(iii) $I = \int \frac{2\sin 2x - \cos x}{6 - \cos^2 x - 4\sin x} \, dx$

$$= \int \frac{(4\sin x - 1)\cos x}{6 - (1 - \sin^2 x) - 4\sin x} \, dx$$

$$= \int \frac{(4\sin x - 1)\cos x}{\sin^2 x - 4\sin x + 5} \, dx$$

Put $\sin x = t$, so that $\cos x \, dx = dt$

$$\therefore \quad I = \int \frac{(4t-1)\, dt}{(t^2 - 4t + 5)} \quad \text{...(i)}$$

Now, let $\quad (4t - 1) = \lambda (2t - 4) + \mu$

Comparing coefficients of like powers of t, we get

$$2\lambda = 4, -4\lambda + \mu = -1$$

$$\Rightarrow \quad \lambda = 2, \mu = 7 \quad \text{...(ii)}$$

$$\therefore I = \int \frac{2(2t-4) + 7}{t^2 - 4t + 5} dt \quad \text{[using Eqs. (i) and (ii)]}$$

$$= 2\int \frac{2t - 4}{t^2 - 4t + 5} \, dt + 7\int \frac{dt}{t^2 - 4t + 5}$$

$$= 2\log |t^2 - 4t + 5| + 7\int \frac{dt}{t^2 - 4t + 4 - 4 + 5}$$

$$= 2\log |t^2 - 4t + 5| + 7\int \frac{dt}{(t-2)^2 + (1)^2}$$

$$= 2\log |t^2 - 4t + 5| + 7\tan^{-1}(t - 2) + C$$

$$= 2\log |\sin^2 x - 4\sin x + 5| + 7\tan^{-1}(\sin x - 2) + C$$

Type II

(i) $\int \frac{(px + q)\, dx}{ax^2 + bx + c}$ (ii) $\int \frac{(px + q)}{\sqrt{ax^2 + bx + c}} \, dx$

(iii) $\int (px + q)\sqrt{ax^2 + bx + c} \, dx$

The linear factor $(px + q)$ is expressed in terms of the derivative of the quadratic factor $ax^2 + bx + c$ together with a constant as $px + q = \frac{\lambda d}{dx}(ax^2 + bx + c) + \mu$

$$\Rightarrow \quad px + q = \lambda (2ax + b) + \mu$$

Here, we have to find λ and μ and replace $(px + q)$ by $\{\lambda (2ax + b) + \mu\}$ in (i), (ii) and (iii).

Example 22 Evaluate

(i) $\int \sqrt{\frac{a - x}{a + x}} \, dx$ (ii) $\int x \sqrt{\frac{a^2 - x^2}{a^2 + x^2}} \, dx$

Sol. (i) Let $I = \int \sqrt{\frac{a - x}{a + x}} \, dx$

$$I = \int \sqrt{\frac{a - x}{a + x} \times \frac{a - x}{a - x}} \, dx = \int \frac{a - x}{\sqrt{a^2 - x^2}} \, dx$$

$$I = \int \frac{a}{\sqrt{a^2 - x^2}} \, dx - \int \frac{x}{\sqrt{a^2 - x^2}} \, dx$$

$$= a \cdot \sin^{-1}\left(\frac{x}{a}\right) + \int \frac{t \, dt}{t}$$

Put $a^2 - x^2 = t^2 \Rightarrow -2x \, dx = 2t \, dt \Rightarrow x \, dx = -t \, dt$

$$= a \cdot \sin^{-1}\left(\frac{x}{a}\right) + t + C$$

$$= a \cdot \sin^{-1}\left(\frac{x}{a}\right) + \sqrt{a^2 - x^2} + C$$

(ii) Let $I = \int x \sqrt{\frac{a^2 - x^2}{a^2 + x^2}}\, dx$

Put $x^2 = t \Rightarrow 2x\, dx = dt$

$$\therefore \quad I = \int \sqrt{\frac{a^2 - t}{a^2 + t}} \cdot \frac{dt}{2} = \frac{1}{2}\int \sqrt{\frac{a^2 - t}{a^2 + t} \cdot \frac{a^2 - t}{a^2 - t}}\, dt$$

$$= \frac{1}{2}\int \frac{a^2 - t}{\sqrt{a^4 - t^2}}\, dt$$

$$= \frac{1}{2} a^2 \int \frac{dt}{\sqrt{(a^2)^2 - (t)^2}} - \frac{1}{2}\int \frac{t\, dt}{\sqrt{a^4 - t^2}}$$

$$= \frac{1}{2} a^2 \cdot \sin^{-1}\left(\frac{t}{a^2}\right) + \frac{1}{4}\int \frac{du}{\sqrt{u}},$$

where $a^4 - t^2 = u \Rightarrow -2t\, dt = du$

$$= \frac{1}{2} a^2 \cdot \sin^{-1}\left(\frac{t}{a^2}\right) + \frac{1}{4} \cdot \left(\frac{u^{1/2}}{1/2}\right) + C$$

[where $t = x^2$ and $u = a^4 - x^4$]

$$= \frac{1}{2} a^2 \cdot \sin^{-1}\left(\frac{x^2}{a^2}\right) + \frac{1}{2} \cdot \sqrt{a^4 - x^4} + C$$

Integrals of the Form $\int \frac{k(x)}{ax^2 + bx + c}\, dx$, where $k(x)$ is a Polynomial of Degree Greater than 2

To evaluate this type of integrals we divide the numerator by denominator and express the integral as

$Q(x) + \frac{R(x)}{ax^2 + bx + c}$, where $R(x)$ is a linear function of x.

| Example 23 Evaluate

(i) $\int x\sqrt{1 + x - x^2}\, dx$ (ii) $\int (x + 1)\sqrt{1 - x - x^2}\, dx$

Sol. (i) Let $I = \int x\sqrt{1 + x - x^2}\, dx$

Put $x = \lambda\left\{\frac{d}{dx}(1 + x - x^2)\right\} + \mu$

Then, comparing the coefficients of like powers of x, we get

$$1 = -2\lambda \text{ and } \lambda + \mu = 0 \Rightarrow \lambda = -1/2, \mu = 1/2$$

$$\therefore \quad I = \int x\sqrt{1 + x - x^2}\, dx$$

$$= \int\left\{-\frac{1}{2}(1 - 2x) + \frac{1}{2}\right\}\sqrt{1 + x - x^2}\, dx$$

$$= -\frac{1}{2}\int (1 - 2x)\sqrt{1 + x - x^2}\, dx + \frac{1}{2}\int\sqrt{1 + x - x^2}\, dx$$

$$= -\frac{1}{2}\int\sqrt{t}\, dt + \frac{1}{2}\int\sqrt{-\left(x^2 - x + \frac{1}{4} - \frac{1}{4} - 1\right)}\, dx$$

[where $t = 1 + x - x^2$]

$$= -\frac{1}{2}\left(\frac{t^{3/2}}{3/2}\right) + \frac{1}{2}\int\sqrt{\left(\frac{\sqrt{5}}{2}\right)^2 - \left(x - \frac{1}{2}\right)^2}\, dx$$

$$= -\frac{1}{3}t^{3/2} + \frac{1}{2}\left[\frac{(x - 1/2)}{2}\sqrt{\left(\frac{\sqrt{5}}{2}\right)^2 - \left(x - \frac{1}{2}\right)^2} + \frac{1}{2}\left(\frac{\sqrt{5}}{2}\right)^2 \sin^{-1}\left(\frac{x - 1/2}{\sqrt{5}/2}\right)\right] + C$$

$$= -\frac{1}{3}(1 + x - x^2)^{3/2} + \frac{1}{2}\left[\frac{(x - 1/2)}{2}\sqrt{1 + x - x^2} + \frac{5}{8}\sin^{-1}\left(\frac{2x - 1}{\sqrt{5}}\right)\right] + C$$

(ii) Let $I = \int (x + 1)\sqrt{1 - x - x^2}\, dx$

Put, $(x + 1) = \lambda \cdot \left(\frac{d}{dx}(1 - x - x^2)\right) + \mu$

Then, $(x + 1) = \lambda(-1 - 2x) + \mu$ comparing the coefficients of like powers of x, we get $-2\lambda = 1$ and $\mu - \lambda = 1 \Rightarrow \lambda = -1/2$ and $\mu = 1/2$.

$$\therefore \quad (x + 1) = -\frac{1}{2}(-1 - 2x) + \frac{1}{2}$$

So, $\int (x + 1)\sqrt{1 - x - x^2}\, dx = \int\left\{-\frac{1}{2}(-1 - 2x) + \frac{1}{2}\right\}\sqrt{1 - x - x^2}\, dx$

$$= -\frac{1}{2}\int (-1 - 2x)\sqrt{1 - x - x^2}\, dx + \frac{1}{2}\int\sqrt{1 - x - x^2}\, dx$$

$$= -\frac{1}{2}\int (-1 - 2x)\sqrt{1 - x - x^2}\, dx + \frac{1}{2}\int\sqrt{\left\{1 - \left(x^2 + x + \frac{1}{4} - \frac{1}{4}\right)\right\}}\, dx$$

$$= -\frac{1}{2}\sqrt{t}\, dt + \frac{1}{2}\int\sqrt{(\sqrt{5}/2)^2 - (x + 1/2)^2}\, dx$$

[where $t = 1 + x - x^2$]

$$= -\frac{1}{2}\left(\frac{t^{3/2}}{3/2}\right) + \frac{1}{2}\left\{\frac{1}{2}\left(x + \frac{1}{2}\right)\sqrt{1 - x - x^2} + \frac{1}{2} \cdot \frac{5}{4}\sin^{-1}\left(\frac{x + 1/2}{\sqrt{5}/2}\right)\right\} + C$$

$$= -\frac{1}{3}(1 - x - x^2)^{3/2} + \frac{1}{8}(2x + 1)\sqrt{1 - x - x^2} + \frac{5}{16}\sin^{-1}\left(\frac{2x + 1}{\sqrt{5}}\right) + C$$

Example 24 Evaluate $\int \frac{x^2+x+3}{x^2-x-2}\,dx.$

Sol. Let $I = \int \frac{x^2+x+3}{x^2-x-2}\,dx$

$\therefore \quad I = \int \left(1 + \frac{2x+5}{x^2-x-2}\right) dx$

$\Rightarrow \quad I = \int 1\,dx + \int \frac{2x+5}{x^2-x-2}\,dx$

$I = x + \int \frac{2x+5}{x^2-x-2}\,dx$

Put, $2x+5 = \lambda \left\{\frac{d}{dx}(x^2-x-2)\right\} + \mu$. Then, obtaining $2x+5 = \lambda(2x-1)+\mu$, comparing the coefficients of like terms. We get, $2 = 2\lambda$ and $5 = \mu - \lambda$

$\therefore \quad \lambda = 1$ and $\mu = 6$

$\therefore \quad I = x + \int \frac{\lambda(2x-1)+\mu}{x^2-x-2}\,dx$

$= x + \int \frac{2x-1}{x^2-x-2}\,dx + 6\int \frac{1}{x^2-x-2}\,dx$

$= x + \int \frac{1}{t}\,dt + 6\int \frac{1}{x^2 - x + \frac{1}{4} - \frac{1}{4} - 2}$

[where $t = x^2 - x - 2$]

$= x + \log|t| + 6\int \frac{dx}{(x-1/2)^2 - (3/2)^2}\,dx$

$= x + \log|x^2-x-2| + 6\cdot\frac{1}{2(3/2)}\log\left|\frac{x-\frac{1}{2}-\frac{3}{2}}{x-\frac{1}{2}+\frac{3}{2}}\right| + C$

$= x + \log|x^2-x-2| + 2\cdot\log\left|\frac{x-2}{x+1}\right| + C$

Example 25 Evaluate $\int \frac{2x^2+5x+4}{\sqrt{x^2+x+1}}\,dx.$

Sol. Let $I = \int \frac{2x^2+5x+4}{\sqrt{x^2+x+1}}\,dx$

Put $2x^2+5x+4 = \lambda(x^2+x+1) + \mu\left\{\frac{d}{dx}(x^2+x+1)\right\} + \gamma$

or $2x^2+5x+4 = \lambda(x^2+x+1) + \mu(2x+1) + \gamma$

Comparing the coefficients of like terms, we get

$2 = \lambda,\quad 5 = \lambda + 2\mu,\quad 4 = \lambda + \mu + \gamma$

$\therefore \quad \lambda = 2,\quad \mu = 3/2,\quad \gamma = 1/2$

Hence, the above integral reduces to

$I = \int \frac{2x^2+5x+4}{\sqrt{x^2+x+1}}\,dx$

$= \int \left(2\cdot\frac{(x^2+x+1)}{\sqrt{x^2+x+1}} + \frac{3}{2}\cdot\frac{(2x+1)}{\sqrt{x^2+x+1}} + \frac{1}{2}\cdot\frac{1}{\sqrt{x^2+x+1}}\right) dx$

$= 2\int \sqrt{x^2+x+1}\,dx + \frac{3}{2}\int \frac{dt}{\sqrt{t}} + \frac{1}{2}\int \frac{dx}{\sqrt{x^2+x+1}}$

[where $t = x^2+x+1$]

$= 2\int \sqrt{(x+1/2)^2 + (\sqrt{3}/2)^2}\,dx + \frac{3}{2}\cdot\frac{t^{1/2}}{1/2}$

$+ \frac{1}{2}\int \frac{dx}{\sqrt{(x+1/2)^2 + (\sqrt{3}/2)^2}}$

$= 2\left[\frac{1}{2}\left(x+\frac{1}{2}\right)\sqrt{x^2+x+1} + \frac{1}{2}\cdot\frac{3}{4}\cdot\log\left|\left(x+\frac{1}{2}\right) + \sqrt{x^2+x+1}\right|\right]$

$+ 3\sqrt{x^2+x+1} + \frac{1}{2}\log\left|\left(x+\frac{1}{2}\right) + \sqrt{x^2+x+1}\right| + C$

$\therefore \quad I = \left(x+\frac{1}{2}\right)\sqrt{x^2+x+1} + \frac{3}{4}\log\left\{\left(x+\frac{1}{2}\right) + \sqrt{x^2+x+1}\right\}$

$+ 3\sqrt{x^2+x+1} + \frac{1}{2}\log\left\{\left(x+\frac{1}{2}\right) + \sqrt{x^2+x+1}\right\} + C$

$\Rightarrow I = \left(x+\frac{7}{2}\right)\sqrt{x^2+x+1} + \frac{5}{4}\log\left\{\left(x+\frac{1}{2}\right) + \sqrt{x^2+x+1}\right\} + C$

Integrals of the Type

1. $\int \frac{ax^2+bx+c}{(px^2+qx+r)}\,dx$

2. $\int \frac{(ax^2+bx+c)}{\sqrt{px^2+qx+r}}\,dx$

3. $\int (ax^2+bx+c)\sqrt{px^2+qx+r}\,dx$

In above cases; substitute

$$ax^2+bx+c = \lambda(px^2+qx+r) + \mu\left\{\frac{d}{dx}(px^2+qx+r)\right\} + \gamma.$$

Find λ, μ and γ. These integrations reduces to integration of three independent functions.

Trigonometric Integrals

(a) Integrals of the Form

$$\int \frac{1}{a\cos^2 x + b\sin^2 x}\,dx,\ \int \frac{1}{a + b\sin^2 x}\,dx,\ \int \frac{1}{a+b\cos^2 x}\,dx,$$

$$\int \frac{1}{(a\sin x + b\cos x)^2}\,dx,\ \int \frac{1}{a + b\sin^2 x + c\cos^2 x}\,dx$$

To evaluate this type of integrals, divide numerator and denominator both by $\cos^2 x$, replace $\sec^2 x$, if any, in denominator by $(1+\tan^2 x)$ and put $\tan x = t$. So that $\sec^2 x\, dx = dt$.

| Example 26 Evaluate

(i) $\int \frac{1}{4\sin^2 x + 9\cos^2 x} dx$ (ii) $\int \frac{\sin x}{\sin 3x} dx$

Sol. (i) $I = \int \frac{dx}{4\sin^2 x + 9\cos^2 x}$

Here, dividing numerator and denominator by $\cos^2 x$. We get

$$I = \int \frac{\sec^2 x}{4\tan^2 x + 9} dx$$

Put $\tan x = t$

$\Rightarrow \sec^2 x\, dx = dt$

$$\therefore \quad I = \int \frac{dt}{4t^2 + 9} = \frac{1}{4} \int \frac{dt}{t^2 + (3/2)^2}$$

$$= \frac{1}{4} \cdot \frac{1}{3/2} \tan^{-1}\left(\frac{t}{3/2}\right) + C$$

$$I = \frac{1}{6} \tan^{-1}\left(\frac{2\tan x}{3}\right) + C$$

(ii) Let $I = \int \frac{\sin x}{\sin 3x} dx = \int \frac{\sin x}{3\sin x - 4\sin^3 x} dx$

$$I = \int \frac{dx}{3 - 4\sin^2 x}$$

Dividing numerator and denominator by $\cos^2 x$, we get

$$I = \int \frac{\sec^2 x\, dx}{3\sec^2 x - 4\tan^2 x} = \int \frac{\sec^2 x\, dx}{3(1+\tan^2 x) - 4\tan^2 x}$$

$$I = \int \frac{\sec^2 x\, dx}{3 - \tan^2 x}$$

Let $\tan x = t \Rightarrow \sec^2 x\, dx = dt$

$$\therefore \quad I = \int \frac{dt}{(\sqrt{3})^2 - (t)^2} = \frac{1}{2\sqrt{3}} \log\left|\frac{\sqrt{3}+t}{\sqrt{3}-t}\right| + C$$

$$I = \frac{1}{2\sqrt{3}} \log\left|\frac{\sqrt{3}+\tan x}{\sqrt{3}-\tan x}\right| + C$$

(b) Integrals of the Form

$$\int \frac{1}{a\sin x + b\cos x} dx, \int \frac{1}{a + b\sin x} dx,$$

$$\int \frac{1}{a + b\cos x} dx, \int \frac{1}{a\sin x + b\cos x + c} dx$$

To evaluate this type of integrals we put

$\sin x = \frac{2\tan x/2}{1+\tan^2 x/2}$ and $\cos x = \frac{1-\tan^2 x/2}{1+\tan^2 x/2}$ and replace $\tan x/2 = t$, by performing these steps the integral reduces to the form $\int \frac{1}{at^2 + bt + c} dt$ which can be evaluated by methods discussed earlier.

| Example 27 Evaluate

(i) $\int \frac{dx}{2 + \sin x + \cos x}$ (ii) $\int \frac{dx}{\sqrt{3}\sin x + \cos x}$

Sol. For this type we use, $\sin x = \frac{2\tan x/2}{1+\tan^2 x/2}$,

$$\cos x = \frac{1-\tan^2 x/2}{1+\tan^2 x/2}.$$

(i) Let $I = \int \frac{dx}{2 + \sin x + \cos x}$

$$= \int \frac{dx}{2 + \frac{2\tan x/2}{1+\tan^2 x/2} + \frac{1-\tan^2 x/2}{1+\tan^2 x/2}}$$

$$= \int \frac{\sec^2 \frac{x}{2} dx}{2 + 2\tan^2 \frac{x}{2} + 2\tan \frac{x}{2} + 1 - \tan^2 \frac{x}{2}}$$

$$I = \int \frac{\sec^2 \frac{x}{2} dx}{\tan^2 \frac{x}{2} + 2\tan \frac{x}{2} + 3}$$

Put $\tan \frac{x}{2} = t$

$$\Rightarrow \frac{1}{2}\sec^2 \frac{x}{2} dx = dt = \int \frac{2\, dt}{t^2 + 2t + 3} = 2\int \frac{dt}{t^2 + 2t + 1 + 2}$$

$$= 2\int \frac{dt}{(t+1)^2 + (\sqrt{2})^2}$$

$$= 2 \cdot \frac{1}{\sqrt{2}} \tan^{-1}\left(\frac{t+1}{\sqrt{2}}\right) + C$$

$$I = \sqrt{2} \tan^{-1}\left(\frac{\tan x/2 + 1}{\sqrt{2}}\right) + C$$

(ii) Let $I = \int \frac{dx}{\sqrt{3}\sin x + \cos x}$

$$= \int \frac{dx}{\frac{\sqrt{3} \cdot 2\tan x/2}{1+\tan^2 x/2} + \frac{1-\tan^2 x/2}{1+\tan^2 x/2}}$$

$$= \int \frac{\sec^2 \frac{x}{2} dx}{2\sqrt{3}\tan \frac{x}{2} + 1 - \tan^2 \frac{x}{2}}$$

Put $\tan\frac{x}{2}=t \Rightarrow \frac{1}{2}\sec^2\frac{x}{2}\,dx=dt$

$\therefore \quad I=\int\frac{2dt}{-t^2+2\sqrt{3}t+1}=2\int\frac{dt}{-t^2+2\sqrt{3}t-3+3+1}$

$=2\int\frac{dt}{4-(t-\sqrt{3})^2}=2\int\frac{dt}{(2)^2-(t-\sqrt{3})^2}$

$=2\cdot\frac{1}{2(2)}\log\left|\frac{2+t-\sqrt{3}}{2-t+\sqrt{3}}\right|+C$

$\therefore \quad I=\frac{1}{2}\log\left|\frac{2-\sqrt{3}+\tan x/2}{2+\sqrt{3}-\tan x/2}\right|+C$

(c) Alternative Method to Evaluate the Integrals of the Form

$$\int\frac{1}{a\sin x+b\cos x}\,dx$$

To evaluate this type of integrals we substitute $a=r\cos\theta, b=r\sin\theta$ and so

$$r=\sqrt{a^2+b^2},\quad \theta=\tan^{-1}\left(\frac{b}{a}\right)$$

$\therefore \quad a\sin x+b\cos x=r\sin(x+\theta)$

So, $\int\frac{1}{a\sin x+b\cos x}\,dx=\frac{1}{r}\int\frac{1}{\sin(x+\theta)}\,dx$

$=\frac{1}{r}\int\operatorname{cosec}(x+\theta)\,dx=\frac{1}{r}\log\left|\tan\left(\frac{x}{2}+\frac{\theta}{2}\right)\right|+C$

$\therefore \quad \int\frac{1}{a\sin x+b\cos x}\,dx=\frac{1}{\sqrt{a^2+b^2}}\log\left|\tan\left(\frac{x}{2}+\frac{1}{2}\tan^{-1}\frac{b}{a}\right)\right|+C$

| Example 28 Evaluate $\int\frac{1}{\sqrt{3}\sin x+\cos x}\,dx.$

Sol. Let $\sqrt{3}=r\sin\theta$ and $1=r\cos\theta$.

Then, $r=\sqrt{(\sqrt{3})^2+(1)^2}=2$ and $\tan\theta=\frac{\sqrt{3}}{1} \Rightarrow \theta=\frac{\pi}{3}$

$\therefore \quad I=\int\frac{1}{\sqrt{3}\sin x+\cos x}\,dx$

$=\int\frac{1}{r\sin\theta\sin x+r\cos\theta\cos x}\,dx$

$=\frac{1}{r}\int\frac{dx}{\cos(x-\theta)}=\frac{1}{r}\int\sec(x-\theta)\,dx$

$=\frac{1}{r}\log\left|\tan\left(\frac{\pi}{4}+\frac{x}{2}-\frac{\theta}{2}\right)\right|+C$

$=\frac{1}{2}\log\left|\tan\left(\frac{\pi}{4}+\frac{x}{2}-\frac{\pi}{6}\right)\right|+C$

$=\frac{1}{2}\log\left|\tan\left(\frac{x}{2}+\frac{\pi}{12}\right)\right|+C$

(d) Integrals of the Form

$$\int\frac{p\cos x+q\sin x+r}{a\cos x+b\sin x+c}\,dx,\quad \int\frac{p\cos x+q\sin x}{a\cos x+b\sin x}\,dx$$

Rule for (i) In this integral express numerator as,

λ (denominator) + μ (diffn. of denominator) + γ.

Find λ,μ and γ by comparing coefficients of $\sin x, \cos x$ and constant term and split the integral into sum of three integrals.

$$\lambda\int dx+\mu\int\frac{\text{d.c. of (denominator)}}{\text{denominator}}\,dx+\gamma\int\frac{dx}{a\sin x+b\cos x+c}$$

Rule for (ii) Express numerator as λ (denominator) + μ (differentiation of denominator) and find λ and μ as above.

| Example 29 Evaluate $\int\frac{(2+3\cos x)}{\sin x+2\cos x+3}\,dx.$

Sol. Write the numerator = λ (denominator) + μ (d.c. of denominator) + γ

$\Rightarrow \quad 2+3\cos x=\lambda(\sin x+2\cos x+3)+\mu(\cos x-2\sin x)+\gamma$

Comparing the coefficients of $\sin x$, $\cos x$ and constant terms, we get

$$0=\lambda-2\mu,\ 3=2\lambda+\mu,\ 2=3\lambda+\gamma$$

$\Rightarrow \quad \lambda=6/5,\ \mu=3/5,\ \gamma=-8/5$

Hence, $I=\frac{6}{5}\int 1\,dx+\frac{3}{5}\int\frac{\cos x-2\sin x}{\sin x+2\cos x+3}\,dx-\frac{8}{5}\int\frac{dx}{\sin x+2\cos x+3}$

$=\frac{6}{5}\cdot x+\frac{3}{5}\log|\sin x+2\cos x+3|-\frac{8}{5}I_3 \quad \text{...(i)}$

Where, $I_3=\int\frac{dx}{\sin x+2\cos x+3}$

$=\int\frac{dx}{\frac{2\tan x/2}{1+\tan^2 x/2}+\frac{2(1-\tan^2 x/2)}{1+\tan^2 x/2}+3}$

$=\int\frac{\sec^2\frac{x}{2}\,dx}{2\tan\frac{x}{2}+2-2\tan^2\frac{x}{2}+3+3\tan^2\frac{x}{2}}$

$=\int\frac{\sec^2\frac{x}{2}\,dx}{\tan^2\frac{x}{2}+2\tan\frac{x}{2}+5}$, let $\tan\frac{x}{2}=t$

$$\Rightarrow \frac{1}{2}\sec^2\frac{x}{2}\,dx = dt = \int\frac{2dt}{t^2+2t+5} = 2\int\frac{dt}{(t+1)^2+2^2}$$

$$I_3 = 2\cdot\frac{1}{2}\cdot\tan^{-1}\left(\frac{t+1}{2}\right) = \tan^{-1}\left(\frac{\tan\frac{x}{2}+1}{2}\right) \quad \text{...(ii)}$$

From Eqs. (i) and (ii),

$$I = \frac{6}{5}x + \frac{3}{5}\log|\sin x + 2\cos x + 3| - \frac{8}{5}\tan^{-1}\left|\left(\frac{\tan\frac{x}{2}+1}{2}\right)\right| + C$$

Example 30 The value of $\int\{1+\tan x\cdot\tan(x+A)\}\,dx$ is equal to

(a) $\cot A\cdot\log\left|\frac{\sec x}{\sec(x+A)}\right|+C$

(b) $\tan A\cdot\log|\sec(x+A)|+C$

(c) $\cot A\cdot\log\left|\frac{\sec(x+A)}{\sec(x)}\right|+C$

(d) None of the above

Sol. Let $I = \int\{1+\tan x\cdot\tan(x+A)\}\,dx$

$$= \int\left\{1+\frac{\sin x\cdot\sin(x+A)}{\cos x\cdot\cos(x+A)}\right\}dx$$

$$= \int\frac{\cos x\cdot\cos(x+A)+\sin x\cdot\sin(x+A)}{\cos x\cdot\cos(x+A)}\,dx$$

$$= \int\frac{\cos(x+A-x)\,dx}{\cos x\cdot\cos(x+A)}$$

$$= \cos A\cdot\int\frac{dx}{\cos x\cdot\cos(x+A)}$$

Multiplying and dividing by $\sin A$, we get

$$= \cot A\cdot\int\frac{\sin A\,dx}{\cos x\cdot\cos(x+A)}$$

$$= \cot A\cdot\int\frac{\sin(x+A-x)\,dx}{\cos x\cdot\cos(x+A)}$$

$$= \cot A\cdot\int\left\{\frac{\sin(x+A)\cdot\cos x}{\cos x\cos(x+A)} - \frac{\cos(x+A)\cdot\sin x}{\cos x\cdot\cos(x+A)}\right\}dx$$

$$= \cot A\cdot\{\int\tan(x+A)dx - \int\tan x\,dx\}$$

$$= \cot A\cdot\{\log|\sec(x+A)| - \log|\sec x|\} + C$$

Hence, (c) is the correct answer.

Example 31 The value of $\int\frac{\sqrt{\cos 2x}}{\sin x}\,dx$, is equal to

(a) $\log|\cot x+\sqrt{\cot^2 x-1}|+\sqrt{2}\log|\cos x + \sqrt{\cos^2 x-1/2}|+C$

(b) $-\log|\cot x+\sqrt{\cot^2 x-1}|+\sqrt{2}\log|\cos x + \sqrt{\cos^2 x-1/2}|+C$

(c) $\log|\cot x+\sqrt{\cot^2 x-1}|+2\log|\cos x + \sqrt{\cos^2 x-1/2}|+C$

(d) $-\log|\cot x+\sqrt{\cot^2 x-1}|+2\log|\cos x + \sqrt{\cos^2 x-1/2}|+C$

Sol. Let $I = \int\frac{\sqrt{\cos 2x}}{\sin x}\,dx = \int\frac{\cos 2x}{\sin x\sqrt{\cos 2x}}\,dx$

$$= \int\frac{1-2\sin^2 x}{\sin x\sqrt{\cos 2x}}\,dx$$

$$= \int\frac{1}{\sin x\sqrt{\cos^2 x-\sin^2 x}}\,dx - 2\int\frac{\sin x}{\sqrt{2\cos^2 x-1}}\,dx$$

$$= \int\frac{\text{cosec}^2 x}{\sqrt{\cot^2 x-1}}\,dx - \frac{2}{\sqrt{2}}\int\frac{\sin x}{\sqrt{\cos^2 x-1/2}}\,dx$$

$$= -\int\frac{dt}{\sqrt{t^2-1}} - \sqrt{2}\int\frac{-ds}{\sqrt{s^2-(1/\sqrt{2})^2}}$$

[where $t=\cot x$ and $s=\cos x$]

$$= -\log|t+\sqrt{t^2-1}| + \sqrt{2}\log|s+\sqrt{s^2-1/2}|+C$$

$$= -\log|\cot x+\sqrt{\cot^2 x-1}| + \sqrt{2}\log|\cos x + \sqrt{\cos^2 x-1/2}|+C$$

Hence, (b) is the correct answer.

Exercise for Session 3

■ **Evaluate the following integrals**

1. $\int \frac{x\,dx}{9-16x^4}$

2. $\int \frac{x^2}{9+16x^6}\,dx$

3. $\int \frac{x^3\,dx}{16x^8-25}$

4. $\int \sqrt{\frac{x}{a^3-x^3}}\,dx$

5. $\int \sqrt{\frac{x^4}{a^6+x^6}}\,dx$

6. $\int \frac{1}{4e^{-x}-9e^{x}}\,dx$

7. $\int \frac{2^x}{\sqrt{4^x-25}}\,dx$

8. $\int \frac{8x-11}{\sqrt{5+2x-x^2}}\,dx$

9. $\int \frac{x+2}{x^2+2x+2}\,dx$

10. $\int \frac{x-3}{3-2x-x^2}\,dx$

11. $\int \frac{3x-1}{4x^2-4x+17}\,dx$

12. $\int \frac{\sqrt{x}\,dx}{\sqrt{2x+3}}$

13. $\int \sqrt{\frac{a-x}{x-b}}\,dx$

14. $\int \sqrt{\frac{1-x}{1+x}}\,dx$

15. $\int \frac{x^2+2x+3}{\sqrt{x^2+x+1}}\,dx$

16. $\int \frac{dx}{1+\sin x+\cos x}$

17. $\int \frac{dx}{\sin x+\sqrt{3}\cos x}$

18. $\int \frac{\cos^2 x\sin x}{\sin x-\cos x}\,dx$

19. $\int \frac{e^x}{\sqrt{5-4e^x-e^{2x}}}\,dx$

20. $\int \sqrt{\frac{\cos x-\cos^3 x}{(1-\cos^3 x)}}\,dx$

21. Evaluate $\int \frac{3\sin x+2\cos x}{3\cos x+2\sin x}\,dx$

22. Evalute $\int (2x-4)\sqrt{4+3x-x^2}\,dx$.

23. $\int \frac{(2x^2+5x+9)\,dx}{(x+1)\sqrt{x^2+x+1}}$

24. The value of $\int \frac{dx}{\sec x+\operatorname{cosec} x}$, is equal to

(a) $\left\{(\sin x+\cos x)+\frac{1}{\sqrt{2}}\log\left|\frac{\tan x/2-1-\sqrt{2}}{\tan x/2-1+\sqrt{2}}\right|\right\}+C$

(b) $2\left\{(\sin x+\cos x)+\frac{1}{\sqrt{2}}\log\left|\frac{\tan x/2-1-\sqrt{2}}{\tan x/2-1+\sqrt{2}}\right|\right\}+C$

(c) $\frac{1}{2}\left\{(\sin x-\cos x)+\frac{1}{\sqrt{2}}\log\left|\frac{\tan x/2-1-\sqrt{2}}{\tan x-1+\sqrt{2}}\right|\right\}+C$

(d) None of these

Session 4

Integration by Parts

Integration by Parts

Theorem If u and v are two functions of x, then

$$\int uv\,dx = u\int v\,dx - \int\left\{\frac{du}{dx}\int v\,dx\right\}dx$$

i.e. The integral of product of two functions = (first function) × (integral of second function) − integral of (differential of first function × integral of second function).

Proof For any two functions $f(x)$ and $g(x)$, we have

$$\frac{d}{dx}\{f(x)\cdot g(x)\} = f(x)\cdot\frac{d}{dx}\{g(x)\} + g(x)\cdot\frac{d}{dx}\{f(x)\}$$

$$\therefore \int\left(f(x)\cdot\frac{d}{dx}\{g(x)\}+g(x)\cdot\frac{d}{dx}\{f(x)\}\right)dx=\int f(x)\cdot g(x)\,dx$$

$$\Rightarrow \int\left(f(x)\cdot\frac{d}{dx}\{g(x)\}\right)dx + \int\left(g(x)\cdot\frac{d}{dx}\{f(x)\}\right)dx$$

$$= \int f(x)\cdot g(x)dx$$

$$\Rightarrow \int\left(f(x)\cdot\frac{d}{dx}\{g(x)\}\right)dx$$

$$= \int f(x)\cdot g(x)\,dx - \int\left(g(x)\cdot\frac{d}{dx}\{f(x)\}\right)dx$$

Let $\quad f(x) = u \quad$ and $\quad \frac{d}{dx}\{g(x)\} = v$

So that, $g(x) = \int v\,dx$

$$\therefore \quad \int uv\,dx = u\cdot\int v\,dx - \int\left\{\frac{du}{dx}\cdot\int v\,dx\right\}\cdot dx$$

Remarks

While applying the above rule, care has to be taken in the selection of first function (u) and selection of second function (v). Normally we use the following methods :

1. If in the product of the two functions, one of the functions is not directly integrable (e.g. $\log|x|, \sin^{-1}x, \cos^{-1}x, \tan^{-1}x, \ldots$, etc.) Then, we take it as the first function and the remaining function is taken as the second function. i.e. In the integration of $\int x\tan^{-1}x\,dx$, $\tan^{-1}x$ is taken as the first function and x as the second function.
2. If there is no other function, then unity is taken as the second function. e.g. In the integration of $\int \tan^{-1}x\,dx$, $\tan^{-1}x$ is taken as first function and 1 as the second function.
3. If both of the function are directly integrable, then the first function is chosen in such a way that the derivative of the function thus obtained under integral sign is easily integrable.

Usually we use the following preference order for selecting the first function. (Inverse, Logarithmic, Algebraic, Trigonometric, Exponent).

In above stated order, the function on the left is always chosen as the first function. This rule is called as **ILATE**.

Example 32 Evaluate

(i) $\int \sin^{-1}x\,dx$ (ii) $\int \log_e|x|\,dx$

Sol. (i) $I = \int \sin^{-1}x\,dx = \int \underset{\text{I}}{\sin^{-1}x}\cdot \underset{\text{II}}{1}\,dx$

Here, we know by definition of integration by parts that order of preference is taken according to ILATE. So, '$\sin^{-1}x$' should be taken as first and '1' as the second function to apply by parts.

Applying integration by parts, we get

$$I = \sin^{-1}x\cdot(x) - \int\frac{1}{\sqrt{1-x^2}}\cdot x\,dx$$

$$= x\cdot\sin^{-1}x + \frac{1}{2}\int\frac{dt}{t^{1/2}}$$

Let $\quad 1 - x^2 = t$

$$-2x\,dx = dt \Rightarrow x\,dx = -\frac{1}{2}dt$$

$$= x\sin^{-1}x + \frac{1}{2}\cdot\frac{t^{1/2}}{1/2} + C$$

$$I = x\sin^{-1}x + \sqrt{1-x^2} + C$$

$$\therefore \int\sin^{-1}x\,dx = x\sin^{-1}x + \sqrt{1-x^2} + C$$

(ii) $I = \int \log_e|x|\,dx = \int \underset{\text{I}}{\log_e|x|}\cdot \underset{\text{II}}{1}\,dx$

Applying integration by parts, we get

$$= \log|x|\cdot x - \int\frac{1}{x}\cdot x\,dx$$

$$= x\log|x| - \int 1\,dx$$

$$I = x\log|x| - x + C$$

Example 33 Evaluate

(i) $\int x\cos x\,dx$ (ii) $\int x^2\cos x\,dx$

Sol. (i) $\int x\cos x\,dx,\quad I = \int \underset{\text{I}}{x}\,\underset{\text{II}}{\cos x}\,dx$

Applying integration by parts,

$$I = x\left(\int \cos x\, dx\right) - \int \left\{\frac{d}{dx}(x)\right\} \left\{\int (\cos x)\, dx\right\} dx$$

$$I = x \sin x - \int 1 \cdot \sin x\, dx = x \sin x + \cos x + C$$

(ii) $I = \int \underset{\text{I}}{x^2} \underset{\text{II}}{\cos x}\, dx$

Applying integration by parts,

$$I = x^2 \left(\int \cos x\, dx\right) - \int \left\{\frac{d}{dx}(x^2)\right\} \cdot \left\{\int \cos x\right\} dx$$

$$= x^2 \sin x - \int 2x \cdot (\sin x)\, dx$$

$$= x^2 \sin x - 2 \int x (\sin x)\, dx$$

We again have to integrate $\int x \sin x\, dx$ using integration by parts,

$$= x^2 \cdot \sin x - 2 \int \underset{\text{I}}{x} \cdot \underset{\text{II}}{\sin x}\, dx$$

$$= x^2 \sin x - 2\left\{x\left(\int \sin x\, dx\right) - \int \left(\frac{dx}{dx}\right)\left(\int \sin x\, dx\right) dx\right\}$$

$$= x^2 \sin x - 2\{- x \cos x - \int 1 \cdot (- \cos x)\, dx\}$$

$$I = x^2 \sin x + 2x \cos x - 2 \sin x + C$$

Example 34 Evaluate $\int \dfrac{\sin^{-1} \sqrt{x} - \cos^{-1} \sqrt{x}}{\sin^{-1} \sqrt{x} + \cos^{-1} \sqrt{x}}\, dx.$

Sol. Let $I = \int \dfrac{\sin^{-1} \sqrt{x} - \cos^{-1} \sqrt{x}}{\sin^{-1} \sqrt{x} + \cos^{-1} \sqrt{x}}\, dx$

$$= \int \frac{\sin^{-1} \sqrt{x} - (\pi/2 - \sin^{-1} \sqrt{x})}{\pi/2}\, dx$$

$$[\because \sin^{-1} \theta + \cos^{-1} \theta = \pi/2]$$

$$\Rightarrow \quad I = \frac{2}{\pi} \int (2 \sin^{-1} \sqrt{x} - \pi/2)\, dx$$

$$= \frac{4}{\pi} \int \sin^{-1} \sqrt{x}\, dx - \int 1\, dx$$

$$I = \frac{4}{\pi} \int \sin^{-1} \sqrt{x}\, dx - x + C \qquad \text{...(i)}$$

Let $x = \sin^2 \theta$, then $dx = 2 \sin \theta \cos \theta\, d\theta = \sin 2\theta\, d\theta$

$$\therefore \quad \int \sin^{-1} \sqrt{x}\, dx = \int \underset{\text{I}}{\theta} \cdot \underset{\text{II}}{\sin 2\theta}\, d\theta$$

Applying integration by parts

$$\int \sin^{-1} \sqrt{x} dx = - \theta \cdot \frac{\cos 2\theta}{2} + \int \frac{1}{2} \cos 2\theta\, d\theta$$

$$= \frac{-\theta}{2} \cdot \cos 2\theta + \frac{1}{4} \sin 2\theta$$

$$= \frac{-1 \cdot \theta}{2} \cdot (1 - 2 \sin^2 \theta) + \frac{1}{2} \cdot \sin \theta \cdot \sqrt{1 - \sin^2 \theta}$$

$$= \frac{-1}{2} \sin^{-1} \sqrt{x}\, (1 - 2x) + \frac{1}{2} \cdot \sqrt{x}\, \sqrt{1 - x} \qquad \text{...(ii)}$$

From Eqs. (i) and (ii), we get

$$I = \frac{4}{\pi} \left\{\frac{-1}{2} (\sin^{-1} \sqrt{x})(1 - 2x) + \frac{1}{2} \sqrt{x} \sqrt{1 - x}\right\} - x + C$$

$$= \frac{2}{\pi} \{\sqrt{x - x^2} - (1 - 2x) \sin^{-1} \sqrt{x}\} - x + C$$

Integral of Form $\int e^x \{f(x) + f'(x)\} dx$

Theorem Prove that

$$\int e^x \{f(x) + f'(x)\}\, dx = e^x f(x) + C$$

Proof We have, $\int e^x \{f(x) + f'(x)\}\, dx$

$$= \int \underset{\text{II}}{e^x} \cdot \underset{\text{I}}{f(x)}\, dx + \int e^x \cdot f'(x)\, dx$$

$$= f(x) \cdot e^x - \int f'(x) \cdot e^x dx + \int e^x \cdot f'(x)\, dx + C$$

$$= f(x) \cdot e^x + C$$

Thus, to evaluate the integrals of the type

$$\int e^x \{f(x) + f'(x)\}\, dx,$$

we first express the integral as the sum of two integrals $\int e^x f(x)\, dx$ and $\int e^x f'(x)\, dx$ and then integrate the integral involving $e^x f(x)$ as integral by parts taking e^x as second function.

Remark

The above theorem is also true, if we have e^{kx} in place of e^x

i.e. $\int e^{kx} \{f(kx) + f'(kx)\}\, dx = e^{kx} f(kx) + C$

General Concept

$$\int e^{g(x)} \{f(x) g'(x) + f'(x)\}\, dx$$

Proof $I = \int \underbrace{e^{g(x)}}_{\text{II}} \underbrace{f(x)}_{\text{I}} \underbrace{g'(x)}_{\text{II}}\, dx + \underbrace{\int e^{g(x)} f'(x)\, dx}_{\text{as it is}}$

Using, $\int e^{g(x)} \cdot g'(x)\, dx = e^{g(x)}$, we get

$$= f(x) \cdot e^{g(x)} - \int f'(x) \cdot e^{g(x)} dx + \int e^{g(x)} \cdot f'(x)\, dx$$

$$= f(x) \cdot e^{g(x)} + C$$

e.g. $= \int e^{(x \sin x + \cos x)} \left(\dfrac{x^2 \cos^2 x - (x \sin x + \cos x)}{x^2}\right) dx$

$$\Rightarrow \quad \int e^{(x \sin x + \cos x)} \left(\cos^2 x - \frac{x \sin x + \cos x}{x^2}\right) dx$$

$$\Rightarrow \int e^{(x\sin x+\cos x)}\left(x\cos x\left(\frac{\cos x}{x}\right)+\left(\frac{\cos x}{x}\right)'\right)dx$$

$$\Rightarrow e^{(x\sin x+\cos x)}\cdot\frac{\cos x}{x}+C$$

e.g. $= \int e^{\tan x}(\sin x-\sec x)\,dx$

$$=\int e^{\tan x}\sin x\,dx-\int e^{\tan x}\sec x\,dx$$

$$\Rightarrow -e^{\tan x}\cdot\cos x+\int e^{\tan x}\sec^2 x\cos x\,dx-\int e^{\tan x}\sec x\,dx$$

$$\Rightarrow -e^{\tan x}\cdot\cos x$$

Example 35 Evaluate

(i) $\int e^x\left(\frac{1+\sin x\cos x}{\cos^2 x}\right)dx$ (ii) $\int e^{2x}\left(\frac{1+\sin 2x}{1+\cos 2x}\right)dx$

Sol. (i) $I=\int e^x\left(\frac{1+\sin x\cos x}{\cos^2 x}\right)dx$

$$I=\int e^x\left\{\frac{1}{\cos^2 x}+\frac{\sin x\cos x}{\cos^2 x}\right\}dx$$

$$I=\int e^x\{\tan x+\sec^2 x\}\,dx$$

$$I=\int \underset{\text{II}}{e^x}\cdot\underset{\text{I}}{\tan x}\,dx+\int e^x(\sec^2 x)\,dx$$

$$I=\tan x\cdot e^x-\int\sec^2 x\cdot e^x\,dx+\int e^x\cdot\sec^2 x\,dx+C$$

$$I=e^x\tan x+C$$

(ii) $I=\int e^{2x}\left\{\frac{1+\sin 2x}{1+\cos 2x}\right\}dx$

$$=\int e^{2x}\left\{\frac{1+2\sin x\cos x}{2\cos^2 x}\right\}dx$$

$$=\int e^{2x}\left\{\frac{1}{2\cos^2 x}+\frac{2\sin x\cos x}{2\cos^2 x}\right\}dx$$

$$=\int e^{2x}\left\{\frac{1}{2}\sec^2 x+\tan x\right\}dx$$

$$=\int \underset{\text{II}}{e^{2x}}\cdot\underset{\text{I}}{\tan x}\,dx+\frac{1}{2}\int e^{2x}\cdot\sec^2 x\,dx$$

$$=\tan x\cdot\frac{e^{2x}}{2}-\int\sec^2 x\cdot\frac{e^{2x}}{2}\,dx+\frac{1}{2}\int e^{2x}\cdot\sec^2 x\,dx$$

$$I=\frac{1}{2}e^{2x}\cdot\tan x+C$$

Example 36 Evaluate $\int e^x\left(\frac{1-x}{1+x^2}\right)^2dx.$

Sol. $I=\int e^x\left(\frac{1-x}{1+x^2}\right)^2dx=\int e^x\frac{(1-2x+x^2)}{(1+x^2)^2}dx$

$$=\int e^x\left\{\frac{1+x^2}{(1+x^2)^2}-\frac{2x}{(1+x^2)^2}\right\}dx$$

$$=\int e^x\left\{\frac{1}{1+x^2}-\frac{2x}{(1+x^2)^2}\right\}dx\quad\left[\text{as }\frac{d}{dx}\left(\frac{1}{1+x^2}\right)=-\frac{2x}{(1+x^2)^2}\right]$$

$$=\frac{e^x}{1+x^2}+C$$

$$\therefore\quad I=\frac{e^x}{1+x^2}+C$$

Integrals of the Form $\int e^{ax}\sin bx\,dx$, $\int e^{ax}\cos bx\,dx$

Let $I=\int e^{ax}(\sin bx)\,dx$

Then, $I=\int \underset{\text{I}}{\sin bx}\cdot\underset{\text{II}}{e^{ax}}\,dx$

$$=\sin bx\cdot\left(\frac{e^{ax}}{a}\right)-\int b\cos bx\cdot\frac{e^{ax}}{a}\,dx$$

$$=\frac{1}{a}\sin bx\cdot e^{ax}-\frac{b}{a}\left\{\cos bx\cdot\frac{e^{ax}}{a}-\int(-b\sin bx)\cdot\frac{e^{ax}}{a}\,dx\right\}$$

$$=\frac{1}{a}\sin bx\cdot e^{ax}-\frac{b}{a^2}\cos bx\cdot e^{ax}-\frac{b^2}{a^2}\int\sin bx\cdot e^{ax}\,dx$$

$$I=\frac{1}{a}\sin bx\cdot e^{ax}-\frac{b}{a^2}\cos bx\cdot e^{ax}-\frac{b^2}{a^2}I$$

$$\therefore\quad I+\frac{b^2}{a^2}I=\frac{1\cdot e^{ax}}{a^2}\cdot(a\sin bx-b\cos bx)$$

$$\Rightarrow\quad I\left(\frac{a^2+b^2}{a^2}\right)=\frac{e^{ax}}{a^2}(a\sin bx-b\cos bx)$$

or $$I=\frac{e^{ax}}{a^2+b^2}(a\sin bx-b\cos bx)+C$$

Thus, $\int e^{ax}\sin bx\,dx=\frac{e^{ax}}{a^2+b^2}(a\sin bx-b\cos bx)+C$

Similarly, $\int e^{ax}\cos bx\,dx=\frac{e^{ax}}{a^2+b^2}(a\cos bx+b\sin bx)+C$

Aliter Use Euler's equation

Let $P=\int e^{ax}\cos bx\,dx$ and $Q=\int e^{ax}\sin bx\,dx$

Hence, $P+iQ=\int e^{ax}\cdot e^{ibx}\,dx=\int e^{(a+ib)x}\,dx$

$$P+iQ=\frac{1}{a+ib}e^{(a+ib)x}=\frac{a-ib}{a^2+b^2}e^{ax}(\cos bx+i\sin bx)$$

$$= \frac{(ae^{ax}\cos bx + be^{ax}\sin bx) - i\,(ae^{ax}\sin bx - be^{ax}\cos bx)}{a^2+b^2}$$

$$\therefore \quad P = \frac{e^{ax}\,(a\cos bx + b\sin bx)}{a^2+b^2}$$

$$Q = \frac{e^{ax}\,(a\sin bx - b\cos bx)}{a^2+b^2}$$

Example 37 Evaluate

(i) $\int e^x \cos^2 x\, dx$

(ii) $\int \sin(\log x)\, dx$

Sol. (i) $I = \int e^x \cdot \cos^2 x\, dx = \int e^x \cdot \left\{\frac{1+\cos 2x}{2}\right\} dx$

$$I = \frac{1}{2}\int e^x\, dx + \frac{1}{2}\int \cos 2x \cdot e^x\, dx$$

$$I = \frac{1}{2}e^x + \frac{1}{2}I_1 \qquad \text{...(i)}$$

where, $I_1 = \int \cos 2x \cdot e^x\, dx$

$$I_1 = \int \underset{\text{I}}{\cos 2x} \cdot \underset{\text{II}}{e^x}\, dx = \cos 2x \cdot e^x - \int -2\sin 2x \cdot e^x\, dx$$

$$= e^x \cdot \cos 2x + 2\int \underset{\text{I}}{\sin 2x} \cdot \underset{\text{II}}{e^x}\, dx$$

$$= e^x \cdot \cos 2x + 2\left\{\sin 2x \cdot e^x - \int 2\cos 2x \cdot e^x\, dx\right\}$$

$$= e^x \cdot \cos 2x + 2\sin 2x \cdot e^x - 4\,I_1$$

$$\therefore \quad I_1 = \frac{1}{5}\{e^x \cos 2x + 2\sin 2x\, e^x\} \qquad \text{...(ii)}$$

From Eqs. (i) and (ii), we get

$$I = \frac{1}{2}e^x + \frac{1}{2}\cdot\frac{1}{5}\{e^x \cos 2x + 2\sin 2x \cdot e^x\}$$

$$I = \frac{1}{2}e^x + \frac{1}{10}e^x\{\cos 2x + 2\sin 2x\} + C$$

(ii) $I = \int \sin(\log x)\, dx$

Let $\log x = t$

$$\Rightarrow \quad x = e^t \text{ or } dx = e^t\, dt$$

$$\therefore \quad I = \int \underset{\text{I}}{(\sin t)} \cdot \underset{\text{II}}{e^t}\, dt = \sin t \cdot e^t - \int \underset{\text{I}}{\cos t} \cdot \underset{\text{II}}{e^t}\, dt$$

$$I = \sin t \cdot e^t - \left\{\cos t \cdot e^t - \int -\sin t \cdot e^t\, dt\right\}$$

$$I = e^t \cdot \sin t - e^t \cdot \cos t - I$$

$$\therefore \quad I = \frac{1}{2}e^t(\sin t - \cos t) + C$$

$$I = \frac{x}{2}\{\sin(\log x) - \cos(\log x)\} + C$$

Example 38 Evaluate $\int \frac{x^2\, dx}{(x\sin x + \cos x)^2}$.

Sol. Let $I = \int \frac{x^2}{(x\sin x + \cos x)^2}\, dx$

Multiplying and dividing it by $(x\cos x)$, we get

$$I = \int \underset{\text{I}}{(x\sec x)} \cdot \underset{\text{II}}{\frac{(x\cos x)}{(x\sin x + \cos x)^2}}\, dx$$

$$I = x\sec x \cdot \int \frac{x\cos x}{(x\sin x + \cos x)^2}\, dx$$

$$- \int \left\{\frac{d}{dx}(x\sec x)\right\}\left\{\int \frac{x\cos x}{(x\sin x + \cos x)^2}\, dx\right\} dx$$

$$= x\sec x \cdot \frac{-1}{(x\sin x + \cos x)}$$

$$- \int (x\sec x \cdot \tan x + \sec x) \cdot \frac{-1}{(x\sin x + \cos x)}\, dx$$

$$= \frac{-x\sec x}{(x\sin x + \cos x)} + \int \frac{(x\sin x + \cos x)}{\cos^2 x \cdot (x\sin x + \cos x)}\, dx$$

$$= \frac{-x\sec x}{(x\sin x + \cos x)} + \int \sec^2 x\, dx$$

$$I = \frac{-x\sec x}{(x\sin x + \cos x)} + \tan x + C$$

Example 39 The value of

$\int \sqrt{\frac{3-x}{3+x}} \cdot \sin^{-1}\left(\frac{1}{\sqrt{6}}\sqrt{3-x}\right) dx$, is equal to

(a) $\frac{1}{4}\left\{-3\left(\cos^{-1}\left(\frac{x}{3}\right)\right)^2 + 2\sqrt{9-x^2} \cdot \cos^{-1}\left(\frac{x}{3}\right) + 2x\right\} + C$

(b) $\frac{1}{4}\left\{-3\left(\cos^{-1}\left(\frac{x}{3}\right)\right)^2 + 2\sqrt{9-x^2}\, \sin^{-1}\left(\frac{x}{3}\right) + 2x\right\} + C$

(c) $\frac{1}{4}\left\{-3\left(\sin^{-1}\left(\frac{x}{3}\right)\right)^2 + 2\sqrt{9-x^2}\, \sin^{-1}\left(\frac{x}{3}\right) + 2x\right\} + C$

(d) None of the above

Sol. Here, $I = \int \sqrt{\frac{3-x}{3+x}} \cdot \sin^{-1}\left(\frac{1}{\sqrt{6}}\sqrt{3-x}\right) dx$

Put $x = 3\cos 2\theta$

$$\Rightarrow \quad dx = -6\sin 2\theta\, d\theta$$

$$\therefore \quad I = \int \sqrt{\frac{3-3\cos 2\theta}{3+3\cos 2\theta}} \cdot \sin^{-1}\left(\frac{1}{\sqrt{6}}\sqrt{3-3\cos 2\theta}\right)(-6\sin 2\theta)\, d\theta$$

$$= \int \frac{\sin\theta}{\cos\theta} \cdot \sin^{-1}(\sin\theta) \cdot (-6\sin 2\theta)\, d\theta$$

$$= -6\int \theta \cdot (2\sin^2\theta)\, d\theta = -6\int \theta\,(1-\cos 2\theta)\, d\theta$$

$$= -6\left\{\frac{\theta^2}{2} - \int \theta \cos 2\theta \, d\theta\right\}$$

$$= -6\left\{\frac{\theta^2}{2} - \left(\theta \frac{\sin 2\theta}{2} - \int 1 \cdot \left(\frac{\sin 2\theta}{2}\right) d\theta\right)\right\}$$

$$= -3\theta^2 + 6\left\{\frac{\theta \sin 2\theta}{2} + \frac{\cos 2\theta}{4}\right\} + C$$

$$= \frac{1}{4}\left\{-3\left(\cos^{-1}\left(\frac{x}{3}\right)\right)^2 + 2\sqrt{9 - x^2} \cdot \cos^{-1}\left(\frac{x}{3}\right) + 2x\right\} + C$$

Hence, (a) is the correct answer.

| Example 40 The value of $\int \frac{\sec x \,(2 + \sec x)}{(1 + 2\sec x)^2} dx$, is equal to

(a) $\frac{\sin x}{2 + \cos x} + C$ (b) $\frac{\cos x}{2 + \cos x} + C$

(c) $\frac{-\sin x}{2 + \sin x} + C$ (d) $\frac{\cos x}{2 + \sin x} + C$

Sol. Let $I = \int \frac{\sec x \,(2 + \sec x)}{(1 + 2\sec x)^2} dx = \int \frac{2\cos x + 1}{(\cos x + 2)^2} dx$

$$= \int \frac{\cos x \,(\cos x + 2) + \sin^2 x}{(2 + \cos x)^2} dx$$

$$= \int \frac{\cos x}{2 + \cos x} dx + \int \frac{\sin^2 x}{(2 + \cos x)^2} dx$$

$$= \int \underset{\text{II}}{\cos x} \cdot \underset{\text{I}}{\frac{1}{(2 + \cos x)}} dx + \int \frac{\sin^2 x}{(2 + \cos x)^2} dx$$

Applying integration by parts to first by taking $\cos x$ as second function, keeping $\int \frac{\sin^2 x}{(2 + \cos x)^2} dx$ as it is.

$$\therefore \quad I = \frac{1}{2 + \cos x} \cdot (\sin x) - \int \sin x \cdot \frac{\sin x}{(2 + \cos x)^2} dx + \int \frac{\sin^2 x}{(2 + \cos x)^2} dx$$

$$\therefore \quad I = \frac{\sin x}{2 + \cos x} + C$$

Hence, (a) is the correct answer.

| Example 41 The value of $\int \log(\sqrt{1 - x} + \sqrt{1 + x}) \, dx$, is equal to

(a) $x \log(\sqrt{1 - x} + \sqrt{1 + x}) + \frac{1}{2}x - \frac{1}{2}\sin^{-1}(x) + C$

(b) $x \log(\sqrt{1 - x} + \sqrt{1 + x}) + \frac{1}{2}x + \frac{1}{2}\sin^{-1}(x) + C$

(c) $x \log(\sqrt{1 - x} + \sqrt{1 + x}) - \frac{1}{2}x + \frac{1}{2}\sin^{-1}(x) + C$

(d) None of the above

Sol. Here, we have only one function. This can be solved easily by applying integration by parts taking unity as second function.

If we take $u = \log(\sqrt{1 - x} + \sqrt{1 + x})$ as the first function and $v = 1$ as the second function.

Then,

$$I = \int 1 \cdot \log(\sqrt{1 - x} + \sqrt{1 + x}) \, dx$$

$$= \{\log(\sqrt{1 - x} + \sqrt{1 + x})\} \cdot x - \int \frac{1}{\sqrt{1 - x} + \sqrt{1 + x}} \left(-\frac{1}{2\sqrt{1 - x}} + \frac{1}{2\sqrt{1 + x}}\right) \cdot x \, dx$$

$$= x \log(\sqrt{1 - x} + \sqrt{1 + x}) - \frac{1}{2}\int \frac{\sqrt{1 - x} - \sqrt{1 + x}}{\sqrt{1 - x} + \sqrt{1 + x}} \cdot \frac{1}{\sqrt{1 - x^2}} \cdot x \, dx$$

$$= x \log(\sqrt{1 - x} + \sqrt{1 + x}) - \frac{1}{2}\int \frac{(1 - x) + (1 + x) - 2\sqrt{1 - x^2}}{(1 - x) - (1 + x)} \cdot \frac{1}{\sqrt{1 - x^2}} \cdot 2x \, dx$$

$$= x \log(\sqrt{1 - x} + \sqrt{1 + x}) - \frac{1}{2}\int \frac{\sqrt{1 - x^2} - 1}{\sqrt{1 - x^2}} dx$$

$$= x \log(\sqrt{1 - x} + \sqrt{1 + x}) - \frac{1}{2}\int 1 \, dx + \frac{1}{2}\int \frac{1}{\sqrt{1 - x^2}} dx$$

$$= x \log(\sqrt{1 - x} + \sqrt{1 + x}) - \frac{1}{2}x + \frac{1}{2}\sin^{-1} x + C$$

Hence, (c) is the correct answer.

| Example 42 The value of $\int e^x \left(\frac{x^4 + 2}{(1 + x^2)^{5/2}}\right) dx$, is equal to

(a) $\frac{e^x (x + 1)}{(1 + x^2)^{3/2}}$ (b) $\frac{e^x (1 - x + x^2)}{(1 + x^2)^{3/2}}$

(c) $\frac{e^x (1 + x)}{(1 + x^2)^{3/2}}$ (d) None of these

Sol. Let $I = \int e^x \left(\frac{x^4 + 2}{(1 + x^2)^{5/2}}\right) dx$

$$= \int e^x \left(\frac{1}{(1 + x^2)^{1/2}} + \frac{1 - 2x^2}{(1 + x^2)^{5/2}}\right) dx$$

$$= \int e^x \left(\frac{1}{(1 + x^2)^{1/2}} - \frac{x}{(1 + x^2)^{3/2}} + \frac{x}{(1 + x^2)^{3/2}} + \frac{1 - 2x^2}{(1 + x^2)^{5/2}}\right) dx$$

$$= \frac{e^x}{(1 + x^2)^{1/2}} + \frac{xe^x}{(1 + x^2)^{3/2}} + C = \frac{e^x \{1 + x^2 + x\}}{(1 + x^2)^{3/2}} + C$$

Hence, (d) is the correct answer.

Example 43 If $\int (\sin 3\theta + \sin\theta)\, e^{\sin\theta} \cos\theta\, d\theta = (A\sin^3\theta + B\cos^2\theta + C\sin\theta + D\cos\theta + E)\, e^{\sin\theta} + F$, then

(a) $A = -4, B = 12$ (b) $A = -4, B = -12$
(c) $A = 4, B = 12$ (d) $A = 4, B = -12$

Sol. Let $I = \int (\sin 3\theta + \sin\theta)\, e^{\sin\theta} \cdot \cos\theta\, d\theta$

$$= \int (3\sin\theta - 4\sin^3\theta) \cdot e^{\sin\theta} \cdot \cos\theta\, d\theta;$$

Put $\sin\theta = t \Rightarrow \cos\theta\, d\theta = dt$

$$= \int (3t - 4t^3)\, e^t\, dt \quad \text{...(i)}$$

As, $I = (A\sin^3\theta + B\cos^2\theta + C\sin\theta + D\cos\theta + E)e^{\sin\theta} + F$

$$= (A\sin^3\theta - B\sin^2\theta + C\sin\theta + D\cos\theta + B + E)e^{\sin\theta} + F$$

When, $\sin\theta = t$

$$I = (At^3 - Bt^2 + Ct + B + E)\, e^t + F$$

as by Eq. (i) $D = 0$ ...(ii)

From Eqs. (i) and (ii),

$$\int (3t - 4t^3)\, e^t\, dt = \underbrace{(At^3 - Bt^2 + Ct + B + E)}_{f(t)}\, e^t + F,$$

differentiating both sides

$$(3t - 4t^3)\, e^t = (At^3 - Bt^2 + Ct + B + E)e^t + (3At^2 - 2Bt + C)e^t$$

$$\Rightarrow \quad A = -4 \text{ and } 3A = B \Rightarrow B = -12$$

Hence, (b) is the correct answer.

Example 44 The value of

$\int e^{(x\sin x + \cos x)} \cdot \left(\dfrac{x^4\cos^3 x - x\sin x + \cos x}{x^2\cos^2 x}\right) dx$, is equal to

(a) $e^{(x\sin x + \cos x)} \cdot \left(x + \dfrac{1}{x\cos x}\right) + C$

(b) $e^{(x\sin x + \cos x)} \cdot \left(x\cos x + \dfrac{1}{x}\right) + C$

(c) $e^{(x\sin x + \cos x)} \cdot \left(x - \dfrac{1}{x\cos x}\right) + C$

(d) None of the above

Sol. Let $I = \int e^{(x\sin x + \cos x)} \cdot \left(\dfrac{x^4\cos^3 x - x\sin x + \cos x}{x^2\cos^2 x}\right) dx$

$$= \int (x \cdot e^{(x\sin x + \cos x)} \cdot x\cos x)\, dx - \int e^{(x\sin x + \cos x)} \cdot \left(\frac{x\sin x - \cos x}{(x\cos x)^2}\right) dx$$

Applying integration by parts

$$= \{x \cdot e^{(x\sin x + \cos x)} - \int e^{(x\sin x + \cos x)}\, dx\} - \left\{e^{(x\sin x + \cos x)} \cdot \frac{1}{x\cos x} - \int e^{(x\sin x + \cos x)}\, dx\right\}$$

$$= e^{(x\sin x + \cos x)}\left(x - \frac{1}{x\cos x}\right) + C$$

Hence, (c) is the correct answer.

Example 45 Evaluate $\int \sin^{-1}\left\{\dfrac{2x+2}{\sqrt{4x^2 + 8x + 13}}\right\} dx$.

[IIT JEE 2001]

Sol. Here, $I = \int \sin^{-1}\left(\dfrac{2x+2}{\sqrt{4x^2 + 8x + 13}}\right) dx$

$$= \int \sin^{-1}\left(\frac{2x+2}{\sqrt{(2x+2)^2 + 3^2}}\right) dx$$

Put $2x + 2 = 3\tan\theta \Rightarrow 2\, dx = 3\sec^2\theta\, d\theta$

$$= \int \sin^{-1}\left(\frac{3\tan\theta}{3\sec\theta}\right)\frac{3}{2}\sec^2\theta\, d\theta = \frac{3}{2}\int \theta\sec^2\theta\, d\theta$$

$$= \frac{3}{2}\{\theta\tan\theta - \int \tan\theta\, d\theta\}$$

$$= \frac{3}{2}\{\theta\tan\theta - \log|\sec\theta|\} + C$$

$$\Rightarrow I = \frac{3}{2}\left\{\frac{2x+2}{3}\tan^{-1}\left(\frac{2x+2}{3}\right) - \log\left(\sqrt{1 + \left(\frac{2x+2}{3}\right)^2}\right)\right\} + C$$

$$= \frac{3}{2}\left\{\frac{2}{3}(x+1)\tan^{-1}\left(\frac{2}{3}(x+1)\right) - \log\sqrt{4x^2 + 8x + 13}\right\} + C$$

$$\Rightarrow I = (x+1)\tan^{-1}\left(\frac{2}{3}(x+1)\right) - \frac{3}{4}\log(4x^2 + 8x + 13) + C$$

Example 46 Evaluate $\int \dfrac{x^2\,(x\sec^2 x + \tan x)\, dx}{(x\tan x + 1)^2}$

Sol. Here, $I = \int x^2 \cdot \dfrac{x\sec^2 x + \tan x}{(x\tan x + 1)^2}\, dx$

$$= x^2\left(-\frac{1}{(x\tan x + 1)}\right) - \int 2x \cdot \left(-\frac{1}{(x\tan x + 1)}\right) dx \quad \text{...(i)}$$

$$\left[\text{using} \int \frac{x\sec^2 x + \tan x}{(x\tan x + 1)^2}\, dx = \int \frac{dt}{t^2} = -\frac{1}{t} = -\frac{1}{(x\tan x + 1)}\right]$$

$$\Rightarrow I = -\left(\frac{x^2}{x\tan x + 1}\right) + \int \frac{2x\,(\cos x)}{x\sin x + \cos x}\, dx$$

[put, $x\sin x + \cos x = u$
$\Rightarrow (x\cos x + \sin x - \cos x)\, dx = du$]

$$\Rightarrow \quad I = -\frac{x^2}{(x\tan x + 1)} + 2\int \frac{du}{u}$$

$$= -\frac{x^2}{x\tan x + 1} + 2\log|u| + C$$

$$= -\frac{x^2}{x\tan x + 1} + 2\log|x\sin x + \cos x| + C$$

Exercise for Session 4

1. $\int x^2e^x dx$

2. $\int x^2 \sin x \, dx$

3. $\int \log x \cdot dx$

4. $\int (\log x)^2 dx$

5. $\int (\tan^{-1} x) \, dx$

6. $\int (\sec^{-1} x) \, dx$

7. $\int x \tan^{-1} x \, dx$

8. $\int \frac{\log x}{x^2} dx$

9. $\int \frac{x - \sin x}{1 - \cos x} dx$

10. $\int \log (1 + x^2) \, dx$

11. $\int e^x (\tan x + \log \sec x) \, dx$

12. $\int e^x \left\{ \frac{1 + \sin x \cos x}{\cos^2 x} \right\} dx$

13. $\int \left(\log (\log x) + \frac{1}{(\log x)^2} \right) dx$

14. $\int e^{2x} \cdot \left\{ \frac{1 + \sin 2x}{1 + \cos 2x} \right\} dx$

15. $\int e^x \frac{(1 - x)^2}{(1 + x^2)^2} dx$

16. $\int \frac{e^x \cdot (2 - x^2)}{(1 - x)\sqrt{1 - x^2}} dx$

17. $\int e^{ax} \cdot \cos (bx + c) \, dx$

18. $\int \sec^3 x \, dx$

19. $\int \sin \sqrt{x} \, dx$

20. $\int (\sin^{-1} x)^2 dx$

21. $\int \cot^{-1} (1 - x + x^2) \, dx$

22. $\int \sin^{-1} \sqrt{\frac{x}{a + x}} \, dx$

23. $\int \frac{\sqrt{x^2 + 1} \{\log (x^2 + 1) - 2 \log x\}}{x^4} dx$

24. $\int \frac{\cos^2 x + \sin 2x}{(2 \cos x - \sin x)^2} dx$

25. $\int e^{\sin x} \left(\frac{x \cos^2 x - \sin x}{\cos^2 x} \right) dx$

Session 5

Integration Using Partial Fraction

This section deals with the integration of general algebraic rational functions, of the form $\frac{f(x)}{g(x)}$, where $f(x)$ and $g(x)$ are both polynomials. We already have seen some examples of this form. For example, we know how to integrate functions of the form $\frac{1}{Q(x)}$ or $\frac{L(x)}{Q(x)}$ or $\frac{P(x)}{Q(x)}$ where $L(x)$ is a linear factor, $Q(x)$ is a quadratic factor and $P(x)$ is a polynomial of degree $n \geq 2$. We intend to generalise that previous discussion in this section.

We are assuming the scenario where $g(x)$ (the denominator) is decomposible into linear or quadratic factors. These are the only cases relevant to us right now. Any linear or quadratic factor in $g(x)$ might also occur repeatedly.

Thus, $g(x)$ could be of the following general forms.

- $g(x) = L_1(x)L_2(x)\ldots L_n(x)$ (n linear factors)
- $g(x) = L_1(x)\ldots L_r^k(x)\ldots L_n(x)$ $\left(\begin{array}{l} n \text{ linear factors; the } r\text{th} \\ \text{factor is repeated } k \text{ times} \end{array}\right)$
- $g(x) = L_1^{k_1}(x)L_2^{k_2}(x)\ldots L_n^{k_n}(x)$ $\left(\begin{array}{l} n \text{ linear factors, the } i\text{th} \\ \text{factor is repeated } k_i \text{ times} \end{array}\right)$
- $g(x) = L_1(x)L_2(x)\ldots L_n(x)Q(x)Q_2(x)\ldots Q_m(x)$ $\left(\begin{array}{l} n \text{ linear factors and} \\ m \text{ quadratic factors} \end{array}\right)$
- $g(x) = \ldots Q_r^k(x)\ldots$ $\left(\begin{array}{l} \text{a particular quadratic factor} \\ \text{repeats more than once} \end{array}\right)$
- A combination of any of the above

Suppose that the degree of $g(x)$ is n and that of $f(x)$ is m. If $m \geq n$, we can always divide $f(x)$ by $g(x)$ to obtain a quotient $q(x)$ and a remainder $r(x)$ whose degree would be less than n.

$$\frac{f(x)}{g(x)} = q(x) + \frac{r(x)}{g(x)} \qquad \ldots(\text{i})$$

If $m < n$, $\frac{f(x)}{g(x)}$ is termed a proper rational function.

The partial fraction expansion technique says that a proper rational function can be expressed as a sum of simpler rational functions each possessing one of the factors of $g(x)$. The simpler rational functions are called partial fractions.

From now on, we consider only proper rational functions. If $\frac{f(x)}{g(x)}$ is not proper, we make it proper $\left(\frac{r(x)}{g(x)}\right)$ by the procedure described in (1) above. Let us consider a few examples.

Let $g(x)$ be a product of non-repeated, linear factors :

$$g(x) = L_1(x)L_2(x)\ldots L_n(x)$$

Then, we can expand $\frac{f(x)}{g(x)}$ in terms of partial fractions as

$$\frac{f(x)}{g(x)} = \frac{A_1}{L_1(x)} + \frac{A_2}{L_2(x)} + \ldots + \frac{A_n}{L_n(x)}$$

where the $A_i's$ are all constants that need to be determined. Suppose $f(x) = x + 1$ and $g(x) = (x-1)(x-2)(x-3)$. Let us write down the partial fraction expansion of $\frac{f(x)}{g(x)}$:

$$\frac{f(x)}{g(x)} = \frac{x+1}{(x-1)(x-2)(x-3)} = \frac{A}{x-1} + \frac{B}{x-2} + \frac{C}{x-3}$$

We need to determine A, B and C. Cross multiplying in the expression above, we obtain :

$$(x+1) = A(x-2)(x-3) + B(x-1)(x-3) + C(x-1)(x-2)$$

A, B, C can now be determined by comparing coefficients on both sides. More simply since this relation that we have obtained should held true for all x,we substitute those values of x that would straight way give us the required values of A, B and C. These values are obviously the roots of $g(x)$.

$x = 1 \quad \Rightarrow \quad 2 = A(-1)(-2) + B(0) + C(0)$

$\Rightarrow \quad A = 1$

$x = 2 \quad \Rightarrow \quad 3 = A(0) + B(1)(-1) + C(0)$

$\Rightarrow \quad B = -3$

$x = 3 \quad \Rightarrow \quad 4 = A(0) + B(0) + C(2)(1)$

$\Rightarrow \quad C = 2$

Thus, $A = 1$, $B = -3$ and $C = 2$.

We can therefore write $\frac{f(x)}{g(x)}$ as a sum of partial fractions.

$$\frac{f(x)}{g(x)} = \frac{1}{x-1} - \frac{3}{x-2} + \frac{2}{x-3}$$

Integrating $\frac{f(x)}{g(x)}$ is now a simple matter of integrating the partial fractions. This was our sole motive in writing such an expansion, so that integration could be carried out easily. In the example above :

$$\int \frac{f(x)}{g(x)}\,dx = \ln(x-1) - 3\ln(x-2) + 2\ln(x-3) + C$$

Now, suppose that $g(x)$ contains all linear factors, but a particular factor, say $L_1(x)$, is repeated k times.

Thus, $\quad g(x) = L_1^k(x) L_2(x) \dots L_n(x)$

$\frac{f(x)}{g(x)}$ can now be expanded into partial fractions as follows

$$\frac{f(x)}{g(x)} = \underbrace{\frac{A_1}{L_1(x)} + \frac{A_2}{L_1^2(x)} + \frac{A_3}{L_1^3(x)} + \dots \frac{A_k}{L_1^k(x)}}_{k \text{ partial fractions corresponding to } L_1(x)} + \frac{B_2}{L_2(x)} + \dots + \frac{B_n}{L_n(x)}$$

This means that we will have k terms corresponding to $L_1(x)$. The rest of the linear factors will have single corresponding terms in the expansion. Here are some examples.

$\Rightarrow \quad \frac{1}{(x-1)^2(x-2)}$

can be expanded as $\frac{A}{x-1} + \frac{B}{(x-1)^2} + \frac{C}{x-2}$

$\Rightarrow \quad \frac{1}{(x-1)^3(x-2)(x-3)}$

can be expanded as

$\Rightarrow \quad \frac{A}{x-1} + \frac{B}{(x-1)^2} + \frac{C}{(x-1)^3} + \frac{D}{(x-2)} + \frac{C}{(x-3)}$

$\Rightarrow \quad \frac{1}{(x-1)^2(x+5)^3}$

can be expanded as

$$\frac{A}{x-1} + \frac{B}{(x-1)^2} + \frac{C}{(x+5)} + \frac{D}{(x+5)^2} + \frac{E}{(x+5)^3}$$

| Example 47 $\frac{2x+1}{(x+1)(x-2)}$ into partial fractions

Sol. Here, $\frac{2x+1}{(x+1)(x-2)}$ has $Q(x) = (x+1)(x-2)$ i.e linear and non-repeated roots.

$\therefore \quad \frac{2x+1}{(x+1)(x-2)} = \frac{A}{x+1} + \frac{B}{x-2}$

$\Rightarrow \quad (2x+1) = A(x-2) + B(x+1)$

On putting, $x = 2$ we get

$5 = A(0) + B(3) \Rightarrow B = \frac{5}{3}$

Again, let $x = -1$

$\Rightarrow \quad 2(-1) + 1 = A(-1-2) + B(0)$

$\therefore \quad A = \frac{1}{3}.$

$\therefore \quad \frac{2x+1}{(x+1)(x-2)} = \frac{1/3}{x+1} + \frac{5/3}{x-2}$

| Example 48 Resolve $\frac{1}{(x-1)(x+2)(2x+3)}$ into partial fractions.

Sol. Let $\frac{1}{(x-1)(x+2)(2x+3)} = \frac{A}{x-1} + \frac{B}{x+2} + \frac{C}{2x+3}$,

where A, B, C are constants.

$1 = A(x+2)(2x+3) + B(x-1)(2x+3) + C(x-1)(x+2)$ ...(i)

For finding A, let $x - 1 = 0$ or $x = 1$ in Eq. (i), we get

$1 = A(1+2)(2+3) + B(0) + C(0)$

$\therefore \quad A = \frac{1}{15}$

Similarly, for getting B, let $x + 2 = 0$ or $x = -2$ in Eq. (i), we get

$1 = A(0) + B(-2-1)(-4+3) + C(0)$

$\Rightarrow \quad B = \frac{1}{3}$

For getting C, let $2x + 3 = 0$ or $x = -3/2$ in Eq. (i), we get

$1 = A(0) + B(0) + C\left(-\frac{3}{2} - 1\right)\left(-\frac{3}{2} + 2\right)$

$\Rightarrow \quad C = -\frac{4}{5}$

Hence, $\frac{1}{(x-1)(x+2)(2x+3)} = \frac{1}{15(x-1)} + \frac{1}{3(x+2)} - \frac{4}{5(2x+3)}$

| Example 49 Resolve $\frac{3x^3 + 2x^2 + x + 1}{(x+1)(x+2)}$ into partial fractions.

Sol. This is not a proper fraction. Hence, by division process it is to be expressed as the sum of an integral polynomial and a fraction.

Now, $3x^3 + 2x^2 + x + 1 = 3x(x^2 + 3x + 2)$

$\qquad - 7(x^2 + 3x + 2) + (16x + 15)$

So, the given polynomial

$$\frac{3x^3 + 2x^2 + x + 1}{(x+1)(x+2)} = (3x - 7) + \frac{(16x+15)}{(x+1)(x+2)} \quad \text{...(i)}$$

Now, the second term is proper fraction hence it can be expressed as a sum of partial fractions.

$$\frac{16x+15}{(x+1)(x+2)} = \frac{A}{x+1} + \frac{B}{x+2}$$

To find A put $x+1=0$, *ie*, $x=-1$ in the fraction except in the factor $(x+1)$.

$$\therefore \quad \frac{16(-1)+15}{(-1+2)}=A \Rightarrow A=-1 \quad \text{...(ii)}$$

To find B put $x+2=0$, *ie*, $x=-2$ in the fraction except in the factor $(x+2)$.

$$\therefore \quad \frac{16(-2)+15}{(-2+1)}=B \Rightarrow B=17 \quad \text{...(iii)}$$

$\Rightarrow$ The given expression $=(3x-7)-\frac{1}{x+1}+\frac{17}{x+2}$

[using Eqs. (i), (ii) and (iii)]

Case II When the denominator $g(x)$ is expressible as the product of the linear factors such that some of them are repeating. (Linear and Repeated)

Let $Q(x)=(x-a)^k(x-a_1)(x-a_2)\dots(x-a_r)$. Then, we assume that

$$\frac{P(x)}{Q(x)}=\frac{A_1}{(x-a)}+\frac{A_2}{(x-a)^2}+\dots+\frac{A_k}{(x-a)^k}+\frac{B_1}{(x-a_1)}+\frac{B_2}{(x-a_2)}+\dots+\frac{B_r}{(x-a_r)}$$

| Example 50 Expression $\frac{x+5}{(x-2)^2}$ has repeated (twice) linear factors in denominator, so find partial fractions.

Sol. Let $$\frac{x+5}{(x-2)^2}=\frac{A}{(x-2)}+\frac{B}{(x-2)^2}$$

$$\therefore \quad (x+5)=A(x-2)+B$$

Comparing the like terms, $A=1,-2A+B=5$ or $B=7$

$$\therefore \quad \frac{x+5}{(x-2)^2}=\frac{1}{(x-2)}+\frac{7}{(x-2)^2}$$

| Example 51 Resolve $\frac{3x-2}{(x-1)^2(x+1)(x+2)}$ into partial fractions.

Sol. Let $$\frac{3x-2}{(x-1)^2(x+1)(x+2)}=\frac{A}{(x-1)}+\frac{B}{(x-1)^2}+\frac{C}{(x+1)}+\frac{D}{(x+2)}$$

$$\therefore \ 3x-2=A(x-1)(x+1)(x+2)+B(x+1)(x+2)+C(x-1)^2(x+2)+D(x-1)^2(x+1)$$

Putting $(x-1)=0$, we get $B=1/6$,

Putting $(x+1)=0$, we get $C=-5/4$

Putting $(x+2)=0$, we get $D=8/9$

Now, equating the coefficient of x^3 on both the sides, we get

$$0=A+C+D \Rightarrow A=\frac{5}{4}-\frac{8}{9}=\frac{13}{36}$$

$$\therefore \quad \frac{3x-2}{(x-1)^2(x+1)(x+2)}=\frac{13}{36(x-1)}+\frac{1}{6(x-1)^2}-\frac{5}{4(x+1)}+\frac{8}{9(x+2)}$$

Case III When some of the factors in denominator are quadratic but non-repeating. Corresponding to each quadratic factor ax^2+bx+c, we assume the partial fraction of the type $\frac{Ax+B}{ax^2+bx+c}$, where A and B are constants to be determined by comparing coefficients of similar powers of x in numerator of both the sides.

| Example 52 Resolve $\frac{2x+7}{(x+1)(x^2+4)}$ into partial fractions.

Sol. Let $$\frac{2x+7}{(x+1)(x^2+4)}=\frac{A}{x+1}+\frac{Bx+C}{x^2+4}$$

$$\therefore \quad 2x+7=A(x^2+4)+(Bx+C)(x+1)$$

Put $x=-1$

$\therefore \quad 5=5A$ or $A=1$

Comparing the terms, $0=A+B \Rightarrow B=-1$

$7=4A+C \Rightarrow C=3$

$$\therefore \quad \frac{2x+7}{(x+1)(x^2+4)}=\frac{1}{x+1}+\frac{(-x+3)}{x^2+4}$$

Aliter To obtain values of A, B and C from

$$2x+7=A(x^2+4)+(Bx+C)(x+1)$$

i.e., $2x+7=(A+B)x^2+(B+C)x+4A+C$

Equating the coefficients of identical powers of x, we get

$$A+B=0, B+C=2 \text{ and } 4A+C=7.$$

Solving, we get $A=1, B=-1, C=3$

| Example 53 Find the partial fraction $\frac{2x+1}{(3x+2)(4x^2+5x+6)}$.

Sol. Let $$\frac{2x+1}{(3x+2)(4x^2+5x+6)}=\frac{A}{(3x+2)}+\frac{Bx+C}{(4x^2+5x+6)},$$

then $2x+1=A(4x^2+5x+6)+(Bx+C)(3x+2)$

where A, B, C are constants.

For A, let $3x+2=0$,

i.e., $x=-2/3$

$$2\left(-\frac{2}{3}\right)+1=A\left\{4\cdot\frac{4}{9}-\frac{10}{3}+6\right\}+\left\{B\left(-\frac{2}{3}\right)+C\right\}(0)$$

$$-\frac{1}{3}=A\left(\frac{40}{9}\right) \Rightarrow A=-\frac{3}{40}$$

Comparing coefficients of x^2 and constant term on both the sides for B and C, we get

$$4A + 3B = 0,$$

$$\therefore \quad B = -\frac{4}{3}A \Rightarrow B = \frac{1}{10} \text{ and } 6A + 2C = 1,$$

$$\therefore \quad C = \frac{1-6A}{2} \Rightarrow C = \frac{29}{40}$$

$$\therefore \quad \frac{2x+1}{(3x+2)(4x^2+5x+6)} = \frac{-3}{40(3x+2)} + \frac{\left(x+\frac{29}{4}\right)}{10(4x^2+5x+6)}$$

Case IV When some of the factors of the denominator are quadratic and repeating. For every quadratic repeating factor of the type $(ax^2+bx+c)^k$, we assume :

$$\frac{A_1x+A_2}{ax^2+bx+c} + \frac{A_3x+A_4}{(ax^2+bx+c)^2} + \ldots + \frac{A_{2k-1}x+A_{2k}}{(ax^2+bx+c)^k}$$

Example 54 Resolve $\dfrac{2x^4+2x^2+x+1}{x(x^2+1)^2}$ into partial fractions.

Sol. Let $\dfrac{2x^4+2x^2+x+1}{x(x^2+1)^2} = \dfrac{A}{x} + \dfrac{Bx+C}{x^2+1} + \dfrac{Dx+E}{(x^2+1)^2}$

or $2x^4+2x^2+x+1 = A(x^2+1)^2 + (Bx+C)x(x^2+1) + (Dx+E)x$

Comparing coefficients of x^4, x^3, x^2, x and constant term

$$\therefore \quad A+B=2, C=0, 2A+D+B=2, E=1, A=1$$

$\therefore$ we get $A=1, B=1, C=0, D=-1, E=1$

Hence, the partial fraction,

$$\frac{2x^4+2x^2+x+1}{x(x^2+1)^2} = \frac{1}{x} + \frac{x}{1+x^2} + \frac{1-x}{(1+x^2)^2}$$

Example 55 Evaluate the following integrals:

(i) $\displaystyle\int \frac{(1-x^2)\,dx}{x(1-2x)}$ (ii) $\displaystyle\int \frac{3x-1}{(x-2)^2}dx$

(iii) $\displaystyle\int \frac{x^2+x+1}{x^2(x+2)}dx$ (iv) $\displaystyle\int \frac{8dx}{(x+2)(x^2+4)}$

Sol. (i) Let, $\dfrac{1-x^2}{x(1-2x)} = \dfrac{1}{2} + \dfrac{A}{x} + \dfrac{B}{(1-2x)}$

$$\Rightarrow \quad (1-x^2) = \frac{1}{2}x(1-2x) + A(1-2x) + B(x)$$

On putting $x=0$ and $x=\frac{1}{2}$, we get

$$1 = A \text{ and } 1 - \frac{1}{4} = B \cdot \frac{1}{2} \Rightarrow A = 1, B = \frac{3}{2}$$

$$\therefore \quad \int \frac{1-x^2}{x(1-2x)}dx = \int\left(\frac{1}{2} + \frac{1}{x} + \frac{3}{2(1-2x)}\right)dx$$

$$= \frac{1}{2}x + \log|x| + \frac{3}{2}\frac{\log|1-2x|}{-2} + C$$

$$= \frac{1}{2}x + \log|x| - \frac{3}{4}\log|1-2x| + C.$$

(ii) Let, $\dfrac{3x-1}{(x-2)^2} = \dfrac{A}{(x-2)} + \dfrac{B}{(x-2)^2}$

$$\Rightarrow \quad 3x-1 = A(x-2) + B, \quad \ldots(i)$$

On putting $x=2$ in Eq. (i), we get $B=5$.

On equating coefficients of x on both sides of (i), we get $A=3$,

$$\therefore \quad \int \frac{3x-1}{(x-2)^2}dx = \int\left(\frac{3}{(x-2)} + \frac{5}{(x-2)^2}\right)dx$$

$$= 3\log|x-2| - \frac{5}{x-2} + C$$

(iii) Let, $\dfrac{x^2+x+1}{x^2(x+2)} = \dfrac{A}{x} + \dfrac{B}{x^2} + \dfrac{C}{x+2}$

$$\Rightarrow \quad x^2+x+1 = Ax(x+2) + B(x+2) + C(x^2) \quad \ldots(i)$$

On putting, $x=-2$ and $x=0$ in Eq. (i), we get

$$C = 3/4 \text{ and } B = 1/2$$

On equation Coefficient of x^2 on both sides of (i), we get $1 = A + C \Rightarrow A = 1/4$.

$$\therefore \quad \int \frac{x^2+x+1}{x^2(x+2)}dx = \int\left(\frac{1/4}{x} + \frac{1/2}{x^2} + \frac{3/4}{x+2}\right)dx$$

$$= \frac{1}{4}\log|x| - \frac{1}{2x} + \frac{3}{4}\log|x+2| + C$$

(iv) Let, $\dfrac{8}{(x+2)(x^2+4)} = \dfrac{A}{x+2} + \dfrac{Bx+C}{x^2+4}$

$$\Rightarrow \quad 8 = A(x^2+4) + (Bx+C)(x+2) \quad \ldots(i)$$

On putting $x=-2$ in Eq. (i), we get $A=1$.

On equating coefficient of x^2 on both sides we get,

$$0 = A + B \Rightarrow B = -1$$

On equating constant term on both sides, we get,

$$8 = 4A + 2C \Rightarrow C = 2$$

$$\therefore \quad \int \frac{8}{(x+2)(x^2+4)}dx = \int\left(\frac{1}{x+2} + \frac{(-x+2)}{x^2+4}\right)dx$$

$$= \int \frac{1}{x+2}dx - \frac{1}{2}\int \frac{2x\,dx}{x^2+4} + 2\int \frac{dx}{x^2+4}$$

$$= \log|x+2| - \frac{1}{2}\log|x^2+4| + 2\cdot\frac{1}{2}\tan^{-1}\left(\frac{x}{2}\right) + C.$$

Example 56 Evaluate $\displaystyle\int \frac{1}{\sin x - \sin 2x}dx.$

Sol. Let $I = \displaystyle\int \frac{1}{\sin x - \sin 2x}dx = \int \frac{1}{\sin x - 2\sin x\cos x}dx$

$$= \int \frac{1}{\sin x(1-2\cos x)}dx = \int \frac{\sin x}{\sin^2 x(1-2\cos x)}dx$$

$$= \int \frac{\sin x}{(1-\cos^2 x)(1-2\cos x)}\, dx$$

(put $\cos x = t \Rightarrow -\sin x\, dx = dt$)

$$\therefore \quad I = \int \frac{-dt}{(1-t^2)(1-2t)} = \int \frac{-1}{(1-t)(1+t)(1-2t)}\, dt \quad ...(i)$$

Here, in Eq. (i) we have linear and non-repeated factors thus we use partial fractions for;

$$\frac{-1}{(1-t)(1+t)(1-2t)} = \frac{A}{(1-t)} + \frac{B}{(1+t)} + \frac{C}{(1-2t)}$$

or $-1 = A(1+t)(1-2t) + B(1-t)(1-2t) + C(1-t)(1+t)$ ...(ii)

Putting $(t+1) = 0$ or $t = -1$, we get

$$-1 = B(2)(1+2) \Rightarrow B = -\frac{1}{6}$$

Putting $(1-t) = 0$ or $t = 1$, we get

$$-1 = A(2)(-1) \Rightarrow A = \frac{1}{2}$$

Putting $(1-2t) = 0$ or $t = 1/2$, we get

$$-1 = C\left(1-\frac{1}{2}\right)\left(1+\frac{1}{2}\right) \Rightarrow C = -\frac{4}{3}$$

$$\therefore \quad \frac{-1}{(1-t)(1+t)(1-2t)} = \frac{1}{2(1-t)} - \frac{1}{6(1+t)} - \frac{4}{3(1-2t)}$$

So, Eq. (i) reduces to

$$I = \frac{1}{2}\int \frac{1}{1-t}\, dt - \frac{1}{6}\int \frac{1}{1+t}\, dt - \frac{4}{3}\int \frac{1}{1-2t}\, dt$$

$$= -\frac{1}{2}\log|1-t| - \frac{1}{6}\log|1+t| - \frac{4}{3} \times -\frac{1}{2}\log|1-2t| + C$$

$$= -\frac{1}{2}\log|1-\cos x| - \frac{1}{6}\log|1+\cos x| + \frac{2}{3}\log |1-2\cos x| + C$$

| Example 57 Evaluate $\int \frac{(1-x\sin x)\, dx}{x(1-x^3 e^{3\cos x})}$.

Sol. Here, $I = \int \frac{(1-x\sin x)\, dx}{x(1-(xe^{\cos x})^3)}$

Put $xe^{\cos x} = t$

$\Rightarrow \quad (xe^{\cos x}.(-\sin x) + e^{\cos x})\, dx = dt$

$$\therefore \quad I = \int \frac{dt}{t(1-t^3)} = \int \frac{dt}{t(1-t)(1+t+t^2)}$$

$$= \int \left(\frac{A}{t} + \frac{B}{1-t} + \frac{Ct+D}{1+t+t^2}\right) dt$$

Comparing coefficients, we get

$$A = 1, B = \frac{1}{3}, C = -\frac{2}{3}, D = -\frac{1}{3}$$

$$\therefore \quad I = \int \frac{dt}{t} + \frac{1}{3}\int \frac{dt}{1-t} + \int \frac{\left(-\frac{2}{3}t - \frac{1}{3}\right)}{1+t+t^2}\, dt$$

$$= \log|t| - \frac{1}{3}\log|1-t| - \frac{1}{3}\log|1+t+t^2|$$

[where, $t = xe^{\cos x}$]

| Example 58 Evaluate $\int \sin 4x \cdot e^{\tan^2 x}\, dx$.

Sol. The given integral could be written as,

$$I = \int 4\sin x \cdot \cos x \cdot \cos 2x \cdot e^{\tan^2 x} dx$$

$$= 4\int \tan x \cdot \cos^2 x\,(\cos^2 x - \sin^2 x) \cdot e^{\tan^2 x} dx$$

$$= 4\int \tan x \cdot \cos^4 x\,(1-\tan^2 x) \cdot e^{\tan^2 x}\, dx$$

$$= 4\int \frac{\tan x}{(\sec^2 x)^2} \cdot (1-\tan^2 x) \cdot e^{\tan^2 x}\, dx$$

Put $\tan^2 x = t$

$\Rightarrow \quad 2\tan x \cdot \sec^2 x\, dx = dt$

$$\Rightarrow \quad I = 4\int \frac{(1-t)\, e^t}{(1+t)^3} \cdot \frac{dt}{2} = 2\int \frac{(1-t)\, e^t}{(1+t)^3}\, dt$$

$$= 2\left\{\int \frac{2e^t - (1+t)\, e^t}{(1+t)^3}\, dt\right\}$$

$$= 2\left\{\int e^t \left\{\frac{2}{(1+t)^3} - \frac{1}{(1+t)^2}\right\} dt\right.$$

$$= -2\frac{1}{(1+t)^2}\, e^t + C$$

[using $\int e^x(f(x)) + f'(x))dx = e^x . f(x) + c$]

$$= -\frac{2e^{\tan^2 x}}{(1+\tan^2 x)^2} + C$$

$$I = -2\cos^4 x \cdot e^{\tan^2 x} + C$$

| Example 59 Solve $\int \frac{1+x\cos x}{x(1-x^2 e^{2\sin x})}\, dx$.

Sol. Let $I = \int \frac{1+x\cos x}{x(1-x^2 e^2 \sin x)}\, dx$

Put $(x\, e^{\sin x}) = t$

Differentiating both the sides, we get

$$(x\, e^{\sin x} \cdot \cos x + e^{\sin x})\, dx = dt$$

$\Rightarrow \quad e^{\sin x}(x\cos x + 1)\, dx = dt$

$$\Rightarrow \quad I = \int \frac{dt}{t(1-t^2)}$$

$$= \int \frac{dt}{t(1-t)(1+t)} \quad \text{[using partial fraction]}$$

$$= \int \left\{\frac{1}{t} + \frac{1}{2(1-t)} - \frac{1}{2(1+t)}\right\} dt$$

$$= \log|t| - \frac{1}{2}\log|1-t| - \frac{1}{2}\log|1+t| + C$$

$$= \log|x\, e^{\sin x}| - \frac{1}{2}\log|1-x^2 e^{2\sin x}| + C$$

| Example 60 Evaluate;

$$\int \frac{1}{x}\{\log e^{ex} \cdot \log e^{e^2 x} \cdot \log e^{e^3 x}\} dx$$

Sol. We have,

$$I = \int \frac{1}{x}\{\log e^{ex} \cdot \log e^{e^2 x} \cdot \log_e e^3 x\} dx$$

$$= \int \frac{1}{x}\left\{\frac{1}{\log e^{ex}} \cdot \frac{1}{\log e^{e^2 x}} \cdot \frac{1}{\log e^{e^3 x}}\right\} dx$$

$$= \int \frac{dx}{x\{\log e^e + \log e^x\}\{\log e^{e^2} + \log e^{x^2}\}\{\log e^{e^3} + \log x^2\}}$$

$$= \int \frac{dx}{x\{1 + \log e^x\}\{2 + \log e^x\}\{3 + \log e^x\}}$$

Put $\log e^x = t \Rightarrow \frac{1}{x} dx = dt$

$$I = \int \frac{dt}{(1+t)(2+t)(3+t)} = \int \left(\frac{1}{2} \cdot \frac{1}{(1+t)} - \frac{1}{(2+t)} + \frac{1}{(3+t)}\right) dt$$

[using partial fraction]

$$= \frac{1}{2} \log|1+t| - \log|2+t| + \log|3+t| + C.$$

$$= \frac{1}{2} \log|1+\log e^x| - \log|2+\log e^x| + \log|3+\log e^x| + C.$$

Exercise for Session 5

- Evaluate the following Integrals :

1. $\int \frac{x^2}{(x-1)(x-2)(x-3)} dx$

2. $\int \frac{dx}{1+x^3}$

3. $\int \frac{dx}{x(x^n+1)}$

4. $\int \frac{2x}{(x^2+1)(x^2+3)}$

5. $\int \frac{\cos x}{(1+\sin x)(2+\sin x)} dx$

6. $\int \frac{dx}{\sin x(3+2\cos x)} dx$

7. $\int \frac{\sec x}{1+\operatorname{cosec} x} dx$

8. $\int \frac{\tan x + \tan^3 x}{1+\tan^3 x} dx$

9. $\int \frac{dx}{x|6(\log x)^2 + 7\log x + 2|}$

10. $\int \frac{\tan^{-1}}{x^2} \cdot dx$

Session 6

Indirect and Derived Substitutions

Indirect and Derived Substitutions

(i) Indirect Substitution

If the integral is of the form $f(x) \cdot g(x)$, where $g(x)$ is a function of the integral of $f(x)$, then put integral of $f(x) = t$.

| Example 61 The value of $\int \frac{d(x^2+1)}{\sqrt{x^2+2}}$, is

(a) $2\sqrt{x^2+2}+C$ (b) $\sqrt{x^2+2}+C$

(c) $x\sqrt{x^2+2}+C$ (d) None of these

Sol. Here, $I = \int \frac{d(x^2+1)}{\sqrt{x^2+2}}$

We know, $d(x^2+1) = 2x\,dx$

$$\therefore \quad I = \int \frac{2x\,dx}{\sqrt{x^2+2}}$$

Put, $x^2+2 = t^2$

$$\therefore \quad 2x\,dx = 2t\,dt \Rightarrow I = \int \frac{2t\,dt}{t} = 2t + C$$

$$\Rightarrow \quad I = 2\sqrt{x^2+2} + C$$

Hence, (a) is the correct answer.

| Example 62 If $\int \frac{(\sqrt{x})^5}{(\sqrt{x})^7 + x^6}\,dx = a\log\left(\frac{x^k}{1+x^k}\right) + c$, then a and k are

(a) $2/5, 5/2$ (b) $1/5, 2/5$

(c) $5/2, 1/2$ (d) $2/5, 1/2$

Sol. Here, $I = \int \frac{(\sqrt{x})^5}{(\sqrt{x})^7 + x^6}\,dx = \int \frac{dx}{(\sqrt{x})^2 + (\sqrt{x})^7}$

$$= \int \frac{dx}{x^{7/2}\left\{1 + \frac{1}{x^{5/2}}\right\}},$$

Put $\frac{1}{x^{5/2}} = y \Rightarrow -\frac{5}{2x^{7/2}}\,dx = dy$

$$I = -\frac{2}{5}\int \frac{dy}{1+y}$$

$$= -\frac{2}{5}\log|1+y| + C = \frac{2}{5}\log\left|\frac{1}{1+y}\right| + C$$

$$= \frac{2}{5}\log\left|\frac{x^{5/2}}{x^{5/2}+1}\right| + C \quad \text{...(i)}$$

where, $I = a\log\left(\frac{x^k}{1+x^k}\right) + C$ (given) ...(ii)

$\therefore$ From Eqs. (i) and (ii), we get

$$a\log\left(\frac{x^k}{1+x^k}\right) + C = \frac{2}{5}\log\left(\frac{x^{5/2}}{1+x^{5/2}}\right) + C$$

$$\Rightarrow \quad a = 2/5 \text{ and, } k = 5/2$$

Hence, (a) is the correct answer.

| Example 63 Evaluate $\int \frac{5x^4 + 4x^5}{(x^5+x+1)^2}\,dx.$

Sol. Here, $I = \int \frac{5x^4+4x^5}{(x^5+x+1)^2}\,dx = \int \frac{x^4(5+4x)}{x^{10}\left(1 + \frac{1}{x^4} + \frac{1}{x^5}\right)^2}\,dx$

$$= \int \frac{5/x^6 + 4/x^5}{\left(1 + \frac{1}{x^4} + \frac{1}{x^5}\right)^2}\,dx$$

Put $1 + \frac{1}{x^4} + \frac{1}{x^5} = t$

$$\Rightarrow \quad \left(-\frac{4}{x^5} - \frac{5}{x^6}\right)dx = dt$$

$$I = \int -\frac{dt}{t^2} = \frac{1}{t} + C = \frac{1}{1 + \frac{1}{x^4} + \frac{1}{x^5}} + C$$

$$= \frac{x^5}{x^5+x+1} + C$$

| Example 64 For any natural number m, evaluate $\int (x^{3m} + x^{2m} + x^m)(2x^{2m} + 3x^m + 6)^{1/m}\,dx,\ x > 0$

[IIT JEE 2002]

Sol. Here, $I = \int (x^{3m} + x^{2m} + x^m)(2x^{2m} + 3x^m + 6)^{1/m}\,dx$

$$= \int (x^{3m} + x^{2m} + x^m)\frac{(2x^{3m} + 3x^{2m} + 6x^m)^{1/m}}{x}\,dx$$

$$= \int (x^{3m-1} + x^{2m-1} + x^{m-1})(2x^{3m} + 3x^{2m} + 6x^m)^{1/m}\,dx \quad \text{...(i)}$$

Put $\quad 2x^{3m} + 3x^{2m} + 6x^m = t$

$\Rightarrow \quad 6m\,(x^{3m-1} + x^{2m-1} + x^{m-1})\,dx = dt$

$\therefore$ Eq. (i) becomes,

$$I = \int t^{1/m} \frac{dt}{6m} = \frac{1}{6m} \cdot \frac{t^{(1/m)+1}}{(1/m)+1} + C$$

$$I = \frac{1}{6(m+1)} \{2x^{3m} + 3x^{2m} + 6x^m\}^{\frac{m+1}{m}} + C$$

| Example 65 $\displaystyle\int \frac{x\,dx}{\sqrt{1+x^2+\sqrt{(1+x^2)^3}}}$ is equal to

(a) $\frac{1}{2}\ln(1+\sqrt{1+x^2}) + C$ (b) $2\sqrt{1+\sqrt{1+x^2}} + C$

(c) $2(1+\sqrt{1+x^2}) + C$ (d) None of these

Sol. $\displaystyle\int \frac{x\,dx}{\sqrt{(1+x^2)}\sqrt{1+\sqrt{1+x^2}}}$

Put $\quad 1+\sqrt{1+x^2} = t^2 \Rightarrow \dfrac{2x}{2\sqrt{1+x^2}}\,dx = 2t\,dt$

$$\therefore \quad \frac{x\,dx}{\sqrt{1+x^2}} = 2t\,dt$$

$$\therefore \quad I = \int \frac{2t\,dt}{t} = 2t + C = 2\sqrt{1+\sqrt{1+x^2}} + C$$

Hence, (b) is the correct answer.

| Example 66 $\displaystyle\int \frac{(2x+1)}{(x^2+4x+1)^{3/2}}\,dx$

(a) $\dfrac{x^3}{(x^2+4x+1)^{1/2}} + C$ (b) $\dfrac{x}{(x^2+4x+1)^{1/2}} + C$

(c) $\dfrac{x^2}{(x^2+4x+1)^{1/2}} + C$ (d) $\dfrac{1}{(x^2+4x+1)^{1/2}} + C$

Sol. $\displaystyle\int \frac{2x+1}{(x^2+4x+1)^{3/2}}\,dx = \int \frac{2x+1}{x^3\left(1+\frac{4}{x}+\frac{1}{x^2}\right)^{3/2}}\,dx$

$$= \int \frac{2x^{-2}+x^{-3}}{\left(1+\frac{4}{x}+\frac{1}{x^2}\right)^{3/2}}\,dx$$

Now, put $\dfrac{1}{x^2} + \dfrac{4}{x} + 1 = t^2 \Rightarrow \left(-\dfrac{2}{x^3} - \dfrac{4}{x^2}\right)dx = 2t\,dt$

$$\therefore \quad I = \int \frac{-t\,dt}{t^3} = \frac{1}{t} + C$$

$$= \frac{x}{\sqrt{x^2+4x+1}} + C$$

Hence, (b) is the correct answer.

| Example 67 The evaluation of $\displaystyle\int \frac{p\,x^{p+2q-1} - qx^{q-1}}{x^{2p+2q} + 2x^{p+q} + 1}\,dx$ is

(a) $-\dfrac{x^p}{x^{p+q}+1} + C$ (b) $\dfrac{x^q}{x^{p+q}+1} + C$

(c) $-\dfrac{x^q}{x^{p+q}+1} + C$ (d) $\dfrac{x^p}{x^{p+q}+1} + C$

Sol. Here, $I = \displaystyle\int \frac{px^{p+2q-1} - qx^{q-1}}{x^{2p+2q} + 2x^{p+q} + 1}$

$$\int \frac{px^{p+2q-1} - qx^{q-1}}{(x^{p+q}+1)^2}\,dx = \int \frac{px^{p-1} - qx^{-q-1}}{(x^p + x^{-q})^2}\,dx$$

Taking x^q as x^{2q} common from denominator and take it in numerator.

Put $\quad x^p + x^{-q} = t \Rightarrow (px^{p-1} - qx^{-q-1})\,dx = dt$

$$\therefore \quad I = \int \frac{dt}{t^2} = -\frac{1}{t} + C = -\left(\frac{x^q}{x^{p+q}+1}\right) + C$$

Hence, (c) is the correct answer.

| Example 68 $\displaystyle\int \frac{x^2(1-\ln x)}{\ln^4 x - x^4}\,dx$ is equal to

(a) $\dfrac{1}{2}\ln\left(\dfrac{x}{\ln x}\right) - \dfrac{1}{4}\ln(\ln^2 x - x^2) + C$

(b) $\dfrac{1}{4}\ln\left(\dfrac{\ln x - x}{\ln x + x}\right) - \dfrac{1}{2}\tan^{-1}\left(\dfrac{\ln x}{x}\right) + C$

(c) $\dfrac{1}{4}\ln\left(\dfrac{\ln x + x}{\ln x - x}\right) + \dfrac{1}{2}\tan^{-1}\left(\dfrac{\ln x}{x}\right) + C$

(d) $\dfrac{1}{4}\left(\ln\left(\dfrac{\ln x - x}{\ln x + x}\right) + \tan^{-1}\left(\dfrac{\ln x}{x}\right)\right) + C$

Sol. Here, $I = \displaystyle\int \frac{x^2(1-\ln x)}{\ln x^4 x - x^4}$

$$I = \int \frac{x^2(1-\ln x)}{x^4\left(\left(\frac{\ln x}{x}\right)^4 - 1\right)}\,dx = \int \frac{1-\ln x}{x^2\left(\left(\frac{\ln x}{x}\right)^4 - 1\right)}\,dx$$

Put $\dfrac{\ln x}{x} = t \Rightarrow \dfrac{1-\ln x}{x^2} = dt$

$$I = \int \frac{dt}{(t^4-1)} = \int \frac{dt}{(t^2+1)(t^2-1)}$$

$$= \frac{1}{2}\int \frac{(t^2+1)-(t^2-1)}{(t^2+1)(t^2-1)}\,dt$$

$$I = \frac{1}{2}\left(\int \frac{dt}{t^2-1} - \int \frac{dt}{t^2+1}\right) = \frac{1}{2}\left(\frac{1}{2}\ln\frac{t-1}{t+1} - \tan^{-1} t\right)$$

$$= \frac{1}{4} \ln \left(\frac{\ln x - x}{\ln x + x} \right) - \frac{1}{2} \tan^{-1} \left(\frac{\ln x}{x} \right) + C$$

Hence, (b) is the correct answer.

| Example 69 $\int \frac{x^2 - 1}{x^3 \sqrt{2x^4 - 2x^2 + 1}} dx$ is equal to

[IIT JEE 2006]

(a) $\frac{\sqrt{2x^4 - 2x^2 + 1}}{x^2} + C$ (b) $\frac{\sqrt{2x^4 - 2x^2 + 1}}{x^3} + C$

(c) $\frac{\sqrt{2x^4 - 2x^2 + 1}}{x} + C$ (d) $\frac{\sqrt{2x^4 - 2x^2 + 1}}{2x^2} + C$

Sol. Let $I = \int \frac{x^2 - 1}{x^3 \sqrt{2x^4 - 2x^2 + 1}} dx$

$$= \int \frac{x^2 - 1}{x^5} \cdot \frac{dx}{\sqrt{2 - \frac{2}{x^2} + \frac{1}{x^4}}}$$

$$= \frac{1}{4} \int \frac{\frac{4}{x^3} - \frac{4}{x^5}}{\sqrt{2 - \frac{2}{x^2} + \frac{1}{x^4}}} dx = \frac{1}{4} \cdot 2 \sqrt{2 - \frac{2}{x^2} + \frac{1}{x^4}}$$

$$\left(\because \int \frac{f'(x)}{\sqrt{f(x)}} dx = 2\sqrt{f(x)} + C \right)$$

$$= \frac{\sqrt{2x^4 - 2x^2 + 1}}{2x^2} + C$$

Hence, (d) is the correct answer.

| Example 70 Let $f(x) = \frac{x}{(1 + x^n)^{1/n}}$ for $n \geq 2$ and $g(x) = \underbrace{fofo \ldots of}_{n \text{ times}}(x)$, then $\int x^{n-2} g(x) \, dx$ equals to

[IIT JEE 2007]

(a) $\frac{1}{n(n-1)} (1 + nx^n)^{1 - \frac{1}{n}} + C$ (b) $\frac{1}{n-1} (1 + nx^n)^{1 - \frac{1}{n}} + C$

(c) $\frac{1}{n(n+1)} (1 + nx^n)^{1 + \frac{1}{n}} + C$ (d) $\frac{1}{n+1} (1 + nx^n)^{1 + \frac{1}{n}} + C$

Sol. $\because$ $f(x) = \frac{x}{(1 + x^n)^{1/n}}$

$\therefore$ $f(f(x)) = \frac{y}{(1 + x^n)^{1/n}}$,

Where, $y = \frac{x}{(1 + x^n)^{1/n}} = \frac{x}{(1 + 2x^n)^{1/n}}$

Similarly, $f(f(f(x))) = \frac{x}{(1 + 3x^n)^{1/n}}$

and $\underbrace{(fofofo \ldots of)}_{n \text{ times}}(x) = g(x) = \frac{x}{(1 + nx^n)^{1/n}}$

$$\therefore \int x^{n-2} g(x) \, dx = \int \frac{x^{n-1}}{(1 + nx^n)^{1/n}} dx$$

$$= \frac{1}{n^2} \int n^2 \cdot x^{n-1} \cdot (1 + nx^n)^{-1/n} dx$$

$$= \frac{1}{n^2} \cdot \frac{(1 + nx^n)^{1 - \frac{1}{n}}}{1 - \frac{1}{n}} + C$$

$$= \frac{(1 + nx^n)^{1 - \frac{1}{n}}}{n(n-1)} + C$$

Hence, (a) is the correct answer.

Derived Substitutions

Some times it is useful to write the integral as a sum of two related integrals which can be evaluated by making suitable substitutions.

Examples of such integrals are

Type I

(a) Algebraic Twins

$$\int \frac{2x^2}{x^4 + 1} dx = \int \frac{x^2 + 1}{x^4 + 1} dx + \int \frac{x^2 - 1}{x^4 + 1} dx$$

$$\int \frac{2}{x^4 + 1} dx = \int \frac{x^2 + 1}{x^4 + 1} dx - \int \frac{x^2 - 1}{x^4 + 1} dx$$

$$\int \frac{2x^2}{x^4 + 1 + kx^2} dx, \int \frac{2}{(x^4 + 1 + kx^2)} dx$$

(b) Trigonometric Twins

$$\int \sqrt{\tan x} \, dx, \int \sqrt{\cot x} \, dx,$$

$$\int \frac{1}{(\sin^4 x + \cos^4 x)} dx, \int \frac{1}{\sin^6 x + \cos^6 x} dx,$$

$$\int \frac{\pm \sin x \pm \cos x}{a + b \sin x \cos x} dx$$

Method of evaluating these integral are illustrated by mean of the following examples :

Integral of the Form

1. $\int f\left(x + \frac{1}{x}\right)\left(1 - \frac{1}{x^2}\right) dx$

Put $x + \frac{1}{x} = t \Rightarrow \left(1 - \frac{1}{x^2}\right) dx = dt$

2. $\int f\left(x-\frac{1}{x}\right)\left(1+\frac{1}{x^2}\right)dx.$

Put $x-\frac{1}{x}=t \Rightarrow \left(1+\frac{1}{x^2}\right)dx=dt$

3. $\int \frac{x^2+1}{x^4+kx^2+1}dx.$

Divide numerator and denominator by x^2.

4. $\int \frac{x^2-1}{x^4+kx^2+1}dx$

Divide numerator and denominator by x^2.

Example 71 Evaluate $\int \frac{5}{1+x^4}dx.$

Sol. Let $I=\int \frac{5}{1+x^4}dx=\frac{5}{2}\int \frac{2}{1+x^4}dx$

$$=\frac{5}{2}\left[\int \frac{1+x^2}{1+x^4}dx+\int \frac{1-x^2}{1+x^4}dx\right]$$

$$=\frac{5}{2}\left[\int \frac{x^2+1}{x^4+1}dx-\int \frac{x^2-1}{x^4+1}dx\right]$$

Remark

Here, dividing Numerator and Denominator by x^2 and converting Denominator into perfect square so as to get differential in Numerator

i.e. $I=\frac{5}{2}\left[\int \frac{1+1/x^2}{x^2+1/x^2}dx-\int \frac{1-1/x^2}{x^2+1/x^2}dx\right]$

$$=\frac{5}{2}\left[\int \frac{1+1/x^2}{(x-1/x)^2+2}dx-\int \frac{1-1/x^2}{(x+1/x)^2-2}dx\right]$$

$$=\frac{5}{2}\left[\int \frac{dt}{t^2+(\sqrt{2})^2}-\int \frac{du}{u^2-(\sqrt{2})^2}\right],$$

[where $t=x-\frac{1}{x}$ and $u=x+\frac{1}{x}$]

$$=\frac{5}{2}\left[\frac{1}{\sqrt{2}}\tan^{-1}\left(\frac{t}{\sqrt{2}}\right)-\frac{1}{2\sqrt{2}}\log\left|\frac{u-\sqrt{2}}{u+\sqrt{2}}\right|\right]+C$$

$$\therefore \quad I=\frac{5}{2}\left[\frac{1}{\sqrt{2}}\tan^{-1}\left(\frac{x-1/x}{\sqrt{2}}\right)-\frac{1}{2\sqrt{2}}\log\left|\frac{x+\frac{1}{x}-\sqrt{2}}{x+\frac{1}{x}+\sqrt{2}}\right|\right]+C$$

Example 72 Evaluate $\int \frac{1}{x^4+5x^2+1}dx.$

Sol. Let $I=\frac{1}{2}\int \frac{2}{x^4+5x^2+1}dx$

$$\Rightarrow I=\frac{1}{2}\int \frac{1+x^2}{x^4+5x^2+1}dx+\frac{1}{2}\int \frac{1-x^2}{x^4+5x^2+1}dx$$

$$=\frac{1}{2}\int \frac{1+1/x^2}{x^2+5+1/x^2}dx-\frac{1}{2}\int \frac{1-1/x^2}{x^2+5+1/x^2}dx$$

[(dividing Numerator and Denominator by x^2)]

$$=\frac{1}{2}\int \frac{(1+1/x^2)}{(x-1/x)^2+7}dx-\frac{1}{2}\int \frac{(1-1/x^2)}{(x+1/x)^2+3}dx$$

$$=\frac{1}{2}\int \frac{dt}{t^2+(\sqrt{7})^2}-\frac{1}{2}\int \frac{du}{u^2+(\sqrt{3})^2}$$

where $t=x-\frac{1}{x}$ and $u=x+\frac{1}{x}$

$$\therefore \quad I=\frac{1}{2}\cdot\frac{1}{\sqrt{7}}\left(\tan^{-1}\frac{t}{\sqrt{7}}\right)-\frac{1}{2}\frac{1}{\sqrt{3}}\left(\tan^{-1}\frac{u}{\sqrt{3}}\right)+C$$

$$=\frac{1}{2}\left[\frac{1}{\sqrt{7}}\tan^{-1}\left(\frac{x-1/x}{\sqrt{7}}\right)-\frac{1}{\sqrt{3}}\tan^{-1}\left(\frac{x+1/x}{\sqrt{3}}\right)\right]+C$$

Example 73 Evaluate $\int \sqrt{\tan x}\,dx.$

Sol. Here $I=\int \sqrt{\tan x}\,dx$

Put $\tan x=t^2$

$\Rightarrow \sec^2 x\,dx=2t\,dt \quad \Rightarrow dx=\frac{2t\,dt}{1+t^4}$

$$\therefore \quad I=\int t\cdot\frac{2t}{1+t^4}dt=\int \frac{2t^2}{t^4+1}dt$$

$$=\int \frac{t^2+1}{t^4+1}dt+\int \frac{t^2-1}{t^4+1}dt$$

$$=\int \frac{1+1/t^2}{t^2+1/t^2}dt+\int \frac{1-1/t^2}{t^2+1/t^2}dt$$

$$=\int \frac{1+1/t^2}{(t-1/t)^2+2}dt+\int \frac{1-1/t^2}{(t+1/t)^2-2}dt$$

$$I=\int \frac{ds}{s^2+(\sqrt{2})^2}+\int \frac{dr}{r^2-(\sqrt{2})^2},\left[s=t-\frac{1}{t}\text{ and } r=t+\frac{1}{t}\right]$$

$$=\frac{1}{\sqrt{2}}\tan^{-1}\left(\frac{s}{\sqrt{2}}\right)+\frac{1}{2\sqrt{2}}\log\left|\frac{r-\sqrt{2}}{r+\sqrt{2}}\right|+C$$

$$=\frac{1}{\sqrt{2}}\left[\tan^{-1}\left(\frac{t-1/t}{\sqrt{2}}\right)+\frac{1}{2}\log\left|\frac{t+\frac{1}{t}-\sqrt{2}}{t+\frac{1}{t}+\sqrt{2}}\right|\right]+C$$

[(where $t=\sqrt{\tan x}$)]

Example 74 Evaluate $\int \frac{4}{\sin^4 x+\cos^4 x}dx.$

Sol. Let $I=4\int \frac{dx}{\sin^4 x+\cos^4 x}$

Dividing numerator and denominator by $\cos^4 x$, we get

$$I = 4\int \frac{\sec^4 x}{\tan^4 x + 1}\,dx$$

$$I = 4\int \frac{\sec^2 x\,(1+\tan^2 x)}{1+\tan^4 x}\,dx$$

Put $\tan x = t \Rightarrow \sec^2 x\,dx = dt$

$$\therefore \quad I = 4\int \frac{t^2+1}{t^4+1}\,dt$$

$$= 4\int \frac{1+1/t^2}{t^2+1/t^2}\,dt = 4\int \frac{1+1/t^2}{(1-1/t)^2+2}\,dt$$

Again, put $z = t - \dfrac{1}{t}$

$$\therefore \quad I = 4\int \frac{dz}{z^2+2} = \frac{4}{\sqrt{2}}\tan^{-1}\left(\frac{z}{\sqrt{2}}\right) + C$$

$$I = 2\sqrt{2}\tan^{-1}\left(\frac{\tan x - 1/\tan x}{\sqrt{2}}\right) + C$$

| Example 75 The value of $\displaystyle\int \frac{(ax^2-b)\,dx}{x\sqrt{c^2x^2-(ax^2+b)^2}}$, is equal to

(a) $\dfrac{1}{c}\sin^{-1}\left(ax - \dfrac{b}{x}\right) + k$ (b) $c\sin^{-1}\left(ax + \dfrac{b}{x}\right) + k$

(c) $\sin^{-1}\left[\dfrac{ax+b/x}{c}\right] + k$ (d) None of these

Sol. Here, $$I = \int \frac{(ax^2-b)\,dx}{x\sqrt{c^2x^2-(ax^2+b)^2}} = \int \frac{\left(a - \dfrac{b}{x^2}\right)dx}{\sqrt{c^2 - \left(ax + \dfrac{b}{x}\right)^2}}$$

Put $ax + \dfrac{b}{x} = t$

$$\therefore \quad \left(a - \frac{b}{x^2}\right)dx = dt$$

$$I = \int \frac{dt}{\sqrt{c^2-t^2}} = \sin^{-1}\left(\frac{t}{c}\right) + k$$

$$\Rightarrow \quad \sin^{-1}\left(\frac{ax+b/x}{c}\right) + k$$

Hence (c) is the correct answer.

| Example 76 $\displaystyle\int \frac{x^x\,(x^{2x}+1)(\ln x + 1)}{x^{4x}+1}\,dx$

Sol. $$I = \int \frac{x^x\,(x^{2x}+1)(\ln x+1)}{x^{4x}+1}\,dx$$

Put $x^x = y \Rightarrow x^x(\ln x + 1)\,dx = dy$

$$I = \int \frac{y^2+1}{y^4+1}\,dy = \int \frac{1+\dfrac{1}{y^2}}{y^2+\dfrac{1}{y^2}}\,dy = \int \frac{1+\dfrac{1}{y^2}}{\left(y-\dfrac{1}{y}\right)^2+2}\,dy$$

Put, $y - \dfrac{1}{y} = t \Rightarrow \left(1 + \dfrac{1}{y^2}\right)dy = dt$

$$I = \int \frac{dt}{t^2+2} = \frac{1}{\sqrt{2}}\left(\tan^{-1}\frac{t}{\sqrt{2}}\right) + C$$

$$= \frac{1}{\sqrt{2}}\tan^{-1}\left(\frac{y-\dfrac{1}{y}}{\sqrt{2}}\right) + C = \frac{1}{\sqrt{2}}\tan^{-1}\left(\frac{x^x - \dfrac{1}{x^x}}{\sqrt{2}}\right) + C$$

| Example 77 Evaluate

$$\int \frac{(x^2-1)\,dx}{(x^4+3x^2+1)\tan^{-1}\left(x+\dfrac{1}{x}\right)}.$$

Sol. Here $$I = \int \frac{(x^2-1)}{(x^4+x^3+1)\tan^{-1}\left(x+\dfrac{1}{x}\right)}$$

The given integral can be written as

$$I = \int \frac{(1-1/x^2)\,dx}{(x^2+3+1/x^2)\tan^{-1}\left(x+\dfrac{1}{x}\right)}$$

(dividing numerator and denominator by x^2)

$$I = \int \frac{(1-1/x^2)\,dx}{\{(x+1/x)^2+1\}\tan^{-1}\left(x+\dfrac{1}{x}\right)}$$

Put, $x + \dfrac{1}{x} = t \Rightarrow \left(1 - \dfrac{1}{x^2}\right)dx = dt$

$$\therefore \quad I = \int \frac{dt}{(t^2+1)\cdot\tan^{-1}(t)} \quad \text{...(i)}$$

Now, make one more substitution

$\tan^{-1} t = u$. Then, $\dfrac{dt}{t^2+1} = du$

$\therefore$ Eq. (i) becomes, $I = \displaystyle\int \frac{du}{u} = \log|u| + C$

$\Rightarrow I = \log|\tan^{-1} t| + C = \log|\tan^{-1}(x + 1/x)| + C$

| Example 78 $\displaystyle\int \frac{(x^{-7/6} - x^{5/6})\,dx}{x^{1/3}(x^2+x+1)^{1/2} - x^{1/2}(x^2+x+1)^{1/3}}$

Sol. $$I = \int \frac{x^{7/6}(x^{-7/6}-x^{5/6})\,dx}{x^{7/6}\cdot x^{1/3}(x^2+x+1)^{1/2} - x^{1/2}\cdot x^{7/6}(x^2+x+1)^{1/3}}$$

$$= \int \frac{(1-x^2)\,dx}{x^{3/2}(x^2+x+1)^{1/2} - x^{5/3}(x^2+x+1)^{1/3}}$$

$$= \int \frac{-\left(1 - \frac{1}{x^2}\right) dx}{\left(x + \frac{1}{x} + 1\right)^{1/2} - \left(x + \frac{1}{x} + 1\right)^{1/3}} \quad \left[\begin{array}{l}\text{Putting } x + \frac{1}{x} = t \\ \Rightarrow \left(1 - \frac{1}{x^2}\right) dx = dt\end{array}\right]$$

$$= -\int \frac{dt}{(t+1)^{1/2} - (t+1)^{1/3}}$$

Substitute, $(t+1) = u^6$

$$= -\int \frac{6u^5\, du}{u^3 - u^2} = -6 \int \frac{u^3}{u-1}\, du,$$

Put $\quad u - 1 = z$

$$dz = -6 \int \frac{(z+1)^3}{z}\, dz$$

$$= -6 \int \frac{z^3 + 3z^2 + 3z + 1}{z}\, dz$$

$$= -6 \int \left(z^2 + 3z + 3 + \frac{1}{z}\right) dz$$

$$= -6 \left\{\frac{z^3}{3} + \frac{3z^2}{2} + 3z + \log|z|\right\} + C$$

where, $\quad z = \left(x + \frac{1}{x} + 1\right)^{1/6} - 1$

| Example 79 The value of $\int \{\{[x]\}\}\, dx$, where {.} and [.] denotes fractional part of x and greatest integer function, is equal to

(a) 0 (b) 1 (c) 2 (d) –1

Sol. Let $\quad I = \int \{\{[x]\}\}\, dx$

where, $[x]$ = Integer and we know $\{n\} = 0; n \in$ Integer.

$\therefore \quad I = \int 0\, dx = 0$

Hence, (a) is the correct answer.

Type II

Integration of Some Special Irrational Algebraic Functions

In this case we shall discuss four integrals of the form $\int \frac{\phi(x)}{P\sqrt{Q}}\, dx$, where P and Q are polynomial functions of x and $\phi(x)$ is polynomial in x.

(a) Integrals of the Form $\int \frac{\phi(x)}{P\sqrt{Q}}\, dx$, where P and Q are both linear of x

To evaluate this type of integrals we put $Q = t^2$, i.e. to evaluate integrals of the form $\int \frac{1}{(ax+b)\sqrt{cx+d}}\, dx$, put $cx + d = t^2$.

The following examples illustrate the procedure :

| Example 80 Evaluate $\int \frac{1}{(x+1)\sqrt{x-2}}\, dx$.

Sol. Let $I = \int \frac{1}{(x+1)\sqrt{x-2}}\, dx$

Here, P and Q both are linear, so we put $Q = t^2$

i.e. $\quad x - 2 = t^2$

So that $dx = 2t\, dt$

$$\therefore \quad I = \int \frac{1}{(t^2 + 2 + 1)\sqrt{t^2}} \cdot 2t\, dt = 2 \int \frac{dt}{t^2 + 3}$$

$$= 2 \times \frac{1}{\sqrt{3}} \tan^{-1}\left(\frac{t}{\sqrt{3}}\right) + C$$

$$\therefore \quad I = \frac{2}{\sqrt{3}} \tan^{-1}\left(\frac{\sqrt{x-2}}{\sqrt{3}}\right) + C$$

(b) Integrals of the Form $\int \frac{\phi(x)}{P\sqrt{Q}}\, dx$, where P is a quadratic expression and Q is a linear expression

To evaluate this type of integrals we put $Q = t^2$ i.e. to evaluate the integrals of the form

$$\int \frac{1}{(ax^2 + bx + c)\sqrt{px + q}}\, dx$$

put $px + q = t^2$.

| Example 81 Evaluate $\int \frac{x+2}{(x^2 + 3x + 3)\sqrt{x+1}}\, dx$.

Sol. Let $\quad I = \int \frac{x+2}{(x^2 + 3x + 3)\sqrt{x+1}}\, dx$

Put $x + 1 = t^2 \Rightarrow dx = 2t\, dt$

$$\therefore \quad I = \int \frac{(t^2 - 1) + 2}{\{(t^2 - 1)^2 + 3(t^2 - 1) + 3\}\sqrt{t^2}} \cdot (2t)\, dt$$

$$= 2 \int \frac{t^2 + 1}{t^4 + t^2 + 1}\, dt = 2 \int \frac{1 + 1/t^2}{t^2 + 1 + 1/t^2}\, dt$$

$$= 2 \int \frac{1 + 1/t^2}{(t - 1/t)^2 + (\sqrt{3})^2}\, dt = 2 \int \frac{du}{u^2 + (\sqrt{3})^2}$$

$$\left[\text{where } u = t - \frac{1}{t}\right]$$

$$= \frac{2}{\sqrt{3}} \tan^{-1}\left(\frac{u}{\sqrt{3}}\right) + C$$

$$\therefore \quad I = \frac{2}{\sqrt{3}} \tan^{-1}\left(\frac{t^2 - 1}{\sqrt{3}t}\right) + C$$

$$= \frac{2}{\sqrt{3}} \tan^{-1}\left(\frac{x}{\sqrt{3(x+1)}}\right) + C$$

(c) Integral of the Form $\int \frac{1}{(ax+b)} \cdot \frac{dx}{\sqrt{px^2+qx+r}}$**, where in** $\int \frac{dx}{P\sqrt{Q}}$ **P is linear and Q is a quadratic put,** $ax+b=\frac{1}{t}$.

Example 82 Evaluate $\int \frac{dx}{(x-1)\sqrt{x^2+x+1}}$.

Sol. Let $I=\int \frac{dx}{(x-1)\sqrt{x^2+x+1}}$

Put $x-1=\frac{1}{t} \Rightarrow dx=-\frac{1}{t^2}dt$

$$\therefore \quad I=\int \frac{-1/t^2\,dt}{1/t\sqrt{\left(\frac{1}{t}+1\right)^2+\left(\frac{1}{t}+1\right)+1}}$$

$$=-\int \frac{dt}{\sqrt{3t^2+3t+1}}=-\frac{1}{\sqrt{3}}\int \frac{dt}{\sqrt{\left(t+\frac{1}{2}\right)^2+\frac{1}{12}}}$$

$$=-\frac{1}{\sqrt{3}}\log|(t+1/2)+\sqrt{(t+1/2)^2+1/12}|+C$$

$$=-\frac{1}{\sqrt{3}}\log\left|\left(\frac{1}{x-1}+\frac{1}{2}\right)+\sqrt{\frac{12\left(\frac{1}{x-1}+\frac{1}{2}\right)^2+1}{12}}\right|+C$$

(d) Integrals of the Form $\int \frac{dx}{P\sqrt{Q}}$**, where P and Q both are pure quadratic expression in x, i.e.** $P=ax^2+b$ **and** $Q=cx^2+d$**, i.e.** $\int \frac{dx}{(ax^2+b)\sqrt{cx^2+d}}$.

To evaluate this type of integrals of the form we put $x=\frac{1}{t}$

Example 83 Evaluate $\int \frac{dx}{(1+x^2)\sqrt{1-x^2}}$.

Sol. Let $I=\int \frac{dx}{(1+x^2)\sqrt{1-x^2}}$

Put $x=\frac{1}{t}$, so that $dx=-\frac{1}{t^2}dt$

$$\therefore \quad I=\int \frac{-1/t^2\,dt}{(1+1/t^2)\sqrt{1-1/t^2}}=-\int \frac{t\,dt}{(t^2+1)\sqrt{t^2-1}}$$

Again, $t^2=u \Rightarrow 2t\,dt=du$.

$$=-\frac{1}{2}\int \frac{du}{(u+1)\sqrt{u-1}}$$ which reduces to the form $\int \frac{dx}{P\sqrt{Q}}$

where both P and Q are linear so that we put $u-1=z^2$ so that $du=2z\,dz$

$$\therefore \quad I=-\frac{1}{2}\int \frac{2z\,dz}{(z^2+1+1)\sqrt{z^2}}=-\int \frac{dz}{(z^2+2)}$$

$$I=-\frac{1}{\sqrt{2}}\tan^{-1}\left(\frac{z}{\sqrt{2}}\right)+C$$

$$I=-\frac{1}{\sqrt{2}}\tan^{-1}\left(\frac{\sqrt{u-1}}{\sqrt{2}}\right)+C$$

$$=-\frac{1}{\sqrt{2}}\tan^{-1}\left(\frac{\sqrt{t^2-1}}{\sqrt{2}}\right)+C$$

$$=-\frac{1}{\sqrt{2}}\tan^{-1}\left(\frac{\sqrt{1-x^2}}{\sqrt{2}x}\right)+C$$

Aliter Put $x=\cos\theta$, $dx=-\sin\theta\,d\theta$

$$\therefore \quad I=-\int \frac{\sin\theta\,d\theta}{(1+\cos^2\theta)\sin\theta}=-\int \frac{d\theta}{1+\cos^2\theta}$$

$$=-\int \frac{\sec^2\theta\,d\theta}{\sec^2\theta+1}=-\int \frac{\sec^2\theta\,d\theta}{\tan^2\theta+2}$$

Put $\tan\theta=t$. $\Rightarrow \sec^2\theta\,d\theta=dt$

$$\therefore \quad I=-\int \frac{dt}{t^2+2}=-\frac{1}{\sqrt{2}}\tan^{-1}\left(\frac{t}{\sqrt{2}}\right)+C$$

$$=-\frac{1}{\sqrt{2}}\tan^{-1}\left(\frac{\tan\theta}{\sqrt{2}}\right)+C$$

$$=-\frac{1}{\sqrt{2}}\tan^{-1}\left(\frac{\sqrt{1-x^2}}{\sqrt{2}\,x}\right)+C$$

$\left[\text{where, } \cos\theta=x,\ \sin\theta=\sqrt{1-x^2},\ \therefore \tan\theta=\frac{\sqrt{1-x^2}}{x}\right]$

Example 84 Evaluate

$$I=\int \frac{(x-1)\sqrt{x^4+2x^3-x^2+2x+1}}{x^2(x+1)}dx.$$

Sol. Here, $I=\int \frac{(x^2-1)\sqrt{x^4+2x^3-x^2+2x+1}}{x^2(x+1)^2}dx$

$$=\int \frac{\left(1-\frac{1}{x^2}\right)\sqrt{x^2\left(x^2+2x-1+\frac{2}{x}+\frac{1}{x^2}\right)}}{\frac{x^2(x^2+2x+1)}{x^2}}dx$$

$$=\int \frac{\left(1-\frac{1}{x^2}\right)\sqrt{\left(x^2+\frac{1}{x^2}\right)+2\left(x+\frac{1}{x}\right)-1}}{\left(x+\frac{1}{x}+2\right)}dx$$

Put $x+\frac{1}{x}=t$, i.e. $\left(1-\frac{1}{x^2}\right)dx=dt$

$$=\int \frac{\sqrt{(t^2-2)+2t-1}}{(t+2)}dt=\int \frac{\sqrt{t^2+2t-3}}{(t+2)}dt$$

$$= \int \frac{t^2 + 2t - 3}{(t+2)\sqrt{t^2 + 2t - 3}}\, dt$$

$$= \int \frac{t(t+2)}{(t+2)\sqrt{t^2 + 2t - 3}}\, dt - 3\int \frac{dt}{(t+2)\sqrt{t^2 + 2t - 3}}$$

$$I = I_1 - 3I_2 \qquad \text{...(i)}$$

Where, $I_1 = \int \frac{t\, dt}{\sqrt{t^2 + 2t - 3}}$ and $I_2 = \int \frac{dt}{(t+2)\sqrt{t^2 + 2t - 3}}$

$$\therefore \quad I_1 = \int \frac{t\, dt}{\sqrt{(t+1)^2 - 4}}$$

Put, $t + 1 = z = \int \frac{(z-1)\, dz}{\sqrt{z^2 - 2^2}}$

$$= \int \frac{z dz}{\sqrt{z^2 - 2^2}} - \int \frac{dz}{\sqrt{z^2 - 2^2}}$$

$$= \sqrt{z^2 - 2^2} - \log|z + \sqrt{z^2 - 4}|$$

$$= \sqrt{t^2 + 2t - 3} - \log|(t+1) + \sqrt{t^2 + 2t + 3}| \quad \text{...(ii)}$$

Also, $I_2 = \int \frac{dy}{y^2 \cdot \frac{1}{y}\sqrt{\left(\frac{1}{y} - 2\right)^2 + 2\left(\frac{1}{y} - 2\right) - 3}}$

Put $t + 2 = \frac{1}{y} = \int \frac{dy}{\sqrt{1 - 2y - 3y^2}} = \frac{1}{\sqrt{3}} \int \frac{dy}{\sqrt{\left(\frac{2}{3}\right)^2 - \left(y + \frac{1}{3}\right)^2}}$

$$= \frac{1}{\sqrt{3}} \sin^{-1}\left(\frac{y + \frac{1}{3}}{\frac{2}{3}}\right) = \frac{1}{\sqrt{3}} \sin^{-1}\left(\frac{5+t}{2+t}\right) \quad \text{...(iii)}$$

$$\therefore \quad I = \sqrt{t^2 + 2t - 3} - \log(t + 1 + \sqrt{t^2 + 2t - 3}) - \sqrt{3}\sin^{-1}\left(\frac{t+5}{t+2}\right)$$

where, $t = x + \frac{1}{x}$

(e) Integrals of the Form $\int \frac{dx}{(x-k)^r \sqrt{ax^2 + bx + c}}$, **where $r \geq 2$ and $r \in I$**

Here, we substitute, $x - k = \frac{1}{t}$

| Example 85 Evaluate $\int \frac{dx}{(x-3)^3 \sqrt{x^2 - 6x + 10}}$.

Sol. Substitute $(x - 3) = \frac{1}{t} \Rightarrow dx = -\frac{1}{t^2}\, dt$

We get, $\int \frac{dx}{(x-3)^3 \sqrt{x^2 - 6x + 10}}$

$$= \int \frac{-1/t^2\, dt}{1/t^3 \sqrt{(1/t + 3)^2 - 6(1/t + 3) + 10}}$$

$$= -\int \frac{t^2\, dt}{\sqrt{1 + t^2}} = \int \frac{dt}{\sqrt{1 + t^2}} - \int \sqrt{1 + t^2}\, dt$$

$$= \log|t + \sqrt{1 + t^2}| - \frac{t}{2}\sqrt{1 + t^2} - \frac{1}{2}\log|t + \sqrt{1 + t^2}| + C$$

$$= \frac{1}{2}\log|t + \sqrt{1 + t^2}| - \frac{t}{2}\sqrt{1 + t^2} + C$$

$$= \frac{1}{2}\left[\log\left|\frac{1 + \sqrt{x^2 - 6x + 10}}{|x - 3|}\right| - \frac{\sqrt{x^2 - 6x + 10}}{|x - 3|^2}\right] + C$$

(f) Integrals of the Form $\int \frac{ax^2 + bx + c}{(dx + e)\sqrt{fx^2 + gx + h}}\, dx$

Here, we write

$$ax^2 + bx + c = A_1(dx + e)(2fx + g) + B_1(dx + e) + C_1$$

Where A_1, B_1 and C_1 are constants which can be obtained by comparing the coefficients of like terms on both the sides.

| Example 86 Evaluate $\int \frac{2x^2 + 5x + 9}{(x+1)\sqrt{x^2 + x + 1}}\, dx$.

Sol. Let $2x^2 + 5x + 9 = A(x+1)(2x+1) + B(x+1) + C$

or $2x^2 + 5x + 9 = x^2(2A) + x(3A + B) + (A + B + C)$

$$\Rightarrow \qquad A = 1, B = 2, C = 6$$

Thus, $\int \frac{2x^2 + 5x + 9}{(x+1)\sqrt{x^2 + x + 1}}\, dx$

$$= \int \frac{(x+1)(2x+1)}{(x+1)\sqrt{x^2 + x + 1}}\, dx + 2\int \frac{x+1}{(x+1)\sqrt{x^2 + x + 1}}\, dx + 6\int \frac{dx}{(x+1)\sqrt{x^2 + x + 1}}$$

$$= \int \frac{2x+1}{\sqrt{x^2 + x + 1}}\, dx + 2\int \frac{dx}{\sqrt{x^2 + x + 1}} + 6\int \frac{dx}{(x+1)\sqrt{x^2 + x + 1}}$$

$$= \int \frac{du}{\sqrt{u}} + 2\int \frac{dx}{\sqrt{(x + 1/2)^2 + (3/4)}} + 6\int \frac{-dt}{\sqrt{t^2 - t + 1}}$$

[where $u = x^2 + x + 1$ and $\frac{1}{t} = x + 1$]

$$= 2\sqrt{x^2 + x + 1} + 2 \cdot 1 \log|(x + 1/2) + \sqrt{x^2 + x + 1}| - 6\int \frac{dt}{\sqrt{(t - 1/2)^2 + 3/4}}$$

$$= 2\sqrt{x^2 + x + 1} + 2\log\left|\left(x + \frac{1}{2}\right) + \sqrt{x^2 + x + 1}\right| - 6\log\left|\left(t - \frac{1}{2}\right) + \sqrt{t^2 - t + 1}\right| + C$$

$$= 2\sqrt{x^2 + x + 1} + 2\log\left|\left(x + \frac{1}{2}\right) + \sqrt{x^2 + x + 1}\right| - 6\log\left|\frac{1 - x + \sqrt{x^2 + x + 1}}{2(x+1)}\right| + C$$

Type III

Integration of Type $\int (\sin^m x \cdot \cos^n x)\, dx$

(i) Where m, n belongs to natural number.
(ii) If one of them is odd, then substitute for term of even power.
(iii) If both are odd, substitute either of them.
(iv) If both are even, use trigonometric identities only.
(v) If m and n are rational numbers and $\left(\frac{m+n-2}{2}\right)$ is a negative integer, then substitute $\cot x = p$ or $\tan x = p$ which so ever is found suitable.

Example 87 Evaluate $\int \sin^3 x \cdot \cos^5 x\, dx$.

Sol. $I = \int \sin^3 x \cdot \cos^5 x\, dx$

Let $\cos x = t \Rightarrow -\sin x\, dx = dt$

$$I = -\int (1-t^2) \cdot t^5 dt$$

$$I = \int t^7\, dt - \int t^5\, dt = \frac{t^8}{8} - \frac{t^6}{6} + C$$

$$I = \frac{\cos^8 x}{8} - \frac{\cos^6 x}{6} + C$$

Aliter $I = \int R^3 (1-R^2)^2\, dR$,

if $\sin x = R$, $\cos x\, dx = dR$

$$I = \int R^3\, dR - \int 2R^5\, dR + \int R^7 dR$$

$$I = \frac{\sin^4 x}{4} - \frac{2\sin^6 x}{6} + \frac{\sin^8 x}{8} + C$$

Remark

This problem can also be handled by successive reduction or by trigonometrical identities. Answers will be in different form but identical with modified constant of integration.

Example 88 Evaluate $\int \sin^{-11/3} x \cdot \cos^{-1/3} x\, dx$.

Sol. Here, $\int \sin^{-11/3} x \cdot \cos^{-1/3} x\, dx$ i.e. $\left(\frac{-\frac{11}{3} - \frac{1}{3} - 2}{2}\right) = -3$

$$\therefore \quad I = \int \frac{\cos^{-1/3} x}{\sin^{-1/3} x \cdot \sin^4 x}\, dx = \int (\cot^{-1/3} x)(\text{cosec}^2 x)^2 dx$$

$$I = \int (\cot^{-1/3} x)(1 + \cot^2 x)\, \text{cosec}^2 x\, dx$$

$$= -\int t^{-1/3}(1+t^2)\, dt = -\int (t^{-1/3} + t^{5/3})\, dt$$

[Put $\cot x = t, \Rightarrow -\text{cosec}^2 x\, dx = dt$]

$$= -\left\{\frac{3}{2} t^{2/3} + \frac{3}{8} t^{8/3}\right\} + C$$

$$= -\left\{\frac{3}{2}(\cot^{2/3} x) + \frac{3}{8}(\cot^{8/3} x)\right\} + C$$

Example 89 Evaluate $\int \frac{dx}{2\sin x + \sec x}$.

Sol. Let $I = \int \frac{dx}{2\sin x + \sec x} = \int \frac{\cos x\, dx}{\sin 2x + 1} = \frac{1}{2}\int \frac{2\cos x\, dx}{1 + \sin 2x}$

$$= \frac{1}{2}\int \frac{(\cos x + \sin x) + (\cos x - \sin x)}{(\sin^2 + \cos^2 x + 2\sin x \cos x)}\, dx$$

$$= \frac{1}{2}\int \frac{\cos x + \sin x}{(\sin x + \cos x)^2}\, dx + \frac{1}{2}\int \frac{(\cos x - \sin x)}{(\sin x + \cos x)^2}\, dx$$

$$= \frac{1}{2}\int \frac{dx}{\sin x + \cos x} + \frac{1}{2}\int \frac{dv}{v^2}, \text{ where, } v = \sin x + \cos x$$

$$= \frac{1}{2\sqrt{2}} \int \frac{dx}{\frac{1}{\sqrt{2}}\sin x + \frac{1}{\sqrt{2}}\cos x} - \frac{1}{2v} + C$$

$$= \frac{1}{2\sqrt{2}} \int \frac{dx}{\sin\left(x + \frac{\pi}{4}\right)} - \frac{1}{2(\sin x + \cos x)} + C$$

$$= \frac{1}{2\sqrt{2}} \log\left|\text{cosec}\left(x + \frac{\pi}{4}\right) - \cot\left(x + \frac{\pi}{4}\right)\right| - \frac{1}{2(\sin x + \cos x)} + C$$

Type IV

Integrals of the Form $\int x^m (a + bx^n)^P dx$

Case I If $P \in N$. We expand using binomial and integrate.

Case II If $P \in I^-$ (ie, negative integer), write $x = t^k$, where k is the LCM of m and n.

Case III If $\frac{m+1}{n}$ is an integer and $P \leftrightarrow$ fraction, put $(a + b\, x^n) = t^k$, where k is denominator of the fraction P.

Case IV If $\left(\frac{m+1}{n} + P\right)$ is an integer and $P \in$ fraction.

We put $(a + b\, x^n) = t^k x^n$, where k is denominator of the fraction P.

Example 90 Evaluate $\int x^{1/3} (2 + x^{1/2})^2\, dx$.

Sol. $I = \int x^{1/3} (2 + x^{1/2})^2\, dx$

Since, P is natural number.

$$\therefore \quad I = \int x^{1/3} (4 + x + 4x^{1/2})\, dx$$

$$= \int (4x^{1/3} + x^{4/3} + 4x^{5/6})\, dx$$

$$= \frac{4x^{4/3}}{4/3} + \frac{x^{7/3}}{7/3} + \frac{4x^{11/6}}{11/6} + C$$

$$= 3x^{4/3} + \frac{3}{7} x^{7/3} + \frac{24}{11} x^{11/6} + C$$

Example 91 Evaluate $\int x^{-2/3}(1+x^{2/3})^{-1}\,dx$.

Sol. If we substitute $x=t^3$ (as we know $P\in$ negative integer)

$\therefore$ Let $x=t^k$, where k is the LCM of m and n.

$$\therefore \quad x=t^3 \Rightarrow dx=3t^2\,dt$$

or $$I=\int\frac{3t^2}{t^2(1+t^2)}dt=3\int\frac{dt}{t^2+1}=3\tan^{-1}(t)+C$$

$$\Rightarrow \quad I=3\tan^{-1}(x^{1/3})+C$$

Example 92 Evaluate $\int x^{-2/3}(1+x^{1/3})^{1/2}\,dx$.

Sol. If we substitute $1+x^{1/3}=t^2$, then $\frac{1}{3x^{2/3}}dx=2t\,dt$

$$\therefore \quad I=\int\frac{t\cdot 6t\,dt}{1}=6\int t^2\,dt=2t^3+C$$

or $$I=2(1+x^{1/3})^{3/2}+C$$

Example 93 Evaluate $\int\sqrt{x}\,(1+x^{1/3})^4\,dx$.

Sol. Here, $m=\frac{1}{2}$ and $n=\frac{1}{3}$

Put $x=t^6\Rightarrow dx=6t^5\,dt$

$$\Rightarrow \quad I=\int t^3(1+t^2)^4\,6t^5\,dt$$

$$\Rightarrow \quad I=6\int t^8(1+4t^2+6t^4+4t^6+t^8)\,dt$$

$$=6\int(t^8+4t^{10}+6t^{12}+4t^{14}+t^{16})\,dt$$

$$=6\left\{\frac{t^9}{9}+\frac{4t^{11}}{11}+\frac{6t^{13}}{13}+\frac{4t^{15}}{15}+\frac{t^{17}}{17}\right\}+C$$

$$I=6\left\{x^{2/3}+\frac{4}{11}x^{11/6}+\frac{6}{13}x^{13/6}+\frac{4}{15}x^{5/2}+\frac{1}{17}x^{17/6}\right\}+C$$

Example 94 Evaluate $\int x^5(1+x^3)^{2/3}\,dx$.

Sol. Here, $\int x^5(1+x^3)^{2/3}\,dx$ have $m=5$, $n=3$ and $p=\frac{2}{3}$

$$\therefore \quad \frac{m+1}{n}=\frac{6}{3}=2 \qquad \text{[an integer]}$$

So, we substitute $1+x^3=t^2$ and $3x^2\,dx=2t\,dt$

$$\therefore \int x^5(1+x^3)^{2/3}dx=\int x^3(1+x^3)^{2/3}x^2dx$$

$$=\int(t^2-1)(t^2)^{2/3}\frac{2}{3}t\,dt$$

$$=\frac{2}{3}\int(t^2-1)\,t^{7/3}dt=\frac{2}{3}\int(t^{13/3}-t^{7/3})\,dt$$

$$=\frac{2}{3}\left\{\frac{3}{16}t^{16/3}-\frac{3}{10}t^{10/3}\right\}+C$$

$$=\frac{1}{8}(1+x^3)^{8/3}-\frac{1}{5}(1+x^3)^{5/3}+C$$

Example 95 Evaluate $\int x^{-11}(1+x^4)^{-1/2}\,dx$.

Sol. Here, $\left(\frac{m+1}{n}+p\right)=\left[\frac{-11+1}{4}-\frac{1}{2}\right]=-3$

If we substitute $(1+x^4)=t^2x^4$,

then $1+\frac{1}{x^4}=t^2$ and $\frac{-4}{x^5}dx=2t\,dt$

$$\therefore \quad I=\int\frac{dx}{x^{11}(1+x^4)^{1/2}}=\int\frac{dx}{x^{11}\cdot x^2(1+1/x^4)^{1/2}}$$

$$=\int\frac{dx}{x^{13}(1+1/x^4)^{1/2}}=-\frac{1}{4}\int\frac{2t\,dt}{x^8\,t}$$

$$=-\frac{1}{2}\int(t^2-1)^2\,dt=-\frac{1}{2}\int(t^4-2t^2+1)\,dt$$

$$=-\frac{1}{2}\left[\frac{t^5}{5}-\frac{2t^3}{3}+t\right]+C$$

Where $t=\sqrt{1+\frac{1}{x^4}}$

Example 96 Evaluate $\int\frac{1}{\sqrt[3]{x}+\sqrt[4]{x}}\,dx$.

Sol. Let $I=\int\frac{1}{\sqrt[3]{x}+\sqrt[4]{x}}\,dx$

Put $x^{1/12}=t$, $\Rightarrow x=t^{12}$ and $dx=12t^{11}\,dt$

$$\therefore \quad I=\int\frac{1}{t^4+t^3}\cdot 12\,t^{11}\,dt=12\int\frac{t^8}{t+1}\,dt$$

Again put $(t+1)=y$

$$\therefore\ dt=dy=12\int\frac{(y-1)^8}{y}\,dy$$

$$=12\int\frac{(y^8-8y^7+28y^6-56y^5+70y^4-56y^3+28y^2-8y+1)}{y}dy$$

[using binomial]

$$=12\int(y^7-8y^6+28y^5-56y^4+70y^3-56y^2+28y-8+1/y)dy$$

$$=12\begin{pmatrix}\frac{y^8}{8}-\frac{8y^7}{7}+\frac{28y^6}{6}-\frac{56y^5}{5}+\frac{70y^4}{4}\\ -\frac{56y^3}{3}+\frac{28y^2}{2}-8y+\log|y|\end{pmatrix}+C_1$$

Where $y=x^{1/12}+1$

Exercise for Session 6

- Evaluate the following integrals

1. $\int \frac{x^4 - 1}{x^2(x^4 + x^2 + 1)^{1/2}} dx$

2. $\int \frac{(x + 2)\, dx}{(x^2 + 3x + 3)\sqrt{x + 1}}$

3. $\int \frac{dx}{(x + 1)^{1/3} + (x + 1)^{1/2}}$

4. $\int \frac{dx}{(x + a)^{8/7}(x - b)^{6/7}}$

5. $\int \frac{\sec x \,.\, dx}{\sqrt{\sin (x + 2A) + \sin A}}$

6. The value of $\int [\{x\}]\, dx$; (where [.] and {.} denotes greatest integer and fractional part of x) is equal to

(a) 0
(b) 1
(c) 2
(d) – 1

7. If $\int f(x) \cos x \, dx = \frac{1}{2} f^2(x) + C$, then $f(x)$ can be

(a) x
(b) 1
(c) $\cos x$
(d) $\sin x$

8. The value of, $\int \frac{\sin x + \cos x}{9 + 16 \sin 2x} dx$ is

(a) $\frac{1}{40} \log \left| \frac{5+ 4 (\sin x - \cos x)}{5 - 4 (\sin x - \cos x)} \right| + C$
(b) $\log \left| \frac{5+ 4 (\sin x - \cos x)}{5 - 4 (\sin x - \cos x)} \right| + C$
(c) $\frac{1}{10} \log \left| \frac{5+ 4 (\sin x + \cos x)}{5 - 4 (\sin x + \cos x)} \right| + C$
(d) None of these

9. The value of $\int \frac{\cos 7x - \cos 8x}{1 + 2 \cos 5x} dx$, is

(a) $\frac{\sin 2x}{2} + \frac{\cos 3x}{3} + C$
(b) $\sin x - \cos x + C$
(c) $\frac{\sin 2x}{2} - \frac{\cos 3x}{3} + C$
(d) None of these

10. The value of $\int \frac{\cos 5x + \cos 4x}{1 - 2 \cos 3x} dx$, is

(a) $\sin x + \sin 2x + C$
(b) $\sin x - \frac{\sin 2x}{2} + C$
(c) $- \sin x - \frac{\sin 2x}{2} + C$
(d) None of these

Session 7

Euler's Substitution, Reduction Formula and Integration Using Diffrentiation

Euler's Substitution, Reduction and Integration Using Diffrentiation

Integration Using Euler's Substitutions

Integrals of the form $\int f(x), \sqrt{ax^2+bx+c}\,dx$ are calculated with the aid of one of the three Euler's substitutions

(i) $\sqrt{ax^2+bx+c} = t \pm x\sqrt{a}$, if $a>0$.

(ii) $\sqrt{ax^2+bx+c} = tx + \sqrt{c}$, if $c>0$.

(iii) $\sqrt{ax^2+bx+c} = (x-\alpha)\,t$, if $ax^2+bx+c = a(x-\alpha)(x-\beta)$, i.e. If α is real root of (ax^2+bx+c).

Remark

The Euler's substitutions often lead to rather cumbersome calculations, therefore they should be applied only when it is difficult to find another method for calculating a given integral.

| Example 97 Evaluate $I = \int \dfrac{x\,dx}{(\sqrt{7x-10-x^2})^3}$.

Sol. In this case $a<0$ and $c<0$. Therefore, neither (I) nor (II) Euler's Substitution is applicable. But the quadratic $7x-10-x^2$ has real roots $\alpha = 2, \beta = 5$.

$\therefore$ We use the substitution (III)

i.e. $\sqrt{7x-10-x^2} = \sqrt{(x-2)(5-x)} = (x-2)\,t$

Where $(5-x) = (x-2)\,t^2$

or $5+2t^2 = x(1+t^2)$

$$\therefore \quad x = \frac{5+2t^2}{1+t^2}$$

$$(x-2)\,t = \left(\frac{5+2t^2}{1+t^2} - 2\right)t = \frac{3t}{1+t^2}$$

$$\therefore \quad dx = \frac{-6t}{(1+t^2)^2}\,dt$$

Hence, $$I = \int \frac{x\,dx}{(\sqrt{7x-10-x^2})^3} = \int \frac{\left(\dfrac{5+2t^2}{1+t^2}\right)\cdot \dfrac{-6t}{(1+t^2)^2}\,dt}{\left(\dfrac{3t}{1+t^2}\right)^3}$$

$$= \frac{-6}{27}\int \frac{5+2t^2}{t^2}\,dt$$

$$= \frac{-2}{9}\int \left(\frac{5}{t^2}+2\right)dt = \frac{-2}{9}\left[\frac{-5}{t}+2t\right]+C$$

$$\therefore \quad \int \frac{x\,dx}{(\sqrt{7x-10-x^2})^3} = -\frac{2}{9}\left(\frac{-5}{t}+2t\right)+C,$$

where, $t = \dfrac{\sqrt{7x-10-x^2}}{x-2}$

| Example 98 Evaluate $\int \dfrac{dx}{x+\sqrt{x^2-x+1}}$.

Sol. Since, here $c=1$, we can apply the second Euler's Substitution.

$$\sqrt{x^2-x+1} = tx-1$$

Therefore, $(2t-1)\,x = (t^2-1)\,x^2 \Rightarrow x = \dfrac{2t-1}{t^2-1}$

$$\therefore \quad dx = -\frac{2(t^2-t+1)\,dt}{(t^2-1)^2} \text{ and } x+\sqrt{x^2-x+1} = \frac{t}{t-1}$$

$$\therefore \quad I = \int \frac{dx}{x+\sqrt{x^2-x+1}} = \int \frac{-2t^2+2t-2}{t(t-1)(t+1)^2}\,dt$$

Using partial fractions, we have

$$\frac{-2t^2+2t-2}{t(t-1)(t+1)^2} = \frac{A}{t} + \frac{B}{t-1} + \frac{C}{(t+1)} + \frac{D}{(t+1)^2}$$

or $(-2t^2+2t-2) = A(t-1)(t+1)^2 + Bt(t+1)^2 + C(t-1)(t+1)t + Dt$

we get $A = 2$, $B = -1/2$, $C = -3/2$, $D = -3$

Hence, $$I = 2\int \frac{dt}{t} - \frac{1}{2}\int \frac{dt}{t-1} - \frac{3}{2}\int \frac{dt}{(t+1)} - 3\int \frac{dt}{(t+1)^2}$$

$$= 2\log_e|t| - \frac{1}{2}\log_e|t-1| - \frac{3}{2}\log_e|t+1| + \frac{3}{(t+1)} + C$$

$$\left[\text{where } t = \frac{\sqrt{x^2-x+1}+1}{x}\right]$$

Introduction of Reduction Formulae (a recursive relation) Over Indefinite Integrals

Reduction formulae makes it possible to reduce an integral depending on the index $n > 0$, called the order of the integral, to an integral of the same type with smaller index. (i.e. To reduce the integrals into similar integrals of order less than or greater than given integral).

Application of reduction formula is given with the help of some examples.

Reduction Formula for $\int \sin^n x\, dx$

Let $I_n = \int \sin^n x\, dx = \int \underset{\text{I}}{\sin^{n-1} x}\, \underset{\text{II}}{\sin x}\, dx$

$$= -\sin^{n-1} x \cos x + \int (n-1) \sin^{n-2} x \cos^2 x\, dx$$

$$= -\sin^{n-1} x \cos x + (n-1) \int \sin^{n-2} x (1 - \sin^2 x)\, dx$$

$$= -\sin^{n-1} x \cos x + (n-1) \int (\sin^{n-2} x - \sin^n x)\, dx$$

$$= -\sin^{n-1} x \cos x + (n-1) I_{n-2} - (n-1) I_n$$

$$\therefore n I_n = -\sin^{n-1} x \cos x + (n-1) I_{n-2}$$

$$\Rightarrow I_n = -\frac{\sin^{n-1} x \cos x}{n} + \frac{n-1}{n} I_{n-2}$$

Thus, $\int \sin^n x\, dx = \dfrac{-\sin^{n-1} x \cos x}{n} + \dfrac{n-1}{n} \int \sin^{n-2} x\, dx$

Reduction Formula for $\int \cos^n x\, dx$

Let $I_n = \int \cos^n x\, dx = \int \underset{\text{I}}{\cos^{n-1} x}\, \underset{\text{II}}{\cos x}\, dx$

$$= \cos^{n-1} x \sin x + \int (n-1) \cos^{n-2} x \sin^2 x\, dx$$

$$= \cos^{n-1} x \sin x + (n-1) \int \cos^{n-2} x (1 - \cos^2 x)\, dx$$

$$= \cos^{n-1} x \sin x + (n-1) I_{n-2} - (n-1) I_n$$

$$\therefore \quad nI_n = \cos^{n-1} x \sin x + (n-1) I_{n-2}$$

or $\int \cos^n x\, dx = \dfrac{\cos^{n-1} x \sin x}{n} + \dfrac{n-1}{n} \int \cos^{n-2} x\, dx$

Reduction Formula for $\int \tan^n x\, dx$

Let $I_n = \int \tan^n x\, dx$

$$\Rightarrow I_n = \int \tan^{n-2} x \tan^2 x\, dx = \int \tan^{n-2} x (\sec^2 x - 1)\, dx$$

$$= \int \tan^{n-2} x \sec^2 x - I_{n-2} = \int t^{n-2}\, dt - I_{n-2}$$

where, $\tan x = t \Rightarrow \sec^2 x\, dx = dt$

$$I_n = \frac{t^{n-1}}{n-1} - I_{n-2}.$$

$$\therefore \quad I_n = \frac{\tan^{n-1} x}{n-1} - I_{n-2}$$

$$\Rightarrow \quad \int \tan^n x\, dx = \frac{\tan^{n-1} x}{n-1} - \int \tan^{n-2} x\, dx$$

Reduction Formula for $\int \operatorname{cosec}^n x\, dx$

Let $I_n = \int \operatorname{cosec}^n x\, dx = \int \underset{\text{I}}{\operatorname{cosec}^{n-2} x}\, \underset{\text{II}}{\operatorname{cosec}^2 x}\, dx$

$$= \operatorname{cosec}^{n-2} x (-\cot x) - \int (n-2) \operatorname{cosec}^{n-2} x (\operatorname{cosec}^2 x - 1) dx$$

$$= -\operatorname{cosec}^{n-2} x \cot x - (n-2) \int (\operatorname{cosec}^n x - \operatorname{cosec}^{n-2} x)\, dx$$

$$= -\operatorname{cosec}^{n-2} x \cot x - (n-2) I_n + (n-2) I_{n-2}.$$

$$\therefore \quad (n-1) I_n = -\operatorname{cosec}^{n-2} x \cot x + (n-2) I_{n-2}$$

or $I_n = -\dfrac{\operatorname{cosec}^{n-2} x \cot x}{n-1} + \dfrac{n-2}{n-1} I_{n-2}$

$$\therefore \int \operatorname{cosec}^n x dx = -\frac{\operatorname{cosec}^{n-2} x \cot x}{n-1} + \frac{n-2}{n-1} \int \operatorname{cosec}^{n-2} x\, dx$$

Reduction Formula for $\int \sec^n x\, dx$

Let $I_n = \int \sec^n x\, dx = \int \underset{\text{I}}{\sec^{n-2} x}\, \underset{\text{II}}{\sec^2 x}\, dx$

$$= \sec^{n-2} x \tan x - \int (n-2) \sec^{n-3} x \sec x \tan x \cdot \tan x\, dx$$

$$= \sec^{n-2} x \tan x - (n-2) \int \sec^{n-2} x (\sec^2 x - 1)\, dx$$

$$= \sec^{n-2} x \tan x - (n-2) I_n + (n-2) I_{n-2}$$

$$\Rightarrow (n-1) I_n = \sec^{n-2} x \tan x + (n-2) I_{n-2}$$

or $I_n = \dfrac{\sec^{n-2} x \tan x}{(n-1)} + \dfrac{(n-2)}{(n-1)} I_{n-2}$

$$\therefore \int \sec^n x\, dx = \frac{\sec^{n-2} x \tan x}{(n-1)} + \frac{(n-2)}{(n-1)} \int \sec^{n-2} x\, dx$$

Reduction Formula for $\int \cot^n x\, dx$

Let $I_n = \int \cot^n x\, dx = \int \cot^{n-2} x \cot^2 x\, dx$

$$= \int \cot^{n-2} x (\operatorname{cosec}^2 x - 1)\, dx$$

$$= \int \cot^{n-2} x (\operatorname{cosec}^2 x - 1)\, dx = \int \cot^{n-2} x\, dx$$

$$= \int t^{n-2}\, dt - I_{n-2}, \qquad \text{where } t = \cot x$$

$$I_n = -\frac{\cot^{n-1} x}{n-1} - I_{n-2}$$

$$\therefore \quad \int \cot^n x \, dx = -\frac{\cot^{n-1} x}{n-1} - \int \cot^{n-2} x \, dx$$

Reduction Formula for $\int \sin^m x \cos^n x \, dx$

Let $A = \sin^{m-1} x \cos^{n+1} x$

$$\therefore \quad \frac{dA}{dx} = (m-1)\sin^{m-2} x \cos^{n+2} x - (n+1)\sin^m x \cos^n x$$

$$= (m-1)\sin^{m-2} x \cos^n x (1 - \sin^2 x) - (n+1)\sin^m x \cos^n x$$

$$= (m-1)\sin^{m-2} x \cos^n x - (m-1+n+1) \sin^m x \cos^n x$$

$$\Rightarrow \quad \frac{dA}{dx} = (m-1)\sin^{m-2} x \cos^n x - (m+n)\sin^m x \cos^n x$$

Integrating with respect to x on both the sides, we get

$$A = (m-1)\int \sin^{m-2} x \cos^n x \, dx - (m+n) \int \sin^m x \cos^n x \, dx$$

$$\Rightarrow \quad (m+n)\int \sin^m x \cos^n x \, dx = (m-1) \int \sin^{m-2} x \cos^n x \, dx - P$$

$$\Rightarrow \quad \int \sin^m x \cos^n x \, dx = \frac{(m-1)}{(m+n)} \int \sin^{m-2} x \cos^n x \, dx - \frac{\sin^{m-1} x \cos^{n+1} x}{m+n}$$

$$\text{or} \quad I_{m,n} = \frac{(m-1)}{(m+n)} I_{m-2,n} - \frac{\sin^{m-1} x \cos^{n+1} x}{(m+n)}$$

Remarks

Similarly, we can show

1. $\int \sin^m x \cos^n x \, dx = \frac{\sin^{m+1} x \cos^{n+1} x}{m+n} + \frac{n-1}{m+n} \int \sin^m x \cos^{n-2} x \, dx$
2. $\int \sin^m x \cos^n x \, dx = \frac{\sin^{m+1} x \cos^{n+1} x}{m+1} + \frac{m+n+2}{m+1} \int \sin^{m+2} x \cos^n x \, dx$
3. $\int \sin^m x \cos^n x \, dx = \frac{\sin^{m+1} x \cos^{n+1} x}{n+1} + \frac{m+n+2}{n+1} \int \sin^m x \cos^{n+2} x \, dx$
4. $\int \sin^m x \cos^n x \, dx = -\frac{\sin^{m-1} x \cos^{n+1} x}{n+1} + \frac{m-1}{n+1} \int \sin^{m-2} x \cos^{n+2} x \, dx$
5. $\int \sin^m x \cos^n x \, dx = \frac{\sin^{m+1} x \cos^{n-1} x}{m+1} + \frac{n-1}{m+1} \int \sin^{m+2} x \cos^{n-2} x \, dx$

Reduction Formula for $\int \cos^m x \sin nx \, dx$

Let $I_{m,n} = \int \underset{\text{I}}{\cos^m x} \underset{\text{II}}{\sin nx} \, dx$

$$= -\frac{\cos^m x \cos nx}{n} - \frac{m}{n} \int \cos^{m-1} x \sin x \cos nx \, dx$$

$$= -\frac{\cos^m x \cos nx}{n} - \frac{m}{n} \int \cos^{m-1} x \{\sin nx \cos x - \sin (n-1) x\} \, dx$$

[using $\sin (n-1) x = \sin nx \cos x - \cos nx \sin x$
$\Rightarrow \sin x \cos nx = \sin nx \cos x - \sin (n-1) x$]

$$= -\frac{\cos^m x \cos nx}{n} - \frac{m}{n} \int \cos^m x \sin nx \, dx + \frac{m}{n} \int \cos^{m-1} x \sin (n-1) x \, dx$$

$$I_{m,n} = -\frac{\cos^m x \cos nx}{n} - \frac{m}{n} I_{m,n} + \frac{m}{n} I_{m-1,n-1}$$

$$\Rightarrow \quad \frac{m+n}{n} I_{m,n} = -\frac{\cos^m x \cos nx}{n} + \frac{m}{n} I_{m-1,n-1}$$

$$\text{or} \quad I_{m,n} = -\frac{\cos^m x \cos nx}{m+n} + \frac{m}{m+n} I_{m-1,n-1}$$

Remarks

Similarly, we can show

1. $\int \cos^m x \cos nx \, dx = \frac{\cos^m x \sin nx}{m+n} + \frac{m}{m+n} \int \cos^{m-1} x \cos (n-1) x \, dx$
2. $\int \sin^m x \sin nx \, dx = \frac{n \sin^m x \cos nx}{m^2 - n^2} - \frac{m \sin^{m-1} x \cos x \cos nx}{m^2 - n^2} + \frac{m(m-1)}{m^2 - n^2} \int \sin^{m-2} x \sin nx \, dx$
3. $\int \sin^m x \cos nx \, dx = \frac{n \sin^m x \sin nx}{m^2 - n^2} - \frac{m \sin^{m-1} x \cos x \cos nx}{m^2 - n^2} + \frac{m(m-1)}{m^2 - n^2} \int \sin^{m-2} x \cos nx \, dx$

Example 99 Evaluate $I_n = \int \frac{dx}{(x^2 + a^2)^n}$.

Sol. Here, $I_n = \int \frac{dx}{(x^2 + a^2)^n} = \int \frac{1}{(x^2 + a^2)^n} \cdot 1 \, dx$

Applying Integration by parts, we get

$$= \frac{1}{(x^2 + a^2)^n} \cdot x - \int \frac{(2x)}{(x^2 + a^2)^{n+1}} \cdot (-n) \cdot (x) \, dx$$

$$= \frac{x}{(x^2 + a^2)^n} + 2n \int \frac{x^2}{(x^2 + a^2)^{n+1}} \, dx$$

$$= \frac{x}{(x^2 + a^2)^n} + 2n \int \frac{x^2 + a^2 - a^2}{(x^2 + a^2)^{n+1}} \, dx$$

$$\therefore\ I_n = \frac{x}{(x^2+a^2)^n} + 2n\int \frac{1}{(x^2+a^2)^n}\,dx - 2a^2 n\int \frac{dx}{(x^2+a^2)^{n+1}}$$

$$I_n = \frac{x}{(x^2+a^2)^n} + 2n\,I_n - 2n\,a^2\,I_{n+1}$$

$$\therefore\ 2n\,a^2\,I_{n+1} = \frac{x}{(x^2+a^2)^n} + (2n-1)\,I_n$$

or $$I_{n+1} = \frac{1}{2n\,a^2}\cdot\frac{x}{(x^2+a^2)^n} + \frac{(2n-1)}{2n}\cdot\frac{1}{a^2}\,I_n$$

Remark

Above obtained formula reduces the calculations of the integral I_{n+1} to the calculations of the integral I_n and consequently, allows us to calculate completely an integral with natural index, as

$$I_1 = \int \frac{dx}{x^2+a^2} = \frac{1}{a}\tan^{-1}\left(\frac{x}{a}\right) + C$$

$\therefore$ From above formula

Let $n = 1$

$$I_2 = \int \frac{dx}{(x^2+a^2)^2} = \frac{1}{2a^2}\cdot\frac{x}{x^2+a^2} + \frac{1}{2a^2}\cdot I_1$$

$$= \frac{1}{2a^2}\cdot\frac{x}{x^2+a^2} + \frac{1}{2a^2}\cdot\frac{1}{a}\cdot\tan^{-1}\left(\frac{x}{a}\right) + C$$

$$= \frac{1}{2a^2}\cdot\frac{x}{x^2+a^2} + \frac{1}{2a^3}\cdot\tan^{-1}\left(\frac{x}{a}\right) + C$$

Let $n = 2$

$$I_3 = \int \frac{dx}{(x^2+a^2)^3} = \frac{1}{4a^2}\cdot\frac{x}{(x^2+a^2)^2} + \frac{3}{4a^2}\,I_2$$

$$= \frac{1}{4a^2}\cdot\frac{x}{(x^2+a^2)^2} + \frac{3}{8a^4}\cdot\frac{x}{x^2+a^2} + \frac{3}{8a^5}\tan^{-1}\left(\frac{x}{a}\right) + C$$

...and so on.

Example 100 Derive reduction formula for $I_{(n,\,m)} = \int \frac{\sin^n x}{\cos^m x}\,dx.$

Sol. Using Integration by parts for $I_{(n,\,m)}$, we get

$$I_{(n,\,m)} = \int \underset{\text{I}}{\sin^{n-1} x}\ \underset{\text{II}}{\frac{\sin x}{\cos^m x}}\,dx$$

$$= \sin^{n-1} x\cdot\frac{(\cos x)^{-m+1}}{(m-1)} - \int (n-1)\sin^{n-2} x\cdot\cos x\cdot\frac{(\cos x)^{-m+1}}{(m-1)}\,dx$$

$$= \frac{1}{m-1}\cdot\frac{\sin^{n-1} x}{\cos^{m-1} x} - \frac{(n-1)}{(m-1)}\cdot\int \frac{\sin^{n-2} x}{\cos^{m-2} x}\,dx$$

$$I_{n,\,m} = \frac{1}{(m-1)}\cdot\frac{\sin^{n-1} x}{\cos^{m-1} x} - \frac{(n-1)}{(m-1)}\cdot I_{(n-2,\,m-2)}$$

is required reduction formula.

Integration Using Differentiation

In $\int \frac{dx}{(a+b\cos x)^2}$, $\int \frac{dx}{(a+b\sin x)^2}$, $\int \frac{dx}{(\sin x + a\sec x)^2}$, $\int \frac{a+b\sin x}{(b+a\sin x)^2}\,dx, \ldots$ we follow the following method.

1. Let $A = \frac{\sin x}{a+b\cos x}$ or $A = \frac{\cos x}{a+b\sin x}$ according to the integral to evaluated is of the form
$$\int \frac{dx}{(a+b\cos x)^2} \text{ or } \int \frac{dx}{(a+b\sin x)^2}$$
2. Find $\frac{dA}{dx}$ and express it in terms of $\frac{1}{a+b\cos x}$ or $\frac{1}{a+b\sin x}$ as the case may be.
3. Integrate both the sides of the expression obtained in step 2 to obtain the value of the required integral.

Example 101 Evaluate $\int \frac{dx}{(5+4\cos x)^2}$.

Sol. Here, $A = \frac{\sin x}{5+4\cos x}$, then

$$\frac{dA}{dx} = \frac{(5+4\cos x)(\cos x) - \sin x(-4\sin x)}{(5+4\cos x)^2}$$

$$\Rightarrow\ \frac{dA}{dx} = \frac{5\cos x + 4}{(5+4\cos x)^2} = \frac{\frac{5}{4}(4\cos x + 5) + 4 - \frac{25}{4}}{(5+4\cos x)^2}$$

$$\Rightarrow\ \frac{dA}{dx} = \frac{5}{4}\cdot\frac{1}{(5+4\cos x)} - \frac{9}{4}\cdot\frac{1}{(5+4\cos x)^2}$$

Integrating both the sides w.r.t. 'x', we get

$$A = \frac{5}{4}\int \frac{dx}{5+4\cos x} - \frac{9}{4}\int \frac{dx}{(5+4\cos x)^2}$$

$$\Rightarrow\ \frac{9}{4}\int \frac{dx}{(5+4\cos x)^2} = \frac{5}{4}\int \frac{dx}{5+4\cos x} - A$$

$$= \frac{5}{4}\int \frac{dx}{5 + 4\,\frac{(1-\tan^2 x/2)}{(1+\tan^2 x/2)}} - \frac{\sin x}{(5+4\cos x)}$$

$$\Rightarrow\ \int \frac{dx}{(5+4\cos x)^2} = \frac{5}{9}\int \frac{1+\tan^2 x/2}{9+\tan^2 x/2}\,dx - \frac{4}{9}\cdot\frac{\sin x}{5+4\cos x}$$

$$\Rightarrow\ \int \frac{dx}{(5+4\cos x)^2} = \frac{5}{9}\int \frac{2\,dt}{9+t^2} - \frac{4}{9}\cdot\frac{\sin x}{5+4\cos x}$$

(where $\tan x/2 = t$)

$$\Rightarrow \int \frac{dx}{(5+4\cos x)^2} = \frac{10}{9} \cdot \frac{1}{3} \tan^{-1}\left(\frac{t}{3}\right) - \frac{4}{9} \cdot \frac{\sin x}{5+4\cos x}$$

$$\Rightarrow \int \frac{dx}{(5+4\cos x)^2} = \frac{10}{27} \tan^{-1}\left(\frac{\tan x/2}{3}\right) - \frac{4}{9}\left(\frac{\sin x}{5+4\cos x}\right) + C$$

| Example 102 Evaluate $\int \frac{dx}{(16+9\sin x)^2}$.

Sol. Let $A = \frac{\cos x}{16+9\sin x}$ ...(i)

$$\Rightarrow \frac{dA}{dx} = \frac{(16+9\sin x)(-\sin x) - \cos x(9\cos x)}{(16+9\sin x)^2}$$

$$\Rightarrow \frac{dA}{dx} = \frac{-16\sin x - 9}{(16+9\sin x)^2}$$

$$\Rightarrow \frac{dA}{dx} = \frac{-\frac{16}{9}(9\sin x + 16) + \frac{256}{9} - 9}{(16+9\sin x)^2}$$

$$\Rightarrow \frac{dA}{dx} = -\frac{16}{9} \cdot \frac{1}{(16+9\sin x)} + \frac{175}{9(16+9\sin x)^2} \quad \text{...(ii)}$$

Integrating both the sides of Eq. (ii) w.r.t. 'x', we get

$$A = -\frac{16}{9}\int \frac{dx}{16+9\sin x} + \frac{175}{9}\int \frac{dx}{(16+9\sin x)^2}$$

$$\Rightarrow \frac{175}{9}\int \frac{dx}{(16+9\sin x)^2} = A + \frac{16}{9}\int \frac{(1+\tan^2 x/2)\,dx}{16+16\tan^2 x/2 + 18\tan x/2}$$

$$\Rightarrow \frac{175}{9}\int \frac{dx}{(16+9\sin x)^2} = A + \frac{16}{9}\int \frac{2\,dt}{16t^2+18t+16}$$

[where $\tan x/2 = t$]

$$\Rightarrow \frac{175}{9}\int \frac{dx}{(16+9\sin x)^2} = A + \frac{2}{9}\int \frac{dt}{t^2 + \frac{9}{8}t + 1}$$

$$= A + \frac{2}{9}\int \frac{dt}{\left(t+\frac{9}{16}\right)^2 + \left(\frac{\sqrt{175}}{16}\right)^2}$$

$$= A + \frac{2}{9} \times \frac{16}{\sqrt{175}} \tan^{-1}\left(\frac{16t+9}{\sqrt{175}}\right)$$

$$\Rightarrow \int \frac{dx}{(16+9\sin x)^2} = \frac{9}{175} \cdot \frac{\cos x}{(16+9\sin x)} + \frac{2}{(175)^{3/2}} \tan^{-1}\left(\frac{16\tan x/2 + 9}{\sqrt{175}}\right) + C$$

| Example 103 Evaluate $\int \frac{dx}{(\sin x + a\sec x)^2}$ when $|a| > 1/2$.

Sol. Here, $I = \int \frac{dx}{(\sin x + a\sec x)^2}$ or $I = \int \frac{\cos^2 x\,dx}{(\sin x\cos x + a)^2}$

$$= \int \frac{\cos^2 x\,dx}{a^2 + 2a\sin x\cos x + \sin^2 x\cos^2 x}$$

$$= \int \frac{\cos^2 x\,dx}{a^2 + a\sin 2x + \frac{1}{4}\sin^2 2x}$$

$$= \int \frac{4\cos^2 x\,dx}{(4a^2 + 4a\sin 2x + \sin^2 2x)} = 2\int \frac{(1+\cos 2x)\,dx}{(2a+\sin 2x)^2}$$

$$= 2\int \frac{dx}{(2a+\sin 2x)^2} + 2\int \frac{\cos 2x\,dx}{(2a+\sin 2x)^2}$$

$$\Rightarrow I = 2I_1 + \int \frac{dt}{t^2} \text{ [where } (2a+\sin 2x) = t, (2\cos 2x)\,dx = dt]$$

$$\Rightarrow I = 2I_1 - \frac{1}{(2a+\sin 2x)} + C$$

where $I_1 = \int \frac{dx}{(2a+\sin 2x)^2}$ ...(i)

Put $A = \frac{\cos 2x}{2a+\sin 2x}$

$$\Rightarrow \frac{dA}{dx} = \frac{(2a+\sin 2x)(-2\sin 2x) - \cos 2x(2\cos 2x)}{(2a+\sin 2x)^2}$$

$$\Rightarrow \frac{dA}{dx} = \frac{-4a\sin 2x - 2}{(2a+\sin 2x)^2}$$

$$\Rightarrow \frac{dA}{dx} = \frac{-4a(\sin 2x + 2a) - 2 + 8a^2}{(2a+\sin 2x)^2}$$

$$\Rightarrow \frac{dA}{dx} = -\frac{4a}{(2a+\sin 2x)} + \frac{(8a^2-2)}{(2a+\sin 2x)^2}$$

Integrating both the sides w.r.t. 'x', we get

$$\Rightarrow A = -4a\int \frac{dx}{(2a+\sin 2x)} + (8a^2-2)I_1$$

$$\Rightarrow (8a^2-2)I_1 = A + 4a\int \frac{\sec^2 x\,dx}{2a + 2\tan x + 2a\tan^2 x}$$

$$= A + \frac{4a}{2a}\int \frac{dt}{t^2 + \frac{t}{a} + 1}$$

$$= A + 2\int \frac{dt}{\left(t+\frac{1}{2a}\right)^2 + \left(1 - \frac{1}{4a^2}\right)}$$

$$= A + 2\frac{(2a)}{\sqrt{4a^2-1}} \tan^{-1}\left(\frac{(2at+1)}{\sqrt{4a^2-1}}\right)$$

$$\Rightarrow (8a^2-2)I_1 = \frac{\cos 2x}{2a+\sin 2x} + \frac{4a}{\sqrt{4a^2-1}} \tan^{-1}\left(\frac{(2a\tan x + 1)}{\sqrt{4a^2-1}}\right) \quad \text{...(ii)}$$

From Eqs. (i) and (ii)

$$I = \frac{1}{(4a^2-1)} \cdot \frac{\cos 2x}{(2a+\sin 2x)} + \frac{4a}{(4a^2-1)^{3/2}} \tan^{-1}\left(\frac{2a\tan x + 1}{\sqrt{4a^2-1}}\right) - \frac{1}{(2a+\sin 2x)} + C$$

JEE Type Solved Examples : Single Option Correct Type Questions

● **Ex. 1** *The value of* $\int \frac{dx}{\cos^6 x + \sin^6 x}$, *is equal to*

(a) $\tan^{-1}(2\cot 2x) + C$ (b) $\tan^{-1}(\cot 2x) + C$

(c) $\tan^{-1}\left(\frac{1}{2}\cot 2x\right) + C$ (d) $\tan^{-1}(-2\cot 2x) + C$

Sol. Let $I = \int \frac{dx}{\cos^6 x + \sin^6 x} = \int \frac{\sec^6 x\, dx}{1 + \tan^6 x}$

$$= \int \frac{(1+\tan^2 x)^2 \cdot \sec^2 x}{1 + \tan^6 x} dx$$

Put $\tan x = t \Rightarrow \sec^2 x\, dx = dt = \int \frac{(1+t^2)^2}{1+t^6} dt$

$$= \int \frac{(1+t^2)^2}{(1+t^2)(1-t^2+t^4)} dt$$

$$= \int \frac{1+t^2}{1-t^2+t^4} dt = \int \frac{(1+1/t^2)\, dt}{(1/t^2 - 1 + t^2)} = \int \frac{\left(1+\frac{1}{t^2}\right) dt}{(t-1/t)^2+1},$$

Put $t - \frac{1}{t} = z$

$\therefore \left(1+\frac{1}{t^2}\right) dt = dz = \int \frac{dz}{z^2+1} = \tan^{-1}(z) + C$

$$= \tan^{-1}\left(\frac{t^2-1}{t}\right) + C = \tan^{-1}\left(\frac{\tan^2 x - 1}{\tan x}\right) + C$$

$$= \tan^{-1}(-2\cot 2x) + C$$

Hence, (d) is the correct answer.

● **Ex. 2** $\int \frac{e^{\tan^{-1} x}}{(1+x^2)}\left[(\sec^{-1}\sqrt{1+x^2})^2 + \cos^{-1}\left(\frac{1-x^2}{1+x^2}\right)\right] dx,$

$(x > 0)$ is equal to

(a) $e^{\tan^{-1} x} \cdot \tan^{-1} x + C$

(b) $\frac{e^{\tan^{-1} x} \cdot (\tan^{-1} x)^2}{2} + C$

(c) $e^{\tan^{-1} x} \cdot (\sec^{-1}(\sqrt{1+x^2}))^2 + C$

(d) $e^{\tan^{-1} x} \cdot (\operatorname{cosec}^{-1}(\sqrt{1+x^2}))^2 + C$

Sol. Note that $\sec^{-1}\sqrt{1+x^2} = \tan^{-1} x$; $\cos^{-1}\left(\frac{1-x^2}{1+x^2}\right) = 2\tan^{-1} x$,

For $x > 0$

$$\Rightarrow \quad I = \int \frac{e^{\tan^{-1} x}}{1+x^2}\{(\tan^{-1} x)^2 + 2\tan^{-1} x\}\, dx,$$

Put $\tan^{-1} x = t$

$$= \int e^t (t^2 + 2t)\, dt = e^t \cdot t^2 = e^{\tan^{-1} x}(\tan^{-1} x)^2 + C$$

Hence, (c) is the correct answer.

● **Ex. 3** *Let* $I = \int \frac{e^x}{e^{4x} + e^{2x} + 1} dx$, $J = \int \frac{e^{-x}}{e^{-4x} + e^{-2x} + 1} dx$.

Then, for an arbitrary constant c, the value of J − I equals to **[IIT JEE 2008]**

(a) $\frac{1}{2}\log\left(\frac{e^{4x} - e^{2x} + 1}{e^{4x} + e^{2x} + 1}\right) + C$ (b) $\frac{1}{2}\log\left(\frac{e^{2x} + e^x + 1}{e^{2x} - e^x + 1}\right) + C$

(c) $\frac{1}{2}\log\left(\frac{e^{2x} - e^x + 1}{e^{2x} + e^x + 1}\right) + C$ (d) $\frac{1}{2}\log\left(\frac{e^{4x} + e^{2x} + 1}{e^{4x} - e^{2x} + 1}\right) + C$

Sol. $J = \int \frac{e^{3x}}{1 + e^{2x} + e^{4x}} dx$

$$J - I = \int \frac{(e^{3x} - e^x)}{1 + e^{2x} + e^{4x}} dx = \int \frac{(u^2-1)}{1+u^2+u^4} du \qquad (u = e^x)$$

$$= \int \frac{\left(1 - \frac{1}{u^2}\right) du}{1 + \frac{1}{u^2} + u^2} = \int \frac{\left(1-\frac{1}{u^2}\right) du}{\left(u+\frac{1}{u}\right)^2 - 1} = \int \frac{dt}{t^2-1} \quad \left(t = u + \frac{1}{u}\right)$$

$$= \frac{1}{2}\log\left|\frac{t-1}{t+1}\right| + C = \frac{1}{2}\log\left|\frac{u^2-u+1}{u^2+u+1}\right| + C$$

$$= \frac{1}{2}\log\left|\frac{e^{2x} - e^x + 1}{e^{2x} + e^x + 1}\right| + C$$

Hence, (c) is the correct answer.

● **Ex. 4** *Integral of* $\sqrt{1 + 2\cot x(\cot x + \operatorname{cosec} x)}$ *w.r.t. x, is*

(a) $2\ln\cos\frac{x}{2} + C$ (b) $2\ln\sin\frac{x}{2} + C$

(c) $\frac{1}{2}\ln\cos\frac{x}{2} + C$ (d) $\ln\sin x - \ln(\operatorname{cosec} x - \cot x) + C$

Sol. $I = \int \sqrt{1 + 2\operatorname{cosec} x \cot x + 2\cot^2 x}\, dx$

$$= \int \sqrt{\operatorname{cosec}^2 x + 2\operatorname{cosec} x \cot x + \cot^2 x}\, dx$$

$$= \int (\operatorname{cosec} x + \cot x)\, dx$$

$$= \int \frac{1+\cos x}{\sin x} dx = \int \cot\left(\frac{x}{2}\right) dx = 2\log\left|\sin\frac{x}{2}\right| + C$$

Hence, (b) is the correct answer.

● **Ex. 5** *If* $I_n = \int \cot^n x\, dx$, *then* $I_0 + I_1 + 2(I_2 + I_3 + \dots + I_8) + I_9 + I_{10}$ *equals to (where* $u = \cot x$*)*

(a) $u + \frac{u^2}{2} + \dots + \frac{u^9}{9}$ (b) $-\left(u + \frac{u^2}{2} + \dots + \frac{u^9}{9}\right)$

(c) $-\left(u + \frac{u^2}{2!} + \dots + \frac{u^9}{9!}\right)$ (d) $\frac{u}{2} + \frac{2u^2}{3} + \dots + \frac{9u^9}{10}$

Sol. $I_n = \int \cot^n x\, dx = \int \cot^{n-2} x \cdot (\operatorname{cosec}^2 x - 1)\, dx$

$$I_n = -\frac{u^{n-1}}{n-1} - I_{n-2} \text{ or } I_n + I_{n-2} = -\frac{u^{n-1}}{n-1} \quad [\text{put } n = 2, 3, 4, \ldots, 10]$$

$$I_2 + I_0 = -\frac{u}{1}$$

$$I_3 + I_1 = -\frac{u^2}{2}$$

$$I_4 + I_2 = -\frac{u^3}{3}$$

....

....

$$I_{10} + I_9 = -\frac{u^9}{9}$$

Adding, $I_0 + I_1 + 2(I_2 + I_3 + \ldots + I_8) + I_9 + I_{10}$

$$= -\left(u + \frac{u^2}{2} + \ldots + \frac{u^9}{9}\right)$$

Hence, (b) is the correct answer.

● ***Ex. 6** Let $f(x) = x + \sin x$. Suppose g denotes the inverse function of f. The value of $g'\left(\frac{\pi}{4} + \frac{1}{\sqrt{2}}\right)$ has the value equal to*

(a) $\sqrt{2} - 1$ (b) $\frac{\sqrt{2}+1}{\sqrt{2}}$

(c) $2 - \sqrt{2}$ (d) $\sqrt{2} + 1$

Sol. $f(x) = y = x + \sin x$

$$\Rightarrow \quad \frac{dy}{dx} = 1 + \cos x$$

$$g'(y) = \frac{dx}{dy} = \frac{1}{1 + \cos x}$$

where $y = \frac{\pi}{4} + \frac{1}{\sqrt{2}} = x + \sin x \Rightarrow x = \frac{\pi}{4}$

$$\therefore \quad g'\left(\frac{\pi}{4} + \frac{1}{\sqrt{2}}\right) = \frac{1}{1 + (1/\sqrt{2})}$$

$$= \frac{\sqrt{2}}{\sqrt{2}+1} = \sqrt{2}(\sqrt{2} - 1) = 2 - \sqrt{2}$$

Hence, (c) is the correct answer.

● ***Ex. 7** The value of $\int \frac{dx}{\sqrt{(x-a)(b-x)}}$, is*

(a) $2\sin^{-1}\sqrt{\frac{x-a}{b-a}} + C$ (b) $2\sin^{-1}\sqrt{\frac{x-b}{b-a}} + C$

(c) $\sin^{-1}\sqrt{\frac{x-a}{b-a}} + C$ (d) None of these

Sol. Let $x = a\cos^2\theta + b\sin^2\theta$ in the given integral.

So that, $dx = a(2\cos\theta)(-\sin\theta) + b(2\sin\theta)(\cos\theta)\, d\theta$

$dx = 2(b-a)\sin\theta\cos\theta\, d\theta$

$$\therefore \quad I = \int \frac{2(b-a)\sin\theta\cos\theta\, d\theta}{\sqrt{(a\cos^2\theta + b\sin^2\theta - a)(b - a\cos^2\theta - b\sin^2\theta)}}$$

$$= 2(b-a)\int \frac{\sin\theta\cos\theta\, d\theta}{\sqrt{(b\sin^2\theta - a\sin^2\theta)(b\cos^2\theta - a\cos^2\theta)}}$$

$$= 2(b-a)\int \frac{\sin\theta\cos\theta\, d\theta}{(b-a)\sin\theta\cos\theta} = 2\int 1\, d\theta$$

$$= 2\theta + C = 2\sin^{-1}\sqrt{\frac{x-a}{b-a}} + C$$

Hence, (a) is the correct answer.

● ***Ex. 8** The value of $\int \frac{(x-1)}{(x+1)\sqrt{x^3 + x^2 + x}}\, dx$, is*

(a) $2\tan^{-1}\sqrt{\frac{x+1}{x}} + C$ (b) $\tan^{-1}\sqrt{\frac{x^2+x+1}{x}} + C$

(c) $2\tan^{-1}\sqrt{\frac{x^2+x+1}{x}} + C$ (d) None of these

Sol. Let $I = \int \frac{(x-1)}{(x+1)\sqrt{x^3 + x^2 + x}}\, dx$

$$= \int \frac{(x^2 - 1)}{(x+1)^2\sqrt{x^3 + x^2 + x}}\, dx$$

$$= \int \frac{x^2(1 - 1/x^2)}{(x^2 + 2x + 1)\sqrt{x^3 + x^2 + x}}\, dx$$

$$= \int \frac{x^2(1 - 1/x^2)}{x(x + 2 + 1/x) \cdot x\sqrt{x + 1 + 1/x}}\, dx$$

Put $x + \frac{1}{x} = t$,

$\Rightarrow (1 - 1/x^2)\, dx = dt$

$$= \int \frac{dt}{(t+2)\sqrt{t+1}}, \text{ which reduces to } \int \frac{dx}{P\sqrt{Q}}.$$

Let $t + 1 = z^2$

$$\therefore \quad dt = 2z\,dz = \int \frac{2z\, dz}{(z^2+1)\sqrt{z^2}}$$

$$= 2\int \frac{dz}{z^2+1} = 2\tan^{-1}(z) + C$$

$$= 2\tan^{-1}(\sqrt{t+1}) + C = 2\tan^{-1}\sqrt{\frac{x^2+x+1}{x}} + C$$

Hence, (c) is the correct answer.

● ***Ex. 9** The value of $\int \frac{(1+x^2)\, dx}{(1-x^2)\sqrt{1+x^2+x^4}}$, is*

(a) $-\frac{1}{2\sqrt{3}}\log\left|\frac{\sqrt{x^4+x^2+1} - \sqrt{3}x}{\sqrt{x^4+x^2+1} + \sqrt{3}x}\right| + C$

(b) $\frac{1}{2\sqrt{3}}\log\left|\frac{\sqrt{x^4+x^2+1} + \sqrt{2}x}{\sqrt{x^4+x^2+1} - \sqrt{2}x}\right| + C$

(c) $\frac{1}{2\sqrt{3}}\log\left|\frac{\sqrt{x^4-x^2+1} - \sqrt{3}x}{\sqrt{x^4+x^2+1} + \sqrt{3}x}\right| + C$

(d) None of the above

Sol. Let $I = \int \frac{(1+x^2)\,dx}{(1-x^2)\sqrt{1+x^2+x^4}}$

$$= \int \frac{x^2\left(1+\frac{1}{x^2}\right)dx}{x\left(\frac{1}{x}-x\right)x\sqrt{\frac{1}{x^2}+1+x^2}}$$

$$= -\int \frac{(1+1/x^2)\,dx}{(1-1/x)\sqrt{(x-1/x)^2+3}}$$

Put $x - \frac{1}{x} = t = \left(1+\frac{1}{x^2}\right)dx = dt \Rightarrow -\int \frac{dt}{t\sqrt{t^2+3}}$

Again, put $t^2 + 3 = s^2$

$$\Rightarrow \quad 2t\,dt = 2s\,ds = -\int \frac{s\,ds}{s(s^2-3)} = -\int \frac{ds}{s^2-(\sqrt{3})^2}$$

$$= -\frac{1}{2\sqrt{3}}\log\left|\frac{s-\sqrt{3}}{s+\sqrt{3}}\right| + C$$

$$= -\frac{1}{2\sqrt{3}}\log\left|\frac{\sqrt{t^2+3}-\sqrt{3}}{\sqrt{t^2+3}+\sqrt{3}}\right| + C$$

$$= -\frac{1}{2\sqrt{3}}\log\left|\frac{\sqrt{(x-1/x)^2+3}-\sqrt{3}}{\sqrt{(x-1/x)^2+3}+\sqrt{3}}\right| + C$$

$$= -\frac{1}{2\sqrt{3}}\log\left|\frac{\sqrt{x^2+\frac{1}{x^2}+1}-\sqrt{3}}{\sqrt{x^2+\frac{1}{x^2}+1}+\sqrt{3}}\right| + C$$

$$= -\frac{1}{2\sqrt{3}}\log\left|\frac{\sqrt{x^4+x^2+1}-\sqrt{3}x}{\sqrt{x^4+x^2+1}+\sqrt{3}x}\right| + C$$

Hence (a) is the correct answer.

• ***Ex. 10*** *The value of* $I = \int \frac{dx}{(a+bx^2)\sqrt{b-ax^2}}$, *is*

(a) $\frac{1}{\sqrt{a(a^2+b^2)}}\tan^{-1}\left(\frac{x\sqrt{a^2+b^2}}{a\sqrt{b-ax^2}}\right)+C$

(b) $\frac{1}{\sqrt{(a^2+b^2)}}\tan^{-1}\left(\frac{x\sqrt{a^2+b^2}}{a\sqrt{b-ax^2}}\right)+C$

(c) $\frac{1}{\sqrt{a(a^2+b^2)}}\tan^{-1}\left(\frac{x\sqrt{a^2+b^2}}{a}\right)+C$

(d) None of the above

Sol. Substituting $ax^2 = b\sin^2\theta$

$$\Rightarrow \quad dx = \sqrt{\frac{b}{a}}\cos\theta\,d\theta$$

$$\therefore \quad I = \int \frac{\sqrt{\frac{b}{a}}\cos\theta\,d\theta}{\left(a+\frac{b^2}{a}\sin^2\theta\right)\sqrt{b-b\sin^2\theta}}$$

$$= \sqrt{a}\int \frac{\cos\theta\,d\theta}{(a^2+b^2\sin^2\theta)\cdot\cos\theta}$$

$$= \sqrt{a}\int \frac{d\theta}{a^2+b^2\sin^2\theta},$$

dividing numerator and denominator by $\cos^2\theta$, we get

$$= \sqrt{a}\int \frac{\sec^2\theta\,d\theta}{a^2\sec^2\theta+b^2\tan^2\theta}, \text{ put } \tan\theta = t$$

$$= \sqrt{a}\int \frac{dt}{a^2(1+t^2)+b^2t^2} = \sqrt{a}\int \frac{dt}{(a^2+b^2)t^2+a^2}$$

$$= \frac{\sqrt{a}}{a^2+b^2}\int \frac{dt}{t^2+\frac{a^2}{a^2+b^2}}$$

$$= \frac{\sqrt{a}}{a^2+b^2}\cdot\left(\frac{\sqrt{a^2+b^2}}{a}\right)\tan^{-1}\left(\frac{t\sqrt{a^2+b^2}}{a}\right)+C$$

$$= \frac{1}{\sqrt{a(a^2+b^2)}}\cdot\tan^{-1}\left(\frac{x\sqrt{a^2+b^2}}{a\sqrt{b-ax^2}}\right)+C \quad \left[\because t=\tan\theta=\frac{x}{\sqrt{b-ax^2}}\right]$$

Hence (a) is the correct answer.

• ***Ex. 11*** *The value of* $I = \int \frac{dx}{2x\sqrt{1-x}\sqrt{(2-x)+\sqrt{1-x}}}$

$$= -\frac{1}{2}\left\{\log\left(z+\frac{3}{2}+\sqrt{z^2+3z+3}\right)\right\}+\frac{1}{2}\left|\log s-\frac{1}{2}+\sqrt{s^2-s+1}\right|+C$$

and $s - z = \frac{k}{x}$, *then value of k, is*

(a) 1 (b) 2 (c) 3 (d) 4

Sol. Here, $I = \int \frac{dx}{2x\sqrt{1-x}\sqrt{(2-x)+\sqrt{1-x}}}$,

put $(1-x) = t^2 - dx = 2t\,dt$

$$= -\int \frac{2t\,dt}{2(1-t^2)\cdot t\sqrt{1+t^2+t}}$$

$$= -\int \frac{dt}{(1-t^2)\sqrt{t^2+t+1}}$$

$$= \int \frac{dt}{(t-1)(t+1)\sqrt{t^2+t+1}} = \frac{1}{2}\int\left(\frac{1}{t-1}-\frac{1}{t+1}\right)\frac{dt}{\sqrt{t^2+t+1}}$$

$$\because \frac{1}{(t-1)(t+1)} = \frac{1}{2}\left(\frac{1}{t-1}-\frac{1}{t+1}\right)$$

$$= \frac{1}{2}\int \frac{1}{(t-1)\sqrt{t^2+t+1}}dt - \frac{1}{2}\int \frac{1}{(t+1)\sqrt{t^2+t+1}}dt$$

Let $\quad I = \frac{1}{2}I_1 - \frac{1}{2}I_2 \quad$ ...(i)

where, $\quad I_1 = \int \frac{dt}{(t-1)\sqrt{t^2+t+1}}$

and $\quad I_2 = \int \frac{dt}{(t+1)\sqrt{t^2+t+1}}$

For I_1, put $(t-1) = \frac{1}{z} \Rightarrow dt = -\frac{1}{z^2}dz$

$$I_1 = \int \frac{-1/z^2\, dz}{\frac{1}{z}\sqrt{\left(1+\frac{1}{z}\right)^2 + \left(1+\frac{1}{z}\right)+1}} = -\int \frac{dz}{\sqrt{\left(z+\frac{3}{2}\right)^2 + \left(\frac{\sqrt{3}}{2}\right)^2}}$$

$$= -\log\left|\left(z+\frac{3}{2}\right)+\sqrt{z^2+3z+3}\right| \quad \text{...(ii)}$$

For I_2, put $(t+1) = \frac{1}{S}$

$$\Rightarrow \quad dt = -\frac{1}{s^2} ds$$

$$I_2 = -\int \frac{ds}{\sqrt{\left(s-\frac{1}{2}\right)^2 + \frac{3}{4}}}$$

$$= -\log\left|\left(s-\frac{1}{2}\right)+\sqrt{s^2-s+1}\right| \quad \text{...(iii)}$$

$$\therefore \quad I = -\frac{1}{2}\left\{\log\left(z+\frac{3}{2}+\sqrt{z^2+3z+3}\right)\right\} + \frac{1}{2}\log\left|\left(s-\frac{1}{2}\right)+\sqrt{s^2-s+1}\right| + C$$

where, $z = \frac{1}{\sqrt{1-x}-1}$ and $s = \frac{1}{\sqrt{1-x}+1}$

$$\therefore \quad s - z = \frac{1}{\sqrt{1-x}+1} - \frac{1}{\sqrt{1-x}-1} = \frac{2}{x} \Rightarrow k = 2$$

Hence (b) is the correct answer.

Ex. 12 *If* $\int \frac{dx}{(x^2+a^2)^2} = \frac{1}{ka^2}\left\{\frac{x}{x^2+a^2} + \frac{1}{a}\tan^{-1}\frac{x}{a}\right\} + C$. *Then the value of k, is*

(a) 1 (b) 2 (c) 3 (d) 4

Sol. Here, we know

$$\int \frac{dx}{x^2+a^2} = \frac{1}{a}\tan^{-1}\frac{x}{a} + C \quad \text{...(i)}$$

Also, $\int \frac{1}{x^2+a^2}\cdot 1\, dx = \frac{1}{x^2+a^2}\, x - \int \frac{-2x}{(x^2+a^2)^2}\, x\, dx$

$$= \frac{x}{x^2+a^2} + 2\int \frac{x^2+a^2-a^2}{(x^2+a^2)^2}\, dx$$

I II

$$\int \frac{dx}{x^2+a^2} = \frac{x}{x^2+a^2} + 2\int \frac{dx}{x^2+a^2} - 2a^2 \int \frac{dx}{(x^2+a^2)^2} \quad \text{...(ii)}$$

From Eqs. (i) and (ii), we get

$$\frac{1}{a}\tan^{-1}\frac{x}{a} = \frac{x}{x^2+a^2} + 2\,\frac{1}{a}\tan^{-1}\frac{x}{a} - 2a^2\int \frac{dx}{(x^2+a^2)^2}$$

$$\Rightarrow \quad 2a^2 \int \frac{dx}{(x^2+a^2)^2} = \frac{x}{x^2+a^2} + \frac{1}{a}\tan^{-1}\frac{x}{a}$$

or $\int \frac{dx}{(x^2+a^2)^2} = \frac{1}{2a^2}\left\{\frac{x}{x^2+a^2} + \frac{1}{a}\tan^{-1}\frac{x}{a}\right\} + C$

$$= \frac{1}{ka^2}\left\{\frac{x}{x^2+a^2} + \frac{1}{a}\tan^{-1}\frac{x}{a}\right\} + C$$

$$\therefore \quad k = 2$$

Hence, (b) is the correct answer.

Ex. 13 *If* $\int \frac{dx}{(x^2+a^2)^3} = \frac{x}{4a^2(x^2+a^2)} + \frac{m}{na^2}\left\{\frac{x}{2a^2(x^2+a^2)} + \frac{1}{2a^3}\tan^{-1}\left(\frac{x}{a}\right)\right\} + C$. *Then* $|m-n|$ *is equal to*

(a) 4 (b) 3 (c) 2 (d) 1

Sol. Let $I = \int \frac{dx}{(x^2+a^2)^3}$ ...(i)

and $I_1 = \int \frac{1}{(x^2+a^2)^2}\, dx$ ...(ii)

$$= \int \frac{1}{(x^2+a^2)^2}\cdot 1\, dx = \frac{1}{(x^2+a^2)^2}\cdot x - \int \frac{-2(2x)}{(x^2+a^2)^3}\, x\, dx$$

I II

$$= \frac{x}{(x^2+a^2)^2} + 4\int \frac{x^2+a^2-a^2}{(x^2+a^2)^3}\, dx$$

$$= \frac{x}{(x^2+a^2)^2} + 4\int \frac{1}{(x^2+a^2)^2}\, dx - 4a^2\int \frac{dx}{(x^2+a^2)^3}$$

$$\Rightarrow \quad I_1 = \frac{x}{(x^2+a^2)^2} + 4I_1 - 4a^2\cdot I \quad \text{[using Eqs. (i) and (ii)]}$$

$$\Rightarrow 4a^2 I = \frac{x}{(x^2+a^2)^2} + 3I_1$$

$$\Rightarrow \quad I = \frac{x}{4a^2(x^2+a^2)^2} + \frac{3}{4a^2} I_1 \quad \text{...(iii)}$$

[using previous example,

$$I_1 = \int \frac{dx}{(x^2+a^2)^2} = \frac{x}{2a^2(x^2+a^2)} + \frac{1}{2a^3}\tan^{-1}\left(\frac{x}{a}\right) + C]$$

$$\Rightarrow I = \frac{x}{4a^2(x^2+a^2)^2} + \frac{3}{4a^2}\left\{\frac{x}{2a^2(x^2+a^2)} + \frac{1}{2a^3}\tan^{-1}\left(\frac{x}{a}\right)\right\} + C \quad \text{...(iv)}$$

$m = 3$ and $n = 4$

$|m-n| = |3-4| = |-1| = 1$

Hence, (d) is the correct answer.

Ex. 14 *If* $y(x-y)^2 = x$, *then* $\int \frac{dx}{(x-3y)} = \frac{m}{n}\ln[(x-y)^2-1]$. *Then* $(m+2n)$ *is equal to*

(a) 1 (b) 3 (c) 5 (d) 7

Sol. Let $P = \int \frac{dx}{(x-3y)} = \frac{1}{2}\ln[(x-y)^2-1]$

$$\therefore \quad \frac{dP}{dx} = \frac{1}{x-3y} = \frac{(x-y)\left\{1-\frac{dy}{dx}\right\}}{\{(x-y)^2-1\}} \quad \text{...(i)}$$

Given, $y(x-y)^2 = x$, on differentiating both the sides, we get

$$\frac{dy}{dx} = \frac{1-2y(x-y)}{(x-y)(x-3y)} \quad \text{...(ii)}$$

$$\therefore \quad \frac{dP}{dx} = \frac{(x-y)\left\{1-\frac{1-2y(x-y)}{(x-y)(x-3y)}\right\}}{\{(x-y)^2-1\}}$$

$$=\frac{(x-y)(x-3y)-1+2y(x-y)}{(x-3y)\{(x-y)^2-1\}}=\frac{(x-y)^2-1}{(x-3y)\{(x-y)^2-1\}}$$

$$\therefore \frac{dP}{dx}=\frac{1}{(x-3y)} \quad \text{...(iii)}$$

which is true as given

$$\therefore \int \frac{dx}{(x-3y)}=\frac{1}{2}\log\{(x-y)^2-1\},$$

$$\therefore \quad m=1, n=2$$

$$\Rightarrow \quad m+2n=5$$

Hence, (c) is the correct answer.

● **Ex. 15** *If* $\int (x+\sqrt{1+x^2})^n\, dx.$

$$=\frac{1}{a(n+1)}\{x+\sqrt{1+x^2}\}^{n+1}+\frac{1}{-b(n-1)}\{x+\sqrt{1+x^2}\}^{n-1}+C$$

Then $(a+b)$ *is equal to*

(a) 2 (b) 3 (c) 4 (d) 5

Sol. Let $I=\int (x+\sqrt{1+x^2})^n\, dx$

Put $\quad x+\sqrt{1+x^2}=t \quad \text{...(i)}$

$$\Rightarrow \left(1+\frac{1}{2\sqrt{1+x^2}}\cdot 2x\right)dx=dt$$

$$\Rightarrow \left(\frac{\sqrt{1+x^2}+x}{\sqrt{1+x^2}}\right)dx=dt \quad \text{...(ii)}$$

We know, $t=x+\sqrt{1+x^2}=x+\sqrt{1+x^2}\times\dfrac{x-\sqrt{1+x^2}}{x-\sqrt{1+x^2}}$

$$t=\frac{-1}{x-\sqrt{1+x^2}} \Rightarrow t=x+\sqrt{1+x^2}$$

$$-\frac{1}{t}=x-\sqrt{1+x^2}$$

Subtracting, we get

$$2\sqrt{1+x^2}=t+\frac{1}{t} \quad \text{or} \quad \frac{1}{\sqrt{1+x^2}}=\frac{2t}{t^2+1} \quad \text{...(iii)}$$

From Eqs. (i), (ii) and (iii), we get

$$dx=\frac{t^2+1}{2t^2}\, dt$$

$$\therefore \quad I=\int t^n\cdot\frac{t^2+1}{(2t^2)}\, dt=\frac{1}{2}\int (t^n+t^{n-2})\, dt$$

$$=\frac{1}{2}\left[\frac{t^{n+1}}{n+1}+\frac{t^{n-1}}{n-1}\right]+C$$

$$\Rightarrow \quad I=\frac{1}{2(n+1)}[x+\sqrt{(1+x^2)}]^{n+1}$$

$$+\frac{1}{2(n-1)}(x+\sqrt{(1+x^2)})^{n-1}+C \quad \text{...(iv)}$$

Then comparing the values of a and b by Eq. (iv) $a=2$, $b=2$

$$\therefore \quad (a+b)=(2+2)=4$$

Hence, (c) is the correct answer.

● **Ex. 16** *If* $\int \frac{f(x)}{x^3-1}\, dx$, *where* $f(x)$ *is a polynomial of degree 2 in x such that* $f(0)=f(1)=3f(2)=-3$ *and* $\int \frac{f(x)}{x^3-1}\, dx=-\log|x-1|+\log|x^2+x+1|$ $+\frac{m}{\sqrt{n}}\tan^{-1}\left(\frac{2x+1}{\sqrt{3}}\right)+C$. *Then* $(2m+n)$ *is*

(a) 3 (b) 5 (c) 7 (d) 9

Sol. Let $\quad f(x)=ax^2+bx+c$

Given, $\quad f(0)=f(1)=3f(2)=-3$

$$\therefore \quad f(0)=c=-3$$

$$f(1)=a+b+c=-3$$

$$3f(2)=3(4a+2b+c)=-3$$

On solving, we get $a=1$, $b=-1$, $c=-3$

$$\therefore \quad f(x)=x^2-x-3$$

$$\Rightarrow \quad I=\int\frac{f(x)}{x^3-1}\, dx=\int\frac{x^2-x-3}{(x-1)(x^2+x+1)}\, dx$$

Using partial fractions, we get

$$\frac{(x^2-x-3)}{(x-1)(x^2+x+1)}=\frac{A}{(x-1)}+\frac{Bx+C}{(x^2+x+1)}$$

we get, $A=-1$, $B=2$, $C=2$

$$\therefore I=\int -\frac{1}{x-1}\, dx+\int\frac{(2x+2)}{(x^2+x+1)}\, dx$$

$$=-\log|x-1|+\int\frac{(2x+1)\, dx}{x^2+x+1}+\int\frac{1\, dx}{x^2+x+1}$$

$$=-\log|x-1|+\log|x^2+x+1|+\int\frac{dx}{(x+1/2)^2+(\sqrt{3}/2)^2}$$

$$=-\log|x-1|+\log|x^2+x+1|+\frac{2}{\sqrt{3}}\tan^{-1}\left(\frac{2x+1}{\sqrt{3}}\right)+C$$

$\therefore$ On comparing $m=2, n=3 \Rightarrow 2m+n=7$.

Hence, (c) is the correct answer.

● **Ex. 17** *The value of* $\int\frac{(1+x)}{x(1+xe^x)^2}\, dx$, *is equal to*

(a) $\log\left|\frac{x}{1+xe^x}\right|+\frac{1}{(1+xe^x)}+C$

(b) $\log\left|\frac{xe^x}{1+xe^x}\right|+\frac{1}{1+xe^x}+C$

(c) $\log\left|\frac{xe^x}{1+e^x}\right|+\frac{1}{1+xe^x}+C$

(d) None of the above

Sol. Let $I=\int\frac{(1+x)}{x(1+xe^x)^2}\, dx=\int\frac{(1+x)e^x}{(xe^x)(1+xe^x)^2}\, dx,$

put $1+xe^x=t$

$\therefore (1+x)e^x\, dx=dt=\int\frac{dt}{(t-1)\cdot t^2}$, applying partial fraction,

we get $\dfrac{1}{(t-1)t^2}=\dfrac{A}{t-1}+\dfrac{B}{t}+\dfrac{C}{t^2}$

$$\Rightarrow \quad 1 = A(t^2) + Bt(t-1) + C(t-1)$$

For $\quad t = 1 \Rightarrow A = 1$

For $\quad t = 0 \Rightarrow C = -1$ and $B = -1$

$$\therefore \quad I = \int \left\{ \frac{1}{t-1} - \frac{1}{t} - \frac{1}{t^2} \right\} dt = \log|t-1| - \log|t| + \frac{1}{t} + C$$

$$= \log|xe^x| - \log|1 + xe^x| + \frac{1}{1+xe^x} + C$$

$$= \log\left|\frac{xe^x}{1+xe^x}\right| + \frac{1}{1+xe^x} + C$$

Hence, (b) is the correct answer.

● ***Ex. 18*** *The value of* $\int \frac{dx}{x + \sqrt{a^2 - x^2}}$*, is equal to*

(a) $\frac{1}{2}\sin^{-1}\left(\frac{x}{a}\right) + \frac{1}{2}\log|x + \sqrt{a^2 - x^2}| + C_1$

(b) $\frac{1}{2}\sin^{-1}\left(\frac{x}{a}\right) - \frac{1}{2}\log|x + \sqrt{a^2 - x^2}| + C_1$

(c) $\frac{1}{2}\sin^{-1}\left(\frac{x}{a}\right) - \log|x + \sqrt{a^2 - x^2}| + C_1$

(d) $\frac{1}{2}\cos^{-1}\left(\frac{x}{a}\right) + \frac{1}{2}\log|x + \sqrt{a^2 - x^2}| + C_1$

Sol. Let $I = \int \frac{dx}{x + \sqrt{a^2 - x^2}}$, Put $x = a\sin\theta$

$$\therefore \quad dx = a\cos\theta\, d\theta = \int \frac{a\cos\theta\, d\theta}{a\sin\theta + \sqrt{a^2 - a^2\sin^2\theta}}$$

$$= \int \frac{\cos\theta\, d\theta}{\sin\theta + \cos\theta} = \frac{1}{2}\int \frac{\cos\theta + \sin\theta + \cos\theta - \sin\theta}{\sin\theta + \cos\theta}\, d\theta$$

$$= \frac{1}{2}\int 1\, d\theta + \frac{1}{2}\int \frac{\cos\theta - \sin\theta}{\sin\theta + \cos\theta}\, d\theta$$

$$= \frac{1}{2}\cdot\theta + \frac{1}{2}\log(\sin\theta + \cos\theta) + C$$

$$= \frac{1}{2}\sin^{-1}\left(\frac{x}{a}\right) + \frac{1}{2}\log\left|\frac{x}{a} + \sqrt{1 - \frac{x^2}{a^2}}\right| + C$$

$$= \frac{1}{2}\sin^{-1}\left(\frac{x}{a}\right) + \frac{1}{2}\{\log|x + \sqrt{a^2 - x^2}|\} - \frac{1}{2}\log a + C$$

$$= \frac{1}{2}\sin^{-1}\left(\frac{x}{a}\right) + \frac{1}{2}\log|x + \sqrt{a^2 - x^2}| + C_1$$

$$\left[\text{where } C_1 = C - \frac{1}{2}\log a\right]$$

Hence, (a) is the correct answer.

● ***Ex. 19*** *The value of* $\int \frac{x^2 - 1}{(x^2+1)\sqrt{x^4+1}}\, dx$*, is equal to*

(a) $\frac{1}{\sqrt{2}}\sec^{-1}\left(\frac{x^2+1}{\sqrt{2}x}\right) + C$ (b) $\sqrt{2}\sec^{-1}\left(\frac{x^2+1}{\sqrt{2}x}\right) + C$

(c) $\frac{1}{\sqrt{2}}\text{cosec}^{-1}\left(\frac{x^2+1}{\sqrt{2}x}\right) + C$ (d) $\sqrt{2}\,\text{cosec}^{-1}\left(\frac{x^2+1}{\sqrt{2}x}\right) + C$

Sol. Let $I = \int \frac{(x^2-1)}{(x^2+1)\sqrt{x^4+1}}\, dx = \int \frac{x^2(1 - 1/x^2)\, dx}{x^2\left(x + \frac{1}{x}\right)\sqrt{x^2 + \frac{1}{x^2}}}$

$$= \int \frac{(1 - 1/x^2)\, dx}{\left(x + \frac{1}{x}\right)\sqrt{\left(x + \frac{1}{x}\right)^2 - 2}}$$

Put $x + \frac{1}{x} = t \quad \Rightarrow \quad \left(1 - \frac{1}{x^2}\right) dx = dt$

$$= \int \frac{dt}{t\sqrt{t^2 - 2}} = \frac{1}{\sqrt{2}}\sec^{-1}\left(\frac{t}{\sqrt{2}}\right) + C$$

$$= \frac{1}{\sqrt{2}}\sec^{-1}\left(\frac{x^2+1}{\sqrt{2}x}\right) + C$$

Hence, (a) is the correct answer.

JEE Type Solved Examples : More than One Correct Option Type Questions

● ***Ex. 20*** $\int \frac{\sqrt{4+x^2}}{x^6}\, dx = \frac{A(4+x^2)^{3/2}(Bx^2 - 6)}{x^5} + C,$

then

(a) $A = \frac{1}{120}$ (b) $B = 1$

(c) $A = -\frac{1}{120}$ (d) $B = -1$

Sol. Here, $I = \int \frac{\sqrt{4 - x^2}}{x^6}\, dx = \int \frac{\sqrt{1 + \frac{4}{x^2}}}{x^5}\, dx = \int \frac{\sqrt{1 + \frac{4}{x^2}}}{x^2 \cdot x^3}\, dx$

Put $\quad t = \sqrt{1 + \frac{4}{x^2}} \Rightarrow t^2 = 1 + \frac{4}{x^2}$

$$\therefore\ 2t\, dt = -\frac{8}{x^3}\, dx$$

$$\Rightarrow \quad I = \frac{1}{16}\int (t^2 - t^4)\, dx = \frac{1}{16}\left\{\frac{t^3}{3} - \frac{t^5}{5}\right\} + C$$

$$= \frac{1}{120}\cdot\frac{(4+x^2)^{3/2}}{x^5}(x^2 - 6) + C$$

$$A = \frac{1}{120},\ B = 1$$

Hence, (a) and (b) are the correct answers.

• Ex. 21 *The value of the integral* $\int e^{\sin^2 x}(\cos x + \cos^3 x)\sin x\, dx$ *is*

(a) $\frac{1}{2}e^{\sin^2 x}(3-\sin^2 x)+C$

(b) $e^{\sin^2 x}\left(1+\frac{1}{2}\cos^2 x\right)+C$

(c) $e^{\sin^2 x}(3\cos^2 x + 2\sin^2 x)+C$

(d) $e^{\sin^2 x}(2\cos^2 x + 3\sin^2 x)+C$

Sol. Put $t=\sin^2 x$

The integral reduces to $I=\frac{1}{2}\int e^t(2-t)\,dt=\frac{3}{2}e^t-\frac{te^t}{2}+C$

$=\frac{1}{2}e^{\sin^2 x}(3-\sin^2 x)+C$ [option (a)]

$=e^{\sin^2 x}\left(1+\frac{1}{2}\cos^2 x\right)+C$ [option (b)]

Hence, (a) and (b) are the correct answers.

• Ex. 22 *If* $I=\int(\sqrt{\tan x}+\sqrt{\cot x})\,dx=f(x)+c$, *then* $f(x)$ *is equal to*

(a) $\sqrt{2}\sin^{-1}(\sin x-\cos x)$ (b) $\frac{\pi}{\sqrt{2}}-\sqrt{2}\cos^{-1}(\sin x-\cos x)$

(c) $\sqrt{2}\tan^{-1}\left(\frac{\tan x-1}{\sqrt{2}\sqrt{\tan x}}\right)$ (d) None of these

Sol. $I=\int(\sqrt{\tan x}+\sqrt{\cot x})\,dx=\int\sqrt{2}\cdot\frac{\sin x+\cos x}{\sqrt{2\sin x\cos x}}\,dx$

If $\sin x-\cos x=p$, then $(\cos x+\sin x)\,dx=dp$

$I=\sqrt{2}\int\frac{dp}{\sqrt{1-p^2}}=\sqrt{2}\sin^{-1}p+c=\sqrt{2}\sin^{-1}(\sin x-\cos x)+c$

$=\frac{\pi}{\sqrt{2}}-\sqrt{2}\cos^{-1}(\sin x-\cos x)=\sqrt{2}\tan^{-1}\frac{\sin x-\cos x}{\sqrt{1-(\sin x-\cos x)^2}}$

$=\sqrt{2}\tan^{-1}\frac{\sin x-\cos x}{\sqrt{2\sin x\cos x}}=\sqrt{2}\tan^{-1}\left(\frac{\tan x-1}{\sqrt{2\tan x}}\right)$

Hence, (a), (b) and (c) are the correct answers.

JEE Type Solved Examples : Passage Based Questions

Passage
(Q. Nos. 23 to 25)

For integral $\int f\left(x-\frac{a}{x}\right)\cdot\left(1+\frac{a}{x^2}\right)dx$, *put* $x-\frac{a}{x}=t$

For integral $\int f\left(x+\frac{a}{x}\right)\cdot\left(1-\frac{a}{x^2}\right)dx$, *put* $x+\frac{a}{x}=t$

For integral $\int f\left(x^2-\frac{a}{x^2}\right)\cdot\left(x+\frac{a}{x^3}\right)dx$, *put* $x^2-\frac{a}{x^2}=t$

For integral $\int f\left(x^2+\frac{a}{x^2}\right)\cdot\left(x-\frac{a}{x^3}\right)dx$, *put* $x^2+\frac{a}{x^2}=t$

many integrands can be brought into above forms by suitable reductions or transformations.

• Ex. 23 $\int\frac{x^4-2}{x^2\sqrt{x^4+x^2+2}}\,dx$

(a) $\sqrt{x^2+1+\frac{1}{x^2}}+C$ (b) $\sqrt{x^2+1+\frac{2}{x^2}}+C$

(c) $\sqrt{x^2+\frac{1}{x^2}}+C$ (d) $\sqrt{x^2+\frac{2}{x^2}}+C$

Sol. Here, $I=\int\frac{x-\frac{2}{x^3}}{\sqrt{x^2+1+\frac{2}{x^2}}}\,dx$

Put $x^2+\frac{2}{x^2}+1=t \Rightarrow 2\left(x-\frac{2}{x^3}\right)dx=dt$

$=\frac{1}{2}\int\frac{dt}{\sqrt{t}}=\frac{1}{2}\cdot\frac{t^{1/2}}{1/2}+C=\sqrt{t}+C$

$=\sqrt{x^2+\frac{2}{x^2}+1}+C$

Hence, (b) is the correct answer.

• Ex. 24 $\int\frac{(x-1)}{(x+1)\sqrt{x^3+x^2+x}}\,dx$

(a) $\tan^{-1}\left(x+\frac{1}{x}+1\right)+C$ (b) $\tan^{-1}\sqrt{x+\frac{1}{x}+1}+C$

(c) $2\tan^{-1}\sqrt{x+\frac{1}{x}+1}+C$ (d) None of these

Sol. $\int\frac{x^2-1}{(x+1)^2\sqrt{x^3+x^2+x}}\,dx=\int\frac{\left(1-\frac{1}{x^2}\right)}{\left(x+\frac{1}{x}+2\right)\sqrt{x+\frac{1}{x}+1}}\,dx$

Put $x+\frac{1}{x}+1=t^2 \Rightarrow \left(1-\frac{1}{x^2}\right)dx=2t\,dt$

$=\int\frac{2t\,dt}{(t^2+1)t}=2\int\frac{1}{(t^2+1)}\,dt$

$=2\cdot\tan^{-1}(t)+C=2\tan^{-1}\left(\sqrt{x+\frac{1}{x}+1}\right)+C$

Hence, (c) is the correct answer.

Ex. 25 $\int \frac{5x^4 + 4x^5}{(x^5 + x + 1)^2} dx$

(a) $x^5 + x + 1 + C$ (b) $\frac{x^5}{x^5 + x + 1} + C$

(c) $x^{-4} + x^{-5} + C$ (d) $\frac{x^5}{x^5 + x + 1} + C$

Sol. Here, $I = \sqrt{\frac{5x^4 + 4x^5}{(x^5 + x + 1)^2}}$

Divide numerator and denominator by x^{10}, we get

$$I = \int \frac{5x^{-6} + 4x^{-5}}{(1 + x^{-4} + x^{-5})^2} dx$$

Put $1 + x^{-4} + x^{-5} = t \Rightarrow (-4x^{-5} - 5x^{-6})\, dx = dt$

$$\therefore \quad I = -\int \frac{dt}{t^2} = \frac{1}{t} + C = \frac{1}{1 + x^{-4} + x^{-5}} + C$$

$$= \frac{x^5}{x^5 + x + 1} + C$$

Hence, (d) is the correct answer.

JEE Type Solved Examples : Matching Type Questions

Ex. 26 *If $x \in (0, 1)$ then match the entries of Column I with Column II considering 'c' as an arbitrary constant of integration.*

Column I	Column II
(A) $\int \tan\left(2\tan^{-1}\sqrt{\frac{\sqrt{1+\sqrt{x}} - 1}{\sqrt{1+\sqrt{x}} + 1}}\right) dx$	(p) $\frac{4}{3} x^{3/4} + C$
(B) $\int \cot\left(2\tan^{-1}\sqrt{\frac{\sqrt{1+\sqrt{x}} - \sqrt[4]{x}}{\sqrt{1+\sqrt{x}} + \sqrt[4]{x}}}\right) dx$	(q) $\frac{4}{5} x^{5/4} + C$
(C) $\int \left(\frac{1 - \tan\left(\frac{1}{2}\sin^{-1}\left(\frac{1-\sqrt{x}}{1+\sqrt{x}}\right)\right)}{1 + \tan\left(\frac{1}{2}\sin^{-1}\left(\frac{1-\sqrt{x}}{1+\sqrt{x}}\right)\right)}\right) dx$	(r) $\frac{2}{3} x^{3/4} + C$
(D) $\int \sqrt{x} \tan\left(2\tan^{-1}\left(\frac{\sqrt{\sqrt{1+\sqrt{x}}+1} - \sqrt{\sqrt{1+\sqrt{x}}-1}}{\sqrt{\sqrt{1+\sqrt{x}}+1} + \sqrt{\sqrt{1+\sqrt{x}}-1}}\right)\right) dx$	(s) $\frac{2}{5} x^{5/4} + C$

Sol. Let $\sqrt{x} = \tan^2\theta$

$$x = \tan^4\theta \Rightarrow \tan\theta = x^{1/4}$$

$$\therefore \quad dx = 4\tan^3\theta \sec^2\theta\, d\theta \quad \left[\because x \in (0,1) \quad \therefore \theta \in (0, \pi/4)\right]$$

$$\therefore \quad \sqrt{1+\sqrt{x}} = \sec\theta$$

(A) $I = \int \tan\left(2\tan^{-1}\sqrt{\frac{\sqrt{1+\sqrt{x}} - 1}{\sqrt{1+\sqrt{x}} + 1}}\right) dx$

$$\Rightarrow \tan\left(2\tan^{-1}\sqrt{\frac{\sqrt{1+\sqrt{x}} - 1}{\sqrt{1+\sqrt{x}} + 1}}\right) = \tan\left(2\tan^{-1}\sqrt{\frac{\sec\theta - 1}{\sec\theta + 1}}\right)$$

$$= \tan\left(2\tan^{-1}\left(\tan\frac{\theta}{2}\right)\right) = \tan\theta$$

$$\therefore \quad I = \int \tan\theta \cdot 4\tan^3\theta \sec^2\theta\, d\theta$$

$$= \frac{4}{5}\tan^5\theta + C = \frac{4}{5}(x^{5/4}) + C$$

(B) $I = \int \cot\left(2\tan^{-1}\sqrt{\frac{\sqrt{1+\sqrt{x}} - \sqrt[4]{x}}{\sqrt{1+\sqrt{x}} + \sqrt[4]{x}}}\right) dx$

$$\therefore \quad \cot\left(2\tan^{-1}\sqrt{\frac{\sqrt{1+\sqrt{x}} - \sqrt[4]{x}}{\sqrt{1+\sqrt{x}} + \sqrt[4]{x}}}\right) = \cot\left(2\tan^{-1}\sqrt{\frac{\sec\theta - \tan\theta}{\sec\theta + \tan\theta}}\right)$$

$$= \cot\left(2\tan^{-1}\sqrt{(\sec\theta - \tan\theta)^2}\right)$$

$$= \cot\left(2\tan^{-1}\frac{1 - \sin\theta}{\cos\theta}\right)$$

If $\theta \in (0, \pi/4)$, then $\sec\theta - \tan\theta > 0$

$$= \cot\left(2\tan^{-1}\tan\left(\frac{\pi}{4} - \frac{\theta}{2}\right)\right) = \cot\left(\frac{\pi}{2} - \theta\right) = \tan\theta$$

$$\therefore \quad I = \int \tan\theta \cdot 4\tan^3\theta \sec^2\theta\, d\theta$$

$$= \frac{4}{5}\tan^5\theta + C = \frac{4}{5}(x^{5/4}) + C$$

(C) $\frac{1}{2}\sin^{-1}\left(\frac{1-\sqrt{x}}{1+\sqrt{x}}\right) = \frac{1}{2}\sin^{-1}\left(\frac{1-\tan^2\theta}{1+\tan^2\theta}\right)$

$$= \frac{1}{2}\sin^{-1}(\cos 2\theta) = \frac{1}{2}\sin^{-1}\sin\left(\frac{\pi}{2} - 2\theta\right) = \frac{\pi}{4} - \theta$$

$$\therefore \quad \int \left(\frac{1 - \tan\left(\frac{1}{2}\sin^{-1}\left(\frac{1-\sqrt{x}}{1+\sqrt{x}}\right)\right)}{1 + \tan\left(\frac{1}{2}\sin^{-1}\left(\frac{1-\sqrt{x}}{1+\sqrt{x}}\right)\right)}\right) dx$$

$$= \int \frac{1 - \tan\left(\frac{\pi}{4} - \theta\right)}{1 + \tan\left(\frac{\pi}{4} - \theta\right)} 4\tan^3\theta \sec^2\theta\, d\theta$$

$$= \int \tan\left(\frac{\pi}{4} - \left(\frac{\pi}{4} - \theta\right)\right) 4\tan^3\theta \sec^2\theta\, d\theta$$

$$= \int 4\tan^4\theta \sec^2\theta\, d\theta$$

$$= \frac{4}{5}\tan^5\theta + C = \frac{4}{5}(x^{5/4}) + C$$

(D) Let $\sqrt{x} = \tan^2\theta \Rightarrow x = \tan^4\theta$

$\therefore \quad dx = 4\tan^3\theta\sec^2\theta\, d\theta \qquad \left[\begin{array}{l}\because x \in (0,1)\\ \therefore \theta \in (0, \pi/4)\end{array}\right]$

$\therefore \sqrt{1+\sqrt{x}} = \sec\theta$

$$I = \int \sqrt{x}\tan\left(2\tan^{-1}\left(\frac{\sqrt{\sqrt{1+\sqrt{x}}+1} - \sqrt{\sqrt{1+\sqrt{x}}-1}}{\sqrt{\sqrt{1+\sqrt{x}}+1} + \sqrt{\sqrt{1+\sqrt{x}}-1}}\right)\right)dx$$

$$\therefore \sqrt{x}\tan\left(2\tan^{-1}\left(\frac{\sqrt{\sqrt{1+\sqrt{x}}+1} - \sqrt{\sqrt{1+\sqrt{x}}-1}}{\sqrt{\sqrt{1+\sqrt{x}}+1} + \sqrt{\sqrt{1+\sqrt{x}}-1}}\right)\right)$$

$$= \tan^2\theta \cdot \tan\left(2\tan^{-1}\left(\frac{\sqrt{\sec\theta+1} - \sqrt{\sec\theta-1}}{\sqrt{\sec\theta+1} + \sqrt{\sec\theta-1}}\right)\right)$$

$$= \tan^2\theta \cdot \tan\left(2\tan^{-1}\left(\frac{\cos\frac{\theta}{2} - \sin\frac{\theta}{2}}{\cos\frac{\theta}{2} + \sin\frac{\theta}{2}}\right)\right)$$

$$= \tan^2\theta \cdot \tan\left(2\tan^{-1}\tan\left(\frac{\pi}{4} - \frac{\theta}{2}\right)\right)$$

$$= \tan^2\theta \cdot \tan\left(\frac{\pi}{2} - \theta\right) = \tan^2\theta \cdot \cot\theta = \tan\theta$$

$$\therefore \quad I = \int \tan\theta \cdot 4\tan^3\theta\sec^2\theta\, d\theta = \frac{4\tan^5\theta}{5} + C = \frac{4}{5}(x^{5/4}) + C$$

(A) → (q); (B) → (q); (C) → (q); (D) → (q)

JEE Type Solved Examples : Single Integer Answer Type Questions

• **Ex. 27** *If the primitive of the function* $f(x) = \dfrac{x^{2009}}{(1+x^2)^{1006}}$ *w.r.t. x is equal to* $\dfrac{1}{n}\left(\dfrac{x^2}{1+x^2}\right)^m + C$, *then* $\dfrac{n}{m}$ *is equal to ......*

Sol. $$f(x) = \int \frac{x^{2009}}{(1+x^2)^{1006}}\,dx$$

Put $\quad 1 + x^2 = t \Rightarrow 2x\,dx = dt$

$$\therefore \quad I = \frac{1}{2}\int \frac{(t-1)^{1004}}{t^{1006}}\,dt = \frac{1}{2}\int\left(1 - \frac{1}{t}\right)^{1004} \cdot \frac{1}{t^2}\,dt$$

Put $\quad 1 - \dfrac{1}{t} = y \Rightarrow \dfrac{1}{t^2}\,dt = dy$

$$\therefore \quad I = \frac{1}{2}\int y^{1004}dy = \frac{1}{2}\cdot\frac{y^{1005}}{1005} + C$$

$$= \frac{1}{2010}\cdot\left(\frac{t-1}{t}\right)^{1005} + C = \frac{1}{2010}\cdot\left(\frac{x^2}{1+x^2}\right)^{1005} + C$$

$$\Rightarrow \quad m = 1005, n = 2010 \Rightarrow \frac{n}{m} = \frac{2010}{1005} = 2$$

• **Ex. 28** *Suppose* $\begin{vmatrix} f'(x) & f(x) \\ f''(x) & f'(x)\end{vmatrix} = 0$ *where* $f(x)$ *is continuous differentiable function with* $f'(x) \neq 0$ *and satisfies* $f(0) = 1$ *and* $f'(0) = 2$, *then* $f(x) = e^{\lambda x} + k$, *then* $\lambda + k$ *is equal to ....*

Sol. $f'(x)\cdot f'(x) - f(x)\cdot f''(x) = 0$ or $\dfrac{[f'(x)]^2 - f(x)f''(x)}{[f'(x)]^2} = 0$

$$\frac{d}{dx}\left[\frac{f(x)}{f'(x)}\right] = 0$$

Integrating, $\dfrac{f(x)}{f'(x)} + C$ ...(i)

Put $\quad x = 0, \dfrac{f(0)}{f'(0)} = C \Rightarrow C = \dfrac{1}{2}.$

Hence, $\quad \dfrac{f(x)}{f'(x)} = \dfrac{1}{2}$ ...(ii)

From Eq. (i), $2f(x) = f'(x) \;\therefore\; \dfrac{f'(x)}{f(x)} = 2$

Again, integrating, $\ln[f(x)] = 2x + k$

Put $x = 0$ to get, $k = 0$

$$f(x) = e^{2x} \Rightarrow \lambda + k = 2 + 0 = 2$$

• **Ex. 29** $\int\{\sin(101x)\cdot\sin^{99}x\}\,dx = \dfrac{\sin(100x)(\sin x)^{\lambda}}{\mu}$, *then* $\dfrac{\lambda}{\mu}$ *is equal to ......*

Sol. (1) $I = \int\{\sin(100x + x)\cdot(\sin x)^{99}\}\,dx$

$$= \int\{\sin(100x)\cos x + \cos 100x\sin x\}(\sin x)^{99}\,dx$$

$$= \int \underbrace{\sin(100x)}_{\text{I}}\,\underbrace{\cos x\cdot(\sin x)^{99}}_{\text{II}}\,dx + \int\cos(100x)\cdot(\sin x)^{100}\,dx$$

$$= \frac{\sin(100x)(\sin x)^{100}}{100}$$

$$- \frac{100}{100}\int\cos(100x)(\sin x)^{100}\,dx + \int\cos(100x)(\sin x)^{100}\,dx$$

$$= \frac{\sin(100x)(\sin x)^{100}}{100} + C$$

$$\Rightarrow \lambda = 100, \mu = 100 \Rightarrow \frac{\lambda}{\mu} = \frac{100}{100} = 1$$

Subjective Type Questions

Ex. 30 *If I_n denotes $\int z^n e^{1/z}\, dz$, then show that $(n+1)!\, I_n = I_0 + e^{1/z}(1!\, z^2 + 2!\, z^3 + \ldots + n!\, z^{n+1})$.*

Sol. $I_n = \int z^n e^{1/z}\, dz$, applying integration by parts taking $e^{1/z}$ as first function and z^n as second function. We get,

$$I_n = \frac{e^{1/z}\cdot z^{n+1}}{(n+1)} - \int e^{1/z}\left(-\frac{1}{z^2}\right)\cdot\frac{z^{n+1}}{n+1}\, dz$$

$$= \frac{e^{1/z}\cdot z^{n+1}}{(n+1)} + \frac{1}{(n+1)}\int e^{1/z}\cdot z^{n-1}\, dz$$

$$I_n = \frac{e^{1/z}\cdot z^{n+1}}{(n+1)} + \frac{I_{n-1}}{(n+1)}$$

$$= \frac{e^{1/z}\cdot z^{n+1}}{(n+1)} + \frac{1}{(n+1)}\left[\frac{e^{1/z}\cdot z^n}{n} + \frac{1}{n} I_{n-2}\right]$$

$$= \frac{e^{1/z}(z)^{n+1}}{(n+1)} + \frac{e^{1/z}\cdot(z)^n}{(n+1)\, n} + \frac{1}{(n+1)\, n} I_{n-2}$$

$$= \frac{e^{1/z}\cdot(z)^{n+1}}{(n+1)} + \frac{e^{1/z}\cdot(z)^n}{(n+1)n} + \frac{e^{1/z}\cdot(z)^{n-1}}{(n+1)n\cdot(n-1)} + \frac{1}{(n+1)n(n-1)} I_{n-3}$$

... ...

... ...

$$= \frac{e^{1/z}\cdot(z)^{n+1}}{n+1} + \frac{e^{1/z}\cdot(z)^n}{(n+1)\, n} + \ldots + \frac{e^{1/z}\cdot(z)^1}{(n+1)\, n\ldots 3\cdot 2} + \frac{1}{(n+1)\, n\,(n-1)\ldots 3\cdot 2} I_0$$

Multiplying both the sides by $(n+1)!$. We get,

$$(n+1)!\, I_n = (e^{1/z}\cdot z^{n+1}\cdot n! + e^{1/z}\cdot z^n\,(n-1)! + \ldots + \ldots + e^{1/z}\cdot z^3\cdot(2)! + e^{1/z}\cdot z^2\cdot 1!) + I_0$$

$$\Rightarrow \quad I_n\,(n+1)! = I_0 + e^{1/z}(1!\, z^2 + 2!\, z^3 + \ldots + n!\, z^{n+1})$$

Hence Proved.

Ex. 31 *If $I_n = \int x^n \sqrt{a^2 - x^2}\, dx$, prove that*

$$I_n = -\frac{x^{n-1}(a^2 - x^2)^{3/2}}{(n+2)} + \frac{(n-1)}{(n+2)} a^2 I_{n-2}.$$

Sol. $I_n = \int x^n \sqrt{a^2 - x^2}\, dx = \int \underset{\text{I}}{x^{n-1}} \cdot \underset{\text{II}}{\{x\sqrt{a^2 - x^2}\}}\, dx$

Applying integration by parts, we get

$$= x^{n-1}\cdot\left\{-\frac{(a^2 - x^2)^{3/2}}{3}\right\} + \int (n-1)\, x^{n-2}\cdot\left\{-\frac{(a^2 - x^2)^{3/2}}{3}\right\} dx$$

$$= -\frac{x^{n-1}(a^2 - x^2)^{3/2}}{3} + \frac{(n-1)}{3}\int x^{n-2}\cdot(a^2 - x^2)\sqrt{a^2 - x^2}\, dx$$

$$\Rightarrow I_n = -\frac{x^{n-1}(a^2 - x^2)^{3/2}}{3} + \frac{(n-1)\, a^2}{3} I_{n-2} - \frac{(n-1)}{3} I_n$$

$$\therefore\ I_n + \frac{(n-1)}{3} I_n = -\frac{x^{n-1}(a^2 - x^2)^{3/2}}{3} + \frac{(n-1)\, a^2}{3} I_{n-2}$$

$$\left(\frac{n+2}{3}\right) I_n = -\frac{x^{n-1}(a^2 - x^2)^{3/2}}{3} + \frac{(n-1)\, a^2}{3} I_{n-2}$$

$$I_n = -\frac{x^{n-1}(a^2 - x^2)^{3/2}}{(n+2)} + \frac{(n-1)\, a^2}{(n+2)} I_{n-2}$$

Hence Proved.

Ex. 32 *If $I_m = \int (\sin x + \cos x)^m\, dx$, then show that $m\, I_m = (\sin x + \cos x)^{m-1}\cdot(\sin x - \cos x) + 2(m-1)\, I_{m-2}$*

Sol. $\because I_m = \int (\sin x + \cos x)^m\, dx$

$$= \int (\sin x + \cos x)^{m-1}\cdot(\sin x + \cos x)\, dx,$$

Applying integration by parts

$$= (\sin x + \cos x)^{m-1}(\cos x + \sin x) - \int (m-1)(\sin x + \cos x)^{m-2}\cdot(\cos x - \sin x)\cdot(\sin x - \cos x)\, dx$$

$$= (\sin x + \cos x)^{m-1}(\sin x - \cos x) + (m-1)\int(\sin x + \cos x)^{m-2}(\sin x - \cos x)^2\, dx$$

As we know, $(\sin x + \cos x)^2 + (\sin x - \cos x)^2 = 2$,

$$\therefore I_m = (\sin x + \cos x)^{m-1}(\sin x - \cos x) + (m-1)\int(\sin x + \cos x)^{m-2}\cdot\{2 - (\sin x + \cos x)^2\}\, dx$$

$$= (\sin x + \cos x)^{m-1}(\sin x - \cos x) + (m-1)\int 2(\sin x + \cos x)^{m-2}\, dx - (m-1)\int(\sin x + \cos x)^m\, dx$$

$$I_m = (\sin x + \cos x)^{m-1}(\sin x - \cos x) + 2(m-1) I_{m-2} - (m-1) I_m$$

or $(m-1)I_m + I_m = (\sin x + \cos x)^{m-1}(\sin x - \cos x) + 2(m-1)I_{m-2}$

or $m\, I_m = (\sin x + \cos x)^{m-1}(\sin x - \cos x) + 2(m-1)\, I_{m-2}$

Hence Proved.

Ex. 33 *If $I_{m,n} = \int \cos^m x\cdot\cos nx\, dx$, show that $(m+n)\, I_{m,n} = \cos^m x\cdot\sin nx + m\, I_{(m-1,\, n-1)}$*

Sol. We have,

$$I_{m,n} = \int \underset{\text{I}}{\cos^m x}\cdot\underset{\text{II}}{\cos n x}\, dx$$

$$= (\cos^m x)\left[\frac{\sin nx}{n}\right] - \int m\cos^{m-1} x\,(-\sin x)\cdot\frac{\sin nx}{n}\, dx$$

$$= \frac{1}{n}\cos^m x\cdot\sin nx + \frac{m}{n}\int\cos^{m-1} x\,\{\sin x\cdot\sin nx\}\, dx$$

As we have, $\cos(n-1)\, x = \cos nx\cos x + \sin nx\sin x$

$$\therefore\ I_{m,n} = \frac{1}{n}\cos^m x\cdot\sin x + \frac{m}{n}\int\cos^{m-1} x\,\{\cos(n-1)\, x - \cos nx\cdot\cos x\}\, dx$$

$$= \frac{1}{n}\cos^m x\cdot\sin x + \frac{m}{n}\int\cos^{m-1} x\cdot\cos(n-1)\, x\, dx - \frac{m}{n}\int\cos^m x\cdot\cos n x\, dx$$

$$= \frac{1}{n}\cos^m x\cdot\sin nx + \frac{m}{n} I_{m-1,n-1} - \frac{m}{n} I_{m,n}$$

$$I_{m,n} + \frac{m}{n} I_{m,n} = \frac{1}{n}[\cos^m x \cdot \sin nx + m\, I_{m-1,n-1}]$$

$$\left(\frac{m+n}{n}\right) I_{m,n} = \frac{1}{n}[\cos^m x \cdot \sin nx + m\, I_{m-1,n-1}]$$

$$(m+n)\, I_{m,n} = \cos^m x \cdot \sin nx + m\, I_{m-1,n-1}$$

• **Ex. 34** Evaluate $\displaystyle\int \frac{\tan\left(\frac{\pi}{4} - x\right)}{\cos^2 x\sqrt{\tan^3 x + \tan^2 x + \tan x}}\, dx.$

Sol. $\displaystyle I = \int \frac{\tan\left(\frac{\pi}{4} - x\right) dx}{\cos^2 x\sqrt{\tan^3 x + \tan^2 x + \tan x}}$

$$= \int \frac{(1 - \tan^2 x)\, dx}{(1 + \tan x)^2 \cos^2 x\sqrt{\tan^3 x + \tan^2 x + \tan x}}$$

$$I = \int \frac{-\left(1 - \frac{1}{\tan^2 x}\right) \sec^2 x\, dx}{\left(\tan x + 2 + \frac{1}{\tan x}\right)\sqrt{\tan x + 1 + \frac{1}{\tan x}}}$$

let $\quad y = \sqrt{\tan x + 1 + \frac{1}{\tan x}}$

$$\Rightarrow \quad 2y\, dy = \left(\sec^2 x - \frac{1}{\tan^2 x} \cdot \sec^2 x\right) dx$$

$$\therefore \quad I = \int \frac{-2y\, dy}{(y^2 + 1) \cdot y} = -2\int \frac{dy}{1 + y^2} = -2\tan^{-1} y + C$$

$$= -2\tan^{-1}\left(\sqrt{\tan x + 1 + \frac{1}{\tan x}}\right) + C$$

• **Ex. 35** Evaluate $\displaystyle\int \frac{x^2 + n(n-1)}{(x \sin x + n \cos x)^2}\, dx.$

Sol. Here, $\displaystyle I = \int \frac{x^2 + n(n-1)}{(x \sin x + n \cos x)^2}\, dx$

Multiplying and dividing by x^{2n-2}, we get

$$I = \int \frac{\{x^2 + n(n-1)\}\, x^{2n-2}}{(x^n \sin x + n\, x^{n-1} \cos x)^2}\, dx$$

We know $x^n \sin x + n\, x^{n-1} \cos x = t$

$$\Rightarrow \{(n\, x^{n-1} \sin x) + (x^n \cos x) + n(n-1)\, x^{n-2} \cos x - (n\, x^{n-1} \sin x)\, dx = dt\}$$

$$\Rightarrow \quad x^{n-2} \cos x \cdot \{x^2 + n(n-1)\}\, dx = dt$$

Keeping this in mind, we put

$$I = \int \underset{\text{II}}{\frac{\{x^2 + n(n-1)\} \cdot x^{n-2} \cdot \cos x}{(x^n \sin x + n\, x^{n-1} \cos x)^2}} \cdot \underset{\text{I}}{x^n \cdot \sec x}\, dx$$

Applying integration by parts, we get

$$= x^n \sec x \cdot \left(-\frac{1}{(x^n \sin x + n\, x^{n-1} \cos x)}\right) + \int \frac{(x^n \sec x \tan x + n\, x^{n-1} \cdot \sec x)}{(x^n \sin x + n\, x^{n-1} \cos x)}\, dx$$

$$= -\frac{(x \sec x)}{(x \sin x + n \cos x)} + \int \sec^2 x\, dx$$

$$= -\frac{(x \sec x)}{(x \sin x + n \cos x)} + \tan x + C \qquad \textbf{Hence Proved.}$$

• **Ex. 36** *If* $\cos\theta > \sin\theta > 0$, *then evaluate*

$$\int \left\{\log\left(\frac{1 + \sin 2\theta}{1 - \sin 2\theta}\right)^{\cos^2\theta} + \log\left(\frac{\cos 2\theta}{1 + \sin 2\theta}\right)\right\} d\theta$$

Sol. Here, $\displaystyle I = \int \left\{\log\left(\frac{1 + \sin 2\theta}{1 - \sin 2\theta}\right)^{\cos^2\theta} + \log\left(\frac{\cos 2\theta}{1 + \sin 2\theta}\right)\right\} d\theta$

$$= \int \left\{2\cos^2\theta \log\left(\frac{\cos\theta + \sin\theta}{\cos\theta - \sin\theta}\right) - \log\left(\frac{\cos\theta + \sin\theta}{\cos\theta - \sin\theta}\right)\right\} d\theta$$

$$= \int (2\cos^2\theta - 1) \log\left(\frac{\cos\theta + \sin\theta}{\cos\theta - \sin\theta}\right) d\theta$$

$$= \int \underset{\text{II}}{\cos 2\theta} \cdot \underset{\text{I}}{\log\left(\frac{\cos\theta + \sin\theta}{\cos\theta - \sin\theta}\right)} d\theta, \text{ applying integration by parts}$$

$$= \log\left(\frac{\cos\theta + \sin\theta}{\cos\theta - \sin\theta}\right) \cdot \frac{\sin 2\theta}{2} - \int \frac{2}{\cos 2\theta} \cdot \frac{\sin 2\theta}{2}\, d\theta$$

$$= \frac{\sin 2\theta}{2} \log\left(\frac{\cos\theta + \sin\theta}{\cos\theta - \sin\theta}\right) + \frac{1}{2} \log|\cos 2\theta| + C$$

• **Ex. 37** Evaluate $\displaystyle\int \frac{\tan^{-1} x}{x^4}\, dx.$

Sol. $\displaystyle I = \int \frac{\tan^{-1} x}{x^4}\, dx = \int \underset{\text{I}}{\tan^{-1} x} \cdot \underset{\text{II}}{\frac{1}{x^4}}\, dx$

$$= (\tan^{-1} x)\left(-\frac{1}{3x^3}\right) - \int \frac{1}{1 + x^2} \cdot \frac{1}{(-3x^3)}\, dx$$

$$= -\frac{\tan^{-1} x}{3x^3} + \frac{1}{3}\int \frac{dx}{x^3(1 + x^2)},$$

Put $1 + x^2 = t$,

$$2x\, dx = dt = -\frac{\tan^{-1} x}{3x^3} + \frac{1}{6}\int \frac{dt}{(t-1)^2 \cdot t}$$

$$I = -\frac{\tan^{-1} x}{3x^3} + \frac{1}{6} I_1 \qquad \text{...(i)}$$

Where, $\displaystyle I_1 = \int \frac{1}{(t-1)^2 \cdot t}\, dt = \int \left\{\frac{A}{t-1} + \frac{B}{(t-1)^2} + \frac{C}{t}\right\} dt$

Comparing coefficients, we get

$$A = -1, B = 1, C = 1$$

$$\therefore \quad I_1 = \int \left\{-\frac{1}{(t-1)} + \frac{1}{(t-1)^2} + \frac{1}{t}\right\} dt$$

$$= -\log|t - 1| - \frac{1}{(t-1)} + \log|t| \qquad \text{...(ii)}$$

$\therefore$ From Eqs. (i) and (ii), we get

$$I = -\frac{\tan^{-1} x}{3x^3} + \frac{1}{6}\left\{-\log|x^2| - \frac{1}{x^2} + \log|1+x^2|\right\} + C$$

$$= -\frac{\tan^{-1} x}{3x^3} - \frac{1}{6}\log\left|\frac{x^2+1}{x^2}\right| - \frac{1}{6x^2} + C$$

Ex. 38 *Evaluate* $\int x^2 \log(1-x^2)\, dx$, *and hence prove that* $\frac{1}{1\cdot 5} + \frac{1}{2\cdot 7} + \frac{1}{3\cdot 9} + \ldots = \frac{2}{3}\log 2 - \frac{8}{9}$.

Sol. We know, $\log(1-x) = -\left\{x + \frac{x^2}{2} + \frac{x^3}{3} + \frac{x^4}{4} + \ldots \infty\right\}$

Put x^2 instead of x in the above identity,

$$\Rightarrow \quad \log(1-x^2) = -\left\{x^2 + \frac{x^4}{2} + \frac{x^6}{3} + \frac{x^8}{4} + \ldots \infty\right\}$$

$$\Rightarrow \quad x^2\log(1-x^2) = -\left\{x^4 + \frac{x^6}{2} + \frac{x^8}{3} + \frac{x^{10}}{4} + \ldots \infty\right\}$$

Integrating both the sides, we get

$$\int x^2 \log(1-x^2)\, dx = -\left\{\frac{x^5}{1\cdot 5} + \frac{x^7}{2\cdot 7} + \frac{x^9}{3\cdot 9} + \ldots \infty\right\} + C$$

Now, to find constant of integration, put $x = 0$

$$\Rightarrow \quad 0 = 0 + C$$

$$\Rightarrow \quad C = 0$$

$$\therefore \quad \int \underset{\text{II}}{x^2} \underset{\text{I}}{\log(1-x^2)}\, dx = -\left\{\frac{x^5}{1\cdot 5} + \frac{x^7}{2\cdot 7} + \frac{x^9}{3\cdot 9} + \ldots \infty\right\}$$

Applying integration by parts, and taking limits 0 to 1 for LHS

$$\Rightarrow \quad \left(\frac{x^3}{3}\log(1-x^2)\right)_0^1 - \int_0^1 \frac{x^3}{3}\cdot\frac{1(-2x)}{1-x^2}\, dx$$

$$\Rightarrow \quad \left(\frac{x^3}{3}\log(1-x^2)\right)_0^1 + \frac{2}{3}\left(-\frac{x^3}{3} - x + \frac{1}{2}\log\left|\frac{1+x}{1-x}\right|\right)_0^1$$

Taking $\log(1-x^2) = \log(1+x) + \log(1-x)$

and $\log\left(\frac{1+x}{1-x}\right) = \log(1+x) - \log(1-x)$

$$\Rightarrow \quad \frac{1}{3}\log 2 + \frac{1}{3}\log 2 - \frac{2}{3} - \frac{2}{9} + \lim_{x\to 1}\left(\frac{x^3}{3} - \frac{1}{3}\right)\log(1-x)$$

$$\left[\because \lim_{x\to 1}(x^3-1)\log(1-x) = 0\right]$$

$$\Rightarrow \quad \frac{2}{3}\log 2 - \frac{8}{9} = \text{RHS}$$

$$\therefore \quad \frac{1}{1\cdot 5} + \frac{1}{2\cdot 7} + \frac{1}{3\cdot 9} + \ldots = \frac{2}{3}\log(2) - \frac{8}{9}$$

Ex. 39 *Evaluate* $\int \frac{a + b\sin x}{(b + a\sin x)^2}\, dx$

Sol. Here, $I = \int \frac{a + b\sin x}{(b + a\sin x)^2}\, dx = \frac{b}{a}\int \frac{\frac{a^2}{b} - b + (b + a\sin x)}{(b + a\sin x)^2}\, dx$

$$I = \frac{a^2 - b^2}{a}\int \frac{dx}{(b + a\sin x)^2} + \frac{b}{a}\int \frac{dx}{(b + a\sin x)} \quad \ldots\text{(i)}$$

Now, let $A = \frac{\cos x}{b + a\sin x} \Rightarrow \frac{dA}{dx} = \frac{-b\sin x - a}{(b + a\sin x)^2}$

$$\Rightarrow \quad \frac{dA}{dx} = -\frac{b}{a}\left\{\frac{a\sin x + b + \frac{a^2}{b} - b}{(b + a\sin x)^2}\right\}$$

$$\Rightarrow \quad \frac{dA}{dx} = -\frac{b}{a}\left\{\frac{1}{b + a\sin x} + \frac{a^2 - b^2}{b(b + a\sin x)^2}\right\}$$

Integrating both the sides w.r.t. 'x', we get

$$A = -\frac{b}{a}\int \frac{dx}{b + a\sin x} - \frac{(a^2 - b^2)}{a}\int \frac{dx}{(b + a\sin x)^2}$$

$$\Rightarrow \quad \frac{a^2 - b^2}{a}\int \frac{dx}{(b + a\sin x)^2} = -\frac{b}{a}\int \frac{dx}{b + a\sin x} - A \quad \ldots\text{(ii)}$$

From Eqs. (i) and (ii), we get

$$I = -\frac{b}{a}\int \frac{dx}{(b + a\sin x)} - A + \frac{b}{a}\int \frac{dx}{(b + a\sin x)}$$

$$\Rightarrow \quad I = -A + C \Rightarrow I = -\left(\frac{\cos x}{b + a\sin x}\right) + C$$

Ex. 40 *Evaluate* $\int \frac{dx}{(x-1)^{3/4}(x+2)^{5/4}}$.

Sol. Let $I = \int \frac{dx}{(x-1)^{3/4}(x+2)^{5/4}} = \int \frac{dx}{(x+2)^2\left(\frac{(x-1)}{(x+2)}\right)^{3/4}}$

Let $\quad \frac{x-1}{x+2} = t$

So that, $\quad \frac{3}{(x+2)^2}\, dx = dt$

$$\therefore \quad I = \int \frac{dt}{3\, t^{3/4}} = \frac{1}{3}\int t^{-3/4}\, dt$$

$$= \frac{1}{3}\cdot\frac{t^{1/4}}{1/4} + C = \frac{4}{3}\left(\frac{x-1}{x+2}\right)^{1/4} + C$$

Indefinite Integral Exercise 1 : Single Option Correct Type Questions

1. Let $f(x)=\int \frac{x^2}{(1+x^2)(1+\sqrt{1+x^2})}\,dx$ and $f(0)=0$. Then $f(1)$ is equal to

(a) $\log_e(1+\sqrt{2})$
(b) $\log_e(1+\sqrt{2})-\frac{\pi}{4}$
(c) $\log_e(1+\sqrt{2})+\frac{\pi}{4}$
(d) None of these

2. If $\int f(x)\,dx=f(x)$, then $\int \{f(x)\}^2\,dx$ is equal to

(a) $\frac{1}{2}\{f(x)\}^2$
(b) $\{f(x)\}^3$
(c) $\frac{\{f(x)\}^3}{3}$
(d) $\{f(x)\}^2$

3. If $\int f(x)\,dx=F(x)$, then $\int x^3 f(x^2)\,dx$ is equal to

(a) $\frac{1}{2}[x^2\{F(x)\}^2-\int\{F(x)\}^2\,dx]$
(b) $\frac{1}{2}[x^2F(x^2)-\int F(x^2)\,d(x^2)]$
(c) $\frac{1}{2}[x^2F(x)-\frac{1}{2}\int\{F(x)\}^2\,dx]$
(d) None of the above

4. If n is an odd positive integer, then $\int |x^n|\,dx$ is equal to

(a) $\left|\frac{x^{n+1}}{n+1}\right|+C$
(b) $\frac{x^{n+1}}{n+1}+C$
(c) $\frac{|x|^n x}{n+1}+C$
(d) None of these

5. Let $F(x)$ be the primitive of $\frac{3x+2}{\sqrt{x-9}}$ w.r.t. x. If $F(10)=60$, then the value of $F(13)$ is

(a) 66
(b) 132
(c) 248
(d) 264

6. $\int (x^x)^x(2x\log_e x+x)\,dx$ is equal to

(a) $x^{(x^x)}+C$
(b) $(x^x)^x+C$
(c) $x^2\cdot\log_e x+C$
(d) None of these

7. The value of $\int x\log x(\log x-1)\,dx$ is equal to

(a) $2(x\log x-x)^2+C$
(b) $\frac{1}{2}(x\log x-x)^2+C$
(c) $(x\log x)^2+C$
(d) $\frac{1}{2}(x\log x)^3+C$

8. $\int \frac{x^2-1}{x^3\sqrt{2x^4-2x^2+1}}\,dx$ is equal to

(a) $\frac{\sqrt{2x^4-2x^5+1}}{x^2}+C$
(b) $\frac{\sqrt{2x^4-2x^2+1}}{x^3}+C$
(c) $\frac{\sqrt{2x^4+2x^2+1}}{x}+C$
(d) $\frac{\sqrt{2x^4-2x^2+1}}{2x^2}+C$

9. Let $f(x)$ be a polynomial satisfying $f(0)=2$, $f'(0)=3$ and $f''(x)=f(x)$. Then $f(4)$ is equal to

(a) $\frac{5(e^8+1)}{2e^4}$
(b) $\frac{5(e^8-1)}{2e^4}$
(c) $\frac{2e^4}{5(e^8-1)}$
(d) $\frac{2e^4}{5(e^8+1)}$

10. $\int \frac{e^{(x^2+4\ln x)}-x^3e^{x^2}}{x-1}\,dx$ is equal to

(a) $\left(\frac{e^{3\ln x}-e^{\ln x}}{2x}\right)e^{x^2}+C$
(b) $\frac{(x-1)\,xe^{x^2}}{2}+C$
(c) $\frac{(x^2-1)}{2x}-e^{x^2}+C$
(d) None of these

11. $\int \tan^4 x\,dx=A\tan^3 x+B\tan x+f(x)$, then

(a) $A=\frac{1}{3}$, $B=-1$, $f(x)=x+C$
(b) $A=\frac{2}{3}$, $B=-1$, $f(x)=x+C$
(c) $A=\frac{1}{3}$, $B=1$, $f(x)=x+C$
(d) $A=\frac{2}{3}$, $B=1$, $f(x)=-x+C$

12. If the anti-derivative of $\int \frac{\sin^4 x}{x}\,dx$ is $f(x)$, then $\int \frac{\sin^4\{(p+q)x\}}{x}\,dx$ in terms of $f(x)$ is

(a) $f\{(p+q)x\}$
(b) $\frac{f\{(p+q)x\}}{p+q}$
(c) $f\{(p+q)x\}(p+q)$
(d) None of these

13. $\int\left(\frac{\sin\theta}{\cos 3\theta}+\frac{\sin 3\theta}{\cos 9\theta}+\frac{\sin 9\theta}{\cos 27\theta}\right)d\theta$ is equal to

(a) $\frac{1}{2}\log\left|\frac{\sec 27\theta}{\sec\theta}\right|+C$
(b) $\frac{1}{2}\log\left|\frac{\sec\theta}{\sec 27\theta}\right|+C$
(c) $\frac{1}{2}\log\left|\frac{\sqrt[27]{\sec 27\theta}}{\sec\theta}\right|+C$
(d) None of these

14. Let $x^2 \neq n\pi - 1, n \in N$. Then, the value of

$$\int x \sqrt{\frac{2\sin(x^2+1) - \sin 2(x^2+1)}{2\sin(x^2+1) + \sin 2(x^2+1)}}\, dx \text{ is equal to}$$

(a) $\log\left|\frac{1}{2}\sec(x^2+1)\right| + C$ (b) $\log\left|\sec\left(\frac{x^2+1}{2}\right)\right| + C$

(c) $\frac{1}{2}\log|\sec(x^2+1)| + C$ (d) None of these

15. $\int \frac{dx}{\cos(2x)\cos(4x)}$ is equal to

(a) $\frac{1}{2\sqrt{2}}\log\left|\frac{1+\sqrt{2}\sin 2x}{1-\sqrt{2}\sin 2x}\right| - \frac{1}{2}(\log|\sec 2x - \tan 2x|) + C$

(b) $\frac{1}{2\sqrt{2}}\log\left|\frac{1+\sqrt{2}\sin 2x}{1+\sqrt{2}\sin x}\right| - \frac{1}{2}(\log|\sec 2x - \tan 2x|) + C$

(c) $\frac{1}{\sqrt{2}}\log\left|\frac{1+\sqrt{2}\sin 2x}{1-\sqrt{2}\sin 2x}\right| - \frac{1}{2}(\log|\sec 2x - \tan 2x|) + C$

(d) None of the above

16. $\int \frac{1 - 7\cos^2 x}{\sin^7 x \cos^2 x}\, dx = \frac{f(x)}{(\sin x)^7} + C$, then $f(x)$ is equal to

(a) $\sin x$ (b) $\cos x$ (c) $\tan x$ (d) $\cot x$

17. $\int \frac{\sin^3 x}{(\cos^4 x + 3\cos^2 x + 1)\tan^{-1}(\sec x + \cos x)}\, dx$ is equal to

(a) $\tan^{-1}(\sec x + \cos x) + C$ (b) $\log_e|\tan^{-1}(\sec x + \cos x)| + C$

(c) $\frac{1}{(\sec x + \cos x)^2} + C$ (d) None of these

18. The primitive of the function $f(x) = x|\cos x|$, when $\frac{\pi}{2} < x < \pi$ is given by

(a) $\cos x + x\sin x + C$

(b) $-\cos x - x\sin x + C$

(c) $x\sin x - \cos x + C$

(d) None of the above

19. The primitive of the function $f(x) = (2x+1)|\sin x|$, when $\pi < x < 2\pi$ is

(a) $-(2x+1)\cos x + 2\sin x + C$

(b) $(2x+1)\cos x - 2\sin x + C$

(c) $(x^2 + x)\cos x + C$

(d) None of the above

20. Given, $f(x) = \begin{vmatrix} 0 & x^2 - \sin x & \cos x - 2 \\ \sin x - x^2 & 0 & 1 - 2x \\ 2 - \cos x & 2x - 1 & 0 \end{vmatrix}$, then

$\int f(x)\, dx$ is equal to

(a) $\frac{x^3}{3} - x^2\sin x + \sin 2x + C$

(b) $\frac{x^3}{3} - x^2\sin x - \cos 2x + C$

(c) $\frac{x^3}{3} - x^2\cos x - \cos 2x + C$

(d) None of the above

Indefinite Integral Exercise 2 :
More than One Option Correct Type Questions

21. $\int \frac{dx}{(x+1)(x-2)} = A\log(x+1) + B\log(x-2) + C$, where

(a) $A + B = 0$ (b) $AB = 0$

(c) $A/B = -1$ (d) None of these

22. If $\int \frac{dx}{(x^2+1)(x^2+4)} = k\tan^{-1} x + l\tan^{-1}\frac{x}{2} + C$, then

(a) $k = \frac{1}{3}$ (b) $l = \frac{2}{3}$ (c) $k = -\frac{1}{3}$ (d) $l = -\frac{1}{6}$

23. If $\int x\log(1+x^2)\, dx = \phi(x)\log(1+x^2) + x(\psi) + C$, then

(a) $\phi(x) = \frac{1+x^2}{2}$ (b) $\psi(x) = \frac{1+x^2}{2}$

(c) $\psi(x) = -\frac{1+x^2}{2}$ (d) $\phi(x) = -\frac{1+x^2}{2}$

24. If $\int \frac{4e^x + 6e^{-x}}{9e^x - 4e^{-x}}\, dx = Ax + B\log_e(9e^{2x} - 4) + C$, then

(a) $A = \frac{3}{2}$ (b) $B = \frac{35}{36}$

(c) C is indefinite (d) $A + B = -\frac{19}{36}$

25. If $\int \tan^5 x\, dx = A\tan^4 x + B\tan^2 x + g(x) + C$, then

(a) $A = \frac{1}{4}, B = -\frac{1}{2}$

(b) $g(x) = \ln|\sec x|$

(c) $g(x) = \ln|\cos x|$

(d) $A = -\frac{1}{4}, B = \frac{1}{3}$

Indefinite Integral Exercise 3 : Statement I and II Type Questions

- **Directions** (Q. Nos. 26 to 30) For the following questions, choose the correct answers from the codes (a), (b), (c) and (d) defined as follows :
  - (a) Statement I is true, Statement II is also true; Statement II is the correct explanation of Statement I.
  - (b) Statement I is true, Statement II is also true; Statement II is not the correct explanation of Statement I.
  - (c) Statement I is true, Statement II is false.
  - (d) Statement I is false, Statement II is true.

26. Statement I If y is a function of x such that $y(x-y)^2 = x$, then $\int \frac{dx}{x-3y} = \frac{1}{2}[\log (x-y)^2 - 1]$.

Statement II $\int \frac{dx}{x-3y} = \log (x-3y) + C$

27. Statement I Integral of an even function is not always an odd function.

Statement II Integral of an odd function is an even function.

28. Statement I If $a > 0$ and $b^2 - 4ac < 0$, then the value of the integral $\int \frac{dx}{ax^2 + bx + c}$ will be of the type $\mu \tan^{-1} \frac{x+A}{B} + C$, where A, B, C, μ are constants.

Statement II If $a > 0$, $b^2 - 4ac < 0$, then $ax^2 + bx + C$ can be written as sum of two squares.

29. Statement I $\int \left(\frac{1}{1+x^4}\right) dx = \tan^{-1}(x^2) + C$

Statement II $\int \frac{1}{1+x^2} dx = \tan^{-1} x + C$

30. Statement I $\int 2^{\tan^{-1} x} d(\cot^{-1} x) = \frac{2^{\tan^{-1} x}}{\ln 2} + C$

Statement II $\frac{d}{dx}(a^x + C) = a^x \ln a$

Indefinite Integral Exercise 4 : Passage Based Questions

Passage I

(Q. Nos. 31 to 33)

Let us consider the integral of the following forms

$$f(x_1, \sqrt{mx^2 + nx + p})^{1/2}$$

Case I *If* $m > 0$, *then put* $\sqrt{mx^2 + nx + C} = u \pm x\sqrt{m}$

Case II *If* $p > 0$, *then put* $\sqrt{mx^2 + nx + C} = ux \pm \sqrt{p}$

Case III *If quadratic equation* $mx^2 + nx + p = 0$ *has real roots* α *and* β *there put* $\sqrt{mx^2 + nx + p} = (x-\alpha)u$ or $(x-\beta)u$

31. If $I = \int \frac{dx}{x - \sqrt{9x^2 + 4x + 6}}$ to evaluate I, one of the most proper substitution could be

(a) $\sqrt{9x^2 + 4x + 6} = u \pm 3x$

(b) $\sqrt{9x^2 + 4x + 6} = 3u \pm x$

(c) $x = \frac{1}{t}$

(d) $9x^2 + 4x + 6 = \frac{1}{t}$

32. $\int \frac{(x + \sqrt{1+x^2})^{15}}{\sqrt{1+x^2}} dx$ is equal to

(a) $\frac{(x + \sqrt{1+x^2})^{16}}{10} + C$

(b) $\frac{1}{15(\sqrt{1+x^2} + x)} + C$

(c) $\frac{15}{(\sqrt{1+x^2} - x)} + C$

(d) $\frac{(x + \sqrt{1+x^2})^{15}}{15} + C$

33. To evaluate $\int \frac{dx}{(x-1)\sqrt{-x^2 + 3x - 2}}$ one of the most suitable substitution could be

(a) $\sqrt{-x^2 + 3x - 2} = u$

(b) $\sqrt{-x^2 + 3x - 2} = (ux\sqrt{2})$

(c) $\sqrt{-x^2 + 3x - 2} = u(1-x)$

(d) $\sqrt{-x^2 + 3x - 2} = u(x+2)$

Passage II

(Q. Nos. 34 to 36)

Let $I_{n,m}=\int \sin^n x\cos^m x\,dx$. *Then, we can relate* $I_{n,m}$ *with each of the following :*

(i) $I_{n-2,m}$ (ii) $I_{n+2,m}$
(iii) $I_{n,m-2}$ (iv) $I_{n,m+2}$
(v) $I_{n-2,m+2}$ (vi) $I_{n+2,m-2}$

Suppose we want to establish a relation between $I_{n,m}$ *and* $I_{n,m-2}$, *then we get*

$$P(x)=\sin^{n+1} x\cos^{m-1} x \qquad \ldots\text{(i)}$$

In $I_{n,m}$ *and* $I_{n,m-2}$ *the exponent of* $\cos x$ *is* m *and* $m-2$ *respectively, the minimum of the two is* $m-2$, *adding 1 to the minimum we get* $m-2+1=m-1$. *Now, choose the exponent* $m-1$ *of* $\cos x$ *in* $P(x)$. *Similarly, choose the exponent of* $\sin x$ *for* $P(x)=(nH)\sin^n x\cos^m x-(m-1)\sin^{n+2} x\cos^{m-2} x$.

Now, differentiating both the sides of Eq. (i), we get

$$=(n+1)\sin^n x\cos^m x-(m-1)\sin^n x(1-\cos^2 x)\cos^{m-2} x$$

$$=(n+1)\sin^n x\cos^m x-(m-1)\sin^n x\cos^{m-2} x+(m-1)\sin^n x\cos^n x$$

$$=(n+m)\sin^n x\cos^m x-(m-1)\sin^n x\cos^{m-2} x$$

Now, integrating both the sides, we get

$$\sin^{n+1} x\cos^{m-1} x=(n+m)I_{n,m}-(m-1)I_{n,m-2}$$

Similarly, we can establish the other relations.

34. The relation between $I_{4,2}$ and $I_{2,2}$ is

(a) $I_{4,2}=\frac{1}{6}(-\sin^3 x\cos^3 x+3I_{2,2})$

(b) $I_{4,2}=\frac{1}{6}(\sin^3 x\cos^3 x+3I_{2,2})$

(c) $I_{4,2}=\frac{1}{6}(\sin^3 x\cos^3 x-3I_{2,2})$

(d) $I_{4,2}=\frac{1}{4}(-\sin^3 x\cos^3 x+2I_{2,2})$

35. The relation between $I_{4,2}$ and $I_{6,2}$ is

(a) $I_{4,2}=\frac{1}{5}(\sin^5 x\cos^3 x+8I_{6,2})$

(b) $I_{4,2}=\frac{1}{5}(-\sin^5 x\cos^3 x+8I_{6,2})$

(c) $I_{4,2}=\frac{1}{5}(\sin^5 x\cos^3 x-8I_{6,2})$

(d) $I_{4,2}=\frac{1}{6}(\sin^5 x\cos^3 x+8I_{6,2})$

36. The relation between $I_{4,2}$ and $I_{4,4}$ is

(a) $I_{4,2}=\frac{1}{3}(\sin^5 x\cos^3 x+8I_{4,4})$

(b) $I_{4,2}=\frac{1}{3}(-\sin^5 x\cos^3 x+8I_{4,4})$

(c) $I_{4,2}=\frac{1}{3}(\sin^5 x\cos^3 x-8I_{4,4})$

(d) $I_{4,2}=\frac{1}{3}(\sin^5 x\cos^3 x+6I_{4,4})$

Passage III

(Q. Nos. 37 to 38)

If $f:R\to(0,\infty)$ be a differentiable function $f(x)$ satisfying $f(x+y)-f(x-y)=f(x)\cdot\{f(y)-f(y)-y\}$, $\forall\, x,y\in R$, $(f(y)\neq f(-y)$ for all $y\in R)$ and $f'(0)=2010$.

Now, answer the following questions.

37. Which of the following is true for $f(x)$

(a) $f(x)$ is one-one and into
(b) $\{f(x)\}$ is non-periodic, where $\{\}$ denotes fractional part of x.
(c) $f(x)=4$ has only two solutions.
(d) $f(x)=f^{-1}(x)$ has only one solution.

38. let $g(x)=\log_e(\sin x)$, and $\int f(g(x))\cos x\,dx=h(x)+c$, (where c is constant of integration), then $h\left(\frac{\pi}{2}\right)$ is equal to

(a) 0 (b) $\frac{1}{2010}$
(c) 1 (d) $\frac{1}{2011}$

Passage IV

(Q. Nos. 39 to 41)

Let $f:R\to R$ *be a function as* $f(x)=(x-1)(x+2)(x-3)(x-6)-100$. *If* $g(x)$ *is a polynomial of degree* ≤ 3 *such that* $\int\frac{g(x)}{f(x)}dx$ *does not contain any logarithm function and* $g(-2)=10$. *Then*

39. The equation $f(x)=0$ has

(a) all four distinct roots
(b) three distinct real roots
(c) two real and two imaginary
(d) all four imaginary roots

40. The minimum value of $f(x)$ is

(a) – 136 (b) – 100
(c) – 84 (d) – 68

41. $\int\frac{g(x)}{f(x)}dx$, equals

(a) $\tan^{-1}\left(\frac{x-2}{2}\right)+c$ (b) $\tan^{-1}\left(\frac{x-1}{1}\right)+c$
(c) $\tan^{-1}(x)+c$ (d) None of these

Indefinite Integral Exercise 5 : Matching Type Questions

42. Match the following :

	Column I		Column II
(A)	If $I = \int \frac{\sin x - \cos x}{\vert \sin x - \cos x \vert} dx$, where $\frac{\pi}{4} < x < \frac{3\pi}{8}$, then I is equal to	(p)	$\sin x$
(B)	If $\int \frac{x^2}{(x^3+1)(x^3+2)} dx = \frac{1}{3} f\left(\frac{x^3+1}{x^3+2}\right) + C$, then $f(x)$ is equal to	(q)	$x + C$
(C)	If $\int \sin^{-1} x \cdot \cos^{-1} x \, dx = f^{-1}(x)\left[\frac{\pi}{2} x - xf^{-1}(x) - 2\sqrt{1-x^2}\right] + 2x + C$, then $f(x)$ is equal to	(r)	$\ln \vert x \vert$
(D)	If $\int \frac{dx}{xf(x)} = f(f(x)) + C$, then $f(x)$ is equal to	(s)	$\sin^{-1} x$

43. Match the following :

	Column I		Column II
(A)	If $\int \left(\frac{x^2 + \cos^2 x}{1 + x^2}\right) \text{cosec}^2 x \, dx = A \cot^{-1} x + B \frac{\text{cosec } x}{\sec x}$, then	(p)	$A = 1$
(B)	If $\int \sqrt{x + \sqrt{x^2+2}} \, dx = \frac{A}{3}(x + \sqrt{x^2+2})^{3/2} - \frac{B}{(x+\sqrt{x^2+2})}$, then	(q)	$B = -1$
(C)	If $\int \frac{\sqrt{2-x-x^2}}{x^2} dx = A\sqrt{\frac{2-x-x^2}{x}} + \frac{B}{4\sqrt{2}} \log\left(\frac{4 - x + 4\sqrt{2-x-x^2}}{x}\right) - \sin^{-1}\left(\frac{2x+1}{3}\right)$, then	(r)	$B = 2$
(D)	If $\int \frac{\sin 2x}{\sin^4 x + \cos^4 x} dx = B \cot^{-1}(\tan^2 x)$, then	(s)	$A = -1$

Indefinite Integral Exercise 6 : Single Integer Answer Type Questions

44. If $\int \frac{(2x+3)\,dx}{x(x+1)(x+2)(x+3)+1} = C - \frac{1}{f(x)}$, where $f(x)$ is of the form of $ax^2 + bx + c$, then $(a+b+c)$ equals to ....

45. Let $F(x)$ be the primitive of $\frac{3x+2}{\sqrt{x-9}}$ w.r.t. x. If $F(10) = 60$, then the sum of digits of the value of $F(13)$, is ....

46. Let $u(x)$ and $v(x)$ are differentiable function such that $\frac{u(x)}{v(x)} = 7$. If $\frac{u'(x)}{v'(x)} = p$ and $\left(\frac{u(x)}{v(x)}\right)' = q$, then $\frac{p+q}{p-q}$ has the value equal to ....

47. If $\int \frac{1}{(x^2-1)} \ln\left(\frac{x-1}{x+1}\right) dx = 6A\left[\ln\left(\frac{x-1}{x+1}\right)\right]^2 + C$, then find 24 A.

48. If $\int \frac{e^x(2-x^2)}{(1-x)\sqrt{1-x^2}} dx = \mu e^x \left(\frac{1+x}{1-x}\right)^{\lambda} + C$, then $2(\lambda + \mu)$ is equal to ....

49. If $\int \frac{\cos x - \sin x + 1 - x}{e^x + \sin x + x} dx = \ln \{f(x)\} + g(x) + C$, where C is the constant of integrating and $f(x)$ is positive, then $\frac{f(x) + g(x)}{e^x + \sin x}$ is equal to ....

50. Suppose $A = \int \frac{dx}{x^2 + 6x + 25}$ and $B = \int \frac{dx}{x^2 - 6x - 27}$.

If $12(A + B) = \lambda \cdot \tan^{-1}\left(\frac{x+3}{4}\right) + \mu \cdot \ln \left|\frac{x-9}{x+3}\right| + C$, then the value of $(\lambda + \mu)$ is ... .

51. If $\int \frac{\cos 6x + \cos 9x}{1 - 2\cos 5x} dx = -\frac{\sin 4x}{k} - \sin x + C$, then the value of k is ....

52. The value of $\int \frac{\tan x}{1 + \tan x + \tan^2 x} dx = x - \frac{1}{\sqrt{A}} \tan^{-1}\left(\frac{2\tan x + 1}{\sqrt{A}}\right) + C$, then the value of A is......... .

53. $\int \sin^{5/2} x \cos^3 x \, dx = 2 \sin^{A/2} x \left[\frac{1}{B} - \frac{1}{C}\sin^2 x\right] + C$, then the value of $(A + B) - C$ is equal to ....

54. If $\int (x^{2010} + x^{804} + x^{402})(2x^{1608} + 5x^{402} + 10)^{1/402} \, dx = \frac{1}{10a}(2x^{2010} + 5x^{804} + 10x^{402})^{a/402}$. Then $(a - 400)$ is equal to ....

55. If $\int e^{x^3 + x^2 - 1}(3x^4 + 2x^3 + 2x) \, dx = h(x) + c$ Then the value of $h(1) \cdot h(-1)$, is ....

Indefinite Integral Exercise 7 :
Subjective Type Questions

56. Evaluate $e^{(x \sin x + \cos x)} dx \left[\frac{x^4 \cos^3 x - x \sin x + \cos x}{x^2 \cos^2 x}\right]$

57. Evaluate $\int \sqrt{x + \sqrt{x^2 + 2}} \, dx.$

58. Evaluate $\int \frac{dx}{(\sqrt{(x-\alpha)^2 - \beta^2})(ax + b)}$.

59. Evaluate $\int \frac{\sqrt{1 + \sqrt[3]{x}}}{\sqrt[3]{x^2}} dx.$

60. Evaluate $\int \frac{\sin^3(\theta/2) \, d\theta}{\cos \theta/2 \sqrt{\cos^3 \theta + \cos^2 \theta + \cos \theta}}$.

61. Evaluate $\int \frac{(2\sin \theta + \sin 2\theta) \, d\theta}{(\cos \theta - 1)\sqrt{\cos \theta + \cos^2 \theta + \cos^3 \theta}}$.

62. Connect $\int x^{m-1}(a + bx^n)^p \, dx$ with $\int x^{m-n-1}(a + bx^n)^p \, dx$ and evaluate $\int \frac{x^8 \, dx}{(1 - x^3)^{1/3}}$.

63. Evaluate $\int \operatorname{cosec}^2 x \ln(\cos x + \sqrt{\cos 2x}) \, dx.$

64. Evaluate $\int \frac{dx}{(\sin x + a \sec x)^2}$, $a \in N$.

65. Evaluate $\int \frac{dx}{x - \sqrt{x^2 + 2x + 4}}$.

66. Evaluate $\int \frac{dx}{1 + \sqrt{x^2 + 2x + 2}}$.

67. Evaluate $\int \frac{x^4 + 1}{x^6 + 1} dx.$

68. Evaluate $\int \frac{dx}{(1 - x^3)^{1/3}} dx.$

69. Evaluate $\int \frac{(x + \sqrt{1 + x^2})^{15}}{\sqrt{1 + x^2}} dx.$

70. If $y^2 = ax^2 + 2bx + c$, and $u_n = \int \frac{x^n}{y} dx$, prove that $(n+1) a u_{n+1} + (2n+1) bu_n + {}^n c \, y_{n-1} = x^n y$ and deduce that $au_1 = y - b u_0$; $2a^2 u_2 = y(ax - 3b) - (ac - 3b^2) u_0$.

Indefinite Integrals Exercise 8 : Questions Asked in Previous 10 Years' Exams

(i) JEE Advanced & IIT-JEE

71. $\int \frac{\sec^2 x}{(\sec x + \tan x)^{9/2}} dx$ equals to (for some arbitrary constant K) **[Only One Correct Option 2012]**

(a) $\frac{-1}{(\sec x + \tan x)^{11/2}}\left\{\frac{1}{11} - \frac{1}{7}(\sec x + \tan x)^2\right\} + K$

(b) $\frac{1}{(\sec x + \tan x)^{11/2}}\left\{\frac{1}{11} - \frac{1}{7}(\sec x + \tan x)^2\right\} + K$

(c) $\frac{-1}{(\sec x + \tan x)^{11/2}}\left\{\frac{1}{11} + \frac{1}{7}(\sec x + \tan x)^2\right\} + K$

(d) $\frac{1}{(\sec x + \tan x)^{11/2}}\left\{\frac{1}{11} + \frac{1}{7}(\sec x + \tan x)^2\right\} + K$

72. If $I = \int \frac{e^x}{e^{4x} + e^{2x} + 1} dx$, $J = \int \frac{e^{-x}}{e^{-4x} + e^{-2x} + 1} dx$. Then, for an arbitrary constant c, the value of $J - I$ equals **[Only One Correct Option 2008]**

(a) $\frac{1}{2}\log\left|\frac{e^{4x} - e^{2x} + 1}{e^{4x} + e^{2x} + 1}\right| + C$ (b) $\frac{1}{2}\log\left|\frac{e^{2x} + e^x + 1}{e^{2x} - e^x + 1}\right| + C$

(c) $\frac{1}{2}\log\left|\frac{e^{2x} - e^x + 1}{e^{2x} + e^x + 1}\right| + C$ (d) $\frac{1}{2}\log\left|\frac{e^{4x} + e^{2x} + 1}{e^{4x} - e^{2x} + 1}\right| + C$

(ii) JEE Main & AIEEE

73. The integral $\int \frac{2x^{12} + 5x^9}{(x^5 + x^3 + 1)^3} dx$ is equal to **[2016 JEE Main]**

(a) $\frac{-x^5}{(x^5 + x^3 + 1)^2} + C$ (b) $\frac{x^{10}}{2(x^5 + x^3 + 1)^2} + C$

(c) $\frac{x^5}{2(x^5 + x^3 + 1)^2} + C$ (d) $\frac{-x^{10}}{2(x^5 + x^3 + 1)^2} + C$

where, C is an arbitrary constant.

74. The integral $\int \frac{dx}{x^2(x^4 + 1)^{\frac{3}{4}}}$ equals **[2015 JEE Main]**

(a) $\left(\frac{x^4 + 1}{x^4}\right)^{\frac{1}{4}} + C$ (b) $(x^4 + 1)^{\frac{1}{4}} + C$

(c) $-(x^4 + 1)^{\frac{1}{4}} + C$ (d) $-\left(\frac{x^4 + 1}{x^4}\right)^{\frac{1}{4}} + C$

75. The integral $\int \left(1 + x - \frac{1}{x}\right) e^{x + \frac{1}{x}} dx$ is equal to **[2014 JEE Main]**

(a) $(x - 1) e^{x + \frac{1}{x}} + C$ (b) $x e^{x + \frac{1}{x}} + C$

(c) $(x + 1) e^{x + \frac{1}{x}} + C$ (d) $-x e^{x + \frac{1}{x}} + C$

76. If $\int f(x)\,dx = \psi(x)$, then $\int x^5 f(x^3)\,dx$ is equal to **[2013 JEE Main]**

(a) $\frac{1}{3}[x^3\psi(x^3) - \int x^2\psi(x^3)dx] + C$

(b) $\frac{1}{3}x^3\psi(x^3) - 3\int x^3\psi(x^3)\,dx + C$

(c) $\frac{1}{3}x^3\psi(x^3) - \int x^2\psi(x^3)\,dx + C$

(d) $\frac{1}{3}[x^3\psi(x^3) - \int x^3\psi(x^3)\,dx] + C$

77. If the integral $\int \frac{5 \tan x}{\tan x - 2} dx = x + a \log |\sin x - 2\cos x| + k$, then a is equal to **[2012 AIEEE]**

(a) -1 (b) -2

(c) 1 (d) 2

78. The value of $\sqrt{2}\int \frac{\sin x\,dx}{\sin\left(x - \frac{\pi}{4}\right)}$ is **[2012 AIEEE]**

(a) $x + \log\left|\cos\left(x - \frac{\pi}{4}\right)\right| + C$ (b) $x + \log\left|\sin\left(x - \frac{\pi}{4}\right)\right| + C$

(c) $x - \log\left|\sin\left(x - \frac{\pi}{4}\right)\right| + C$ (d) $x - \log\left|\cos\left(x - \frac{\pi}{4}\right)\right| + C$

Answers

Exercise for Session 1

1. $\frac{2}{3}(x+1)^{3/2}+\frac{2}{3}x^{3/2}+c$
2. $-\frac{2}{x}+\frac{2}{3x^3}-\frac{3}{5x^5}-2\tan^{-1}x+c$
3. $\log x+2\tan^{-1}x+c$
4. $\frac{x^3}{3}-x+\tan^{-1}x+c$
5. $\frac{1}{2}\left(\frac{x^3}{3}+\tan^{-1}x\right)+c$
6. $\tan x-\tan^{-1}x+c$
7. $\frac{1}{b^3}\left\{bx-2a\log|bx+a|-\frac{a^2}{a+bx}\right\}+c$
8. $\frac{2^x e^x}{1+\log_e 2}+c$
9. $\frac{e^{4x}}{4}+c$
10. $\frac{x^{a+1}}{a+1}+\frac{a^x}{\log a}+c$
11. $-\frac{1}{8}\cos 4x+C$
12. $\frac{1}{3}\ln|\sec 3x|-\frac{1}{2}\ln|\sec 2x|-\ln|\sec x|+e$
13. $\frac{2}{3}\sin 3x+2\sin x+C$
14. $\frac{3}{4}\sin x+\frac{1}{12}\sin 3x+C$
15. $-\frac{3}{64}\cos 2x+\frac{1}{192}\cos 6x+C$

Exercise for Session 2

1. $\tan x-\sec x+C$
2. $\sin 2x+C$
3. $-\frac{\cos 3x}{3}+C$
4. $\frac{180}{\pi}\sin x^\circ+C$
5. $x+C$
6. $2(\sin x+x\cos\alpha)+C$
7. $\sec x-\operatorname{cosec} x+C$
8. $\tan x-\cot x+C$
9. $(\sin x+\cos x)\sin(\cos x-\sin x)+C$
10. $\tan x-\cot x-3x+C$
11. $-\sqrt{2}\cos\left(\frac{x}{2}\right)+C$
12. $\frac{-\cos 4x}{8}+C$
13. $\frac{1}{2}(x-\sin x)+C$
14. $-2\cos x+C$
15. $\frac{x}{\sqrt{2}}+C$

Exercise for Session 3

1. $\frac{1}{48}\tan^{-1}\left(\frac{3x^4}{4}\right)+C$
2. $\frac{1}{36}\tan^{-1}\left(\frac{4x^3}{3}\right)+C$
3. $\frac{1}{160}\log\left|\frac{4x^4-5}{4x^4+5}\right|+C$
4. $\frac{2}{3}\sin^{-1}\left(\frac{x^{3/2}}{a^{3/2}}\right)+C$
5. $\frac{1}{3}\log|x^3+\sqrt{a^6+x^6}|+C$
6. $\frac{1}{12}\log\left|\frac{2+3e^x}{2-3e^x}\right|+C$
7. $\frac{1}{\log_e 2}\log|2^x+\sqrt{4^x-25}|+C$
8. $-8\sqrt{5+2x-x^2}-3\sin^{-1}\left(\frac{x-1}{\sqrt{6}}\right)+C$
9. $\frac{1}{2}\log|x^2+2x+2|+\tan^{-1}(x+1)+C$
10. $-\sqrt{3-2x-x^2}-4\sin^{-1}\left(\frac{x-1}{\sqrt{6}}\right)+C$
11. $\frac{3}{8}\left\{\log|4x^2-4x+17|+\frac{1}{6}\tan^{-1}\left(\frac{2x-1}{4}\right)+C\right\}$
12. $\frac{1}{2}\sqrt{2x^2+3x}-\frac{3}{4\sqrt{2}}\log\left|x+\frac{3}{4}\sqrt{x^2+\frac{3}{2}x}\right|+C$
13. $\sqrt{a-x(x-b)}-(a-b)\tan^{-1}\sqrt{\frac{a-x}{x-b}}+C$
14. $\sin^{-1}x+\sqrt{1-x^2}+C$
15. $\frac{(2x+5)}{4}\sqrt{x^2+x+1}+\frac{15}{8}\log\left|\left(x+\frac{1}{2}\right)+\sqrt{x^2+x+1}\right|+C$
16. $\log\left|\tan\frac{x}{2}+1\right|+C$
17. $\frac{1}{2}\log\left|\tan\left(\frac{x}{2}+\frac{\pi}{6}\right)\right|+C$
18. $\frac{1}{4}\log|\sin x-\cos x|+\frac{1}{8}\cos 2x+\frac{1}{8}\sin 2x+C$
19. $\sin^{-1}\left(\frac{e^x+2}{3}\right)+C$
20. $-\frac{2}{3}\sin^{-1}(\cos^{3/2}x)+C$
21. $\frac{12}{13}(3\sin x-2\cos x)-\frac{5}{13}\log(3\cos x+2\sin x)+C$
22. $-\frac{2}{3}(4+3x-x^2)^{3/2}-\frac{1}{2}\left[\left(x-\frac{3}{2}\right)\sqrt{4+3x-x^2}+\frac{25}{4}\sin^{-1}\left(\frac{2x-3}{5}\right)\right]+C$
23. $2\sqrt{x^2+x+1}+2\log\left|\left(x+\frac{1}{2}\right)+\sqrt{x^2+x+1}\right|-6\log\left|\frac{1-x+\sqrt{x^2+x+1}}{2(x+1)}\right|+C$
24. (c)

Exercise for Session 4

1. $x^2e^x-2(xe^x-e^x)+C$
2. $-x^2\cos x+2(x\sin x+\cos x)+C$
3. $x(\log x)-x+C$
4. $x(\log x)^2-2(x\log x-x)+C$
5. $x\tan^{-1}x-\frac{1}{2}\log|1+x^2|+C$
6. $x(\sec^{-1}x)-\log|x+\sqrt{x^2-1}|+C$
7. $\frac{x^2}{2}\tan^{-1}-\frac{1}{2}(x-\tan^{-1}x)+C$
8. $-\frac{1}{x}(1+\log x)+C$
9. $-x\cot\frac{x}{2}+C$
10. $x\log(x^2+1)-2x+2\tan^{-1}x+C$
11. $e^x\cdot\log(\sec x)+C$
12. $e^x\tan x+C$
13. $x\log(\log x)-\frac{x}{\log x}+C$
14. $\frac{1}{2}e^{2x}\tan x+C$
15. $\frac{e^x}{x^2+1}+C$
16. $e^x\cdot\sqrt{\frac{1+x}{1-x}}+C$
17. $\frac{e^{ax}}{a^2+b^2}\{a\cos(bx+c)+b\sin(bx+c)\}+C$
18. $\frac{1}{2}\sec x\tan x+\frac{1}{2}\log|sec\, x+\tan x|+C$
19. $-2(-\sqrt{x}\cos\sqrt{x}+\sin\sqrt{x})+C$
20. $x(\sin^{-1}x)^2-2(-\sin^{-1}x\cdot\sqrt{1-x^2}+x)+C$
21. $x\tan^{-1}x-\frac{1}{2}\log(1+x^2)-(1-x)\tan^{-1}(1-x)+\frac{1}{2}\log\{1+(1+x^2)\}+C$
22. $a\left\{\frac{x}{a}\tan^{-1}\sqrt{\frac{x}{a}}-\sqrt{\frac{x}{a}}+\tan^{-1}\sqrt{\frac{x}{a}}\right\}+C$
23. $-\frac{1}{3}\left(1+\frac{1}{x^2}\right)^{3/2}\cdot\log\left(1+\frac{1}{x^2}\right)+\frac{2}{9}\left(1+\frac{1}{x^2}\right)^{3/2}+C$
24. $\frac{\cos x}{2\cos x-\sin x}-\frac{x}{5}-\frac{2}{5}\log|2\cos x-\sin x|+C$
25. $e^{\sin x}(x-\sec x)+C$

Exercise for Session 5

1. $\frac{1}{2}\log|x-1|-4\log|x-2|+\frac{9}{2}\log|x-3|+C$
2. $\frac{1}{3}\log|1+x|-\frac{1}{6}\log|1-x+x^2|+\frac{1}{\sqrt{3}}\tan^{-1}\left(\frac{2x-1}{\sqrt{3}}\right)+C.$
3. $\frac{1}{n}\log\left|\frac{x^n}{x^n+1}\right|+C$
4. $\frac{1}{2}\log\left|\frac{x^2+1}{x^2+3}\right|+C$
5. $\log\left|\frac{1+\sin x}{2+\sin x}\right|+C$
6. $\frac{1}{10}\log|1-\cos x|-\frac{1}{2}\log|1+\cos x|+\frac{2}{5}\log|3+2\cos x|+C$
7. $\frac{1}{4}\log\left|\frac{1+\sin x}{1-\sin x}\right|+\frac{1}{2(1+\sin x)}+C$
8. $-\frac{1}{3}\log|1+\tan x|+\frac{1}{6}\log|\tan^2 x-\tan x+1|$ $+\frac{1}{\sqrt{3}}\tan^{-1}\left(\frac{2\tan x-1}{\sqrt{3}}\right)+C$
9. $\log\left|\frac{2\log x+1}{3\log x+2}\right|+C$
10. $-\frac{\tan^{-1}x}{x}+\log|x|-\frac{1}{2}\log|1+x^2|+C$

Exercise for Session 6

1. $\sqrt{\frac{x^4+x^2+1}{x^2}}+C,$
2. $\frac{2}{\sqrt{3}}\tan^{-1}\left(\frac{x}{\sqrt{3}\sqrt{x+1}}\right)+C.$
3. $2t^3-3t^2+6t-6\log|1+t|+C$, where, $t=(x+1)^{1/6}$.
4. $\frac{7}{(a+b)}\left(\frac{x-b}{x+a}\right)^{1/7}+C.$
5. $\sqrt{2}\sec A\left(\sqrt{\tan x\sin A+\cos A}\right)+C$
6. (a)
7. (d)
8. (c)
9. (d)
10. (c)

Chapter Exercises

1. (b) **2.** (a) **3.** (b) **4.** (c) **5.** (b) **6.** (b)
7. (b) **8.** (d) **9.** (b) **10.** (d) **11.** (a) **12.** (a)
13. (c) **14.** (b) **15.** (a) **16.** (c) **17.** (b) **18.** (b)
19. (b) **20.** (d) **21.** (a,c) **22.** (a, d) **23.** (a, c) **24.** (b,c,d)
25. (a, b) **26.** (c) **27.** (c) **28.** (a) **29.** (d) **30.** (d)
31. (a) **32.** (d) **33.** (c) **34.** (a) **35.** (a) **36.** (b)
37. (b) **38.** (d) **39.** (c) **40.** (c) **41.** (a)
42. A → q; B → r; C → p; D → r
43. A → p, q; B → p, r; C → r; D → q **44.** (5) **45.** (6)
46. (1) **47.** (1) **48.** (3) **49.** (1) **50.** (4) **51.** (4)
52. (3) **53.** (3) **54.** (3) **55.** (1)

56. $e^{(x\sin x+\cos x)}\cdot\left[\left(x-\frac{1}{x\cos x}\right)\right]+C$

57. $\frac{1}{3}(x+\sqrt{x^2+2})^{3/2}-2\frac{1}{\sqrt{x+\sqrt{x^2+2}}}+C$

58. $\tan\frac{\theta}{2}=t$

59. $2(1+x^{1/3})^{3/2}+C$

60. $\tan^{-1}(\cos\theta+\sec\theta+1)^{1/2}+C$

61. $-\frac{2}{3}\log\left|\frac{\sqrt{\cos\theta+\sec\theta+1}-\sqrt{3}}{\sqrt{\cos\theta+\sec\theta+1}+\sqrt{3}}\right|+C$

62. $-\frac{1}{8}x^6(1-x^3)^{2/3}-\frac{3}{20}x^3(1-x^3)^{2/3}-\frac{9}{40}(1-x^3)^{2/3}+C$

63. $-\cot x\log(\cos x+\sqrt{\cos 2x})-\cot x-x+\sqrt{\cot^2 x-1}+C$

64. $\frac{1}{(4a^2-1)^{3/2}}\left\{2a\sin^{-1}\left(\frac{2a\sin 2x+1}{2a+\sin 2x}\right)+\sqrt{1-\left(\frac{2a\sin 2x+1}{2a+\sin 2x}\right)}\right\}$ $-\frac{1}{(2a+\sin 2x)}+C$

65. $2\ln|\sqrt{x^2+2x+4}-x|-\frac{3\log}{2(\sqrt{x^2+2x+4}-(x+1))}$ $-\frac{3}{2}\ln\sqrt{x^2+2x+4}-x-1+C$

66. $\log(x+1+\sqrt{x^2+2x+2})+\frac{2}{(x+2)+\sqrt{(x^2+2x+2)}}+C$

67. $\tan^{-1}\left(x-\frac{1}{x}\right)-\frac{2}{3}\tan^{-1}(x^3)+C$

68. $\frac{1}{3}\log\left|\frac{(1-x^3)^{1/3}+x}{x}\right|-\frac{1}{6}\log\left|\frac{(1-x^3)^{2/3}-x(1-x^3)^{1/3}+x^2}{x^2}\right|$ $-\frac{1}{\sqrt{3}}\tan^{-1}\left\{\frac{2(1-x^3)}{\sqrt{3x}}-x\right\}^{1/3}+C$

69. $\frac{(x+\sqrt{1+x^2})^{15}}{15}+C$

71. (c) 72. (c) 73. (b)
74. (d) 75. (b) 76. (c) 77. (d) 78. (b)

Solutions

1. Let $I = \sqrt{\dfrac{x^2}{(1+x^2)1+(1+x^2)}dx}$

Put $x = \tan\theta \Rightarrow dx = \sec^2 d\theta$

Putting, $x = \tan\theta$, $I = \int \dfrac{\tan^2\theta}{1+\sec\theta}\,d\theta$

$$= \int (\sec\theta - 1)\,d\theta$$

$$= \log(\sec\theta + \tan\theta) - \theta + C$$

$$f(x) = \log_e(x + \sqrt{x^2+1}) - \tan^{-1}x + C$$

$$f(0) = 0 \Rightarrow C = 0$$

$\Rightarrow$ $f(1) = \log_e(1+\sqrt{2}) - \tan^{-1}1$

$$= \log_e(1+\sqrt{2}) - \frac{\pi}{4}$$

2. We have, $\int f(x)\,dx = f(x)$

$\Rightarrow$ $\dfrac{d}{dx}\{f(x)\} = f(x)$ $\Rightarrow$ $\dfrac{1}{f(x)}\,d\{f(x)\} = dx$

$\Rightarrow$ $\log\{f(x)\} = x + \log C \Rightarrow f(x) = Ce^x$

$\Rightarrow$ $\{f(x)\}^2 = C^2e^{2x}$

$\Rightarrow$ $\int \{f(x)\}^2\,dx = \int C^2e^{2x}\,dx = \dfrac{C^2e^{2x}}{2} = \dfrac{1}{2}\{f(x)\}^2$

3. We have, $\int f(x)\,dx = F(x)$

$\therefore$ $\int x^3 f(x^2)\,dx = \dfrac{1}{2}\int \underbrace{x^2}_{\text{I}}\ \underbrace{f(x^2)\,d(x^2)}_{\text{II}}$

$$= \frac{1}{2}\left[x^2F(x^2) - \int F(x^2)\,d(x^2)\right]$$

4. We have the following cases :

***Case* I** When $x \ge 0$

In this case, we have

$$\int |x^n|\,dx = \int |x|^n\,dx = \int x^n\,dx \qquad [\because |x| = x]$$

$$= \frac{x^{n+1}}{n+1} + C = \frac{|x|^n\,x}{n+1} + C \qquad [\because x \ge 0 \Rightarrow |x| = x]$$

***Case* II** When $x \le 0$

In this case, we have $|x| = -x$

$\therefore$ $\int |x^n|\,dx = \int |x|^n\,dx$

$$= \int (-x)^n\,dx = -\int x^n\,dx \qquad [\because n \text{ in odd}]$$

$$= -\frac{x^{n+1}}{n+1} + C = \frac{(-x)^n x}{n+1} + C = \frac{|x|^n\,x}{n+1} + C$$

Hence, $\int |x^n|\,dx = \dfrac{|x|^n\,x}{n+1} + C$

5. $F(x) = \int \dfrac{3x+2}{\sqrt{x-9}}\,dx$. Let $x - 9 = t^2$

$\Rightarrow$ $dx = 2t\,dt$

$\therefore$ $F(x) = \int \left(\dfrac{3(t^2+9)+2}{t}\cdot 2t\right)dt$

$$= 2\int (29 + 3t^2)\,dt = 2[29t + t^3]$$

$$F(x) = 2[29\sqrt{x-9} + (x-9)^{3/2}] + C$$

Given, $F(10) = 60 = 2[29+1] + C \Rightarrow C = 0$

$\therefore$ $F(x) = 2[29\sqrt{x-9} + (x-9)^{3/2}]$

$$F(13) = 2[29 \times 2 + 4 \times 2] = 132$$

6. We have, $\int (x^x)^x (2x\log_e x + x)\,dx$

$$= \int x^{x^2}(2x\log_e x + x)\,dx$$

$$= \int 1 \cdot d(x^{x^2}) = x^{x^2} + C = (x^x)^x + C$$

7. We have, $\int x\log x(\log x - 1)\,dx$

$$= \int \log x(x\log x - x)\,dx$$

$$= \int (x\log x - x)\,d(x\log x - x)$$

$$= \frac{(x\log x - x)^2}{2} + C$$

8. $\displaystyle\int \frac{\left(\dfrac{1}{x^3} - \dfrac{1}{x^5}\right)dx}{\sqrt{2 - \dfrac{2}{x^2} + \dfrac{1}{x^4}}}$

Let $2 - \dfrac{2}{x^2} + \dfrac{1}{x^4} = z \Rightarrow \dfrac{1}{4}\int \dfrac{dz}{\sqrt{z}}$

$\Rightarrow$ $\dfrac{1}{2}\sqrt{z} + C \Rightarrow \dfrac{1}{2}\sqrt{2 - \dfrac{2}{x^2} + \dfrac{1}{x^4}} + C$

or $\sqrt{\dfrac{2x^4 - 2x^2 + 1}{2x^2}} + C$

9. We have, $f''(x) = f(x)$

$\Rightarrow$ $2f'(x)\,f''(x) = 2f(x)\,f'(x)$

$\Rightarrow$ $\dfrac{d}{dx}\{f'(x)\}^2 = \dfrac{d}{dx}\{f(x)\}^2$

$\Rightarrow$ $\{f'(x)\}^2 = \{f(x)\}^2 + C$ ...(i)

Now, $f(0) = 2$ and $f'(0) = 3$. Therefore, from Eq. (i), we get

$$\{f'(0)\}^2 = \{f(0)\}^2 + C$$

$\Rightarrow$ $9 = 4 + C \Rightarrow C = 5$

$\therefore$ $\{f'(x)\}^2 = \{f(x)\}^2 + 5$

$\Rightarrow$ $f'(x) = \sqrt{5 + \{f(x)\}^2}$

$\Rightarrow$ $\int \dfrac{1}{\sqrt{(\sqrt{5})^2 + \{f(x)\}^2}}\,d\{f(x)\} = \int dx$

$\Rightarrow$ $\log\left|f(x) + \sqrt{5 + \{f(x)\}^2}\right| = x + C_1$

$\therefore \quad f(0) = 2 \Rightarrow \log|2+3| = C_1$

$\Rightarrow \quad C_1 = \log 5$

$\therefore \quad \log|f(x) + \sqrt{5 + \{f(x)\}^2}| = x + \log 5$

$\Rightarrow \log\left\{\dfrac{f(x) + \sqrt{5 + \{f(x)\}^2}}{5}\right\} = x$

$\Rightarrow f(x) + \sqrt{5 + \{f(x)\}^2} = 5e^x$

$\Rightarrow \sqrt{5 + \{f(x)\}^2} + f(x) = 5e^x$ and $\sqrt{5 + \{f(x)\}^2} - f(x) = 5e^{-x}$

$\Rightarrow \quad 2f(x) = 5(e^x - e^{-x})$

$\Rightarrow \quad f(x) = \dfrac{5}{2}(e^x - e^{-x})$

$\Rightarrow \quad f(4) = \dfrac{5}{2}(e^4 - e^{-4}) \Rightarrow f(4) = \dfrac{5(e^8 - 1)}{2e^4}$

10. We have, $\displaystyle\int \frac{e^{x^2 + 4\ln x} - x^3 e^{x^2}}{x-1}\,dx = \int \frac{e^{x^2}\cdot x^4 - x^3 e^{x^2}}{x-1}\,dx$

$$= \int x^3 e^{x^2}\,dx = \frac{1}{2}\int te^t\,dt, \text{ [where } t = x^2]$$

$$= \frac{1}{2}(t-1)e^t + C = \frac{1}{2}(x^2 - 1)e^{x^2} + C$$

11. $\displaystyle\int \tan^4 x\,dx = \int (\tan^2 x \sec^2 x - \sec^2 x + 1)\,dx$

$$= \frac{\tan^3 x}{3} - \tan x + x + C$$

$\Rightarrow \quad A = \dfrac{1}{3}, B = -1$ and $f(x) = x + C$

12. $\displaystyle\int \frac{\sin^4 x}{x}\,dx = f(x) \Rightarrow \int \frac{\sin^4 (p+q)x}{(p+q)x}\,dx = \frac{f\{(p+q)x\}}{p+q}$

$\displaystyle\int \frac{\sin^4 (p+q)x}{x}\,dx = f\{(p+q)x\}$

13. On solving, $\dfrac{\sin\theta}{\cos 3\theta} = \dfrac{1}{2}[\tan 3\theta - \tan\theta]$

$$\frac{\sin 3\theta}{\cos 9\theta} = \frac{1}{2}[\tan 9\theta - \tan 3\theta]$$

$$\frac{\sin 9\theta}{\cos 27\theta} = \frac{1}{2}[\tan 27\theta - \tan 9\theta]$$

$$\therefore \int\left(\frac{\sin\theta}{\cos 3\theta} + \frac{\sin 3\theta}{\cos 9\theta} + \frac{\sin 9\theta}{\cos 27\theta}\right)d\theta = \frac{1}{2}\int (\tan 27\theta - \tan\theta)\,d\theta$$

$$= \frac{1}{2}\left\{\frac{1}{27}\log(\sec 27\theta) - \log(\sec\theta)\right\} + C$$

$$= \frac{1}{2}\log\frac{\sqrt[27]{\sec 27\theta}}{\sec\theta} + C$$

14. We have, $\displaystyle\int x\sqrt{\frac{2\sin(x^2+1) - \sin 2(x^2+1)}{2\sin(x^2+1) + \sin 2(x^2+1)}}\,dx$

$$= \int x\sqrt{\frac{2\sin(x^2+1) - 2\sin(x^2+1)\cos(x^2+1)}{2\sin(x^2+1) + 2\sin(x^2+1)\cos(x^2+1)}}\,dx$$

$$= \int x\sqrt{\frac{1 - \cos(x^2+1)}{1 + \cos(x^2+1)}}\,dx = \int x\tan\left(\frac{x^2+1}{2}\right)dx$$

$$= \int \tan\left(\frac{x^2+1}{2}\right)d\left(\frac{x^2+1}{2}\right) = \log\left|\sec\left(\frac{x^2+1}{2}\right)\right| + C$$

15. $\displaystyle\int \frac{\sin(4x - 2x)\,dx}{\sin(2x)\cos(2x)\cos(4x)} = \int \frac{\sin(4x)\,dx}{\sin(2x)\cos(4x)} - \int \sec 2x\,dx$

$$= 2\int \frac{\cos 2x\,dx}{\cos 4x} - \frac{1}{2}(\log|\sec 2x - \tan 2x|)$$

$$= 2\int \frac{\cos 2x}{(1 - 2\sin^2 2x)}\,dx - \frac{1}{2}(\log|\sec 2x - \tan 2x|)$$

$$= \frac{2}{2\sqrt{2}}\left[\frac{1}{2\times 1}\log\left|\frac{1 + \sqrt{2}\sin 2x}{1 - \sqrt{2}\sin 2x}\right|\right] - \frac{1}{2}\log|\sec 2x - \tan 2x| + C$$

$$= \frac{1}{2\sqrt{2}}\left[\log\left|\frac{1 + \sqrt{2}\sin 2x}{1 - \sqrt{2}\sin 2x}\right|\right] - \frac{1}{2}\log|\sec 2x - \tan 2x| + C$$

16. $\displaystyle\int \frac{1 - 7\cos^2 x}{\sin^7 x\cos^2 x}\,dx = \int\left(\frac{\sec^2 x}{\sin^7 x} - \frac{7}{\sin^7 x}\right)dx$

$$= \int \frac{\sec^2 x}{\sin^7 x}\,dx - \int \frac{7}{\sin^7 x}\,dx = I_1 + I_2$$

Now, $\displaystyle I_1 = \int \frac{\sec^2 x}{\sin^7 x}\,dx = \frac{\tan x}{\sin^7 x} + 7\int \frac{\tan x\cdot\cos x}{\sin^8 x}\,dx$

$$= \frac{\tan x}{\sin^7 x} + I_2$$

$\therefore \quad I_1 + I_2 = \dfrac{\tan x}{\sin^7 x} + C \quad \Rightarrow f(x) = \tan x$

17. We have, $\displaystyle\int \frac{\sin^3 x}{(\cos^4 x + 3\cos^2 x + 1)\tan^{-1}(\sec x + \cos x)}\,dx$

$$= \int \frac{\dfrac{\sin^3 x}{\cos^2 x}}{(\cos^2 x + 3 + \sec^2 x)\tan^{-1}(\sec x + \tan x)}\,dx$$

$$= \int \frac{1}{1 + (\sec x + \cos x)^2} \times \frac{\sin x(1 - \cos^2 x)}{\cos^2 x} \times \frac{1}{\tan^{-1}(\sec x + \tan x)}\,dx$$

$$= \int \frac{1}{\tan^{-1}(\sec x + \cos x)} \times \frac{1}{1 + (\sec x + \cos x)^2}(\tan x\sec x - \sin x)\,dx$$

$$= \int \frac{1}{\tan^{-1}(\sec x + \cos x)}\,d\,|\tan^{-1}(\sec x + \cos x)|$$

$$= \log_e|\tan^{-1}(\sec x + \cos x)| + C$$

18. We have, $\quad f(x) = x|\cos x|, \dfrac{\pi}{2} < x < \pi$

$\Rightarrow \quad f(x) = -x\cos x \quad [\because \cos x < 0 \text{ for } x \in (\pi/2, \pi)]$

Hence, required primitive is given by

$$\int f(x)\,dx = -\int x\cos x\,dx + C = -x\sin x - \cos x + C$$

19. We have, $f(x) = (2x+1)|\sin x|, \pi < x < 2\pi$

$\Rightarrow \quad f(x) = -(2x+1)\sin x$

Hence, required primitive is given by

$$-\int \underset{\text{I}}{(2x+1)} \underset{\text{II}}{\sin x}\, dx = -[-(2x+1)\cos x + 2\sin x] + C$$

$$= (2x+1)\cos x - 2\sin x + C$$

20. We have, $f(x) = \begin{vmatrix} 0 & x^2 - \sin x & \cos x - 2 \\ \sin x - x^2 & 0 & 1-2x \\ 2-\cos x & 2x-1 & 0 \end{vmatrix}$

$$\Rightarrow \quad f(x) = \begin{vmatrix} 0 & \sin x - x^2 & 2-\cos x \\ x^2 - \sin x & 0 & 2x-1 \\ \cos x - 2 & 1-2x & 0 \end{vmatrix}$$

[Interchanging rows and columns]

$$\Rightarrow \quad f(x) = (-1)^3 \begin{vmatrix} 0 & x^2 - \sin x & \cos x - 2 \\ \sin x - x^2 & 0 & 1-2x \\ 2-\cos x & 2x-1 & 0 \end{vmatrix}$$

[Taking (-1) common from each column]

$\Rightarrow \quad f(x) = -f(x)$

$\Rightarrow \quad f(x) = 0$

$\Rightarrow \quad \int f(x)\,dx = 0$

21. $\displaystyle\int \frac{dx}{(x+1)(x-2)} = \int \left(-\frac{1}{3(x+1)} + \frac{1}{3(x-2)}\right) dx$

$$= -\frac{1}{3}\log(x+1) + \frac{1}{3}\log(x-2) + C$$

$\therefore \quad A = -\frac{1}{3}, B = \frac{1}{3}$

$\therefore \quad A + B = 0 \Rightarrow \dfrac{A}{B} = \dfrac{-\frac{1}{3}}{\frac{1}{3}} = -1$

22. $\displaystyle\frac{1}{3}\int\left(\frac{1}{x^2+1} - \frac{1}{x^2+4}\right) dx$

$\Rightarrow \quad \frac{1}{3}\tan^{-1} x - \frac{1}{6}\tan^{-1}\frac{x}{2} = k\tan^{-1} x + l\tan^{-1}\frac{x}{2}$

$\therefore \quad k = \frac{1}{3}$ and $l = -\frac{1}{6}$

23. $\displaystyle I = \int \underset{\text{I}}{x} \underbrace{\log(1+x^2)}_{\text{II}}\, dx = \log(1+x^2)\cdot\frac{x^2}{2} - \int \frac{1}{1+x^2}\cdot 2x\cdot\frac{x^2}{2}\,dx$

$$= \frac{x^2}{2}\log(1+x^2) - \int \frac{x^3}{x^2+1}\,dx$$

$$I = \left(\frac{x^2+1}{2}\right)\log(1+x^2) - \left(\frac{x^2+1}{2}\right) + C$$

$\therefore \quad \phi(x) = \dfrac{x^2+1}{2}, \psi(x) = -\left(\dfrac{1+x^2}{2}\right)$

24. $\displaystyle I = \int \frac{4e^2 + 6^{-x}}{9e^x - 4e^{-x}}\,dx$

$\displaystyle I = \int \frac{4e^{2x}+6}{9e^{2x}-4}\,dx$, put $9e^{2x} - 4 = z \Rightarrow 18e^{2x}dx = dz$

Then, $\displaystyle I = \int \frac{1}{z}\left\{4\cdot\frac{z+4}{9} + 6\right\}\frac{1}{18}\frac{dz}{\frac{z+4}{9}}$

$$= \int \frac{1}{z(z+4)}\left\{\frac{2z+8}{9} + 3\right\} dz$$

$$= \frac{1}{9}\int \frac{2z+35}{z(z+4)}\,dz = \frac{1}{9}\int \frac{2(z+4)+27}{z(z+4)}\,dz$$

$$= \frac{2}{9}\int \frac{dz}{z} + \frac{3}{4}\int\left(\frac{1}{z} - \frac{1}{z+4}\right) dz$$

$$= \left(\frac{2}{9} + \frac{3}{4}\right)\log z - \frac{3}{4}\log(z+4) + C$$

$$= \frac{35}{36}\log(9e^{2x} - 4) = \frac{3}{4}\log(e^{2x}) + C$$

$$= -\frac{3}{2}x + \frac{35}{36}\log(9e^{2x} - 4) - \frac{3}{2}\log 3 + C$$

25. $\int \tan^3 x(\sec^2 x - 1)\,dx = \int \tan^3 x\sec^2 x\,dx - \int \tan^3 x\,dx$

$$I_1 = \int \tan^3 x\sec^2 x\,dx = \frac{\tan^4 x}{4} + C_1$$

$$I_2 = \int \tan x(\sec^2 x - 1)\,dx$$

$$= \frac{\tan^2 x}{2} - \ln|\sec x| + C_2$$

26. The Statement II is false since while writing

$$\int \frac{dx}{x-3y} = \log(x-3y) + C,$$

we are assuming that y is a constant. We will know prove the Statement I. From the given relation $(x-y)^2 = \dfrac{x}{y}$ and

$$2\log(x-y) = \log x - \log y.$$

Also, $\dfrac{dy}{dx} = \left(-\dfrac{y}{x}\right)\cdot\dfrac{x+y}{x-3y}$. To prove the integral relation it is sufficient to show that $\dfrac{d}{dx}$ RHS $= \dfrac{1}{x-3y}$.

Now, $\quad$ RHS $= \dfrac{1}{2}\log\left[\dfrac{x}{y} - 1\right] \qquad \left[\because (x-y)^2 = \dfrac{x}{y}\right]$

$$= \frac{1}{2}[\log(x-y) - \log y]$$

$$= \frac{1}{2}\left[\frac{\log x - \log y}{2} - \log y\right] = \frac{1}{4}[\log x - 3\log y]$$

$$\Rightarrow \quad \frac{d}{dx}\text{RHS} = \frac{1}{4}\left[\frac{1}{x} - \frac{3}{y}\frac{dy}{dx}\right]$$

$$= \frac{1}{4}\left[\frac{1}{x} - \frac{3}{y}\left(-\frac{y}{x}\right)\frac{x+y}{x-3y}\right] = \frac{1}{x-3y}$$

Thus, Statement I is true. Hence, choice (c) is correct.

27. Let $g(x) = f(x) + f(-x)$

Assuming, $\quad \int f(x)\,dx = F(x) + C$

$$\int g(x)\,dx = \int \{f(x) + f(-x)\}\,dx$$
$$= \int f(x)\,dx + \int f(-x)\,dx$$
$$= F(x) + C + \{-F(-x) + C'\}$$
$$= F(x) - F(-x) + C + C'$$

which may be an odd function, if $C + C' = 0$.

Similarly, integral of an odd function is not always an even function.

Hence, Statement I is true and Statement II is false.

28. If $a > 0$ and $b^2 - 4ac < 0$, then

$$ax^2 + bx + c = a\left(x + \frac{b}{2a}\right)^2 + \frac{4ac - b^2}{4a}$$

$$\Rightarrow \int \frac{dx}{ax^2 + bx + c} = \int \frac{dx}{a\left(x + \frac{b}{2a}\right)^2 + k^2}$$

where $k^2 = \dfrac{4ac - b^2}{4a} > 0$. which will have an answer of the type

$$\frac{1}{a}\cdot\frac{1}{k/\sqrt{a}}\tan^{-1}\frac{x + \frac{b}{2a}}{k/\sqrt{a}} + C \text{ or } \mu\tan^{-1}\frac{x + A}{B} + C$$

Thus, choice (a) is correct.

29. $I = \displaystyle\int \frac{dx}{x^4 + 1} \Rightarrow I = \frac{1}{2}\int \frac{\frac{2}{x^2}}{x^2 + \frac{1}{x^2}}\,dx$

$$= \frac{1}{2}\int \frac{\left(1 + \frac{1}{x^2}\right)}{\left(x - \frac{1}{x}\right)^2 + 2}\,dx - \frac{1}{2}\int \frac{\left(1 - \frac{1}{x^2}\right)}{\left(x + \frac{1}{x}\right)^2 - 2}\,dx$$

$$I = \frac{1}{2}\cdot\frac{1}{\sqrt{2}}\tan^{-1}\left(\frac{x - \frac{1}{x}}{2}\right) + \frac{1}{2}\cdot\frac{1}{2}\log\left(\frac{x + \frac{1}{x} - 1}{x + \frac{1}{x} + 1}\right) + C$$

$\therefore$ Statement I is false.

30. Since, $\cot^{-1} x = \dfrac{\pi}{2} - \tan^{-1} x$,

$\therefore \quad d(\cot^{-1} x) = -d(\tan^{-1} x)$

Thus, $\displaystyle\int 2^{\tan^{-1} x}\,d(\cot^{-1} x) = -\int 2^{\tan^{-1} x}\,d(\tan^{-1} x)$

$$= -\frac{2^{\tan^{-1} x}}{\ln 2} + C$$

$\therefore$ Statement I is false. Statement II is true.

31. As $m = 9 > 0$, hence, we can substitute

$$\sqrt{9x^2 + 4x + 6} = u \pm 3x$$

32. Here, as per notations given, we can substitute

$$\sqrt{1 + x^2} = (u - x)$$

As $m = 1 > 0$ and $p = 1 > 0$

$$\Rightarrow \quad I = \int \frac{u^{15}}{u}\,du = \int u^{14}\,du = \frac{1}{15}u^{15} + C$$
$$= \frac{1}{15}(x + \sqrt{1 + x^2})^{15} + C$$

33. Here, $m = -1 < 0$

$p = -2 < 0$

Also, $-x^2 + 3x - 2 = -(x - 1)(x - 2)$

We can use case III

$\Rightarrow$ Putting, $\sqrt{-x^2 + 3x - 2} = u(x - 2)$

or $\quad (x - 1)u$ or $u(1 - x)$

34. Let $P = \sin^3 x \cos^3 x$

$$\frac{dP}{dx} = 3\sin^2 x\cos^4 x - 3\sin^4 x\cos^2 x$$
$$= 3\sin^2 x(1 - \sin^2 x)\cos^2 x - 3\sin^4 x\cos^2 x$$
$$= 3\sin^2 x\cos^2 x - 6\sin^4 x\cos^2 x$$

$\therefore \quad P = 3I_{2,2} - 6I_{4,2}$

$\therefore \quad I_{4,2} = \dfrac{1}{6}(-P + 3I_{2,2})$

35. Let $P = \sin^5 x\cos^3 x$

$$\therefore \quad \frac{dP}{dx} = 5\sin^4 x\cos^4 x - 3\sin^6 x\cos^2 x$$
$$= 5\sin^4 x(1 - \sin^2 x)\cos^2 x - 3\sin^6 x\cos^2 x$$
$$= 5\sin^4 x\cos^2 x - 8\sin^6 x\cos^2 x$$

$\therefore \quad P = 5I_{4,2} - 8I_{6,2}$

$\therefore \quad I_{4,2} = \dfrac{1}{5}(P + 8I_{6,2})$

36. Let $P = \sin^5 x\cos^3 x$

$$\therefore \quad \frac{dP}{dx} = 5\sin^4 x\cos^4 x - 3\sin^6 x\cos^2 x$$
$$= 5\sin^4 x\cos^4 x - 3\sin^4 x(1 - \cos^2 x)\cos^2 x$$
$$= 8\sin^4 x\cos^4 x - 3\sin^4 x\cos^2 x$$

$\therefore \quad P = 8I_{4,4} - 3I_{4,2}$

$\therefore \quad I_{4,2} = \dfrac{1}{3}(-P + 8I_{4,4})$

37. Here, $2f'(x) = \displaystyle\lim_{h \to 0}\left(\frac{f(x + h) - f(x)}{h} + \frac{f(x\ x - h) - f(x)}{-h}\right)$

$$= \lim_{h \to 0}\left(\frac{f(x + h) - f(x - h)}{h}\right) \quad \text{...(i)}$$

$$\therefore \quad 2f'(0)\lim_{h \to 0}\left(\frac{f(h) - f(0)}{h} + \frac{f(-h) - f(0)}{-h}\right)$$

$$= \lim_{h \to 0}\frac{f(h) - f(-h)}{h} \text{...(ii)}$$

Now by given relation, we have

$$f(h) - f(-h) = \frac{f(x + h) - f(x - h)}{-h} \text{ and } f(0) = 1$$

From Eqs. (i) and (ii), we have $\dfrac{f'(x)}{f(x)} = 2010$

$\Rightarrow \quad f(x) = e^{2010x}, f(0) = 1$

$\therefore$ $\{f(x)\}$ is non-periodic.

38. Here, $\int f(g(x)) \cos x\, dx = \int f(\log(\sin x)) . \cos x\, dx$

$$= \int e^{2010 \log (\sin x)} . \cos x\, dx$$
$$= \int (\sin x)^{2010} . \cos x\, dx$$
$$= \int (\sin x)^{2010} . \cos x\, dx$$
$$= \frac{(\sin x)^{2011}}{2011} + C$$

$\therefore \quad h(x) = \dfrac{(\sin x)^{2011}}{2011}$

$\Rightarrow \quad h\left(\dfrac{\pi}{2}\right) = \dfrac{1}{2011}$

Sol. (Q.Nos. 39 to 41)

Here, $f(x) = (x-1)(x+2)(x-3)(x-6) - 100$

$$= (x^2 - 4x + 3)(x^2 - 4x - 12) - 100$$
$$= (x^2 - 4x)^2 - 9(x^2 - 4x) - 136$$
$$= (x^2 - 4x + 8)(x^2 - 4x - 17)$$

39. $\therefore f(x) = 0 \Rightarrow \underbrace{(x^2 - 4x + 8)}_{D > 0} \underbrace{(x^2 - 4x + 17}_{D < 0} = 0$

$\therefore$ Equation has two distinct and two imaginary roots.

40. $f(x) = (x^2 - 4x - 17)(x^2 - 4x + 8)$

$$= \{((x-2)^2 - 21\}\{(x-2)^2 + 4\}$$

$\because \quad (f(x))_{\min} = (-21)(4) = -84$

which occurs at $x = 2$

41. $\because \quad \int \dfrac{g(x)}{f(x)} = \dfrac{g(x)}{(x^2 - 4x - 17)(x^2 - 4x + 8)}$

$$= \frac{Ax + B}{x^2 - 4x - 17} + \frac{Cx + D}{x^2 - 4x + 8}$$

Clearly, A, B and C must be zero.

$\therefore \quad \dfrac{g(x)}{(x^2 - 4x - 17)(x^2 - 4x + 8)} = \dfrac{D}{x^2 - 4x + 8}$

$\therefore \quad g(x) = D(x^2 - 4x - 17)$

$g(-2) = D(4 + 8 - 17) = -10$ [given]

$\Rightarrow \quad \dfrac{g(x)}{f(x)} = \dfrac{2(x^2 - 4x - 17)}{(x^2 - 4x - 17)(x^2 - 4x + 8)} = \dfrac{2}{x^2 - 4x + 8}$

$\therefore \quad \int \dfrac{g(x)}{f(x)} dx = \int \dfrac{2}{x^2 - 4x + 8} dx = 2\int \dfrac{dx}{(x-2)^2 + (2)^2}$

$$= 2 \cdot \frac{1}{2} \tan^{-1}\left(\frac{x-2}{2}\right) + C = \tan^{-1}\left(\frac{x-2}{2}\right) + C$$

42. (A) If $\dfrac{\pi}{4} < x < \dfrac{3\pi}{8}$, then $\sin x > \cos x$

$\therefore \quad \int \dfrac{\sin x - \cos x}{|\sin x - \cos x|} dx = \int 1\, dx = x + C$

(B) $\int \dfrac{x^2 dx}{(x^3 + 1)(x^3 + 2)} = \dfrac{1}{3} \int 3x^2 \left(\dfrac{1}{x^3 + 1} - \dfrac{1}{x^3 + 2}\right) dx$

$$= \frac{1}{3} \ln\left|\frac{x^3 + 1}{x^3 + 2}\right| + C$$

(C) $\int \sin^{-1} x \cos^{-1} x\, dx = \int \left[\dfrac{\pi}{2} \sin^{-1} x - (\sin^{-1} x)^2\right] dx$

$\Rightarrow \dfrac{\pi}{2}(x \sin^{-1} x + \sqrt{1 - x^2}) - \{x (\sin^{-1} x)^2$

$+ \sin^{-1} x \sqrt{1 - x^2} - x\} + C$ (by parts)

$\Rightarrow \sin^{-1} x \left[\dfrac{\pi}{2} x - x \sin^{-1} x - 2\sqrt{1 - x^2}\right] + \dfrac{\pi}{2} \sqrt{1 - x^2} + 2x + C$

$\therefore \quad f^{-1}(x) = \sin^{-1} x$, $f(x) = \sin x$

(D) $\int \dfrac{dx}{x \ln |x|} = \ln|\ln|x|| + C$

$\therefore \quad f(x) = \ln|x|$

43. (A) $I = \int \left(\dfrac{x^2 + \cos^2 x}{1 + x^2}\right) \cdot \operatorname{cosec}^2 x\, dx$

$$= \int \left(\frac{x^2 + 1 - \sin^2 x}{1 + x^2}\right) \cdot \operatorname{cosec}^2 x\, dx$$
$$= \int \left(\operatorname{cosec}^2 x - \frac{1}{1 + x^2}\right) dx = -\cot x + \cot^{-1} x + k$$

$\Rightarrow \quad A = 1, B = -1$

(B) $I = \int \sqrt{x + \sqrt{x^2 + 2}}\, dx$

Put $\sqrt{x^2 + 2} + x = t \Rightarrow \sqrt{x^2 + 2} - x = \dfrac{2}{t}$

$\therefore \quad 2x = t - \dfrac{2}{t} \Rightarrow 2\, dx = \left(1 + \dfrac{2}{t^2}\right) dt$

$$= \frac{1}{2} \int \left(\sqrt{t} + \frac{2}{t^{3/2}}\right) dt$$

$\Rightarrow \quad I = \dfrac{1}{2} \cdot \dfrac{t^{3/2}}{\frac{3}{2}} + \dfrac{1}{-\frac{1}{2} t^{1/2}} + k$

$$= \frac{1}{3}(x + \sqrt{x^2 + 2})^{3/2} - \frac{2}{\sqrt{x + \sqrt{x^2 + 2}}} + k$$

$\Rightarrow \quad A = 1$ and $B = 2$

(C) $I = \int \dfrac{2 - x - x^2}{x^2 \sqrt{2 - x - x^2}} dx$

$$= -\int \frac{dx}{\sqrt{2 - x - x^2}} + 2\int \frac{dx}{x^2 \sqrt{2 - x - x^2}} - \int \frac{dx}{x\sqrt{2 - x - x^2}}$$

$$= -\int \frac{dx}{\sqrt{\frac{9}{4}-\left(x+\frac{1}{2}\right)^2}} + 2\int -\frac{dt}{\sqrt{2-\frac{1}{t}-\frac{1}{t^2}}} + \int \frac{\frac{1}{t}dt}{\sqrt{2-\frac{1}{t}-\frac{1}{t^2}}}$$

$$\left(\text{put } x = \frac{1}{t}\right)$$

$$= -\sin^{-1}\left(\frac{2x+1}{3}\right) - \frac{1}{2}\int \frac{(4t-1)dt}{\sqrt{2t^2-t-1}} + \frac{1}{2}\int \frac{dt}{\sqrt{2t^2-t-1}}$$

$$= -\sin^{-1}\left(\frac{2x+1}{3}\right) - \frac{1}{2}\frac{\sqrt{2t^2-t-1}}{\frac{1}{2}} + \frac{1}{2\sqrt{2}}\int \frac{dt}{\sqrt{t^2-\frac{t}{2}-\frac{1}{2}+\frac{1}{16}-\frac{1}{16}}}$$

$$= -\sin^{-1}\left(\frac{2x+1}{3}\right) - \frac{\sqrt{2-x-x^2}}{x} + \frac{1}{2\sqrt{2}}\log\left|\left(t-\frac{1}{4}\right)+\sqrt{2t^2-t-1}\right| + K$$

$$= -\frac{\sqrt{2-x-x^2}}{x} + \frac{1}{2\sqrt{2}}\log\left|\frac{(4-x)+\sqrt{2-x-x^2}}{4x}\right| - \sin^{-1}\left(\frac{2x+1}{3}\right) + K$$

(D) $\int \frac{\sin 2x}{\sin^4 x + \cos^4 x}\,dx$, dividing N^r and D^r by $\cos^4 x$

$$I = \int \frac{2\tan x \cdot \sec^2 x}{\tan^4 x + 1}\,dx, \text{ put } \tan^2 x = t$$

$$\Rightarrow 2\tan x \cdot \sec^2 x\,dx = dt = \int \frac{dt}{t^2+1} = -\cot^{-1}(t) + C$$

$$\Rightarrow \; -\cot^{-1}(\tan^2 x) + C \quad \therefore \; B = -1$$

44. $\int \frac{2x+3}{(x^2+3x)(x^2+3x+2)+1}\,dx$

Put $x^2 + 3x = t \Rightarrow (2x+3)\,dx = dt$

$$\int \frac{dt}{t(t+2)+1} = \int \frac{dt}{(t+1)^2} = C - \frac{1}{t+1} = C - \frac{1}{x^2+3x+1}$$

$\Rightarrow \quad a = 1, b = 3, c = 1 \Rightarrow a + b + c = 5$

45. $F(x) = \int \frac{3x+2}{\sqrt{x-9}}\,dx.$

Let $\quad x - 9 = t^2 \Rightarrow dx = 2t\,dt$

$\therefore \quad F(x) = \int \left(\frac{3(t^2+9)+2}{t} \cdot 2t\right) dt$

$$= 2\int (29 + 3t^2)\,dt = 2[29t + t^3]$$

$$F(x) = 2[29\sqrt{x-9} + (x-9)^{3/2}] + C$$

Given, $\quad F(10) = 60 = 2[29+1] + C$

$\Rightarrow \quad C = 0$

$\therefore \quad F(x) = 2[29\sqrt{x-9} + (x-9)^{3/2}]$

$$F(13) = 2[29 \times 2 + 4 \times 2]$$

$$= 4 \times 33 = 132$$

Hence, sum of digits $= 1 + 3 + 2 = 6$

46. $u(x) = 7v(x) \Rightarrow u'(x) = 7v'(x)$

$\Rightarrow \quad p = 7 \quad$ (given)

Again, $\quad \frac{u(x)}{v(x)} = 7 \Rightarrow \left(\frac{u(x)}{v(x)}\right)' = 0$

$\Rightarrow \quad q = 0$

Now, $\quad \frac{p+q}{p-q} = \frac{7+0}{7-0} = 1$

47. Let $t = \ln\left(\frac{x-1}{x+1}\right) \Rightarrow \frac{dt}{dx} = \frac{2}{x^2-1}$

$$I = \int \frac{1}{2}t\,dt = \frac{1}{4}t^2 + C$$

$$I = \frac{1}{4}\left[\ln\left(\frac{x-1}{x+1}\right)\right]^2 + C$$

$\Rightarrow \quad 6A = \frac{1}{4} \Rightarrow 24A = 1$

48. $I = \int e^x \left(\frac{1}{(1-x)\sqrt{1-x^2}} + \sqrt{\frac{1+x}{1-x}}\right) dx$

As $\quad \frac{d}{dx}\left(\sqrt{\frac{1+x}{1-x}}\right) = \frac{1}{(1-x)\sqrt{1-x^2}}$

$\therefore \quad I = e^x\sqrt{\frac{1+x}{1-x}} + C \Rightarrow I = e^x\left(\frac{1+x}{1-x}\right)^{1/2} + C$

$\Rightarrow \quad \mu = 1, \lambda = \frac{1}{2}$

$\Rightarrow \quad 2(\mu + \lambda) = 2\left(1 + \frac{1}{2}\right) = 2 \times \frac{3}{2} = 3$

49. $I = \int \frac{(e^x + \cos x + 1) - (e^x + \sin x + x)}{e^x + \sin x + x}\,dx$

$$= \ln(e^x + \sin x + x) - x + C$$

$\therefore \quad f(x) = e^x + \sin x + x$ and $g(x) = -x$

$\Rightarrow \quad f(x) + g(x) = e^x + \sin x$

$\Rightarrow \quad \frac{f(x)+g(x)}{e^x + \sin x} = 1$

50. $12\left[\frac{1}{4}\tan^{-1}\frac{x+3}{4} + \frac{1}{2\cdot 6}\ln\left|\frac{x-9}{x+3}\right|\right] = 3\tan^{-1}\left(\frac{x+3}{4}\right) + \ln\left|\frac{x-9}{x+3}\right|$

$\Rightarrow \quad \lambda = 3, \mu = 1$

$\Rightarrow \quad \lambda + \mu = 4$

51. $\frac{2\cos\frac{15}{2}x\cos\frac{3}{2}x}{1-2\left(2\cos^2\frac{5x}{2}-1\right)} = \frac{2\left(4\cos^3\frac{5x}{2} - 3\cos\frac{5x}{2}\right)\cos\frac{3x}{2}}{3-4\cos^2\frac{5x}{2}}$

$$= -2\cos\frac{5x}{2}\cos\frac{3x}{2}$$

$$= -(\cos 4x + \cos x)$$

$$I = -\frac{\sin 4x}{4} - \sin x + C$$

52. $I = \int \frac{\tan x}{1 + \tan x + \tan^2 x} dx = \int \frac{\frac{\sin x}{\cos x}}{\frac{1}{\cos^2 x} + \frac{\sin x}{\cos x}} dx$

$= \int \frac{\sin 2x}{2 + \sin 2x} dx = \int dx - 2 \int \frac{dx}{2 + \sin 2x}$

$= x - 2\int \frac{\sec^2 x}{2\sec^2 x + 2\tan x} dx$

Let $t = \tan x, dt = \sec^2 x\, dx$

$= x - \frac{2}{2} \int \frac{dx}{t^2 + t + 1} = x - \int \frac{dt}{\left(t + \frac{1}{2}\right)^2 + \left(\frac{\sqrt{3}}{2}\right)^2}$

$I = x - \frac{1}{\sqrt{3}} \tan^{-1} \left(\frac{2\tan x + 1}{\sqrt{3}}\right) + C$

53. $\int \sin^{5/2} x \cos^3 x\, dx = \int \sin^2 x \sin^{1/2} x \cos^2 x \cos x\, dx$

$= \int \sin^2 x \sin^{1/2} x (1 - \sin^2 x) \cos x\, dx$

$= \int t^2 t^{1/2} (1 - t^2)\, dt = \int [t^{5/2} - t^{9/2}] dt$

$= \int t^{5/2} dt - \int t^{9/2} dt = \frac{t^{7/2}}{7/2} - \frac{t^{11/2}}{11/2} + C$

$= \frac{2}{7} t^{7/2} - \frac{2}{11} t^{11/2} + C = \frac{2}{7} \sin^{7/2} x - \frac{2}{11} \sin^{11/2} x + C$

$= 2 \sin^{7/2} x \left[\frac{1}{7} - \frac{1}{11} \sin^2 x\right] + C$

$\Rightarrow \quad A = 7, B = 7, C = 11$

$\Rightarrow \quad (A + B) - C = (7 + 7) - 11 = 3$

54. Let $I = \int (x^{2010} + x^{804} + x^{402})(2x^{1608} + 5x^{402} + 10)^{1/402} dx$

$= \int x(x^{2009} + x^{508} + x^{401}) \cdot (2x^{1608} + 5x^{402} + 10)^{1/402} dx$

$= \int (x^{2009} + x^{803} + x^{401}) \cdot (2x^{2010} + 5x^{804} + 10^{402})^{1/402} dx$

Put $2x^{2010} + 5x^{804} + 10^{x^{402}} = t$

$\Rightarrow \quad 4020(x^{2009} + x^{803} + x^{401})\, dx = dt$

$\therefore \quad I = \int \frac{1}{4020} \cdot (t)^{1/402} dt = \frac{1}{4020} \cdot \frac{t^{1/420 + 1}}{1/402 + 1}$

$= \frac{1}{4020} \cdot \frac{t^{403/402}}{403/402}$

$= \frac{1}{4030} (2x^{2010} + 5x^{804} + 10^{402})^{403/402}$

$\therefore \; a - 400 = 3$

55. Let $e^{x^3 + x^2 - 1}(3x^4 + 2x^3 + 2x)\, dx$

$= \underset{\text{I}}{\int x^2 \cdot e^{x^3 + x^2 - 1} \cdot (3x^2 + 2x)\, dx} + \underset{\text{II}}{\int e^{x^3 + x^2 - 1} \cdot (2x)\, dx}$

Applying by parts in first internal, we get

$I = x e^{x^3 + x^2 - 1} - \int 2x \cdot e^{x^3 + x^2 - 1} dx + \int e^{x^3 - x^2 - 1} (2x)\, dx$

$= x^2 \cdot e^{x^3 + x^2 - 1} + C = h(x) + C$

$\therefore \quad h(x) = x^2 \cdot e^{x^3 + x^2 - 1}$

$\Rightarrow \quad h(1) \cdot h(-1) = e^1 \cdot e^{-1} = 1$

56. $I = \int e^{(x \sin x + \cos x)} \left\{\frac{x^4 \cos^3 x - x \sin x + \cos x}{x^2 \cos^2 x}\right\} dx$

$= \int e^{(x \sin x + \cos x)} \cdot (x^2 \cos x)\, dx - \int e^{(x \sin x + \cos x)} \cdot \frac{d}{dx}\left(\frac{1}{x \cos x}\right) dx$

$= e^{(x \sin x + \cos x)} \cdot \left(x - \frac{1}{x \cos x}\right) + C$

57. $I = \int \sqrt{x + \sqrt{x^2 + 2}}\, dx$

Let $x + \sqrt{x^2 + 2} = p$ or $x^2 + 2 = p^2 + x^2 - 2px$

$\Rightarrow \quad x = \frac{p^2 - 2}{2p}$ or $dx = \frac{(p^2 + 2)\, dp}{2p^2}$

$I = \int \frac{p^{1/2}(p^2 + 2)}{2p^2} dp = \frac{1}{2} \int p^{1/2} dp + \int p^{-3/2} dp$

$= \frac{1}{3}(x + \sqrt{x^2 + 2})^{3/2} - 2 \frac{1}{\sqrt{x + \sqrt{x^2 + 2}}} + C$

58. $I = \int \frac{dx}{(ax + b)\sqrt{(x - \alpha)^2 - \beta^2}}$

Put $(x - \alpha) = \beta \sec\theta \Rightarrow dx = \beta \sec\theta \tan\theta\, d\theta$

$\therefore \quad I = \int \frac{d\theta}{a(\alpha \cos\theta + \beta) + b\cos\theta}$

$= \int \frac{d\theta}{(a\alpha + b)\cos\theta + a\beta}$

$= \frac{1}{(a\alpha + b)} \int \frac{d\theta}{\cos\theta + \left(\frac{a\beta}{a\alpha + b}\right)}$

if $\left|\frac{a\beta}{a\alpha + b}\right| < 1$ ...(i)

Then, $I = \frac{1}{(a\alpha + b)} \cdot \operatorname{cosec} \alpha^1 \log \left|\frac{\cot\frac{\alpha^1}{2} + 1}{\cot\frac{\alpha^1}{2} - 1}\right| + C$

where $\frac{a\beta}{a\alpha + b} = \cos\alpha^1, \; \tan\frac{\theta}{2} = t$

Again, if $\left|\frac{a\beta}{a\alpha + b}\right| > 1$

$I = \frac{1}{a\alpha + b} \cot\alpha^1 \tan^{-1}\left(t \tan\frac{\alpha^1}{2}\right)$

where $\sec\alpha^1 = \frac{a\beta}{a\alpha + b} \Rightarrow \tan\frac{\theta}{2} = t$

59. $I = \int \frac{\sqrt{1 + \sqrt[3]{x}}}{\sqrt[3]{x^2}} dx = \int x^{-2/3}(1 + x^{1/3})^{1/2} dx,$

$m = -\frac{2}{3}, n = \frac{1}{3}, p = \frac{1}{2}$

$\therefore \quad \frac{m+1}{n} = 1$ ie, integer

$\therefore$ Let us make the substitution,

$$1 + x^{1/3} = t^2 \quad \therefore \quad \frac{1}{3} x^{-2/3}\, dx = 2t\, dt$$

Hence, $\quad I = 6 \int t^2\, dt = 2t^3 + C = 2(1 + x^{1/3})^{3/2} + C$

60. $I = \int \frac{\sin^3 (\theta/2)}{\cos \theta/2 \sqrt{\cos^3 \theta + \cos^2 \theta + \cos \theta}}\, d\theta$

$$= \frac{1}{2} \int \frac{2 \sin \theta/2 \cdot \cos \theta/2 \cdot 2 \sin^2 \theta/2}{2 \cos^2 \theta/2 \sqrt{\cos^3 \theta + \cos^2 \theta + \cos \theta}}\, d\theta$$

$$= \frac{1}{2} \int \frac{\sin \theta\, (1 - \cos \theta)}{(1 + \cos \theta) \sqrt{\cos^3 \theta + \cos^2 \theta + \cos \theta}}\, d\theta$$

Put $\quad \cos \theta = t \Rightarrow -\sin \theta\, d\theta = dt$

$$\therefore \quad I = \frac{1}{2} \int \frac{(t-1)}{(t+1)\sqrt{t^3 + t^2 + t}}\, dt$$

$$= \frac{1}{2} \int \frac{t^2 - 1}{(t+1)^2 \sqrt{t^3 + t^2 + t}}\, dt$$

$$= \frac{1}{2} \int \frac{(1 - 1/t^2)}{(t + \frac{1}{t} + 2)\sqrt{t + 1 + \frac{1}{t}}}\, dt$$

Put $\quad t + 1 + \frac{1}{t} = u^2 \quad \Rightarrow (1 - \frac{1}{t^2})\, dt = 2u du$

$$I = \frac{1}{2} \int \frac{2u\, du}{(u^2 + 1) \cdot u} = \int \frac{du}{u^2 + 1} = \tan^{-1}(u) + C$$

$$= \tan^{-1} \left(t + 1 + \frac{1}{t} \right)^{1/2} + C$$

$$= \tan^{-1} (\cos \theta + \sec \theta + 1)^{1/2} + C$$

61. $I = \int \frac{(2 \sin \theta + \sin 2\theta)\, d\theta}{(\cos \theta - 1)\sqrt{\cos \theta + \cos^2 \theta + \cos^3 \theta}}$

Put $\cos \theta = x^2$

$\Rightarrow \quad -\sin \theta\, d\theta = 2x\, dx$

$$= 2 \int \frac{(1 + x^2)}{(1 - x^2)} \cdot \frac{2x\, dx}{\sqrt{x^2 + x^4 + x^6}}$$

$$= 4 \int \frac{(1 + 1/x^2)\, dx}{(1/x - x)\sqrt{(1/x - x)^2 + 3}},$$

Put $\quad \frac{1}{x} - x = t$

$\Rightarrow \left(-\frac{1}{x^2} - 1 \right) dx = dt$

$$= -4 \int \frac{dt}{t\sqrt{t^2 + 3}}$$

Again, put $\; t^2 + 3 = u^2$

$\Rightarrow \quad 2t\, dt = 2u\, du$

$$\therefore \quad I = 4 \int \frac{-u\, du}{u(u^2 - 3)} = -4 \int \frac{du}{u^2 - 3}$$

$$= -\frac{2}{\sqrt{3}} \log \left| \frac{u - \sqrt{3}}{u + \sqrt{3}} \right| + C$$

$$= -\frac{2}{\sqrt{3}} \log \left| \frac{\sqrt{t^2 + 3} - \sqrt{3}}{\sqrt{t^2 + 3} + \sqrt{3}} \right| + C$$

$$= -\frac{2}{\sqrt{3}} \log \left| \frac{\sqrt{x^2 + 1/x^2 + 1} - \sqrt{3}}{\sqrt{x^2 + 1/x^2 + 1} + \sqrt{3}} \right| + C$$

$$= -\frac{2}{3} \log \left| \frac{\sqrt{\cos \theta + \sec \theta + 1} - \sqrt{3}}{\sqrt{\cos \theta + \sec \theta + 1} + \sqrt{3}} \right| + C$$

62. Let $\quad I_{m-1} = \int x^{m-1} (a + bx^n)^p\, dx$

and $\quad I_{m-n-1} = \int x^{m-n-1} (a + bx^n)^p\, dx$

Let $\quad p = x^{\lambda + 1} (a + bx^n)^{\mu + 1}$

where λ and μ are the smaller indices of x and $(a + bx^n)$.

Here, $\lambda = m - n - 1, \mu = p$

$$\therefore \quad p = x^{m-n} (a + bx^n)^{p+1}$$

Differentiating w.r.t. x, we have

$$\frac{dp}{dx} = x^{m-n} (p+1)(a + bx^n)^p (n\, bx^{n-1}) + (a + bx^n)^{p+1} (m - n)\, x^{m-n-1}$$

$$= nb\,(p+1)\, x^{m-1} (a + bx^n)^p + (m - n)\, x^{m-n-1} (a + bx^n)^p \{a + bx^n\}$$

$$= nb\,(p+1)\, x^{m-1} (a + bx^n)^p + a\,(m-n)\, x^{m-n-1} (a + bx^n)^p + b\,(m-n)\, x^{m-1} (a + bx^n)^p$$

$= b\,(np + m)\, x^{m-1} (a + bx^n)^p + a\,(m - n)\, x^{m-n-1} (a + bx^n)^p$Integrating both the sides w.r.t. x, we get

$$p = b\,(np + m)\, I_{m-1} + a\,(m - n)\, I_{m-n-1}$$

$$\therefore x^{m-n} (a + bx^n)^{p+1} = b\,(np + m)\, I_{m-1} + a\,(m-n)\, I_{m-n-1}$$

or $\quad I_{m-1} = \frac{x^{m-n} (a + bx^n)^{p+1}}{b\,(np + m)} - \frac{a\,(m-n)}{b\,(np+m)} \cdot I_{m-n-1}$

Hence Proved.

Again, $\int \frac{x^8}{(1 - x^3)^{1/3}}\, dx = \int x^{9-1} (1 - x^3)^{-1/3}\, dx$

Here, $m = 9, \quad b = -1, \quad n = 3, \quad p = -1/3, \quad a = 1$

$$\therefore \quad I_8 = \frac{(x^6 (1 - x^3)^{2/3})}{-8} + \frac{6}{8} I_5 \qquad \text{...(i)}$$

$$\Rightarrow \quad I_5 = \frac{x^3 (1 - x^3)^{2/3}}{-5} + \frac{3}{5} I_2 \qquad \text{(here } m = 6)$$

$$\Rightarrow \quad I_2 = \frac{(1 - x^3)^{2/3}}{2}$$

Hence, $I_8 = -\frac{1}{8} x^6 (1 - x^3)^{2/3} - \frac{3}{20} x^3 (1 - x^3)^{2/3} - \frac{9}{40} (1 - x^3)^{2/3} + C$

63. Let $I = \int \text{cosec}^2\, x \ln (\cos x + \sqrt{\cos 2x})\, dx$

$$= \int \text{cosec}^2\, x \cdot \ln \{\sin x (\cot x + \sqrt{\cot^2 x - 1})\}\, dx$$

$$= \int \text{cosec}^2 x \ln (\sin x)\, dx + \int \text{cosec}^2 x \cdot \ln (\cot x + \sqrt{\cot^2 x - 1})\, dx$$

In second integral put $\cot x = 1$

$\therefore \quad \text{cosec}^2 x\, dx = dt$

$\therefore \quad I = \int \text{cosec}^2 x \cdot \ln (\sin x)\, dx - \int \ln(t + \sqrt{t^2 - 1})\, dt$

In first integral (integrating by parts taking $\text{cosec}^2 x$ as second integral) and in second integral (integration by parts taking unity as second function).

We have, $(\ln \sin x)(-\cot x) - \int \cot x (-\cot x)\, dx$

$$- \ln (t + \sqrt{t^2 - 1})\, t + \int \frac{t\, dt}{\sqrt{t^2 - 1}}$$

$$= - \cot x (\ln \sin x) - \cot x - x - t \ln (t + \sqrt{t^2 - 1}) + \sqrt{t^2 - 1} + C$$

$$= - \cot x (\ln \sin x) - \cot x - x - \cot x \{\ln (\cot x + \sqrt{\cot^2 x - 1})\} + \sqrt{\cot^2 x - 1} + C$$

$$= - \cot x \cdot \ln (\cos x + \sqrt{\cos 2x}) - \cot x - x + \sqrt{\cot^2 x - 1} + C$$

64. $I = \int \dfrac{dx}{(\sin x + a \sec x)^2}\ a \in N = \int \dfrac{\cos^2 x\, dx}{(a + \sin x \cos x)^2}$

$$= \int \frac{\cos^2 x\, dx}{(a^2 + \sin^2 x \cdot \cos^2 x + 2a \sin x \cdot \cos x)}$$

$$= \int \frac{4 \cos^2 x\, dx}{4a^2 + \sin^2 2x + 4a \sin 2x} = 2 \int \frac{1 + \cos 2x}{(2a + \sin 2x)^2}\, dx$$

$$= 2 \int \frac{1}{(2a + \sin 2x)^2}\, dx + 2 \int \frac{\cos 2x}{(2a + \sin 2x)^2}\, dx$$

$$= 2I_1 - \frac{1}{(2a + \sin 2x)} \qquad \text{...(i)}$$

$$I_1 = \int \frac{dx}{(2a + \sin 2x)^2},$$

we know

$$\therefore \quad I_1 = \int \frac{du}{(4a^2 - 1) \dfrac{\sqrt{4a^2 - 1}\, \sqrt{1 - u^2}}{(2a - u)}}$$

$$u = 2a \frac{\sin 2x + 1}{2a + \sin 2x} = \frac{1}{(4a^2 - 1)^{3/2}} \int \frac{(2a - u)}{\sqrt{1 - u^2}}\, du$$

$$\Rightarrow \frac{du}{dx} = \frac{(4a^2 - 1) \cos 2x}{(2a + \sin 2x)^2}$$

$$\Rightarrow \frac{1}{(4a^2 - 1)^{3/2}} [2a \sin^{-1} u + \sqrt{1 - u^2}\,] = I_1 \text{ and } \sin 2x = \frac{2au - 1}{2a - u}$$

$$\therefore \quad I = \frac{1}{(4a^2 - 1)^{3/2}} \left[2a \sin^{-1} \left(\frac{2a \sin 2x + 1}{2a + \sin 2x} \right) + \sqrt{1 - \left(\frac{2a \sin 2x + 1}{2a + \sin 2x} \right)} \right] - \frac{1}{(2a + \sin 2x)} + C$$

65. $I = \int \dfrac{dx}{x - \sqrt{x^2 + 2x + 4}}$

Put $\sqrt{x^2 + 2x + 4} = t + x$

$\Rightarrow \quad x^2 + 2x + 4 = t^2 + x^2 + 2tx$

$\Rightarrow \quad 2x - 2tx = t^2 - 4$

$$\Rightarrow \quad x = \frac{t^2 - 4}{2 - 2t} = \frac{1}{2} \frac{(t^2 - 4)}{(1 - t)}$$

$$\Rightarrow \quad dx = -\frac{1}{2} \left[\frac{t^2 - 2t + 4}{(1 - t)^2} \right]$$

$$\therefore \quad I = -\frac{1}{2} \int \frac{t^2 - 2t + 4}{-t (1 - t)^2}\, dt$$

$$= \frac{1}{2} \int \left[\frac{4}{t} + \frac{3}{(1 - t)} + \frac{3}{(1 - t)^2} \right] dt$$

$$= \frac{1}{2} \left[4 \log |t| - 3 \log |1 - t| + \frac{3}{(1 - t)} \right]$$

$$= 2 \log |\sqrt{x^2 + 2x + 4} - x| - \frac{3}{2} \log |1 - \sqrt{x^2 + 2x + 4} + x| + \frac{3}{2 (1 - \sqrt{x^2 + 2x + 4} + x)}$$

$$= 2 \log |\sqrt{x^2 + 2x + 4} - x| - \frac{3}{2} \log |\sqrt{x^2 + 2x + 4} - 1 - x| - \frac{3}{2 (\sqrt{x^2 + 2x + 4} - x - 1)}$$

66. $I = \int \dfrac{dx}{1 + \sqrt{x^2 + 2x + 2}}$

$\sqrt{x^2 + 2x + 2} = t - x$, squaring both the sides, we get

$$x^2 + 2x + 2 = t^2 + x^2 - 2tx$$

$$2x + 2tx = t^2 - 2$$

$$x = \frac{t^2 - 2}{2 (1 + t)}$$

$$\Rightarrow \quad dx = \frac{t^2 + 2t + 2}{2 (1 + t)^2}\, dt$$

$$\therefore \quad 1 + \sqrt{x^2 + 2x + 2} = 1 + t - \frac{t^2 - 2}{2 (1 + t)} = \frac{t^2 + 4t + 4}{2 (1 + t)}$$

$$\Rightarrow \quad I = \int \frac{2 (1 + t)(t^2 + 2t + 2)}{(t^2 + 4t + 4) \cdot 2 \cdot (1 + t)^2}\, dt = \int \frac{(t^2 + 2t + 2)}{(1 + t)(t + 2)^2}\, dt$$

Using partial fractions, we get

$$I = \int \frac{dt}{t + 1} - 2 \int \frac{dt}{(t + 2)^2}$$

$$= \ln |t + 1| + \frac{2}{(t + 2)} + C$$

$$I = \ln (x + 1 + \sqrt{x^2 + 2x + 2}) + \frac{2}{(x + 2) + \sqrt{x^2 + 2x + 2}} + C$$

67. $$I=\int \frac{x^4+1}{x^6+1}\,dx=\int \frac{(x^2+1)^2-2x^2}{(x^2+1)(x^4-x^2+1)}\,dx$$

$$=\int \frac{(1+1/x^2)\,dx}{(x^2+1/x^2-1)}-2\int \frac{x^2\,dx}{(x^3)^2+1}$$

$$=\int \frac{(1+1/x^2)\,dx}{(x-1/x)^2+1}-2\int \frac{x^2\,dx}{(x^3)^2+1}$$

In first integral put $x-1/x=t$ and in second integral put $x^3=u$

$$=\int \frac{dt}{t^2+1}-\frac{2}{3}\int \frac{du}{u^2+1}$$

$$=\tan^{-1}(t)-\frac{2}{3}\tan^{-1}(u)+C$$

$$=\tan^{-1}(x-1/x)-\frac{2}{3}\tan^{-1}(x^3)+C$$

68. $$I=\int \frac{dx}{(1-x^3)^{1/3}}$$

Put $x=1/t,\ dx=-1/t^2\,dt$

$$\therefore\quad I=-\int \frac{dt}{t^2(1-1/t^3)^{1/3}}=-\int \frac{dt}{t\,(t^3-1)^{1/3}}$$

Again, put $t^3-1=u^3 \Rightarrow 3t^2\,dt=3u^2\,du$

$$=-\int \frac{u^2\,du}{(1+u^3)\cdot u}=-\int \frac{u\,du}{(1+u)(1-u+u^2)}$$

$$=\frac{1}{3}\int \frac{du}{1+u}-\frac{1}{3}\int \frac{u+1}{u^2-u+1}\,du$$

(using partial fractions)

$$=\frac{1}{3}\int \frac{du}{u+1}-\frac{1}{3}\int \frac{1/2\,(2u-1)+3/2}{(u^2-u+1)}\,du$$

$$=\frac{1}{3}\int \frac{du}{u+1}-\frac{1}{6}\int \frac{2u-1}{u^2-u+1}\,du-\frac{1}{2}\int \frac{du}{(u-1/2)^2+3/4}$$

$$=\frac{1}{3}\log|u+1|-\frac{1}{6}\log|u^2-u+1|-\frac{1}{2}\cdot\frac{1}{\sqrt{3}/2}\tan^{-1}\left\{\frac{2u-1}{\sqrt{3}}\right\}+C$$

$$=\frac{1}{3}\log|(t^3-1)^{1/3}+1|-\frac{1}{6}\log|(t^3-1)^{2/3}-(t^3-1)^{1/3}+1|-\frac{1}{\sqrt{3}}\tan^{-1}\left\{\frac{2(t^3-1)^{1/3}-1}{\sqrt{3}}\right\}+C$$

$$=\frac{1}{3}\log\left|\frac{(1-x^3)^{1/3}+x}{x}\right|-\frac{1}{6}\log\left|\frac{(1-x^3)^{2/3}-(1-x^3)^{1/3}+x^2}{x^2}\right|-\frac{1}{\sqrt{3}}\tan^{-1}\left\{\frac{2(1-x^3)^{1/3}-x}{\sqrt{3}x}\right\}+C$$

69. $$I=\int \frac{(x+\sqrt{1+x^2})^{15}}{\sqrt{1+x^2}}\,dx$$

Put $(x+\sqrt{1+x^2})=t$

$$\therefore\quad \left(1+\frac{x}{\sqrt{1+x^2}}\right)dx=dt \quad\text{or}\quad \frac{t\,dx}{\sqrt{1+x^2}}=dt$$

$$\therefore\ I=\int t^{15}\cdot\frac{dt}{t}=\int t^{14}\,dt=\frac{t^{15}}{15}+C=\frac{(x+\sqrt{1+x^2})^{15}}{15}+C$$

70. $$\because\ u_{n+1}=\int \frac{x^{n+1}}{y}\,dx=\int \frac{x^{n+1}}{\sqrt{ax^2+2bx+c}}\,dx$$

$$=\frac{1}{2a}\int \frac{x^n(2ax+2b)-2bx^n}{\sqrt{ax^2+2bx+c}}\,dx$$

$$=\frac{1}{2a}\int x^n\frac{(2ax+2b)\,dx}{\sqrt{ax^2+2bx+c}}-\frac{b}{a}\int \frac{x^n}{\sqrt{ax^2+2bx+c}}\,dx$$

$$u_{n+1}=\frac{1}{2a}\int \underset{\text{I}}{x^n}\ \underset{\text{II}}{\frac{(2ax+2b)}{\sqrt{ax^2+2bx+c}}}-\frac{b}{a}u_n$$

$$u_{n+1}=\frac{1}{2a}\left[x^n\cdot 2\sqrt{ax^2+2bx+c}-\int nx^{n-1}\cdot 2\sqrt{(ax^2+bx+c)}\,dx\right]-\frac{b}{a}u_n$$

$$=\frac{1}{a}x^n y-\frac{n}{a}\int x^{n-1}\cdot\sqrt{ax^2+2bx+c}\,dx-\frac{b}{a}u_n$$

$$au_{n+1}=x^n y-n\int \frac{x^{n-1}(ax^2+2bx+c)}{\sqrt{ax^2+2bx+c}}\,dx-\frac{b}{a}u_n$$

$$au_{n+1}=x^n y-n[au_{n+1}+2bu_n+cu_{n-1}]-bu_n$$

$$\Rightarrow\ (n+1)\,a\,u_{n+1}+(2n+1)\,bu_n+nc\cdot u_{n-1}=x^n y \qquad \text{...(i)}$$

Now, putting, $n=0$ in both the sides, we get

$$au_1+bu_0=x^0y$$

$$au_1=y-bu_0 \qquad \text{...(ii)}$$

Putting $n=1$ in Eq. (i), we get

$$2au_2+3bu_1+cu_0=xy$$

$$2au_2+3b\left(\frac{y-bu_0}{a}\right)+cu_0=xy \qquad \text{[from Eq. (ii)]}$$

$$\Rightarrow\ 2a^2u_2+3by-3b^2u_0+acu_0=axy$$

$$\Rightarrow\ 2a^2u_2=y(ax-3b)+(3b^2-ac)\,u_0$$

71. Plan Integration by Substitution

i.e. $I=\int f\{g(x)\}\cdot g'(x)\,dx$

Put $g(x)=t \Rightarrow g'(x)\,dx=dt$

$\therefore\ I=\int f(t)\,dt$

Description of Situation Generally, students gets confused after substitution, i.e. $\sec x+\tan x=t$.

Now, for $\sec x$, we should use

$$\sec^2 x-\tan^2 x=1$$

$$\Rightarrow\ (\sec x-\tan x)(\sec x+\tan x)=1$$

$$\Rightarrow\ \sec x-\tan x=\frac{1}{t}$$

Here, $I=\int \frac{\sec^2 dx}{(\sec x+\tan x)^{9/2}}$

Put $\sec x+\tan x=t$

$\Rightarrow \quad (\sec x\tan x+\sec^2 x)dx=dt$

$\Rightarrow \quad \sec x\cdot t\,dx=dt$

$\Rightarrow \quad \sec x dx=\frac{dt}{t}$

$\therefore \quad \sec x-\tan x=\frac{1}{t} \Rightarrow \sec x=\frac{1}{2}\left(t+\frac{1}{t}\right)$

$\therefore \quad I=\int \frac{\sec x\cdot \sec x dx}{(\sec x+\tan x)^{9/2}}$

$\Rightarrow \quad I=\int \frac{\frac{1}{2}\left(t+\frac{1}{t}\right)\cdot\frac{dt}{t}}{t^{9/2}}=\frac{1}{2}\int\left(\frac{1}{t^{9/2}}+\frac{1}{t^{13/2}}\right)dt$

$=-\frac{1}{2}\left\{\frac{2}{7t^{7/2}}+\frac{2}{11t^{11/2}}\right\}+K$

$=-\left[\frac{1}{7(\sec x+\tan x)^{7/2}}+\frac{1}{11(\sec x+\tan x)^{11/2}}\right]+K$

$=\frac{-1}{(\sec x+\tan x)^{11/2}}\left\{\frac{1}{11}+\frac{1}{7}(\sec x+\tan x)^2\right\}+K$

72. Since, $I=\int \frac{e^x}{e^{4x}+e^{2x}+1}dx$ and $J=\int \frac{e^{3x}}{1+e^{2x}+e^{4x}}dx$

$\therefore \quad J-I=\int \frac{(e^{3x}-e^x)}{1+e^{2x}+e^{4x}}dx$

Put $\quad e^x=u \Rightarrow e^x dx=du$

$\therefore \quad J-I=\int \frac{(u^2-1)}{1+u^2+u^4}du=\int \frac{\left(1-\frac{1}{u^2}\right)}{1+\frac{1}{u^2}+u^2}du$

$=\int \frac{\left(1-\frac{1}{u^2}\right)}{\left(u+\frac{1}{u}\right)^2-1}du$

Put $u+\frac{1}{u}=t \Rightarrow \left(1-\frac{1}{u^2}\right)du=dt$

$=\int \frac{dt}{t^2-1}=\frac{1}{2}\log\left|\frac{t-1}{t+1}\right|+C$

$=\frac{1}{2}\log\left|\frac{u^2-u+1}{u^2+u+1}\right|+C=\frac{1}{2}\log\left|\frac{e^{2x}-e^x+1}{e^{2x}+e^x+1}\right|+C$

73. Let $I=\int \frac{2x^{12}+5x^9}{(x^5+x^3+1)^3}dx=\int \frac{2x^{12}+5x^9}{x^{15}(1+x^{-2}+x^{-5})^3}dx$

$=\int \frac{2x^{-3}+5x^{-6}}{(1+x^{-2}+x^{-5})^3}dx$

Now, put $1+x^{-2}+x^{-5}=t$

$\Rightarrow \quad (-2x^{-3}-5x^{-6})\,dx=dt$

$\Rightarrow \quad (2x^{-3}+5x^{-6})\,dx=-dt$

$\therefore \quad I=-\int \frac{dt}{t^3}=-\int t^{-3}\,dt$

$=-\frac{t^{-3+1}}{-3+1}+C=\frac{1}{2t^2}+C=\frac{x^{10}}{2(x^5+x^3+1)^2}+C$

74. $\int \frac{dx}{x^2(x^4+1)^{\frac{3}{4}}}=\int \frac{dx}{x^5\left(1+\frac{1}{x^4}\right)^{\frac{3}{4}}}$

Put $1+\frac{1}{x^4}=t^4 \Rightarrow -\frac{4}{x^5}dx=4t^3dt$

$\Rightarrow \quad \frac{dx}{x^5}=-t^3dt$

$\therefore \quad I=\int \frac{-t^3dt}{t^3}=-\int dt=-t+C=-\left(1+\frac{1}{x^4}\right)^{\frac{1}{4}}+C$

75. $\int\left(1+x-\frac{1}{x}\right)e^{x+\frac{1}{x}}dx=\int e^{x+\frac{1}{x}}dx+\int x\left(1-\frac{1}{x^2}\right)e^{x+\frac{1}{x}}dx$

$=\int e^{x+\frac{1}{x}}dx+xe^{x+\frac{1}{x}}-\int \frac{d}{dx}(x)e^{x+\frac{1}{x}}dx$

$=\int e^{x+\frac{1}{x}}dx+xe^{x+\frac{1}{x}}-\int e^{x+\frac{1}{x}}dx$

$\left[\because \int\left(1-\frac{1}{x^2}\right)e^{x+\frac{1}{x}}dx=e^{x+\frac{1}{x}}\right]$

$=\int e^{x+\frac{1}{x}}dx+xe^{x+\frac{1}{x}}-\int ex^{x+\frac{1}{x}}dx$

$=xe^{x+\frac{1}{x}}+C$

76. Given, $\int f(x)\,dx=\psi(x)$

Let $\quad I=\int x^5 f(x^3)\,dx$

Put $\quad x^3=t$

$\Rightarrow \quad x^2dx=\frac{dt}{3}$ ...(i)

$\therefore \quad I=\frac{1}{3}\int t\,f(t)\,dt$

$=\frac{1}{3}\left[t\int f(t)\,dt-\int\left\{\frac{d}{dtt}(t)\,dt\right\}dt\right]$

[Integration by parts]

$=\frac{1}{3}[t\,\psi(t)-\int \psi(t)\,dt]$

$=\frac{1}{3}[x^3\psi(x^3)-3\int x^2\psi(x^3)\,dx]+C$ [from Eq. (i)]

$=\frac{1}{3}x^3\psi(x^3)-\int x^2\psi(x^3)\,dx+C$

77. **Given** Integral is $\int \frac{5 \tan x}{\tan x - 2} dx$

To find The value of a, if

$$\int \frac{5 \tan x}{\tan x - 2} dx = x + a \log |\sin x - 2 \cos x| + k \quad \text{...(i)}$$

Now, let us assume that $I = \int \frac{5 \tan x}{\tan x - 2} dx$

Multiplying by $\cos x$ in numerator and denominator, we get

$$I = \int \frac{5 \sin x}{\sin x - 2 \cos x} dx$$

This special integration requires special substitution of type

$$N^r = A(D^r) + B\left(\frac{dD^r}{dx}\right)$$

$\Rightarrow$ Let $5 \sin x = A(\sin x - 2 \cos x) + B(\cos x + 2 \sin x)$

$\Rightarrow 0 \cos x + 5 \sin x = (A + 2B) \sin x + (B - 2A) \cos x$

Comparing the coefficients of $\sin x$ and $\cos x$, we get

$$A + 2B = 5 \quad \text{and} \quad B - 2A = 0$$

Solving the above two equations in A and B, we get

$$A = 1 \quad \text{and} \quad B = 2$$

$\Rightarrow 5 \sin x = (\sin x - 2 \cos x) + 2(\cos x + 2 \sin x)$

$$\Rightarrow I = \int \frac{5 \sin x}{\sin x - 2 \cos x} dx$$

$$= \int \frac{(\sin x - 2 \cos x) + 2(\cos x + 2 \sin x)}{(\sin x - 2 \cos x)} dx$$

$$\Rightarrow I = \int \frac{\sin x - 2 \cos x}{\sin x - 2 \cos x} dx + 2 \int \frac{(\cos x + 2 \sin x)}{(\sin x - 2 \cos x)} dx$$

$$\Rightarrow I = \int 1\, dx + 2 \int \frac{d(\sin x - 2 \cos x)}{(\sin x - 2 \cos x)}$$

$$\Rightarrow I = x + 2 \log |(\sin x - 2 \cos x)| + k \quad \text{...(ii)}$$

where, k is the constant of integration.

Now, by comparing the value of I in Eqs. (i) and (ii), we get $a = 2$.

78. Let $I = \sqrt{2} \int \frac{\sin x}{\sin\left(x - \frac{\pi}{4}\right)} dx$

Put $x - \frac{\pi}{4} = t \Rightarrow dx = dt$

$$\therefore \quad I = \sqrt{2} \int \frac{\sin\left(\frac{\pi}{4} + t\right) dt}{\sin t}$$

$$= \sqrt{2} \int \left[\frac{1}{\sqrt{2}} \cot t + \frac{1}{\sqrt{2}}\right] dt$$

$$= 1 + \log |\sin t| + C$$

$$= x + \log \left|\sin\left(x - \frac{\pi}{4}\right)\right| + C$$

CHAPTER

02

Definite Integral

Learning Part

Session 1
- Integration Basics
- Geometrical Interpretation of Definite Integral
- Evaluation of Definite Integrals by Substitution

Session 2
- Properties of Definite Integral

Session 3
- Applications of Piecewise Function Property

Session 4
- Applications of Even-Odd Property and Half the Integral Limit Property

Session 5
- Applications of Periodic Functions and Newton-Leibnitz's Formula

Session 6
- Integration as Limit of a Sum
- Applications of Inequality
- Gamma Function
- Beta Function
- Walli's Formula

Practice Part
- JEE Type Examples
- Chapter Exercise

Arihant on Your Mobile !
Exercises with the ▯ *symbol can be practised on your mobile. See inside cover page to activate for free.*

Session 1

Integration Basics, Geometrical Interpretation of Definite Integral, Evaluation of Definite Integrals by Substitution

Integration Basics

What is Definite Integral ?

Let f be a function of x defined in the closed interval $[a, b]$ and ϕ be another function, such that $\phi'(x) = f(x)$ for all x in the domain of f, then

$$\int_a^b f(x)\,dx = [\phi(x) + c]_a^b = \phi(b) - \phi(a)$$

is called the definite integral of the function $f(x)$ over the interval $[a, b]$, a and b are called the limits of integration, a being the lower limit and b be the upper limit.

Remark

In definite integrals constant of integration is never present.

Working Rules

To evaluate definite integral $\int_a^b f(x)\,dx$.

1. First evaluate the indefinite integral $\int f(x)\,dx$ and suppose the result is $g(x)$.
2. Next find $g(b)$ and $g(a)$.
3. Finally, the value of the definite integral is obtained by subtracting $g(a)$ from $g(b)$.

Thus, $\int_a^b f(x)\,dx = [g(x)]_a^b = g(b) - g(a)$

| Example 1 Evaluate

(i) $\int_0^1 \frac{1}{3+4x}\,dx$ (ii) $\int_0^{\pi/2} \sin^4 x\,dx$

Sol. (i) Here, $I = \int_0^1 \frac{1}{3+4x}\,dx = \left[\frac{\ln(3+4x)}{4}\right]_0^1$

$$= \frac{1}{4}[\ln 7 - \ln 3] = \frac{1}{4}\ln\left(\frac{7}{3}\right)$$

(ii) Let $I = \int_0^{\pi/2} \sin^4 x\,dx$

$$= \frac{1}{4}\int_0^{\pi/2} (2\sin^2 x)^2\,dx = \frac{1}{4}\int_0^{\pi/2} (1 - \cos 2x)^2\,dx$$

$$= \frac{1}{4}\int_0^{\pi/2} (1 - 2\cos 2x + \cos^2 2x)\,dx$$

$$= \frac{1}{4}\int_0^{\pi/2} \left(1 - 2\cos 2x + \frac{1+\cos 4x}{2}\right) dx$$

$$= \frac{1}{4}\int_0^{\pi/2} \left(\frac{3 - 4\cos 2x + \cos 4x}{2}\right) dx$$

$$= \frac{1}{8}\left[3x - \frac{4}{2}\sin 2x + \frac{\sin 4x}{4}\right]_0^{\pi/2}$$

$$= \frac{1}{8}\left[\left(\frac{3\pi}{2} - 2\sin\pi + \frac{1}{4}\sin 2\pi\right) - 0\right]$$

$$= \frac{1}{8}\left(\frac{3\pi}{2} - 0 + 0\right) = \frac{3\pi}{16}$$

| Example 2 The value of $\int_{-1}^{1}\left[\frac{d}{dx}\left(\tan^{-1}\frac{1}{x}\right)\right]dx$ is

(a) $\pi/2$ (b) $\pi/4$ (c) $-\pi/2$ (d) None of these

Sol. Let $I = \int_{-1}^{1}\left[\frac{d}{dx}\left(\tan^{-1}\frac{1}{x}\right)\right]dx$

Here, $\frac{d}{dx}\left(\tan^{-1}\frac{1}{x}\right) = \frac{d}{dx}(\cot^{-1} x) = \frac{-1}{1+x^2}$

$$\therefore \quad I = \int_{-1}^{1} -\frac{1}{1+x^2}\,dx = -\int_{-1}^{1}\frac{1}{1+x^2}\,dx$$

$$= -(\tan^{-1} x)_{-1}^{1} = -[\tan^{-1}(1) - \tan^{-1}(-1)]$$

$$= -\left(\frac{\pi}{4} + \frac{\pi}{4}\right) = -\frac{\pi}{2}$$

Hence, (c) is the correct answer.

Remark

Note that $\int_{-1}^{1}\left(\frac{d}{dx}\tan^{-1}\frac{1}{x}\right)dx = \left(\tan^{-1}\frac{1}{x}\right)_{-1}^{1} = \tan^{-1}(1) - \tan^{-1}(-1)$

$$= \frac{\pi}{4} - \left(-\frac{\pi}{4}\right) = \frac{\pi}{2}$$

is incorrect, because $\tan^{-1}\left(\frac{1}{x}\right)$ is not a anti-derivative (primitive) of $\frac{d}{dx}\left(\tan^{-1}\frac{1}{x}\right)$ on the interval $[-1, 1]$.

Example 3 If $I_n = \int_1^e (\log x)^n \, dx$, then $I_n + nI_{n-1}$ is equal to

(a) $\frac{1}{e}$ (b) e (c) $e-1$ (d) None of these

Sol. We have, $I_n = \int_1^e (\log x)^n \, dx = \int_1^e \underbrace{(\log x)^n}_{\text{I}} \cdot \underbrace{1}_{\text{II}} \, dx$

$$\therefore \quad I_n = [x \cdot (\log x)^n]_1^e - \int_1^e n \cdot (\log x)^{n-1} \cdot \frac{1}{x} \cdot x dx$$

$$= (e-0) - n\int_1^e (\log_e x)^{n-1} dx = e - n \cdot I_{n-1}$$

$\therefore I_n + n \cdot I_{n-1} = e$

Hence, (b) is the correct answer.

Example 4 All the values of 'a' for which $\int_1^2 \{a^2 + (4-4a)x + 4x^3\} dx \le 12$ are given by

(a) $a = 3$ (b) $a \le 4$

(c) $0 \le a < 3$ (d) None of these

Sol. We have, $\int_1^2 \{a^2 + (4-4a)x + 4x^3\} dx \le 12$

$$\Rightarrow \quad [a^2 x + (2-2a)x^2 + x^4]_1^2 \le 12$$

$$\Rightarrow a^2(2-1) + (2-2a)(4-1) + (2^4 - 1^4) \le 12$$

$$\Rightarrow \quad a^2 + 3(2-2a) + 15 \le 12$$

$$\Rightarrow \quad a^2 - 6a + 9 \le 0$$

$$\Rightarrow \quad (a-3)^2 \le 0$$

$$\therefore \quad a = 3$$

Hence, (a) is the correct answer.

Geometrical Interpretation of Definite Integral

If $f(x) > 0$ for all $x \in [a, b]$, then $\int_a^b f(x) \, dx$ is numerically equal to the area bounded by the curve $y = f(x)$, the X-axis and the straight lines $x = a$ and $x = b$ i.e. $\int_a^b f(x) \, dx$

In general, $\int_a^b f(x) \, dx$ represents the algebraic sum of the areas of the figures bounded by the curve $y = f(x)$, the X-axis and the straight lines $x = a$ and $x = b$. The areas above X-axis are taken with plus sign and the areas below X-axis are taken with minus sign,

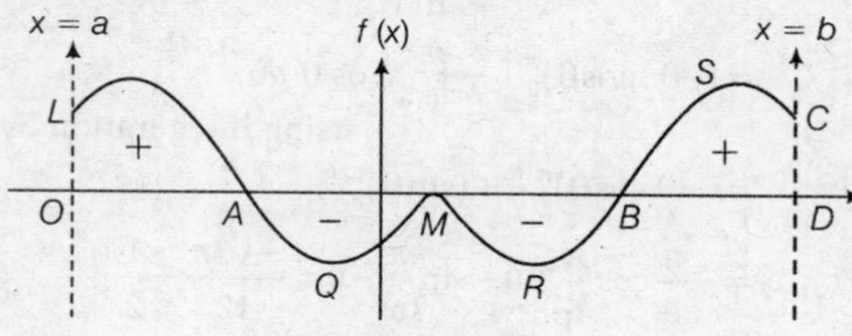

Figure 2.1

i.e. $\int_a^b f(x) \, dx = \text{Area}(OLA) - \text{Area}(AQM) - \text{Area}(MRB) + \text{Area}(BSCD)$

Remark

$\int_a^b f(x) \, dx$, represents algebraic sum of areas means that area of function $y = f(x)$ is asked between a to b.

$\Rightarrow$ Area bounded $= \int_a^b |f(x)| \, dx$ and not been represented by $\int_a^b f(x) \, dx$. e.g. If someone asks for the area of $y = x^3$ between -1 to 1, then $y = x^3$ could be plotted as

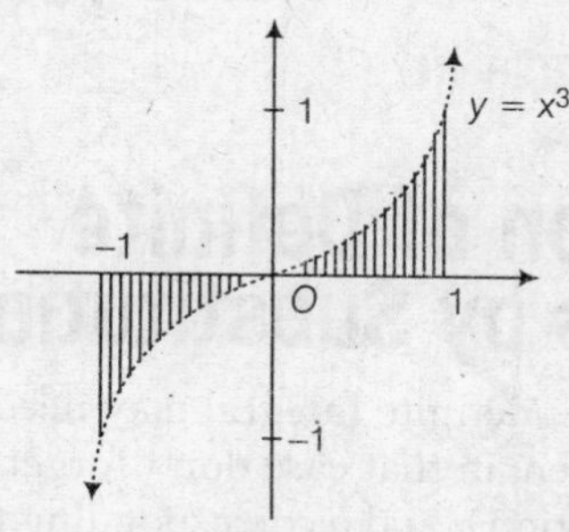

Figure 2.2

$$\therefore \quad \text{Area} = \int_{-1}^0 -x^3 \, dx + \int_0^1 x^3 \, dx = \frac{1}{2}$$

or using above definition, area $= \int_{-1}^1 |x^3| \, dx = 2\int_0^1 x^3 \, dx$

$$= 2\left[\frac{x^4}{4}\right]_0^1 = \frac{1}{2}$$

But, if we integrate x^3 between -1 to 1.

$\Rightarrow \quad \int_{-1}^1 x^3 \, dx = 0$ which does not represent the area.

Thus, students are adviced to make difference between area and definite integral.

Example 5 Evaluate $\int_0^3 |(x-1)(x-2)| \, dx$.

Sol. Let $\quad I = \int_0^3 |(x-1)(x-2)| \, dx$

We know,

$$|(x-1)(x-2)| = \begin{cases} (x-1)(x-2), & x < 1 \text{ or } x > 2 \\ -(x-1)(x-2), & 1 < x < 2 \end{cases}$$

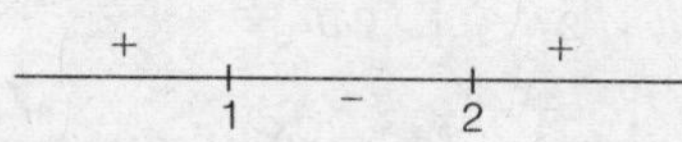

Using number line rule,

$$I = \int_0^3 |(x-1)(x-2)| \, dx$$

$$= \int_0^1 (x-1)(x-2)\,dx - \int_1^2 (x-1)(x-2)\,dx + \int_2^3 (x-1)(x-2)\,dx$$

$$= \int_0^1 (x^2-3x+2)\,dx - \int_1^2 (x^2-3x+2)\,dx + \int_2^3 (x^2-3x+2)\,dx$$

$$= \left[\frac{x^3}{3} - \frac{3x^2}{2} + 2x\right]_0^1 - \left[\frac{x^3}{3} - \frac{3x^2}{2} + 2x\right]_1^2 + \left[\frac{x^3}{3} - \frac{3x^2}{2} + 2x\right]_2^3$$

$$= \left(\frac{1}{3} - \frac{3}{2} + 2\right) - \left(\frac{8}{3} - \frac{12}{2} + 4 - \frac{1}{3} + \frac{3}{2} - 2\right) + \left(\frac{27}{3} - \frac{27}{2} + 6 - \frac{8}{3} + \frac{12}{2} - 4\right) = \frac{11}{6}$$

Evaluation of Definite Integrals by Substitution

Sometimes, the indefinite integral may need substitution, say $x = \phi(t)$. Then, in that case don't forget to change the limits of integration a and b corresponding to the new variable t. The substitution $x = \phi(t)$ is not valid, if it is not continuous in the interval $[a, b]$.

Example 6 Show that

$$\int_0^{\pi/2} \frac{dx}{a^2\cos^2 x + b^2 \sin^2 x} = \frac{\pi}{2ab};\ a, b > 0.$$

Sol. Let $I = \int_{x=0}^{x=\pi/2} \frac{dx}{a^2\cos^2 x + b^2\sin^2 x}$

$$= \int_{x=0}^{x=\pi/2} \frac{\sec^2 x\,dx}{a^2 + b^2\tan^2 x}$$

(divide numerator and denominator by $\cos^2 x$)

Put $\tan x = t \Rightarrow \sec^2 x\,dx = dt$

$\therefore \quad I = \int_{t=0}^{t=\infty} \frac{dt}{a^2 + b^2t^2}$

We find the new limits of integration $t = \tan x \Rightarrow t = 0$ when $x = 0$ and $t = \infty$ when $x = \pi/2$.

$$\Rightarrow \quad I = \frac{1}{b^2}\int_0^\infty \frac{dt}{\left(\frac{a}{b}\right)^2 + t^2} = \frac{1}{b^2}\cdot\frac{1}{a/b}\left[\tan^{-1}\frac{bt}{a}\right]_0^\infty$$

$$= \frac{1}{ab}\left[\frac{\pi}{2} - 0\right] = \frac{\pi}{2ab}$$

Example 7 Evaluate $\int_{-2}^{2} \frac{dx}{4+x^2}$ directly as well as by the substitution $x = 1/t$. Examine as to why the answer don't valid?

Sol. Let $I = \int_{-2}^{2} \frac{dx}{4+x^2}$

$$= \left[\frac{1}{2}\tan^{-1}\left(\frac{x}{2}\right)\right]_{-2}^{2} = \frac{1}{2}\left[\tan^{-1}(1) - \tan^{-1}(-1)\right]$$

$$= \frac{1}{2}\left[\frac{\pi}{4} - \left(-\frac{\pi}{4}\right)\right] = \frac{\pi}{4}$$

$$\Rightarrow \quad I = \frac{\pi}{4}$$

On the other hand; if $x = 1/t$, then

$$I = \int_{-2}^{2}\frac{dx}{4+x^2} = -\int_{-1/2}^{1/2}\frac{dt}{t^2(4+1/t^2)} = -\int_{-1/2}^{1/2}\frac{dt}{4t^2+1}$$

$$= -\left[\frac{1}{2}\tan^{-1}(2t)\right]_{-1/2}^{1/2}$$

$$= -\frac{1}{2}\tan^{-1}(1) - \left(-\frac{1}{2}\tan^{-1}(-1)\right)$$

$$= -\frac{\pi}{8} - \frac{\pi}{8} = -\frac{\pi}{4}$$

$$\therefore \quad I = -\frac{\pi}{4}, \text{ when } x = \frac{1}{t}$$

In above two results, $I = -\pi/4$ is wrong. Since, the integrand $\frac{1}{4+x^2} > 0$ and therefore the definite integral of this function cannot be negative.

Since, $x = 1/t$ is discontinuous at $t = 0$, then substitution is not valid. $(\because I = \pi/4)$

Remark

It is important that the substitution must be continuous in the interval of integration.

Example 8 Evaluate $\int_0^{1/2} x \cdot \frac{\sin^{-1} x}{\sqrt{1-x^2}}dx$.

Sol. Let $I = \int_0^{1/2} x\cdot\frac{\sin^{-1}x}{\sqrt{1-x^2}}dx$

Put $\sin^{-1} x = \theta$, then $x = \sin\theta \Rightarrow dx = \cos\theta\,d\theta$

Also when $x = 0$, then $\theta = 0$ and when $x = \frac{1}{2}$,

then $\theta = \sin^{-1}\left(\frac{1}{2}\right) = \frac{\pi}{6}$

$$\therefore \quad I = \int_0^{\pi/6} \sin\theta\cdot\frac{\theta}{\sqrt{1-\sin^2\theta}}\cdot\cos\theta\,d\theta = \int_0^{\pi/6}\theta\cdot\sin\theta\,d\theta$$

$$= (-\theta\cdot\cos\theta)_0^{\pi/6} + \int_0^{\pi/6}\cos\theta\,d\theta,$$

using integeration by parts.

$$= (-\theta\cos\theta)_0^{\pi/6} + (\sin\theta)_0^{\pi/6}$$

$$= -\frac{\pi}{6}\cos\frac{\pi}{6} + 0 + \sin\frac{\pi}{6} - 0 = \frac{-\sqrt{3}\pi}{12} + \frac{1}{2}$$

Example 9 For any $n > 1$, evaluate the integral $\int_0^{\infty} \frac{1}{(x+\sqrt{x^2+1})^n}\, dx$.

Sol. Let $I = \int_0^{\infty} \frac{1}{(x+\sqrt{1+x^2})^n} dx$

Put $x + \sqrt{1+x^2} = t \quad \Rightarrow \sqrt{1+x^2} = t - x$

$\Rightarrow 1 + x^2 = (t-x)^2 \quad \Rightarrow x = \frac{t^2-1}{2t}$ or $x = \frac{1}{2}\left(t - \frac{1}{t}\right)$

$\therefore \quad dx = \frac{1}{2}\left(1 + \frac{1}{t^2}\right) dt$

$$\therefore \quad I = \int_{t=1}^{\infty} \frac{1}{t^n} \cdot \frac{1}{2}\left(1+\frac{1}{t^2}\right) dt = \frac{1}{2}\int_1^{\infty} (t^{-n} + t^{-n-2}) dt$$

$$= \frac{1}{2}\left[\frac{t^{1-n}}{1-n} + \frac{t^{-n-1}}{-(n+1)}\right]_1^{\infty} = \frac{1}{2}\left[0 - \left(\frac{1}{1-n} - \frac{1}{n+1}\right)\right]$$

$$= \frac{1}{2}\left[\frac{-2n}{1-n^2}\right] = \frac{n}{n^2-1}$$

Example 10 The value of

$$\int_0^{e-1} \frac{e^{\frac{x^2+2x-1}{2}}}{(x+1)} dx + \int_1^e x \log x \cdot e^{\frac{x^2-2}{2}} dx \text{ is equal to}$$

(a) $(\sqrt{e})^{(e^2+1)}$ (b) $(\sqrt{e})^{e^2-1}$ (c) 0 (d) $(\sqrt{e})^{e^2-2}$

Sol. Let $I = \int_0^{e-1} \frac{e^{\frac{x^2+2x-1}{2}}}{(x+1)} dx + \int_1^e x \log x \cdot e^{\frac{x^2-2}{2}} dx$

Put $x + 1 = t$ in first integral

$$\therefore \quad I = \int_1^e \frac{e^{\frac{t^2-2}{2}}}{t} dt + \int_1^e x \log x \cdot e^{\frac{x^2-2}{2}} dx$$

$$= \int_1^e e^{\frac{t^2-2}{2}} \left\{\frac{1}{t} + t \cdot \log t\right\} dt = \left(\log t \cdot e^{\frac{t^2-2}{2}}\right)_1^e$$

$$= (\sqrt{e})^{e^2-2}$$

Hence, (d) is the correct answer.

Example 11 Let $f(x) = \int_2^x \frac{dt}{\sqrt{1+t^4}}$ and g be the inverse of f. Then, the value of $g'(0)$ is

(a) 1 (b) 17 (c) $\sqrt{17}$ (d) None of these

Sol. Here, $f'(x) = \frac{1}{\sqrt{1+x^4}} = \frac{dy}{dx}$

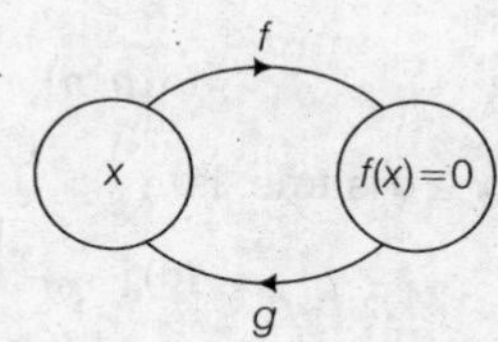

Now, $g'(x) = \frac{dx}{dy} = \sqrt{1+x^4}$

When $y = 0$ i.e. $\int_2^x \frac{dt}{\sqrt{1+t^4}} = 0$, then $x = 2$

Therefore, $g'(0) = \sqrt{1+16} = \sqrt{17}$

Hence, (c) is the correct answer.

Example 12 Let $a_n = \int_0^{\pi/2} (1-\sin t)^n \sin 2t$, then $\lim_{n\to\infty} \sum_{n=1}^{n} \frac{a_n}{n}$ is equal to

(a) 1/2 (b) 1
(c) 4/3 (d) 3/2

Sol. We have, $a_n = \int_0^{\pi/2} (1-\sin t)^n \sin 2t\, dt$

Let $1 - \sin t = u \Rightarrow -\cos t\, dt = du$

$$\therefore \quad a_n = 2\int_0^1 u^n (1-u) du = 2\left(\int_0^1 u^n du - \int_0^1 u^{n+1} du\right)$$

$$= 2\left(\frac{1}{n+1} - \frac{1}{n+2}\right)$$

Therefore, $\frac{a_n}{n} = 2\left(\frac{1}{n(n+1)} - \frac{1}{n(n+2)}\right)$

$$\therefore \lim_{n\to\infty} \sum_{n=1}^{n} \frac{a_n}{n} = 2\left[\sum\left(\frac{1}{n} - \frac{1}{n+1}\right) - \frac{1}{2}\sum\left(\frac{1}{n} - \frac{1}{n+2}\right)\right]$$

$$= 2\sum_{n=1}^{n}\left(\frac{1}{n} - \frac{1}{n+1}\right) - \sum_{n=1}^{n}\left(\frac{1}{n} - \frac{1}{n+2}\right)$$

$$= 2(1) - \left[\left(1 - \frac{1}{3}\right) + \left(\frac{1}{2} - \frac{1}{4}\right) + \left(\frac{1}{3} - \frac{1}{5}\right) + \ldots\right] = 2 - \frac{3}{2} = \frac{1}{2}$$

Hence, (a) is the correct answer.

Example 13 The value of $x > 1$ satisfying the equation $\int_1^x t \ln t\, dt = \frac{1}{4}$ is

(a) $\sqrt{e}$ (b) e (c) e^2 (d) $e - 1$

Sol. Let $I = \int_1^x t \ln t\, dt = \left[\ln t \cdot \frac{t^2}{2}\right]_1^x$

$$-\frac{1}{2}\int_1^x \frac{1}{t} \cdot t^2 dt = \frac{x^2}{2}\ln x - \frac{1}{2}\left[\frac{t^2}{2}\right]_1^x$$

$$= \frac{x^2 \ln x}{2} - \frac{1}{4}[x^2 - 1] = \frac{1}{4}$$

$$\therefore \frac{x^2 \ln x}{2} - \frac{1}{4}x^2 = 0 \Rightarrow [2\ln x - 1] = 0 \qquad (\text{as } x > 1)$$

$$\Rightarrow \quad \ln x = \frac{1}{2} \Rightarrow x = \sqrt{e}$$

Hence, (a) is the correct answer.

Example 14 If $\lim_{a \to \infty} \frac{1}{a} \int_0^{\infty} \frac{x^2 + ax + 1}{1 + x^4} \cdot \tan^{-1}\left(\frac{1}{x}\right) dx$ is equal to $\frac{\pi^2}{k}$, where $k \in N$, then k equals to

(a) 4 (b) 8 (c) 16 (d) 32

Sol. Let $I = \int_0^{\infty} \frac{x^2 + ax + 1}{1 + x^4} \cdot \tan^{-1}\left(\frac{1}{x}\right) dx$

Put $x = 1/t$ and adding, we get

[using $\tan^{-1}(1/x) + \cot^{-1} x = \pi/2$]

$$I = \frac{\pi}{4} \int_0^{\infty} \frac{(x^2 + 1) + ax}{1 + x^4} dx$$

$$= \frac{\pi}{4} \left[\int_0^{\infty} \frac{(x^2 + 1)}{1 + x^4} dx + a \int_0^{\infty} \frac{x\,dx}{1 + x^4} \right]$$

$$= \frac{\pi}{4} \left[\frac{\pi}{2\sqrt{2}} + \frac{a\pi}{4} \right] = \left[\frac{\pi^2}{8\sqrt{2}} + \frac{\pi^2 a}{16} \right]$$

$$\therefore \quad l = \lim_{a \to \infty} \frac{1}{a} \left[\frac{\pi^2}{8\sqrt{2}} + \frac{\pi^2 a}{16} \right] = \lim_{a \to \infty} \left[\frac{\pi^2}{(8\sqrt{2})a} + \frac{\pi^2}{16} \right] = \frac{\pi^2}{16}$$

$\Rightarrow \quad k = 16$

Hence, (c) is the correct answer.

Example 15 If the value of definite integral $\int_1^a x \cdot a^{-[\log_a x]} dx$, where $a > 1$ and $[x]$ denotes the greatest integer, is $\frac{e-1}{2}$, then the value of 'a' equals to

(a) $\sqrt{e}$ (b) e (c) $\sqrt{e+1}$ (d) $e - 1$

Sol. Let $I = \int_1^a x \cdot a^{-[\log_a x]} dx$

Put $\log_a x = t \Rightarrow a^t = x$

$$\therefore \quad I = \ln a \cdot \int_0^1 (a^t \cdot a^{-[t]} \cdot a^t)\, dt = \ln a \cdot \int_0^1 (a^{t-[t]} \cdot a^t) dt$$

$$= \ln a \cdot \int_0^1 (a^{\{t\}} \cdot a^t) dt = \ln a \cdot \int_0^1 a^{2t}\, dt$$

$$= \left[\frac{\ln a}{2} \cdot \frac{a^{2t}}{\ln a} \right]_0^1 = \frac{1}{2}(a^2 - 1) \qquad [\text{as } \{t\} = t, \text{ if } t \in (0,1)]$$

$$\therefore \quad \frac{1}{2}(a^2 - 1) = \frac{e-1}{2} \Rightarrow a = \sqrt{e}$$

Aliter $\quad x \in (1, a)$

$\Rightarrow \quad \log_a x \in (0, 1) \Rightarrow [\log_a x] = 0$

$$\therefore \quad I = \int_1^a x\,dx = \frac{1}{2}(a^2 - 1) = \frac{e-1}{2} \Rightarrow a = \sqrt{e}$$

Hence, (a) is the correct answer.

Exercise for Session 1

1. $\int_0^{\pi/4} \cos^2 x\, dx$

2. $\int_0^{\pi/2} \frac{dx}{1 + \cos x}$

3. $\int_0^{\pi/2} \sqrt{1 + \cos x}\, dx$

4. $\int_0^{\pi/6} \sin 2x \cdot \cos x\, dx$

5. $\int_1^2 \frac{dx}{\sqrt{x} - \sqrt{x-1}}$

6. $\int_0^1 \log x\, dx$

7. $\int_0^{\pi/4} \frac{(\sin x + \cos x)}{9 + 16 \sin 2x} dx$

8. $\int_a^b \frac{1}{\sqrt{(x-a)(b-x)}} dx, b > a$

9. $\int_a^b \sqrt{\frac{x-a}{b-x}} dx$

10. $\int_0^{\pi/4} \sqrt{\tan x}\, dx$

11. $\int_0^{\pi} \cos 2x . \log(\sin x) dx$

12. $\int_0^{\pi/4} e^{\sin x} \left(\frac{x \cos^3 x - \sin x}{\cos^2 x} \right) dx$

13. If $f(x)$ is a function satisfying $f\left(\frac{1}{x}\right) + x^2 f(x) = 0$ for all non-zero x, then $\int_{\sin\theta}^{\operatorname{cosec}\theta} f(x) dx$ is equal to

14. The value of $\int_0^1 \left(\prod_{r=1}^{n} (n + r) \right) \left(\sum_{k=1}^{n} \frac{1}{x + k} \right) dx$ equals to

(a) n (b) $n!$ (c) $(n+1)!$ (d) $n \cdot n!$

15. The true set of values of 'a' for which the inequality $\int_x^0 (3^{-2x} - 2 \cdot 3^{-x})\, dx \ge 0$ is true, is

(a) $[0, 1]$ (b) $[-\infty, -1]$ (c) $[0, \infty]$ (d) $[-\infty, -1] \cup [1, \infty]$

Session 2

Properties of Definite Integral

Properties of Definite Integrals

Property I. $\int_a^b f(x)\,dx = \int_a^b f(t)\,dt$

i.e. The integration is independent of the change of variable.

Proof Let $\phi(x)$ be a primitive of $f(x)$, then

$$\frac{d}{dx}[\phi(x)] = f(x) \Rightarrow \frac{d}{dt}[\phi(t)] = f(t)$$

Therefore, $\int_a^b f(x)\,dx = [\phi(x)]_a^b = \phi(b) - \phi(a)$ ...(i)

and $\int_a^b f(t)\,dt = [\phi(t)]_a^b = \phi(b) - \phi(a)$ ...(ii)

From Eqs. (i) and (ii), we have

$$\int_a^b f(x)\,dx = \int_a^b f(t)\,dt$$

Property II. $\int_a^b f(x)\,dx = -\int_b^a f(x)\,dx$

i.e. if the limits of definite integral are interchanged, then its value changes by minus sign only.

Proof Let $\phi(x)$ be a primitive of $f(x)$, then

$$\int_a^b f(x)\,dx = \phi(b) - \phi(a)$$

and $-\int_b^a f(x)\,dx = -[\phi(a) - \phi(b)] = \phi(b) - \phi(a)$

$\therefore$ $\int_a^b f(x)\,dx = -\int_b^a f(x)\,dx$

Property III. $\int_0^a f(x)\,dx = \int_0^a f(a-x)\,dx$ (King's property)

Proof On RHS put $(a - x) = t$, so that $dx = -dt$

Also, when $x = 0$, then $t = a$ and when $x = a$, then $t = 0$

$\therefore$ $\int_0^a f(a-x)\,dx = -\int_a^0 f(t)\,dt = \int_0^a f(t)\,dt = \int_0^a f(x)\,dx$

$\therefore$ $\int_0^a f(a-x)\,dx = \int_0^a f(x)\,dx$

Remark

This property is useful to evaluate a definite integral without first finding the corresponding indefinite integrals which may be difficult or sometimes impossible to find.

Geometrically $\int_0^a f(x)\,dx = \int_0^a f(a-x)\,dx$

This property says that when integrating from 0 to a, we will get the same result whether we use the function $f(x)$ or $f(a-x)$. The justification for this property will become clear from the figures below :

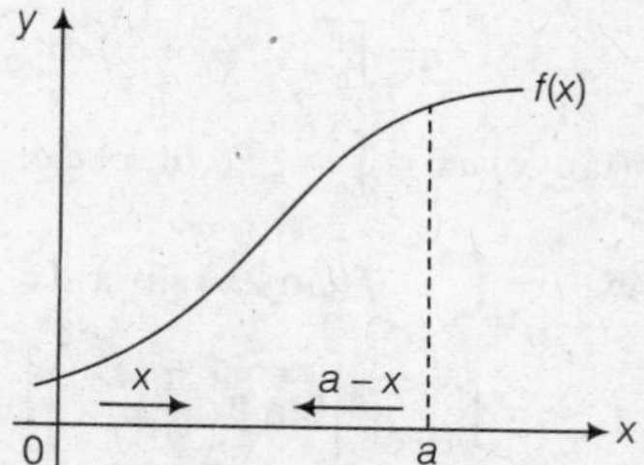

As x progresses from 0 to a, the variable $a - x$ progresses from a to 0. Thus, whether we use x or $a - x$, the entire interval $[0, a]$ is still covered.

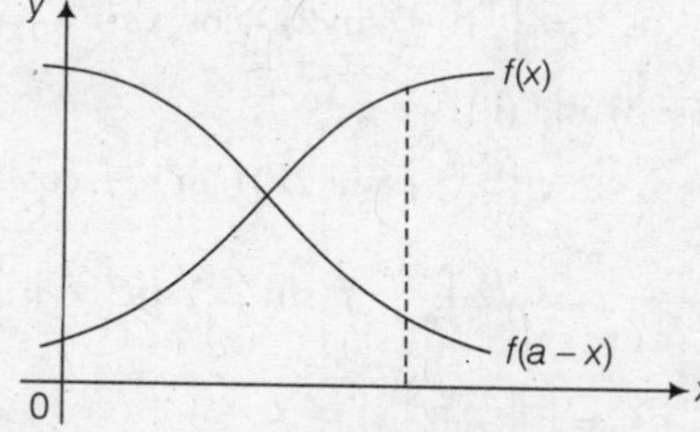

The function $f(a-x)$ can be obtained from the function $f(x)$ by first flipping $f(x)$ along the y-axis and then shifting it right by a units. Notice that in the interval $[0, a]$, $f(x)$ and $f(a-x)$ describe precisely the same area.

There are two ways to look at the justification of this property, as described in the figures on the left and right respectively.

Example 16 Show that

(i) $\int_0^{\pi/2} f(\sin x)\,dx = \int_0^{\pi/2} f(\cos x)\,dx$

(ii) $\int_0^{\pi/2} f(\tan x)\,dx = \int_0^{\pi/2} f(\cot x)\,dx$

(iii) $\int_0^{\pi/2} f(\sin 2x)\sin x\,dx = \int_0^{\pi/2} \sqrt{2}\, f(\cos 2x)\cdot\cos x\,dx$

$= \int_0^{\pi/2} f(\sin 2x)\cdot\cos x\,dx$

(iv) $\int_0^{\pi} x\, f(\sin x)\,dx = \frac{\pi}{2}\int_0^{\pi} f(\sin x)\,dx$ **[IIT JEE 1982]**

Sol. (i) We know,

$$\int_0^{\pi/2} f(\sin x)\,dx = \int_0^{\pi/2} f\left[\sin\left(\frac{\pi}{2}-x\right)\right]dx$$

$$\left[\text{using } \int_0^a f(x)\,dx = \int_0^a f(a-x)\,dx\right]$$

$$= \int_0^{\pi/2} f(\cos x)\,dx$$

$$\therefore \int_0^{\pi/2} f(\sin x)\,dx = \int_0^{\pi/2} f(\cos x)\,dx$$

(ii) $$\int_0^{\pi/2} f(\tan x)\,dx = \int_0^{\pi/2} f\left(\tan\left(\frac{\pi}{2}-x\right)\right)dx$$

$$\left[\text{using } \int_0^a f(x)\,dx = \int_0^a f(a-x)\,dx\right]$$

$$= \int_0^{\pi/2} f(\cot x)\,dx$$

$$\therefore \int_0^{\pi/2} f(\tan x)\,dx = \int_0^{\pi/2} f(\cot x)\,dx$$

(iii) We know, $$I = \int_0^{\pi/2} f(\sin 2x)\sin x\,dx \quad \text{...(i)}$$

$$= \int_0^{\pi/2} f\left[\sin 2\left(\frac{\pi}{2}-x\right)\right]\cdot \sin\left(\frac{\pi}{2}-x\right)dx$$

$$\left[\text{using } \int_0^a f(x)\,dx = \int_0^a f(a-x)\,dx\right]$$

$$= \int_0^{\pi/2} f(\sin(\pi-2x))\cos x\,dx$$

$$I = \int_0^{\pi/2} f(\sin 2x)\cos x\,dx \quad \text{...(ii)}$$

Adding Eqs. (i) and (ii), we get

$$2I = \int_0^{\pi/2} f(\sin 2x)(\sin x + \cos x)\,dx$$

$$= \sqrt{2}\int_0^{\pi/2} f(\sin 2x)\sin\left(x+\frac{\pi}{4}\right)dx$$

Put $x + \frac{\pi}{4} = \left(\frac{\pi}{2}-\theta\right)$ $\left(\text{i.e. } x = \frac{\pi}{4}-\theta\right)$

$$\Rightarrow \quad 2I = -\sqrt{2}\int_{\pi/4}^{-\pi/4} f(\cos 2\theta)\cos\theta\,d\theta$$

$$= \sqrt{2}\int_{-\pi/4}^{\pi/4} f(\cos 2\theta)\cos\theta\,d\theta$$

$$= 2\sqrt{2}\int_0^{\pi/4} f(\cos 2\theta)\cos\theta\,d\theta \text{ (since it is even)}$$

$$\therefore \quad I = \sqrt{2}\int_0^{\pi/4} f(\cos 2\theta)\cos\theta\,d\theta$$

(iv) Let $$I = \int_0^{\pi} x f(\sin x)\,dx \quad \text{...(i)}$$

Replacing x by $(\pi - x)$, we get

$$I = \int_0^{\pi} (\pi - x) f(\sin(\pi - x))\,dx$$

$$\Rightarrow \quad I = \int_0^{\pi} (\pi - x) f(\sin x)\,dx \quad \text{...(ii)}$$

Adding Eqs. (i) and (ii), we get

$$2I = \int_0^{\pi} \pi f(\sin x)\,dx \Rightarrow I = \frac{\pi}{2}\int_0^{\pi} f(\sin x)\,dx$$

$$\therefore \int_0^{\pi} x f(\sin x)\,dx = \frac{\pi}{2}\int_0^{\pi} f(\sin x)\,dx$$

Example 17 If f and g are continuous functions satisfying $f(x) = f(a-x)$ and $g(x) + g(a-x) = 2$, then show that $\int_0^a f(x)\,g(x)\,dx = \int_0^a f(x)\,dx$.

Sol. Let $$I = \int_0^a f(x)\,g(x)\,dx = \int_0^a f(a-x)\,g(a-x)\,dx$$

$$= \int_0^a f(x)\cdot[2-g(x)]\,dx$$

$$\left[\text{using } \int_0^a f(x)\,dx = \int_0^a f(a-x)\,dx\right]$$

$\because$ $f(x) = f(a-x)$ and $g(a-x) + g(x) = 2$ (given)

$$\therefore \quad \int_0^a f(x)\cdot g(x)\,dx = 2\int_0^a f(x)\,dx - \int_0^a f(x)\cdot g(x)\,dx$$

or $$2\int_0^a f(x)\cdot g(x)\,dx = 2\int_0^a f(x)\,dx$$

$$\Rightarrow \quad \int_0^a f(x)\,g(x)\,dx = \int_0^a f(x)\,dx$$

Example 18 Evaluate

(i) $\int_0^{\pi/2} \frac{dx}{1+\sqrt{\tan x}}$ (ii) $\int_0^{\pi/2} \log(\tan x)\,dx$

(iii) $\int_0^{\pi/4} \log(1+\tan x)\,dx$ (iv) $\int_0^{\pi/2} \frac{\sin x - \cos x}{1+\sin x\cos x}\,dx$

Sol. (i) Let $$I = \int_0^{\pi/2} \frac{dx}{1+\sqrt{\tan x}} = \int_0^{\pi/2} \frac{\sqrt{\cos x}}{\sqrt{\cos x}+\sqrt{\sin x}}\,dx \quad \text{...(i)}$$

Then, $$I = \int_0^{\pi/2} \frac{\sqrt{\cos(\pi/2-x)}}{\sqrt{\cos(\pi/2-x)}+\sqrt{\sin(\pi/2-x)}}\,dx$$

$$= \int_0^{\pi/2} \frac{\sqrt{\sin x}}{\sqrt{\sin x}+\sqrt{\cos x}}\,dx \quad \text{...(ii)}$$

Adding Eqs. (i) and (ii), we get

$$2I = \int_0^{\pi/2} \frac{\sqrt{\sin x}}{\sqrt{\sin x}+\sqrt{\cos x}}\,dx + \int_0^{\pi/2} \frac{\sqrt{\cos x}}{\sqrt{\sin x}+\sqrt{\cos x}}\,dx$$

$$= \int_0^{\pi/2} \frac{\sqrt{\sin x}+\sqrt{\cos x}}{\sqrt{\sin x}+\sqrt{\cos x}}\,dx = \int_0^{\pi/2} 1\,dx$$

$$= [x]_0^{\pi/2} = \frac{\pi}{2} - 0 \Rightarrow 2I = \frac{\pi}{2} \Rightarrow I = \frac{\pi}{4}$$

(ii) Let $$I = \int_0^{\pi/2} \log(\tan x)\,dx \quad \text{...(i)}$$

Then, $$I = \int_0^{\pi/2} \log\left\{\tan\left(\frac{\pi}{2}-x\right)\right\}dx$$

$$\Rightarrow \quad I = \int_0^{\pi/2} \log(\cot x)\,dx \quad \text{...(ii)}$$

Adding Eqs. (i) and (ii), we get

$$2I = \int_0^{\pi/2} \log(\tan x)\,dx + \int_0^{\pi/2} \log(\cot x)\,dx$$

$$= \int_0^{\pi/2} (\log\tan x + \log\cot x)\,dx$$

$$= \int_0^{\pi/2} \log(\tan x\cdot\cot x)\,dx = \int_0^{\pi/2} \log(1)\,dx$$

$$\Rightarrow 2I = 0 \Rightarrow \quad I = 0$$

(iii) Let $I = \int_0^{\pi/4} \log(1 + \tan x)\, dx$ ...(i)

$$= \int_0^{\pi/4} \log[1 + \tan(\pi/4 - x)]\, dx$$

$$= \int_0^{\pi/4} \log\left(1 + \frac{\tan \pi/4 - \tan x}{1 + \tan(\pi/4)\cdot \tan x}\right) dx$$

$$= \int_0^{\pi/4} \log\left(\frac{1 + \tan x + 1 - \tan x}{1 + \tan x}\right) dx$$

$$= \int_0^{\pi/4} \log\left(\frac{2}{1 + \tan x}\right) dx$$

$$= \int_0^{\pi/4} \log(2)\, dx - \int_0^{\pi/4} \log(1 + \tan x)\, dx$$

$\Rightarrow I = (\log 2)(x)_0^{\pi/4} - I$ [using Eq. (i)]

$$\Rightarrow 2I = \frac{\pi}{4} \log 2 \Rightarrow I = \frac{\pi}{8} \log 2$$

(iv) Let $I = \int_0^{\pi/2} \frac{\sin x - \cos x}{1 + \sin x \cos x} dx$ ...(i)

Then, $I = \int_0^{\pi/2} \frac{\sin\left(\frac{\pi}{2} - x\right) - \cos\left(\frac{\pi}{2} - x\right)}{1 + \sin\left(\frac{\pi}{2} - x\right)\cos\left(\frac{\pi}{2} - x\right)} dx$

$\Rightarrow I = \int_0^{\pi/2} \frac{\cos x - \sin x}{1 + \cos x \cdot \sin x} dx$ ...(ii)

Adding Eqs. (i) and (ii), we get

$$2I = \int_0^{\pi/2} \frac{\sin x - \cos x}{1 + \sin x \cos x} dx + \int_0^{\pi/2} \frac{\cos x - \sin x}{1 + \sin x \cos x} dx \Rightarrow$$

$2I = 0 \Rightarrow I = 0$

Example 19 The value of $\int_0^a \log(\cot a + \tan x)\, dx$, where $a \in (0, \pi/2)$ is equal to

(a) $a \log(\sin a)$ (b) $-a \log(\sin a)$
(c) $-a \log(\cos a)$ (d) None of these

Sol. Let $I = \int_0^a \log(\cot a + \tan x)\, dx$

$$= \int_0^a \log\left(\frac{\cos a}{\sin a} + \frac{\sin x}{\cos x}\right) dx$$

$$= \int_0^a \log\left(\frac{\cos(a - x)}{\sin a \cos x}\right) dx$$

$$= \int_0^a \log[\cos(a - x)]\, dx - \int_0^a \log(\sin a)\, dx - \int_0^a \log(\cos x)\, dx$$

$$= \int_0^a \log\cos(x) dx - \int_0^a \log(\sin a) dx - \int_0^a \log(\cos x)\, dx$$

$\left[\text{using } \int_0^a f(x)\, dx = \int_0^a f(a - x)\, dx \text{ to first integral}\right]$

$$= -\log(\sin a) \int_0^a dx = -a \log(\sin a)$$

Hence, (b) is the correct answer.

Property IV. $\int_a^b f(x)\, dx = \int_a^b f(a + b - x)\, dx$ (King's property)

Proof Put $x = a + b - t \Rightarrow dx = -dt$

Also, when $x = a$, then $t = b$, and when $x = b$

$$\therefore \int_a^b f(x)\, dx = \int_b^a f(a + b - t)(-dt) = -\int_b^a f(a + b - t)\, dt$$

$$= \int_a^b f(a + b - t)\, dt = \int_a^b f(a + b - x)\, dx$$

$$\therefore \int_a^b f(x)\, dx = \int_a^b f(a + b - x)\, dx$$

Geometrically $\int_0^a f(x) dx = \int_a^b f(a + b - x)\, dx$

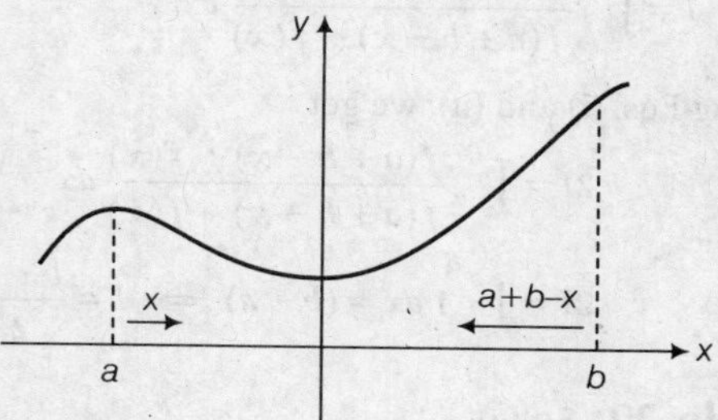

As the variable x varies from a to b, the variable $a + b - x$ varies from b to a. Thus, whether we use x or $a + b - x$, the entire interval $[a, b]$ is covered in both the cases and the areas will be the same.

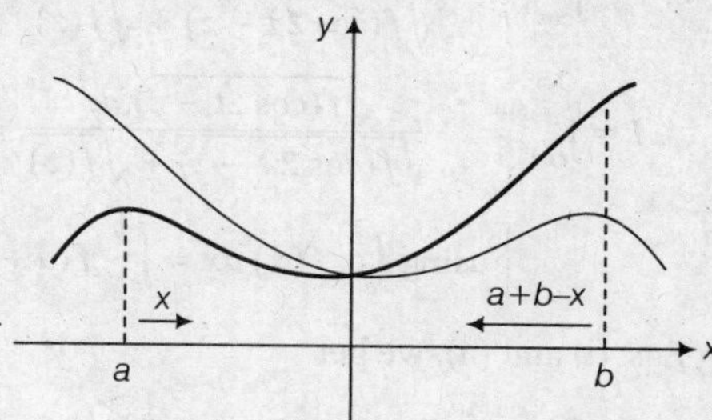

The graph of $f(a + b - x)$ can be obtained from the graph of $f(x)$ by first flipping the graph of $f(x)$ along the y-axis and then shifting it $(a + b)$ units towards the right; the areas described by $f(x)$ and $f(a + b - x)$ in the interval $[a, b]$ are precisely the same.

Example 20 Evaluate $\int_{\pi/6}^{\pi/3} \frac{dx}{1 + \sqrt{\tan x}}$.

Sol. Let $I = \int_{\pi/6}^{\pi/3} \frac{dx}{1 + \sqrt{\tan x}} = \int_{\pi/6}^{\pi/3} \frac{\sqrt{\cos x}\cdot dx}{\sqrt{\cos x} + \sqrt{\sin x}}$ ... (i)

then, $I = \int_{\pi/6}^{\pi/3} \frac{\sqrt{\cos(\pi/2 - x)}}{\sqrt{\cos(\pi/2 - x)} + \sqrt{\sin(\pi/2 - x)}} dx$

($\because a + b = \pi/2$)

$\Rightarrow I = \int_{\pi/6}^{\pi/3} \frac{\sqrt{\sin x}}{\sqrt{\sin x} + \sqrt{\cos x}} dx$ ...(ii)

Adding Eqs. (i) and (ii), we get

$$2I = \int_{\pi/6}^{\pi/3} 1\, dx = \frac{\pi}{3} - \frac{\pi}{6} = \frac{\pi}{6} \Rightarrow I = \frac{\pi}{12}$$

| Example 21 Prove that

$$\int_a^b \frac{f(x)}{f(x)+f(a+b-x)}\, dx = \frac{b-a}{2}.$$

Sol. Let $\quad I = \int_a^b \frac{f(x)}{f(x)+f(a+b-x)}\, dx \quad$ ...(i)

then, $\quad I = \int_a^b \frac{f(a+b-x)}{f(a+b-x)+f(a+b-(a+b-x))}\, dx$

$\Rightarrow \quad I = \int_a^b \frac{f(a+b-x)}{f(a+b-x)+f(x)}\, dx \quad$ ...(ii)

Adding Eqs. (i) and (ii), we get

$$2I = \int_a^b \frac{f(a+b-x)+f(x)}{f(a+b-x)+f(x)}\, dx$$

$$\Rightarrow \quad 2I = \int_a^b 1\, dx = (b-a) \Rightarrow I = \frac{b-a}{2}$$

| Example 22 Solve

$$I = \int_{\cos^4 t}^{-\sin^4 t} \frac{\sqrt{f(z)}\, dz}{\sqrt{f(\cos 2t - z)} + \sqrt{f(z)}}.$$

Sol. We have, $I = \int_{\cos^4 t}^{-\sin^4 t} \frac{\sqrt{f(z)}\, dz}{\sqrt{f(\cos 2t - z)} + \sqrt{f(z)}} \quad$ ...(i)

$\therefore \quad I = \int_{\cos^4 t}^{-\sin^4 t} \frac{\sqrt{f(\cos 2t - z)}\, dz}{\sqrt{f(\cos 2t - z)} + \sqrt{f(z)}} \quad$ ..(ii)

$$\left[\text{using } \int_a^b f(x)\, dx = \int_a^b f(a+b-x)\, dx\right]$$

Adding Eqs. (i) and (ii), we get

$$2I = \int_{\cos^4 t}^{-\sin^4 t} dz \Rightarrow 2I = (z)_{\cos^4 t}^{-\sin^4 t}$$

$$\therefore \quad I = -\frac{1}{2}(\sin^4 t + \cos^4 t) = -\frac{1}{2}(1 - 2\sin^2 t \cos^2 t)$$

$$= -\frac{1}{2}\left(1 - \frac{1}{2}\sin^2 2t\right) = -\frac{1}{2} + \frac{1}{4}\sin^2 2t$$

Directions (Ex 23-25) *Let the function f satisfies* $f(x) \cdot f'(-x) = f(-x) \cdot f'(x)$ *for all x and* $f(0) = 3$.

| Example 23 The value of $f(x) \cdot f(-x)$ for all x is

(a) 4 (b) 9

(c) 12 (d) 16

Sol. Given, $\quad f(x) \cdot f'(-x) = f(-x) \cdot f'(x)$

$$\Rightarrow \quad \frac{f'(x)}{f(x)} = \frac{f'(-x)}{f(-x)}$$

Integrating both sides, we get

$$\ln f(x) = -f(-x) + C$$

$$\ln[f(x) \cdot f(-x)] = C$$

$$f(x) \cdot f(-x) = C$$

But $\quad f(0) = 3$

$\Rightarrow \quad f^2(0) = C \therefore C = 9$

$\therefore \quad f(x) \cdot f(-x) = 9$

Aliter $\quad f(x) \cdot f'(x) - f(-x) \cdot f'(x) = 0$

$$\Rightarrow \quad \frac{d}{dx}[f(-x) \cdot f(x)] = 0$$

Integrating both sides, we get $f(x) \cdot f(-x) =$ Constant

Hence, (b) is the correct answer.

| Example 24 $\int_{-51}^{51} \frac{dx}{3+f(x)}$ has the value equal to

(a) 17 (b) 34

(c) 102 (d) 0

Sol. Let $I = \int_{-51}^{51} \frac{dx}{3+f(x)} = \int_{-51}^{51} \frac{dx}{3+f(-x)}$

$$\left[\text{using } \int_a^b f(x) dx = \int_a^b f(a+b-x) dx\right]$$

$$2I = \int_{-51}^{51} \frac{6+f(x)+f(-x)}{[3+f(x)][3+f(-x)]}\, dx$$

$$= \int_{-51}^{51} \frac{6+f(x)+f(-x)}{9+3[f(x)+f(-x)]+f(x) \cdot f(-x)}\, dx$$

$$= \int_{-51}^{51} \frac{6+f(x)+f(-x)}{18+3[f(x)+f(-x)]}\, dx$$

$$= \frac{1}{3}\int_{-51}^{51} dx = \frac{2 \cdot 51}{3}$$

$$\Rightarrow \quad I = \frac{51}{3} = 17$$

Hence, (a) is the correct answer.

| Example 25 Number of roots of $f(x) = 0$ in $[-2, 2]$ is

(a) 0 (b) 1

(c) 2 (d) 4

Sol. Let $x = \alpha$ be the root of $f(x) = 0$.

$\therefore \quad f(\alpha) = 0$

$$f(x) \cdot f(-x) = 9$$

Put $x = \alpha$, then $\quad 0 = 9 \quad$ (impossible)

Therefore, $f(x)$ has no root but $f(0) = 3$.

$\therefore f(x) > 0, \forall x \in R$ as f is continuous possible function $f(x) = 3e^{-x}$.

Hence, (a) is the correct answer.

Exercise for Session 2

1. The value of $\int_0^{\pi/4} \log(1+\tan\theta)\, d\theta$ is equal to

(a) $\frac{\pi}{2}\log 2$ (b) $-\frac{\pi}{4}\log 2$ (c) $\frac{\pi}{8}\log 2$ (d) None of these

2. For any integer n, the value of $\int_0^{\pi} e^{\cos^2 x}\cdot\cos^3(2n+1)x\cdot dx$ is equal to

(a) 0 (b) 1 (c) -1 (d) None of these

3. The value of $\int_2^3 \frac{\sqrt{x}}{\sqrt{5-x}+\sqrt{x}}\, dx$ is equal to

(a) 1/2 (b) 1/3 (c) 1/4 (d) None of these

4. The value of $\int_0^2 \frac{dx}{(17+8x-4x^2)(e^{6(1-x)}+1)}$ is equal to

(a) $-\frac{1}{8\sqrt{21}}\log\left|\frac{2-\sqrt{21}}{2+\sqrt{21}}\right|$ (b) $-\frac{1}{8\sqrt{21}}\log\left|\frac{2+\sqrt{21}}{\sqrt{21}-2}\right|$

(c) $-\frac{1}{8\sqrt{21}}\left\{\log\left|\frac{2-\sqrt{21}}{2+\sqrt{21}}\right|-\log\left|\frac{2+\sqrt{21}}{\sqrt{21}-2}\right|\right\}$ (d) None of these

5. If f is an odd function, then the value of $\int_{-a}^{a}\frac{f(\sin x)}{f(\cos x)+f(\sin^2 x)}\, dx$ is equal to

(a) 0 (b) $f(\cos x)+f(\sin x)$ (c) 1 (d) None of these

6. If $[x]$ stands for the greatest integar function, then $\int_4^{10}\frac{[x^2]\,dx}{[x^2-28x+196]+[x^2]}$ is

(a) 1 (b) 2 (c) 3 (d) 4

7. The value of $\int_0^{\pi}\frac{x dx}{1+\cos\alpha\cdot\sin\alpha}(0<\alpha<\pi)$ is

(a) $\frac{\pi}{\sin\alpha}$ (b) $\frac{\pi\alpha}{\sin\alpha}$ (c) $\frac{\alpha}{\sin\alpha}$ (d) $\frac{\sin\alpha}{\alpha}$

8. If f, g, h be continuous functions on $[0, a]$ such that $f(a-x)=f(x)$, $g(a-x)=-g(x)$ and $3h(x)=5+4h(a-x)$, then the value of $\int_0^a f(x)\cdot g(x)\cdot h(x)dx$ is

(a) 0 (b) 1 (c) a (d) $2a$

9. If $2f(x)+f(-x)=\frac{1}{x}\sin\left(x-\frac{1}{x}\right)$, then the value of $\int_{1/e}^{e} f(x)dx$ is

(a) 0 (b) e (c) $1/e$ (d) $e+1/e$

10. Prove that $\int_0^{\pi} xf(\sin x)dx=\frac{\pi}{2}\int_0^{\pi} f(\sin x)dx$.

11. Evaluate $\int_0^{\pi}\frac{x^2\sin 2x\cdot\sin\left(\frac{\pi}{2}\cos x\right)dx}{(2x-\pi)}$.

12. Number of positive continuous function $f(x)$ defined on [0, 1] for which $\int_0^1 f(x)dx=1$, $\int_0^1 xf(x)dx=2$ and $\int_0^1 x^2 f(x)dx=4$.

13. Let $I_1=\int_0^1\frac{e^x}{1+x}dx$ and $I_2=\int_0^1\frac{x^2}{e^{x^3}(2-x^3)}dx$. Then $\frac{I_1}{I_2}$ is equal to

(a) $\frac{3}{e}$ (b) $\frac{3}{e}$ (c) $3e$ (d) $\frac{1}{3e}$

14. If $f(x)=\frac{e^x}{1+e^x}$, $I_1=\int_{f(-a)}^{f(x)} x\cdot g\{x(1-x)\}dx$ and $I_2=\int_{f(-a)}^{f(a)} g\{x(1-x)\}dx$, then the value of $\frac{I_2}{I_1}$ is

(a) 1 (b) -3 (c) -1 (d) 2

Session 3

Applications of Piecewise Function Property

Applications of Piecewise Function Property

Property V (a). $\int_a^b f(x)\,dx = \int_a^c f(x)\,dx + \int_c^b f(x)\,dx,$

where $c \leftrightarrow R$

Proof Let $\phi(x)$ be primitive of $f(x)$, then

$$\int_a^b f(x)\,dx = \phi(b) - \phi(a) \qquad \text{...(i)}$$

and $\int_a^c f(x)dx + \int_c^b f(x)dx = [\phi(c) - \phi(a)] + [\phi(b) - \phi(c)]$

$$= \phi(b) - \phi(a) \qquad \text{...(ii)}$$

From Eqs. (i) and (ii), we get

$$\int_a^b f(x)\,dx = \int_a^c f(x)\,dx + \int_c^b f(x)\,dx$$

Generalisation Property V(a) can be generalised into the following form

$$\int_a^b f(x)dx = \int_a^{c_1} f(x)dx + \int_{c_1}^{c_2} f(x)\,dx + \ldots + \int_{c_n}^b f(x)dx$$

where, $a < c_1 < c_2 < \ldots < c_{n-1} < c_n < b$

Property V (b).

$$\int_0^a f(x)\,dx = \int_0^{a/2} f(x)\,dx + \int_0^{a/2} f(a-x)\,dx$$

Proof As we know,

$$\int_0^a f(x)\,dx = \int_0^{a/2} f(x)\,dx + \int_{a/2}^a f(x)\,dx$$

Put $x = a - t \Rightarrow dx = -\,dt$ in the second integral also, when $x = a/2$, then $t = a/2$ and when $x = a$, then $t = 0$.

$$\therefore \quad \int_0^a f(x)\,dx = \int_0^{a/2} f(x)\,dx + \int_{a/2}^0 f(a-t)(-\,dt)$$

$$= \int_0^{a/2} f(x)\,dx + \int_0^{a/2} f(a-t)\,dt$$

$$\int_0^a f(x)\,dx = \int_0^{a/2} f(x)\,dx + \int_0^{a/2} f(a-x)\,dx$$

Property V (c).

$$\int_a^b f(x)\,dx = \begin{cases} 0, & \text{if } f(a+x) = -\,f(b-x) \\ 2\int_a^{\frac{a+b}{2}} f(x)\,dx, & \text{if } f(a+x) = f(b-x) \end{cases}$$

Proof Let us consider the function $f(x)$ on $[a, b]$ when $f(a+x) = f(b-x)$, then f is even symmetric about the mid-point $x = \dfrac{a+b}{2}$ on the interval $[a, b]$ when $f(a+x) = -\,f(b-x)$, then f is odd symmetric about the mid-point $x = \dfrac{a+b}{2}$ of the interval $[a, b]$.

$$\therefore \text{Using } \int_{-a}^a f(x)\,dx = \begin{cases} 0, & \text{if } f \text{ is an odd function} \\ 2f(x)dx, & \text{if } f \text{ is an even function} \end{cases}$$

$$\Rightarrow \int_a^b f(x)dx = \begin{cases} 0, & \text{if } f(a+x) = -\,f(b-x) \\ 2\int_a^{\frac{a+b}{2}} f(x)\,dx, & \text{if } f(a+x) = f(b-x) \end{cases}$$

| Example 26 Given function, $f(x) = \begin{cases} x^2, & \text{for } 0 \le x < 1 \\ \sqrt{x}, & \text{for } 1 \le x \le 2 \end{cases}$.

Evaluate $\int_0^2 f(x)\,dx$.

Sol. Here, $\int_0^2 f(x)\,dx = \int_0^1 f(x)\,dx + \int_1^2 f(x)\,dx$

$$\therefore \quad \int_0^2 f(x)\,dx = \int_0^1 x^2\,dx + \int_1^2 \sqrt{x}\,dx$$

$$= \left[\frac{x^3}{3}\right]_0^1 + \left[\frac{x^{3/2}}{3/2}\right]_1^2$$

$$= \left[\frac{x^3}{3}\right]_0^1 + \left[\frac{2}{3}x\sqrt{x}\right]_1^2$$

$$= \left[\frac{1}{3} - 0\right] + \frac{2}{3}[2\sqrt{2} - 1]$$

$$= \frac{1}{3} + \frac{4\sqrt{2}}{3} - \frac{2}{3} = \frac{4\sqrt{2}}{3} - \frac{1}{3} = \frac{1}{3}(4\sqrt{2} - 1)$$

| Example 27 Evaluate the integral $I = \int_0^2 |1 - x|\,dx$.

Sol. By definition, $|a - b| = \begin{cases} b - a, & \text{if } a < b \\ a - b, & \text{if } a > b \end{cases}$

Then, $|1 - x| = \begin{cases} (1 - x), & 0 \le x \le 1 \\ (x - 1), & 1 \le x \le 2 \end{cases}$

$$\therefore \int_0^2 |1-x|\,dx = \int_0^1 (1-x)\,dx + \int_1^2 (x-1)\,dx$$

$$= \left[x - \frac{x^2}{2}\right]_0^1 + \left[\frac{x^2}{2} - x\right]_1^2$$

$$= \left\{\left(1-\frac{1}{2}\right)-(0-0)\right\} + \left\{\left(\frac{4}{2}-2\right)-\left(\frac{1}{2}-1\right)\right\}$$

$$= \frac{1}{2} + \left\{0 + \frac{1}{2}\right\} = 1$$

Example 28 Evaluate

(i) $\int_0^{\pi} |\cos x|\,dx$ (ii) $\int_0^2 |x^2+2x-3|\,dx$

Sol. (i) $\int_0^{\pi} |\cos x|\,dx = \int_0^{\pi/2} |\cos x|\,dx + \int_{\pi/2}^{\pi} |\cos x|\,dx$

$$= \int_0^{\pi/2} (\cos x)\,dx - \int_{\pi/2}^{\pi} (\cos x)\,dx$$

$$= [\sin x]_0^{\pi/2} - [\sin x]_{\pi/2}^{\pi}$$

$$= (1-0) - (0-1) = 2$$

(ii) $\int_0^2 |x^2+2x-3|\,dx$

$$= \int_0^1 |x^2+2x-3|\,dx + \int_1^2 |x^2+2x-3|\,dx \quad \text{...(i)}$$

We have, $x^2+2x-3 = (x+3)(x-1)$

$\therefore$ $x^2+2x-3 > 0$ for $x < -3$ or $x > 1$

and $x^2+2x-3 < 0$ for $-3 < x < 1$

So, $|x^2+2x-3|$

$$= \begin{cases} (x^2+2x-3), & \text{for } x < -3 \text{ or } x > 1 \\ -(x^2+2x-3), & \text{for } -3 < x < 1 \end{cases}$$

$\therefore$ Eq. (i) becomes

$$I = \int_0^1 -(x^2+2x-3)\,dx + \int_1^2 (x^2+2x-3)\,dx$$

$$= -\left[\frac{x^3}{3} + x^2 - 3x\right]_0^1 + \left[\frac{x^3}{3} + x^2 - 3x\right]_1^2$$

$$= 4$$

Example 29 Evaluate $\int_{-1}^1 (x-[x])\,dx$, where [.] denotes the greatest integral part of x.

Sol. Let $I = \int_{-1}^1 (x-[x])\,dx = \int_{-1}^1 x \cdot dx - \int_{-1}^1 [x]\,dx$

$$= \left(\frac{x^2}{2}\right)_{-1}^1 - \left(\int_{-1}^0 [x]\,dx + \int_0^1 [x]\,dx\right)$$

$$= \frac{1}{2}(1-1) - \left(\int_{-1}^0 -1\,dx + \int_0^1 0\,dx\right)$$

$$= 0 + (x)_{-1}^1 - 0 = 1$$

Example 30 Evaluate $\int_0^2 \{x\}\,dx$, where $\{x\}$ denotes the fractional part of x.

Sol. $\int_0^2 \{x\}\,dx = \int_0^2 (x-[x])\,dx = \int_0^2 x\,dx - \int_0^2 [x]\,dx$

$$= \left(\frac{x^2}{2}\right)_0^2 - \left(\int_0^1 [x]\,dx + \int_1^2 [x]\,dx\right)$$

$$= \frac{1}{2}(4-0) - \left(\int_0^1 0\,dx + \int_1^2 1\,dx\right)$$

$$= 2 - (x)_1^2 = 2 - (1) = 1$$

Remark

In above example, for greatest integer less than or equal to x, it is compulsory to break it at integral limits.

Example 31 Evaluate $\int_0^9 \{\sqrt{x}\}\,dx$, where $\{x\}$ denotes the fractional part of x.

Sol. $\int_0^9 \{\sqrt{x}\}\,dx = \int_0^9 \left(\sqrt{x} - [\sqrt{x}]\right)dx$

$$= \int_0^9 (x^{1/2})\,dx - \int_0^9 [\sqrt{x}]\,dx$$

$$= \frac{2}{3}(x^{3/2})_0^9 - \int_0^9 [\sqrt{x}]\,dx$$

$$= \frac{2}{3}[27] - \int_0^9 [\sqrt{x}]\,dx$$

As $\int_0^9 [\sqrt{x}]\,dx \Rightarrow 0 \le x \le 9$ and $0 \le \sqrt{x} \le 3$

Thus, it should be divided into three parts

$$0 \le \sqrt{x} \le 1,\ 1 \le \sqrt{x} \le 2,\ 2 \le \sqrt{x} \le 3$$

i.e. $I = 2(9) - \int_0^9 [\sqrt{x}]\,dx$

$$= 18 - \left[\int_0^1 [\sqrt{x}]\,dx + \int_1^4 [\sqrt{x}]\,dx + \int_4^9 [\sqrt{x}]\,dx\right]$$

$$= 18 - \left(\int_0^1 0\,dx + \int_1^4 1\,dx + \int_4^9 2\,dx\right)$$

$$= 18 - \left(0 + (x)_1^4 + (2x)_4^9\right) = 18 - (3+10) = 5$$

Example 32 If for a real number y, $[y]$ is the greatest integer less than or equal to y, then find the value of the integral $\int_{\pi/2}^{3\pi/2} [2\sin x]\,dx$.

Sol. We know, $-1 \le \sin x \le 1$ as $x \in [\pi/2, 3\pi/2]$

$\Rightarrow$ $-2 \le 2\sin x \le 2$

$\therefore$ $2\sin x$ must be divided (or broken) at $x = 5\pi/6, \pi, 7\pi/6$.

As $2\sin x = +1, 0, -1$ at these points.

$$\therefore \int_{\pi/2}^{3\pi/2} [2\sin x]\,dx = \int_{\pi/2}^{5\pi/6} [2\sin x]\,dx + \int_{5\pi/6}^{\pi} [2\sin x]\,dx$$

$$+ \int_{\pi}^{7\pi/6} [2\sin x]\,dx + \int_{7\pi/6}^{3\pi/2} [2\sin x]\,dx$$

$$= \int_{\pi/2}^{5\pi/6} 1\,dx + \int_{5\pi/6}^{\pi} 0\,dx + \int_{\pi}^{7\pi/6} (-1)\,dx + \int_{7\pi/6}^{3\pi/2} (-2)\,dx$$

$$= \left(\frac{5\pi}{6} - \frac{\pi}{2}\right) + 0 - \left(\frac{7\pi}{6} - \pi\right) - 2\left(\frac{3\pi}{2} - \frac{7\pi}{6}\right) = -\frac{\pi}{2}$$

Example 33 The value of $\int_0^{100} [\tan^{-1} x]\,dx$ is equal to (where [.] denotes the greatest integer function)

(a) $\tan 1 - 100$ (b) $\pi/2 - \tan 1$
(c) $100 - \tan 1$ (d) None of these

Sol. Let $I = \int_0^{100} [\tan^{-1} x]\,dx$

where $[\tan^{-1} x]$ is shown as

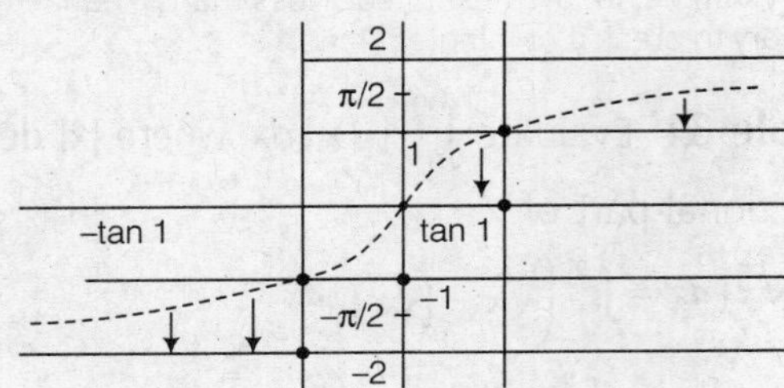

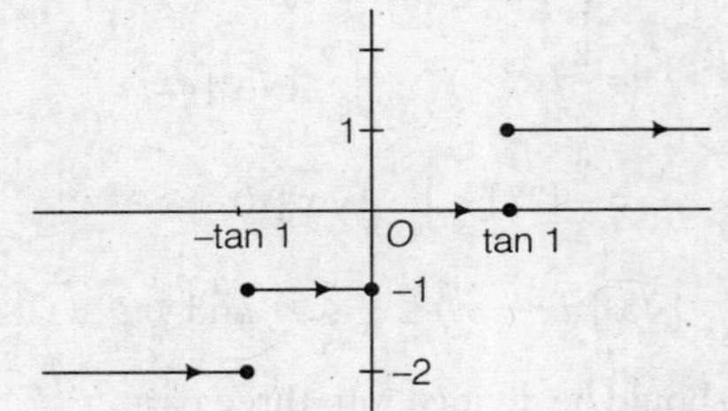

$\therefore \int_0^{100} [\tan^{-1} x]\,dx$ is shown as

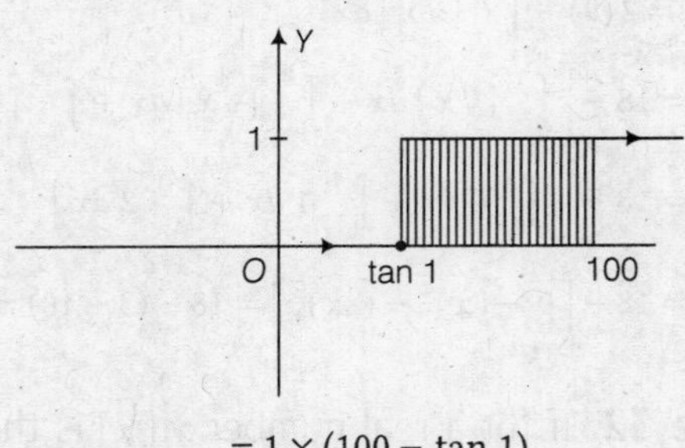

$$= 1 \times (100 - \tan 1)$$

Hence, (c) is the correct answer.

Example 34 The value of $\int_{-2}^{2} \min\{x - [x], -x - [-x]\}\,dx$ is equal to (where [.] denotes the greatest integer function)

(a) 1/2 (b) 1
(c) 3/2 (d) 2

Sol. Let $f(x) = \min(x - [x], -x - [-x]) = \min(\{x\}, \{-x\})$

Graphically, $\{x\}$ and $\{-x\}$ could be plotted as;

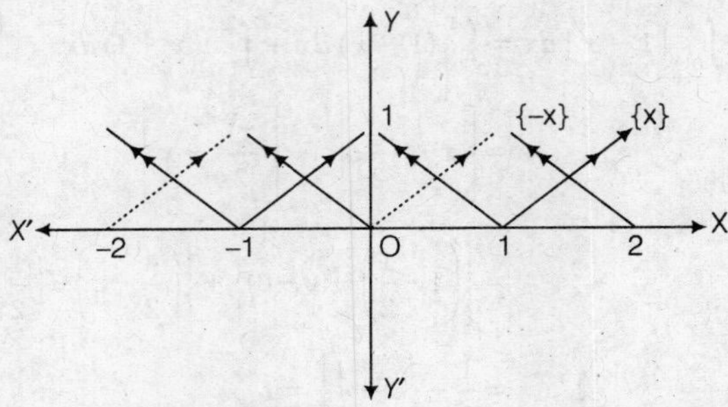

From the above graph, we need $\int_{-2}^{2} \min(\{x\}, \{-x\})$ shown as

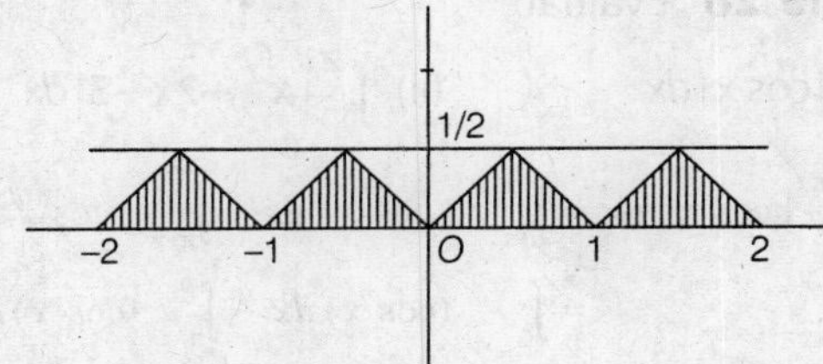

$$\therefore \quad \int_{-2}^{2} f(x)\,dx = 4\int_0^1 f(x)\,dx = 4 \times \frac{1}{2} \times 1 \times \frac{1}{2} = 1$$

Hence, (b) is the correct answer.

Example 35 The value of $\int_1^2 (x^{[x^2]} + [x^2]^x)\,dx$ is equal to where [.] denotes the greatest integer function

(a) $\frac{5}{4} + \sqrt{3} + (2^{\sqrt{3}} - 2^{\sqrt{2}}) + \frac{1}{\log 3}(9 - 3^{\sqrt{3}})$

(b) $\frac{5}{4} + \sqrt{3} + \frac{\sqrt{2}}{3} + \frac{1}{\log 2}(2^{\sqrt{3}} - 2^{\sqrt{2}}) + \frac{1}{\log 3}(9 - 3^{\sqrt{3}})$

(c) $\frac{5}{4} + \frac{\sqrt{2}}{3} + \frac{1}{\log 2}(2^{\sqrt{3}} - 2^{\sqrt{2}}) + \frac{1}{\log 3}(9 - 3^{\sqrt{3}})$

(d) None of the above

Sol. Let $I = \int_1^2 (x^{[x^2]} + [x^2]^x)\,dx$

$$= \int_1^{\sqrt{2}} (x + 1)\,dx + \int_{\sqrt{2}}^{\sqrt{3}} (x^2 + 2^x)\,dx + \int_{\sqrt{3}}^{2} (x^3 + 3^x)\,dx$$

$$= \left[\frac{x^2}{2} + x\right]_1^{\sqrt{2}} + \left[\frac{x^3}{3} + \frac{2^x}{\log 2}\right]_{\sqrt{2}}^{\sqrt{3}} + \left[\frac{x^4}{4} + \frac{3^x}{\log 3}\right]_{\sqrt{3}}^{2}$$

$$= \frac{5}{4} + \sqrt{3} + \frac{\sqrt{2}}{3} + \frac{1}{\log 2}(2^{\sqrt{3}} - 2^{\sqrt{2}}) + \frac{1}{\log 3}(3^2 - 3^{\sqrt{3}})$$

Hence, (b) is the correct answer.

Example 36 The value of $\int_0^{2\pi} [|\sin x| + |\cos x|]\,dx$ is equal to

(a) $\frac{\pi}{2}$ (b) π (c) $\frac{3\pi}{2}$ (d) 2π

Sol. Let $f(x) = [|\sin x| + |\cos x|]$

As, $|\sin x| \geq \sin^2 x$ and $|\cos x| \geq \cos^2 x$

$\therefore \quad |\sin x| + |\cos x| \geq 1$

and $\quad |\sin x| + |\cos x| \leq \sqrt{1^2 + 1^2}$

$\Rightarrow \quad 1 \leq |\sin x| + |\cos x| \leq \sqrt{2}$

Thus, $[|\sin x| + |\cos x|] = 1$

$\therefore \quad \int_0^{2\pi} [|\sin x| + |\cos x|]\, dx = \int_0^{2\pi} 1\, dx = 2\pi$

Hence, (d) is the correct answer.

Example 37 The value of the definite integral $\int_0^{\pi/2} \sin|2x - \alpha|\, dx$, where $\alpha \in [0, \pi]$, is

(a) 1 (b) $\cos\alpha$ (c) $\frac{1+\cos\alpha}{2}$ (d) $\frac{1-\cos\alpha}{2}$

Sol. Let $I = \int_{-\alpha}^{(\pi-\alpha)} \sin|t|\, dt$, where $2x - \alpha = t \Rightarrow dx = \frac{dt}{2}$

$= \frac{1}{2}\int_{-\alpha}^{0} -\sin t\, dt + \frac{1}{2}\int_0^{\pi-\alpha} \sin t\, dt$

$= \left[\frac{1}{2}\cos t\right]_{-\alpha}^{0} - \left[\frac{1}{2}\cos t\right]_0^{\pi-\alpha}$

$= \frac{1}{2}[1 - \cos\alpha] - \frac{1}{2}[-\cos\alpha - 1]$

$= \frac{1}{2}(1 - \cos\alpha) + \frac{1}{2}(1 + \cos\alpha) = 1$

$= \frac{1}{2}(1 - \cos\alpha) + \frac{1}{2}(1 + \cos\alpha) = 1$

Hence, (a) is the correct answer.

Example 38 Let f be a continuous functions satisfying

$$f'(\ln x) = \begin{cases} 1 & \text{for } 0 < x \leq 1 \\ e^x - 1 & \text{for } x > 1 \end{cases}$$

and $f(0) = 0$, then $f(x)$ can be defined as

(a) $f(x) = \begin{cases} 1, & \text{if } x \leq 0 \\ 1 - e^x, & \text{if } x > 0 \end{cases}$ (b) $f(x) = \begin{cases} 1, & \text{if } x \leq 0 \\ e^x - 1, & \text{if } x > 0 \end{cases}$

(c) $f(x) = \begin{cases} x, & \text{if } x < 0 \\ e^x, & \text{if } x > 0 \end{cases}$ (d) $f(x) = \begin{cases} x, & \text{if } x \leq 0 \\ e^x - 1, & \text{if } x > 0 \end{cases}$

Sol. $f'(\ln x) = \begin{cases} 1, & \text{for } 0 < x \leq 1 \\ x, & \text{for } x > 1 \end{cases}$

Put $\quad \ln x = t \Rightarrow x = e^t$

For $x > 1$; $\quad f'(t) = e^t$ for $t > 0$

Integrating $f(t) = e^t + C$; $f(0) = e^0 + C \Rightarrow C = -1$

[given, $f(0) = 0$]

$\therefore \quad f(t) = e^t - 1$, for $t > 0$ (corresponding to $x > 1$)

Therefore, $\quad f(x) = e^x - 1$, for $x > 0$ ...(i)

Again, for $0 < x \leq 1$,

$f'(\ln x) = 1 \quad (\because x = e^t)$

$f'(t) = 1$, for $t \leq 0$

$f(t) = t + C$

$f(0) = 0 + C \Rightarrow C = 0 \Rightarrow f(t) = t$, for $t \leq 0$

$\Rightarrow \quad f(x) = x$, for $x \leq 0$

Hence, (d) is the correct answer.

Example 39 The integral $\int_{\pi/4}^{5\pi/4} (|\cos t|\sin t + |\sin t|\cos t)\, dt$ has the value equal to

(a) 0 (b) 1/2

(c) $1/\sqrt{2}$ (d) 1

Sol. Let

$$I = \int_{\pi/4}^{\pi/2} 2\sin t\cos t\, dt + \underbrace{\int_{\pi/2}^{\pi} [(-\sin t\cos t) + (\sin t\cos t)]\, dt}_{\text{zero}} + \int_{\pi}^{5\pi/4} (-2\sin t\cos t)\, dt$$

$= \int_{\pi/4}^{\pi/2} \sin 2t\, dt - \int_{\pi}^{5\pi/4} \sin 2t\, dt$

These two integrals cancels

$\Rightarrow$ Zero.

Hence, (a) is the correct answer.

Example 40 The value of $\int_0^2 f(x)\, dx$, where

$$f(x) = \begin{cases} 0, \text{ when } x = \frac{n}{n+1}, n = 1, 2, 3 \ldots \\ 1, \text{elsewhere} \end{cases}$$ 3 is equal to

(a) 1 (b) 2

(c) 3 (d) None of these

Sol. Here, $\int_0^2 f(x)\, dx = \int_0^{1/2} 1\, dx + \int_{1/2}^{2/3} 1\, dx + \int_{2/3}^{3/4} 1\, dx + \ldots$

$+ \int_{\frac{n-1}{n}}^{\frac{n}{n+1}} 1\, dx + \ldots + \int_1^2 1\, dx$

$= \left(\frac{1}{2}\right) + \left(\frac{2}{3} - \frac{1}{2}\right) + \left(\frac{3}{4} - \frac{2}{3}\right) + \ldots + \left(\frac{n}{n+1} - \frac{n-1}{n}\right) + \ldots + 1$

$= \frac{n}{n+1} + \ldots + 1$, as $n \to \infty$

We take, limit $n \to \infty$

We have, $\quad \int_0^2 f(x)\, dx = 1 + 1 = 2$

Hence, (b) is the correct answer.

Exercise for Session 3

1. The value of $\int_{-1}^{3} \{|x-2| + [x]\}\, dx$, where [.] denotes the greatest integer function, is equal to

(a) 5 (b) 6 (c) 7 (d) None of these

2. The value of $\int_{-1}^{3} (|x| + |x-1|)\, dx$ is equal to

(a) 9 (b) 6 (c) 3 (d) None of these

3. Let $f(x) = x - [x]$, for every real number x (where, $[x]$ is integral part of x). Then, the value of $\int_{-1}^{1} f(x)\, dx$ is equal to

(a) 0 (b) 1 (c) 2 (d) None of these

4. The value of $\int_{0}^{2} [x + [x + [x]]]\, dx$ (where, [.] denotes the greatest integer function) is equal to

(a) 2 (b) 3 (c) –3 (d) None of these

5. The value of $\int_{0}^{[x]} \frac{2^x}{2^{[x]}}\, dx$ is equal to (where, [.] denotes the greatest integer function)

(a) $\frac{[x]}{\log 2}$ (b) $\frac{[x]}{2 \log 2}$ (c) $\frac{[x]}{4 \log 2}$ (d) None of these

6. The value of $\int_{0}^{4} \{x\}\, dx$ (where, {.} denotes fractional part of x) is equal to

(a) $\frac{4}{3}$ (b) $\frac{5}{3}$ (c) $\frac{7}{3}$ (d) None of these

7. The value of $\int_{1}^{4} \{x\}^{[x]}\, dx$ (where, [.] and {.} denote the greatest integer and fractional part of x) is equal to

(a) $\frac{11}{12}$ (b) $\frac{13}{12}$

(c) $\frac{7}{12}$ (d) $\frac{19}{12}$

8. The value of $\int_{0}^{x} [t+1]^3\, dt$ (where, [.] denotes the greatest integer function of x) is equal to

(a) $\left(\frac{[x]([x]+1)}{2}\right)^2 + ([x]+1)^3 \{x\}$ (b) $\left(\frac{[x]([x]+1)}{2}\right)^3 + ([x]+1)^3 \{x\}$

(c) $\left(\frac{[x]([x]+1)}{2}\right)^3 + ([x]+1)^2 \{x\}$ (d) None of these

9. The value of $\int_{0}^{10\pi} [\tan^{-1} x]\, dx$ (where, [·] denotes the greatest integer function of x) is equal to

(a) $\tan 1$ (b) 10π

(c) $10\pi - \tan 1$ (d) None of these

10. If $f(x) = \min\{|x-1|, |x|, |x+1|\}$, then the value of $\int_{-1}^{1} f(x)\, dx$ is equal to

(a) 1 (b) $\frac{1}{2}$

(c) $\frac{1}{4}$ (d) $\frac{1}{8}$

11. The value of $\int_{0}^{\infty} [2e^{-x}]\, dx$ (where, [·] denotes the greatest integer function of x) is equal to

(a) 1 (b) $\log_e 2$

(c) 0 (d) $\frac{1}{e}$

12. The value of $\int_1^{10\pi}([\sec^{-1}x]+[\cot^{-1}x])dx$ (where, $[\cdot]$ denotes the greatest integer function) is equal to

(a) $(\sec 1)-10\pi$
(b) $10\pi-\sec 1$
(c) $\pi-\sec 1$
(d) None of these

13. The value of $\int_{-\pi/2}^{\pi/2}[\cot^{-1}x]dx$ (where, $[\cdot]$ denotes greatest integer function) is equal to

(a) $\pi+\cot 1$
(b) $\pi+\cot 2$
(c) $\pi+\cot 1+\cot 2$
(d) $\cot 1+\cot 2$

14. The value of $\int_0^{\pi/4}(\tan^n(x-[x])+\tan^{n-2}(x-[x]))dx$ (where, $[\cdot]$ denotes greatest integer function) is equal to

(a) $\frac{1}{n}$
(b) $\frac{1}{n-1}$
(c) $\frac{1}{n(n-1)}$
(d) $\frac{1}{n(n+1)}$

15. The value of $\int_0^2[x^2-x+1]dx$ (where, $[\cdot]$ denotes the greatest integer function) is equal to

(a) $\frac{5+\sqrt{5}}{2}$
b) $\frac{1+\sqrt{5}}{2}$
(c) $\frac{1-\sqrt{5}}{2}$
(d) $\frac{5-\sqrt{5}}{2}$

16. Evaluate $\int_0^a[x^n]dx$, (where, $[\cdot]$ denotes the greatest integer function).

17. Prove that $\int_0^x[x]dx=x[x]-\frac{1}{2}[x]([x]+1)$, where $[\cdot]$ denotes the greatest integer function.

18. If $f(n)=\frac{\int_0^n[x]dx}{\int_0^n\{x\}dx}$ (where, $[\cdot]$ and $\{\}$ denotes greatest integer and fractional part of x and $n\in N$). Then, the value of $f(4)$ is ...

19. If $f(n)=\int_0^x[\cos t]dt$, where $x\in\left(2n\pi, 2n\pi+\frac{\pi}{2}\right)$; $n\in N$ and $[\cdot]$ denotes the greatest integer function. Then, the value of $\left|f\left(\frac{1}{\pi}\right)\right|$ is ...

20. If $\int_0^x[x]dx=\int_0^{[x]}xdx$, $x\notin$ integer (where, $[\cdot]$ and $\{\}$ denotes the greatest integer and fractional parts respectively, then the value of $4\{x\}$ is equal to ...

Session 4

Applications of Even-Odd Property and Half the Integral Limit Property

Applications of Even-Odd Property and Half the Integral Limit Property

Property VI.

$$\int_{-a}^{a} f(x)\,dx = \begin{cases} 2\int_0^a f(x)\,dx, & \text{if } f(x) \text{ is an even function} \\ 0, & \text{if } f(x) \text{ is an odd function} \end{cases}$$

Proof We know,

$$\int_a^b f(x)\,dx = \int_a^c f(x)\,dx + \int_c^b f(x)\,dx, \text{if } a < c < b$$

$$\therefore \quad \int_{-a}^{a} f(x)\,dx = \int_{-a}^{0} f(x)\,dx + \int_0^a f(x)\,dx \quad \text{...(i)}$$

Now, $\int_{-a}^{0} f(x)\,dx = \int_a^0 f(-t)(-dt)$, where $t = -x$

$$= -\int_a^0 f(-t)\,dt = \int_0^a f(-t)\,dt$$

$$= \int_0^a f(-x)\,dx \text{ (using properties I and II)}$$

$$= \begin{cases} \int_0^a f(x)\,dx, & \text{if } f(x) \text{ is even} \\ -\int_0^a f(x)\,dx, & \text{if } f(x) \text{ is odd} \end{cases} \quad \text{...(ii)}$$

From Eqs. (i) and (ii), we get

$$\int_{-a}^{a} f(x)\,dx = \begin{cases} 2\int_0^a f(x)\,dx, & f(x) \text{ is even} \\ 0, & \text{if } f(x) \text{ is odd} \end{cases}$$

| Example 41 Evaluate $\int_{-1}^{1} (x^3 + 5x + \sin x)dx$.

Sol. Let, $f(x) = x^3 + 5x + \sin x$

$\therefore \quad f(-x) = -x^3 - 5x - \sin x = -f(x)$

So, $f(x)$ is an odd function).

Hence, $\int_{-1}^{1} (x^3 + 5x + \sin x)dx = 0$

$$\left[\text{using } \int_{-a}^{a} f(x)\,dx = \begin{cases} 2\int_0^a f(x)dx, f(x) \text{ is even} \\ 0, f(x) \text{ is odd} \end{cases}\right]$$

| Example 42 Evaluate $\int_{-\pi/4}^{\pi/4} x^3 \sin^4 x\,dx$.

Sol. Let $f(x) = x^3 \sin^4 x$, then

$$f(-x) = (-x)^3 \sin^4(-x) = -x^3 [\sin(-x)]^4$$

$$= -x^3(-\sin x)^4 = -x^3 \sin^4 x = -f(x)$$

So, $f(x)$ is an odd function.

Hence, $\int_{-\pi/4}^{\pi/4} f(x)\,dx = 0$

i.e. $\int_{-\pi/4}^{\pi/4} x^3 \sin^4 x\,dx = 0$

| Example 43 Evaluate $\int_{-\pi/2}^{\pi/2} \sin^2 x\,dx$.

Sol. Let $f(x) = \sin^2 x$, then

$$f(-x) = \sin^2(-x) = [\sin(-x)]^2 = (-\sin x)^2$$

$$= \sin^2 x = f(x)$$

So, $f(x)$ is an even function, hence

$$\int_{-\pi/2}^{\pi/2} (\sin^2 x)\,dx = 2\int_0^{\pi/2} (\sin^2 x)\,dx$$

$$= 2\int_0^{\pi/2} \frac{1 - \cos 2x}{2}\,dx$$

$$= \left(x - \frac{\sin 2x}{2}\right)_0^{\pi/2} = \frac{\pi}{2}$$

$$\therefore \int_{-\pi/2}^{\pi/2} \sin^2 x\,dx = \frac{\pi}{2}$$

| Example 44 The value of $\int_{-1}^{1} \log\left(\frac{2-x}{2+x}\right)dx$ is equal to

(a) $\frac{1}{2}$ (b) 1 (c) −1 (d) 0

Sol. Let $f(x) = \log\left(\frac{2-x}{2+x}\right)$

Now, $f(-x) = \log\left(\frac{2+x}{2-x}\right) = \log\left(\frac{2-x}{2+x}\right)^{-1}$

$$= -\log\left(\frac{2-x}{2+x}\right)$$

$$\therefore \quad f(-x) = -\log\left(\frac{2-x}{2+x}\right) = -f(x)$$

i.e. $f(x)$ is an odd function.

So, $\int_{-1}^{1} f(x)\,dx = \int_{-1}^{1} \log\left(\frac{2-x}{2+x}\right) dx = 0$

$$\left[\because \int_{-a}^{a} f(x)\,dx = \begin{cases} 0, & \text{if } f(x) \text{ is odd} \\ 2\int_0^a f(x)\,dx, & \text{if } f(x) \text{ is even} \end{cases}\right]$$

Hence, (d) is the correct answer.

Example 45 The value of

$$\int_0^{\pi} \frac{x \sin(2x) \cdot \sin\left(\frac{\pi}{2}\cos x\right)}{(2x-\pi)}\,dx \text{ is equal to}$$

(a) $\frac{8}{\pi}$ (b) $\frac{\pi}{8}$ (c) $\frac{8}{\pi^2}$ (d) $\frac{\pi^2}{8}$

Sol. Let $I = \int_0^{\pi} \frac{x \sin(2x) \cdot \sin\left(\frac{\pi}{2}\cos x\right)}{(2x-\pi)}\,dx$ ...(i)

$$I = \int_0^{\pi} \frac{(\pi - x)\cdot \sin 2(\pi - x)\cdot \sin\left(\frac{\pi}{2}\cos(\pi - x)\right)}{2(\pi - x) - \pi}\,dx$$

$$I = \int_0^{\pi} \frac{(\pi - x)\cdot \sin(2x)\cdot \sin\left(\frac{\pi}{2}\cos x\right)}{-(2x-\pi)}\,dx \quad \text{...(ii)}$$

Adding Eqs. (i) and (ii), we get

$$2I = \int_0^{\pi} \frac{(2x-\pi)\sin 2x \cdot \sin\left(\frac{\pi}{2}\cos x\right)}{(2x-\pi)}\,dx$$

$$\therefore\ I = \frac{1}{2}\int_0^{\pi} 2\sin x \cos x \cdot \sin\left(\frac{\pi}{2}\cos x\right) dx$$

(put $\cos x = t$, then $-\sin x\,dx = dt$)

$$= -\int_1^{-1} t \sin\left(\frac{\pi}{2} t\right) dt$$

$$= 2\int_0^1 t \cdot \sin\left(\frac{\pi}{2} t\right) dt \quad \text{(using by parts)}$$

$$= 2\left\{\left(t \cdot \frac{\cos\left(\frac{\pi}{2} t\right)}{-\frac{\pi}{2}}\right)_0^1 - \int_0^1 1 \cdot \frac{\cos\left(\frac{\pi}{2} t\right)}{-\frac{\pi}{2}}\,dt\right\}$$

$$= 2\left\{0 + \frac{2}{\pi}\cdot\left(\frac{\sin\left(\frac{\pi}{2} t\right)}{\frac{\pi}{2}}\right)_0^1\right\} = \frac{8}{\pi^2}$$

Hence, (c) is the correct answer.

Example 46 If $f(x) = \begin{vmatrix} \cos x & e^{x^2} & 2x\cos^2 x/2 \\ x^2 & \sec x & \sin x + x^3 \\ 1 & 2 & x + \tan x \end{vmatrix}$,

then value of $\int_{-\pi/2}^{\pi/2} (x^2+1)[f(x) + f''(x)]\,dx$ is equal to

(a) 1 (b) -1 (c) 2 (d) None of these

Sol. As, $f(x) = \begin{vmatrix} \cos x & e^{x^2} & 2x\cos^2 x/2 \\ x^2 & \sec x & \sin x + x^3 \\ 1 & 2 & x + \tan x \end{vmatrix}$

$\Rightarrow f(-x) = -f(x)$

$\Rightarrow f(x)$ is odd. $\Rightarrow f'(x)$ is even.

$\Rightarrow f''(x)$ is odd.

Thus, $f(x) + f''(x)$ is odd function, let

$$\phi(x) = (x^2+1)\cdot\{f(x) + f''(x)\}$$

$$\Rightarrow \quad \phi(-x) = -\phi(x)$$

i.e. $\phi(x)$ is odd.

$$\therefore \quad \int_{-\pi/2}^{\pi/2} \phi(x)\,dx = 0$$

Hence, (d) is the correct answer.

Example 47 The value of

$$\int_{-1}^{1} \frac{x}{\sqrt{1-x^2}} \cdot \sin^{-1}(2x\sqrt{1-x^2})\,dx \text{ is equal to}$$

(a) $4\sqrt{2}$ (b) $4(\sqrt{2}-1)$ (c) $4(\sqrt{2}+1)$ (d) None of these

Sol. Let $I = \int_{-1}^{1} \frac{x}{\sqrt{1-x^2}} \cdot \sin^{-1}(2x\sqrt{1-x^2})\,dx$

$$= 2\int_0^1 \frac{x}{\sqrt{1-x^2}} \cdot \sin^{-1}(2x\sqrt{1-x^2})\,dx$$

$$\left[\text{using } \int_{-a}^{a} f(x)\,dx = 2\int_0^a f(x)\,dx, \text{ if } f(-x) = f(x)\right]$$

Put $x = \sin\theta \Rightarrow dx = \cos\theta\,d\theta$

$$\therefore \quad I = 2\int_0^{\pi/2} \frac{\sin\theta}{\sqrt{1-\sin^2\theta}} \cdot \sin^{-1}(2\sin\theta\cos\theta)\cdot\cos\theta\,d\theta$$

$$= 2\int_0^{\pi/4} \sin\theta \cdot 2\theta\,d\theta + 2\int_{\pi/4}^{\pi/2} (\pi - 2\theta)\sin\theta\,d\theta$$

$$\left[\text{using } \sin^{-1}(\sin 2\theta) = \begin{cases} 2\theta, & 0 < \theta < \pi/4 \\ \pi - 2\theta, & \pi/4 < \theta < \pi/2 \end{cases}\right]$$

$$= 4\int_0^{\pi/4} \theta \cdot \sin\theta\,d\theta + 2\pi\int_{\pi/4}^{\pi/2} \sin\theta\,d\theta - 4\int_{\pi/4}^{\pi/2} \theta \cdot \sin\theta\,d\theta$$

$$= 4\{\theta(-\cos\theta)\}_0^{\pi/4} - 4\int_0^{\pi/4} 1\cdot(-\cos\theta)d\theta + 2\pi(-\cos\theta)_{\pi/4}^{\pi/2}$$

$$- 4\{\theta(-\cos\theta)\}_{\pi/4}^{\pi/2} + 4\int_{\pi/4}^{\pi/2} (-\cos\theta)\,d\theta$$

$$= -\frac{\pi}{\sqrt{2}} + 2\sqrt{2} + \sqrt{2}\pi - \frac{\pi}{\sqrt{2}} - 4 + 2\sqrt{2} = 4\sqrt{2} - 4$$

$$= 4(\sqrt{2} - 1)$$

Hence, (b) is the correct answer.

| Example 48 Suppose the function $g_n(x) = x^{2n+1} + a_n x + b_n (n \in N)$ satisfies the equation $\int_{-1}^{1} (px+q) g_n(x) dx = 0$ for all linear functions $(px+q)$, then

(a) $a_n = b_n = 0$ (b) $b_n = 0 ; a_n = -\frac{3}{2n+3}$

(c) $a_n = 0 ; b_n = -\frac{3}{2n+3}$ (d) $a_n = \frac{3}{2n+3} ; b_n = -\frac{3}{2n+3}$

Sol. We have, $\int_{-1}^{1} (px+q)(x^{2n+1} + a_n x + b_n) dx = 0$

Equating the odd component to be zero and integrating, we get

$$\frac{2p}{2n+3} + \frac{2a_n p}{3} + 2b_n q = 0 \text{ for all } p, q$$

Therefore, $b_n = 0$ and $a_n = -\frac{3}{2n+3}$

Hence, (b) is the correct answer.

Property VII (a).

$$\int_0^{2a} f(x)\, dx = \begin{cases} 2\int_0^a f(x)\, dx, & \text{if } f(2a-x) = f(x) \\ 0, & \text{if } f(2a-x) = -f(x) \end{cases}$$

Proof We know,

$$\int_0^{2a} f(x)\, dx = \int_0^a f(x)\, dx + \int_a^{2a} f(x)\, dx \quad \text{...(i)}$$

Consider the integral $\int_0^{2a} f(x)\, dx$; putting $x = 2a - t$, so that $dx = -dt$

Also, when $x = a$, then $t = a$ and when $x = 2a$, then $t = 0$.

$$\therefore \int_a^{2a} f(x)\, dx = \int_a^0 f(2a-t)(-dt) = -\int_a^0 f(2a-t)\, dt$$

$$= \int_0^a f(2a-t)\, dt = \int_0^a f(2a-x)\, dx$$

$$= \begin{cases} \int_0^a f(x)\, dx, & \text{if } f(2a-x) = f(x) \\ -\int_0^a f(x)\, dx, & \text{if } f(2a-x) = -f(x) \end{cases} \quad \text{...(ii)}$$

From Eqs. (i) and (ii), we have

$$\int_0^{2a} f(x)\, dx = \begin{cases} 2\int_0^a f(x)\, dx, & \text{if } f(2a-x) = f(x) \\ 0, & \text{if } f(2a-x) = -f(x) \end{cases}$$

| Example 49 Evaluate $\int_0^{\pi} \frac{x}{1+\cos^2 x} dx.$

Sol. Let $I = \int_0^{\pi} \frac{x}{1+\cos^2 x} dx$

$$= \int_0^{\pi} \frac{(\pi - x)\, dx}{1+\cos^2(\pi - x)} = \int_0^{\pi} \frac{\pi\, dx}{1+\cos^2 x} - \int_0^{\pi} \frac{x\, dx}{1+\cos^2 x}$$

$$\therefore \quad I = \pi \int_0^{\pi} \frac{dx}{1+\cos^2 x} - I$$

$$\Rightarrow \quad 2I = \pi \int_0^{\pi} \frac{dx}{1+\cos^2 x} = 2\pi \int_0^{\pi/2} \frac{dx}{1+\cos^2 x}$$

$$\left[\text{using} \int_0^{2a} f(x)\, dx = \begin{cases} 0, & f(2a-x) = -f(x) \\ 2\int_0^a f(x)\, dx, & f(2a-x) = f(x) \end{cases}\right]$$

$$\Rightarrow \quad I = \pi \int_0^{\pi/2} \frac{\sec^2 x}{\sec^2 x + 1} dx$$

(dividing numerator and denominator by $\cos^2 x$)

$$I = \pi \int_0^{\pi/2} \frac{\sec^2 x}{2 + \tan^2 x} dx$$

Put $\tan x = t \Rightarrow \sec^2 x\, dx = dt$

Also, when $x = 0$, then $t = 0$ and when $x = \pi/2$, then $t = \infty$

Hence, $$I = \pi \int_0^{\infty} \frac{dt}{2+t^2} = \frac{\pi}{\sqrt{2}} \left(\tan^{-1} \frac{t}{\sqrt{2}} \right)_0^{\infty}$$

$$= \frac{\pi}{\sqrt{2}} \left(\frac{\pi}{2} - 0 \right) = \frac{\pi^2}{2\sqrt{2}}$$

| Example 50 Prove that $\int_0^{\pi/2} \log(\sin x)\, dx = \int_0^{\pi/2} \log(\cos x)\, dx = -\frac{\pi}{2} \log 2.$

Sol. Let $$I = \int_0^{\pi/2} \log(\sin x)\, dx \quad \text{...(i)}$$

Then, $$I = \int_0^{\pi/2} \log \sin(\pi/2 - x)\, dx$$

$$= \int_0^{\pi/2} \log(\cos x)\, dx \quad \text{...(ii)}$$

Adding eqs. (i) and (ii), we get

$$2I = \int_0^{\pi/2} \log \sin x\, dx + \int_0^{\pi/2} \log \cos x\, dx$$

$$= \int_0^{\pi/2} (\log \sin x + \log \cos x)\, dx$$

$$= \int_0^{\pi/2} \log(\sin x \cos x)\, dx = \int_0^{\pi/2} \log\left(\frac{2 \sin x \cos x}{2} \right) dx$$

$$= \int_0^{\pi/2} \log\left(\frac{\sin 2x}{2} \right) dx$$

$$= \int_0^{\pi/2} \log(\sin 2x)\, dx - \int_0^{\pi/2} (\log 2)\, dx$$

$$= \int_0^{\pi/2} \log \sin 2x\, dx - (\log 2)(x)_0^{\pi/2}$$

$$\Rightarrow \quad 2I = \int_0^{\pi/2} \log(\sin 2x)\, dx - \frac{\pi}{2} \log 2 \quad \text{...(iii)}$$

Let $$I_1 = \int_0^{\pi/2} \log(\sin 2x)\, dx$$

$$I_1 = \int_0^{\pi} \log \sin t \frac{dt}{2} = \frac{1}{2}\int_0^{\pi} \log \sin t \, dt \text{ (putting } 2x = t)$$

$$= \frac{1}{2} \cdot 2 \int_0^{\pi/2} \log (\sin t) \, dt$$

$$\left[\text{using } \int_0^{2a} f(x)\,dx = \begin{cases} 0, & f(2a-x) = -f(x) \\ 2\int_0^a f(x)\,dx, & f(2a-x) = f(x), \end{cases}\right.$$

$$= \int_0^{\pi/2} \log (\sin x) \, dx$$

$\therefore$ Eq. (iii) becomes $2I = I - \frac{\pi}{2} \log 2$

Hence, $\int_0^{\pi/2} \log \sin x \, dx = -\frac{\pi}{2} \log 2.$

Remark

Students are advised to learn

$$\int_0^{\pi/2} \log(\sin x)\,dx = \int_0^{\pi/2} \log(\cos x)\,dx = -\frac{\pi}{2}\log 2.$$

Example 51 If $f(x) = -\int_0^x \log(\cos t)\,dt$, then the value of $f(x) - 2f\left(\frac{\pi}{4}+\frac{x}{2}\right) + 2f\left(\frac{\pi}{4}-\frac{x}{2}\right)$ is equal to

(a) $-x\log 2$ (b) $\frac{x}{2}\log 2$

(c) $\frac{x}{3}\log 2$ (d) None of these

Sol. Here, $f\left(\frac{\pi}{4}+\frac{x}{2}\right) = -\int_0^{\pi/4 + x/2} \log(\cos t)\,dt$

$$= -\int_0^{\pi/4} \log(\cos t)\,dt - \int_{\pi/4}^{\pi/4 + x/2} \log(\cos t)\,dt \quad \text{...(i)}$$

$$f\left(\frac{\pi}{4}-\frac{x}{2}\right) = -\int_0^{\pi/4 - x/2} \log(\cos t)\,dt$$

$$= -\int_0^{\pi/4} \log(\cos t)\,dt - \int_{\pi/4}^{\pi/4 - x/2} \log(\cos t)\,dt \quad \text{...(ii)}$$

$$\therefore 2f\left(\frac{\pi}{4}+\frac{x}{2}\right) - 2f\left(\frac{\pi}{4}-\frac{x}{2}\right)$$

$$= 2\int_{\pi/4}^{\pi/4 - x/2} \log(\cos t)\,dt - 2\int_{\pi/4}^{\pi/4 + x/2} \log(\cos t)\,dt$$

Put $t = \frac{\pi}{4} - z$ in first integral and $t = \frac{\pi}{4} + z$ in second integral, we get

$$= -2\int_0^{x/2} \log\cos\left(\frac{\pi}{4} - z\right)dz - 2\int_0^{x/2} \log\cos\left(z + \frac{\pi}{4}\right)dz$$

$$= -2\int_0^{x/2} \log\left(\frac{1}{2}(\cos^2 z - \sin^2 z)\right)dz$$

$$= 2\int_0^{x/2} (\log 2)\,dx - 2\int_0^{x/2} \log(\cos 2z)\,dz$$

$$= x\log 2 - 2\int_0^{x/2} \log(\cos 2z)\,dz$$

$$\therefore 2f\left(\frac{\pi}{4}+\frac{x}{2}\right) - 2f\left(\frac{\pi}{4}-\frac{x}{2}\right) = x(\log 2) - 2\int_0^{x/2} \log(\cos 2z)\,dz$$

$$\Rightarrow \quad 2f\left(\frac{\pi}{4}+\frac{x}{2}\right) - 2f\left(\frac{\pi}{4}-\frac{x}{2}\right) = x(\log 2) + f(x)$$

or $\quad f(x) - 2f\left(\frac{\pi}{4}+\frac{x}{2}\right) + 2f\left(\frac{\pi}{4}-\frac{x}{2}\right) = -x\log 2$

Hence, (a) is the correct answer.

Example 52 If $\int_0^{\pi}\left(\frac{x}{1+\sin x}\right)^2 dx = A$, then the value for $\int_0^{\pi} \frac{2x^2 \cdot \cos^2 x/2}{(1+\sin x)^2}\,dx$ is equal to

(a) $A + 2\pi - \pi^2$ (b) $A - 2\pi + \pi^2$

(c) $2\pi - A - \pi^2$ (d) None of these

Sol. Let $\quad B = \int_0^{\pi} \frac{2x^2 \cos^2 x/2}{(1+\sin x)^2}\,dx$

$$\therefore \quad B - A = \int_0^{\pi} \frac{x^2(2\cos^2 x/2 - 1)}{(1+\sin x)^2}\,dx$$

$$= \int_0^{\pi} \frac{x^2 \cdot \cos x}{(1+\sin x)^2}\,dx$$

Using by parts,

$$B - A = \left\{\frac{x^2}{1+\sin x}\right\}_0^{\pi} + 2\int_0^{\pi} \frac{x}{(1+\sin x)}\,dx$$

$$B - A = -\pi^2 + 2K \quad \text{...(i)}$$

where, $\quad K = \int_0^{\pi} \frac{x\,dx}{1+\sin x} = \int_0^{\pi} \frac{(\pi - x)\,dx}{1+\sin x}$

$$\therefore \quad K = \pi\int_0^{\pi} \frac{dx}{1+\sin x} - K,$$

$$\left[\text{using } \int_0^{2a} f(x)\,dx = \begin{cases} 0, & f(2a-x) = -f(x) \\ 2\int_0^a f(x)\,dx, & f(2a-x) = f(x), \end{cases}\right.$$

$$\Rightarrow 2K = 2\pi\int_0^{\pi/2} \frac{dx}{1+\sin x} = 2\pi\int_0^{\pi/2} \frac{dx}{1+\cos x}$$

$$= 2\pi\int_0^{\pi/2} \frac{1}{2}\sec^2\frac{x}{2}\,dx = 2\pi\left\{\tan\frac{x}{2}\right\}_0^{\pi/2} = 2\pi$$

$\therefore \quad K = \pi$

Thus, $\quad B - A = -\pi^2 + 2K$

$\Rightarrow \quad B = A - \pi^2 + 2\pi$

Hence, (a) is the correct answer.

Example 53 The value of $\int_{-a}^{a}(\cos^{-1}x-\sin^{-1}\sqrt{1-x^2})\,dx\ (a>0)$ (where, $\int_0^a \cos^{-1}x\,dx=A$) is

(a) $\pi a-A$ (b) $\pi a+2A$
(c) $\pi a-2A$ (d) $\pi a+A$

Sol. Let $I=\int_{-a}^{a}(\cos^{-1}x-\sin^{-1}\sqrt{1-x^2})\,dx$ (as $a>0$)

$$=\int_{-a}^{0}(\cos^{-1}x-\sin^{-1}\sqrt{1-x^2})\,dx+\int_0^a(\cos^{-1}x-\sin^{-1}\sqrt{1-x^2})\,dx$$

$$=\int_{-a}^{0}\cos^{-1}x\,dx+A-2\int_0^a\sin^{-1}\sqrt{1-x^2}\,dx$$

$$=-\int_a^0(\pi-\cos^{-1}x)\,dx+A-2A$$

$$=\pi a-\int_0^a\cos^{-1}x\,dx-A$$

$$=\pi a-A-A=\pi a-2A$$

Hence, (c) is the correct answer.

Property VII (b)

$$\int_a^b f(x)\,dx=(b-a)\int_0^1 f[(b-a)x+a]\,dx$$

Sometimes, it is convenient to change the limits of integration into some other limits. For example, suppose we have to add two definite integrals I_1 and I_2; the limits of integration of these integrals are different. if we could somehow change the limits of I_2 into those of I_1 or vice-versa, or infact change the limits of both I_1 and I_2 into a third (common) set of limits, the addition could be accomplished easily.

Suppose that $I=\int_a^b f(x)\,dx$. We need to change the limits (a to b) to (a' to b'). As x varies from a to b, we need a new variable t (in terms of x) which varies from a' to b'.

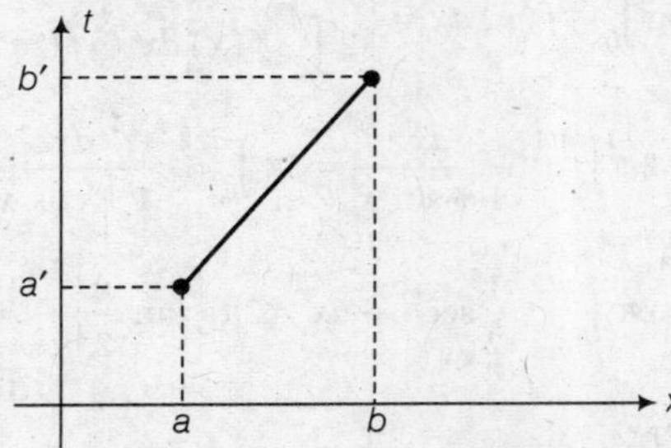

As x varies from a to b, t varies from a to b, t varies from a' to b'.

Thus, $$\frac{t-a'}{x-a}=\frac{b'-a'}{b-a}$$

As described in the figure above, the new variable t is given by,

$$t=a'+\left(\frac{b'-a'}{b-a}\right)(x-a).$$

Thus, $$dt=\frac{b'-a'}{b-a}dx$$

$$\Rightarrow\quad I=\int_0^b f(x)\,dx$$

$$=\int_{a'}^{b'}f\left(a+\left(\frac{b-a}{b'-a'}\right)(t-a')\right)\left(\frac{b-a}{b'-a'}\right)dt$$

The modified integral has the limits (a' to b'). A particular case of this property is modifying the arbitrary integration limits (a to b) to (0 to 1) i.e. $a'=0$ and $b'=1$. For this case,

$$I=\int_a^b f(x)\,dx=(b-a)\int_0^1 f(a+(b-a)t)\,dt$$

Example 54 Evaluate

$$\int_{-4}^{-5}e^{(x+5)^2}dx+3\int_{1/3}^{2/3}e^{9\left(x-\frac{2}{3}\right)^2}dx.$$

Sol. Here, we know $\int e^{x^2}dx$ cannot be evaluated by indefinite integral.

Let $I_1=\int_{-4}^{-5}e^{(x+5)^2}dx=(-5+4)\int_0^1 e^{[(-5+4)x-4+5]^2}dx$

$$\therefore\quad I_1=-\int_0^1 e^{(x-1)^2}dx \quad ...(i)$$

Again, let $I_2=\int_{1/3}^{2/3}e^{9(x-2/3)^2}dx$

$$=\left(\frac{2}{3}-\frac{1}{3}\right)\int_0^1 e^{9\left[\left(\frac{2}{3}-\frac{1}{2}\right)x+\frac{1}{3}-\frac{2}{3}\right]^2}dx$$

$$=\frac{1}{3}\int_0^1 e^{(x-1)^2}dx=\frac{1}{3}(-I_1) \quad ...(ii)$$

where, $I=I_1+3I_2=I_1+3\left(-\frac{I_1}{3}\right)=I_1-I_1=0$

$$\therefore\quad \int_{-4}^{-5}e^{(x+5)^2}dx+3\int_{1/3}^{2/3}e^{9(x-2/3)^2}dx=0$$

Property VII (c) If $f(t)$ is an odd function, then $\phi(x)=\int_a^x f(t)\,dt$ is an even function.

Proof We have, $\phi(-x)=\int_a^{-x}f(t)\,dt$

$$\Rightarrow\quad \phi(-x)=\int_a^{-a}f(t)\,dt+\int_{-a}^{-x}f(t)\,dt$$

$$\Rightarrow\quad \phi(-x)=0+\int_{-a}^{-x}f(t)\,dt$$

$$\left[\because f(t)\text{ is an odd function, then }\int_{-a}^{a}f(t)\,dt=0\right]$$

$\Rightarrow \quad \phi(-x) = -\int_a^x f(-y)\,dy$, where $t = -y$

$\Rightarrow \quad \phi(-x) = \int_a^x f(y)\,dy$

[$\because f$ is an odd function, then $f(-y) = -f(y)$]

$\Rightarrow \quad \phi(-x) = \int_a^x f(t)\,dt$

$\Rightarrow \quad \phi(-x) = \phi(x)$

Hence, $\phi(x) = \int_a^x f(t)\,dt$ is an even function, if $f(t)$ is odd.

Example 55 If $f(x) = \int_0^x \log\left(\frac{1-t}{1+t}\right) dt$, then discuss whether even or odd?

Sol. Let $\quad \phi(t) = \log\left(\frac{1-t}{1+t}\right)$

$\therefore \quad \phi(-t) = \log\left(\frac{1+t}{1-t}\right) = -\log\left(\frac{1-t}{1+t}\right) = -\phi(t)$

$\Rightarrow \quad \phi(-t) = -\phi(t)$, i.e. $\phi(t)$ is odd function

$\therefore \quad \phi(x) = \int_0^x \log\left(\frac{1-t}{1+t}\right) dt$ is an even function.

Property VII (d) If $f(t)$ is an even function, then $\phi(x) = \int_0^x f(t)\,dt$ is an odd function.

Proof We have, $\phi(-x) = \int_0^{-x} f(t)\,dt = -\int_0^x f(-y)\,dy$, where $t = -y$

$\Rightarrow \quad \phi(-x) = -\int_0^x f(y)\,dy$

[$\because f$ is even function $\Rightarrow f(-y) = f(y)$]

$\Rightarrow \quad \phi(-x) = -\int_0^x f(t)\,dt$

$\Rightarrow \quad \phi(-x) = -\phi(x)$

Hence, $\phi(x)$ is an odd function.

Remark

If $f(t)$ is an even function, then for non-zero 'a', $\int_a^x f(t)\,dt$ is not necessarily an odd function. It will be an odd function, if $\int_0^a f(t)\,dt = 0$, because, if $\phi(x) = \int_a^x f(t)\,dt$, it is an odd function.

$\Rightarrow \quad \phi(-x) = -\phi(x)$

$\Rightarrow \quad \int_a^{-x} f(t)\,dt = -\int_a^x f(t)\,dt$

$\Rightarrow \quad \int_a^0 f(t)\,dt + \int_0^{-x} f(t)\,dt = -\int_a^0 f(t)\,dt - \int_0^x f(t)\,dt$

$\Rightarrow \quad \int_a^0 f(t)\,dt - \int_0^x f(-y)\,dy = -\int_0^a f(t)\,dt - \int_0^x f(t)\,dt$

[where, $y = -t$ in second integral of LHS $\Rightarrow f(-y) = f(y)$]

$\Rightarrow \quad 2\int_a^0 f(t)\,dt = \int_0^x f(y)\,dy - \int_0^x f(t)\,dt$

$\Rightarrow \quad 2\int_a^0 f(t)\,dt = 0$

$\Rightarrow \quad -\int_0^a f(t)\,dt = 0 \Rightarrow \int_0^a f(t)\,dt = 0$

or $\quad \phi(x) = \int_a^x f(t)\,dt$ is an odd function, [when $f(t)$ is even.]

Only, if $\int_0^a f(t)\,dt = 0$

Exercise for Session 4

1. Let $f: R \to R$ and $g: R \to R$ be continous functions, then the value of $\int_{-\pi/2}^{\pi/2} [f(x)+f(-x)][g(x)-g(-x)]\,dx$ is equal to

(a) -1 (b) 0 (c) 1 (d) None of these

2. The value of $\int_{-1}^{1} (x|x|)\,dx$ is equal to

(a) 1 (b) $\frac{1}{2}$ (c) 0 (d) None of these

3. The value of $\int_{-1}^{1} \left(\frac{x^2+\sin x}{1+x^2}\right) dx$ is equal to

(a) $2-\pi$ (b) $\pi-2$ (c) $2-\frac{\pi}{2}$ (d) None of these

4. If $f(x)$ is an odd function, then the value of $\int_{-a}^{a} \frac{f(\sin x)}{f(\cos x)+f(\sin^2 x)}\,dx$ is equal to

(a) 0 (b) $f(\cos x)+f(\sin x)$ (c) 1 (d) None of these

5. The value of $\int_{-1/\sqrt{3}}^{1/\sqrt{3}} \frac{\cos^{-1}\left(\frac{2x}{1+x^2}\right)+\tan^{-1}\left(\frac{2x}{1-x^2}\right)}{1+e^x}\,dx$ is equal to

(a) $\frac{\pi}{2}$ (b) $\frac{\pi}{\sqrt{3}}$ (c) $\frac{\pi}{2\sqrt{3}}$ (d) $\frac{\pi}{3\sqrt{3}}$

6. The value of $\int_{-\pi}^{\pi} \frac{\cos^2 x}{1+a^x}\,dx$, where $a>0$, is

[IITJEE 2001]

(a) π (b) $a\pi$ (c) 2π (d) $\frac{\pi}{2}$

7. The integral $\int_{-1/2}^{1/2} \left\{[x]+\log_e\left(\frac{1+x}{1-x}\right)\right\}dx$ is equal to (where, [·] denotes greatest integer function)

(a) $-\frac{1}{2}$ (b) 0 (c) 1 (d) $2\log\left(\frac{1}{2}\right)$

8. The value of $\int_{-\pi/2}^{\pi/2} \frac{1}{e^{\sin x}+1}\,dx$ is equal to

(a) 0 (b) 1 (c) $\frac{\pi}{2}$ (d) $-\frac{\pi}{2}$

9. If [·] denotes greatest integer function, then the value of $\int_{-\pi/2}^{\pi/2} \left(\left[\frac{\pi}{2}\right]+\right) dx$ is

(a) π (b) $\frac{\pi}{2}$ (c) 0 (d) $-\frac{\pi}{2}$

10. The equation $\int_{-\pi/4}^{\pi/4} \left\{a|\sin x|+\frac{b\sin x}{1+\cos^2 x}+c\right\}dx=0$, where *a*, *b*, *c* are constants gives a relation between

(a) *a*, *b* and *c* (b) *a* and *c* (c) *a* and *b* (d) *b* and *c*

11. The value of $\int_{-2}^{2} \frac{\sin^2 x}{\left[\frac{x}{\pi}\right]+\frac{1}{2}}\,dx$, where [·] denotes greatest integer function, is

(a) 1 (b) 0 (c) $4-\sin 4$ (d) None of these

12. Let $f(x)$ be a continuous function such that $\int_{m}^{n+1} f(x)dx = n^3, n \in Z$. Then, the value of $\int_{-3}^{3} f(x)dx$ is

(a) 9 (b) -27 (c) -9 (d) 27

13. Let $f(x)=\dfrac{e^x+1}{e^x-1}$ and $\int_0^1 x^3\cdot\dfrac{e^x+1}{e^x-1}dx=\alpha$. Then, $\int_{-1}^1 t^3 f(t)\,dt$ is equal to

(a) 0 (b) α (c) 2α (d) None of these

14. Let $f: R\to R$ be a continuous function given by $f(x+y)=f(x)+f(y)$ for all $x, y\in R$. if $\int_0^2 f(x)\,dx=\alpha$, then $\int_{-2}^2 f(x)\,dx$ is equal to

(a) 2α (b) α (c) 0 (d) None of these

15. The value of $\int_{-2}^2 |[x]|\,dx$ is equal to

(a) 1 (b) 2 (c) 3 (d) 4

▪ **Directions** (Q. Nos. 16 to 17)

Let $f(x)=\begin{cases}1-|x|, & |x|\le 1\\ 0, & |x|>1\end{cases}$ and $g(x)=f(x+1)+f(x-1)$ for all $x\in R$.

16. The graph for $g(x)$ is given by

(a) 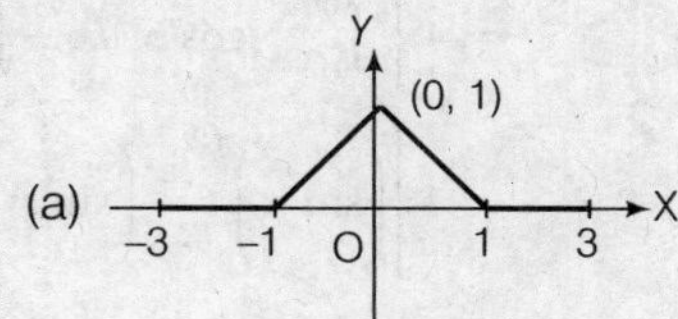

(b) 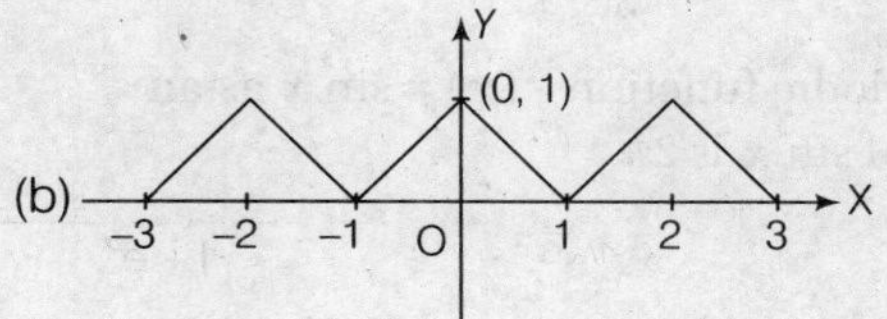

(c) 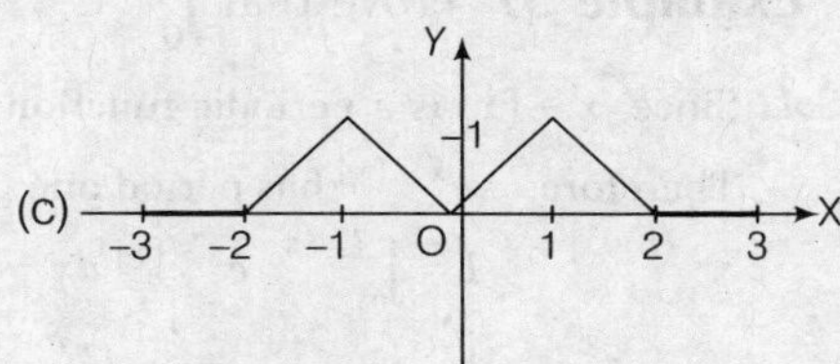

(d) 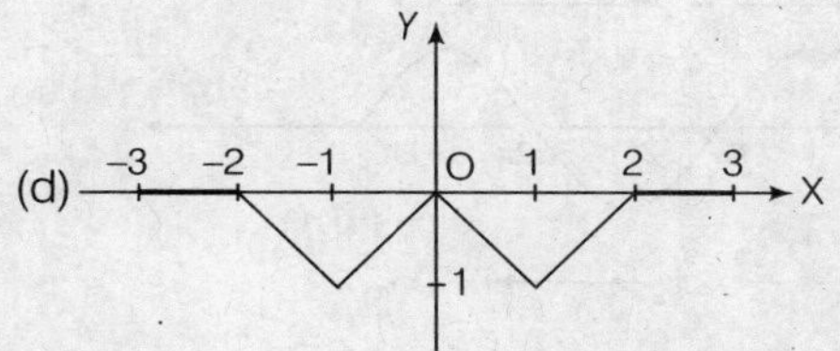

17. The value of $\int_{-3}^3 g(x)dx$ is

(a) 2 (b) 3 (c) 4 (d) 5

▪ **Direction** (Q. Nos. 18 to 20)

Let $I_n=\int_{-\pi}^{\pi}\dfrac{\sin x}{(1+\pi^x)\sin x}dx;\ n=0,1,2,\ldots$

18. The value of $I_{n+2}-I_n$ is equal to

(a) $n\pi$ (b) π (c) $-\pi$ (d) 0

19. The value of $\sum_{m=1}^{10} I_{2m+1}$ is equal to

(a) 0 (b) 5π
(c) 10π (d) None of these

20. The value of $\sum_{m=1}^{10} I_{2m}$ is equal to

(a) 0 (b) 5π
(c) 10π (d) None of these

Session 5

Applications of Periodic Functions and Newton- Leibnitz's Formula

Applications of Periodic Functions and Newton-Leibnitz's Formula

If $f(x)$ is a periodic function with period T, then the area under $f(x)$ for n periods would be n times the area under $f(x)$ for one period, i.e.

$$\int_0^{nT} f(x)\,dx = n\int_0^T f(x)\,dx$$

Now, consider the periodic function $f(x) = \sin x$ as an example. The period of $\sin x$ is 2π.

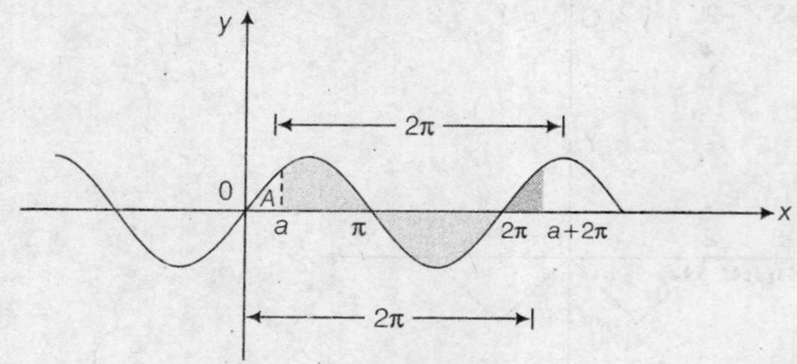

Figure 2.6

Suppose we intend to calculate $\int_a^{a+2\pi} \sin x\,dx$ as depicted above. Notice that the darkly shaded area in the interval $[2\pi, a+2\pi]$ can precisely cover the area marked as

Thus, $$\int_a^{a+2\pi} \sin x\,dx = \int_0^{2\pi} \sin x\,dx$$

This will hold true for every periodic function, i.e.

$$\int_a^{a+T} f(x)\,dx = \int_0^T f(x)\,dx$$

(where T is the period of $f(x)$)

This also implies that

$$\int_a^{a+nT} f(x)\,dx = \int_0^{nT} f(x)dx = n\int_0^T f(x)\,dx$$

and $$\int_{a+nT}^{b+nT} f(x)\,dx = \int_a^b f(x)\,dx$$

and $$\int_a^{b+nT} f(x)\,dx = \int_a^b f(x)dx + n\int_0^T f(x)\,dx$$

| Example 56 Evaluate $\int_0^{4\pi} |\cos x|\,dx$.

Sol. Note that $|\cos x|$ is a periodic with period π.

Let $$I = 4\int_0^{\pi} |\cos x|\,dx$$

$$\left[\text{using property, } \int_0^{nT} f(x)\,dx = n\int_0^T f(x)\,dx\right]$$

$$= 4\left\{\int_0^{\pi/2} \cos x\,dx - \int_{\pi/2}^{\pi} \cos x\,dx\right\}$$

$$= 4\left\{\left(\sin x\right)_0^{\pi/2} - \left(\sin x\right)_{\pi/2}^{\pi}\right\} = 4\{1+1\} = 8$$

| Example 57 Prove that $\int_0^{25} e^{x-[x]}\,dx = 25(e-1)$.

Sol. Since, $x-[x]$ is a periodic function with period one.

Therefore, $e^{x-[x]}$ has period one

$$\therefore \quad I = \int_0^{25\times 1} e^{x-[x]}\,dx = 25\int_0^1 e^{x-[x]}\,dx$$

$$\left[\text{using property, } \int_0^{nT} f(x)\,dx = n\int_0^T f(x)\,dx\right]$$

$$= 25\int_0^1 e^{x-0}\,dx = 25(e^x)_0^1 = 25(e^1 - e^0)$$

$$= 25(e-1)$$

| Example 58 The value of $\int_0^{2n\pi} [\sin x + \cos x]\,dx$ is equal to

(a) $-n\pi$ (b) $n\pi$ (c) $-2n\pi$ (d) None of these

(where [.] denotes the greatest integer function)

Sol. Let $I = \int_0^{2n\pi} [\sin x + \cos x]\,dx$

We know, $\sin x + \cos x = \sqrt{2}\sin\left(x + \frac{\pi}{4}\right)$ ...(i)

$$\therefore \quad \sin x + \cos x = \begin{cases} 1, & 0 \le x \le \pi/2 \\ 0, & \pi/2 < x \le 3\pi/4 \\ -1, & 3\pi/4 < x \le \pi \\ -2, & \pi < x < 3\pi/2 \\ -1, & 3\pi/2 \le x < 7\pi/4 \\ 0, & 7\pi/4 \le x \le 2\pi \end{cases}$$

$$\therefore \int_0^{2\pi} [\sin x + \cos x]dx = \int_0^{\pi/2} (1)\,dx + \int_{\pi/2}^{3\pi/4} (0)\,dx$$

$$+\int_{3\pi/4}^{\pi}(-1)dx+\int_{\pi}^{3\pi/2}(-2)\,dx+\int_{3\pi/2}^{7\pi/4}(-1)\,dx+\int_{7\pi/4}^{2\pi}(0)\,dx$$

$$=\left(\frac{\pi}{2}\right)+(0)-\left(\pi-\frac{3\pi}{4}\right)-2\left(\frac{3\pi}{2}-\pi\right)-1\left(\frac{7\pi}{4}-\frac{3\pi}{2}\right)+0$$

$$=-\pi$$

Since, $\sin x+\cos x$ has the period 2π.

So, $I=\int_0^{2n\pi}[\sin x+\cos x]\,dx=n\int_0^{2\pi}[\sin x+\cos x]\,dx$

$$=-n\pi$$

Hence, (a) is the correct answer.

Example 59 The value of $\int_{-5}^{5}f(x)\,dx$; where $f(x)=$ *minimum* $(\{x+1\},\{x-1\})$, $\forall\, x\in R$ and $\{.\}$ denotes fractional part of x, is equal to

(a) 3 (b) 4 (c) 5 (d) 6

Sol. We know, $\{x+1\}=\{x-1\}=\{x\}$

Thus, $f(x)=\text{minimum}(\{x+1\},\{x-1\})=\{x\}$

$$\Rightarrow \int_{-5}^{5}f(x)\,dx=\int_{-5}^{5}\{x\}\,dx=(5-(-5))\int_0^1\{x\}\,dx$$

[as $\{x\}$ is periodic with period '1']

$$=10\int_0^1(x-[x])\,dx=10\int_0^1 x\,dx$$

$$=10\left(\frac{x^2}{2}\right)_0^1=5$$

Hence, (c) is the correct answer.

Example 60 Show $\int_0^{n\pi+V}|\sin x|\,dx=(2n+1)-\cos V$, where n is a positive integer and $0\le V<\pi$.

[IIT JEE 1994, 2004]

Sol. $\int_0^{n\pi+V}|\sin x|\,dx=\int_0^{V}|\sin x|\,dx+\int_V^{n\pi+V}|\sin x|\,dx$

$$=\int_0^V\sin x\,dx+n\int_0^{\pi}|\sin x|\,dx$$

$$\left[\text{using property, }\int_a^{a+nT}f(x)dx=n\int_0^T f(x)dx\ \text{ i.e. }\int_V^{n\pi V}|\sin x|dx=n\int_V^{\pi}|\sin x|dx\right]$$

$$=\left(-\cos x\right)_0^V+n\int_0^{\pi}\sin x\,dx$$

$$=(-\cos V+1)+n\left(-\cos x\right)_0^{\pi}$$

$$=-(\cos V)+1+n(1+1)=(2n+1)-\cos V$$

$\therefore \int_0^{n\pi+V}|\sin x|\,dx=(2n+1)-\cos V$, where n is a positive integer and $0\le V<\pi$.

Example 61 The value of $\int_{-2\pi}^{5\pi}\cot^{-1}(\tan x)\,dx$ is equal to

(a) $\frac{7\pi}{2}$ (b) $\frac{7\pi^2}{2}$

(c) $\frac{3\pi}{2}$ (d) π^2

Sol. Let $I=\int_{-2\pi}^{5\pi}\cot^{-1}(\tan x)\,dx$

$$\Rightarrow I=7\int_0^{\pi}\cot^{-1}\left(\cot\left(\frac{\pi}{2}-x\right)\right)dx \quad \text{...(i)}$$

$$\left[\because \int_{nT}^{mT}f(x)\,dx=(m-n)\int_0^T f(x)\,dx\right]$$

As we know, $\cot^{-1}(\cot x)=\begin{cases}x &, 0<x<\pi/2\\ \pi+x, & \pi/2<x<\pi\end{cases}$

$$\therefore\quad I=7\left\{\int_0^{\pi/2}\left(\frac{\pi}{2}-x\right)dx+\int_{\pi/2}^{\pi}\left(\pi+\frac{\pi}{2}-x\right)dx\right\}$$

$$=7\left\{\left(\frac{\pi}{2}x-\frac{x^2}{2}\right)_0^{\pi/2}+\left(\frac{3\pi}{2}x-\frac{x^2}{2}\right)_{\pi/2}^{\pi}\right\}$$

$$=7\left\{\left(\frac{\pi^2}{4}-\frac{\pi^2}{8}\right)+\left(\frac{3\pi^2}{2}-\frac{\pi^2}{2}-\frac{3\pi^2}{4}+\frac{\pi^2}{8}\right)\right\}=\frac{7\pi^2}{2}$$

Hence, (b) is the correct answer.

Example 62 Let $g(x)$ be a continuous and differentiable function such that $\int_0^2\left\{\int_{\sqrt{2}}^{\sqrt{5/2}}[2x^2-3]\,dx\right\}\cdot g(x)\,dx=0$, then $g(x)=0$ when $x\in(0,2)$ has (where, [.] denotes the greatest integer function)

(a) exactly one real root (b) atleast one real root

(c) no real root (d) None of these

Sol. As, $1<2x^2-3<2,\ \forall\ x\in(\sqrt{2},\sqrt{5/2})$

$$\Rightarrow \int_{\sqrt{2}}^{\sqrt{5/2}}[2x^2-3]\,dx>0,\ \forall\ x\in(0,2)$$

$\Rightarrow$ **$g(x)=0$ should have atleast one root in (0, 2).**

$[\because g'(x)\neq 0]$

Hence, (b) is the correct answer.

Example 63 The value of x satisfying $\int_0^{2[x+14]}\left\{\frac{x}{2}\right\}dx=\int_0^{\{x\}}[x+14]\,dx$ is equal to (where, [.] and {.} denotes the greatest integer and fractional part of x)

(a) $[-14,-13)$ (b) $(0,1)$

(c) $(-15,-14]$ (d) None of these

Sol. Given, $\displaystyle\int_0^{2[x+14]}\left\{\frac{x}{2}\right\}dx=\int_0^{\{x\}}[x+14]\,dx$

$$\Rightarrow \int_0^{28+2[x]}\left\{\frac{x}{2}\right\}dx=\int_0^{\{x\}}(14+[x])\,dx$$

$$\Rightarrow \int_0^{28}\left\{\frac{x}{2}\right\}dx+\int_{28}^{28+2[x]}\left\{\frac{x}{2}\right\}dx=(14+[x])\{x\}$$

$$\Rightarrow 14\int_0^{2}\left\{\frac{x}{2}\right\}dx+\int_0^{2[x]}\left\{\frac{x}{2}\right\}dx=(14+[x])\{x\}$$

$$\left[\begin{array}{l}\text{using } \int_0^{nT} f(x)\,dx = n\int_0^{T} f(x)\,dx \quad\text{and}\\ \int_a^{a+nT} f(x)\,dx=\int_0^{nT} f(x)\,dx;\text{ where } T \text{ is period of } f(x)\end{array}\right]$$

$$\Rightarrow 14+[x]=(14+[x])\{x\}$$

$$\Rightarrow (14+[x])(1-\{x\})=0$$

$$\Rightarrow [x]=-14$$

$$\Rightarrow x\in[-14,-13)$$

Hence, (a) is the correct answer.

Property IX. Leibnitz's Rule for the Differentiation under the Integral Sign

(i) If the functions $\phi(x)$ and $\psi(x)$ are defined on $[a,b]$ and are differentiable at a point $x\in(a,b)$ and $f(x,t)$ is continuous, then

$$\frac{d}{dx}\left[\int_{\phi(x)}^{\psi(x)} f(x,t)\,dt\right]$$
$$=\int_{\phi(x)}^{\psi(x)}\frac{\partial}{\partial x}f(x,t)\,dt+\left\{\frac{d\,\psi(x)}{dx}\right\}f^{(x,\,\psi(x))}-\left\{\frac{d\,\phi(x)}{dx}\right\}f^{(x,f(x))}$$

(ii) If the functions $\phi(x)$ and $\psi(x)$ are defined on $[a,b]$ and differentiable at a point $x\in(a,b)$ and $f(t)$ is continuous on $[\phi(a),\phi(b)]$, then

$$\frac{d}{dx}\left(\int_{\phi(x)}^{\psi(x)} f(t)\,dt\right)=\frac{d}{dx}\{\psi(x)\}\,f(\psi(x))-\frac{d}{dx}\{\phi(x)\}\,f(\phi(x))$$

Example 64 Find the derivative of the following with respect to x.

(i) $\displaystyle\int_0^x \cos t\,dt$ (ii) $\displaystyle\int_0^{x^2}\cos t^2\,dt$

Sol. (i) Let $f(x)=\displaystyle\int_0^x \cos t\,dt$

$$\therefore \frac{d}{dx}(f(x))=\cos(x)\left\{\frac{d}{dx}(x)\right\}-\cos 0\cdot\left\{\frac{d}{dx}(0)\right\}=\cos x$$

$$\left[\begin{array}{l}\text{using Leibnitiz's rule, } \dfrac{d}{dx}\\ \int_{\phi(x)}^{\psi(x)} f(t)dt=\dfrac{d}{dx}\{\psi(x)\}f(\psi(x))-\dfrac{d}{dx}\{\phi(x)\}+f(\phi(x))\end{array}\right]$$

$$\Rightarrow \frac{d}{dx}\left\{\int_0^x \cos t\,dt\right\}=\cos x$$

(ii) Let $f(x)=\displaystyle\int_0^{x^2}\cos t^2\,dt$

$$\therefore \frac{d}{dx}(f(x))=\cos(x^2)^2\cdot\left\{\frac{d}{dx}(x^2)\right\}-\cos(0)^2\left\{\frac{d}{dx}(0)\right\}$$
$$=2x\cdot\cos x^4$$

$$\Rightarrow \frac{d}{dx}\left(\int_0^{x^2}(\cos t^2)\,dt\right)=2x\cos x^4$$

Example 65 Evaluate $\dfrac{d}{dx}\left(\displaystyle\int_{1/x}^{\sqrt{x}}\cos t^2\,dt\right)$.

Sol. Let $f(x)=\displaystyle\int_{1/x}^{\sqrt{x}}\cos t^2\,dt$

$$\therefore \frac{d}{dx}(f(x))=\cos(\sqrt{x})^2\cdot\left\{\frac{d}{dx}(\sqrt{x})\right\}-\cos\left(\frac{1}{x}\right)^2\left\{\frac{d}{dx}\left(\frac{1}{x}\right)\right\}$$
$$=\frac{1}{2\sqrt{x}}\cos x+\frac{1}{x^2}\cdot\cos\left(\frac{1}{x^2}\right)$$

$$\Rightarrow \frac{d}{dx}\left(\int_{1/x}^{\sqrt{x}}\cos t^2\,dt\right)=\frac{1}{2\sqrt{x}}\cos x+\frac{1}{x^2}\cos\left(\frac{1}{x^2}\right)$$

Example 66 If $\dfrac{d}{dx}\left(\displaystyle\int_0^y e^{-t^2}\,dt+\int_0^{x^2}\sin^2 t\,dt\right)=0$, find $\dfrac{dy}{dx}$.

Sol. We know, $\dfrac{d}{dx}\left(\displaystyle\int_0^y e^{-t^2}\,dt+\int_0^{x^2}\sin^2 t\,dt\right)=0$

$$\Rightarrow e^{-y^2}\cdot\left\{\frac{d}{dx}(y)\right\}-e^{-0}\left\{\frac{d}{dx}(0)\right\}+\sin^2(x^2)\left\{\frac{d}{dx}(x^2)\right\}-\sin^2 0\left\{\frac{d}{dx}(0)\right\}=0$$

$$\Rightarrow e^{-y^2}\frac{dy}{dx}+2x\sin^2 x^2=0 \Rightarrow \frac{dy}{dx}=-2x\,e^{y^2}\sin^2 x^2$$

Example 67 Find the points of maxima/minima of $\displaystyle\int_0^{x^2}\frac{t^2-5t+4}{2+e^t}\,dt$.

Sol. Let $f(x)=\displaystyle\int_0^{x^2}\frac{t^2-5t+4}{2+e^t}\,dt$

$$\therefore f'(x)=\frac{x^4-5x^2+4}{2+e^{x^2}}\cdot 2x-0$$
$$=\frac{(x-1)(x+1)(x-2)(x+2)\cdot 2x}{2+e^{x^2}}$$

–	+	–	+	–	+

Number line points: –2, –1, 0, 1, 2

From the wavy curve, it is clear that $f'(x)$ changes its sign at $x = \pm 2 \pm 1\ 0$ and hence the points of maxima are $-1, 1$ (as sign changes from + ve to − ve) and of the minima are $-2, 0, 2$ (as sign changes from − ve to + ve).

Example 68 Find $\frac{d}{dx}\left(\int_{x^2}^{x^3} \frac{1}{\log t}\, dt\right)$.

Sol. $\frac{d}{dx}\left(\int_{x^2}^{x^3} \frac{1}{\log t}\, dt\right) = \frac{1}{\log x^3} \cdot \frac{d}{dx}(x^3) - \frac{1}{\log x^2} \cdot \frac{d}{dx}(x^2)$

$$= \frac{3x^2}{3\log x} - \frac{2x}{2\log x}$$

$$\therefore \quad \frac{d}{dx}\left(\int_{x^2}^{x^3} \frac{1}{\log t}\, dt\right) = \frac{1}{\log x}(x^2 - x)$$

Example 69 If $y = \int_0^x f(t)\sin\{K(x-t)\}\, dt$, then prove that $\frac{d^2y}{dx^2} + K^2 y = Kf(x)$.

Sol. We have, $y = \int_0^x f(t)\sin\{K(x-t)\}\, dt$

Differentiating w.r.t. x, we get

$$\frac{dy}{dx} = \int_0^x \frac{\partial}{\partial x}\{f(t)\sin K(x-t)\}\, dt + \frac{d}{dx}(x)$$

$$\cdot \{f(x)\sin K(x-x)\} - \frac{d}{dx}(0)\{f(0)\sin K(x-0)\}$$

$$= K\int_0^x f(t)\cos K(x-t)\, dt + 0 - 0$$

$$\Rightarrow \frac{dy}{dx} = K\int_0^x f(t)\cos K(x-t)\, dt$$

Again, differentiating both the sides w.r.t. x, we get

$$\frac{d^2y}{dx^2} = K\left\{\int_0^x \frac{\partial}{\partial x}\{f(t)\cos K(x-t)\}\, dt\right.$$

$$\left. + \left\{f(x)\cdot\cos K(x-x)\cdot\frac{d}{dx}(x)\right\} - \left\{f(0)\cos K(x-0)\cdot\frac{d}{dx}(0)\right\}\right\}$$

$$= K\left[-K\int_0^x f(t)\sin K(x-t)\, dt + f(x) - 0\right]$$

$$= -K^2\int_0^x f(t)\sin K(x-t)\, dt + K f(x)$$

$$\Rightarrow \frac{d^2y}{dx^2} = -K^2 y + K f(x) \Rightarrow \frac{d^2y}{dx^2} + K^2 y = Kf(x)$$

Example 70 If $\int_{\pi/3}^x \sqrt{3 - \sin^2 t}\, dt + \int_0^y \cos t\, dt = 0$, then evaluate $\frac{dy}{dx}$.

Sol. Differentiating w.r.t. x, we have

$$\frac{d}{dx}\left(\int_{\pi/3}^x \sqrt{3-\sin^2 t}\, dt\right) + \frac{d}{dx}\int_0^y (\cos t)\, dt = 0$$

$$\Rightarrow \sqrt{3-\sin^2 x}\cdot\frac{d}{dx}(x) - \sqrt{3 - \sin^2\frac{\pi}{3}}\cdot\frac{d}{dx}\left(\frac{\pi}{3}\right) + \cos y \cdot \frac{dy}{dx}$$

$$- \cos(0)\frac{d}{dx}(0) = 0$$

$$\Rightarrow \sqrt{3-\sin^2 x} + \cos y\frac{dy}{dx} = 0$$

$$\Rightarrow \frac{dy}{dx} = -\frac{\sqrt{3-\sin^2 x}}{\cos y}$$

Example 71 Let $\frac{d}{dx}(F(x)) = \frac{e^{\sin x}}{x}$, $x > 0$. If $\int_1^4 \frac{2e^{\sin x^2}}{x}\, dx = F(K) - F(1)$, then the possible value of K is

(a) 10 (b) 14 (c) 16 (d) 18

Sol. We have, $\frac{d}{dx}(F(x)) = \frac{e^{\sin x}}{x}$

$$\Rightarrow \int \frac{e^{\sin x}}{x}\, dx = F(x) \quad \text{...(i)}$$

Now, $\int_1^4 \frac{2e^{\sin x^2}}{x}\, dx = \int_1^4 \frac{e^{\sin(x^2)}}{x^2}\, d(x^2) = \int_1^{16} \frac{e^{\sin t}}{t}\, dt$

$$(\because x^2 = t)$$

$$= [F(t)]_1^{16} = F(16) - F(1)$$

$$\Rightarrow K = 16$$

Hence, (c) is the correct answer.

Example 72 The function $f(x) = \int_0^x \log_{|\sin t|}\left(\sin t + \frac{1}{2}\right) dt$, where $x \in (0, 2\pi)$, then $f(x)$ strictly increases in the interval

(a) $\left(\frac{\pi}{6}, \frac{5\pi}{6}\right)$ (b) $\left(\frac{5\pi}{6}, 2\pi\right)$

(c) $\left(\frac{\pi}{6}, \frac{7\pi}{6}\right)$ (d) $\left(\frac{5\pi}{6}, \frac{7\pi}{6}\right)$

Sol. Here, $f'(x) = \log_{|\sin x|}\left(\sin x + \frac{1}{2}\right) > 0$

$$\Rightarrow \sin x + \frac{1}{2} < 1 \text{ and } \left(\sin x + \frac{1}{2}\right) > 0$$

$$\Rightarrow 0 < \sin x + \frac{1}{2} < 1$$

$$\Rightarrow -1/2 < \sin x < 1/2$$

$$\Rightarrow x \in \left(\frac{5\pi}{6}, \frac{7\pi}{6}\right) \text{ as } x \in (0, 2\pi)$$

Hence, (d) is the correct answer.

| Example 73 Let $f:(0,\infty)\to R$ and $F(x)=\int_0^x t\,f(t)\,dt$.

If $F(x^2)=x^4+x^5$, then $\sum_{r=1}^{12} f(r^2)$ is equal to

(a) 216 (b) 219 (c) 221 (d) 223

Sol. Here, $F(x^2)=x^4+x^5=\int_0^{x^2} t\,f(t)\,dt$

Differentiating w.r.t. *x*, we get

$$x^2\,f(x^2)\cdot 2x=4x^3+5x^4$$

$$\Rightarrow \quad f(x^2)=2+\frac{5}{2}x \Rightarrow f(r^2)=2+\frac{5}{2}r$$

$$\therefore \quad \sum_{r=1}^{n} f(r^2)=2n+\frac{5}{2}n(n+1)=\frac{n(5n+13)}{4}$$

$$\Rightarrow \quad \sum_{r=1}^{12} f(r^2)=\frac{12(60+13)}{4}=219$$

Hence, (b) is the correct answer.

| Example 74 A function $f(x)$ satisfies $f(x)=\sin x+\int_0^x f'(t)(2\sin t-\sin^2 t)\,dt$, then $f(x)$ is

(a) $\frac{x}{1-\sin x}$ (b) $\frac{\sin x}{1-\sin x}$ (c) $\frac{1-\cos x}{\cos x}$ (d) $\frac{\tan x}{1-\sin x}$

Sol. Differentiating both the sides w.r.t. *x*, we get

$$f'(x)=\cos x+f'(x)(2\sin x-\sin^2 x)$$

$$\Rightarrow (1+\sin^2 x-2\sin x)f'(x)=\cos x$$

$$\Rightarrow \quad f'(x)=\frac{\cos x}{1+\sin^2 x-2\sin x}=\frac{\cos x}{(1-\sin x)^2}$$

Integrating, we get $f(x)=\int\frac{\cos x}{(1-\sin x)^2}\,dx$

Put $1-\sin x=t$, $\quad f(x)=-\int\frac{dt}{t^2}=\frac{1}{t}=\frac{1}{1-\sin x}+C$

Also, $f(0)=0$, hence $C=-1$

$$f(x)=\frac{1}{1-\sin x}-1=\frac{1-1+\sin x}{1-\sin x}=\frac{\sin x}{1-\sin x}$$

Hence, (b) is the correct answer.

| Example 75 If $F(x)=\int_1^x f(t)\,dt$, where $f(t)=\int_1^{t^2}\frac{\sqrt{1+u^4}}{u}\,du$, then the value of $F''(2)$ equals to

(a) $\frac{7}{4\sqrt{17}}$ (b) $\frac{15}{\sqrt{17}}$ (c) $\sqrt{257}$ (d) $\frac{15\sqrt{17}}{68}$

Sol. Here, $f'(t)=\frac{\sqrt{1+t^8}\cdot 2t}{t^2}=\frac{2\sqrt{1+t^8}}{t}$ ...(i)

Now, $F(x)=\int_1^x f(t)\,dt \Rightarrow F'(x)=f(x)$

$$F''(x)=f'(x) \Rightarrow F''(2)=f'(2)$$

From Eq. (i), $f'(2)=\sqrt{256+1}=\sqrt{257}$

Hence, (c) is the correct answer.

Property X. Let a function $f(x,\alpha)$ be continuous for $a\le x\le b$ and $c\le\alpha\le d$, then for any $\alpha\in[c,d]$, if $I(\alpha)=\int_a^b f(x,\alpha)\,dx$, then $\frac{dI(\alpha)}{d\alpha}=\int_a^b\frac{\partial f(x,\alpha)}{\partial\alpha}\,dx$

| Example 76 Evaluate $I(b)=\int_0^1\frac{x^b-1}{\ln x}\,dx; b\ge 0.$

Sol. We have, $I(b)=\int_0^1\frac{x^b-1}{\ln x}\,dx$

$$\Rightarrow \quad \frac{d}{db}(I(b))=\int_0^1\frac{\partial}{\partial b}\left(\frac{x^b-1}{\ln x}\right)dx+0-0$$

$$=\int_0^1\frac{x^b\ln x}{\ln x}\,dx=\int_0^1(x^b)\,dx=\left(\frac{x^{b+1}}{b+1}\right)_0^1$$

$$=\frac{1}{b+1}[1-0]=\frac{1}{b+1}$$

$$\therefore \quad \frac{d}{dx}(I(b))=\frac{1}{b+1}$$

Integrating both the sides w.r.t. *b*, we get

$$I(b)=\log(b+1)+C \quad \text{...(i)}$$

Given, $\quad I(b)=\int_0^1\frac{x^b-1}{\ln x}\,dx$

$\therefore \quad I(0)=0$ (when $b=0$) ...(ii)

Also, from Eq. (i), $I(0)=\log(1)+C$

$\therefore \quad I(0)=C$ ...(iii)

From Eqs. (ii) and (iii), $C=0$

$$\Rightarrow \quad I(b)=\log(b+1)$$

| Example 77 Prove that

$$\int_0^{\pi/2}\frac{dx}{(a^2\sin^2 x+b^2\cos^2 x)^2}=\frac{\pi(a^2+b^2)}{4a^3b^3}.$$

Sol. Let $I=\int_0^{\pi/2}\frac{1\,dx}{a^2\sin^2 x+b^2\cos^2 x}$

Then, $I=\int_0^{\pi/2}\frac{\sec^2 x}{a^2\tan^2 x+b^2}\,dx=\int_0^{\infty}\frac{dt}{a^2t^2+b^2}$

(where, $t=\tan x$)

$$\Rightarrow \quad I=\frac{1}{ab}\left[\tan^{-1}\left(\frac{at}{b}\right)\right]_0^{\infty}=\frac{1}{ab}\left(\frac{\pi}{2}-0\right)=\frac{\pi}{2ab}$$

Thus, $\int_0^{\pi/2}\frac{1}{a^2\sin^2 x+b^2\cos^2 x}\,dx=\frac{\pi}{2ab}=f(a,b)$ ...(i)

Differentiating both the sides w.r.t. 'a', we get

$$\int_0^{\pi/2} \frac{-2a\sin^2 x}{(a^2\sin^2 x + b^2\cos^2 x)^2}\,dx = -\frac{\pi}{2a^2b}$$

$$\Rightarrow \int_0^{\pi/2} \frac{\sin^2 x}{(a^2\sin^2 x + b^2\cos^2 x)^2}\,dx = \frac{\pi}{4a^3b} \quad \text{...(ii)}$$

Similarly, by differentiating Eq. (i) w.r.t. 'b', we get

$$\int_0^{\pi/2} \frac{\cos^2 x}{(a^2\sin^2 x + b^2\cos^2 x)^2}\,dx = \frac{\pi}{4ab^3} \quad \text{...(iii)}$$

Adding Eqs. (ii) and (iii), we get

$$\int_0^{\pi/2} \frac{(\sin^2 x + \cos^2 x)\,dx}{(a^2\sin^2 x + b^2\cos^2 x)^2} = \frac{\pi}{4a^3b} + \frac{\pi}{4ab^3}$$

$$\Rightarrow \int_0^{\pi/2} \frac{dx}{(a^2\sin^2 x + b^2\cos^2 x)^2} = \frac{\pi}{4a^3b^3}(a^2 + b^2)$$

Example 78 The value of $\int_0^{\pi/2} \frac{\log(1 + x\sin^2\theta)}{\sin^2\theta}\,d\theta\,;\, x \geq 0$ is equal to

(a) $\pi(\sqrt{1+x} - 1)$ (b) $\pi(\sqrt{1+x} - 2)$

(c) $\sqrt{\pi}(\sqrt{1+x} - 1)$ (d) None of these

Sol. Given, $f(x) = \int_0^{\pi/2} \frac{\log(1 + x\sin^2\theta)}{\sin^2\theta}\,d\theta;\ x \geq 0$

As above integral is function of x. Thus, differentiating both the sides w.r.t. 'x', we get

$$f'(x) = \int_0^{\pi/2} \frac{1}{1 + x\sin^2\theta}\cdot\frac{\sin^2\theta}{\sin^2\theta}\,d\theta + 0 - 0$$

(using Newton-Leibnitz's formula)

$$= \int_0^{\pi/2} \frac{d\theta}{1 + x\sin^2\theta} = \int_0^{\pi/2} \frac{\operatorname{cosec}^2\theta\,d\theta}{\cot^2\theta + (1 + x)}$$

$$= \left(-\frac{1}{\sqrt{1+x}}\cdot\tan^{-1}\frac{\cot\theta}{\sqrt{1+x}}\right)_0^{\pi/2} = \frac{\pi}{2\sqrt{1+x}}$$

$$\therefore \quad f'(x) = \frac{\pi}{2\sqrt{1+x}}$$

$$\Rightarrow \quad f(x) = \pi\sqrt{1+x} + C$$

where, $f(0) = 0 \Rightarrow C = -\pi$

$$\Rightarrow \quad f(x) = \pi\sqrt{1+x} - \pi = \pi(\sqrt{1+x} - 1)$$

Hence, (a) is the correct answer.

Example 79 Let $f(x)$ be a continuous functions for all x, such that $(f(x))^2 = \int_0^x f(t)\cdot\frac{2\sec^2 t}{4 + \tan t}\,dt$ and $f(0) = 0$, then

(a) $f\left(\frac{\pi}{4}\right) = \log\frac{5}{4}$ (b) $f\left(\frac{\pi}{4}\right) = \frac{3}{4}$

(c) $f\left(\frac{\pi}{2}\right) = 2$ (d) None of these

Sol. Here, $(f(x))^2 = \int_0^x f(t)\cdot\frac{2\sec^2 t}{4 + \tan t}\,dt,$

On differentiating both the sides w.r.t. x, we get

$$2f(x)\,.\,f'(x) = f(x)\cdot\frac{2\sec^2 x}{4 + \tan x}$$

$$\Rightarrow \quad f'(x) = \frac{\sec^2 x}{4 + \tan x}$$

Integrating both the sides, we get

$$f(x) = \int \frac{\sec^2 x}{4 + \tan x}\,dx = \log(4 + \tan x) + C$$

Since, $f(0) = 0$

$$\Rightarrow \quad 0 = \log(4) + C$$

$$\Rightarrow \quad C = -\log 4$$

$$\therefore \quad f(x) = \log(4 + \tan x) - \log(4)$$

$$\Rightarrow \quad f\left(\frac{\pi}{4}\right) = \log(4 + 1) - \log(4) = \log\frac{5}{4}$$

Hence, (a) is the correct answer.

Exercise for Session 5

1. The value of $\int_{-1}^{10} \operatorname{sgn}(x-[x])dx$ is equal to (where, $[\cdot]$ denotes the greatest integer function)

(a) 9 (b) 10 (c) 11 (d) 12

2. The value of $\int_0^{[x]}(x-[x])dx$ (where, $[\cdot]$ denotes the greatest integer function)

(a) $[x]$ (b) $\frac{[x]}{2}$ (c) $x[x]$ (d) None of these

3. The value of $\int_{-\pi/4}^{n\pi-\pi/4}|\sin x+\cos x|dx$ is equal to

(a) $2\sqrt{2}n$ (b) $\sqrt{2}n$ (c) $\frac{1}{2\sqrt{2}}n$ (d) None of these

4. Let $f(x)=x-[x]$ for every real number x (where, $[\cdot]$ denotes greatest integer function), then $\int_{-1}^{1} f(x)dx$ is equal to

(a) 1 (b) 2 (c) 0 (d) $\frac{1}{2}$

5. If $\int_0^x f(t)dt = x+\int_x^1 tf(t)\,dt$, then the value of $f(1)$ is

(a) $\frac{1}{2}$ (b) 0 (c) 1 (d) $-\frac{1}{2}$

6. The least value of the function $\phi(x)=\int_{5\pi/4}^{x}(3\sin t+4\cos t)dt$ on the interval $\left[\frac{5\pi}{4},\frac{4\pi}{3}\right]$ is

(a) $\sqrt{3}+\frac{3}{2}$ (b) $-2\sqrt{3}+\frac{3}{2}+\frac{1}{\sqrt{2}}$

(c) $\frac{3}{2}+\frac{1}{\sqrt{2}}$ (d) None of these

7. The points of extremum of $\phi(x)=\int_1^x e^{-t^2/2}(1-t^2)dt$ are

(a) $x=1,-1$ (b) $x=-1, 2$ (c) $x=2, 1$ (d) $x=-2, 1$

8. If $f(x)$ is periodic function, with period T, then

(a) $\int_a^b f(x)dx=\int_a^{b+T}f(x)dx$ (b) $\int_a^b f(x)dx=\int_{a+T}^{b+T}f(x)dx$

(c) $\int_a^b f(x)dx=\int_{a+T}^{b}f(x)dx$ (d) $\int_a^b f(x)dx=\int_{a+T}^{b+2T}f(x)dx$

9. Let $\frac{d}{dx}(F(x))=\frac{e^{\sin x}}{x}$, $x>0$. If $\int_1^4 \frac{2e^{\sin x^2}}{x}dx=F(k)-F(1)$, then one of the possible value of k is

(a) 4 (b) 8 (c) 16 (d) 32

10. Let $f:(0,\infty)\to R$ and $F(x)=\int_0^x f(t)dt$. If $F(x^2)=x^2(1+x)$, then $f(4)$ is equal to

(a) $\frac{5}{4}$ (b) 7 (c) 4 (d) 2

11. Let $T>0$ be a fixed real number. Suppose f is continuous function such that $f(x+T)=f(x)$ for all $x\in R$. If $I=\int_0^T f(x)dx$, then the value of $\int_3^{3+3T} f(2x)\,dx$ is

(a) $\frac{3}{2}I$ (b) $2I$ (c) $3I$ (d) $6I$

12. Let $f(x)=\int_1^x \sqrt{2-t^2}dt$, then the real roots of the equation $x^2-f'(x)=0$ are

(a) ± 1 (b) $\pm\frac{1}{\sqrt{2}}$ (c) $\pm\frac{1}{2}$ (d) $\pm\sqrt{2}$

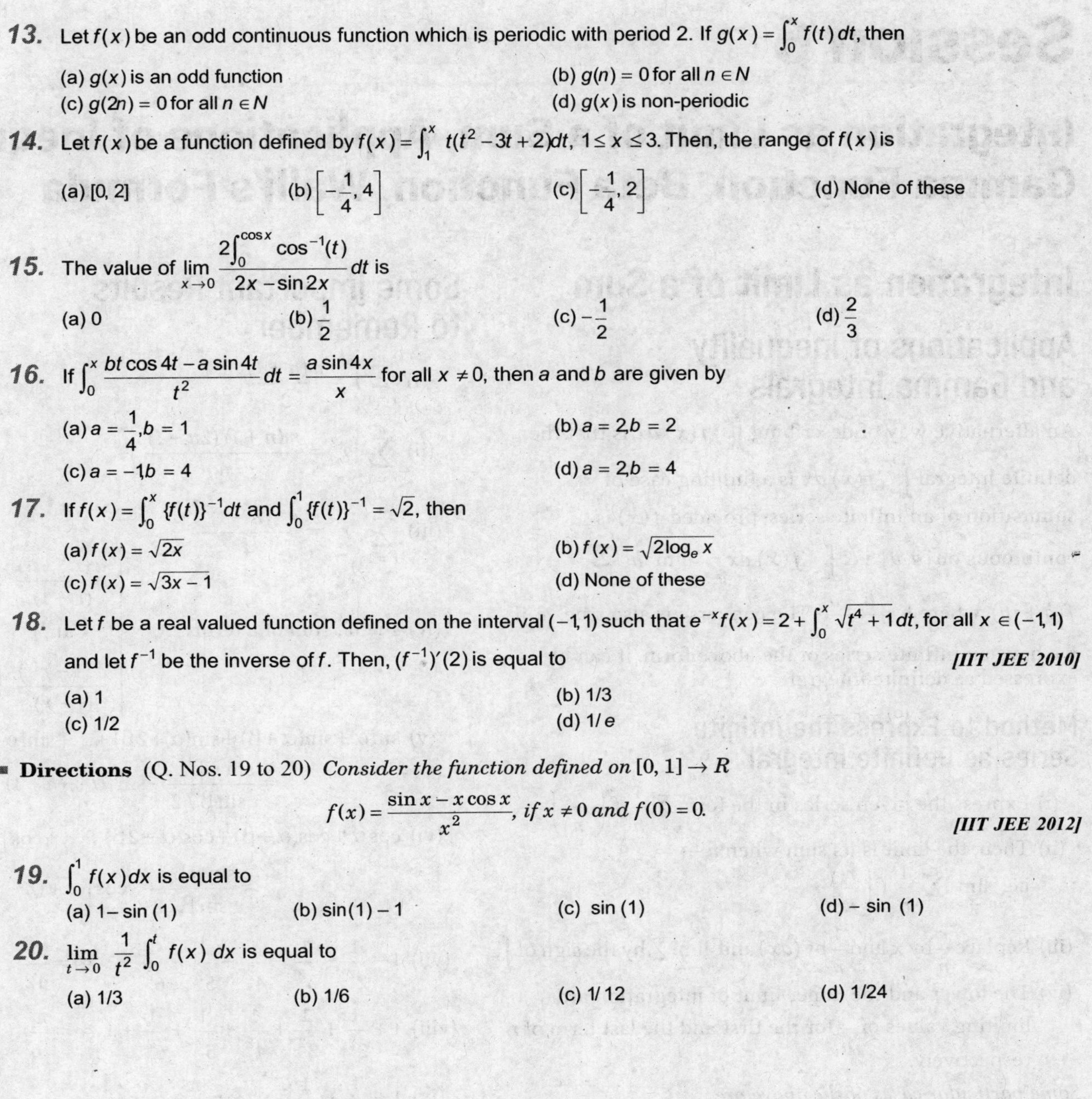

13. Let $f(x)$ be an odd continuous function which is periodic with period 2. If $g(x)=\int_0^x f(t)\,dt$, then

(a) $g(x)$ is an odd function
(b) $g(n)=0$ for all $n\in N$
(c) $g(2n)=0$ for all $n\in N$
(d) $g(x)$ is non-periodic

14. Let $f(x)$ be a function defined by $f(x)=\int_1^x t(t^2-3t+2)dt$, $1\le x\le 3$. Then, the range of $f(x)$ is

(a) [0, 2]
(b) $\left[-\frac{1}{4}, 4\right]$
(c) $\left[-\frac{1}{4}, 2\right]$
(d) None of these

15. The value of $\lim\limits_{x\to 0}\dfrac{2\int_0^{\cos x}\cos^{-1}(t)\,dt}{2x-\sin 2x}$ is

(a) 0
(b) $\frac{1}{2}$
(c) $-\frac{1}{2}$
(d) $\frac{2}{3}$

16. If $\int_0^x \dfrac{bt\cos 4t-a\sin 4t}{t^2}dt=\dfrac{a\sin 4x}{x}$ for all $x\ne 0$, then a and b are given by

(a) $a=\frac{1}{4}, b=1$
(b) $a=2, b=2$
(c) $a=-1, b=4$
(d) $a=2, b=4$

17. If $f(x)=\int_0^x \{f(t)\}^{-1}dt$ and $\int_0^1\{f(t)\}^{-1}=\sqrt{2}$, then

(a) $f(x)=\sqrt{2x}$
(b) $f(x)=\sqrt{2\log_e x}$
(c) $f(x)=\sqrt{3x-1}$
(d) None of these

18. Let f be a real valued function defined on the interval $(-1, 1)$ such that $e^{-x}f(x)=2+\int_0^x\sqrt{t^4+1}\,dt$, for all $x\in(-1,1)$ and let f^{-1} be the inverse of f. Then, $(f^{-1})'(2)$ is equal to ***[IIT JEE 2010]***

(a) 1
(b) 1/3
(c) 1/2
(d) $1/e$

■ **Directions** (Q. Nos. 19 to 20) *Consider the function defined on* $[0, 1]\to R$

$$f(x)=\frac{\sin x-x\cos x}{x^2},\ \text{if } x\ne 0 \text{ and } f(0)=0.$$

[IIT JEE 2012]

19. $\int_0^1 f(x)dx$ is equal to

(a) $1-\sin(1)$
(b) $\sin(1)-1$
(c) $\sin(1)$
(d) $-\sin(1)$

20. $\lim\limits_{t\to 0}\dfrac{1}{t^2}\int_0^t f(x)\,dx$ is equal to

(a) 1/3
(b) 1/6
(c) 1/12
(d) 1/24

Session 6

Integration as Limit of a Sum, Applications of Inequality Gamma Function, Beta Function, Walli's Formula

Integration as Limit of a Sum

Applications of Inequality and Gamma Integrals

An alternative way of describing $\int_a^b f(x)\,dx$ is that the definite integral $\int_a^b f(x)\,dx$ is a limiting case of summation of an infinite series, provided $f(x)$ is continuous on $[a, b]$, i.e. $\int_a^b f(x)\,dx = \lim_{n\to\infty} h \sum_{r=1}^{n-1} f(a+rh)$, where $h = \frac{b-a}{n}$. The converse is also true, *ie*, if we have an infinite series of the above form, it can be expressed as definite integral.

Method to Express the Infinite Series as Definite Integral

(i) Express the given series in the form $\sum \frac{1}{n} f\left(\frac{r}{n}\right)$.

(ii) Then, the limit is its sum when $n \to \infty$, i.e. $\lim_{n\to\infty} \sum \frac{1}{n} f\left(\frac{r}{n}\right)$.

(iii) Replace $\frac{r}{n}$ by x and $\frac{1}{n}$ by (dx) and $\lim_{n\to\infty} \sum$ by the sign of $\int$.

(iv) The lower and the upper limit of integration are limiting values of $\frac{r}{n}$ for the first and the last term of r respectively.

Some particular cases of the above are

(a) $\lim_{n\to\infty} \sum_{r=1}^{n} \frac{1}{n} f\left(\frac{r}{n}\right)$

or $\lim_{n\to\infty} \sum_{r=1}^{n-1} \frac{1}{n} f\left(\frac{r}{n}\right) = \int_0^1 f(x)\,dx$

(b) $\lim_{n\to\infty} \sum_{r=1}^{Pn} \frac{1}{n} f\left(\frac{r}{n}\right) = \int_\alpha^\beta f(x)\,dx$

where, $\alpha = \lim_{n\to\infty} \frac{r}{n} = 0$ (as $r = 1$)

and $\beta = \lim_{n\to\infty} \frac{r}{n} = p$ (as $r = pn$)

Some Important Results to Remember

(i) $\sum_{r=1}^{n} r = \frac{n(n+1)}{2}$

(ii) $\sum_{r=1}^{n} r^2 = \frac{n(n+1)(2n+1)}{6}$

(iii) $\sum_{r=1}^{n} r^3 = \frac{n^2(n+1)^2}{4}$

(iv) In GP, sum of n terms, $S_n = \begin{cases} \frac{a(r^n-1)}{(r-1)}, & |r|>1 \\ an, & r=1 \\ \frac{a(1-r^n)}{(1-r)}, & |r|<1 \end{cases}$

(v) $\sin\alpha + \sin(\alpha+\beta) + \sin(\alpha+2\beta) + \ldots + \sin[\alpha+\overline{(n-1)}\beta]$
$= \frac{\sin n\beta/2}{\sin\beta/2} \cdot \sin[\alpha+(n-1)\beta/2]$

(vi) $\cos\alpha + \cos(\alpha+\beta) + \cos(\alpha+2\beta) + \ldots + \cos[\alpha+\overline{(n-1)}\beta]$
$= \frac{\sin n\beta/2}{\sin\beta/2} \cdot \cos[\alpha+(n-1)\beta/2]$

(vii) $1 - \frac{1}{2^2} + \frac{1}{3^2} - \frac{1}{4^2} + \frac{1}{5^2} - \frac{1}{6^2} + \ldots \infty = \frac{\pi^2}{12}$

(viii) $1 + \frac{1}{2^2} + \frac{1}{3^2} + \frac{1}{4^2} + \frac{1}{5^2} + \frac{1}{6^2} + \ldots \infty = \frac{\pi^2}{6}$

(ix) $1 + \frac{1}{3^2} + \frac{1}{5^2} + \ldots \infty = \frac{\pi^2}{8}$

(x) $\frac{1}{2^2} + \frac{1}{4^2} + \frac{1}{6^2} + \ldots \infty = \frac{\pi^2}{24}$

(xi) $\cos\theta = \frac{e^{i\theta} + e^{-i\theta}}{2}$, and $\sin\theta = \frac{e^{i\theta} - e^{-i\theta}}{2i}$

(xii) $\cos h\theta = \frac{e^{\theta} + e^{-\theta}}{2}$ and $\sin h\theta = \frac{e^{\theta} - e^{-\theta}}{2}$

Remark

The method of evaluate the integral, as limit of the sum of an infinite series is known as integration by first principles.

Example 80 Evaluate the following :

(i) $\lim_{n\to\infty}\left(\frac{1}{n^2}+\frac{2}{n^2}+\frac{3}{n^2}+\ldots+\frac{n-1}{n^2}\right)$

(ii) $\lim_{n\to\infty}\left(\frac{1}{n+1}+\frac{1}{n+2}+\ldots+\frac{1}{2n}\right)$

(iii) $\lim_{n\to\infty}\left(\frac{n}{n^2+1^2}+\frac{n}{n^2+2^2}+\ldots+\frac{n}{2n^2}\right)$

(iv) $\lim_{n\to\infty}\frac{(1^P+2^P+\ldots+n^P)}{n^{P+1}}, P>0$

Sol. Let

(i) $S_n=\frac{1}{n^2}+\frac{2}{n^2}+\frac{3}{n^2}+\ldots+\frac{n-1}{n^2}$

$$=\sum_{r=2}^{n}\frac{r-1}{n^2}=\sum_{r=2}^{n}\frac{1}{n}\left(\frac{r-1}{n}\right)$$

$$\Rightarrow\quad S=\lim_{n\to\infty}\sum_{r=2}^{n}\frac{1}{n}\left(\frac{r}{n}\right)\quad\left(\text{as } n\to\infty\Rightarrow\frac{1}{n}\to 0\right)$$

$$=\int_0^1 x\,dx=\frac{1}{2}$$

(ii) Let $S_n=\frac{1}{n+1}+\frac{1}{n+2}+\ldots+\frac{1}{2n}=\sum_{r=1}^{n}\frac{1}{n+r}$

$$=\sum_{r=1}^{n}\frac{1}{n\left(1+\frac{r}{n}\right)}$$

Hence, $S=\lim_{n\to\infty}S_n=\lim_{n\to\infty}\frac{1}{n}\sum_{r=1}^{n}\frac{1}{1+\frac{r}{n}}$

$$=\int_0^1\frac{dx}{1+x}=[\log(1+x)]_0^1=\log 2$$

(iii) Let $S_n=\frac{n}{n^2+1^2}+\frac{n}{n^2+2^2}+\ldots+\frac{n}{2n^2}$

$$=\sum_{r=1}^{n}\frac{n}{n^2+r^2}=\sum_{r=1}^{n}\frac{1}{n(1+r^2/n^2)}$$

Hence, $S=\lim_{n\to\infty}S_n=\lim_{n\to\infty}\frac{1}{n}\sum_{r=1}^{n}\frac{1}{1+\frac{r^2}{n^2}}$

$$=\int_0^1\frac{dx}{1+x^2}=\left[\tan^{-1}x\right]_0^1=\frac{\pi}{4}$$

(iv) Let $S_n=\frac{1^P+2^P+\ldots+n^P}{n^{P+1}}=\sum_{r=1}^{n}\frac{r^P}{n^{P+1}}=\sum_{r=1}^{n}\frac{1}{n}\left(\frac{r}{n}\right)^P$

$$\therefore\quad S=\lim_{n\to\infty}S_n=\lim_{n\to\infty}\frac{1}{n}\sum_{r=1}^{n}\left(\frac{r}{n}\right)^P$$

$$=\int_0^1 x^P\,dx=\left[\frac{x^{P+1}}{P+1}\right]_0^1=\frac{1}{P+1}$$

Example 81 Evaluate $S=\sum_{r=0}^{n-1}\frac{1}{\sqrt{4n^2-r^2}}$ as $n\to\infty$.

Sol. Let $S_n=\sum_{r=0}^{n-1}\frac{1}{\sqrt{4n^2-r^2}}=\sum_{r=0}^{n-1}\frac{1}{n\sqrt{4-(r/n)^2}}$

$$=\frac{1}{n}\sum_{r=0}^{n-1}\frac{1}{\sqrt{4-(r/n)^2}}$$

Hence, $S=\lim_{n\to\infty}S_n=\lim_{n\to\infty}\frac{1}{n}\sum_{r=0}^{n-1}\frac{1}{\sqrt{4-(r/n)^2}}$

$$=\int_0^1\frac{dx}{\sqrt{4-x^2}}=\left[\sin^{-1}\frac{x}{2}\right]_0^1$$

$$\Rightarrow\quad S=\sin^{-1}\left(\frac{1}{2}\right)=\frac{\pi}{6}\qquad\therefore\ S=\frac{\pi}{6}$$

Example 82 Evaluate

$$\lim_{n\to\infty}\left(\frac{1}{2n+1}+\frac{1}{2n+2}+\ldots+\frac{1}{6n}\right).$$

Sol. Let $S_n=\left(\frac{1}{2n+1}+\frac{1}{2n+2}+\ldots+\frac{1}{6n}\right)$

$$=\sum_{r=1}^{4n}\frac{1}{2n+r}=\sum_{r=1}^{4n}\frac{1}{n}\cdot\frac{1}{2+(r/n)}$$

$$\Rightarrow\quad S=\lim_{n\to\infty}S_n=\int_0^4\frac{dx}{2+x}=[\ln|2+x|]_0^4$$

$$=\log 6-\log 2=\log 3$$

$$\therefore\quad S=\ln 3$$

Example 83 Evaluate $\int_1^4(ax^2+bx+c)\,dx$ from the first principle.

Sol. Let $x=1+rh$, where $h=\frac{4-1}{n}=\frac{3}{n}$

As $x\to 1, r\to 0$ and $x\to 4, r\to n$

$$\therefore\quad\int_1^4(ax^2+bx+c)\,dx=\lim_{n\to\infty}\sum_{r=0}^{n}h\,f(1+rh)$$

$$=\lim_{n\to\infty}\sum_{r=0}^{n}h\,[a(1+rh)^2+b(1+rh)+c]$$

$$=\lim_{n\to\infty}\sum_{r=0}^{n}\frac{3}{n}\left[a\left(1+\frac{3r}{n}\right)^2+b\left(1+\frac{3r}{n}\right)+c\right]$$

$$=3\lim_{n\to\infty}\sum_{r=0}^{n}\frac{1}{n}\left[a\left(1+\frac{9r^2}{n^2}+\frac{6r}{n}\right)+b\left(1+\frac{3r}{n}\right)+c\right]$$

$$=3\lim_{n\to\infty}\frac{1}{n}\left[a\left(n+\frac{9n(n+1)(2n+1)}{6n^2}+\frac{6n(n+1)}{2n}\right)+b\left(n+\frac{3n(n+1)}{2n}\right)+cn\right]$$

$$=3[a(1+3+3)+b(1+3/2)+c]=21a+\frac{15}{2}b+3c$$

Example 84 The value of

$$\lim_{n\to\infty}\left(\sin\frac{\pi}{2n}\cdot\sin\frac{2\pi}{2n}\cdot\sin\frac{3\pi}{2n}\dots\sin\frac{(n-1)\pi}{n}\right)^{1/n}$$ is equal to

(a) $\frac{1}{2}$ (b) $\frac{1}{3}$ (c) $\frac{1}{4}$ (d) None of these

Sol. Let $A=\left\{\lim_{n\to\infty}\sin\frac{\pi}{2n}\cdot\sin\frac{2\pi}{2n}\cdot\sin\frac{3\pi}{2n}\dots\sin\frac{2(n-1)\pi}{2n}\right\}^{1/n}$

$$\therefore \log A=\lim_{n\to\infty}\frac{1}{n}\log\left(\sin\frac{\pi}{2n}\cdot\sin\frac{2\pi}{2n}\dots\sin\frac{2(n-1)\pi}{2n}\right)$$

$$=\lim_{n\to\infty}\frac{1}{n}\sum_{r=1}^{2(n-1)}\log\sin\frac{r\pi}{2n}$$

$$=\int_0^2\log\sin\left(\frac{\pi x}{2}\right)dx$$

$$\left[\text{using }\lim_{n\to\infty}\Sigma\frac{1}{n}f\left(\frac{r}{n}\right)=\int_a^b f(x)\,dx\right]$$

$$=\int_0^{\pi}\log(\sin t)\cdot\frac{2}{\pi}\,dt \qquad \left[\text{putting }\frac{\pi x}{2}=t\right]$$

$$=\frac{2\cdot 2}{\pi}\int_0^{\pi/2}\log(\sin t)\,dt$$

$$\left[\text{using }\int_0^{2a}f(x)\,dx=2\int_0^a f(x)\,dx,\text{ if }f(2a-x)=f(x)\right]$$

$$=\frac{4}{\pi}\left\{-\frac{\pi}{2}\log 2\right\}\left[\text{using}\int_0^{\pi/2}\log(\sin x)dx=-\frac{\pi}{2}\log 2\right]$$

$$=-2\log 2$$

$\therefore \quad \log A=\log(1/4)\Rightarrow A=1/4$

Hence, (c) is the correct answer.

Example 85 The interval [0, 4] is divided into n equal sub-intervals by the points $x_0, x_1, x_2, \dots, x_{n-1}, x_n$ where $0=x_0<x_1<x_2<x_3<\dots<x_n=4$.

If $\delta x=x_i-x_{i-1}$ for $i=1,2,3,\dots,n$, then $\lim_{\delta x\to 0}\sum_{i=1}^{n}x_i\,\delta x$ is equal to

(a) 4 (b) 8 (c) $\frac{32}{3}$ (d) 16

Sol. $\lim_{\delta x\to 0}\delta x(x_1+x_2+x_3+\dots+x_n)$

$$=\lim_{n\to\infty}\frac{4}{n}\left[\frac{4}{n}+\frac{8}{n}+\frac{12}{n}+\dots\dots+4\cdot\frac{n}{n}\right] \qquad \left(\because \delta x=\frac{4}{n}\right)$$

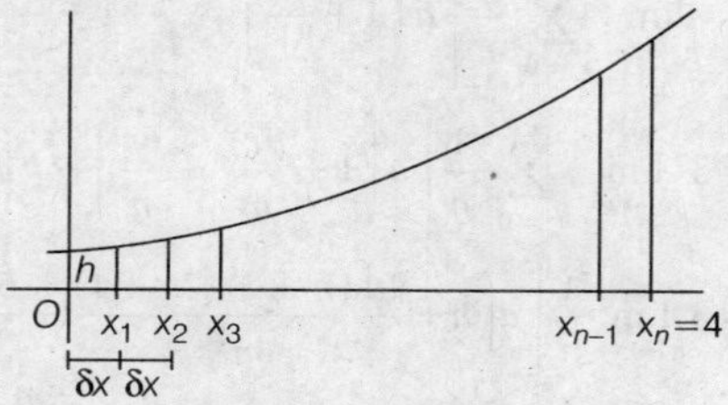

$$=\lim_{n\to\infty}\frac{16}{n^2}(1+2+3+\dots+n)=\lim_{n\to\infty}\frac{16}{n^2}\cdot\frac{n(n+1)}{2}=8$$

Hence, (b) is the correct answer.

Example 86 The value of $\lim_{n\to\infty}\frac{1}{n}\cdot\sum_{r=1}^{2n}\frac{r}{\sqrt{n^2+r^2}}$ is equal to

(a) $1+\sqrt{5}$ (b) $-1+\sqrt{5}$ (c) $-1+\sqrt{2}$ (d) $1+\sqrt{2}$

Sol. We have, $\lim_{n\to\infty}\frac{1}{n}\cdot\sum_{r=1}^{2n}\frac{r}{\sqrt{n^2+r^2}}$

$$=\lim_{n\to\infty}\frac{1}{n}\cdot\sum_{r=1}^{2n}\frac{\frac{r}{n}}{\sqrt{1+\frac{r^2}{n^2}}}=\int_0^2\frac{x}{\sqrt{1+x^2}}dx=(\sqrt{x^2+1})_0^2=\sqrt{5}-1$$

Hence, (b) is the correct answer.

Applications of Inequality

Sometimes you are asked to prove inequalities involving definite integrals or to estimate the upper and lower boundary values of definite integral, where the exact value of the definite integral is difficult to find. Under these circumstances, we use the following types

Type I. If $f(x)$ is defined on $[a, b]$, then

$$\left|\int_a^b f(x)\,dx\right|\le\int_a^b|f(x)|\,dx.$$

Equality sign holds, where $f(x)$ is entirely of the same sign on $[a, b]$.

Example 87 Estimate the absolute value of the integral $\int_{10}^{19}\frac{\sin x}{1+x^8}dx$.

Sol. To find, $I=\left|\int_{10}^{19}\frac{\sin x}{1+x^8}dx\right|\le\int_{10}^{19}\left|\frac{\sin x}{1+x^8}\right|dx$ ...(i)

(using type I)

Since, $|\sin x|\le 1$ for $x\ge 10$

The inequality $\left|\frac{\sin x}{1+x^8}\right|\le\frac{1}{|1+x^8|}$ ...(ii)

Also, $10\le x\le 19\Rightarrow 1+x^8>10^8$

$\Rightarrow \frac{1}{1+x^8}<\frac{1}{10^8}$ or $\frac{1}{|1+x^8|}<10^{-8}$ ...(iii)

From Eqs. (ii) and (iii), $\left|\frac{\sin x}{1+x^8}\right|<10^{-8}$ is fulfilled.

$$\left|\int_{10}^{19}\frac{\sin x}{1+x^8}dx\right|<\int_{10}^{19}10^{-8}\,dx$$

$$\therefore \quad \left|\int_{10}^{19}\frac{\sin x}{1+x^8}dx\right|<(19-10).10^{-8}<10^{-7}$$

($\because$ the true value of integral $\approx 10^{-8}$)

| Example 88 The minimum odd value of 'a' ($a > 1$) for which $\int_{10}^{19} \frac{\sin x}{1+x^a}\, dx < \frac{1}{9}$, is equal to

(a) 1 (b) 3 (c) 5 (d) 9

Sol. Let $I = \int_{10}^{19} \frac{\sin x\, dx}{1+x^a} < \int_{10}^{19} \frac{dx}{1+x^a}$

$$\left(\because \sin x < 1 \Rightarrow \frac{\sin x}{1+x^a} < \frac{1}{1+x^a}\right)$$

$$\therefore \quad I < \int_{10}^{19} \frac{dx}{1+x^a} < \int_{10}^{19} \frac{dx}{1+10^a}$$

$$(\because 10 < x < 19 \Rightarrow 10^a + 1 < 1 + x^a < 19^a + 1)$$

$$\Rightarrow \quad I < \frac{9}{1+10^a}$$

$$\therefore \frac{9}{1+10^a} < \frac{1}{9} \Rightarrow 1 + 10^a > 81 \text{ or } 10^a > 80 \text{ i.e. } a = 2, 3, 4, 5, \ldots$$

$\therefore$ Minimum odd value of 'a' is 3.

Hence, (b) is the correct answer.

Type II.

$$\left| \int_a^b f(x)\, g(x)\, dx \right| \leq \sqrt{\left(\int_a^b f^2(x)\, dx\right)\left(\int_a^b g^2(x)\, dx\right)},$$

where $f^2(x)$ and $g^2(x)$ are integrable on $[a, b]$.

| Example 89 Prove that $\int_0^1 \sqrt{(1+x)(1+x^3)}\, dx$ cannot exceed $\sqrt{15/8}$.

Sol. $\int_0^1 \sqrt{(1+x)(1+x^3)}dx \leq \sqrt{\left(\int_0^1 (1+x)dx\right)\left(\int_0^1 (1+x^3)\, dx\right)}$

$$\leq \sqrt{\left(x + \frac{x^2}{2}\right)_0^1 \left(x + \frac{x^4}{4}\right)_0^1}$$

$$\leq \sqrt{\frac{3}{2} \cdot \frac{5}{4}} \leq \sqrt{\frac{15}{8}}$$

Type III. If $f(x) \,|\, g(x)$ on $[a, b]$, then $\int_a^b f(x)\, dx \geq \int_a^b g(x)\, dx$. In particular, if $f(x) \geq 0$, then $\int_a^b f(x)\, dx \,|\, 0$.

| Example 90 If $f(x)$ is a continuous function such that $f(x) \,|\, 0, \forall\, x \in [2, 10]$ and $\int_4^8 f(x)\, dx = 0$, then find $f(6)$.

Sol. $f(x)$ is above the X-axis or on the X-axis for all $x \in [2, 10]$.

If $f(x)$ is greater than zero at any sub-interval of [4, 8], then $\int_4^8 f(x)\, dx$ must be greater than zero. But $\int_4^8 f(x)\, dx = 0$, which shows $f(x)$ can't have any value greater than zero in the sub-interval [4, 8].

$\Rightarrow f(x)$ is constant in the sub-interval [4, 8] and has to be zero at all points, $x \in [4, 8]$.

$$\Rightarrow \quad f(x) = 0, \quad \forall\, x \in [4, 8]$$

$$\Rightarrow \quad f(6) = 0$$

Type IV. For a given function $f(x)$ continuous on $[a, b]$, if you are able to find two continuous functions $f_1(x)$ and $f_2(x)$ on $[a, b]$ such that $f_1(x) \leq f(x) \leq f_2(x), \forall\, x \in [a, b]$, then

$$\int_a^b f_1(x)\, dx \leq \int_a^b f(x)\, dx \leq \int_a^b f_2(x)\, dx.$$

| Example 91 Prove that $\frac{\pi}{6} \leq \int_0^1 \frac{dx}{\sqrt{4 - x^2 - x^3}} \leq \frac{\pi}{4\sqrt{2}}$.

Sol. Since, $4 - x^2 \,|\, 4 - x^2 - x^3 \,|\, 4 - 2x^2 > 1, \forall\, x \in [0, 1]$

$$\sqrt{4 - x^2} \,|\, \sqrt{4 - x^2 - x^3} \,|\, \sqrt{4 - 2x^2} > 1, \forall\, x \in [0, 1]$$

$$\Rightarrow \frac{1}{\sqrt{4 - x^2}} \leq \frac{1}{\sqrt{4 - x^2 - x^3}} \leq \frac{1}{\sqrt{4 - 2x^2}}, \forall\, x \in [0, 1]$$

$$\Rightarrow \int_0^1 \frac{dx}{\sqrt{4 - x^2}} \leq \int_0^1 \frac{dx}{\sqrt{4 - x^2 - x^3}}$$

$$\leq \int_0^1 \frac{1}{\sqrt{4 - 2x^2}}\, dx, \forall\, x \in [0, 1]$$

$$\Rightarrow \left(\sin^{-1} \frac{x}{2}\right)_0^1 \leq \int_0^1 \frac{dx}{\sqrt{4 - x^2 - x^3}} \leq \frac{1}{\sqrt{2}} \left(\sin^{-1} \frac{x}{\sqrt{2}}\right)_0^1$$

$$\Rightarrow \frac{\pi}{6} \leq \int_0^1 \frac{dx}{\sqrt{4 - x^2 - x^3}} \leq \frac{\pi}{4\sqrt{2}}$$

Type V. If m and M be global minimum and global maximum of $f(x)$ respectively in $[a, b]$, then

$$m\,(b - a) \leq \int_a^b f(x)\, dx \leq M(b - a).$$

Proof We have, $m \leq f(x) \leq M$ for all $x \in [a, b]$

$$\Rightarrow \quad \int_a^b m\, dx \leq \int_a^b f(x)\, dx \leq \int_a^b M\, dx$$

$$\Rightarrow \quad m\,(b - a) \leq \int_a^b f(x)\, dx \leq M\,(b - a)$$

| Example 92 Prove that $4 \leq \int_1^3 \sqrt{3 + x^3}\, dx \leq 2\sqrt{30}$.

Sol. Since, the function $f(x) = \sqrt{3 + x^3}$ increases monotonically on the interval [1, 3].

$$\therefore \quad M = \text{Maximum value of } \sqrt{3 + x^3} = \sqrt{3 + 3^3} = \sqrt{30}$$

$$\text{and} \quad m = \text{Minimum value of } \sqrt{3 + x^3} = \sqrt{3 + 1^3} = 2$$

$\therefore \quad m = 2, M = \sqrt{30}, b - a = 2$

Hence, $\quad 2 \cdot 2 \le \int_1^3 \sqrt{3 + x^3}\, dx \le 2\sqrt{30}$

$\Rightarrow \quad 4 \le \int_1^3 \sqrt{3 + x^3}\, dx \le 2\sqrt{30}$

Example 93 Prove that $1 \le \int_0^1 e^{x^2} dx \le e$.

Sol. For $0 \le x \le 1$, we have $e^0 \le e^{x^2} \le e^1$

$\therefore \quad e^0 (1 - 0) \le \int_0^1 e^{x^2} dx \le e^1 (1 - 0)$

$\Rightarrow \quad 1 \le \int_0^1 e^{x^2} dx \le e$

Gamma Function

If n is a positive number, then the improper integral $\int_0^\infty e^{-x} x^{n-1}\, dx$ is defined as Gamma function and is denoted by Γn.

i.e. $\quad \Gamma n = \int_0^\infty e^{-x} x^{n-1}\, dx$, where $x \in Q^+$.

Example 94 Evaluate

(i) $\Gamma 1$ (ii) $\Gamma 2$

Sol. (i) $\Gamma 1 = \int_0^\infty e^{-x} \,.\, x^{1-1}\, dx = \lim_{b \to \infty} \int_0^b e^{-x}\, dx$

$= \lim_{b \to \infty} \left[-e^{-x} \right]_0^b = \lim_{b \to \infty} (-e^{-b} + e^0)$

$= 0 + 1 = 1$

(ii) $\Gamma 2 = \int_0^\infty e^{-\infty} x^{2-1}\, dx = \lim_{b \to \infty} \int_0^b e^{-x} \cdot x\, dx$

$= \lim_{b \to \infty} \left[-x\, e^{-x} - e^{-x} \right]_0^b$

$= \lim_{b \to \infty} [(-b\, e^{-b} - e^{-b}) - (0 - 1)]$

$= \lim_{b \to \infty} \left[\frac{-b}{e^b} - \frac{1}{e^b} + 1 \right] = \lim_{b \to \infty} \frac{-(b+1)}{e^b} + 1$

$= \left(\lim_{b \to \infty} -\frac{1}{e^b} \right) + 1$ (using L'Hospital's rule)

$= 1$

Properties of Gamma Function

Gamma function has following properties :

(i) $\Gamma 1 = 1, \Gamma 0 = \infty$ and $\Gamma(n+1) = n \Gamma n$

e.g. $\Gamma 5 = 4 \Gamma 4 = 4 \times 3\, \Gamma 3 = 4 \times 3 \times 2\, \Gamma 2$

$= 4 \times 3 \times 2 \times 1\, \Gamma 1 = 4 \times 3 \times 2 \times 1$

(ii) If $n \in N$, then $\Gamma(n+1) = (n)\,!$

(iii) $\Gamma(1/2) = \sqrt{\pi}$

(iv) $\int_0^{\pi/2} \sin^m x \cdot \cos^n x\, dx = \dfrac{\Gamma\left(\frac{m+1}{2}\right) \Gamma\left(\frac{n+1}{2}\right)}{2\, \Gamma\left(\frac{m+n+2}{2}\right)}$

(v) $\Gamma n\, \Gamma(1-n) = \dfrac{\pi}{\sin n\pi}, 0 < n < 1$

(vi) $\Gamma m\, \Gamma\left(m + \frac{1}{2}\right) = \dfrac{\sqrt{\pi}}{2^{2m-1}} \Gamma\, 2m$

(vii) $\Gamma \frac{1}{n} \Gamma\left(\frac{2}{n}\right) \ldots \Gamma\left(\frac{n-1}{n}\right) = \dfrac{(2\pi)^{\frac{n-1}{2}}}{n^{1/2}}$

Example 95 Evaluate $\int_0^\infty e^{-x} x^3\, dx$.

Sol. By definition of Gamma function,

$\int_0^\infty e^{-x} x^3\, dx = \int_0^\infty e^{-x} x^{4-1}\, dx = \Gamma 4$

$\therefore \quad \int_0^\infty e^{-x} x^3\, dx = 6$

Example 96 Evaluate $\int_0^1 \left(\log \frac{1}{x} \right)^{n-1} dx$.

Sol. Let $I = \int_0^1 \left(\log \frac{1}{x} \right)^{n-1} dx$

Put $\log \frac{1}{x} = t \Rightarrow dx = -e^{-t}\, dt$

$\therefore \quad I = \int_\infty^0 t^{n-1} (-e^{-t})\, dt = \int_0^\infty e^{-t}\, t^{n-1}\, dt$

$\therefore \quad \int_0^1 \left(\log \frac{1}{x} \right)^{n-1} dx = \Gamma n$

Beta Function

The beta function is

$$B(m, n) = \int_0^1 x^{m-1} (1-x)^{n-1}\, dx,$$

where $m, n > 0$

Properties of Beta Function

(i) $B(m, n) = B(n, m)$, where $m, n > 0$

(ii) $B(m, n) = \dfrac{\Gamma m\, \Gamma n}{\Gamma (m+n)}$, where $m, n > 0$

(iii) $B(m, n) = \int_0^\infty \dfrac{x^{m-1}}{(1+x)^{m+n}}\, dx$

Example 97 Evaluate $\int_0^1 x^6 \sqrt{(1-x^2)}\, dx$.

Sol. Let, $I = \int_0^1 x^6 \sqrt{(1-x^2)}\, dx$

Put let $x^2 = t$

$\Rightarrow 2x\, dx = dt$

$\therefore \quad I = \frac{1}{2}\int_0^1 t^{5/2} \sqrt{(1-t)}\, dt$

$$I = \frac{1}{2} B\left(\frac{7}{2}, \frac{3}{2}\right) = \frac{1}{2} \cdot \frac{\Gamma 7/2\, \Gamma 3/2}{\Gamma\left(\frac{3}{2}+\frac{7}{2}\right)}$$

$$= \frac{1}{2} \frac{\frac{5}{2}\cdot\frac{3}{2}\cdot\frac{1}{2}\cdot\sqrt{\pi}\cdot\frac{1}{2}\cdot\sqrt{\pi}}{4\cdot 3\cdot 2\cdot 1} = \frac{5\pi}{256}$$

Walli's Formula

An easy way to evaluate $\int_0^{\pi/2} \sin^m x \cdot \cos^n x\, dx$, where $m, n \in I_+$.

We have, $\int_0^{\pi/2} \sin^m x \cdot \cos^n x\, dx = \int_0^{\pi/2} \sin^n x \cdot \cos^m x\, dx$

$$= \frac{(m-1)(m-3)\ldots(1 \text{ or } 2).(n-1)(n-3)\ldots(1 \text{ or } 2)}{(m+n)(m+n-2)\ldots(1 \text{ or } 2)} \cdot \frac{\pi}{2},$$

when both m and $n \in$ even integer.

$$= \frac{(m-1)(m-3)\ldots(1 \text{ or } 2)\cdot(n-1)(n-3)\ldots(1 \text{ or } 2)}{(m+n)(m+n-2)\ldots(1 \text{ or } 2)},$$

when either of m or $n \in$ odd integer.

Remark

If n be a positive integer, then

$$\int_0^{\pi/2} \sin^n x\, dx = \int_0^{\pi/2} \cos^n x\, dx$$

$$= \frac{n-1}{n}\cdot\frac{n-3}{n-2}\cdot\frac{n-5}{n-4}\ldots\frac{3}{4}\cdot\frac{1}{2}\cdot\frac{\pi}{2}, \; n \text{ is even.}$$

$$= \frac{n-1}{n}\cdot\frac{n-3}{n-2}\cdot\frac{n-5}{n-4}\ldots\frac{4}{5}\cdot\frac{2}{3}\cdot 1, \; n \text{ is odd.}$$

Example 98 Evaluate $\int_0^{\pi/2} \sin^4 x \cdot \cos^6 x\, dx$.

Sol. Using Gamma function, we have

$$\int_0^{\pi/4} \sin^4 x \cdot \cos^6 x\, dx = \frac{\Gamma(5/2)\,\Gamma(7/2)}{2\Gamma\left(\frac{4+6+2}{2}\right)} = \frac{\Gamma(5/2)\,\Gamma(7/2)}{2\Gamma 6}$$

$$= \frac{\left(\frac{3}{2}\times\frac{1}{2}\times\Gamma(1/2)\right)\left(\frac{5}{2}\times\frac{3}{2}\times\frac{1}{2}\times\Gamma(1/2)\right)}{2\times 5!} = \frac{3\pi}{512}$$

Example 99 The value of $\int_0^\infty e^{-a^2x^2}\, dx$ is equal to

(a) $\frac{\sqrt{\pi}}{2a}$ (b) $\frac{\pi}{2a}$

(c) $\frac{\pi}{\sqrt{2a}}$ (d) None of these

Sol. Let $I = \int_0^\infty e^{-a^2x^2}\, dx$

$$\therefore \quad I = \int_0^\infty e^{-t} \cdot \frac{1}{2a\sqrt{t}}\, dt = \frac{1}{2a}\int_0^\infty e^{-t} \cdot t^{-1/2}\, dt$$

(put $a^2x^2 = t \Rightarrow 2a^2x\, dx = dt$)

$$= \frac{1}{2a}\int_0^\infty t^{1/2-1} \cdot e^{-t} \cdot dt \quad \left(\text{using } \int_0^\infty e^{-x} x^{n-1} dx = \Gamma n\right)$$

$$= \frac{1}{2a}\Gamma\frac{1}{2} = \frac{1}{2a}\sqrt{\pi} \quad \left(\text{using } \Gamma\frac{1}{2} = \sqrt{\pi}\right)$$

Hence, (a) is the correct answer.

Exercise for Session 6

1. The value of $f(x) = \int_0^{\pi/2} \frac{\log(1 + x\sin^2\theta)}{\sin^2\theta} d\theta, x \geq 0$ is equal to

(a) $\frac{1}{\pi}(\sqrt{1+x} - 1)$ (b) $\sqrt{\pi}(\sqrt{1+x} - 1)$ (c) $\pi(\sqrt{1+x} - 1)$ (d) None of these

2. The value of $\lim_{n \to \infty} \frac{1}{n} \sum_{r-1}^{n} \left(\frac{r}{n+r}\right)$ is equal to

(a) $1 - \log 2$ (b) $\log 4 - 1$ (c) $\log 2$ (d) None of these

3. The value of $\lim_{n \to \infty} \frac{1}{n}\{(n+1)(n+2)(n+3)\ldots(n+n)\}^{1/n}$ is equal to

(a) $4e$ (b) $\frac{e}{4}$ (c) $\frac{4}{e}$ (d) None of these

4. If $m, n \in N$, then the value of $\int_a^b (x-a)^m (b-x)^n dx$ is equal to

(a) $\frac{(b-a)^{m+n} \cdot m!n!}{(m+n)!}$ (b) $\frac{(b-a)^{m+n+1} \cdot m!n!}{(m+n+1)!}$

(c) $\frac{(b-a)^m \cdot m!}{m!}$ (d) None of these

5. The value of $\lim_{n \to \infty} \left(\frac{n!}{n^n}\right)^{\frac{2n^4+1}{5n^5+1}}$ is equal to

(a) e (b) $\frac{2}{e}$ (c) $\left(\frac{1}{e}\right)^{\frac{2}{5}}$ (d) None of these

6. The value of $\lim_{n \to \infty} n \left\{\frac{1}{3n^2 + 8n + 4} + \frac{1}{3n^2 + 16n + 16} + \ldots + n \text{ terms}\right\}$ is equal to

(a) $\frac{1}{2}\log\left(\frac{9}{5}\right)$ (b) $\frac{1}{3}\log\left(\frac{9}{5}\right)$

(c) $\frac{1}{4}\log\left(\frac{9}{5}\right)$ (d) None of these

7. The value of $\lim_{n \to \infty} \frac{1}{n^2}\left\{\sin^3\frac{\pi}{4n} + 2\sin^3\frac{2\pi}{4n} + \ldots + n\sin^3\frac{n\pi}{4n}\right\}$ is equal to

(a) $\frac{\sqrt{2}}{9\pi^2}(52 - 15n)$ (b) $\frac{2}{9\pi^2}(52 - 15n)$

(c) $\frac{1}{9\pi^2}(15n - 15)$ (d) None of these

8. The value of $f(k) = \int_0^{\pi/2} \log(\sin^2\theta + k^2\cos^2\theta)\, d\theta$ is equal to

(a) $\pi\log(1+K) - \pi\log 2$ (b) $\pi\log 2 - \log(1+K)$ (c) $\log(1+K) - \pi\log 2$ (d) None of these

9. If $m, n \in N$, then $I_{m,n} = \int_0^1 x^m (1-x)^n dx$ is equal to

(a) $\frac{m!n!}{(m+n+2)!}$ (b) $\frac{2m!n!}{(m+n+1)!}$ (c) $\frac{m!n!}{(m+n+1)!}$ (d) None of these

10. The value of $I(n) = \int_0^{\pi} \frac{\sin^2 n\theta}{\sin^2\theta} d\theta$ is $(\forall\, n \in N)$

(a) $n\pi$ (b) $\frac{n\pi}{2}$ (c) $\frac{n\pi}{4}$ (d) None of these

JEE Type Solved Examples : Single Option Correct Type Questions

- **Ex. 1** *If $\int_0^{\infty} f(x)dx = \frac{\pi}{2}$ and $f(x)$ is an even function, then $\int_0^{\infty} f\left(x-\frac{1}{x}\right)dx$ is equal to*

(a) $\frac{\pi}{4}$ (b) $\frac{\pi}{2}$ (c) π (d) None of these

Sol. Here, $\int_0^{\infty} f(x)dx = \frac{\pi}{2}$

Put $x = t - \frac{1}{t}$

$$\Rightarrow \quad dx = \left(1+\frac{1}{t^2}\right)dt$$

$$\therefore \int_0^{\infty} f(x)dx = \int_1^{\infty} f\left(t-\frac{1}{t}\right)\cdot\left(1+\frac{1}{t^2}\right)dt$$

$$= \int_1^{\infty} f\left(t-\frac{1}{t}\right)dt + \int_1^{\infty} f\left(t-\frac{1}{t}\right)\cdot\frac{1}{t^2}dt$$

$$= \int_1^{\infty} f\left(t-\frac{1}{t}\right)dt + \int_1^{0} f\left(\frac{1}{y}-y\right)\cdot(-dy) \quad \left(\text{put } t = \frac{1}{y}\right)$$

$$= \int_1^{\infty} f\left(t-\frac{1}{t}\right)dt - \int_1^{0} f\left(y-\frac{1}{y}\right)dy \quad \text{as } f(x) \text{ is even}$$

$$= \int_1^{\infty} f\left(t-\frac{1}{t}\right)dt + \int_0^{1} f\left(t-\frac{1}{t}\right)dt = \int_0^{\infty} f\left(t-\frac{1}{t}\right)dt$$

$$\therefore \quad \int_0^{\infty} f\left(x-\frac{1}{x}\right)dx = \int_0^{\infty} f(x)dx = \frac{\pi}{2}$$

- **Ex. 2** *The value of $\int_0^1 \left(\prod_{r=1}^{n}(x+r)\right)\left(\sum_{k=1}^{n}\frac{1}{x+k}\right)dx$ equals to*

(a) n (b) $n!$ (c) $(n+1)!$ (d) $n\cdot n!$

Sol. The given integrand is perfect coefficient of $\prod_{r=1}^{n}(x+r)$

$$\therefore \quad I = \left[\prod_{r=1}^{n}(x+r)\right]_0^1 = (n+1)! - n! = n\cdot n!$$

Aliter $(x+1)(x+2)(x+3)\ldots(x+n) = e^t$

So that, when $x = 0$, then $t = \ln n!$ when $x = 1$, then $t = \ln(n+1)!$

$[\ln(x+1) + \ln(x+2) + \ldots\ldots + \ln(x+n)] = t$

$$\therefore \quad \left(\frac{1}{(x+1)} + \frac{1}{(x+2)} + \ldots + \frac{1}{(x+n)}\right)dx = dt$$

Therefore, $I = \int_{\ln n!}^{\ln(n+1)!} e^t dt = [e^t]_{\ln n!}^{\ln(n+1)!}$

$$= e^{\ln(n+1)!} - e^{\ln n!} = (n+1)! - n! = n\cdot n!$$

Hence, (d) is the correct answer.

- **Ex. 3** *The true set of values of 'a' for which the inequality $\int_a^0 (3^{-2x} - 2\cdot 3^{-x})\,dx \geq 0$ is true, is*

(a) [0, 1] (b) $(-\infty, -1]$ (c) $[0, \infty)$ (d) $(-\infty, -1] \cup [0, \infty)$

Sol. We have, $\int_a^0 3^{-x}(3^{-x} - 2)\,dx \geq 0$

Put $3^{-x} = t \Rightarrow 3^{-x}\ln 3\,dx = -dt$

$$\Rightarrow \quad \ln 3\int_1^{3^{-a}} (t-2)\,dt \geq 0 = \left[\frac{t^2}{2} - 2t\right]_1^{3^{-a}} \geq 0$$

$$\Rightarrow \quad \left(\frac{3^{-2a}}{2} - 2\cdot 3^{-a}\right) - \left(\frac{1}{2} - 2\right) \geq 0$$

$$\Rightarrow \quad 3^{-2a} - 4\times 3^{-a} + 3 > 0 \Rightarrow (3^{-a} - 3)(3^{-a} - 1) > 0$$

$$\Rightarrow \quad 3^{-a} > 3^1 \Rightarrow a < 1 \text{ or } 3^{-a} < 3^0 \Rightarrow a > 0$$

Thus, $a \in (-\infty, -1] \cup [0, \infty)$

Hence, (d) is the correct answer.

- **Ex. 4** *The value of the definite integral $\int_0^{2n\pi} \max(\sin x, \sin^{-1}(\sin x))dx$ equals to (where, $n \in I$)*

(a) $\frac{n(\pi^2-4)}{2}$ (b) $\frac{n(\pi^2-4)}{4}$

(c) $\frac{n(\pi^2-8)}{4}$ (d) $\frac{n(\pi^2-2)}{4}$

Sol. Let $I = \int_0^{2n\pi} \max(\sin x, \sin^{-1}(\sin x))\,dx$

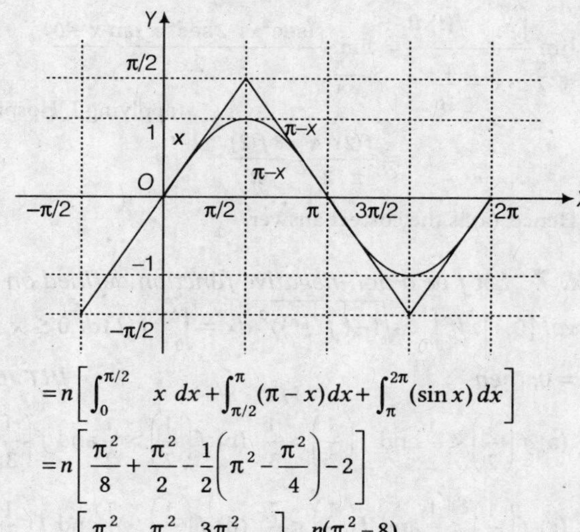

$$= n\left[\int_0^{\pi/2} x\,dx + \int_{\pi/2}^{\pi}(\pi - x)dx + \int_{\pi}^{2\pi}(\sin x)\,dx\right]$$

$$= n\left[\frac{\pi^2}{8} + \frac{\pi^2}{2} - \frac{1}{2}\left(\pi^2 - \frac{\pi^2}{4}\right) - 2\right]$$

$$= n\left[\frac{\pi^2}{8} + \frac{\pi^2}{2} - \frac{3\pi^2}{8} - 2\right] = \frac{n(\pi^2-8)}{4}$$

Hence, (c) is the correct answer.

Ex. 5 *$\lim_{n\to\infty} n^{-\frac{1}{2}\left(1+\frac{1}{n}\right)} \cdot (1^1\cdot 2^2\cdot 3^3 .....n^n)^{\frac{1}{n^2}}$ is equal to*

(a) $\sqrt{e}$ (b) $\frac{1}{\sqrt{e}}$ (c) $\frac{1}{\sqrt[4]{e}}$ (d) $\sqrt[4]{e}$

Sol. Let $L = \lim_{n\to\infty} n^{-\frac{1}{2}\left(1+\frac{1}{n}\right)} \cdot (1^1\cdot 2^2\cdot 3^3 ...n^n)^{\frac{1}{n^2}}$

$$\therefore \ln L = \lim_{n\to\infty} -\frac{1}{2}\left(\frac{n+1}{n}\right)\ln n + \frac{1}{n^2}\sum_{k=1}^{n} k\ln k$$

$$= \lim_{n\to\infty} -\frac{1}{2}\left(\frac{n+1}{n}\right)\ln n + \frac{1}{n^2}\sum_{k=1}^{n}(k\ln k - k\ln n + k\ln n)$$

$$= \lim_{n\to\infty} -\frac{1}{2}\left(\frac{n+1}{n}\right)\ln n + \frac{1}{n^2}\sum_{k=1}^{n} k\ln\frac{k}{n} + \frac{\ln n}{n^2}\sum_{k=1}^{n} k$$

$$= \lim_{n\to\infty} -\frac{1}{2}\left(\frac{n+1}{n}\right)\ln n + \frac{1}{n}\sum_{k=1}^{n}\frac{k}{n}\ln\frac{k}{n} + \frac{\ln n}{n^2}\cdot\frac{n(n+1)}{2}$$

$$= -\frac{1}{2}\left(\frac{n+1}{n}\right)\ln n + \int_0^1 x\ln x\,dx + \frac{1}{2}\left(\frac{n+1}{n}\right)\ln n$$

$$= \int_0^1 \underbrace{x}_{\text{II}}\ \underbrace{\ln x}_{\text{I}}\,dx = -\frac{1}{4} \Rightarrow L = e^{-\frac{1}{4}}$$

Hence, (c) is the correct answer.

Ex. 6 *$\lim_{x\to\frac{\pi}{4}} \frac{\int_2^{\sec^2 x} f(t)\,dt}{x^2 - \frac{\pi^2}{16}}$ is equal to* **[IIT JEE 2007]**

(a) $\frac{8}{\pi}f(2)$ (b) $\frac{2}{\pi}f(2)$ (c) $\frac{2}{\pi}f\left(\frac{1}{2}\right)$ (d) $4f(2)$

Sol. $\lim_{x\to\frac{\pi}{4}} \frac{\int_2^{\sec^2 x} f(t)dt}{x^2 - \frac{\pi^2}{16}} = \lim_{x\to\frac{\pi}{4}} \frac{f(\sec^2 x)\cdot 2\sec^2 x\tan x - 0}{2x}$

(applying L'Hospital rule)

$$= \frac{f(2)\cdot 4}{\pi/2} = \frac{8f(2)}{\pi}$$

Hence, (a) is the correct answer.

Ex. 7 *Let f be a non-negative function defined on the interval [0,1]. If $\int_0^x \sqrt{1-(f'(t))^2}\,dx = \int_0^x f(t)\,dt, 0 \le x \le 1$ and $f(0) = 0$, then* **[IIT JEE 2009]**

(a) $f\left(\frac{1}{2}\right) < \frac{1}{2}$ and $f\left(\frac{1}{3}\right) > \frac{1}{3}$ (b) $f\left(\frac{1}{2}\right) > \frac{1}{2}$ and $f\left(\frac{1}{3}\right) > \frac{1}{3}$

(c) $f\left(\frac{1}{2}\right) < \frac{1}{2}$ and $f\left(\frac{1}{3}\right) < \frac{1}{3}$ (d) $f\left(\frac{1}{2}\right) > \frac{1}{2}$ and $f\left(\frac{1}{3}\right) < \frac{1}{3}$

Sol. Given, $\int_0^x \sqrt{1-(f'(t))^2}\,dt = \int_0^x f(t)\,dt, 0 \le x \le 1$

Applying Leibnitz theorem, we get

$$\sqrt{1-(f'(x))^2} = f(x)$$

$$\Rightarrow 1-(f'(x))^2 = f^2(x)$$

$$\Rightarrow (f'(x))^2 = 1 - f^2(x) \Rightarrow f'(x) = \pm\sqrt{1-f^2(x)}$$

$$\Rightarrow \frac{dy}{dx} = \pm\sqrt{1-y^2}, \text{ where } y = f(x)$$

$$\Rightarrow \frac{dy}{\sqrt{1-y^2}} = \pm\,dx$$

Integrating both the sides, we get $\sin^{-1}(y) = \pm x + C$

$\therefore$ $f(0) = 0 \Rightarrow C = 0$

$\therefore$ $y = \pm\sin x$

$\Rightarrow$ $y = \sin x = f(x)$, given $f(x) \ge 0$ for $x \in [0,1]$

Its known that, $\sin x < x, \forall\, x \in R^+$

$$\sin\left(\frac{1}{2}\right) < \frac{1}{2} \Rightarrow f\left(\frac{1}{2}\right) < \frac{1}{2} \text{ and } \sin\left(\frac{1}{3}\right) < \frac{1}{3}$$

$$\Rightarrow f\left(\frac{1}{3}\right) < \frac{1}{3}$$

Hence, (c) is the correct answer.

Ex. 8 *The value of $\lim_{x\to 0} \frac{1}{x^3}\int_0^x \frac{t\ln(1+t)}{t^4+4}dt$* **[IIT JEE 2010]**

(a) 0 (b) $\frac{1}{12}$ (c) $\frac{1}{24}$ (d) $\frac{1}{64}$

Sol. $\lim_{x\to 0} \frac{1}{x^3}\int_0^x \frac{t\log(1+t)}{4+t^4}dt$

Using L'Hospital's rule,

$$\lim_{x\to 0} \frac{\frac{x\log(1+x)}{4+x^4}}{3x^2} = \lim_{x\to 0} \frac{\log(1+x)}{3x}\cdot\frac{1}{4+x^4} = \frac{1}{12}$$

$$\left[\text{using } \lim_{x\to 0}\frac{\log(1+x)}{x} = 1\right]$$

Hence, (b) is the correct answer.

Ex. 9 *The value(s) of $\int_0^1 \frac{x^4(1-x)^4}{1+x^2}dx$ is (are)* **[IIT JEE 2010]**

(a) $\frac{22}{7} - \pi$ (b) $\frac{2}{105}$ (c) 0 (d) $\frac{71}{15} - \frac{3\pi}{2}$

Sol. Let $I = \int_0^1 \frac{x^4(1-x)^4}{1+x^2}dx$

$$= \int_0^1 \frac{(x^4-1)(1-x)^4 + (1-x)^4}{(1+x^2)}dx$$

$$= \int_0^1 (x^2-1)(1-x)^4 dx + \int_0^1 \frac{(1+x^2-2x)^2}{(1+x^2)}dx$$

$$= \int_0^1 \left\{(x^2-1)(1-x)^4 + (1+x^2) - 4x + \frac{4x^2}{(1+x^2)}\right\}dx$$

$$= \int_0^1 \left((x^2-1)(1-x)^4 + (1+x^2) - 4x + 4 - \frac{4}{1-x^2}\right)dx$$

$$=\int_0^1\left(x^6-4x^5+5x^4+4-\frac{4}{1+x^2}\right)dx$$

$$=\frac{1}{7}-\frac{4}{6}+\frac{5}{5}-\frac{4}{3}+4-4\left(\frac{\pi}{4}-0\right)=\frac{22}{7}-\pi$$

Hence, (a) is the correct answer.

● **Ex. 10** *If* $\int_{\sin\theta}^{\cos\theta} f(x\tan\theta)dx\left(\theta\neq\frac{n\pi}{2}, n\in I\right)$ *is equal to*

(a) $-\cos\theta\int_1^{\tan\theta} f(x\sin\theta)dx$

(b) $-\tan\theta\int_{\cos\theta}^{\sin\theta} f(x)dx$

(c) $\sin\theta\int_1^{\tan\theta} f(x\cos\theta)dx$

(d) $\frac{1}{\tan\theta}\int_{\sin\theta}^{\sin\theta\tan\theta} f(x)dx$

Sol. Let, $I=\int_{\sin\theta}^{\cos\theta} f(x\tan\theta)dx$. Put $x\tan\theta=z\sin\theta$

$\therefore\quad I=\int_{\tan\theta}^{1} f(z\sin\theta)\cos\theta\, dz$

$\Rightarrow\quad dx=\cos\theta\, dz$

$$=-\cos\theta\int_1^{\tan\theta} f(z\sin\theta)\,dz=-\cos\theta\int_1^{\tan\theta} f(x\sin\theta)\,dx$$

Hence, (a) is correct option.

JEE Type Solved Examples : More than One Correct Option Type Questions

● **Ex. 11** *Let $f(x)$ be an even function which is mapped from $(-\pi,\pi)$. Then, the value of* $\int_{-\pi}^{\pi}\left(\int_0^x f(t)\,dt+[f(x)]\right)dx$ *can be (where, $[\cdot]$ denotes greatest integer function)*

(a) 0 (b) π
(c) 2π (d) 4π

Sol. As, $f(x)$ is an even function, then $\int_0^x f(x)\,dx$ is an odd function.

Also, $[f(x)]=1,2$ [as $1<f(x)<3$]

$\therefore\quad g(x)=\int_{-\pi}^{\pi}\left(\int_0^x f(t)\,dt\right)dx+\int_{-\pi}^{\pi}[f(x)]\,dx$

$=0+\int_{-\pi}^{\pi}[f(x)]\,dx,$ [$\because$ since $[f(x)]=1$ or 2]

$=\int_{-\pi}^{\pi}1\,dx$

or $\int_{-\pi}^{\pi}2\,dx=2\pi$ or 4π

Hence, options (c) and (d) are correct.

● **Ex. 12** *Let,* $A_1=\int_n^{n+1}(\min\{|x-n|,|x-(n+1)|\})\,dx$,

$A_2=\int_{n+1}^{n+2}(|x-n|-|x-(n+1)|)\,dx$,

$A_3=\int_{n+2}^{n+3}(|x-(n+4)|-|x-(n+3)|)\,dx$

and $g(x)=A_1+A_2+A_3$, then

(a) $A_1+A_2+A_3=9$ (b) $A_1+A_2+A_3=\frac{9}{4}$

(c) $\sum_{n=1}^{100} g(x)=\frac{900}{4}$ (d) $\sum_{n=1}^{100} g(x)=300$

Sol. Here, $\min\{|x-n|,|x-(n+1)|\}$ can be shown as

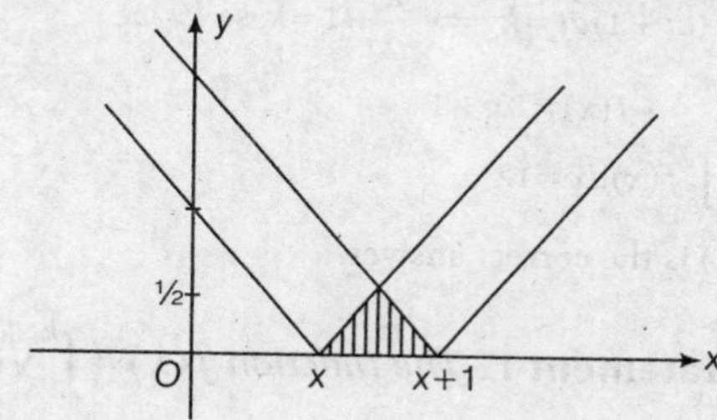

$\therefore\quad A_1=\int_n^{n+1}(\min\{|x-n|,|x-(n+1)|\})\,dx$

$=\frac{1}{2}\times1\times\frac{1}{2}=\frac{1}{4}$

Now, $A_2=\int_{n+1}^{n+2}(|x-n|-|x-(n+1)|)\,dx$

$=\int_1^2(|t|-|t-1|)dt$ [put $x=n+t\Rightarrow dx=dt$]

$=\int_1^2(t-(t-1))dt=\int_1^2 1dt=(t)_1^2=1$

and $A_3=\int_{n+2}^{n+3}(|x-(n+4)|-|x-(n+3)|)dx,$

$=\int_2^3(|t-4|-|t-3|)dt$ [put $x=n+t\Rightarrow dx=dt$]

$=\int_2^3((4-t)-(3-t))dt=\int_2^3 1\,dt=1$

Also, $g(x)=A_1+A_2+A_3=\frac{1}{4}+1+1=\frac{9}{4}$

$\therefore\ \sum_{n=1}^{100} g(x)=g(1)+g(2)+g(3)+\ldots+g(100)$

$=\frac{9}{4}+\frac{9}{4}+\ldots+\frac{9}{4}=\frac{900}{4}$

JEE Type Solved Examples : Statement I and II Type Questions

- **Directions** (Q. Nos. 13 to 15) *For the following questions, choose the correct answers from the codes (a), (b), (c) and (d) defined as follows.*
  (a) Statement I is true, Statement II is also true; Statement II is the correct explanation of Statement I.
  (b) Statement I is true, Statement II is also true; Statement II is not the correct explanation of Statement I.
  (c) Statement I is true, Statement II is false.
  (d) Statement I is false, Statement II is true.

● ***Ex. 13*** **Statement I** *If* $f(x)=\int_0^1 (x f(t)+1)\,dt$, *then* $\int_0^3 f(x)\,dx=12$

Statement II $f(x)=3x+1$

Sol. Let $\int_0^1 f(t)\,dt=k$, so $f(x)=xk+1$

Now, $\int_0^1 (kt+1)\,dt=k \Rightarrow \frac{k}{2}+1=k$, so $k=2$

$\therefore \quad f(x)=2x+1$

Also $\int_0^3 f(x)\,dx=12$

Hence, (c) is the correct answer.

● ***Ex. 14*** **Statement I** *The function* $f(x)=\int_0^x \sqrt{1+t^2}\,dt$ *is an odd function and* $g(x)=f'(x)$ *is an even function.*

Statement II *For a differentiable function* $f(x)$ *if* $f'(x)$ *is an even function, then* $f(x)$ *is an odd function.*

Sol. If $f(x)$ is of odd, then $f'(x)$ is even but converse is not true.
e.g. If $f'(x)=x\sin x$, then $f(x)=\sin x - x\cos x + C$

$$f(-x)=-\sin x + x\cos x + C$$

On adding, $f(x)+f(-x)=$ constant which need not to be zero.

For Statement I $f(x)=\int_0^x \sqrt{1+t^2}\,dt;\ g(x)=\sqrt{1+x^2}$

$$f(-x)=\int_0^{-x}\sqrt{1+t^2}\,dt;\ t=-y$$

$$f(-x)=-\int_0^x \sqrt{1+y^2}\,dy$$

$\therefore \quad f(x)+f(-x)=0$

$\Rightarrow f$ is odd and g is obviously even.

Hence, (c) is the correct answer.

● ***Ex. 15*** *Given,* $f(x)=\sin^3 x$ *and* $P(x)$ *is a quadratic polynomial with leading coefficient unity.*

Statement I $\int_0^{2\pi} P(x)\cdot f''(x)\,dx$ *vanishes.*

Statement II $\int_0^{2\pi} f(x)\,dx$ *vanishes.*

Sol. $P(x)=ax^2+bx+c;\ f(x)=\sin^3 x$

$$I=\int_0^{2\pi} \underbrace{P(x)}_{\text{I}}\cdot \underbrace{f''(x)}_{\text{II}}\,dx$$

Using I.B.P. $\underbrace{P(x)\cdot f'(x)\Big|_0^{2\pi}}_{\text{zero}} - \int_0^{2\pi} \underbrace{P'(x)}_{\text{I}}\cdot \underbrace{f'(x)}_{\text{II}}\,dx$

$$=-\left[[P'(x)\cdot f(x)]_0^{2\pi}-\int_0^{2\pi} P''(x)\cdot f(x)\,dx\right]$$

$$=\int_0^{2\pi} P''(x)\cdot f(x)\,dx=2\int_0^{2\pi}\sin^3 x\,dx=0$$

Hence, (a) is the correct answer.

JEE Type Solved Examples : Passage Based Questions

Passage I

(Q. Nos. 16 to 18)

Suppose we define the definite integral using the following formula $\int_a^b f(x)\,dx=\frac{b-a}{2}(f(a)+f(b))$, *for more accurate result for* $c\in(a,b)$, $F(c)=\frac{c-a}{2}(f(a)+f(c))+\frac{b-c}{2}(f(b)+f(c))$.

When $c=\frac{a+b}{2}$, then $\int_a^b f(x)\,dx=\frac{b-a}{4}(f(a)+f(b)+2f(c))$.

[IIT JEE 2007]

● ***Ex. 16*** $\int_0^{\pi/2} \sin x\,dx$ *is equal to*

(a) $\frac{\pi}{8}(1+\sqrt{2})$ (b) $\frac{\pi}{4}(1+\sqrt{2})$

(c) $\frac{\pi}{8\sqrt{2}}$ (d) $\frac{\pi}{4\sqrt{2}}$

Sol. $\int_0^{\pi/2} \sin x\,dx = \frac{\frac{\pi}{2}-0}{4}\left(\sin(0)+\sin\left(\frac{\pi}{2}\right)+2\sin\left(\frac{0+\frac{\pi}{2}}{2}\right)\right) = \frac{\pi}{8}(1+\sqrt{2})$

Hence, (a) is the correct answer.

● ***Ex. 17*** *If $f(x)$ is a polynomial and if*

$$\lim_{t\to a}\frac{\int_a^t f(x)\,dx-\frac{(t-a)}{2}(f(t)+f(a))}{(t-a)^3}=0 \text{ for all } a, \text{ then the}$$

degree of $f(x)$ can atmost be

(a) 1 (b) 2

(c) 3 (d) 4

Sol. Applying L' Hospital's rule,

$$\lim_{t\to a}\frac{f(t)-\frac{1}{2}(f(t)+f(a))-\frac{(t-a)}{2}f'(t)}{3(t-a)^2}=0$$

$$\Rightarrow \lim_{t\to a}\frac{f(t)-\frac{1}{2}(f(t)+f(a))-\frac{(t-a)}{2}f'(t)}{3(t-a)^2}=0$$

$$\Rightarrow \lim_{t\to a}\frac{f'(t)-\frac{1}{2}(f(t)+f(a))-\frac{(t-a)}{2}f'(t)}{12(t-a)}=0$$

$$\Rightarrow \lim_{t\to a}\frac{f''(t)}{12}=0$$

$$\Rightarrow \lim_{t\to a}\frac{f'(t)-\frac{1}{2}(f(t)+f(a))-\frac{(t-a)}{2}f'(t)}{12(t-a)}=0$$

$$\Rightarrow \lim_{t\to a}\frac{f''(t)}{12}=0\ f''(a)=0 \text{ for any } a.$$

$\Rightarrow$ $f(a)$ is atmost of degree 1.

Hence, (a) is the correct answer.

● ***Ex. 18*** *If $f''(x)<0, \forall\ x\in(a,b)$ and c is a point such that $a<c<b$ and $(c, f(c))$ is the point on the curve for which $F(c)$ is maximum, then $f'(c)$ is equal to*

(a) $\frac{f(b)-f(a)}{b-a}$ (b) $\frac{2(f(b)-f(a))}{b-a}$

(c) $\frac{2f(b)-f(a)}{2b-a}$ (d) 0

Sol. $F'(c)=(b-a)'(c)+f(a)-f(b)$

$F''(c)=f''(c)(b-a)<0$

$\Rightarrow$ $F'(c)=0$

$\Rightarrow$ $f'(c)=\frac{f(b)-f(a)}{b-a}$

Hence, (a) is the correct answer.

Passage II

(Q. Nos. 19 to 20)

$$\text{Let } f(\alpha,\beta)=\begin{vmatrix}\cos(\alpha+\beta) & -\sin(\alpha+\beta) & \cos 2\beta\\ \sin\alpha & \cos\alpha & \sin\beta\\ -\cos\alpha & \sin\alpha & \cos\beta\end{vmatrix}.$$

● ***Ex. 19*** *The value of*

$$I=\int_0^{\pi/2} e^{\beta}\left(f(0,0)+f\left(\frac{\pi}{2},\beta\right)+f\left(\frac{3\pi}{2},\frac{\pi}{2}-\beta\right)\right)d\beta \text{ is}$$

(a) $e^{\pi/2}$ (b) 0

(c) $2(2e^{\pi/2}-1)$ (d) None of these

Sol. Here, $f(\alpha,\beta)=2\cos\beta$ i.e. independent of α

$$\therefore\quad I=\int_0^{\pi/2} e^{\beta}\left(f(0,0)+f\left(\frac{\pi}{2},\pi\right)+f\left(\frac{3\pi}{2},\frac{\pi}{2}-\beta\right)\right)d\beta$$

$$=\int_0^{\pi/2} e^{\beta}(2+2\cos\beta+2\sin\beta)d\beta$$

Hence, $=[e^{\beta}(2+2\sin\beta)]_0^{\pi/2}$

$$=4e^{\pi/2}-2=2(2e^{\pi/2}-1)$$

Hence, (c) is the correct answer.

● ***Ex. 20*** *If* $I=\int_{-\pi/2}^{\pi/2}\cos^2\beta\left(f(0,\beta)+f\left(0,\frac{\pi}{2}-\beta\right)\right)d\beta$, *then* $[I]$ *is*

(a) $e^{\pi/2}$ (b) 2

(c) $2(2e^{\pi/2}-1)$ (d) None of these

Sol. Again, $I=\int_{-\pi/2}^{\pi/2}\cos^2\beta\left(f(0,\beta)+f\left(0,\frac{\pi}{2}-\beta\right)\right)d\beta$

$$=\int_{-\pi/2}^{\pi/2}\cos^2\beta(\cos\beta+\sin\beta)\,d\beta$$

$$=\int_{-\pi/2}^{\pi/2}\cos^3\beta\,d\beta+\int_{-\pi/2}^{\pi/2}\cos^2\beta\sin\beta\,d\beta$$

$$=2\int_0^{\pi/2}\cos^3\beta\,d\beta+0$$

$$\Rightarrow\quad I=\frac{\theta}{3}\Rightarrow[I]=2$$

Hence, (b) is the correct answer.

JEE Type Solved Examples : Matching Type Questions

• Ex. 21 *Match the following.*

Column I	Column II
(A) The function $f(x)=\dfrac{e^{x\cos x}-1-x}{\sin x^2}$ is not defined at $x=0$. The value of $f(0)$, so that f is continuous at $x=0$, is	(p) -1
(B) The value of the definite integral $\int_0^1 \dfrac{dx}{\sqrt{x}+\sqrt[3]{x}}$ is equal to $a+b\ln 2$, where a and b are integers, then $(a+b)$ is equal to	(q) 0
(C) Given, $e^n\int_0^n \dfrac{\sec^2\theta-\tan\theta}{e^\theta}\,d\theta=1$, then the value of $\tan n$ is equal to	(r) 1/2
(D) Let $a_n=\int_{\frac{1}{n+1}}^{\frac{1}{n}}\tan^{-1}(nx)\,dx$ and $b_n=\int_{\frac{1}{n+1}}^{\frac{1}{n}}\sin^{-1}(nx)\,dx$, then $\lim_{n\to\infty}\dfrac{a_n}{b_n}$ has the value equal to	(s) 1

Sol. (A) → (r), (B) → (p), (C) → (s), (D) → (r)

(A) $$\lim_{x\to 0}\frac{e^x\cos x-1-x}{x^2\cdot\dfrac{\sin x^2}{x^2}}=\lim_{x\to 0}\frac{e^{x\cos x}-1-x}{x^2}$$

(applying L'Hospital's twice)

$$=\lim_{x\to 0}\frac{e^{x\cos x}\cdot(-x\sin x+\cos x)-1}{2x}$$

$$=\lim_{x\to 0}\frac{e^{x\cos x}(-x\cos x-\sin x-\sin x)+e^{x\cos x}(-x\sin x+\cos x)}{2}$$

$$=\frac{1}{2}$$

(B) Put $x=u^6\Rightarrow dx=6u^5\,du$

$$\therefore\ I=\int_0^1\frac{6u^5\,du}{u^3+u^2}=6\int_0^1\frac{u^3+1-1}{u+1}\,du=5-6\ln 2$$

$$\Rightarrow a+b=5-6=-1$$

(C) $e^n\int_0^n e^{-\theta}(\sec^2\theta-\tan\theta)\,d\theta=1$

Put $-\theta=t\Rightarrow d\theta=-dt$

$$-e^n\int_0^{-n}e^t(\sec^2 t+\tan t)\,dt=1$$

[use $\int e^x(f(x)+f'(x))=e^x f(x)$]

$$\Rightarrow -e^n[e^t\tan t]_0^{-n}=1\Rightarrow -e^n[-e^{-n}\tan n]=1\Rightarrow \tan n=+1$$

(D) $$\lim_{n\to\infty}\frac{\int_{1/n+1}^{1/n}\tan^{-1}(nx)\,dx}{\int_{1/n+1}^{1/n}\sin^{-1}(nx)\,dx}$$

Put $nx=t\Rightarrow dx=\frac{1}{n}dt$

$$\therefore\ \lim_{n\to\infty}\frac{\frac{1}{n}\int_{n/n+1}^{1}\tan^{-1}(t)\,dt}{\frac{1}{n}\int_{n/n+1}^{1}\sin^{-1}(t)\,dt}\qquad\left(\frac{0}{0}\text{ form}\right)$$

Use L'Hospital's rule, $$\lim_{n\to\infty}\frac{\tan^{-1}\left(\dfrac{n}{n+1}\right)}{\sin^{-1}\left(\dfrac{n}{n+1}\right)}=\frac{\frac{\pi}{4}}{\frac{\pi}{2}}=\frac{1}{2}$$

• Ex. 22 *Match the following* **[IIT JEE 2006]**

Column I	Column II
(A) $\int_{-1}^{1}\dfrac{dx}{1+x^2}$	(p) $\dfrac{1}{2}\log\left(\dfrac{2}{3}\right)$
(B) $\int_0^1\dfrac{dx}{\sqrt{1-x^2}}$	(q) $\dfrac{1}{2}\log\left(\dfrac{3}{2}\right)$
(C) $\int_2^3\dfrac{dx}{1-x^2}$	(r) $\dfrac{\pi}{3}$
(D) $\int_1^2\dfrac{dx}{x\sqrt{x^2-1}}$	(s) $\dfrac{\pi}{2}$

Sol. (A) → (s), (B) → (s), (C) → (q), (D) → (r)

(A) $$\int_{-1}^{1}\frac{dx}{1+x^2}$$

$\because$ $f(x)=\dfrac{1}{1+x^2}$ is an reven function.

$$\therefore\ I=2\int_0^1\frac{dx}{1+x^2}=[2(\tan^{-1}x)]_0^1=\frac{\pi}{2}$$

(B) $$\int_0^1\frac{dx}{\sqrt{1-x^2}}=[\sin^{-1}x]_0^1=\frac{\pi}{2}$$

(C) $$\int_2^3\frac{dx}{1-x^2}=-\int_2^3\frac{dx}{x^2-1}=-\left[\frac{1}{2}\ln\left|\frac{x-1}{x+1}\right|\right]_2^3$$

$$=-\frac{1}{2}\ln\frac{2}{3}=\frac{1}{2}\ln\left(\frac{3}{2}\right)$$

(D) Let $I=\int_1^2\dfrac{dx}{x\sqrt{x^2-1}}$ [put $x=\sec\theta\Rightarrow dx=\sec\theta\tan\theta\,d\theta$]

$$=\int_0^{\pi/3}\frac{\sec\theta\tan\theta\,d\theta}{\sec\theta\tan\theta}$$

$$=\int_0^{\pi/3}1\,d\theta=\frac{\pi}{3}$$

JEE Type Solved Examples : Single Integer Answer Type Questions

● **Ex. 23** *Let $f: R \to R$ be a continuous function which satisfies $f(x) = \int_0^x f(t)\,dt$. Then, the value of $f(\ln 5)$ is____.*

[IIT JEE 2009]

Sol. (0) From given integral equation, $f(0) = 0$

Also, differentiating the given integral equation w.r.t. x, we get

$$f'(x) = f(x)$$

If $f(x) \neq 0$, then $\frac{f'(x)}{f(x)} = 1 \Rightarrow f(x) = e^c e^x$

$\because$ $f(0) = 0 \Rightarrow e^c = 0$, a contradiction

$\therefore$ $f(x) = 0, \forall\, x \in R \Rightarrow f(\ln 5) = 0$

● **Ex. 24** *For any real number x, let $[x]$ denotes the largest integer less than or equal to x. Let f be a real valued function defined on the interval $[-10, 10]$ by*

$$f(x) = \begin{cases} x - [x], & \text{if } [x] \text{ is odd} \\ 1 + [x] - x, & \text{if } [x] \text{ is even} \end{cases}.$$

Then, the value of $\frac{\pi^2}{10}\int_{-10}^{10} f(x) \cos \pi x\,dx$ is.

[IIT JEE 2010]

Sol. (4) We have, $f(x) = \begin{cases} x - [x], & \text{if } [x] \text{ is odd} \\ 1 + [x] - x, & \text{if } [x] \text{ is even} \end{cases}$

$f(x)$ and $\cos \pi x$ are both periodic with period 2 and are both even.

$$\therefore \int_{-10}^{10} f(x) \cos \pi x\,dx = 2\int_0^{10} f(x) \cos \pi x\,dx$$

$$= 10\int_0^2 f(x) \cos \pi x\,dx$$

$$\int_0^1 f(x) \cos \pi x\,dx = \int_0^1 (1 - x) \cos \pi x\,dx = -\int_0^1 u \cos \pi u\,du$$

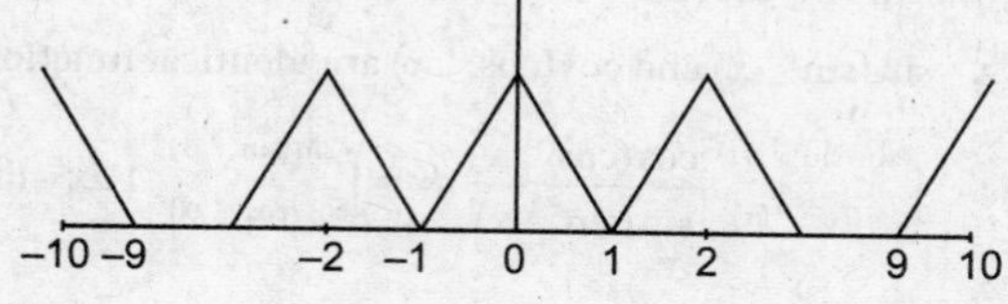

$$\int_1^2 f(x) \cos \pi x\,dx = \int_1^2 (x - 1) \cos \pi x\,dx = -\int_0^1 u \cos \pi u\,du$$

$$\therefore \int_{-10}^{10} f(x) \cos \pi x\,dx = -20\int_0^1 u \cos \pi u\,du = \frac{40}{\pi^2}$$

$$\Rightarrow \frac{\pi^2}{10}\int_{-10}^{10} f(x) \cos \pi x\,dx = 4$$

● **Ex. 25** *Let $f(x)$ be a differentiable function satisfying $f(x) + f\left(x + \frac{1}{2}\right) = 1, \forall x \in R$ and $g(x) = \int_0^x f(t)dt$. If $g(1) = 1$, then the value of $\sum_{n=2}^{\infty}\left(\frac{8}{\sum_{k=1}^{n}(g(x+k^2) - g(x+k))}\right)$ is.*

Sol. (6) Here, $f(x) + f\left(x + \frac{1}{2}\right) = 1$

Replace x by $\left(x + \frac{1}{2}\right)$, we get $f\left(x + \frac{1}{2}\right) + f(x + 1) = 1$

On subtracting, $f(x) = f(x + 1)$ ...(i)

Also, $g(x + 1^2) = \int_0^{x+1^2} f(t)\,dt = \int_0^x f(t)\,dt + \int_n^{x+1^2} f(t)\,dt$

Since; $f(x + 1) = f(x)$

$\therefore$ $g(x + 1^2) = \int_0^x f(t)\,dt + 1^2 \cdot \int_0^1 f(t)dt$

$g(x + 2^2) = \int_0^x f(t)\,dt + 2^2 \cdot \int_0^1 f(t)dt$

$g(x + k^2) = \int_0^x f(t)\,dt + k^2 \cdot \int_0^1 f(t)dt$ ...(ii)

and $g(x + k) = \int_0^x f(t)\,dt + k \cdot \int_0^1 f(t)dt$ ...(iii)

Thus, $\sum_{k=1}^{n} (g(x + k^2) - g(x + k)) = \sum_{k=1}^{n} (k^2 - k) \cdot \int_0^1 f(t)\,dt$

$= \sum_{k=1}^{n} (k^2 - k) \cdot g(1)$, given $g(x) = \int_0^x f(t)\,dt$

$= \left(\frac{n(n+1)(2n+1)}{6} - \frac{n(n+1)}{2}\right) \times 1$

$= \frac{n(n-1)(n+1)}{3}$

$$\therefore \sum_{n=2}^{\infty} \frac{8}{\sum_{k=2}^{n}(g(x+k^2) - g(x+k))} = \sum_{n=2}^{\infty} \frac{8 \times 3}{(n-1)n(n+1)}$$

$$= 12\sum_{n=2}^{\infty}\left(\frac{(n+1)-(n-1)}{(n-1)\cdot n(n+1)} = \frac{1}{(n-1)n} - \frac{1}{n(n+1)}\right)$$

$$= 12\left[\left(\frac{1}{1\times 2} - \frac{1}{2\times 3}\right) + \left(\frac{1}{2\times 3} - \frac{1}{3\times 4}\right) + \dots + \left(\frac{1}{(n-1)n} - \frac{1}{n(n+1)}\right)\right]$$

$$= 12\left(\frac{1}{2} - \frac{1}{n(n+1)}\right)_{n\to\infty} = 6$$

Subjective Type Questions

• **Ex. 26** *Find the error in steps to evaluate the following integral.*

$$\int_0^{\pi} \frac{dx}{1+2\sin^2 x} = \int_0^{\pi} \frac{\sec^2 x\, dx}{\sec^2 x + 2\tan^2 x} = \int_0^{\pi} \frac{\sec^2 x\, dx}{1+3\tan^2 x}$$

$$= \frac{1}{\sqrt{3}} [\tan^{-1}(\sqrt{3}\tan x)]_0^{\pi} = 0$$

Sol. Here, the Newton-Leibnitz's formula for evaluating the definite integrals is not applicable because the anti-derivative,

$$f(x) = \frac{1}{\sqrt{3}} [\tan^{-1}(\sqrt{3}\tan x)]$$

has a discontinuity at the point $x = \frac{\pi}{2}$ which lies in the interval $[0, \pi]$.

$$\text{LHL} = \lim_{h \to 0} \frac{1}{\sqrt{3}} \tan^{-1} \sqrt{3} \left[\tan\left(\frac{\pi}{2} - h\right) \right] \text{ at } x = \frac{\pi}{2}$$

$$= \lim_{h \to 0} \frac{1}{\sqrt{3}} \tan^{-1}(\sqrt{3}\cot h)$$

$$= \lim_{h \to 0} \frac{1}{\sqrt{3}} \tan^{-1}(\infty) = \frac{\pi}{2\sqrt{3}} \quad \text{...(i)}$$

Also, $$\text{RHL} = \lim_{h \to 0} \frac{1}{\sqrt{3}} \tan^{-1} \sqrt{3} \left[\tan\left(\frac{\pi}{2} + h\right) \right] \text{ at } x = \frac{\pi}{2}$$

$$= \lim_{h \to 0} \frac{1}{\sqrt{3}} \tan^{-1}(-\sqrt{3}\cot h)$$

$$= \lim_{h \to 0} \frac{1}{\sqrt{3}} \tan^{-1}(-\infty) = -\frac{\pi}{2\sqrt{3}} \quad \text{...(ii)}$$

From Eqs. (i) and (ii), LHL $\neq$ RHL at $x = \pi/2$

$\Rightarrow$ Anti-derivative $f(x)$ is discontinuous at $x = \pi/2$.

So, the correct solution for above integral;

$$I = \int_0^{\pi} \frac{dx}{1+2\sin^2 x} = \int_0^{\pi} \frac{\sec^2 x\, dx}{1+3\tan^2 x} \quad \text{...(iii)}$$

Using, $\int_0^{2a} f(x)\, dx = \begin{cases} 0, & f(2a-x) = -f(x) \\ 2\int_0^a f(x)\, dx, & f(2a-x) = f(x) \end{cases}$

We know, if $f(x) = \dfrac{\sec^2 x}{1+3\tan^2 x}$ $f(\pi - x) = f(x)$

$\therefore$ Eq. (iii) reduces to $I = 2\displaystyle\int_0^{\pi/2} \frac{\sec^2 x\, dx}{1+3\tan^2 x}$

$$= 2 \cdot \frac{1}{\sqrt{3}} \int_0^{\infty} \frac{dt}{1+t^2} \quad (\text{put } \sqrt{3}\tan x = t \Rightarrow \sqrt{3}\sec^2 x\, dx = dt)$$

$$= \frac{2}{\sqrt{3}} [\tan^{-1}(t)]_0^{\infty}$$

$$= \frac{2}{\sqrt{3}} (\tan^{-1}\infty - \tan^{-1} 0) = \frac{2}{\sqrt{3}} \left(\frac{\pi}{2} - 0\right) = \frac{\pi}{\sqrt{3}}$$

$$\therefore \int_0^{\pi} \frac{dx}{1+2\sin^2 x} = \frac{\pi}{\sqrt{3}}$$

Remark

Students are advised to check continuity of anti-derivatives before substitution of integral limits.

• **Ex. 27** *If* $\int_a^b |\sin x|\, dx = 8$ *and* $\int_0^{a+b} |\cos x|\, dx = 9$, *then find the value of* $\int_a^b x \sin x\, dx$.

Sol. We know, $\int_a^b |\sin x|\, dx$ represents the area under the curve from $x = a$ to $x = b$.

We also know, area from $x = a$ to $x = a + \pi$ is 2.

$$\therefore \int_a^b |\sin x|\, dx = 8$$

$$\Rightarrow b - a = \frac{8\pi}{2} \quad \text{...(i)}$$

Similarly, $$\int_0^{a+b} |\cos x|\, dx = 9$$

$$\Rightarrow a + b - 0 = \frac{9\pi}{2} \quad \text{...(ii)}$$

From Eqs. (i) and (ii), $a = \pi/4$, $b = 17\pi/4$

Hence, $$\int_a^b x \sin x\, dx = \int_{\pi/4}^{17\pi/4} x \sin x\, dx$$

$$= [-x\cos x]_{\pi/4}^{17\pi/4} + \int_{\pi/4}^{17\pi/4} \cos x\, dx$$

$$= -\frac{17\pi}{4}\cos\frac{17\pi}{4} + \frac{\pi}{4}\cos\frac{\pi}{4} + [\sin x]_{\pi/4}^{17\pi/4}$$

$$= -\frac{4\pi}{\sqrt{2}}$$

$$\therefore \int_a^b x \sin x\, dx = -2\sqrt{2}\pi$$

• **Ex. 28** *Evaluate* $\displaystyle\int_{\cos(\cos^{-1}\alpha)}^{\sin(\sin^{-1}\beta)} \left| \frac{\cos(\cos^{-1} x)}{\sin(\sin^{-1} x)} \right| dx.$

Sol. We know, $\cos(\cos^{-1} x)$ and $\sin(\sin^{-1} x)$ could be plotted as

$\therefore$ $\sin(\sin^{-1} x)$ and $\cos(\cos^{-1} x)$ are identical functions.

$$\therefore \int_{\cos(\cos^{-1}\alpha)}^{\sin(\sin^{-1}\beta)} \frac{\cos(\cos^{-1} x)}{\sin(\sin^{-1} x)} dx = \int_{\cos(\cos^{-1}\alpha)}^{\sin(\sin^{-1}\beta)} 1\, dx = (\beta - \alpha)$$

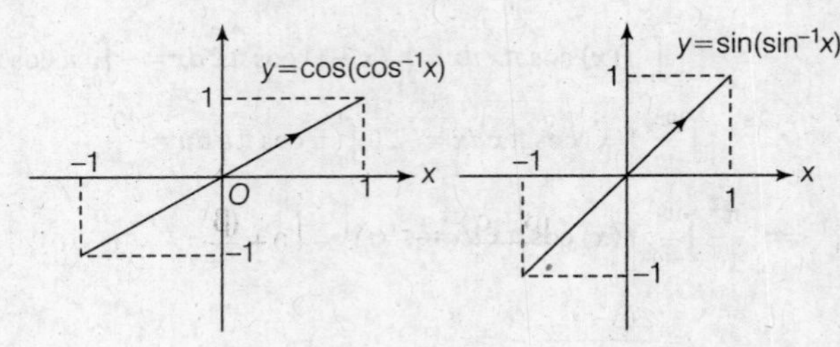

Ex. 29 *Evaluate* $\int_{\alpha}^{\beta}\sqrt{\frac{x-\alpha}{\beta-x}}\,dx.$

Sol. Let $$I=\int_{\alpha}^{\beta}\sqrt{\frac{x-\alpha}{\beta-x}}\,dx \quad \text{...(i)}$$

Put $x=\alpha\cos^2 t+\beta\sin^2 t$

$\therefore \quad x-\alpha=\alpha\cos^2 t+\beta\sin^2 t-\alpha=\beta[\sin^2(t)+\alpha(\cos^2 t-1)]$

$=\beta\sin^2 t-\alpha\sin^2 t \Rightarrow (x-\alpha)=(\beta-\alpha)\sin^2 t$

Similarly, $\beta-x=(\beta-\alpha)\cos^2 t$

$\therefore \quad dx=2(\beta-\alpha)\sin t\cos t\,dt$

where, $x=\alpha\Rightarrow\sin^2 t=0 \Rightarrow t=0 \quad (\because \alpha<\beta)$

and $x=\beta\Rightarrow\cos^2 t=0 \Rightarrow t=\pi/2$

$\therefore$ Eq. (i) reduces to

$$I=\int_0^{\pi/2}\sqrt{\frac{(\beta-\alpha)\sin^2 t}{(\beta-\alpha)\cos^2 t}}\cdot 2(\beta-\alpha)\sin t\cos t\,dt$$

$$=\int_0^{\pi/2}\frac{\sin t}{\cos t}\cdot 2(\beta-\alpha)\sin t\cos t\,dt$$

$$\left[\because \sqrt{\frac{\sin^2 t}{\cos^2 t}}=+\frac{\sin t}{\cos t}\text{ as } t\in[0,\pi/2]\right]$$

$$=(\beta-\alpha)\int_0^{\pi/2}2\sin^2 t\,dt=(\beta-\alpha)\int_0^{\pi/2}(1-\cos 2t)\,dt$$

$$=(\beta-\alpha)\left(t-\frac{\sin 2t}{2}\right)_0^{\pi/2}$$

$$=(\beta-\alpha)\left[\left(\frac{\pi}{2}-\frac{1}{2}\sin\pi\right)-\left(0-\frac{1}{2}\sin 0\right)\right]=(\beta-\alpha)\left[\frac{\pi}{2}\right]$$

$$\therefore \quad I=\frac{\pi}{2}(\beta-\alpha)$$

Aliter Let $I=\int_{\alpha}^{\beta}\sqrt{\frac{x-\alpha}{\beta-x}}\,dx$ $\quad\left[\begin{array}{l}\text{put } \sqrt{\beta-x}=t\\ \text{or } \beta-x=t^2\\ \Rightarrow -dx=2t\,dt\end{array}\right]$

When $x=\alpha$, then $\beta-\alpha=t^2 \Rightarrow \sqrt{\beta-\alpha}=t$

When $x=\beta$, then $0=t^2 \Rightarrow 0=t$

$$\therefore \quad I=\int_{\sqrt{\beta-\alpha}}^{0}\frac{\sqrt{(\beta-t^2)-\alpha}}{t}(-2t)\,dt$$

$$=-2\int_{\sqrt{\beta-\alpha}}^{0}\sqrt{(\beta-\alpha)-t^2}\,dt$$

$$=2\int_0^{\sqrt{\beta-\alpha}}\sqrt{(\sqrt{\beta-\alpha})^2-t^2}\,dt$$

$$=2\left\{\frac{t}{2}\sqrt{(\beta-\alpha)-t^2}+\frac{(\beta-\alpha)}{2}\sin^{-1}\left(\frac{t}{\sqrt{\beta-\alpha}}\right)\right\}_0^{\sqrt{\beta-\alpha}}$$

$$=2\left[\left\{0+\frac{(\beta-\alpha)}{2}\sin^{-1}(1)\right\}-\left\{0+\frac{(\beta-\alpha)}{2}\sin^{-1}(0)\right\}\right]$$

$$=\frac{2(\beta-\alpha)}{2}\cdot\frac{\pi}{2}=\frac{\pi}{2}(\beta-\alpha)$$

Ex. 30 *Evaluate* $\int_{\sqrt{(3a^2+b^2)/4}}^{\sqrt{(a^2+b^2)/2}}\frac{x}{\sqrt{(x^2-a^2)(b^2-x^2)}}\,dx.$

Sol. Let $$I=\int_{\sqrt{(3a^2+b^2)/4}}^{\sqrt{(a^2+b^2)/2}}\frac{x}{\sqrt{(x^2-a^2)(b^2-x^2)}}\,dx \quad \text{...(i)}$$

Put $x^2=a^2\cos^2 t+b^2\sin^2 t$

$\Rightarrow \quad 2x\,dx=[2a^2\cos t(-\sin t)+2b^2\sin t(\cos t)]\,dt$

$\Rightarrow \quad x\,dx=\frac{1}{2}(b^2-a^2)\sin 2t\,dt$

For $x^2=\frac{a^2+b^2}{2}=a^2\cos^2 t+b^2\sin^2 t,$

$a^2+b^2=2(1-\sin^2 t)a^2+2b^2\sin^2 t$

or $(a^2+b^2)=2a^2+2(b^2-a^2)\sin^2 t$

$\Rightarrow \quad \sin^2 t=\frac{1}{2} \Rightarrow \cos 2t=0 \Rightarrow t=\frac{\pi}{4}$

For $x^2=\frac{3a^2+b^2}{4}=a^2\cos^2 t+b^2\sin^2 t,$

$3a^2+b^2=4a^2+4(b^2-a^2)\sin^2 t$

$\Rightarrow \quad \sin^2 t=\frac{1}{4} \Rightarrow \cos 2t=\frac{1}{2} \Rightarrow t=\frac{\pi}{6}$

$\therefore$ Eq. (i) reduces to

$$I=\int_{\pi/6}^{\pi/4}\frac{1}{2}\cdot\frac{(b^2-a^2)\sin 2t}{\sqrt{(b^2-a^2)\sin^2 t(b^2-a^2)\cos^2 t}}\,dt$$

$$=\int_{\pi/6}^{\pi/4}dt=\left(t\right)_{\pi/6}^{\pi/4}=\left(\frac{\pi}{4}-\frac{\pi}{6}\right)=\frac{\pi}{12}$$

Ex. 31 *Evaluate* $\int_0^{\pi/4}\frac{e^{\sec x}\left[\sin\left(x+\frac{\pi}{4}\right)\right]}{\cos x(1-\sin x)}\,dx.$

Sol. Let $$I=\int_0^{\pi/4}\frac{e^{\sec x}\left[\sin\left(x+\frac{\pi}{4}\right)\right]}{\cos x(1-\sin x)}\,dx$$

$$=\frac{1}{\sqrt{2}}\int_0^{\pi/4}\frac{e^{\sec x}(\sin x+\cos x)(1+\sin x)}{\cos x(1-\sin^2 x)}\,dx$$

$$=\frac{1}{\sqrt{2}}\int_0^{\pi/4}\frac{e^{\sec x}(\sin x+\cos x)(1+\sin x)}{\cos^2 x\cdot\cos x}\,dx$$

$$=\frac{1}{\sqrt{2}}\int_0^{\pi/4}e^{\sec x}\cdot(\sec x\tan x+\sec x)(\sec x+\tan x)\,dx$$

$$=\frac{1}{\sqrt{2}}\int_0^{\pi/4}e^{\sec x}\cdot[\sec x\tan x(\sec x+\tan x)+\sec^2 x+\sec x\tan x]\,dx$$

$$=\frac{1}{\sqrt{2}}\int_0^{\pi/4}e^{\sec x}\cdot[\sec x\tan x(\sec x+\tan x+1)+\sec^2 x]\,dx$$

$$=\frac{1}{\sqrt{2}}\int_0^{\pi/4}e^{\sec x}\cdot\sec x\tan x(\sec x+\tan x+1)+\frac{1}{\sqrt{2}}\int_0^{\pi/4}e^{\sec x}\cdot\sec^2 x\,dx$$

Applying integration by parts,

$$I=\frac{1}{\sqrt{2}}\{(\sec x+\tan x+1)\,e^{\sec x}\}_0^{\pi/4}$$

$$-\frac{1}{\sqrt{2}}\int_0^{\pi/4}(\sec x\tan x+\sec^2 x)\cdot e^{\sec x}dx+\frac{1}{\sqrt{2}}\int_0^{\pi/4}e^{\sec x}\cdot\sec^2 x\,dx$$

$$=\frac{1}{\sqrt{2}}\{(\sqrt{2}+1+1)\,e^{\sqrt{2}}-(1+1)\,e\}-\frac{1}{\sqrt{2}}[e^{\sec x}]_0^{\pi/4}$$

$$=\frac{1}{\sqrt{2}}(\sqrt{2}+2)\,e^{\sqrt{2}}-\sqrt{2}e-\frac{1}{\sqrt{2}}(e^{\sqrt{2}}-e)=\frac{1}{\sqrt{2}}(1+\sqrt{2})\,e^{\sqrt{2}}-\frac{e}{\sqrt{2}}$$

• Ex. 32 *Evaluate* $\int_0^{\pi/4}\frac{x^2(\sin 2x-\cos 2x)\,dx}{(1+\sin 2x)\cos^2 x}$.

Sol. Let $I=\int_0^{\pi/4}\frac{x^2(\sin 2x-\cos 2x)\,dx}{(1+\sin 2x)\cos^2 x}$,

$$=\frac{1}{8}\int_0^{\pi/2}\frac{t^2(\sin t-\cos t)}{(1+\sin t)(\cos^2 t/2)}dt \qquad \text{(put } 2x=t)$$

$$I=\frac{1}{4}\int_0^{\pi/2}\frac{t^2(\sin t-\cos t)}{(1+\sin t)(1+\cos t)}dt \qquad \text{...(i)}$$

$$\left[\text{using, } \int_0^a f(x)\,dx=\int_0^a f(a-x)\,dx\right]$$

$$I=\frac{1}{4}\int_0^{\pi/2}\frac{\left(\frac{\pi}{2}-t\right)^2\cdot(\cos t-\sin t)}{(1+\cos t)(1+\sin t)}dt \qquad \text{...(ii)}$$

Adding Eqs. (i) and (ii), we get

$$2I=\frac{1}{4}\int_0^{\pi/2}\frac{\left(\pi t-\frac{\pi^2}{4}\right)(\sin t-\cos t)}{(1+\cos t)(1+\sin t)}dt \qquad \text{...(iii)}$$

where, $\int_0^{\pi/2}\frac{\sin t-\cos t}{(1+\cos t)(1+\sin t)}dt=0$

$$\left[\text{as} \int_0^{2a} f(x)\,dx=0, \text{ if } f(2a-x)=-f(x)\right]$$

$\therefore$ Eq. (iii) becomes

$$I=\frac{1}{8}\int_0^{\pi/2}\frac{\pi t(\sin t-\cos t)\,dt}{(1+\cos t)(1+\sin t)}+0$$

$$=\frac{\pi}{8}\int_0^{\pi/2}\frac{t\{(1+\sin t)-(1+\cos t)\}\,dt}{(1+\cos t)(1+\sin t)}$$

$$=\frac{\pi}{8}\int_0^{\pi/2}\frac{t\,dt}{1+\cos t}-\frac{\pi}{8}\int_0^{\pi/2}\frac{t\,dt}{1+\sin t}$$

$$=\frac{\pi}{8}\int_0^{\pi/2}\frac{t\,dt}{1+\cos t}-\frac{\pi}{8}\int_0^{\pi/2}\frac{(\pi/2-t)\,dt}{1+\cos t}$$

$$=\frac{2\pi}{8}\int_0^{\pi/2}\frac{t\,dt}{1+\cos t}-\frac{\pi^2}{16}\int_0^{\pi/2}\frac{dt}{1+\cos t}$$

$$=\frac{\pi}{8}\int_0^{\pi/2}t(\sec^2 t/2)\,dt-\frac{\pi^2}{16}\int_0^{\pi/2}(\sec^2 t/2)\,dt$$

$$=\frac{\pi}{8}\left\{\left(2t\cdot\tan\frac{t}{2}\right)_0^{\pi/2}-\int_0^{\pi/2}1\cdot 2\tan\frac{t}{2}\,dt\right\}-\frac{\pi^2}{16}\left(2\tan\frac{t}{2}\right)_0^{\pi/2}$$

$$=\frac{\pi}{8}\left\{(\pi-0)+4\left(\log\cos\frac{t}{2}\right)_0^{\pi/2}\right\}-\frac{\pi^2}{8}\{1-0\}$$

$$=\frac{\pi}{8}\left\{\pi+4\log\frac{1}{\sqrt{2}}\right\}-\frac{\pi^2}{8}=\frac{\pi^2}{8}+\pi\log\frac{1}{\sqrt{2}}-\frac{\pi^2}{8}$$

$$=\frac{\pi^2}{8}-\frac{1}{2}\pi\log 2=\frac{\pi^2}{16}-\frac{\pi}{4}\log 2$$

• Ex. 33 *Evaluate* $\int_0^{\pi}\frac{x^2\cos x}{(1+\sin x)^2}dx.$

Sol. Let $I=\int_0^{\pi}\frac{x^2\cos x}{(1+\sin x)^2}dx=\int_0^{\pi}x^2\{(1+\sin x)^{-2}\cos x\}\,dx$

Applying integration by parts,

$$I=\left(x^2\frac{(1+\sin x)^{-1}}{-1}\right)_0^{\pi}-\int_0^{\pi}2x\cdot\frac{(1+\sin x)^{-1}}{-1}dx$$

$$=(-\pi^2+0)+2\int_0^{\pi}\frac{x}{1+\sin x}dx \qquad \text{...(i)}$$

$$\left[\text{using, } \int_0^a f(x)\,dx=\int_0^a f(a-x)\,dx\right]$$

$$I=-\pi^2+2\int_0^{\pi}\frac{(\pi-x)}{1+\sin x}dx \qquad \text{...(ii)}$$

Adding Eqs. (i) and (ii), we get

$$2I=-2\pi^2+2\int_0^{\pi}\frac{\pi}{1+\sin x}dx$$

$$=-2\pi^2+2\pi\int_0^{\pi}\frac{1-\sin x}{\cos^2 x}dx$$

$$=-2\pi^2+2\pi\,[\tan x-\sec x]_0^{\pi}$$

$$=-2\pi^2+2\pi\,[0-(-1-1)]=-2\pi^2+4\pi$$

$$\therefore \quad I=-\pi^2+2\pi$$

• Ex. 34 *Compute the following integrals.*

(i) $\int_0^{\infty}f(x^n+x^{-n})\ln x\frac{dx}{x}=0$

(ii) $\int_0^{\infty}f(x^n+x^{-n})\ln x\frac{dx}{1+x^2}=0$

Sol. (i) Let $\quad t=\ln x \Rightarrow x=e^t$

$$dx=e^t\,dt \quad \text{or} \quad \frac{dx}{x}=dt$$

Also, $\quad x=0 \Rightarrow t=-\infty$

and $\quad x=\infty \Rightarrow t=\infty$

$$\therefore \quad \int_0^{\infty}f(x^n+x^{-n})\ln x\frac{dx}{x}=\int_{-\infty}^{\infty}f(e^{nt}+e^{-nt})\cdot t\,dt=0$$

($\because$ integrand is an odd function of t)

(ii) $\int_0^{\infty}f(x^n+x^{-n})\ln x\cdot\frac{dx}{1+x^2}=\int_{-\infty}^{\infty}f(e^{nt}+e^{-nt})\cdot t\cdot\frac{e^t}{1+e^{2t}}\cdot dt$

Now, if $h(t) = f(e^{nt} + e^{-nt}) \cdot \dfrac{t\, e^t}{1 + e^{2t}}$

Then, $h(-t) = f(e^{-nt} + e^{nt}) \cdot (-t) \cdot \dfrac{1}{e^t + e^{-t}} \quad \left(\because \dfrac{e^t}{1 + e^{2t}} = \dfrac{1}{e^{-t} + e^t} \right)$

$h(-t) = -h(t)$

Thus, integrand is an odd function and hence

$$\int_0^\infty f(x^n + x^{-n}) \ln x \cdot \frac{dx}{1 + x^2} = 0$$

Ex. 35 *Show that*

(a) $\int_0^\infty \sin x \, dx = 1$ (b) $\int_0^\infty \cos x \, dx = 0$

Sol. Let us first evaluate;

$$I = \int e^{-sx} \sin x \, dx \text{ and } J = \int e^{-sx} \cos x \, dx$$

Using integer by parts, we get

$$I = -e^{-sx} \cos x - sJ \quad \text{...(i)}$$

and $$J = e^{-sx} \sin x + sI \quad \text{...(ii)}$$

Subtracting Eqs. (i) and (ii), we get

$$I = -e^{-sx} \left| \frac{\cos x + s \sin x}{1 + s^2} \right|$$

$$\Rightarrow \quad J = e^{-sx} \left| \sin x - \frac{s^2}{s^2 + 1} \sin x - \frac{s}{1 + s^2} \cos x \right|$$

$$= e^{-sx} \left| \frac{\sin x - s \cos x}{1 + s^2} \right|$$

Thus, $\int_0^\infty e^{-sx} \sin x \, dx = \dfrac{1}{s^2 + 1}$

and $\int_0^\infty e^{-sx} \cos x \, dx = \dfrac{s}{s^2 + 1}$

Now, $\int_0^\infty \sin x \, dx = \lim_{s \to 0} \int_0^\infty e^{-sx} \sin x \, dx = \lim_{s \to 0} \dfrac{1}{s^2 + 1} = 1$

and $\int_0^\infty \cos x \, dx = \lim_{s \to 0} \int_0^\infty e^{-sx} \cos x \, dx = \lim_{s \to 0} \dfrac{s}{s^2 + 1} = 0$

Ex. 36 *Find a function $g : R \to R$, continuous in $[0, \infty)$ and positive in $(0, \infty)$ satisfying $g(0) = 1$ and $\frac{1}{2} \int_0^x g^2(t) \, dt = \frac{1}{x} \left(\int_0^x g(t) \, dt \right)^2$.*

Sol. Let $$f(x) = \int_0^x g(t) \, dt$$

$$\Rightarrow \quad f'(x) = g(x)$$

$$\Rightarrow \quad \frac{1}{2} \int_0^x (f'(t))^2 \, dt = \frac{1}{2} \int_0^x g^2(t) \, dt \quad \text{...(i)}$$

$$\Rightarrow \quad \frac{1}{2} \left[\int_0^x g(t) \right]^2 = \frac{1}{2} (f(x))^2$$

$$\Rightarrow \quad \frac{1}{2} \frac{\left[\int_0^x g(t) \right]^2}{x} = \frac{1}{2} \frac{(f(x))^2}{x}$$

$$\Rightarrow \quad \frac{1}{2} \cdot \frac{1}{2} \left[\int_0^x g^2(t) \right] dt = \frac{1}{2} \frac{(f(x))^2}{x}$$

$$\Rightarrow \quad \frac{1}{2} \int_0^x (f'(t))^2 \, dt = \frac{1}{2} \frac{(f(x))^2}{x} \quad \text{[using Eq. (i)]}$$

Differentiating both the sides w.r.t. x, we get

$$\frac{1}{2} [f'(x)]^2 = \frac{x \, 2 f(x) f'(x) - (f(x))^2}{x^2}$$

$$\Rightarrow \quad \frac{1}{2} [g(x)]^2 x^2 = 2x f(x) (g(x)) - (f(x))^2$$

$$\Rightarrow \quad \left(\frac{x \, g(x)}{f(x)} \right)^2 = 4 \left(\frac{x \, g(x)}{f(x)} \right) - 2$$

$$\Rightarrow \quad t^2 - 4t + 2 = 0, \text{ where } t = \frac{x \, g(x)}{f(x)}$$

$$\Rightarrow \quad t = \frac{4 \pm \sqrt{8}}{2} = 2 \pm \sqrt{2} \text{ or } \frac{x f'(x)}{f(x)} = 2 \pm \sqrt{2}$$

$$\Rightarrow \quad \ln f(x) = 2 \pm \sqrt{2} \ln x + \text{constant}$$

$$\Rightarrow \quad f(x) = cx^{2 + \sqrt{2}} \text{ or } cx^{2 - \sqrt{2}}$$

$$\Rightarrow \quad g(x) = f'(x) = c_1 x^{1 + \sqrt{2}} \text{ or } c_2 x^{1 - \sqrt{2}}$$

where, c_1 and c_2 are constants of integration.

But g is continuous on $[0, \infty)$, then $c_2 x^{1 - \sqrt{2}}$ is ruled out.

Hence, $g(x) = c_1 x^{1 + \sqrt{2}}$

Also, $g(0) = c^1 = 1 \Rightarrow g(x) = x^{1 + \sqrt{2}}$

Ex. 37 *Let $I_n = \int_0^{\pi/4} \tan^n x \, dx$ ($n > 1$ and is an integer). Show that*

(i) $I_n + I_{n-2} = \dfrac{1}{n-1}$ (ii) $\dfrac{1}{2(n+1)} < I_n < \dfrac{1}{2(n-1)}$

Sol. (i) Given, $I_n = \int_0^{\pi/4} \tan^n x \, dx = \int_0^{\pi/4} \tan^{n-2} x \cdot \tan^2 x \, dx$

$$= \int_0^{\pi/4} \sec^2 x \cdot \tan^{n-2} x \, dx - \int_0^{\pi/4} \tan^{n-2} x \, dx$$

$$= \int_0^1 t^{n-2} \, dt - I_{n-2}, \text{ where } t = \tan x$$

$$I_n + I_{n-2} = \left(\frac{t^{n-1}}{n-1} \right)_0^1 \quad \therefore \; I_n + I_{n-2} = \frac{1}{n-1}$$

(ii) For $0 < x < \pi/4$, we have $0 < \tan^n x < \tan^{n-2} x$

So that; $$0 < I_n < I_{n-2}$$

$$\therefore \quad I_n + I_{n+2} < 2I_n < I_n + I_{n-2}$$

$$\Rightarrow \quad \frac{1}{n+1} < 2I_n < \frac{1}{n-1}$$

$$\Rightarrow \quad \frac{1}{2(n+1)} < I_n < \frac{1}{2(n-1)}$$

• **Ex. 38** *If* $U_n = \int_0^{\pi} \frac{1-\cos nx}{1-\cos x}\,dx$, *where n is positive integer or zero, then show that* $U_{n+2} + U_n = 2U_{n+1}$.

Hence, deduce that $\int_0^{\pi/2} \frac{\sin^2 n\theta}{\sin^2\theta} = \frac{1}{2}n\pi$.

Sol. $U_{n+2} - U_{n+1} = \int_0^{\pi} \frac{[1-\cos(n+2)x]-[1-\cos(n+1)x]}{1-\cos x}\,dx$

$$= \int_0^{\pi} \frac{\cos(n+1)x - \cos(n+2)x}{1-\cos x}\,dx$$

$$= \int_0^{\pi} \frac{2\sin\left(n+\frac{3}{2}\right)x \cdot \sin\frac{x}{2}}{2\sin^2\frac{x}{2}}\,dx$$

$$U_{n+2} - U_{n+1} = \int_0^{\pi} \frac{\sin\left(n+\frac{3}{2}\right)x}{\sin\frac{x}{2}}\,dx \quad \text{...(i)}$$

$$\Rightarrow U_{n+1} - U_n = \int_0^{\pi} \frac{\sin\left(n+\frac{1}{2}\right)x}{\sin\frac{x}{2}}\,dx \quad \text{...(ii)}$$

From Eqs. (i) and (ii), we get

$$(U_{n+2}-U_{n+1})-(U_{n+1}-U_n) = \int_0^{\pi} \frac{\sin\left(n+\frac{3}{2}\right)x - \sin\left(n+\frac{1}{2}\right)x}{\sin\frac{x}{2}}\,dx$$

$$U_{n+2} + U_n - 2U_{n+1} = \int_0^{\pi} \frac{2\cos(n+1)x \cdot \sin x/2}{\sin x/2}\,dx$$

$$= 2\int_0^{\pi} \cos(n+1)x\,dx = 2\left(\frac{\sin(n+1)x}{n+1}\right)_0^{\pi} = 0$$

$\Rightarrow U_{n+2} + U_n = 2U_{n+1}$

$\Rightarrow U_n, U_{n+1}, U_{n+2}$ are in AP.

Now, $U_0 = \int_0^{\pi} \frac{1-1}{1-\cos x}\,dx = 0$

$U_1 = \int_0^{\pi} \frac{1-\cos x}{1-\cos x}\,dx = \pi$

$U_1 - U_0 = \pi$ (common difference)

$U_n = U_0 + n\pi = n\pi$

$U_n = n\pi$

Now, $I_n = \int_0^{\pi/2} \frac{\sin^2 n\theta}{\sin^2\theta}\,d\theta = \int_0^{\pi/2} \frac{1-\cos 2n\theta}{1-\cos 2\theta}\,d\theta$

$$= \frac{1}{2}\int_0^{\pi} \frac{1-\cos nx}{1-\cos x}\,dx = \frac{1}{2}n\pi$$

• **Ex. 39** *Prove that for any positive integer K,*

$$\frac{\sin 2Kx}{\sin x} = 2[\cos x + \cos 3x + \ldots + \cos(2K-1)x]$$

Hence, prove that $\int_0^{\pi/2} \sin 2Kx \cdot \cot x\,dx = \frac{\pi}{2}$.

Sol. To prove; $\sin 2Kx = 2\sin x[\cos x + \cos 3x + \cos 5x + \ldots + \cos(2K-1)x]$

Taking RHS, $[2\sin x\cos x + 2\sin x\cos 3x + 2\sin x\cos 5x + \ldots + 2\sin x\cos(2K-1)x]$

$$= (\sin 2x) + (\sin 4x - \sin 2x) + [\sin 6x - \sin 4x) + \ldots + (\sin 2Kx - \sin(2K-2)x)$$

$$= \sin 2Kx$$

Now, $\int_0^{\pi/2} \sin 2Kx \cdot \cot x\,dx = \int_0^{\pi/2} \left(\frac{\sin 2Kx}{\sin x}\right) \cdot \cos x\,dx$

$$= \int_0^{\pi/2} 2\cos x[\cos x + \cos 3x + \ldots + \cos(2K-1)x]\,dx$$

$$= \int_0^{\pi/2} (1+\cos 2x)\,dx + \int_0^{\pi/2} (\cos 4x + \cos 2x)\,dx + \ldots + \int_0^{\pi/2} [\cos 2Kx + \cos(2K-2)x]\,dx$$

But we know that,

$$\int_0^{\pi/2} (\cos 2nx)\,dx = 0, \forall n \in I \text{ and } n \neq 0$$

$$\Rightarrow \int_0^{\pi/2} \sin 2Kx \cdot \cot x\,dx = \int_0^{\pi/2} 1\,dx + 0 = \frac{\pi}{2}$$

• **Ex. 40** *Evaluate* $\int_0^{\sqrt{3}} \frac{1}{1+x^2} \cdot \sin^{-1}\left(\frac{2x}{1+x^2}\right)dx$.

Sol. Let $I = \int_0^{\sqrt{3}} \frac{1}{1+x^2}\sin^{-1}\left(\frac{2x}{1+x^2}\right)dx$

Now, $\sin^{-1}\left(\frac{2x}{1+x^2}\right) = \begin{cases} 2\tan^{-1}x, & \text{if } -1 \le x \le 1 \\ \pi - 2\tan^{-1}x, & \text{if } x > 1 \end{cases}$

$$\therefore I = \int_0^1 \frac{1}{1+x^2}\sin^{-1}\left(\frac{2x}{1+x^2}\right)dx + \int_1^{\sqrt{3}} \frac{1}{1+x^2}\cdot\sin^{-1}\left(\frac{2x}{1+x^2}\right)dx$$

$$= \int_0^1 \frac{2\tan^{-1}x}{1+x^2}\,dx + \int_1^{\sqrt{3}} \frac{\pi - 2\tan^{-1}x}{1+x^2}\,dx$$

$$= 2\int_0^1 \frac{\tan^{-1}x}{1+x^2}\,dx + \pi\int_1^{\sqrt{3}} \frac{1}{1+x^2}\,dx - 2\int_1^{\sqrt{3}} \frac{\tan^{-1}x}{1+x^2}\,dx$$

$$= 2\int_0^{\pi/4} t\,dt + \pi(\tan^{-1}x)_1^{\sqrt{3}} - 2\int_{\pi/4}^{\pi/3} t\,dt \quad (\text{put } \tan^{-1}x = t)$$

$$= 2\left(\frac{t^2}{2}\right)_0^{\pi/4} + \pi\{\tan^{-1}\sqrt{3} - \tan^{-1}1\} - 2\left(\frac{t^2}{2}\right)_{\pi/4}^{\pi/3}$$

$$= \frac{\pi^2}{16} + \pi\left\{\frac{\pi}{3} - \frac{\pi}{4}\right\} - \left\{\frac{\pi^2}{9} - \frac{\pi^2}{16}\right\} = \frac{7}{72}\pi^2$$

• **Ex. 41** *Prove that* $\int_0^x e^{xt}\cdot e^{-t^2}\,dt = e^{x^2/4}\int_0^x e^{-t^2/4}\,dt$.

Sol. Let $I = \int_0^x e^{xt}\cdot e^{-t^2}\,dt$. Put $t = \frac{x+z}{2} \Rightarrow dt = \frac{1}{2}dz$

$$\therefore I = \int_0^x e^{tx}\cdot e^{-t^2}\,dt = \frac{1}{2}\int_{-x}^{x} e^{\left(\frac{x+z}{2}\right)x}\cdot e^{-\left(\frac{x+z}{2}\right)^2}dz$$

$$= \frac{1}{2}\int_{-x}^{x} e^{\left(\frac{x+z}{2}\right)\left(x-\frac{x+z}{2}\right)}dz = \frac{1}{2}\int_{-x}^{x} e^{\left(\frac{x+z}{2}\right)\left(\frac{x-z}{2}\right)}dz$$

$$=\frac{1}{2}\int_{-x}^{x} e^{\frac{x^2}{4}-\frac{z^2}{4}}\,dz=\frac{1}{2}e^{x^2/4}\cdot\int_{-x}^{x} e^{-z^2/4}\,dz$$

$$=\frac{1}{2}e^{x^2/4}\int_{-x}^{x} e^{-t^2/4}\,dt=\frac{1}{2}e^{x^2/4}\cdot 2\int_{0}^{x} e^{-t^2/4}\,dt$$

$$\left[\text{using, }\int_{-a}^{a} f(x)\,dx=2\int_0^a f(x)\,dx,\text{ when } f(-x)=f(x)\right]$$

$$=e^{x^2/4}\int_0^x e^{-t^2/4}\,dt$$

$$\Rightarrow\quad \int_0^x e^{xt}\cdot x^{-t^2}\,dt=e^{x^2/4}\int_0^x e^{-t^2/4}\,dt$$

Ex. 42 *If* $f(x)=e^x+\int_0^1 (e^x+te^{-x})\,f(t)\,dt$, *find* $f(x)$.

Sol. We can write $f(x)=Ae^x+Be^{-x}$, where

$$A=1+\int_0^1 f(t)\,dt \quad\text{and}\quad B=\int_0^1 tf(t)\,dt$$

$$\therefore\quad A=1+\int_0^1 (Ae^t+Be^{-t})\,dt=1+(Ae^t-Be^{-t})_0^1$$

$$A=1+A(e^1-1)-B(e^{-1}-1)$$

$$\Rightarrow\quad (2-e)A+(e^{-1}-1)B=1 \qquad \text{...(i)}$$

$$B=\int_0^1 t(Ae^t+Be^{-t})\,dt$$

$$=A(te^t-e^t)_0^t+B(-te^{-t}-e^{-t})_0^1$$

$$B=A+B(1-2e^{-1})$$

$$\Rightarrow\quad A-2e^{-1}B=0 \qquad \text{...(ii)}$$

From Eqs. (i) and (ii), we get

$$A=\frac{2(e-1)}{4e-2e^2},\ B=\frac{e-1}{4-2e}$$

Hence, $$f(x)=\frac{2(e-1)}{4e-2e^2}\cdot e^x+\frac{e-1}{4-2e}\cdot e^{-x}$$

Ex. 43 *If* $|a|<1$, *show that*

$$\int_0^{\pi}\frac{\log(1+a\cos x)}{\cos x}\,dx=\pi\sin^{-1}a.$$

Sol. Given, $|a|<1$

Let $$f(a)=\int_0^{\pi}\frac{\log(1+a\cos x)}{\cos x}\,dx$$

$$\therefore\quad f'(a)=\int_0^{\pi}\frac{\cos x}{\cos x\cdot(1+a\cos x)}\,dx=\int_0^{\pi}\frac{dx}{1+a\cos x}$$

(differentiating w.r.t. 'a' using Leibnitz rule)

$$\left(\begin{array}{l}\text{put }\tan\frac{x}{2}=t\Rightarrow\frac{dx}{dt}=\frac{2}{1+t^2},\text{ when } x=0, t=0\\ \text{and when } x=\pi, t\to\infty\end{array}\right)$$

$$\Rightarrow\quad f'(a)=\int_0^{\infty}\frac{\frac{2dt}{1+t^2}}{1+a\left(\frac{1-t^2}{1+t^2}\right)}$$

$$=\int_0^{\infty}\frac{2dt}{(1+t^2)+a(1-t^2)}=\int_0^{\infty}\frac{2dt}{(1-a)t^2+(1+a)}$$

$$=\frac{2}{1-a}\int_0^{\infty}\frac{dt}{t^2+\left(\sqrt{\frac{1+a}{1-a}}\right)^2}$$

$$=\frac{2}{1-a}\cdot\frac{1}{\sqrt{(1+a)/(1-a)}}\cdot\left(\tan^{-1}t\sqrt{\frac{1-a}{1+a}}\right)_0^{\infty}=\frac{2}{\sqrt{1-a^2}}\cdot\frac{\pi}{2}=\frac{\pi}{\sqrt{1-a^2}}$$

(integrating both the sides w.r.t. 'a')

$$\Rightarrow\quad f(a)=\pi\sin^{-1}a+c$$

But $$f(0)=\int_0^{\pi}\frac{\log(1+0\cos x)\,dx}{\cos x}=0$$

$$\Rightarrow\quad c=0$$

$$\therefore\quad f(a)=\pi\sin^{-1}a$$

Ex. 44 *Evaluate* $\int_0^{\pi/2}\operatorname{cosec}\theta\tan^{-1}(c\sin\theta)\,d\theta.$

Sol. Let $$f(c)=\int_0^{\pi/2}\operatorname{cosec}\theta\cdot\tan^{-1}(c\sin\theta)\,d\theta$$

$$\therefore\quad f'(c)=\int_0^{\pi/2}\operatorname{cosec}\theta\cdot\frac{(\sin\theta)}{1+c^2\sin^2\theta}\,d\theta+0-0$$

$$=\int_0^{\pi/2}\frac{d\theta}{1+c^2\sin^2\theta}$$

$$=\int_0^{\pi/2}\frac{\operatorname{cosec}^2\theta\,d\theta}{c^2+\operatorname{cosec}^2\theta}=\int_0^{\pi/2}\frac{\operatorname{cosec}^2\theta\,d\theta}{(c^2+1)+\cot^2\theta}$$

$$=-\frac{1}{\sqrt{c^2+1}}\left(\tan^{-1}\frac{\cot\theta}{\sqrt{c^2+1}}\right)_0^{\pi/2}$$

$$f'(c)=\frac{\pi}{2\sqrt{c^2+1}}$$

Integrating both the sides, we get

$$f(c)=\int\frac{\pi\,dc}{2\sqrt{c^2+1}}=\frac{\pi}{2}\log(c+\sqrt{c^2+1})+A$$

where, $f(0)=A$

But $$f(0)=\int_0^{\pi/2}\operatorname{cosec}\theta\tan^{-1}(0)\,d\theta=0$$

$$\Rightarrow\quad f(c)=\frac{\pi}{2}\log(c+\sqrt{c^2+1})$$

Ex. 45 *Evaluate* $\int_0^{\pi/2}\sec\theta\cdot\tan^{-1}(a\cos\theta)\,d\theta.$

Sol. Given definite integral is a function of 'a'. Let its value be $I(a)$.

Then, $$I(a)=\int_0^{\pi/2}\sec\theta\cdot\tan^{-1}(a\cos\theta)\,d\theta$$

$$\Rightarrow\quad I'(a)=\int_0^{\pi/2}\sec\theta\cdot\frac{1}{1+a^2\cos^2\theta}\cdot\cos\theta\,d\theta+0-0$$

(using Leibnitz rule)

$$=\int_0^{\pi/2}\frac{1}{1+a^2\cos^2\theta}\,d\theta=\int_0^{\pi/2}\frac{\sec^2\theta}{\sec^2\theta+a^2}\,d\theta$$

$$=\int_0^{\pi/2}\frac{\sec^2\theta}{1+\tan^2\theta+a^2}\,d\theta \qquad \text{(put } \tan\theta=t)$$

$$=\int_0^{\infty}\frac{dt}{t^2+(a^2+1)}=\frac{1}{\sqrt{a^2+1}}\left(\tan^{-1}\frac{t}{\sqrt{a^2+1}}\right)_0^{\infty}$$

$$=\frac{1}{\sqrt{a^2+1}}\left(\frac{\pi}{2}-0\right) \Rightarrow I'(a)=\frac{\pi}{2\sqrt{a^2+1}}$$

Integrating both the sides w.r.t. 'a', we get

$$I(a)=\frac{\pi}{2}\log|a+\sqrt{a^2+1}|+C$$

Since, $\quad I(0)=0+C$

$$\Rightarrow \quad I(a)=\frac{\pi}{2}\log|a+\sqrt{1+a^2}|$$

• Ex. 46 *Let f be a continuous function on $[a, b]$. Prove that there exists a number $x\in[a, b]$ such that $\int_a^x f(t)\,dt=\int_x^b f(t)\,dt$.*

Sol. Let $g(x)=\int_a^x f(t)\,dt-\int_x^b f(t)\,dt,\ x\in[a,b]$

We have, $g(a)=-\int_a^b f(t)\,dt$ and $g(b)=\int_a^b f(t)\,dt$

$$\Rightarrow \quad g(a)\cdot g(b)=-\left(\int_a^b f(t)\,dt\right)^2\le 0$$

Clearly, $g(x)$ is continuous in $[a,b]$ and $g(a)\cdot g(b)\le 0$.

It implies that $g(x)$ will become zero at least once in $[a,b]$.

Hence, $\int_a^x f(t)\,dt=\int_x^b f(t)\,dt$ for atleast one value of $x\in[a,b]$.

• Ex. 47 *If $f(x)=x+\int_0^1(xy^2+x^2y)\,(f(y))\,dy$, find $f(x)$.*

Sol. Given, $f(x)=x+x\int_0^1 y^2 f(y)\,dy+x^2\int_0^1 y\,f(y)\,dy$

$$=x\left(1+\int_0^1 y^2 f(y)\,dy\right)+x^2\left(\int_0^1 y\,f(y)\,dy\right)$$

$\Rightarrow$ $f(x)$ is a quadratic expression.

$$\Rightarrow \quad f(x)=ax+bx^2 \text{ or } f(y)=ay+by^2 \qquad \text{...(i)}$$

where, $$a=1+\int_0^1 y^2 f(y)\,dy=1+\int_0^1 y^2(ay+by^2)\,dy$$

$$=1+\left(\frac{ay^4}{4}+\frac{by^5}{5}\right)_0^1 \quad a=1+\left(\frac{a}{4}+\frac{b}{5}\right)$$

$$\Rightarrow \quad 20a=20+5a+4b \text{ or } 15a-4b=20 \qquad \text{...(ii)}$$

and $$b=\int_0^1 y\,f(y)\,dy=\int_0^1 y(ay+by^2)\,dy$$

$$=\left(\frac{ay^3}{3}+\frac{by^4}{4}\right)_0^1 \Rightarrow b=\frac{a}{3}+\frac{b}{4}$$

$$\Rightarrow \quad 12b=4a+3b \text{ or } 9b-4a=0 \qquad \text{...(iii)}$$

From Eqs. (ii) and (iii),

$$a=\frac{180}{119} \text{ and } b=\frac{80}{119}$$

$\therefore$ Eq. (i) reduces to

$$f(x)=\frac{80x^2+180x}{119}$$

• Ex. 48 *Prove that*

$$\int_0^x\left\{\int_0^u f(t)\,dt\right\}du=\int_0^x(x-u)\,f(u)\,du.$$

Sol. Here, applying integration by parts to

$$\int_0^x \underbrace{1}_{\text{II}}\cdot\underbrace{\left\{\int_0^u f(t)\,dt\right\}}_{\text{I}}du$$

i.e. taking '1' as second function and $\int_0^u f(t)\,dt$ as first function, we have

$$\int_0^x 1\cdot\left\{\int_0^u f(t)\,dt\right\}du=\left\{\int_0^u f(t)\,dt\right\}_0^x\cdot(u)_0^x-\int_0^x f(u)\cdot u\,du$$

$$=\left(u\int_0^u f(t)\,dt\right)_0^x-\int_0^x uf(u)\,du$$

$$=x\int_0^x f(t)\,dt-\int_0^x uf(u)\,du$$

$$=\int_0^x(x-u)\,f(u)\,du$$

• Ex. 49 *Evaluate $\int_0^{3\pi/2}(\log|\sin x|)(\cos(2nx))\,dx,\ n\in N$.*

Sol. Let $I(n)=\int_0^{3\pi/2}\underset{\text{I}}{(\log|\sin x|)}\underset{\text{II}}{(\cos 2nx)}\,dx$

$$I(n)=\left(\log|\sin x|\cdot\frac{\sin 2nx}{2n}\right)_0^{3\pi/2}-\int_0^{3\pi/2}\cot x\cdot\frac{\sin 2nx}{2n}\,dx$$

(using integration by parts)

$$I(n)=0-\frac{1}{2n}\int_0^{3\pi/2}\frac{\sin 2nx\cdot\cos x}{\sin x}\,dx=0-\frac{1}{2}I_1(n) \qquad \text{...(i)}$$

Let $I_1(n)=\int_0^{3\pi/2}\frac{\sin(2nx)\cos x}{\sin x}\,dx$

$$I_1(n+1)=\int_0^{3\pi/2}\frac{\sin(2n+2)x\cdot\cos x}{\sin x}\,dx$$

$$\therefore \quad I_1(n+1)-I_1(n)=\int_0^{3\pi/2}\frac{(\sin(2n+2)x-\sin 2nx)\cdot\cos x}{\sin x}\,dx$$

$$=\int_0^{3\pi/2}\frac{2\cos(2n+1)x\cdot\sin x\cdot\cos x}{\sin x}\,dx$$

$$=\int_0^{3\pi/2}(\cos(2n+2)x+\cos 2nx)\,dx$$

$$=\left(\frac{\sin(2n+2)x}{(2n+2)}+\frac{\sin(2n)x}{2n}\right)_0^{3\pi/2}=0+0$$

$$\Rightarrow \quad I_1(n+1)=I_1(n)=\ldots=I_1(1)$$

$$\therefore \quad I_1(1)=\int_0^{3\pi/2}\frac{\sin 2x\cdot\cos x}{\sin x}\,dx=\int_0^{3\pi/2}\frac{2\sin x\cos x\cdot\cos x}{\sin x}\,dx$$

$$= \int_0^{3\pi/2} 2\cos^2 x\, dx = \int_0^{3\pi/2} (1+\cos 2x)\, dx$$

$$= \left(x + \frac{\sin 2x}{2}\right)_0^{3\pi/2}$$

$$\Rightarrow \quad I_1(1) = \frac{3\pi}{2} = I_1(n) \Rightarrow I(n) = -\frac{1}{2n} I_1(n) \qquad \text{[using Eq. (i)]}$$

$$\therefore \quad I(n) = -\frac{3\pi}{4n}$$

● ***Ex. 50*** *Evaluate* $\int_0^{\infty} e^{-x} \sin^n x\, dx$, *if n is an even integer.*

Sol. Here, $I_n = \int_0^{\infty} e^{-x} \sin^n x\, dx$

$$= (-\sin^n x\, e^{-x})_0^{\infty} + n\int_0^{\infty} \sin^{n-1} x \cos x\, e^{-x}\, dx$$

$$= n\int_0^{\infty} \underset{\text{I}}{(\sin^{n-1} x \cdot \cos x)} \underset{\text{II}}{(e^{-x})}\, dx \text{ [where } (-\sin^n x\, e^{-x})_0^{\infty} = 0]$$

$$\Rightarrow \quad I_n = n\,[(-\sin^{n-1} x \cdot \cos x\, e^{-x})_0^{\infty}$$
$$+ (n-1)\int_0^{\infty} \sin^{n-2} x \cos^2 x\, e^{-x} dx - \int_0^{\infty} \sin^n x\, e^{-x}\, dx]$$

$$I_n = n(n-1)\int_0^{\infty} e^{-x} \sin^{n-2} x\, dx - n^2 \int_0^{\infty} e^{-x} \sin^n x\, dx$$

$$= n(n-1) I_{n-2} - n^2 I_n$$

$$\Rightarrow \quad (n^2+1) I_n = n(n-1) I_{n-2}$$

$$\therefore \quad I_n = \frac{n(n-1)}{n^2+1} I_{n-2}$$

Replacing n by $(n-2), (n-4), \ldots, 2$, we get

$$I_{n-2} = \frac{(n-2)(n-3)}{(n-2)^2+1} I_{n-4} = \frac{(n-1)(n-3)}{(n-2)^2+1} \cdot \frac{(n-4)(n-5)}{(n-4)^2+1} I_{n-6}$$

... and so on.

$$I_2 = \frac{2(2-1)}{2^2+1} I_0$$

$$\therefore \quad I_n = \frac{n(n-1)}{n^2+1} \cdot \frac{(n-2)(n-3)}{(n-2)^2+1} \cdot \frac{(n-4)(n-5)}{(n-3)^2+1} \cdots \frac{2(2-1)}{2^2+1} I_0$$

$$= \frac{n!}{\prod_{r=1}^{n/2} \{1+(2r)^2\}} \cdot I_0 = \frac{n!}{\prod_{r=1}^{n/2} 1+4r^2} \left(\because I_0 = \int_0^{\infty} e^{-x}\, dx = 1\right)$$

● ***Ex. 51*** *Evaluate* $\int_0^1 (tx+1-x)^n\, dx, n \in N$ *and t is independent of x. Hence, show*

$$\int_0^1 x^k (1-x)^{n-k}\, dx = \frac{1}{{}^nC_k (n+1)}.$$

Sol. Here, $I = \int_0^1 (tx+1-x)^n\, dx = \int_0^1 ((t-1)x+1)^n\, dx$

$$= \left\{\frac{((t-1)x+1)^{n+1}}{(n+1)(t-1)}\right\}_0^1$$

$$= \frac{1}{n+1}\{t^n + t^{n-1} + t^{n-2} + \ldots + t + 1\} \qquad \text{...(i)}$$

Again, $I = \int_0^1 (tx+1-x)^n\, dx = \int_0^1 \{(1-x)+tx\}^n\, dx$

$$= \int_0^1 \{{}^nC_0 (1-x)^n + {}^nC_1 (1-x)^{n-1} (tx) + {}^nC_2 (1-x)^{n-2} (tx)^2 + \ldots + {}^nC_r (1-x)^{n-r} (tx)^r + \ldots + {}^nC_n (tx)^n\}\, dx$$

$$= \int_0^1 \left\{\sum_{r=0}^{n} {}^nC_r (1-x)^{n-r} (tx)^r\right\} dx$$

$$= \sum_{r=0}^{n} {}^nC_r\, t^r \int_0^1 \{(1-x)^{n-r}\, x^r\}\, dx \qquad \text{...(ii)}$$

From Eqs. (i) and (ii),

$$\sum_{r=0}^{n} {}^nC_r\, t^r \int_0^1 (1-x)^{n-r}\, x^r\, dx = \frac{1}{n+1}\{t^n + t^{n-1} + t^{n-2} + \ldots + t + 1\}$$

Equating coefficient of t^k on both the sides, we get

$${}^nC_k \int_0^1 (1-x)^{n-k}\, x^k\, dx = \frac{1}{n+1}$$

$$\Rightarrow \quad \int_0^1 (1-x)^{n-k}\, x^k\, dx = \frac{1}{{}^nC_k (n+1)}$$

● ***Ex. 52*** *Given a real valued function f(x) which is monotonic and differentiable, prove that for any real numbers a and b;*

$$\int_a^b \{f^2(x) - f^2(a)\}\, dx = \int_{f(a)}^{f(b)} 2x\{b - f^{-1}(x)\}\, dx$$

Sol. As, $f(x)$ is differentiable and monotonic.

$\therefore\ f^{-1}(x)$ exists.

Let $\quad f^{-1}(x) = t \Rightarrow x = f(t)$ or $dx = f'(t)\, dt$

As, $\quad x = f(a) \Rightarrow f^{-1}\{f(a)\} = t \Rightarrow t = a$

and $\quad x = f(b) \Rightarrow f^{-1}\{f(b)\} = t \Rightarrow t = b$

$$\therefore \quad \int_{f(a)}^{f(b)} 2x\{b - f^{-1}(x)\}\, dx = \int_a^b 2f(t)(b-t)\, f'(t)\, dt$$

$$= \int_a^b \underset{\text{I}}{(b-t)} \underset{\text{II}}{\{2f(t)\, f'(t)\}}\, dt$$

$$= ((b-t)\{f(t)\}^2)_a^b + \int_a^b \{f(t)\}^2\, dt$$

$$= -(b-a)\{f(a)\}^2 + \int_a^b \{f(t)\}^2\, dt$$

$$= \int_a^b (\{f(t)\}^2 - \{f(a)\}^2)\, dt$$

$$= \int_a^b \{f^2(x) - f^2(a)\}\, dx$$

● ***Ex. 53*** *Evaluate*

$$\int_0^1 \frac{\sin\theta\, (\cos^2\theta - \cos^2 \pi/5)(\cos^2\theta - \cos^2 2\pi/5)}{\sin 5\theta}\, d\theta.$$

Sol. We know,

$$z^{10} - 1 = (z^2-1)\left[z^2 - 2\cos\left(\frac{\pi}{5}\right)z + 1\right]\left[z^2 - 2\left(\cos\frac{2\pi}{5}\right)z + 1\right] \times \left(z^2 - 2\cos\frac{4\pi}{5}z + 1\right)\left(z^2 - 2\cos\frac{6\pi}{5}z + 1\right)$$

or $z^5-\frac{1}{z^5}=\left(z-\frac{1}{z}\right)\left(z-2\cos\frac{\pi}{5}+\frac{1}{z}\right)\left(z-2\cos\frac{2\pi}{5}+\frac{1}{z}\right)$

$$\times\left(z-2\cos\frac{4\pi}{5}+\frac{1}{z}\right)\left(z-2\cos\frac{6\pi}{5}+\frac{1}{z}\right)$$

Put $z=\cos\theta+i\sin\theta$

$\Rightarrow 2i\sin 5\theta=(2i\sin\theta)(2\cos\theta-2\cos\pi/5)(2\cos\theta-2\cos 2\pi/5)$
$\times(2\cos\theta-2\cos 4\pi/5)(2\cos\theta-2\cos 6\pi/5)$

$\Rightarrow \sin 5\theta=16\sin\theta(\cos^2\theta-\cos^2\pi/5)(\cos^2\theta-\cos^2 2\pi/5)$

$\Rightarrow \frac{\sin\theta(\cos^2\theta-\cos^2\pi/5)(\cos^2\theta-\cos^2 2\pi/5)}{\sin 5\theta}=\frac{1}{16}$

$\therefore \int_0^1 \frac{\sin\theta(\cos^2\theta-\cos^2\pi/5)(\cos^2\theta-\cos^2 2\pi/5)}{\sin 5\theta}d\theta$

$$=\int_0^1\frac{1}{16}d\theta=\frac{1}{16}$$

● ***Ex. 54*** *Show that* $\lim_{n\to\infty}\sum_{k=0}^{n}\frac{{}^nC_K}{n^K(K+3)}=e-2$.

Sol. $\lim_{n\to\infty}\sum_{K=0}^{n}\frac{{}^nC_K}{n^K(K+3)}=\lim_{n\to\infty}\sum_{K=0}^{n}\frac{1}{K+3}{}^nC_K\cdot\frac{1}{n^K}$

$=\lim_{n\to\infty}\sum_{K=0}^{n}{}^nC_K\cdot\frac{1}{n^K}\int_0^1 x^{K+2}dx\left(\because \frac{1}{K+3}=\int_0^1 x^{K+2}dx\right)$

$=\int_0^1\left(x^2\lim_{n\to\infty}\sum_{K=0}^{n}{}^nC_K\cdot\left(\frac{x}{n}\right)^K\right)dx$

$=\int_0^1 x^2\left\{\lim_{n\to\infty}\left(1+\frac{x}{n}\right)^n\right\}dx$

$=\int_0^1 x^2\cdot e^x dx \quad \left[\because \lim_{n\to\infty}\left(1+\frac{x}{n}\right)^n=e^x\right]$

$=(x^2\cdot e^x)_0^1-\int_0^1 2x\cdot e^x dx=e-2\left\{(xe^x)_0^1-\int_0^1 e^x dx\right\}$

$=e-2\{e-e+1\}=e-2$

● ***Ex. 55*** *Let* $I=\int_0^{\pi/2}\frac{\cos x}{a\cos x+b\sin x}dx$ *and* $J=\int_0^{\pi/2}\frac{\sin x}{a\cos x+b\sin x}dx$, *where* $a>0$ and $b>0$. *Compute the values of I and J.*

Sol. $\because \quad aI+bJ=\frac{\pi}{2}$ ...(i)

and $bI-aJ=\int_0^{\pi/2}\frac{b\cos x-a\sin x}{a\cos x+b\sin x}dx$

$\therefore \quad bI-aJ=\ln[a\cos x+b\sin x]_0^{\pi/2}$

$\Rightarrow \quad bI-aJ=\ln\left(\frac{b}{a}\right)$ ...(ii)

From Eqs. (i) and (ii),

$a^2I+abJ=\frac{a\pi}{2}$

$b^2I-abJ=b\ln(b/a)$

$I=\frac{1}{a^2+b^2}\left[\frac{a\pi}{2}+b\ln\left(\frac{b}{a}\right)\right]$

Again, $abI+b^2J=\frac{b\pi}{2}$

and $abI-a^2J=a\ln(b/a)$

On subtracting, we get $J=\frac{1}{a^2+b^2}\left[\frac{b\pi}{2}-a\ln\left(\frac{b}{a}\right)\right]$

Aliter Convert $a\cos x+b\sin x$ into a single cosine say $\cos(x+\phi)$ and put $(x+\phi)=t$.

● ***Ex. 56*** *Evaluate* $\int_0^\infty\frac{\ln x\,dx}{x^2+2x+4}$.

Sol. $I=\int_0^\infty\frac{\ln x\,dx}{x^2+2x+4}$ (put $x=2t\Rightarrow dx=2dt$ to make coefficient of x^2 and constant term same)

$=2\int_0^\infty\frac{\ln 2+\ln t}{4(t^2+t+1)}dt=\frac{\ln 2}{2}\underbrace{\int_0^\infty\frac{dt}{t^2+t+1}}_{I_1}+\frac{1}{2}\underbrace{\int_0^\infty\frac{\ln t\,dt}{t^2+t+1}}_{I_2=\text{zero}}$

$I_2=\int_0^\infty\frac{\ln t\,dt}{t^2+t+1}\left(\text{put } t=\frac{1}{y}\Rightarrow dt=-\frac{1}{y^2}dy\right)$

$I_2=\int_\infty^0\frac{\ln y\cdot(+1)}{\left(\frac{1}{y^2}+\frac{1}{y}+1\right)y^2}dy$

$I_2=\int_\infty^0\frac{\ln y\,dy}{y^2+y+1}=-\int_\infty^0\frac{\ln y\,dy}{y^2+y+1}=-I_2$

Now, $I_1=\int_0^\infty\frac{dt}{\left(t+\frac{1}{2}\right)^2+\left(\frac{\sqrt{3}}{2}\right)^2}=\left[\frac{2}{\sqrt{3}}\tan^{-1}\frac{[t+(1/2)]^2}{\sqrt{3}}\right]_0^\infty$

$=\frac{2}{\sqrt{3}}\left[\frac{\pi}{2}-\frac{\pi}{6}\right]=\frac{2\pi}{3\sqrt{3}} \qquad \therefore I=\frac{\ln 2}{2}\cdot\frac{2\pi}{3\sqrt{3}}=\frac{\pi\ln 2}{3\sqrt{3}}$

Note For $a>0$, $I=\int_0^\infty\frac{\ln x\,dx}{ax^2+bx+a}=0$

[**Hint** By putting $x=1/t$, we get $I=-I$, so $I=0$]

● ***Ex. 57*** *Find a function f, continuous for all x (and not zero everywhere) such that* $f^2(x)=\int_0^x\frac{f(t)\sin t}{2+\cos t}dt$.

Sol. We have, $f^2(x)=\int_0^x\frac{f(t)\sin t}{2+\cos t}dt$

(Note that $f^2(x)$ being an integral function of a continuous function is continuous and differentiable)

$$2f(x)f'(x)=\frac{f(x)\cdot\sin x}{2+\cos x}$$

Integrating, we get $2f(x)=C-\ln(2+\cos x)$

$\because \quad x=0\Rightarrow f(0)=0\Rightarrow C=\ln 3$

$\therefore \quad f(x)=\frac{1}{2}\ln\frac{3}{2+\cos x}$

● ***Ex. 58*** *Evaluate* $\int_0^{\infty} \frac{\tan^{-1} ax - \tan^{-1} x}{x} dx$*, where a is a parameter.*

Sol. Let $I = \int_0^{\infty} \frac{\tan^{-1} ax - \tan^{-1} x}{x} dx$

$$\therefore \quad \frac{dI}{da} = \int_0^{\infty} \frac{1 \cdot x}{(1+a^2x^2)x} dx = \int_0^{\infty} \frac{dx}{1+a^2x^2}$$

$$= \frac{1}{a^2} \int_0^{\infty} \frac{dx}{x^2 + \frac{1}{a^2}} = \frac{1}{a^2} [a \tan^{-1} x]_0^{\infty} = \frac{\pi}{2a}$$

$$\int dI = \frac{\pi}{2} \int \frac{da}{a} \Rightarrow I = \frac{\pi}{2} \ln a + C$$

When $a = 1$ and $I = 0$ then $C = 0$

Hence, $I = \frac{\pi}{2} \ln a$

● ***Ex. 59*** *Evalute* $\int_0^1 \frac{\ln(1-a^2x^2)}{x^2\sqrt{(1-x^2)}} dx \ (a^2 < 1).$

Sol. Let $I = \int_0^1 \frac{\ln(1-a^2x^2)}{x^2\sqrt{(1-x^2)}} dx, |a| < 1$

$$\therefore \quad \frac{dI}{da} = \int_0^1 \frac{-2ax^2}{(1-a^2x^2)} \cdot \frac{dx}{x^2\sqrt{1-x^2}} \quad \text{(put } x = \sin\theta)$$

$$= \int_0^{\pi/2} \frac{2a\, d\theta}{a^2 \sin^2\theta - 1} = \int_0^{\pi/2} \frac{2a \sec^2\theta\, d\theta}{a^2\tan^2\theta - (1+\tan^2\theta)}$$

$$= -\int_0^{\pi/2} \frac{2a\sec^2\theta\, d\theta}{(1-a^2)\tan^2\theta + 1} \quad \text{(put } \tan\theta = 1)$$

$$= \int_0^{\infty} \frac{2a\, dt}{(1-a^2)t^2+1} \text{ or } -\frac{2a}{(1-a^2)} \int_0^{\infty} \frac{dt}{t^2 + \left(\frac{1}{\sqrt{1-a^2}}\right)^2}$$

$$= -\frac{2a}{\sqrt{1-a^2}} [\tan^{-1} t\sqrt{1-a^2}]_0^{\infty} = -\frac{\pi \cdot 2a}{2\sqrt{1-a^2}} = -\frac{\pi a}{\sqrt{1-a^2}}$$

or $I = \pi\sqrt{1-a^2} + C$

If $a = 0$ and $I = 0$, then $C = -\pi$

$\therefore \quad I = \pi\left(\sqrt{1-a^2} - 1\right)$

● ***Ex. 60*** *Evaluate* $\int_0^{\pi/2} \ln\left(\frac{1+a\sin x}{1-a\sin x}\right) \frac{dx}{\sin x} (|a|<1).$

Sol. Let $I = \int_0^{\pi/2} \ln\left(\frac{1+a\sin x}{1-a\sin x}\right) \frac{dx}{\sin x} (|a|<1)$

$$\therefore \quad \frac{dI}{da} = \int_0^{\pi/2} \frac{2\sin x}{(1-a^2\sin^2 x)} \cdot \frac{dx}{\sin x}$$

$$= \int_0^{\pi/2} \frac{2\sec^2 x}{1+\tan^2 x - a^2\tan^2 x} dx$$

$$= \int_0^{\pi/2} \frac{2\sec^2 x}{(1-a^2)\tan^2 x + 1} dx \quad \text{(put } \tan x = t)$$

$$= \int_0^{\infty} \frac{2\, dt}{(1-a^2)t^2+1} = \frac{2}{(1-a^2)} \int_0^{\infty} \frac{dt}{t^2 + \left(\frac{1}{\sqrt{1-a^2}}\right)^2}$$

$$\Rightarrow \quad = \frac{2}{\sqrt{1-a^2}} [\tan^{-1}(t\sqrt{1-a^2})]_0^{\infty} = \frac{\pi}{\sqrt{1-a^2}}$$

$$\Rightarrow \quad dI = \frac{\pi\, da}{\sqrt{1-a^2}}$$

When $a = 0$ and $I = 0$, then $C = 0$

$\therefore \quad I = \pi \sin^{-1}(a)$

Hence, $I = \pi \sin^{-1} a + C$

Definite Integral Exercise 1 : Single Option Correct Type Questions

1. The value of $\int_0^4 \frac{(y^2-4y+5)\sin(y-2)dy}{(2y^2-8y+1)}$ is

(a) 0 (b) 2
(c) −2 (d) None of these

2. Let $f(x)=x^2+ax+b$ and the only solution of the equation $f(x)=\text{minimum } f(x)$ is $x=0$ and $f(x)=0$ has root α and β, then $\int_\alpha^\beta x^3\,dx$ is equal to

(a) $\frac{1}{4}(\beta^4+\alpha^4)$ (b) $\frac{1}{4}(a^2-b^2)$
(c) 0 (d) None of these

3. $\int_{\pi/2}^x \sqrt{(3-2\sin^2 t)}\,dt+\int_0^y \cos t\,dt=0$, then $\left(\frac{dy}{dx}\right)$ at $x=\pi$ and $y=\pi$ is

(a) $\sqrt{3}$ (b) $-\sqrt{2}$
(c) $-\sqrt{3}$ (d) None of these

4. $\int_{-4}^4 \frac{\sin^{-1}(\sin x)+\cos^{-1}(\cos x)}{(1+x^2)\left(1+\left[\frac{x^2}{17}\right]\right)}dx=\log\left(\frac{(1+x^2)}{a}\right)$ $+b\pi\tan^{-1}\left(\frac{c-\pi}{1+c\pi}\right)$ (where, [·] denotes greatest integer function), then number of ways in which $a-(2b+c)$ distinct object can distributed among $\frac{a-5}{c}$ persons equally, is

(a) $\frac{9!}{(3!)^3}$ (b) $\frac{12!}{(4!)^3}$ (c) $\frac{15!}{(5!)^3}$ (d) $\frac{10!}{(6!)^3}\times 3!$

5. The value of the definite integral $\int_0^\infty \frac{dx}{(1+x^a)(1+x^2)}(a>0)$ is

(a) $\frac{\pi}{4}$ (b) $\frac{\pi}{2}$
(c) π (d) Some function of a

6. The value of the definite integral $\int_0^{3\pi/4}[(1+x)\sin x+(1-x)\cos x]\,dx$ is

(a) $2\tan\frac{3\pi}{8}$ (b) $2\tan\frac{\pi}{4}$
(c) $2\tan\frac{\pi}{8}$ (d) 0

7. Let $C_n=\int_{1/n+1}^{1/n}\frac{\tan^{-1}(nx)}{\sin^{-1}(nx)}dx$, then $\lim_{n\to\infty} n^2\cdot C_n$ is equal to

(a) 1 (b) 0
(c) −1 (d) $\frac{1}{2}$

8. If x satisfies the equation $\left(\int_0^1 \frac{dt}{t^2+2t\cos\alpha+1}\right)x^2-\left(\int_{-3}^3 \frac{t^2\sin 2t}{t^2+1}dt\right)x-2=0\,(0<\alpha<\pi)$, then the value of x is

(a) $\pm\sqrt{\frac{\alpha}{2\sin\alpha}}$ (b) $\pm\sqrt{\frac{2\sin\alpha}{\alpha}}$
(c) $\pm\sqrt{\frac{\alpha}{\sin\alpha}}$ (d) $\pm 2\sqrt{\frac{\sin\alpha}{\alpha}}$

9. If $f(x)=e^{g(x)}$ and $g(x)=\int_2^x \frac{t\,dt}{1+t^4}$, then $f'(2)$ is equal to

(a) 2/17 (b) 0
(c) 1 (d) Cannot be determined

10. If a, b and c are real numbers, then the value of $\lim_{t\to 0}\ln\left(\frac{1}{t}\int_0^t (1+a\sin bx)^{c/x}dx\right)$ equals

(a) abc (b) $\frac{ab}{c}$
(c) $\frac{bc}{a}$ (d) $\frac{ca}{b}$

11. The value of $\lim_{n\to\infty}\sum_{r=1}^{r=4n}\frac{\sqrt{n}}{\sqrt{r}\,(3\sqrt{r}+4\sqrt{n})^2}$ is equal to

(a) $\frac{1}{35}$ (b) $\frac{1}{14}$
(c) $\frac{1}{10}$ (d) $\frac{1}{5}$

12. Let $f(x)=\int_{-1}^x e^{t^2}dt$ and $h(x)=f(1+g(x))$ where $g(x)$ is defined for all x, $g'(x)$ exists for all x, and $g(x)<0$ for $x>0$. If $h'(1)=e$ and $g'(1)=1$, then the possible values which $g(1)$ can take

(a) 0 (b) −1
(c) −2 (d) −4

13. Let $f(x)$ be a function satisfying $f'(x)=f(x)$ with $f(0)=1$ and g be the function satisfying $f(x)+g(x)=x^2$.

The value of the integral $\int_0^1 f(x)\,g(x)\,dx$ is

(a) $e-\frac{1}{2}e^2-\frac{5}{2}$ (b) $e-e^2-3$
(c) $\frac{1}{2}(e-3)$ (d) $e-\frac{1}{2}e^2-\frac{3}{2}$

14. Let $f(x) = \int_0^{g(x)} \frac{dt}{\sqrt{1+t^2}}$, where $g(x) = \int_0^{\cos x} (1 + \sin t^2)\, dt$. Also, $h(x) = e^{-|x|}$ and $f(x) = x^2 \sin \frac{1}{x}$, if $x \neq 0$ and $f(0) = 0$, then $f'\left(\frac{\pi}{2}\right)$ is equal to

(a) $l'(0)$ (b) $h'(0^-)$
(c) $h'(0^+)$ (d) $\lim_{x \to 0} \frac{1 - \cos x}{x \sin x}$

15. For $f(x) = x^4 + |x|$, let $I_1 = \int_0^{\pi} f(\cos x)\, dx$ and $I_2 = \int_0^{\pi/2} f(\sin x)\, dx$, then $\frac{I_1}{I_2}$ has the value equal to

(a) 1 (b) 1/2
(c) 2 (d) 4

16. Let f be a positive function. Let $I_1 = \int_{1-k}^{k} (x) f(x(1-x))\, dx$; $I_2 = \int_{1-k}^{k} f(x(1-x))\, dx$, where $2k - 1 > 0$. Then, $\frac{I_2}{I_1}$ is

(a) k (b) 1/2
(c) 1 (d) 2

17. Suppose that the quadratic function $f(x) = ax^2 + bx + c$ is non-negative on the interval $[-1, 1]$. Then, the area under the graph of f over the interval $[-1, 1]$ and the X-axis is given by the formula

(a) $A = f(-1) + f(1)$
(b) $A = f\left(-\frac{1}{2}\right) + f\left(\frac{1}{2}\right)$
(c) $A = \frac{1}{2}[f(-1) + 2f(0) + f(1)]$
(d) $A = \frac{1}{3}[f(-1) + 4f(0) + f(1)]$

18. Let $I(a) = \int_0^{\pi} \left(\frac{x}{a} + a \sin x\right)^2 dx$, where '$a$' is positive real.
The value of 'a' for which $I(a)$ attains its minimum value, is

(a) $\sqrt{\pi\sqrt{\frac{2}{3}}}$ (b) $\sqrt{\pi\sqrt{\frac{3}{2}}}$ (c) $\sqrt{\frac{\pi}{16}}$ (d) $\sqrt{\frac{\pi}{13}}$

19. The set of values of 'a' which satisfy the equation $\int_0^2 (t - \log_2 a)\, dt = \log_2 \left(\frac{4}{a^2}\right)$, is

(a) $a \in R$ (b) $a \in R^+$
(c) $a < 2$ (d) $a > 2$

20. $\lim_{x \to \infty} \left(x^3 \int_{-1/x}^{1/x} \frac{\ln(1+t^2)}{1+e^t}\, dt \right)$ is equal to

(a) $\frac{1}{3}$ (b) $\frac{2}{3}$
(c) 1 (d) 0

21. The value of $\sqrt{\pi\left(\int_0^{2008} x\,|\sin \pi x|\, dx\right)}$ is equal to

(a) $\sqrt{2008}$ (b) $\pi\sqrt{2008}$ (c) 1004 (d) 2008

22. $\lim_{n \to \infty} \sum_{k=1}^{n} \frac{n}{n^2 + k^2 x^2}$, $x > 0$ is equal to

(a) $x \tan^{-1}(x)$ (b) $\tan^{-1}(x)$
(c) $\frac{\tan^{-1}(x)}{x}$ (d) $\frac{\tan^{-1}(x)}{x^2}$

23. Let $a > 0$ and $f(x)$ is monotonic increasing such that $f(0) = 0$ and $f(a) = b$, then $\int_0^a f(x)\, dx + \int_0^b f^{-1}(x)\, dx$ is equal to

(a) $a + b$ (b) $ab + b$ (c) $ab + a$ (d) ab

24. If $\int_{-1/\sqrt{3}}^{1/\sqrt{3}} \frac{x^4}{1-x^4} \cos^{-1} \frac{2x}{1+x^2}\, dx = k \int_0^{1/\sqrt{3}} \frac{x^4}{1-x^4}$, then '$k$' is equal to

(a) π (b) 2π (c) 2 (d) 1

25. $\int_0^{\infty} f\left(x + \frac{1}{x}\right) \cdot \frac{\ln x}{x}\, dx$ is equal to

(a) 0 (b) 1
(c) $\frac{1}{2}$ (d) Cannot be evaluated

26. $\lim_{\lambda \to 0} \left(\int_0^1 (1+x)^{\lambda}\, dx\right)^{1/\lambda}$ is equal to

(a) $2 \ln 2$ (b) $\frac{4}{e}$ (c) $\ln \frac{4}{e}$ (d) 4

27. If $g(x)$ is the inverse of $f(x)$ and $f(x)$ has domain $x \in [1, 5]$, where $f(1) = 2$ and $f(5) = 10$, then the values of $\int_1^5 f(x)\, dx + \int_2^{10} g(y)\, dy$ is equal to

(a) 48 (b) 64 (c) 71 (d) 52

28. The value of the definite integral $\int_0^{\pi/2} \sin x \sin 2x \sin 3x\, dx$ is equal to

(a) $\frac{1}{3}$ (b) $-\frac{2}{3}$ (c) $-\frac{1}{3}$ (d) $\frac{1}{6}$

29. If $f(x) = \int_0^x (f(t))^2\, dt$, $f: R \to R$ be differentiable function and $f(g(x))$ is differentiable function at $x = a$, then

(a) $g(x)$ must be differentiable at $x = a$
(b) $g(x)$ may be non-differentiable at $x = a$
(c) $g(x)$ may be discontinuous at $x = a$
(d) None of the above

30. The number of integral solutions of the equation $4\int_0^{\infty} \frac{\ln t\, dt}{x^2 + t^2} - \pi \ln 2 = 0$; $x > 0$, is

(a) 0 (b) 1 (c) 2 (d) 3

31. $\int_0^{16n^2/\pi} \cos \frac{\pi}{2}\left[\frac{x\pi}{n}\right] dx$ is equal to

(a) 0 (b) 1 (c) 2 (d) 3

32. If $\int_{-2}^{-1} (ax^2 - 5)\, dx = 0$ and $5 + \int_{1}^{2} (bx + c)\, dx = 0$, then

(a) $ax^2 - bx + c = 0$ has atleast one root in $(1, 2)$
(b) $ax^2 - bx + c = 0$ has atleast one root in $(-2, -1)$
(c) $ax^2 + bx + c = 0$ has atleast one root in $(-2, -1)$
(d) None of the above

33. The value of $\int_0^6 (\sqrt{x + \sqrt{12x - 36}} + \sqrt{x - \sqrt{12x - 36}})\, dx$ is equal to

(a) $6\sqrt{3}$ (b) $4\sqrt{3}$
(c) $12\sqrt{3}$ (d) None of these

34. If $I_n = \int_{-n}^{n} (\{x+1\}\{x^2+2\} + \{x^2+3\}\{x^3+4\})\, dx$, (where, {} denotes the fractional part), then I_1 is equal to

(a) $-\frac{1}{3}$ (b) $-\frac{2}{3}$ (c) $\frac{1}{3}$ (d) None of these

35. Let $I_n = \int_0^{\pi/2} \frac{\sin (2n-1)x}{\sin x}\, dx$, $J_n = \int_0^{\pi/2} \frac{\sin^2 nx}{\sin^2 x}$, $n \in N$, then

(a) $J_{n+1} - J_n = I_n$ (b) $J_{n+1} - J_n = I_{n+1}$
(c) $J_{n+1} + J_n = J_n$ (d) $J_{n+1} - J_{n+1} = J_n$

Definite Integral Exercise 2 :
More than One Option Correct Type Questions

36. If $f(x) = [\sin^{-1} (\sin 2x)]$ (where, [] denotes the greatest integer function), then

(a) $\int_0^{\pi/2} f(x)\, dx = \frac{\pi}{2} - \sin^{-1} (\sin 1)$
(b) $f(x)$ is periodic with period π
(c) $\lim_{x \to \frac{\pi}{2}} f(x) = -1$
(d) None of the above

37. Which of the following definite integral(s) vanishes?

(a) $\int_0^{\pi/2} \ln (\cot x)\, dx$ (b) $\int_0^{2\pi} \sin^3 x\, dx$
(c) $\int_{1/e}^{e} \frac{dx}{x (\ln x)^{1/3}}$ (d) $\int_0^{\pi} \sqrt{\frac{1 + \cos 2x}{2}}\, dx$

38. The equation $10x^4 - 3x^2 - 1 = 0$ has

(a) atleast one root in $(-1, 0)$
(b) atleast one root in $(0, 1)$
(c) atleast two roots in $(-1, 1)$
(d) no root in $(-1, 1)$

39. Suppose $I_1 = \int_0^{\pi/2} \cos (\pi \sin^2 x)\, dx$;

$I_2 = \int_0^{\pi/2} \cos (2\pi \sin^2 x)\, dx$ and $I_3 = \int_0^{\pi/2} \cos (\pi \sin x)\, dx$, then

(a) $I_1 = 0$ (b) $I_2 + I_3 = 0$
(c) $I_1 + I_2 + I_3 = 0$ (d) $I_2 = I_3$

40. Let $f(x) = \int_{-1}^{1} (1 - |t|) \cos (xt)\, dt$, then which of the following holds true?

(a) $f(0)$ is not defined
(b) $\lim_{x \to 0} f(x)$ exists and is equal to 2
(c) $\lim_{x \to 0} f(x)$ exists and is equal to 1
(d) $f(x)$ is continuous at $x = 0$

41. The function f is continuous and has the property $f(f(x)) = 1 - x$ for all $x \in [0, 1]$ and $J = \int_0^1 f(x)\, dx$, then

(a) $f\left(\frac{1}{4}\right) + f\left(\frac{3}{4}\right) = 1$
(b) the value of J equals to 1/2
(c) $f\left(\frac{1}{3}\right) \cdot f\left(\frac{2}{3}\right) = 1$
(d) $\int_0^{\pi/2} \frac{\sin x\, dx}{(\sin x + \cos x)^3}$ has the same value as J

42. Let $f(x)$ is a real valued function defined by $f(x) = x^2 + x^2 \int_{-1}^{1} tf(t)\, dt + x^3 \int_{-1}^{1} f(t)\, dt$, then which of the following hold(s) good?

(a) $\int_{-1}^{1} t f(t)\, dt = \frac{10}{11}$ (b) $f(1) + f(-1) = \frac{30}{11}$
(c) $\int_{-1}^{1} t f(t)\, dt > \int_{-1}^{1} f(t)\, dt$ (d) $f(1) - f(-1) = \frac{20}{11}$

43. Let $f(x)$ and $g(x)$ be differentiable functions such that $f(x) + \int_0^x g(t)\, dt = \sin x (\cos x - \sin x)$ and $(f'(x))^2 + (g(x))^2 = 1$, then $f(x)$ and $g(x)$ respectively, can be

(a) $\frac{1}{2} \sin 2x$, $\sin 2x$ (b) $\frac{\cos 2x}{2}$, $\cos 2x$
(c) $\frac{1}{2} \sin 2x$, $-\sin 2x$ (d) $-\sin^2 x$, $\cos 2x$

44. Let $f(x) = \int_{-x}^{x} (t \sin at + bt + c)dt$, where a, b, c are non-zero real numbers, then $\lim_{x \to 0} \frac{f(x)}{x}$ is

(a) independent of a
(b) independent of a and b, and has the value equals to c
(c) independent a, b and c
(d) dependent only on c

45. Let $L = \lim_{n \to \infty} \int_a^{\infty} \frac{n\, dx}{1 + n^2 x^2}$, where $a \in R$, then L can be

(a) π (b) $\pi/2$ (c) 0 (d) 1

Definite Integral Exercise 3 : Passage Based Questions

Passage I

(Q. Nos. 46 to 48)

Suppose $\lim_{x \to 0} \dfrac{\int_0^x \frac{t^2\, dt}{(a+t^r)^{1/p}}}{bx - \sin x} = l$, *where* $p \in N, p \geq 2, a > 0, r > 0$ *and* $b \neq 0$.

46. If l exists and is non-zero, then

(a) $b > 1$ (b) $0 < b < 1$
(c) $b < 0$ (d) $b = 1$

47. If $p = 3$ and $l = 1$, then the value of 'a' is equal to

(a) 8 (b) 3
(c) 6 (d) 3/2

48. If $p = 2$ and $a = 9$ and l exists, then the value of l is equal to

(a) $\frac{3}{2}$ (b) $\frac{2}{3}$ (c) $\frac{1}{3}$ (d) $\frac{7}{9}$

Passage II

(Q. Nos. 49 to 51)

Suppose $f(x)$ *and* $g(x)$ *are two continuous functions defined for* $0 \leq x \leq 1$. *Given,* $f(x) = \int_0^1 e^{x+1} \cdot f(t)\, dt$ *and* $g(x) = \int_0^1 e^{x+t} \cdot g(t)\, dt + x$.

49. The value of $f(1)$ equals

(a) 0 (b) 1
(c) e^{-1} (d) e

50. The value of $g(0) - f(0)$ equals

(a) $\frac{2}{3-e^2}$ (b) $\frac{3}{e^2-2}$ (c) $\frac{1}{e^2-1}$ (d) 0

51. The value of $\frac{g(0)}{g(2)}$ equals

(a) 0 (b) $\frac{1}{3}$ (c) $\frac{1}{e^2}$ (d) $\frac{2}{e^2}$

Passage III

(Q. Nos. 52 to 54)

We are given the curves $y = \int_{-\infty}^{x} f(t) dt$ *through the point* $\left(0, \frac{1}{2}\right)$ *any* $y = f(x)$, *where* $f(x) > 0$ *and* $f(x)$ *is differentiable,* $\forall x \in R$ *through* $(0, 1)$. *Tangents drawn to both the curves at the points with equal abscissae intersect on the same point on the X-axis.*

52. The number of solutions $f(x) = 2ex$ is equal to

(a) 0 (b) 1
(c) 2 (d) None of these

53. $\lim_{x \to \infty} (f(x))^{f(-x)}$ is

(a) 3 (b) 6
(c) 1 (d) None of these

54. The function $f(x)$ is

(a) increasing for all x (b) non-monotonic
(c) decreasing for all x (d) None of these

Passage IV

(Q. Nos. 55 to 57)

$f(x) = \int_0^x (4t^4 - at^3)\, dt$ *and* $g(x)$ *is quadratic satisfying* $g(0) + 6 = g'(0) - c = g''(c) + 2b = 0$. $y = h(x)$ *and* $y = g(x)$ *intersect in 4 distinct points with abscissae* x_i; $i = 1, 2, 3, 4$ *such that* $\sum \frac{i}{x_i} = 8, a, b, c \in R^+$ *and* $h(x) = f'(x)$.

55. Abscissae of point of intersection are in

(a) AP (b) GP
(c) HP (d) None of these

56. 'a' is equal to

(a) 6 (b) 8 (c) 20 (d) 12

57. 'c' is equal to

(a) 25 (b) 25/2 (c) 25/4 (d) 25/8

Passage V

(Q. Nos. 58 to 60)

Let $y = \int_{u(x)}^{v(x)} f(t)\, dt$, *let us define* $\frac{dy}{dx}$ *as* $\frac{dy}{dx}$ $= v'(x)\, f^2(v(x)) - u'(x)\, f^2(u(x))$ *and the equation of the tangent at* (a, b) *and* $y - b = \left(\frac{dy}{dx}\right)_{(a,b)} (x - a)$.

58. If $y = \int_x^{x^2} t^2\, dt$, then the equation of tangent at $x = 1$ is

(a) $x + y = 1$ (b) $y = x - 1$
(c) $y = x$ (d) $y = x + 1$

59. If $y = \int_{x^2}^{x^4} (\ln t) dt$, then $\lim_{x \to 0^+} \frac{dy}{dx}$ is equal to

(a) 0 (b) 1 (c) 2 (d) −1

60. If $f(x) = \int_1^x e^{t^2/2} (1 - t^2)\, dt$, then $\frac{d}{dx} f(x)$ at $x = 1$ is

(a) 0 (b) 1
(c) 2 (d) −1

Passage VI (Q. Nos. 61 to 62)

Consider $f:(0,\infty)\to\left(-\frac{\pi}{2},\frac{\pi}{2}\right)$*, defined as* $f(x)=\tan^{-1}\left(\frac{\log_e x}{(\log_e x)^2+1}\right)$.

61. The about function can be classified as
(a) Injective but nor surjective
(b) Surjective but not bijective
(c) Neither injective nor surjective
(d) Both injective and surjective

62. The value of $\int_0^\infty [\tan]\,dx$ is equal to (where, [·] denotes the greatest integer function)
(a) $-\frac{\pi}{2}$ (b) $\frac{\pi}{2}$
(c) -1 (d) 1

Definite Integral Exercise 4 : Matching Type Questions

63. Let $\lim_{T\to\infty}\frac{1}{T}\int_0^T(\sin x+\sin ax)^2\,dx=L$, then

	Column I		Column II
(A)	For $a=0$, the value of L is	(p)	0
(B)	For $a=1$, the value of L is	(q)	1/2
(C)	For $a=-1$, the value of L is	(r)	1
(D)	For $a\in R-\{-1,0,1\}$, the value of L is	(s)	2

64. Let $f(\theta)=\int_0^1(x+\sin\theta)^2\,dx$ and $g(\theta)=\int_0^1(x+\cos\theta)^2\,dx$ where $\theta\in[0,2\pi]$. The quantity $f(\theta)-g(\theta)$, $\forall\,\theta$ in the interval given in column I, is

	Column I		Column II
(A)	$\left(\frac{\pi}{4},\frac{3\pi}{4}\right)$	(p)	negative
(B)	$\left(\frac{3\pi}{4},\pi\right]$	(q)	positive
(C)	$\left[\frac{3\pi}{2},\frac{7\pi}{4}\right)$	(r)	non-negative
(D)	$\left(0,\frac{\pi}{4}\right)\cup\left(\frac{7\pi}{4},2\pi\right)$	(s)	non-positive

65. Match the following.

	Column I		Column II
(A)	$\int_0^1(1+2008\,x^{2008})\,e^{x^{2008}}\,dx$ equals	(p)	e^{-1}
(B)	The value of the definite integral $\int_0^1 e^{-x^2}\,dx+\int_1^{1/e}\sqrt{-\ln x}\,dx$ is equal to	(q)	$e^{-1/4}$
(C)	$\lim_{n\to\infty}\left(\frac{1^1\cdot2^2\cdot3^3\ldots(n-1)^{n-1}\cdot n^n}{n^{1+2+3+\ldots+n}}\right)^{\frac{1}{n^2}}$ equals	(r)	$e^{1/2}$
		(s)	e

66. Match the following.

	Column I		Column II
(A)	If $f(x)=\int_0^{g(x)}\frac{dt}{\sqrt{1+t^3}}$, where $g(x)=\int_0^{\cos x}(1+\sin t^2)\,dt$, then value of $f'\left(\frac{\pi}{2}\right)$ is	(p)	-2
(B)	If $f(x)$ is a non-zero differentiable function such that $\int_0^x f(t)\,dt=\{f(x)\}^2$, $\forall x\in R$, then $f(2)$ is equal to	(q)	2
(C)	If $\int_a^b(2+x-x^2)\,dx$ is maximum, then $a+b$ is equal to	(r)	1
(D)	If $\lim_{x\to0}\left(\frac{\sin 2x}{x^3}+a+\frac{b}{x^2}\right)=0$, then $3a+b$ has the value	(s)	-1

Definite Integral Exercise 5 :
Single Integer Answer Type Questions

67. If $f(x)=\sum_{n=1} \frac{\sin nx}{4^n}$ and $\int_0^{\pi} f(x)\,dx=\log\left(\frac{m}{n}\right)$, then the value of $(m+n)$ is ...

68. The value of $I=\int_{-\pi/2}^{\pi/2} \frac{\cos x\,dx}{1+2[\sin^{-1}(\sin x)]}$ (where, [·] denotes greatest integer function) is ...

69. If $f(x)=\frac{1}{\pi}\int_0^{\pi/2} \frac{\sin^2 n\theta}{\sin^2\theta}\,d\theta\,(n\in N)$, then the value of $\frac{f(15)+f(13)}{f(15)-f(a)}$ ...

70. Let $f(x)=\int_{-2}^{x} e^{(1+t)^2}\,dt$ and $g(x)=(h/x)$, where $h(x)$ is defined for all $x\in h$. If $g^{1/2}=e^4$ and $h'(2)=1$. Then, absolute value of sun for all possible value of $h(2)$, is ...

71. If $=\int_0^{\pi/2} \sin x\cdot\log(\sin x)dx=\log\left(\frac{K}{e}\right)$. Then, the value of K is ...

Definite Integrals Exercise 6 :
Questions Asked in Previous 10 Years' Exams

(i) JEE Advanced & IIT-JEE

72. The value of $\int_{-\pi/2}^{\pi/2} \frac{x^2\cos x}{1+e^x}\,dx$ is equal to **[Only One Correct Option 2016]**

(a) $\frac{\pi^2}{4}-2$ (b) $\frac{\pi^2}{4}+2$

(c) $\pi^2-e^{-\pi/2}$ (d) $\pi^2+e^{\pi/2}$

73. The total number of distincts $x\in[0,1]$ for which $\int_0^x \frac{t^2}{1+t^4}\,dt=2x-1$ is **[Integer Type 2016]**

74. Let $f(x)=7\tan^8 x+7\tan^6 x-3\tan^4 x-3\tan^2 x$ for all $x\in\left(-\frac{\pi}{2},\frac{\pi}{2}\right)$. Then, the correct expression(s) is/are **[More than One Correct Option 2015]**

(a) $\int_0^{\pi/4} x f(x)\,dx=\frac{1}{12}$ (b) $\int_0^{\pi/4} f(x)\,dx=0$

(c) $\int_0^{\pi/4} x f(x)\,dx=\frac{1}{6}$ (d) $\int_0^{\pi/4} f(x)\,dx=1$

75. Let $f'(x)=\frac{192x^3}{2+\sin^4\pi x}$ for all $x\in R$ with $f\left(\frac{1}{2}\right)=0$. If $m\le\int_{1/2}^{1} f(x)\,dx\le M$, then the possible values of m and M are **[More than One Correct Option 2015]**

(a) $m=13, M=24$ (b) $m=\frac{1}{4}, M=\frac{1}{2}$

(c) $m=-11, M=0$ (d) $m=1, M=12$

76. The option(s) with the values of a and L that satisfy the equation $\frac{\int_0^{4\pi} e^t(\sin^6 at+\cos^4 at)dt}{\int_0^{\pi} e^t(\sin^6 at+\cos^4 at)dt}=L$, is/are **[More than One Correct Option 2015]**

(a) $a=2, L=\frac{e^{4\pi}-1}{e^{\pi}-1}$ (b) $a=2, L=\frac{e^{4\pi}+1}{e^{\pi}+1}$

(c) $a=4, L=\frac{e^{4\pi}-1}{e^{\pi}-1}$ (d) $a=4, L=\frac{e^{4\pi}+1}{e^{\pi}+1}$

- **Directions** (Q. Nos. 77 to 78) Let $F:R\to R$ be a thrice differentiable function. Suppose that $F(1)=0, F(3)=-4$ and $F'(x)<0$ for all $x\in(1,3)$. Let $f(x)=xF(x)$ for all $x\in R$.

77. The correct statement(s) is/are **[Passage Based Questions 2015]**

(a) $f'(1)<0$

(b) $f(2)<0$

(c) $f'(x)\ne 0$ for any $x\in(1,3)$

(d) $f'(x)=0$ for some $x\in(1,3)$

78. If $\int_1^3 x^2F'(x)\,dx=-12$ and $\int_1^3 x^3F''(x)\,dx=40$, then the correct expression(s) is/are

(a) $9f'(3)+f'(1)-32=0$ (b) $\int_1^3 f(x)\,dx=12$

(c) $9f'(3)-f'(1)+32=0$ (d) $\int_1^3 f(x)\,dx=-12$

79. Let $f : R \to R$ be a function defined by $f(x) = \begin{cases} [x], & x \le 2 \\ 0, & x > 2 \end{cases}$, where $[x]$ denotes the greatest integer less than or equal to x. If $I = \int_{-1}^{2} \frac{x f(x^2)}{2 + f(x+1)} dx$, then the value of $(4I - 1)$ is **[Integer Answer Type 2015]**

80. If $\alpha = \int_0^1 (e^{9x + 3\tan^{-1} x}) \left(\frac{12 + 9x^2}{1 + x^2} \right) dx$, where $\tan^{-1} x$ takes only principal values, then value of $\left(\log_e |1 + \alpha| - \frac{3\pi}{4} \right)$ is **[Integer Answer Type 2015]**

81. The integral $\int_{\pi/4}^{\pi/2} (2 \operatorname{cosec} x)^{17} dx$ is equal to **[Only One Correct Option 2014]**

(a) $\int_0^{\log(1+\sqrt{2})} 2(e^u + e^{-u})^{16} du$ (b) $\int_0^{\log(1+\sqrt{2})} (e^u + e^{-u})^{17} du$

(c) $\int_0^{\log(1+\sqrt{2})} (e^u - e^{-u})^{17} du$ (d) $\int_0^{\log(1+\sqrt{2})} 2(e^u - e^{-u})^{16} du$

82. Let $f : [0, 2] \to R$ be a function which is continuous on $[0, 2]$ and is differentiable on $(0, 2)$ with $f(0) = 1$. Let $F(x) = \int_0^{x^2} f(\sqrt{t})\, dt$, for $x \in [0, 2]$. If $F'(x) = f'(x), \forall x \in (0, 2)$, then $F(2)$ equals **[Only One Correct Option 2014]**

(a) $e^2 - 1$ (b) $e^4 - 1$
(c) $e - 1$ (d) e^4

83. Match the conditions/expressions in Column I with statement in Column II. **[Matching Type 2014]**

	Column I		Column II
A.	$\int_{-1}^{1} \frac{dx}{1+x^2}$	p.	$\frac{1}{2}\log\left(\frac{2}{3}\right)$
B.	$\int_0^1 \frac{dx}{\sqrt{1-x^2}}$	q.	$2\log\left(\frac{2}{3}\right)$
C.	$\int_2^3 \frac{dx}{1-x^2}$	r.	$\frac{\pi}{3}$
D.	$\int_1^2 \frac{dx}{x\sqrt{x^2-1}}$	s.	$\frac{\pi}{2}$

84. Match List I with List II and select the correct answer using codes given below the lists. **[Matching Type 2014]**

	List I		List II
A.	The number of polynomials $f(x)$ with non-negative integer coefficients of degree ≤ 2, satisfying $f(0) = 0$ and $\int_0^1 f(x)\, dx = 1$, is	p.	8
B.	The number of points in the interval $[-\sqrt{13}, \sqrt{13}]$ at which $f(x) = \sin(x^2) + \cos(x^2)$ attains its maximum value, is	q.	2
C.	$\int_{-2}^{2} \frac{3x^2}{1 + e^x} dx$ equals	r.	4
D.	$\dfrac{\left(\int_{-1/2}^{1/2} \cos 2x \log\left(\frac{1+x}{1-x}\right) dx \right)}{\left(\int_0^{1/2} \cos 2x \log\left(\frac{1+x}{1-x}\right) dx \right)}$ equals	s.	0

Codes

	A	B	C	D		A	B	C	D
(a)	r	q	s	p	(b)	q	r	s	p
(c)	r	q	p	s	(d)	q	r	p	s

85. The value of $\int_0^1 4x^3 \left\{ \frac{d^2}{dx^2} (1 - x^2)^5 \right\} dx$ is **[Integer Answer Type 2014]**

86. The value of the integral $\int_{-\pi/2}^{\pi/2} \left(x^2 + \log \frac{\pi - x}{\pi + x} \right) \cos x\, dx$ is **[Only One Correct Option 2012]**

(a) 0 (b) $\frac{\pi^2}{2} - 4$
(c) $\frac{\pi^2}{2} + 4$ (d) $\frac{\pi^2}{2}$

87. The value of $\int_{\sqrt{\log 2}}^{\sqrt{\log 3}} \frac{x \sin x^2}{\sin x^2 + \sin(\log 6 - x^2)} dx$ is **[Integer Answer Type 2011]**

(a) $\frac{1}{4}\log\frac{3}{2}$ (b) $\frac{1}{2}\log\frac{3}{2}$
(c) $\log\frac{3}{2}$ (d) $\frac{1}{6}\log\frac{3}{2}$

88. Let $f : [1, \infty] \to [2, \infty]$ be differentiable function such that $f(1) = 2$. If $6\int_1^x f(x) = dt = 3x\, f(x) - x^3, \forall\, x \ge 1$ then the value of $f(2)$ is .... **[Integer Answer Type 2011]**

89. The value(s) of $\int_0^1 \frac{x^4 (1-x)^4}{1+x^2} dx$ is (are) **[Only One Correct Option 2010]**

(a) $\frac{22}{7} - \pi$ (b) $\frac{2}{105}$
(c) 0 (d) $\frac{71}{15} - \frac{3\pi}{2}$

90. For $a \in R$ (the set of all real numbers), $a \ne -1$,

$$\lim_{n \to \infty} \frac{(1^a + 2^a + \ldots + n^a)}{(n+1)^{a-1} [(na+1) + (na+2) + \ldots + (na+n)]} = \frac{1}{60}.$$

Then, a is equal to **[More than One Correct Option 2010]**

(a) 5 (b) 7
(c) $\frac{-15}{2}$ (d) $\frac{-17}{2}$

- **Directions** (Q Nos. 91 to 92) Let $f(x)=(1-x)^2\sin^2 x+x^2$, $\forall x\in R$ and $g(x)=\int_1^x\left(\frac{2(t-1)}{t+1}-\ln t\right)f(t)\,dt\ \forall x\in(1,\infty)$.

[Passage Based Questions 2010]

91. Consider the statements

P: There exists some $x\in R$ such that, $f(x)+2x=2(1+x^2)$.

Q: There exists some $x\in R$ such that $2f(x)+1=2x(1+x)$.

Then,

(a) both P and Q are true (b) P is true and Q is false

(c) P is false and Q is true (d) both P and Q are false

92. Which of the following is true?

(a) g is increasing on $(1,\infty)$

(b) g is decreasing on $(1,\infty)$

(c) g is increasing on $(1, 2)$ and decreasing on $(2,\infty)$

(d) g is decreasing on $(1, 2)$ and increasing on $(2,\infty)$

93. For any real number x, let $[x]$ denotes the largest integer less than or equal to x. Let f be a real valued function defined on the interval $[-10, 10]$ by

$$f(x)=\begin{cases}x-[x[, & \text{if } f(x) \text{ is odd}\\ 1+[x[-x, & \text{if } f(x) \text{ is even}\end{cases}$$

Then, the value of $\frac{\pi^2}{10}\int_{-10}^{10} f(x)\cos\pi x\,dx$ is...... **[Integer Answer Type 2010]**

94. Let f be a non-negative function defined on the interval $[0, 1]$. If $\int_0^x\sqrt{1-(f'(t))^2}\,dt=\int_0^x f(t)\,dt$, $0\le x\le 1$ and $f(0)=0$, then **[Only One Option Correct 2009]**

(a) $f\left(\frac{1}{2}\right)<\frac{1}{2}$ and $f\left(\frac{1}{3}\right)>\frac{1}{3}$ (b) $f\left(\frac{1}{2}\right)>\frac{1}{2}$ and $f\left(\frac{1}{3}\right)>\frac{1}{3}$

(c) $f\left(\frac{1}{2}\right)<\frac{1}{2}$ and $f\left(\frac{1}{3}\right)<\frac{1}{3}$ (d) $f\left(\frac{1}{2}\right)>\frac{1}{2}$ and $f\left(\frac{1}{3}\right)<\frac{1}{3}$

95. If $I_n=\int_{-\pi}^{\pi}\frac{\sin nx}{(1+\pi^x)\sin x}\,dx$, $n=0,1,2,\ldots$, then **[More than One Correct 2009]**

(a) $I_n=I_{n+2}$ (b) $\sum_{m=1}^{10} I_{2m+1}=10\pi$

(c) $\sum_{m=1}^{10} I_{2m}=0$ (d) $I_n=I_{n+1}$

96. Let $S_n=\sum_{k=0}^{n}\frac{n}{n^2+kn+k^2}$ and $T_n=\sum_{k=0}^{n-1}\frac{n}{n^2+kn+k^2}$, for $n=1,2,3,\ldots$, then **[More than One Correct Option 2008]**

(a) $S_n<\frac{\pi}{3\sqrt{3}}$ (b) $S_n>\frac{\pi}{3\sqrt{3}}$

(c) $T_n<\frac{\pi}{3\sqrt{3}}$ (d) $T_n>\frac{\pi}{3\sqrt{3}}$

(ii) JEE Main & AIEEE

97. The integral $\int_{\pi/4}^{3\pi/4}\frac{dx}{1+\cos x}$ is equal to **[2017 JEE Main]**

(a) -1 (b) -2

(c) 2 (d) 4

98. Let $I_n=\int\tan^n x\,dx,(n>1)$. $I_4+I_6=a\tan^5 x+bx^5+C$, where C is a constant of integration, then the ordered pair (a, b) is equal to **[2017 JEE Main]**

(a) $\left(-\frac{1}{5},0\right)$ (b) $\left(-\frac{1}{5},1\right)$ (c) $\left(\frac{1}{5},0\right)$ (d) $\left(\frac{1}{5},-1\right)$

99. $\lim_{n\to\infty}\left[\frac{(n+1)(n+2)\ldots 3n}{n^{2n}}\right]^{1/n}$ is equal to **[2016 JEE Main]**

(a) $\frac{18}{e^4}$ (b) $\frac{27}{e^2}$ (c) $\frac{9}{e^2}$ (d) $3\log 3-2$

100. The integral $\int_2^4\frac{\log x^2}{\log x^2+\log(36-12x+x^2)}dx$ is equal to **[2015 JEE Main]**

(a) 2 (b) 4 (c) 1 (d) 6

101. The integral $\int_0^{\pi}\sqrt{1+4\sin^2\frac{x}{2}-4\sin\frac{x}{2}}\,dx$ is equal to **[2014 JEE Main]**

(a) $\pi-4$ (b) $\frac{2\pi}{3}-4-4\sqrt{3}$

(c) $4\sqrt{3}-4$ (d) $4\sqrt{3}-4-\pi/3$

102. Statement I The value of the integral $\int_{\pi/6}^{\pi/3}\frac{dx}{1+\sqrt{\tan x}}$ is equal to $\pi/6$. **[2013 JEE Main]**

Statement II $\int_a^b f(x)\,dx=\int_a^b f(a+b-x)\,dx$

(a) Statement I is true; Statement II is true; Statement II is a true explanation for Statement I

(b) Statement I is true; Statement II is true; Statement II is not a true explanation for Statement I

(c) Statement I is true; Statement II is false

(d) Statement I is false; Statement II is true

103. The intercepts on X-axis made by tangents to the curve, $y=\int_0^x|t|\,dt$, $x\in R$, which are parallel to the line $y=2x$, are equal to **[2013 JEE Main]**

(a) ± 1 (b) ± 2

(c) ± 3 (d) ± 4

104. If $g(x)=\int_0^x\cos 4t\,dt$, then $g(x+\pi)$ equals **[2012 AIEEE]**

(a) $\frac{g(x)}{g(\pi)}$ (b) $g(x)+g(\pi)$ (c) $g(x)-g(\pi)$ (d) $g(x)\cdot g(\pi)$

105. The value of $\int_0^1\frac{8\log(1+x)}{1+x^2}dx$ is **[2011 AIEEE]**

(a) $\frac{\pi}{8}\log 2$ (b) $\frac{\pi}{2}\log 2$ (c) $\log 2$ (d) $\pi\log 2$

106. For $x \in \left(0, \dfrac{5\pi}{2}\right)$, define $f(x) = \int_0^x \sqrt{t} \sin t \, dt$. Then, f has **[2011 AIEEE]**

(a) local minimum at π and 2π
(b) local minimum at π and local maximum at 2π
(c) local maximum at π and local minimum at 2π
(d) local maximum at π and 2π

107. Let $p(x)$ be a function defined on R such that $\lim_{x \to \infty} \dfrac{f(3x)}{f(x)} = 1, p'(x) = p'(1-x)$, for all $x \in [0, 1]$, $p(0) = 1$ and $p(1) = 41$. Then, $\int_0^1 p(x)\, dx$ equals **[2010 AIEEE]**

(a) $\sqrt{41}$ (b) 21
(c) 41 (d) 42

108. $\int_0^{\pi} [\cot x]\, dx$, [ ] denotes the greatest integer function, is equal to **[2009 AIEEE]**

(a) $\dfrac{\pi}{2}$ (b) 1
(c) -1 (d) $-\dfrac{\pi}{2}$

109. Let $I = \int_0^1 \dfrac{\sin x}{\sqrt{x}} dx$ and $J = \int_0^1 \dfrac{\cos x}{\sqrt{x}} dx$.

Then, which one of the following is true? **[2008 AIEEE]**

(a) $I > \dfrac{2}{3}$ and $J > 2$ (b) $I < \dfrac{2}{3}$ and $J < 2$
(c) $I < \dfrac{2}{3}$ and $J > 2$ (d) $I > \dfrac{2}{3}$ and $J < 2$

Answers

Exercise for Session 1

1. $\dfrac{\pi + 2}{8}$ 2. 1 3. 2 4. $\dfrac{2}{3} - \dfrac{\sqrt{3}}{4}$ 5. $\dfrac{4\sqrt{2}}{3}$
6. -1 7. $\dfrac{1}{20} \log_e 3$ 8. π 9. $\dfrac{\pi}{2}(b - a)$
10. $\dfrac{\pi}{2\sqrt{2}} + \dfrac{1}{\sqrt{2}} \log(\sqrt{2} - 1)$ 11. $\dfrac{-\pi}{2}$ 12. $1 + \left(\dfrac{\pi}{4} - \sqrt{2}\right) e^{1/\sqrt{2}}$
13. 10 ! 14. (d) 15. (d)

Exercise for Session 2

1. (c) 2. (a) 3. (a) 4. (c) 5. (a) 6. (c)
7. (b) 8. (a) 9. (a) 11. $\dfrac{16}{\pi}$ 12. 0 13. (c)
14. (d)

Exercise for Session 3

1. (c) 2. (a) 3. (b) 4. (b) 5. (a) 6. (d)
7. (b) 8. (d) 9. (c) 10. (b) 11. (b)
12. (b) 13. (c) 14. (b) 15. (d)
16. $\sum_{r=1}^{k} (r-1) \cdot (r^{1/n} - (r-1)^{1/n}) + k(9 - k^{1/n})$
18. 3 19. 1 20. 2

Exercise for Session 4

1. (b) 2. (c) 3. (c) 4. (a) 5. (c) 6. (a)
7. (a) 8. (c) 9. (c) 10. (b) 11. (b) 12. (b)
13. (c) 14. (c) 15. (d) 16. (c) 17. (a) 18. (d)
19. (c) 20. (a)

Exercise for Session 5

1. (c) 2. (b) 3. (a) 4. (a) 5. (a) 6. (b)
7. (a) 8. (a) 9. (c) 10. (c) 11. (c) 12. (a)
13. (c) 14. (c) 15. (c) 16. (a) 17. (a) 18. (b)
19. (a) 20. (b)

Exercise for Session 6

1. (c) 2. (a) 3. (c) 4. (b) 5. (c) 6. (c)
7. (a) 8. (a) 9. (c) 10. (a)

Chapter Exercises

1. (a) 2. (c) 3. (a) 4. (a) 5. (a) 6. (a)
7. (d) 8. (d) 9. (a) 10. (a) 11. (c) 12. (c)
13. (d) 14. (c) 15. (c) 16. (d) 17. (d) 18. (a)
19. (b) 20. (a) 21. (d) 22. (c) 23. (d) 24. (a)
25. (a) 26. (b) 27. (a) 28. (d) 29. (a) 30. (c)
31. (a) 32. (b) 33. (a) 34. (b) 35. (b) 36. (a,b,c)
37. (c,d) 38. (a) 39. (a,b,c) 40. (c,d) 41. (a,b,d)
42. (b,d) 43. (c) 44. (d) 45. (a,b,c) 46. (d) 47. (a)
48. (b) 49. (a) 50. (a) 51. (b) 52. (b) 53. (c)
54. (a) 55. (a) 56. (c) 57. (a) 58. (b) 59. (a)
60. (a) 61. (c) 62. (c)
63. (A) → (q), (B) → (s), (C) → (p), (D) → (r)
64. (A) → (q), (B) → (r), (C) → (s), (D) → (p)
65. (A) → (s), (B) → (p), (C) → (q)
66. (A) → (s), (B) → (r), (C) → (r), (D) → (q)
67. (8) 68. (0) 69. (3) 70. (2) 71. (2) 72. (a)
73. (1) 74. (a,b) 75. (b) 76. (a,c) 77. (a,b,c) 78. (c,d)
79. (0) 80. (9) 81. (a) 82. (b)
83. A→s, B→s, C→p, D→r 84. (d) 85. (2) 86. (b)
87. (a) 88. (8/3) 89. (a) 90. (b,d) 91. (c) 92. (b)
93. (4) 94. (c) 95. (a,b,c) 96. (d) 97. (c) 98. (c)
99. (b) 100. (c) 101. (d) 102. (d) 103. (a) 104. (c)
105. (d) 106. (c) 107. (b) 108. (d) 109. (b)

Solutions

1. Let $I = \int_0^4 \frac{(y^2 - 4y + 5)\sin(y-2)dy}{(2y^2 - 8y + 1)}$

Put $y - 2 = z$

$\Rightarrow$ $dy = dz$

$\therefore$ $I = \int_{z=-2}^{2} \frac{(z^2+1)\sin z}{(2z^2 - 7)} dz$

$\Rightarrow$ $I = 0$, as $\int_{-a}^{a} f(x)\, dx = 0$, when $f(-x) = -f(x)$

and $f(z) = \frac{(z^2+1)\sin z}{(2z^2-7)} dz$ is an odd function.

2. Hence, $f(x) = x^2 + ax - b$

The solution of $f(x) =$ minium $f(x)$ is $x = \frac{-a}{2}$.

Given, $f(x)_{\text{minimum}}$ is at $x = 0$.

$\Rightarrow$ $\frac{-a}{2} = 0$ or $a = 0$

$\therefore$ $f(x) = x^2 - b = 0$ has roots α and β.

$\Rightarrow$ $\alpha = \sqrt{b}$ and $\beta = -\sqrt{b}$

$\Rightarrow$ $\int_\alpha^\beta x^3 dx = \int_{\sqrt{b}}^{-\sqrt{b}} x^3 dx = 0$

$$\left[\int_{-a}^{a} f(x)dx = 0, \text{ when } f(-x) = f(x)\right]$$

3. Here, $\int_{\pi/2}^{x} \sqrt{(3 - 2\sin^2 t)}\, dt + \int_0^y \cos t\, dt = 0$

Differentiating both the sides, we get

$$(\sqrt{3 - 2\sin^2 x})\cdot 1 + (\cos y)\left(\frac{dy}{dx}\right) = 0$$

$\Rightarrow$ $\frac{dy}{dx} = \frac{-\sqrt{3 - 2\sin^2 x}}{\cos y}$

$\therefore$ $\left(\frac{dy}{dx}\right)_{(\pi,\pi)} = \frac{-\sqrt{3}}{-1} = \sqrt{3}$

4. Here, $-4 \le x \le 4 \Rightarrow 0 \le \frac{x^2}{17} < 1$

$\therefore$ $\left[\frac{x^2}{17}\right] = 0$ and $\sin^{-1}(\sin x)$ is an odd function.

Let, $I = \int_{-4}^{4} \frac{\sin^{-1}(\sin x)}{(1+x^2)\times 1} dx + \int_{-4}^{4} \frac{\cos^{-1}(\cos x)}{(1+x^2)\times 1} dx$

$$= 0 + 2\int_0^\pi \frac{\cos^{-1}(\cos x)}{(1+x^2)} dx$$

$$I = 2\left[\int_0^\pi \frac{x}{1+x^2} dx + \int_\pi^4 \frac{2\pi}{(1+x^2)} dx\right]$$

$$= \log(1+\pi^2) + 2\pi(\tan^{-1} x)_\pi^4 - [\log(1+16) - \log(1+\pi^2)]$$

$$= \log(1+\pi^2) + 2\pi(\tan^{-1} 4 - \tan^{-1}\pi) - \log\frac{17}{1+\pi^2}$$

$$= \log\frac{(1+\pi^2)\cdot(1+\pi^2)}{17} + 2\pi\tan^{-1}\left[\tan^{-1}\left(\frac{4-\pi}{1+4\pi}\right)\right]$$

$$= \log\left(\frac{(1+\pi^2)^2}{17}\right) + 2\pi\tan^{-1}\left(\frac{4-\pi}{1+4\pi}\right)$$

On comparing with $\log\left(\frac{(1+\pi^2)^2}{a}\right) + b\pi\tan^{-1}\left(\frac{c-\pi}{1+c\pi}\right)$, we get

$a = 17$, $b = 2$ and $c = 4$

$\therefore$ $a - (2b + c) = 17 - 8 = 9$ and $\frac{a-5}{c} = 3$

Thus, the number of ways to distribute 9 distinct bijective into 3 persons equally is $\frac{9!}{(3!)^3}$.

5. Put $x = \tan\theta$

$\therefore$ $I = \int_0^{\pi/2} \frac{d\theta}{1 + (\tan\theta)^a} = \int_0^{\pi/2} \frac{(\cos\theta)^a}{(\sin\theta)^a + (\cos\theta)^a} d\theta \Rightarrow I = \frac{\pi}{4}$

6. $I = \int_0^{3\pi/4} (\sin x + \cos x)\, dx + \int_0^{3\pi/4} \underbrace{x}_{\text{I}}\underbrace{(\sin x - \cos x)}_{\text{II}}\, dx$

$$= \int_0^{3\pi/4} (\sin x + \cos x)\, dx$$

$$+ [x(-\cos x - \sin x)]_0^{3\pi/4} + \int_0^{3\pi/4} (\sin x + \cos x)\, dx$$

$$= 2\int_0^{3\pi/4} (\sin x + \cos x)\, dx + 0 = 2[-\cos x + \sin x]_0^{3\pi/4}$$

$$= 2\left[+\frac{1}{\sqrt{2}} + \frac{1}{\sqrt{2}} + 1\right] = 2(\sqrt{2} + 1) = 2\tan\frac{3\pi}{8}$$

7. We have, $C_n = \int_{\frac{1}{n+1}}^{\frac{1}{n}} \frac{\tan^{-1}(nx)}{\sin^{-1}(nx)} dx$

$$C_n = \frac{1}{n}\int_{\frac{n}{n+1}}^{1} \frac{\tan^{-1}(t)}{\sin^{-1}(t)} dt \qquad \text{(put } nx = t)$$

Now, $L = \lim_{n\to\infty} n^2 \cdot C_n = \lim_{n\to\infty} n\int_{\frac{n}{n+1}}^{1} \frac{\tan^{-1} t}{\sin^{-1} t} dt\ (\infty \times 0)$

$$L = \frac{\int_{\frac{n}{n+1}}^{1} \frac{\tan^{-1} t}{\sin^{-1} t} dt}{\frac{1}{n}} \qquad \left(\frac{0}{0}\text{ form}\right)$$

Applying Leibnitz rule,

$$L = \lim_{n\to\infty} \frac{0 - \frac{\tan^{-1}\frac{n}{n+1}}{\sin^{-1}\frac{n}{n+1}}\left(\frac{1}{(n+1)^2}\right)}{-\frac{1}{n^2}} = \frac{\pi}{4}\cdot\frac{2}{\pi} = \frac{1}{2}$$

8. $\int_{-3}^{3} \frac{t^2 \sin 2t}{t^2 + 1} dt = 0$ as the integrand is an odd function.

Also, $\int_0^1 \frac{dt}{t^2 + 2t\cos\alpha + 1}$

$$= \frac{1}{\sin\alpha}\left|\tan^{-1}\frac{t + \cos\alpha}{\sin\alpha}\right|_0^1 = \frac{\alpha}{2\sin\alpha}$$

Thus, the given equation reduces to

$$x^2 \cdot \frac{\alpha}{2\sin\alpha} - 2 = 0 \Rightarrow x = \pm 2\sqrt{\frac{\sin\alpha}{\alpha}}$$

9. $f'(x) = e^{g(x)} \cdot g'(x)$ and $g'(x) = \dfrac{x}{1+x^4}$

$\therefore$ $f'(x) = e^{g(x)} \cdot \dfrac{x}{1+x^4}$ $e^{g(2)} = e^0 = 1$

Hence, $f'(2) = e^{g(2)} \cdot g'(2) = e^0 \cdot \dfrac{2}{17} = \dfrac{2}{17}$

10. $\displaystyle\lim_{t\to 0} \ln\left(\frac{1}{t}\int_0^t (1 + a\sin bx)^{c/x}\, dx\right)$

$$= \ln \lim_{t\to 0} \frac{\int_0^t (1 + a\sin b\,x)^{c/x}\, dx}{t}$$

$$= \ln \lim_{t\to 0} \frac{(1 + a\sin bt)^{c/t}}{1} = \ln e^{\lim_{t\to 0} \frac{a\sin bt}{t/c}} = \ln e^{abc} = abc$$

11. $T_r = \dfrac{1}{\sqrt{\dfrac{r}{n}} \cdot n\left(3\sqrt{\dfrac{r}{n}} + 4\right)^2}$

$$S = \frac{1}{n}\sum_1^{4n} \frac{1}{\left(3\sqrt{\frac{r}{n}} + 4\right)^2 \cdot \sqrt{\frac{r}{n}}} = \int_0^4 \frac{dx}{\sqrt{x}\,(3\sqrt{x} + 4)^2}$$

Put $3\sqrt{x} + 4 = t \Rightarrow \dfrac{3}{2}\cdot\dfrac{1}{\sqrt{x}}\, dx = dt$

$$= \frac{2}{3}\int_4^{10} \frac{dt}{t^2} = \frac{2}{3}\left[\frac{1}{t}\right]_{10}^4 = \frac{2}{3}\left[\frac{1}{4} - \frac{1}{10}\right] = \frac{2}{3}\cdot\frac{6}{40} = \frac{1}{10}$$

12. Given, $f(x) = \int_{-1}^x e^{t^2}\, dt; h(x) = f(1 + g(x)); g(x) < 0$ for $x > 0$

Now, $h(x) = \int_{-1}^{1+g(x)} e^{t^2}\, dt = f(1 + g(x))$ (given)

Differentiating, we get $h'(x) = e^{(1+g(x))^2} \cdot g'(x)$

Now, $h'(1) = e$ (given)

$\therefore$ $e^{(1+g(1))^2} \cdot g'(1) = e$

$\Rightarrow$ $(1 + g(1))^2 = 1$

$\Rightarrow$ $1 + g(1) = \pm 1$

$\Rightarrow$ $g(1) = 0$ (not possible)

or $g(1) = -2$

13. Given, $f'(x) = f(x) \Rightarrow f(x) = Ce^x$

Since, $f(0) = 1$ $\therefore$ $1 = f(0) = C$

$\therefore$ $f(x) = e^x$ and hence $g(x) = x^2 - e^x$

Thus, $\int_0^1 f(x)\, g(x)\, dx = \int_0^1 (x^2e^x - e^{2x})\, dx$

$$= [x^2e^x]_0^1 - 2\int_0^1 xe^x\, dx - \left[\frac{e^{2x}}{2}\right]_0^1$$

$$= (e - 0) - 2\,[(xe^x)_0^1 - (e^x)_0^1\,] - \frac{1}{2}(e^2 - 1)$$

$$= (e - 0) - 2\,[(e - 0) - (e - 1)] - \frac{1}{2}(e^2 - 1)$$

$$= e - \frac{1}{2}e^2 - \frac{3}{2}$$

14. Here, $f'(x) = \dfrac{1}{\sqrt{1 + g^2(x)}}\, g'(x);$

Now, $f'\left(\dfrac{\pi}{2}\right) = \dfrac{g'(\pi/2)}{\sqrt{1 + g^2(\pi/2)}};$ $g\left(\dfrac{\pi}{2}\right) = 0 = g'\left(\dfrac{\pi}{2}\right)$

But $g'(x) = [1 + \sin(\cos^2 x)](-\sin x)$

$$g'\left(\frac{\pi}{2}\right) = 1\,(-1) = -1$$

Hence, $f'\left(\dfrac{\pi}{2}\right) = -1$ as $h'(0^+) = -1$

15. Clearly, f is an even function, hence

$$I_1 = \int_0^\pi f[\cos(\pi - x)]\, dx = \int_0^\pi f(-\cos x)\, dx$$

$$= \int_0^\pi f(\cos x)\, dx$$

$\therefore$ $I_1 = 2\displaystyle\int_0^{\pi/2} f(\cos x)\, dx \cdot 2\int_0^{\pi/2} f(\sin x)\, dx = 2I_2$

$\Rightarrow$ $\dfrac{I_1}{I_2} = 2$

Aliter Let $u = \cos x \Rightarrow du = -\sin x\, dx$

$\therefore$ $I_1 = \displaystyle\int_{-1}^1 \frac{f(u)}{\sqrt{1 - u^2}}\, du$

$\Rightarrow$ $I_1 = 2\displaystyle\int_0^1 \frac{f(u)}{\sqrt{1 - u^2}}\, du$ ...(i)

Similarly, with $\sin t = t$,

$$I_2 = \int_0^1 \frac{f(t)}{\sqrt{1 - t^2}}\, dt \quad \text{...(ii)}$$

From Eqs. (i) and (ii), $\dfrac{I_1}{I_2} = 2$

16. Given, $I_1 = \displaystyle\int_{1-k}^k x\, f(x\,(1 - x))\, dx$ and

$$I_2 = \int_{1-k}^k f(x\,(1 - x))\, dx$$

Using King's property $I_1 = \displaystyle\int_{1-k}^k (1 - x)\, f(x\,(1 - x))\, dx$

$$2I_1 = \int_{1-k}^k f(x\,(1 - x))\, dx = I_2$$

$\therefore$ $\dfrac{I_2}{I_1} = 2$

17. $A = \displaystyle\int_{-1}^1 (ax^2 + bx + c)\, dx = 2\int_0^1 (ax^2 + c)\, dx$

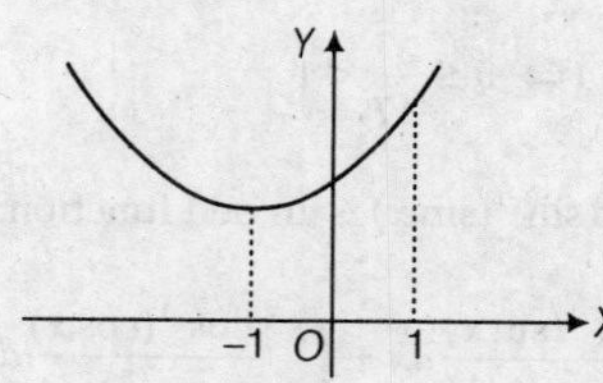

$$= 2\left[\frac{a}{3} + c\right] = \frac{1}{3}\,[2a + 6c]$$

$\therefore$ $A = \dfrac{1}{3}\,[f(-1) + 4f(0) + f(1)]$

18. $I(a)=\int_0^{\pi}\left(\frac{x^2}{a^2}+a^2\sin^2 x+2x\sin x\right)dx \qquad \left(\because \int_0^{\pi} x\sin x\,dx=\pi\right)$

$$\therefore \quad I(a)=\frac{\pi^3}{3a^2}+\frac{\pi a^2}{2}+2\pi=\pi\left[\frac{\pi^2}{3a^2}+\frac{a^2}{2}\right]+2\pi$$

$$=\pi\left[\left(\frac{\pi}{\sqrt{3}a}-\frac{a}{\sqrt{2}}\right)^2+\frac{2\pi}{\sqrt{6}}\right]+2\pi$$

$I(a)$ is minimum when $\frac{\pi}{\sqrt{3}a}=\frac{a}{\sqrt{2}} \Rightarrow a^2=\pi\sqrt{\frac{2}{3}}$

$$\Rightarrow \quad a=\sqrt{\pi\sqrt{\frac{2}{3}}}$$

Also, $\quad [I(a)]_{\min}=2\pi+\pi^2\sqrt{\frac{2}{3}}$

19. $\left[\frac{t^2}{2}-\log_2 a\cdot t\right]_0^2=2-\log_2(a^2) \qquad (\because a>0)$

$\Rightarrow \quad (2-2\log_2 a)=2-2\log_2 a$

$\Rightarrow \quad 2\log_2 a=2\log_2 a \Rightarrow a\in R^+$

20. Consider $I=\int_{-1/x}^{1/x}\frac{\ln(1+t^2)}{1+e^t}dt$ ...(i)

$\Rightarrow \quad I=\int_{-1/x}^{1/x}\frac{\ln(1+t^2)}{1+e^{-t}}dt$ (using King' property)

$I=\int_{-1/x}^{1/x}\frac{\ln(1+t^2)\,e^t}{1+e^t}dt$ ...(ii)

On adding Eqs. (i) and (ii), we get

$$2I=\int_{-1/x}^{1/x}\ln(1+t^2)\,dt=2\int_0^{1/x}\ln(1+t^2)\,dt$$

$\Rightarrow \quad I=\int_0^{1/x}\ln(1+t^2)\,dt$

Hence, $\quad l=\lim_{x\to\infty}x^3\int_0^{1/x}\ln(1+t^2)\,dt$

$$=\lim_{x\to\infty}\frac{\int_0^{1/x}\ln(1+t^2)\,dt}{x^{-3}} \qquad \left(\frac{0}{0}\text{ form}\right)$$

Using L' Hospital's rule,

$$l=\lim_{x\to 0}\frac{x^4\ln\left(1+\frac{1}{x^2}\right)\cdot\left(-\frac{1}{x^2}\right)}{-3}=\frac{1}{3}\lim_{x\to\infty}x^2\ln\left(1+\frac{1}{x^2}\right)$$

$$=\frac{1}{3}\lim_{x\to\infty}\ln\left(1+\frac{1}{x^2}\right)^{x^2} \qquad (1^{\infty}\text{ form})$$

$$=\lim_{x\to\infty}\frac{1}{3}x^2\left(1+\frac{1}{x^2}-1\right)=\frac{1}{3}$$

21. Put $\pi x=t \Rightarrow dx=\frac{dt}{\pi}$

$\therefore \quad I=\frac{1}{\pi}\cdot\frac{\pi}{\pi}\int_0^{2008\pi}t\,|\sin t|\,dt=\frac{1}{\pi}\int_0^{2008\pi}t\,|\sin t|\,dt$ ...(i)

$\Rightarrow \quad I=\frac{1}{\pi}\int_0^{2008\pi}(2008\pi-t)\,|\sin t|\,dt$ ...(ii)

On adding Eqs. (i) and (ii), we get

$$2I=\frac{2008\pi}{\pi}\int_0^{2008\pi}|\sin t|\,dt=(2008)^2\cdot\int_0^{\pi}|\sin t|\,dt$$

$\Rightarrow \quad I=(2008)^2 \qquad \Rightarrow \sqrt{I}=2008$

22. $T_n=\frac{n}{n^2+k^2x^2}=\frac{1}{n[1+(k/n)^2x^2]};$

$$S=\frac{1}{n}\sum_{k=1}^{n}\frac{1}{1+\underbrace{(k/n)^2}_{t}x^2}=\int_0^1\frac{dt}{1+t^2x^2}$$

$$=\frac{1}{x^2}\int_0^1\frac{dt}{t^2+(1/x^2)}=\left[\frac{1}{x}\tan^{-1}(tx)\right]_0^1=\frac{\tan^{-1}(x)}{x}$$

23. Let $y=f(x) \Rightarrow x=g(y)$ and $dy=f'(x)\,dx$

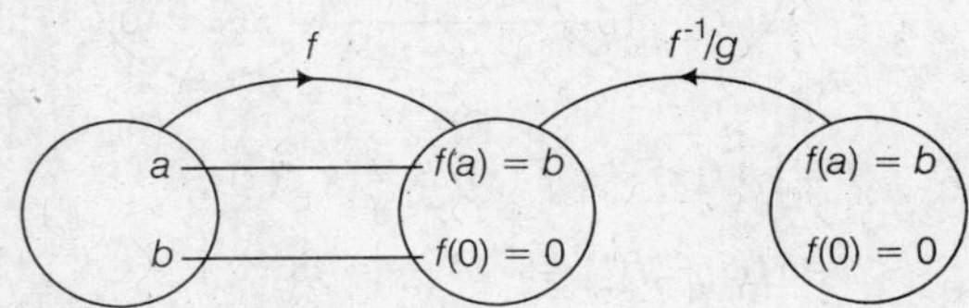

$$I=\int_0^a f(x)\,dx+\int_0^b g(y)\,dy; y=f(x)$$

$$\Rightarrow x=f^{-1}(y)=g(y)=\int_0^a f(x)dx+\int_0^a xf'(x)\,dx$$

$$=\int_0^a(f(x)+xf'(x))\,dx=[xf(x)]_0^a=a\,f(a)=ab$$

24. Let $I=\int_{-1/\sqrt{3}}^{1/\sqrt{3}}\frac{x^4}{1-x^4}\cos^{-1}\frac{2x}{1+x^2}dx$ ...(i)

$\Rightarrow I=\int_{-1/\sqrt{3}}^{1/\sqrt{3}}\frac{x^4}{1-x^4}\cos^{-1}\left(\frac{-2x}{1-x^4}\right)dx$ (using King's property)

$\Rightarrow I=\int_{-1/\sqrt{3}}^{1/\sqrt{3}}\frac{x^4}{1-x^4}\left(\pi-\cos^{-1}\frac{2x}{1-x^4}\right)dx$ ...(ii)

On adding Eqs. (i) and (ii), we get

$$\therefore \quad 2I=\pi\int_{-1/\sqrt{3}}^{1/\sqrt{3}}\frac{x^4}{1-x^4}dx \Rightarrow 2I=2\pi\int_0^{1/\sqrt{3}}\frac{x^4}{1-x^4}dx$$

$\therefore \quad k=\pi$

25. Put $\ln x=t$ or $x=e^t \Rightarrow dx=e^t\,dt$

$$\therefore \quad I=\int_{-\infty}^{\infty}f(e^t+e^{-t})\frac{t}{e^t}e^t\,dt=\int_{-\infty}^{\infty}f(e^t+e^{-t})\,t\,dt=0$$

(as the function is odd)

Aliter I Put $x=\tan\theta$

$$\int_0^{\pi/2}f\left(\tan\theta+\frac{1}{\tan\theta}\right)\frac{\ln\tan\theta}{\tan\theta}\cdot\sec^2\theta\,d\theta$$

$$=\int_0^{\pi/2}f\left(\tan\theta+\frac{1}{\tan\theta}\right)\frac{\ln\tan\theta}{\sin\theta\cos\theta}d\theta$$

Aliter II Put $x=1/t \Rightarrow I=-1 \Rightarrow 2I=0 \Rightarrow I=0$

26. $\lim_{\lambda\to 0}\left(\int_0^1(1+x)^{\lambda}\,dx\right)^{1/\lambda}=\lim_{\lambda\to 0}\left(\left|\frac{(1+x)^{\lambda+1}}{\lambda+1}\right|_0^1\right)^{1/\lambda}$

$$=\lim_{\lambda\to 0}\left(\frac{2^{\lambda+1}-1}{\lambda+1}\right)^{1/\lambda} \qquad (1^{\infty}\text{ form})$$

$$=e^{\lim_{\lambda\to 0}\frac{1}{\lambda}\left(\frac{2^{\lambda+1}-1-\lambda-1}{\lambda+1}\right)}=e^{\lim_{\lambda\to 0}\left(\frac{2^{\lambda+1}-2-\lambda}{\lambda(\lambda+1)}\right)}$$

$$=e^{\lim_{\lambda\to 0}\left(\frac{2(2^{\lambda}-1)}{\lambda}-1\right)}=e^{2\ln 2-1}=e^{\ln\left(\frac{4}{e}\right)}=\frac{4}{e}$$

27. Let $y = f(x) \Rightarrow x = f^{-1}(y) = g(y)$

$$dy = f'(x)\,dx$$

$$\therefore \quad I = \int_1^5 f(x)\,dx + \int_1^5 xf'(x)\,dx$$

When $y = 2$, then $x = 1$

and when $y = 1$, then $x = 5$

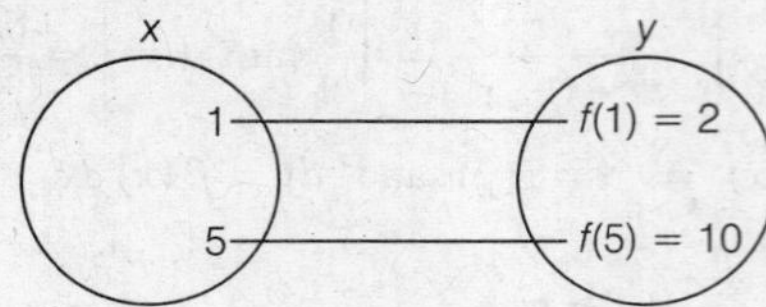

$$\therefore \quad I = \int_1^5 (f(x) + x\,f'(x))dx = |x\,f(x)|_1^5$$

$$= 5f(5) - f(1) = 5 \cdot 10 - 2 = 48$$

28. $I = \int_0^{\pi/2} \sin x \sin 2x \sin 3x\,dx$ ...(i)

$$= \int_0^{\pi/2} \sin\left(\frac{\pi}{2} - x\right) \sin 2\left(\frac{\pi}{2} - x\right) \sin 3\left(\frac{\pi}{2} - x\right) dx$$

$\Rightarrow \quad I = \int_0^{\pi/2} -\cos x \sin 2x \cos 3x\,dx$ ...(ii)

$$\therefore \quad 2I = \int_0^{\pi/2} -\sin 2x\,(\cos x \cos 3x - \sin 3x \sin x)\,dx$$

$$= \int_0^{\pi/2} -\sin 2x \cos(4x)\,dx$$

$$= -\int_0^{\pi/2} \sin 2x\,(2\cos^2 2x - 1)\,dx$$

Put $\cos 2x = t \Rightarrow -\sin 2x \times 2\,dx = dt$

$$\therefore \quad 2I = \int_1^{-1} \frac{1}{2}(2t^2 - 1)\,dt = \frac{1}{2}\left[\frac{2t^3}{3} - t\right]_1^{-1}$$

$$= \frac{1}{2}\left[\frac{2}{3}(-1)^3 - (-1) - \left(\frac{2}{3}(1)^3 - 1\right)\right]$$

$$= \frac{1}{2}\left[-\frac{2}{3} + 1 - \frac{2}{3} + 1\right] = \frac{1}{2}\left[\frac{2}{3}\right] \quad \Rightarrow I = \frac{1}{6}$$

29. Here, $f'(x) = (f(x))^2 > 0$; $\frac{d}{dx} f(g(x))\Big|_{x=a}$

$$= f'(g(x)) \lim_{x \to a} \frac{g(x) - g(a)}{x - a}$$

It implies that $g(x)$ must be differentiable at $x = a$.

30. On putting $t = \frac{x^2}{z}$ and then solving,

$$\int_0^{\infty} \frac{\ln x}{x^2 + t^2}\,dt = \frac{2\pi \ln x}{x}$$

$$\Rightarrow \quad \frac{\ln x}{x} = \frac{\ln 2}{x}$$

$\Rightarrow \quad x = 2$ and 4 i.e. two solutions.

31. Put $\frac{x\pi}{n} = t$

$$\therefore \int_0^{\frac{16n^2}{\pi}} \cos\frac{\pi}{2}\left[\frac{\pi x}{n}\right] dx = \frac{n}{\pi}\int_0^{16n} \cos\frac{\pi}{2}[t]\,dt$$

$$= \frac{4n^2}{\pi}\int_0^4 \cos\frac{\pi}{2}[t]\,dt = 0$$

32. $\int_{-2}^{-1} (ax^2 - 5)\,dx + \int_1^2 (bx + c)\,dx + 5$

$$= \int_{-2}^{-1} (ax^2 - 5 - bx + c + 5)\,dx = 0$$

Hence, $ax^2 - bx + c = 0$ has atleast one root in $(-2, -1)$.

33. $I = \int_3^6 ((\sqrt{x-3} + \sqrt{3}) + (\sqrt{3} - \sqrt{x-3}))\,dx = 6\sqrt{3}$

34. $I_1 = \int_{-1}^{1} (\{x\} + \{x^3\})\{x^2\}\,dx$

$$= -2\int_0^1 \{x^2\}\,dx = \left[-2 \times \frac{x^3}{3}\right]_0^1 = -\frac{2}{3}$$

35. $\mathcal{J}_n - \mathcal{J}_{n-1} = \int_0^{\pi/2} \frac{\sin^2 nx - \sin^2 (n-1)x}{\sin^2 x}\,dx$

$$= \int_0^{\pi/2} \frac{\sin(2n-1)x \cdot \sin x}{\sin^2 x}\,dx = I_n$$

i.e. $\quad \mathcal{J}_n - \mathcal{J}_{n-1} = I_n$

$\Rightarrow \quad \mathcal{J}_{n+1} - \mathcal{J}_n = I_{n+1}$

36.

37. (a) $I = \int_0^{\pi/2} \ln(\cot x)\,dx \Rightarrow I = \int_0^{\pi/2} \ln(\tan x)\,dx$

$$I = -\int_0^{\pi/2} \ln(\cot x)\,dx \Rightarrow I = -I \Rightarrow I = 0$$

(b) $I = \int_0^{2\pi} \sin^3 x\,dx = -\int_0^{2\pi} \sin^3 x\,dx \Rightarrow I = 0$

(c) At $x = \frac{1}{t}$, $I = \int_e^{1/e} \frac{-(1/t^2)\,dt}{-1/t\,(\ln t)^{1/3}} = -\int_{1/e}^{e} \frac{dt}{t\,(\ln t)^{1/3}}$

$$I = -1 \text{ or } I = 0$$

(d) $\sqrt{\frac{1 + \cos 2x}{2}} > 0 \Rightarrow \int_0^{\pi} \sqrt{\frac{1 + \cos 2x}{2}}\,dx > 0$

38. $I = \int_0^1 (10x^4 - 3x^2 - 1)\,dx = [2x^5 - x^3 - x]_0^1 = 0$

Since, $f(x)$ is even, hence must have a root in $(-1, 0)$.

39. We have, $I_1 = \int_0^{\pi/2} \cos(\pi \sin^2 x)\,dx$

$$I_1 = \int_0^{\pi/2} \cos(\pi \cos^2 x)\,dx$$

On adding, $2I_1 = \int_0^{\pi/2} \cos(\pi \sin^2 x) + \cos(\pi \cos^2 x)\,dx$

$$= \int_0^{\pi/2} 2\cos\left(\frac{\pi}{2}\right) \cdot \cos\left(\frac{\pi}{2}\cos 2x\right) dx = 0$$

$\Rightarrow \quad I_1 = 0$ ...(i)

Now, $I_2 = \int_0^{\pi/2} \cos\{\pi(1-\cos 2x)\}\,dx$

$= -\int_0^{\pi/2} \cos(\pi \cos 2x)\,dx$

$= -\frac{1}{2}\int_0^{\pi} \cos(\pi \cos t)\,dt$ (put $2x = t$)

$= -\frac{2}{2}\int_0^{\pi/2} \cos(\pi \cos t)\,dt = I_3$

$\Rightarrow \quad I_2 + I_3 = 0$

$I_3 = -\int_0^{\pi/2} \cos(\pi \sin t)\,dt$

$\therefore \quad I_2 + I_3 = 0$ ...(ii)

Hence, $I_1 + I_2 + I_3 = 0$

40. $f(x) = 2\int_0^1 \underbrace{(1-t)}_{\text{I}}\underbrace{\cos(xt)}_{\text{II}}\,dt$

$$= 2\left[(1-t)\frac{\sin xt}{x}\Big|_0^1 + \frac{1}{x}\int_0^1 \sin xt\,dt\right] = 2\left[\left|0 - \frac{1}{x^2}\cos xt\right|_0^1\right]$$

$$f(x) = 2\left[\frac{1-\cos x}{x^2}\right] \quad (x \neq 0)$$

If $x = 0$, then $f(x) = \int_{-1}^{1}(1-|t|)\,dt = 2\int_0^1 (1-t)\,dt = 1$

$\therefore$ option (c) is correct.

Hence, $f(x) = \begin{cases} 2\left(\dfrac{1-\cos x}{x^2}\right), & \text{if } x \neq 0 \\ 1, & \text{if } x = 0 \end{cases}$

$\therefore$ f is continuous at $x = 0$.

$\therefore$ option (d) is correct.

41. Given, $f(f(x)) = -x + 1$

Replacing x by $f(x)$, we get

$$f(f(f(x))) = -f(x) + 1$$
$$f(1-x) = -f(x) + 1$$
$$f(x) + f(1-x) = 1 \quad \text{...(i)}$$

Now, $J = \int_0^1 f(x)\,dx = \int_0^1 f(1-x)\,dx$ (using King's property)

$\Rightarrow \quad 2J = \int_0^1 (f(x) + f(1-x))\,dx$

$\Rightarrow \quad 2J = \int_0^1 dx = 1 \Rightarrow J = \frac{1}{2}$

Put $x = \frac{1}{4}$ in Eq. (i),

$$F\left(\frac{1}{4}\right) + F\left(1 - \frac{1}{4}\right) = 1 \Rightarrow F\left(\frac{1}{4}\right) + F\left(\frac{3}{4}\right) = 1$$

Now $I = \int_0^{\pi/2} \frac{\sin x}{(\sin x + \cos x)^3}\,dx$

$$I = \int_0^{\pi/2} \frac{\sin\left(\frac{\pi}{2} - x\right)}{\left(\sin\left(\frac{\pi}{2} - x\right) + \cos\left(\frac{\pi}{2} - x\right)\right)^3}\,dx$$

$\Rightarrow I = \int_0^{\pi/2} \frac{\cos x}{(\cos x + \sin x)^3}\,dx$

$$\therefore 2I = \int_0^{\pi/2} \frac{1}{(\sin x + \cos x)^2}\,dx = \frac{1}{2}\int_0^{\pi/2} \frac{dx}{\left(\frac{1}{\sqrt{2}}\sin x + \frac{1}{\sqrt{2}}\cos x\right)^2}$$

$$= \frac{1}{2}\int_0^{\pi/2} \frac{dx}{\sin^2\left(\frac{\pi}{4} + x\right)}$$

$$= \frac{1}{2}\int_0^{\pi/2} \operatorname{cosec}^2\left(\frac{\pi}{4} + x\right)dx = -\frac{1}{2}\left[\cot\left(\frac{\pi}{4} + x\right)\right]_0^{\pi/2}$$

$$= -\frac{1}{2}[-1-1] = 1 \quad \Rightarrow I = \frac{1}{2}$$

42. We have, $f(x) = x^2 + ax^2 + bx^3$

where, $a = \int_{-1}^{1} t\,f(t)\,dt$ and $b = \int_{-1}^{1} f(t)\,dt$

Now, $a = \int_{-1}^{1} t\,[(a+1)t^2 + bt^3]\,dt$

$\Rightarrow \quad a = 2b\int_0^1 t^4 dt = \frac{2b}{5}$ ...(i)

Again, $b = \int_{-1}^{1} f(t)\,dt = \int_{-1}^{1} ((a+1)t^2 + bt^3)\,dt$

$\Rightarrow \quad b = 2\int_0^1 (a+1)t^2\,dt$

$\Rightarrow \quad b = \frac{2(a+1)}{3}$ ...(ii)

From Eqs. (i) and (ii), $\frac{5a}{2} = \frac{2(a+1)}{3}$

$\Rightarrow \quad \left(\frac{5}{2} - \frac{2}{3}\right)a = \frac{2}{3} \Rightarrow \frac{11}{6}a = \frac{2}{3}$

$\Rightarrow \quad a = \frac{4}{11}$ and $b = \frac{10}{11}$

Hence, $\int_{-1}^{1} t\,f(t)\,dt = \frac{4}{11}$ and $\int_{-1}^{1} f(t)\,dt = \frac{10}{11}$

$\therefore$
$$f(x) = (a+1)x^2 + bx^3$$
$$f(1) = (a+1) + b$$
$$f(-1) = (a+1) - b$$

$\Rightarrow \quad f(1) + f(-1) = 2(a+1) = \frac{30}{11}$

and $\quad f(1) - f(-1) = 2b = \frac{20}{11}$

43. Given, $(f'(x))^2 + (g(x))^2 = 1$

$$f(x) + \int_0^x g(t)\,dt = \sin x(\cos x - \sin x)$$

Differentiating both the sides, we get

$$f'(x) + g(x) = \cos 2x - \sin 2x \quad \text{...(i)}$$

Squaring both the sides of Eq. (i), we get

$$(f'(x))^2 + (g(x))^2 = 2f'(x)\cdot g(x) = 1 - \sin 4x$$

$\Rightarrow \quad 1 + 2f'(x)\cdot g(x) = 1 - \sin 4x$

$\therefore \quad 2f'(x)\,g(x) = -\sin 4x$

Now, substituting $g(x) = -\frac{\sin 4x}{2f'(x)}$ in Eq. (i), we get

$$f'(x) - \frac{\sin 4x}{2f'(x)} = \cos 2x - \sin 2x$$

Put $\quad f'(x) = t$

$\Rightarrow\ 2t^2 - 2(\cos 2x - \sin 2x)\,t - \sin 4x = 0$

$\Rightarrow\ t = \dfrac{2(\cos 2x - \sin 2x) \pm \sqrt{4(1 - \sin 4x) + 8\sin 4x}}{4}$

$\therefore\ 4t = 2(\cos 2x - \sin 2x) \pm \sqrt{4(1 - \sin 4x) + 8\sin 4x}$

$\Rightarrow\ 2t = (\cos 2x - \sin 2x) \pm \sqrt{1 + \sin 4x}$

Taking + ve sign, $2t = \cos 2x - \sin 2x + \cos 2x + \sin 2x$

$\Rightarrow\quad t = \cos 2x$

Taking – ve sign, $t = -\sin 2x$

Since, $\quad f'(x) = \cos 2x$ or $f'(x) = -\sin 2x$

$f(x) = \dfrac{1}{2}\sin 2x + C_1$ or $f(x) = \dfrac{\cos 2x}{2} + C_2$

$f(0) = 0$

$\Rightarrow\quad C_1 = 0$ and $C_2 = -1/2$

$\therefore\quad f(x) = \dfrac{1}{2}\sin 2x$ or $f(x) = \dfrac{\cos 2x - 1}{2}$

If $f'(x) = \cos 2x$, then $g(x) = -\sin 2x$

If $f'(x) = -\sin 2x$, then $g(x) = \cos 2x$

i.e. $f(x) = \dfrac{1}{2}\sin 2x$ and $g(x) = -\sin 2x$

$\Rightarrow\ f(x) = \dfrac{\cos 2x - 1}{2}$ and $g(x) = \cos 2x$

44. Consider $f(x) = \int_{-x}^{x} (\underbrace{t\sin at}_{\text{even}} + \underbrace{bt}_{\text{odd}} + \underbrace{c}_{\text{even}})\,dt$

$$= 2\int_0^x (t\sin at + c)\,dt$$

$$= 2\left[\left|-t\frac{\cos at}{a}\right|_0^x + \int_0^x \frac{\cos at}{a}\,dt + |ct|_0^x\right] \text{(using I.B.P.)}$$

$$= 2\left[\frac{-x\cos ax}{a} + \frac{1}{a^2}\sin ax + cx\right]$$

$$\therefore\ \lim_{x\to 0}\frac{f(x)}{x} = \lim_{x\to 0} 2\left[-\frac{\cos ax}{a} + \frac{\sin ax}{a\cdot ax} + c\right]$$

$$= 2\left[-\frac{1}{a} + \frac{1}{a} + c\right] = 2c$$

45. Consider $I = \int_a^{\infty} \dfrac{n\,dx}{n^2\left(x^2 + \dfrac{1}{n^2}\right)} = \dfrac{1}{n}\cdot n\,(\tan^{-1} nx)_0^{\infty} = \left(\dfrac{\pi}{2} - \tan^{-1} an\right)$

$$\therefore\quad L = \lim_{n\to\infty}\left(\frac{\pi}{2} - \tan^{-1} an\right) = \begin{cases} \pi, & \text{if } a < 0 \\ \pi/2, & \text{if } a = 0 \\ 0, & \text{if } a > 0 \end{cases}$$

46. $\lim_{x\to 0} \dfrac{\int_0^x \dfrac{t^2\,dt}{(a + t^r)^{1/p}}}{bx - \sin x} = \lim_{x\to 0} \dfrac{\dfrac{x^2}{(a + x^r)^{1/p}}}{b - \cos x}$ Using L'Hospital's rule

For existence of limit, $\lim_{x\to 0}$ denominator = 0

$\therefore\quad b - 1 = 0 \Rightarrow b = 1$

47. $l = \lim_{x\to 0} \dfrac{x^2}{(a + x^r)^{1/p}}\cdot\dfrac{x^2}{(1 - \cos x)}\cdot\dfrac{1}{x^2}$

$$= 2\lim_{x\to 0}\frac{1}{(a + x^r)^{1/p}} = \frac{2}{a^{1/p}}$$

If $p = 3$ and $l = 1$, then $1 = \dfrac{2}{a^{1/3}} \Rightarrow a = 8$

48. If, $p = 2$ and $a = 9$, then $l = \dfrac{2}{9^{1/2}} = \dfrac{2}{3}$

49. Here, $\quad f(x) = e^x \underbrace{\int_0^1 e^t\cdot f(t)\,dt}_{A\text{ (say)}}$

$f(x) = Ae^x$ ...(i)

$\Rightarrow\quad f(t) = Ae^t$

where, $\quad A = \int_0^1 e^t\cdot f(t)\,dt$

$\Rightarrow\quad A = \int_0^1 e^t\cdot Ae^t\,dt;\ A = A\int_0^1 e^{2t}\,dt$

Now, $A\left[\int_0^1 e^{2t}dt - 1\right] = 0 \Rightarrow A = 0$, as $\int_0^1 e^{2t}\,dt \neq 0$

Hence, $\quad f(x) = 0 \Rightarrow f(1) = 0$

50. Again, $\quad g(x) = e^x\int_0^1 e^t\,g(t)\,dt + x$

$\Rightarrow\quad g(x) = Be^x + x$ ...(ii)

$\Rightarrow\quad g(t) = Be^t + t$

where, $\quad B = \int_0^1 e^t\,g(t)\,dt \Rightarrow B = \int_0^1 e^t\,(Be^t + t)\,dt$

$\Rightarrow\quad B = B\int_0^1 e^{2t}\,dt + \int_0^1 e^t\cdot t\,dt$

But $\quad \int_0^1 e^{2t}\,dt = \dfrac{1}{2}(e^2 - 1)$ and $\int_0^1 te^t\,dt = 1$

$\therefore\quad B = \dfrac{B}{2}(e^2 - 1) + 1$

$\Rightarrow\quad 2B = B(e^2 - 1) + 2$

$\Rightarrow\quad 3B = Be^2 + 2 \Rightarrow B = \dfrac{2}{3 - e^2}$

From Eq. (ii), $\quad g(x) = \left(\dfrac{2}{3 - e^2}\right)e^x + x \Rightarrow g(0) = \dfrac{2}{3 - e^2}$

Also, $\quad f(0) = 0$

$\therefore\quad g(0) - f(0) = \dfrac{2}{3 - e^2} - 0 = \dfrac{2}{3 - e^2}$

51. $g(2) = \dfrac{2e^2}{3 - e^2} + 2 = \dfrac{6}{3 - e^2}$

$\therefore\quad \dfrac{g(0)}{g(2)} = \dfrac{2}{3 - e^2}\cdot\dfrac{3 - e^2}{6} = \dfrac{1}{3}$

Solutions (Q. Nos. 52 to 54)

We have the equations of the tangents to the curve $y = \int_{-\infty}^{x} f(t)dt$ and $y = f(x)$ at arbitrary points on them are

$$Y - \int_{-x}^{x} f(t)\,dt = f(x)\,(X - x) \quad ...(i)$$

and $\quad Y - f(x) = f'(x)\,(X - x)$ ...(ii)

As Eqs. (i) and (ii) intersect at the same point on the X-axis

Putting $Y = 0$ and equating x-coordinates, we have

$$x - \frac{f(x)}{f'(x} = x - \frac{\int_{-\infty}^{x} f(t)\,dt}{f(x)}$$

$$\Rightarrow \quad \frac{f(x)}{\int_{-\infty}^{x} f(t)\,dt} = \frac{f'(x)}{f(x)}$$

$$\Rightarrow \quad \int_{-\infty}^{x} f(t)\,dt = cf(x) \quad \text{...(iii)}$$

As, $f(0) = 1 \Rightarrow \int_{-\infty}^{0} f(t)\,dt = c \times 1 \Rightarrow c = \frac{1}{2}$

$\Rightarrow \int_{-\infty}^{x} f(t)\,dt = \frac{1}{2} f(x)$; differentiating both the sides and integrating and using boundary conditions, we get $f(x) = e^{2x}$; $y = 2ex$ is tangent to $y = e^{2x}$.

$\therefore$ Number of solutions = 1.

Cearly, $f(x)$ is increasing for all x.

$$\therefore \quad \lim_{x \to \infty} (e^{2x})^{e^{-2x}} = 1 \quad (\infty^0 \text{ form})$$

Solutions (Q. Nos. 55 to 57)

We have, $g(x) = g(0) + xg'(0) + \frac{x^2}{2} g''(0) = -bx^2 + cx - 6$

$h(x) = g(x) = 4x^4 - ax^3 + bx^2 - cx + 6 = 0$ has 4 distinct real roots. Using Descarte's rule of signs.

Given biquadratic equation has 4 distinct positive roots.

Let the roots be x_1, x_2, x_3 and x_4.

Now, $$\frac{\frac{1}{x_1} + \frac{2}{x_2} + \frac{3}{x_3} + \frac{4}{x_4}}{4} \geq \sqrt[4]{\frac{24}{x_1\,x_2\,x_3\,x_4}}$$

$$\Rightarrow \quad 2 \geq 2 \Rightarrow \frac{1}{x_1} = \frac{2}{x_2} = \frac{3}{x_3} = \frac{4}{x_4} = k$$

$$\Rightarrow \quad \frac{1}{x_1} \cdot \frac{2}{x_2} \cdot \frac{3}{x_3} \cdot \frac{4}{x_4} = k^4$$

$$\Rightarrow \quad \frac{24}{3/2} = k^4 \Rightarrow k = 2$$

$\therefore$ Roots are $\frac{1}{2}$, 1, $\frac{3}{2}$ and 2. Also, $a = 20$ and $c = 25$

58. At $x = 1$, $y = 0$, $\frac{dy}{dx} = 2x \cdot (x^4)^2 - (x^2)^2 = 1$

$\therefore$ Equation of the tangent is $y = x - 1$.

59. $\frac{dy}{dx} = 4x^3(\ln x^4)^2 - 3x^2 (\ln x^3)^2$

$= 64x^3 (\ln x)^2 - 27x^2 (\ln x)^2$

$\therefore \lim_{x \to 0^+} \frac{dy}{dx} = 64 \lim_{x \to 0^+} x^3 (\ln x)^2 - 27 \lim_{x \to 0^+} x^2 (\ln x)^2 = 0$

60. We have, $f(x) = \int_1^x e^{t^2/2} (1 - t^2)\,dt$

$\therefore \quad f'(x) = [e^{x^2/2} (1 - x^2)]^2$

Now, $\quad f'(1) = e^{1/2} \cdot 0 = 0$

61. Here, $f(x) = \tan^{-1}\left(\frac{\log_e x}{\log_e x + 1}\right), 0 < x < \infty$

attains minimum at $x = \frac{1}{e}$ and maximum at $x = e$.

Also, $f(x)$ has $y = 0$ as asymptotes.

$\therefore$ $f(x)$ can be shown as

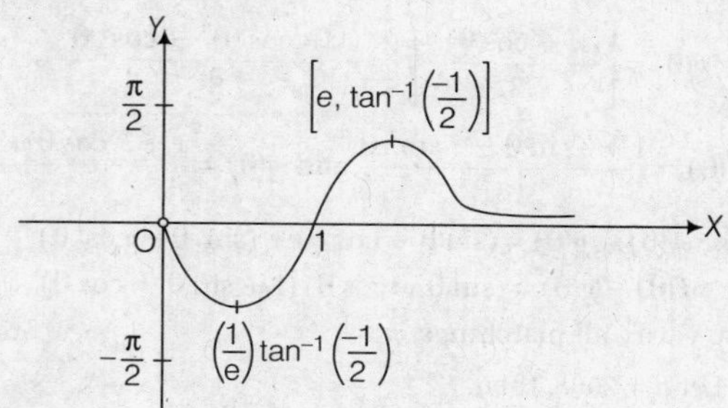

Clearly, $f(x)$ is neither injective nor subjective, also graph for $[f(x)]$ can be shown, as

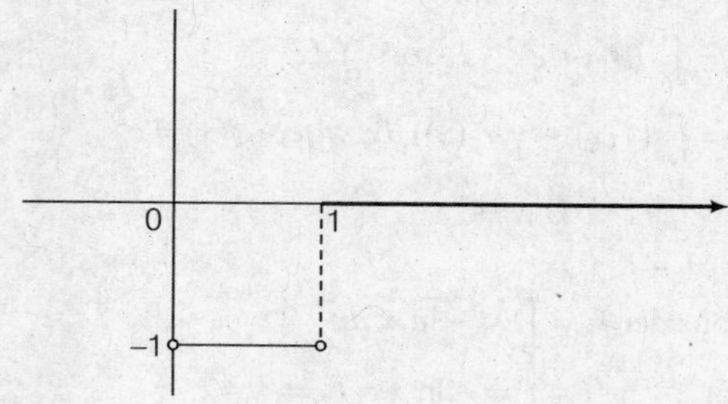

62. $\int_0^\infty [f(x)]dx = \int_0^1 -1 \cdot dx + \int_1^\infty 0 \cdot dx = -(x)\frac{1}{0} = -1$

63. (A) For $a = 0$, $I = \int_0^T \sin^2 x\,dx$

$$= \int_0^T \frac{1 - \cos 2x}{2}\,dx$$

$$= \left[\frac{x}{2} - \frac{1}{4}\sin 2x\right]_0^T = \frac{T}{2} - \frac{1}{4}\sin 2T$$

$$\therefore \quad L = \frac{1}{2} - \lim_{T \to \infty} \frac{1}{4} \frac{\sin 2T}{T} = \frac{1}{2}$$

(B) For $a = 1$, $\int_0^T 4\sin^2 x\,dx \Rightarrow L = 2$

(C) For $a = -1$, $\int_0^T 0\,dx = 0 \Rightarrow L = 0$

(D) For $a \neq 0, -1, 1$,

$$I = \int_0^T (\sin^2 x + \sin^2 ax + 2\sin x \cdot \sin ax)\,dx$$

$$= \int_0^T \left(\frac{1 - \cos 2x}{2} + \frac{1 - \cos 2ax}{2} + \cos(a-1)x - \cos(a+1)x\right)dx$$

$$= \left[x - \frac{1}{4}\sin 2x - \frac{1}{4a}\sin 2ax \frac{\sin(a-1)x}{a-1} - \frac{\sin(a+1)x}{a+1}\right]_0^T$$

$$\therefore L = \lim_{T \to \infty} \frac{T}{T} - \lim_{T \to \infty} \frac{1}{T}$$

$$\left[\frac{1}{4}\sin 2x - \frac{1}{4a}\sin 2ax + \frac{\sin(a-1)x}{a-1} - \frac{\sin(a+1)x}{a+1}\right]_0^T$$

$\Rightarrow L = 1$

64. $\because \quad f(\theta) = \left[\dfrac{(x+\sin\theta)^3}{3}\right]_0^1 = \dfrac{(1+\sin\theta)^3 - \sin^3\theta}{3}$

and $g(\theta) = \left[\dfrac{(x+\cos\theta)^3}{3}\right]_0^1 = \dfrac{(1+\cos\theta)^3 - \cos^3\theta}{3}$

$\therefore f(\theta) = \dfrac{1+3\sin\theta+3\sin^2\theta}{3}$ and $g(\theta) = \dfrac{1+3\cos\theta+3\cos^2\theta}{3}$

Now, $f(\theta) - g(\theta) = (\sin\theta - \cos\theta) + (\sin^2\theta - \cos^2\theta)$

and $f(\theta) - g(\theta) = (\sin\theta - \cos\theta)(1+\sin\theta+\cos\theta)$

Now verify all matchings.

65. (A) Let $a = 2008$, then

$$I = \int_0^1 (1+ax^a)\, e^{x^a}\, dx$$

$$I = \int_0^1 (e^{x^a} + ax^a e^{x^a})\, dx \qquad (\text{note} : ax^a = ax \cdot x^{a-1})$$

$$\therefore \; I = \int_0^1 (e^{x^a} + e^{x^a} \cdot x \cdot ax^{a-1})\, dx$$

$$= \int_0^1 (f(x) + x\, f'(x))\, dx, \text{ where } f(x) = e^{x^a}$$

Hence, $I = [xe^{x^a}]_0^1 = e$

(B) $\quad I = I_1 + I_2$

Consider $I_2 = \int_1^{1/e} \sqrt{-\ln x}\, dx$

Put $\sqrt{-\ln x} = t \Rightarrow -\ln x = t^2 \Rightarrow x = e^{-t^2}$

$$\Rightarrow \quad dx = -2t\, e^{-t^2}\, dt$$

$$\therefore \; I_2 = \int_0^1 \underset{\text{I}}{t} \cdot \underset{\text{II}}{\underbrace{(-2te^{-t^2})}}\, dt = [te^{-t^2}]_0^1 - \int_0^1 e^{-t^2} dt = \frac{1}{e} - \int_0^1 e^{-t^2} dt$$

Hence, $\quad I_2 = \int_0^1 e^{-x}\, dx + \dfrac{1}{e} - \int_0^1 e^{-t^2}\, dt = \dfrac{1}{e} = e^{-1}$

Note that, if $f(x) = e^{-x^2}$, then $f^{-1}(x) = \sqrt{-\ln x}$

(C) $L = \lim\limits_{n\to\infty} \left[\left(\dfrac{1}{n}\right)^1 \cdot \left(\dfrac{2}{n}\right)^2 \cdot \left(\dfrac{3}{n}\right)^3 \cdots \left(\dfrac{n}{n}\right)^n\right]^{\frac{1}{n^2}}$

$$\Rightarrow \quad \ln L = \lim_{n\to\infty} \frac{1}{n^2}$$

$$\left[1 \cdot \ln\left(\frac{1}{n}\right) + 2 \cdot \ln\left(\frac{2}{n}\right) + 3 \cdot \ln\left(\frac{3}{n}\right) + \dots + n \cdot \ln\left(\frac{n}{n}\right)\right]$$

General term of $\ln L = \dfrac{r}{n^2} \ln \dfrac{r}{n}$

$$\text{Sum} = \frac{1}{n} \cdot \sum_{r=1}^{n} \frac{r}{n} \ln\left(\frac{r}{n}\right)$$

$$\ln L = \int_0^1 x \ln x\, dx = \left[\frac{x^2 \cdot \ln x}{2}\right]_0^1 - \frac{1}{2}\int_0^1 x^2 \frac{1}{x}\, dx$$

$$= \left[0 - \frac{1}{2}\frac{x^2}{2}\right]_0^1 = -\frac{1}{4}$$

$\therefore \quad L = e^{-1/4}$

66. (A) We have, $f'(x) = \dfrac{g'(x)}{\sqrt{1+g^3(x)}}$

and $g'(x) = (1+\sin(\cos^2 x))(-\sin x)$

Hence, $\quad f'(x) = \dfrac{(1+\sin(\cos^2 x))(-\sin x)}{\sqrt{1+g^3(x)}}$

$$f'\left(\frac{\pi}{2}\right) = \frac{1+0}{\sqrt{1+g^3\left(\dfrac{\pi}{2}\right)}} = -1,\; g\left(\frac{\pi}{2}\right) = 0$$

$$\therefore \quad f'\left(\frac{\pi}{2}\right) = -1$$

(B) We have, $\int_0^x f(x)\, dx = \{f(x)\}^2$

Differentiating both the sides, we get

$$f(x) = 2f(x) \cdot f'(x) \;\Rightarrow\; f'(x) = \frac{1}{2}$$

Integrating both the sides, $f(x) = \dfrac{1}{2}x + C$

where, $f(0) = 0 \quad \Rightarrow \quad C = 0$

$\Rightarrow \quad f(x) = \dfrac{x}{2} \;\Rightarrow\; f(2) = 1$

(C) Maximum when $a = -1, b = 2 \Rightarrow a + b = 1$

(D) If $\quad \lim\limits_{x\to 0} \dfrac{\sin 2x}{x^3} + a + \dfrac{b}{x^2} = 0$, then

$$\lim_{x\to 0} \frac{\sin 2x + ax^3 + bx}{x^3} = 0$$

For limit to exist $2 + b = 0 \Rightarrow b = -2$

$$\therefore \quad \lim_{x\to 0} \frac{\sin 2x + ax^3 - 2x}{x^3} = 0$$

Using left hand rule and solving, we get $a = \dfrac{4}{3}$

$$\therefore \qquad 3a + b = 2$$

67. Let $B = \sum\limits_{n=1} \dfrac{\sin nx}{4^n} = \dfrac{\sin x}{4} + \dfrac{\sin 2x}{4^2} + \dots$

and $\quad A = 1 + \cos\dfrac{x}{4} + \cos\dfrac{2x}{4^2} + \dots$

$$\therefore A + iB = 1 + \frac{e^{ix}}{4} + \frac{e^{i2x}}{4^2} + \dots = \frac{1}{1 - \dfrac{e^{ix}}{4}}$$

Thus, B imaginary part of $\dfrac{1}{1 - \dfrac{e^{ix}}{4}} = \dfrac{4}{4 - \cos x - i\sin x}$

$$\therefore \qquad B = \frac{4\sin x}{17 - \theta\cos x} \Rightarrow f(x) = \frac{4\sin x}{17 - \theta\cos x}$$

and $\int_0^\pi f(x)dx = \int_0^\pi \dfrac{4\sin x}{17 - \theta\cos x} = \dfrac{1}{2}\log\left(\dfrac{25}{9}\right)$

$$= \log\left(\frac{5}{3}\right) = \log\left(\frac{m}{n}\right)$$

$$\therefore \qquad m + n = 8$$

68. Here, $I = \int_{-\pi/2}^{\pi/2} \dfrac{\cos x dx}{1 + 2[\sin^{-1}(\sin x)]}$

$$= \int_{-\pi/2}^{-1} \frac{\cos x}{-3} dx + \int_{-1}^{0} \frac{\cos x dx}{-1} + \int_0^1 \cos x dx + \int_1^{\pi/2} \frac{\cos x}{3} dx$$

$$= \frac{1}{3}\int_{-1}^{-\pi/2} \cos x dx + \int_0^{-1} \cos x dx + \int_0^1 \cos x dx + \frac{1}{3}\int_1^{\pi/2} \cos x dx$$

$$= \frac{1}{3}\int_0^{\pi/2} \cos t(-dt) + \int_0^1 \cos(t) \cdot (-dt) + \int_0^1 \cos x dx + \frac{1}{3}\int_1^{\pi/2} \cos x dx$$

$$= 0$$

69. Here, $f(x+1)-f(x)=\dfrac{1}{\pi}\displaystyle\int_0^{\pi/2}\frac{\sin^2(n+1)\theta-\sin^2 n\theta}{\sin^2\theta}d\theta$

$$=\frac{1}{\pi}\int_0^{\pi/2}\frac{\sin(2n+1)\theta\cdot\sin\theta}{\sin^2\theta}d\theta$$

$$=\frac{1}{\pi}\int_0^{\pi/2}\frac{\sin(2n+1)\theta}{\sin^2\theta}d\theta$$

$$=\frac{1}{\pi}\left(\int_0^{\pi/2}\frac{\sin 2n\theta\cdot\cos\theta}{\sin\theta}d\theta+\int_0^{\pi/2}\cos 2n\theta\, d\theta\right)$$

Using, $\cos\theta+\cos 3\theta+\cos 5\theta+\ldots+\cos(2n-1)\theta$

$$=\frac{\sin\dfrac{n\cdot(2\theta)}{2}}{\sin\left(\dfrac{2\theta}{2}\right)}\cdot\cos(\theta+(n-1)\theta)$$

i.e. $\cos\theta+\cos 3\theta+\cos 5\theta+\ldots+\cos(2n-1)\theta=\dfrac{1}{2}\left(\dfrac{\sin 2n\theta}{\sin\theta}\right)$

$\therefore f(n+1)-f(n)=\dfrac{1}{\pi}$

$$\left[2\int_0^{\pi/2}\cos\theta+\cos 3\theta+\ldots+\cos(2n-1)\theta\cdot\cos\theta\, d\theta+0\right]$$

$$=\frac{1}{\pi}\int_0^{\pi/2}\{(2\cos\theta\cos\theta)+(2\cos 3\theta\cos\theta)+\ldots(2\cos(2n-1)\cdot\cos\theta)\}d\theta$$

$$=\frac{1}{\pi}\int_0^{\pi/2}1\cdot d\theta,\text{ as }\int_0^{\pi/2}\cos 2n\theta\, d\theta=0$$

$\therefore \quad f(n+1)-f(n)=\dfrac{1}{2}$

If $\quad n=1,\ f(2)-f(1)=\dfrac{1}{2}\left(\text{as } f(1)=\dfrac{1}{2}\right)\Rightarrow f(2)=\dfrac{2}{2}$

If $\quad n=2,\ f(3)-f(2)=\dfrac{1}{2}$

$\Rightarrow f(3)=\dfrac{3}{2}$ and so on $\quad\therefore f(n)=\dfrac{n}{2}$

Hence, $\dfrac{f(15)+f(3)}{f(15)-f(9)}=\dfrac{\dfrac{15}{2}+\dfrac{3}{2}}{\dfrac{15}{2}-\dfrac{9}{2}}=3$

70. Here, $g(x)=\displaystyle\int_{-2}^{h(x)}e^{(1+t)^2}dt$

$\Rightarrow \quad g'(x)=h'(x)\cdot e^{(1+h(x))}$

$\Rightarrow \quad g'(x)=h'(x)\cdot e$

$\Rightarrow \quad g'(2)=h'(2)\cdot e^{(1+h(x))^2}$

$\Rightarrow e^4=1\cdot e^{(1+h(2))^2}$, given $g'(2)=e^4$ and $h'(2)=1$

$\therefore \quad (1+h(2))^2=4$

$\Rightarrow \quad 1+h(2)=2,-2$

$\therefore \quad h(2)=-3,1$

$\therefore$ Absolute sum for all possible values of $h(2)=|-3+1|=2$

71. Let $I=\displaystyle\int_0^{\pi/2}\sin x\cdot\log(\sin x)dx=\frac{1}{2}\int_0^{\pi/2}\sin x\cdot\log(\sin^2 x)dx$

$$=\frac{1}{2}\int_0^{\pi/2}\sin x\cdot\log(1-\cos^2 x)dx$$

Put $\cos x=t\Rightarrow -\sin x\, dx=dt$

$\therefore \quad I=\dfrac{1}{2}\displaystyle\int_0^1\log(1-t^2)dt$

$$=\frac{1}{2}\int_0^1\left(-t^2-\frac{(-t^2)^2}{2}+\frac{(-t^2)^3}{2}\ldots\right)dt$$

$$=\frac{1}{2}\left[\frac{-t^3}{3}-\frac{t^5}{10}+\frac{t^7}{21}\ldots\right]_0^1=\frac{1}{2}\left[\frac{-1}{3}-\frac{1}{10}+\frac{1}{21}\ldots\right]$$

$$=-\frac{1}{2}\left[\frac{1}{3}+\frac{1}{10}+\frac{1}{21}+\ldots\right]=-\left[\frac{1}{2\times 3}+\frac{1}{20}+\frac{1}{42}+\ldots\right]$$

$$=-\left[\left(\frac{1}{2}-\frac{1}{3}\right)+\left(\frac{1}{4}-\frac{1}{5}\right)+\left(\frac{1}{6}-\frac{1}{7}\right)+\ldots\right]$$

$$=\log_e 2-1=\log_e\left(\frac{2}{e}\right)$$

$\therefore \quad K=2$

72. Let $\quad I=\displaystyle\int_{-\pi/2}^{\pi/2}\frac{x^2\cos x}{1+e^x}dx$ ...(i)

$$\left[\because \int_a^b f(x)dx=\int_a^b f(a+b-x)\,dx\right]$$

$\Rightarrow \quad I=\displaystyle\int_{-\pi/2}^{\pi/2}\frac{x^2\cos(-x)}{1+e^{-x}}dx$ ...(ii)

On adding Eqs. (i) and (ii), we get

$$2I=\int_{-\pi/2}^{\pi/2}x^2\cos x\left[\frac{1}{1+e^x}+\frac{1}{1+e^{-x}}\right]dx$$

$$=\int_{-\pi/2}^{\pi/2}x^2\cos x\cdot(1)\,dx$$

$$\left[\because \int_{-a}^{a}f(x)dx=2\int_0^a f(x)dx,\text{ when } f(-x)=f(x)\right]$$

$\Rightarrow \quad 2I=2\displaystyle\int_0^{\pi/2}x^2\cos x\, dx$

Using integration by parts, we get

$$2I=2\left[x^2(\sin x)-(2x)(-\cos x)+(2)(-\sin x)\right]_0^{\pi/2}$$

$\Rightarrow \quad 2I=2\left[\dfrac{\pi^2}{4}-2\right]$

$\therefore \quad I=\dfrac{\pi^2}{4}-2$

73. Let $f(x)=\displaystyle\int_0^x\frac{t^2}{1+t^4}dt$

$\Rightarrow f'(x)=\dfrac{x^2}{1+x^4}>0$, for all $x\in[0,1]$

$\therefore f(x)$ is increasing.

At $x=0$, $f(0)=0$ and at $x=1$,

$$f(1)=\int_0^1\frac{t^2}{1+t^4}dt$$

Because, $\quad 0<\dfrac{t^2}{1+t^4}<\dfrac{1}{2}$

$\Rightarrow \quad \displaystyle\int_0^1 0\cdot dt<\int_0^1\frac{t^2}{1+t^4}dt<\int_0^1\frac{1}{2}\cdot dt$

$\Rightarrow \quad 0<f(1)<\dfrac{1}{2}$

Thus, $f(x)$ can be plotted as

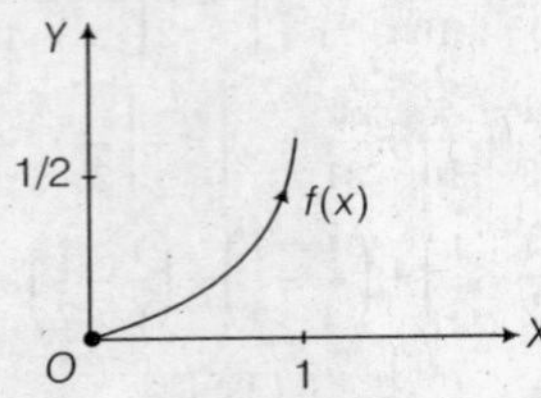

$\therefore y = f(x)$ and $y = 2x - 1$ can be shown as

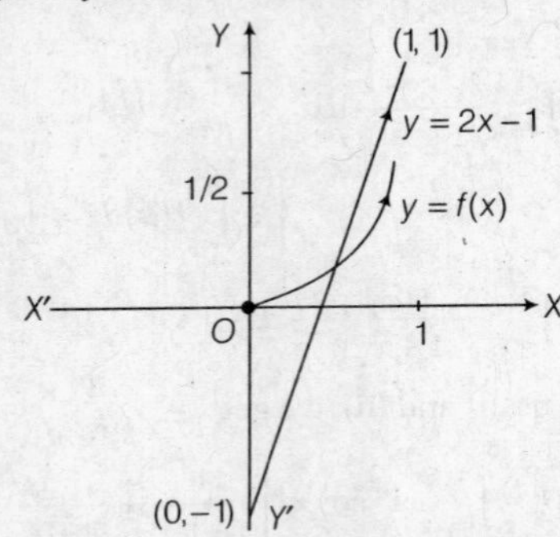

From the graph, the total number of distinct solutions for $x \in (0, 1] = 1$. [as they intersect only at one point]

74. Here, $f(x) = 7\tan^8 x + 7\tan^6 x - 3\tan^4 x - 3\tan^2 x$

for all $x \in \left(\frac{-\pi}{2}, \frac{\pi}{2}\right)$

$$\therefore \quad f(x) = 7\tan^6 x \sec^2 x - 3\tan^2 x \sec^2 x = (7\tan^6 x - 3\tan^2 x)\sec^2 x$$

$$\text{Now,} \quad \int_0^{\pi/4} x f(x)dx = \int_0^{\pi/4} \underset{\text{I}}{x} \underset{\text{II}}{(7\tan^6 x - 3\tan^2 x)\sec^2 x}\, dx$$

$$= [x(\tan^7 x - \tan^3 x)]_0^{\pi/4} - \int_0^{\pi/4} 1\,(\tan^7 x - \tan^3 x)dx$$

$$= 0 - \int_0^{\pi/4} \tan^3 x(\tan^4 x - 1)dx$$

$$= -\int_0^{\pi/4} \tan^3 x\,(\tan^2 x - 1)\sec^2 x\, dx$$

Put $\tan x = t \Rightarrow \sec^2 x\, dx = dt$

$$\therefore \quad \int_0^{\pi/4} x f(x)dx = -\int_0^1 t^3(t^2 - 1)dt$$

$$= \int_0^1 (t^3 - t^5)dt = \left[\frac{t^4}{4} - \frac{t^5}{5}\right]_0^1 = \frac{1}{4} - \frac{1}{6} = \frac{1}{12}$$

$$\text{Also,} \quad \int_0^{\pi/4} f(x)dx = \int_0^{\pi/4} (7\tan^6 x - 3\tan^2 x)\sec^2 x\, dx$$

$$= \int_0^1 (7t^6 - 3t^2)dt = [t^7 - t^3]_0^1 = 0$$

75. Here, $$f'(x) = \frac{192x^3}{2 + \sin^4 \pi x}$$

$$\therefore \quad \frac{192x^3}{3} \le f'(x) \le \frac{192x^3}{2}$$

On integrating between the limits $\frac{1}{2}$ to x, we get

$$\int_{1/2}^{x} \frac{192x^3}{3} dx \le \int_{1/2}^{x} f'(x)dx \le \int_{1/2}^{x} \frac{192x^3}{2} dx$$

$$\Rightarrow \quad \frac{192}{12}\left(x^4 - \frac{1}{16}\right) \le f(x) - f(0) \le 24x^4 - \frac{3}{2}$$

$$\Rightarrow \quad 16x^4 - 1 \le f(x) \le 24x^4 - \frac{3}{2}$$

Again, integrating between the limits $\frac{1}{2}$ to 1, we get

$$\int_{1/2}^{1} (16x^4 - 1)dx \le \int_{1/2}^{1} f(x)dx \le \int_{1/2}^{1} \left(24x^4 - \frac{3}{2}\right)dx$$

$$\Rightarrow \quad \left[\frac{16x^5}{5} - x\right]_{1/2}^{1} \le \int_{1/2}^{1} f(x)dx \le \left[\frac{24x^5}{5} - \frac{3}{2}x\right]_{1/2}^{1}$$

$$\Rightarrow \quad \left(\frac{11}{5} + \frac{2}{5}\right) \le \int_{1/2}^{1} f(x)dx \le \left(\frac{33}{10} + \frac{6}{10}\right)$$

$$\Rightarrow \quad 2.6 \le \int_{1/2}^{1} f(x)dx \le 3.9$$

76. Let $I_1 = \int_0^{4\pi} e^t(\sin^6 at + \cos^6 at)dt$

$$= \int_0^{\pi} e^t(\sin^6 at + \cos^6 at)dt + \int_{\pi}^{2\pi} e^t(\sin^6 at + \cos^6 at)dt + \int_{2\pi}^{3\pi} e^t(\sin^6 at + \cos^6 at)dt + \int_{3\pi}^{4\pi} e^t(\sin^6 at + \cos^6 at)dt$$

$$\therefore \quad I_1 = I_2 + I_3 + I_4 + I_5 \quad \text{...(i)}$$

Now, $I_3 = \int_{\pi}^{2\pi} e^t(\sin^6 at + \cos^6 at)dt$

Put $t = \pi + t \Rightarrow dt = dt$

$$\therefore \quad I_3 = \int_0^{\pi} e^{\pi + t}\cdot(\sin^6 at + \cos^6 at)dt = e^{\pi}\cdot I_2 \quad \text{...(ii)}$$

Now, $I_4 = \int_{2\pi}^{3\pi} e^t(\sin^6 at + \cos^6 at)dt$

Put $t = 2\pi + t \Rightarrow dt = dt$

$$\therefore \quad I_4 = \int_0^{\pi} e^{t + 2\pi}(\sin^6 at + \cos^6 at)dt = e^{2\pi}\cdot I_2 \quad \text{...(iii)}$$

and $I_5 = \int_{3\pi}^{4\pi} e^t(\sin^6 at + \cos^6 at)dt$

Put $t = 3\pi + t$

$$\therefore \quad I_5 = \int_0^{\pi} e^{3\pi + t}(\sin^6 at + \cos^6 at)dt = e^{3\pi}\cdot I_2 \quad \text{...(iv)}$$

From Eqs. (i), (ii), (iii) and (iv), we get

$$I_1 = I_2 + e^{\pi}\cdot I_2 + e^{2\pi}\cdot I_2 + e^{3\pi}\cdot I_2 = (1 + e^{\pi} + e^{2\pi} + e^{3\pi})I_2$$

$$\therefore \quad L = \frac{\int_0^{4\pi} e^t(\sin^6 at + \cos^6 at)dt}{\int_0^{\pi} e^t(\sin^6 at + \cos^6 at)dt}$$

$$= (1 + e^{\pi} + e^{2\pi} + e^{3\pi}) = \frac{1\cdot(e^{4\pi} - 1)}{e^{\pi} - 1} \text{ for } a \in R$$

77. According to the given data, $F(x) < 0, \forall x \in (1, 3)$

We have, $f(x) = xF(x)$

$$\Rightarrow \quad f'(x) = F(x) + xF'(x) \quad \text{...(i)}$$

$$\Rightarrow \quad f'(1) = F(1) + F'(1) < 0$$

[given $F(1) = 0$ and $F'(x) < 0$]

Also, $f(2) = 2F(2) < 0$ [using $F(x) < 0, \forall x \in (1, 3)$]

Now, $f'(x) = F(x) + xF'(x) < 0$

[using $F(x) < 0, \forall x \in (1,3)$]

$$\Rightarrow \quad f'(x) < 0$$

78. Given, $\int_1^3 x^2 F'(x)dx = -12$

$\Rightarrow \quad [x^2 F(x)]_1^3 - \int_1^3 2x \cdot F(x)dx = -12$

$\Rightarrow \quad 9F(3) - F(1) - 2\int_1^3 f(x)dx = -12$ [$\because xF(x) = f(x)$, given]

$\Rightarrow \quad -36 - 0 - 2\int_1^3 f(x)dx = -12$

$\therefore \quad \int_1^3 f(x)dx = -12$

and $\quad \int_1^3 x^3 F''(x)dx = 40$

$\Rightarrow \quad [x^3 F'(x)]_1^3 - \int_1^3 3x^2 F'(x)dx = 40$

$\Rightarrow \quad [x^2(xF'(x))]_1^3 - 3\times(-12) = 40$

$\Rightarrow \quad \{x^2 \cdot [f'(x) - F(x)]\}_1^3 = 4$

$\Rightarrow 9[f'(3) - F(3)] - [f'(1) - F(1)] = 4$

$\Rightarrow \quad 9[f'(3) + 4] - [f'(1) - 0] = 4$

$\Rightarrow \quad 9f'(3) - f'(1) = -32$

79. Here, $f(x) = \begin{cases} [x], & x \le 2 \\ 0, & x > 2 \end{cases}$

$\therefore \quad I = \int_{-1}^{2} \frac{x\,f(x^2)}{2 + f(x+1)}dx$

$$= \int_{-1}^{0} \frac{x\,f(x^2)}{2 + f(x+1)}dx + \int_0^1 \frac{x\,f(x^2)}{2 + f(x+1)}dx + \int_1^{\sqrt{2}} \frac{x\,f(x^2)}{2 + f(x+1)}dx + \int_{\sqrt{2}}^{\sqrt{3}} \frac{x\,f(x^2)}{2 + f(x+1)}dx + \int_{\sqrt{3}}^{2} \frac{x\,f(x^2)}{2 + f(x+1)}dx$$

$$= \int_{-1}^{0} 0\,dx + \int_0^1 0\,dx + \int_1^{\sqrt{2}} \frac{x \cdot 1}{2+0}dx + \int_{\sqrt{2}}^{\sqrt{3}} 0\,dx + \int_{\sqrt{3}}^{2} 0\,dx$$

$\because -1 < x < 0 \Rightarrow 0 < x^2 < 1 \Rightarrow [x^2] = 0,$

$0 < x < 1 \Rightarrow 0 < x^2 < 1 \Rightarrow [x^2] = 0,$

$1 < x < \sqrt{2} \Rightarrow \begin{cases} 1 < x^2 < 2 \quad \Rightarrow [x^2] = 1 \\ 2 < x+1 < 1+\sqrt{2} \Rightarrow f(x+1) = 0, \end{cases}$

$\sqrt{2} < x < \sqrt{3} \Rightarrow 2 < x^2 < 3 \Rightarrow f(x^2) = 0,$

and $\sqrt{3} < x < 2 \Rightarrow 3 < x^2 < 4 \Rightarrow f(x^2) = 0$

$\Rightarrow \quad I = \int_1^{\sqrt{2}} \frac{x}{2}dx = \left[\frac{x^2}{4}\right]_1^{\sqrt{2}} = \frac{1}{4}(2-1) = \frac{1}{4}$

$\therefore \quad 4I = 1 \Rightarrow 4I - 1 = 0$

80. Here, $\alpha = \int_0^1 e^{(9x + 3\tan^{-1} x)}\left(\frac{12+9x^2}{1+x^2}\right)dx$

Put $9x + 3\tan^{-1} x = t$

$\Rightarrow \quad \left(9 + \frac{3}{1+x^2}\right)dx = dt$

$\therefore \quad \alpha = \int_0^{9+3\pi/4} e^t\,dt = [e^t]_0^{9+3\pi/4} = e^{9+3\pi/4} - 1$

$\Rightarrow \quad \log_e|1+\alpha| = 9 + \frac{3\pi}{4}$

$\Rightarrow \log_e|\alpha+1| - \frac{3\pi}{4} = 9$

81. **Plan** This type of question can be done using appropriate substitution.

Given, $I = \int_{\pi/4}^{\pi/2} (2\,\text{cosec}\,x)^{17}\,dx$

$$= \int_{\pi/4}^{\pi/2} \frac{2^{17}(\text{cosec}\,x)^{16}\,\text{cosec}\,x\,(\text{cosec}\,x + \cot x)}{(\text{cosec}\,x + \cot x)}dx$$

Let $\quad \text{cosec}\,x + \cot x = t$

$\Rightarrow (-\text{cosec}\,x \cdot \cot x - \text{cosec}^2 x)\,dx = dt$

and $\quad \text{cosec}\,x - \cot x = 1/t$

$\Rightarrow \quad 2\,\text{cosec}\,x = t + \frac{1}{t}$

$\therefore \quad I = -\int_{\sqrt{2}+1}^{1} 2^{17}\left(\frac{t+\frac{1}{t}}{2}\right)^{16}\frac{dt}{t}$

Let $t = e^u \Rightarrow dt = e^u du$. When $t = 1, e^u = 1 \Rightarrow u = 0$

and when $t = \sqrt{2}+1, e^u = \sqrt{2}+1$

$\Rightarrow \quad u = \ln(\sqrt{2}+1)$

$\Rightarrow \quad I = -\int_{\ln(\sqrt{2}+1)}^{0} 2(e^u + e^{-u})^{16}\frac{e^u du}{e^u}$

$$= 2\int_0^{\ln(\sqrt{2}+1)} (e^u + e^{-u})^{16}\,du$$

82. **Plan** Newton-Leibnitz's formula

$$\frac{d}{dx}\left[\int_{\phi(x)}^{\psi(x)} f(t)\,dt\right] = f\{\psi(x)\}\left\{\frac{d}{dx}\psi(x)\right\} - f\{\phi(x)\}\left\{\frac{d}{dx}\phi(x)\right\}$$

Given, $\quad F(x) = \int_0^{x^2} f(\sqrt{t})\,dt$

$\therefore \quad F'(x) = 2x\,f(x)$

Also, $\quad F'(x) = f'(x)$

$\Rightarrow \quad 2x\,f(x) = f'(x)$

$\Rightarrow \quad \frac{f'(x)}{f(x)} = 2x$

$\Rightarrow \quad \int \frac{f'(x)}{f(x)}dx = \int 2x\,dx$

$\Rightarrow \quad \ln f(x) = x^2 + c \Rightarrow f(x) = e^{x^2+c}$

$\Rightarrow \quad f(x) = K\,e^{x^2} \qquad [K = e^c]$

Now, $\quad f(0) = 1$

$\therefore \quad 1 = K$

Hence, $\quad f(x) = e^{x^2}$

$\quad F(2) = \int_0^4 e^t dt = [e^t]_0^4 = e^4 - 1$

83. (A) Let $I = \int_{-1}^{1} \frac{dx}{1+x^2}$

Put $x = \tan\theta$

$\Rightarrow dx = \sec^2\theta\,d\theta$

$\therefore \quad I = 2\int_0^{\pi/4} d\theta = \frac{\pi}{2}$

(B) Let $I=\int_0^1 \frac{dx}{\sqrt{1-x^2}}$

Put $x=\sin\theta \Rightarrow dx=\cos\theta\, d\theta$

$\therefore \quad I=\int_0^{\pi/2} 1\, d\theta=\frac{\pi}{2}$

(C) $\int_2^3 \frac{dx}{1-x^2}=\frac{1}{2}\left[\log\left(\frac{1+x}{1-x}\right)\right]_2^3$

$=\frac{1}{2}\left[\log\left(\frac{4}{-2}\right)-\log\left(\frac{3}{-1}\right)\right]=\frac{1}{2}\left[\log\left(\frac{2}{3}\right)\right]$

(D) $\int_1^2 \frac{dx}{x\sqrt{x^2-1}}=[\sec^{-1}x]_1^2=\frac{\pi}{3}-0=\frac{\pi}{3}$

84. (A) **Plan**

(p) A polynomial satisfying the given conditions is taken.

(q) The other conditions are also applied and the number of polynomial is taken out.

Let $\quad f(x)=ax^2+bx+c$

$f(0)=0 \Rightarrow c=0$

Now, $\int_0^1 f(x)\,dx=1 \Rightarrow \left(\frac{ax^3}{3}+\frac{bx^2}{2}\right)_0^1=1$

$\Rightarrow \quad \frac{\alpha}{3}+\frac{\beta}{2}=1 \Rightarrow 2a+3b=6$

As a, b are non-negative integers.

So, $\quad a=0, b=2$ or $a=3, b=0$

$\therefore \quad f(x)=2x$ or $f(x)=3x^2$

(B) **Plan** Such type of questions are converted into only sine or cosine expression and then the number of points of maxima in given interval are obtained.

$f(x)=\sin(x^2)+\cos(x^2)$

$=\sqrt{2}\left[\frac{1}{\sqrt{2}}\cos(x^2)+\frac{1}{\sqrt{2}}\sin(x^2)\right]$

$=\sqrt{2}\left[\cos x^2\cos\frac{\pi}{4}+\sin\frac{\pi}{4}\sin(x^2)\right]=\sqrt{2}\cos\left(x^2-\frac{\pi}{4}\right)$

For maximum value, $x^2-\frac{\pi}{4}=2n\pi \Rightarrow x^2=2n\pi+\frac{\pi}{4}$

$\Rightarrow \quad x=\pm\sqrt{\frac{\pi}{4}}$, for $n=0$

$x=\pm\sqrt{\frac{9\pi}{4}}$, for $n=1$

So, $f(x)$ attains maximum at 4 points in $[-\sqrt{13}, \sqrt{13}]$.

(C) **Plan**

(p) $\int_{-a}^a f(x)\,dx=\int_{-a}^a f(-x)\,dx$

(q) $\int_{-a}^a f(x)\,dx=2\int_0^a f(x)\,dx$, if $f(-x)=f(x)$, i.e. f is an even function.

$I=\int_{-2}^2 \frac{3x^2}{1+e^x}dx$ and $I=\int_{-2}^2 \frac{3x^2}{1+e^{-x}}dx$

$\Rightarrow \quad 2I=\int_{-2}^2\left(\frac{3x^2}{1+e^x}+\frac{3x^2(e^x)}{e^x+1}\right)dx$

$2I=\int_{-2}^2 3x^2\,dx \Rightarrow 2I=2\int_0^2 3x^2\,dx$

$I=[x^3]_0^2=8$

(D) **Plan** $\int_{-a}^a f(x)\,dx=0$

If $f(-x)=-f(x)$, i.e. $f(x)$ is an odd function.

Let $f(x)=\cos 2x\log\left(\frac{1+x}{1-x}\right)$

$f(-x)=\cos 2x\log\left(\frac{1-x}{1+x}\right)=-f(x)$

Hence, $f(x)$ is an odd function.

So, $\quad \int_{-1/2}^{1/2} f(x)\,dx=0$

(A) → (q); (B) → (r); (C) → (p); (D) → (s)

85. **Plan** Integration by parts

$$\int f(x)\,g(x)\,dx=f(x)\int g(x)\,dx-\int\left(\frac{d}{dx}[f(x)]\int g(x)\,dx\right)dx$$

Given, $I=\int_0^1 \underset{\text{I}}{4x^3}\,\frac{d^2}{dx^2}\underset{\text{II}}{(1-x^2)^5}\,dx$

$=\left[4x^3\frac{d}{dx}(1-x^2)^5\right]_0^1-\int_0^1 12x^2\frac{d}{dx}(1-x^2)^5\,dx$

$=\left[4x^3\times 5(1-x^2)^4\,(-2x)\right]_0^1$

$-12\left[[x^2(1-x^2)^5]_0^1-\int_0^1 2x(1-x^2)^5\,dx\right]$

$=0-0-12(0-0)+12\int_0^1 2x(1-x^2)^5\,dx$

$=12\times\left[-\frac{(1-x^2)^6}{6}\right]_0^1=12\left[0+\frac{1}{6}\right]=2$

86. $I=\int_{-\pi/2}^{\pi/2}\left[x^2+\log\left(\frac{\pi-x}{\pi+x}\right)\right]\cos x\,dx$

As, $\int_{-a}^a f(x)\,dx=0$, when $f(-x)=-f(x)$

$\therefore \quad I=\int_{-\pi/2}^{\pi/2} x^2\cos x\,dx+0=2\int_0^{\pi/2}(x^2\cos x)\,dx$

$=2\{(x^2\sin x)_0^{\pi/2}-\int_0^{\pi/2} 2x\cdot\sin x\,dx\}$

$=2\left[\frac{\pi^2}{4}-2\{(-x\cdot\cos x)_0^{\pi/2}-\int_0^{\pi/2}1\cdot(-\cos x)\,dx\}\right]$

$=2\left[\frac{\pi^2}{4}-2(\sin x)_0^{\pi/2}\right]=2\left[\frac{\pi^2}{4}-2\right]=\left(\frac{\pi^2}{2}-4\right)$

87. Put $x^2=t \Rightarrow x\,dx=dt/2$

$\therefore \quad I=\int_{\log 2}^{\log 3}\frac{\sin t\cdot\frac{dt}{2}}{\sin t+\sin(\log 6-t)}$ ...(i)

Using, $\int_a^b f(x)\,dx=\int_a^b f(a+b-x)\,dx$

$=\frac{1}{2}\int_{\log 2}^{\log 3}\frac{\sin(\log 2+\log 3-t)}{\sin(\log 2+\log 3-t)+\sin(\log 6-(\log 2+\log 3-t))}dt$

$=\frac{1}{2}\int_{\log 2}^{\log 3}\frac{\sin(\log 6-t)}{\sin(\log 6-t)+\sin(t)}dt$

$\therefore \quad I=\int_{\log 2}^{\log 3}\frac{\sin(\log 6-t)}{\sin(\log 6-t)+\sin t}dt$ ...(ii)

On adding Eqs. (i) and (ii), we get

$$2I = \frac{1}{2}\int_{\log 2}^{\log 3} \frac{\sin t + \sin(\log 6 - t)}{\sin(\log 6 - t) + \sin t}\,dt$$

$$\Rightarrow \quad 2I = \frac{1}{2}(t)_{\log 2}^{\log 3} = \frac{1}{2}(\log 3 - \log 2)$$

$$\therefore \quad I = \frac{1}{4}\log\left(\frac{3}{2}\right)$$

88. Given, $f(1) = \frac{1}{3}$ and $6\int_1^x f(t)dt = 3x\,f(x) - x^3,\ \forall\, x \ge 1$

Using Newton-Leibnitz formula.

Differentiating both sides

$$\Rightarrow \quad 6f(x)\cdot 1 - 0 = 3f(x) + 3xf'(x) - 3x^2$$

$$\Rightarrow \quad 3xf'(x) - 3f(x) = 3x^2 \Rightarrow f'(x) - \frac{1}{x}f(x) = x$$

$$\Rightarrow \quad \frac{xf'(x) - f'(x)}{x^2} = 1 \Rightarrow \frac{d}{dx}\left\{\frac{x}{x}\right\} = 1$$

On integrating both sides, we get

$$\Rightarrow \quad \frac{f(x)}{x} = x + c \qquad \left[\because f(1) = \frac{1}{3}\right]$$

$$\frac{1}{3} = 1 + c \Rightarrow c = \frac{2}{3} \text{ and } f(x) = x^2 - \frac{2}{3}x$$

$$\therefore \quad f(2) = 4 - \frac{4}{3} = \frac{8}{3}$$

Note Here, $f(1) = 2$, does not satisfy given function.

$$\therefore \quad f(1) = \frac{1}{3}$$

For that $f(x) = x^2 - \frac{2}{3}x$ and $f(2) = 4 - \frac{4}{3} = \frac{8}{3}$

89. Let $I = \int_0^1 \frac{x^4(1-x)^4}{1+x^2}dx$

$$= \int_0^1 \frac{(x^4-1)(1-x)^4 + (1-x)^4}{(1+x^2)}dx$$

$$= \int_0^1 (x^2-1)(1-x)^4\,dx + \int_0^1 \frac{(1+x^2-2x)^2}{(1+x^2)}dx$$

$$= \int_0^1 \left\{(x^2-1)(1-x)^4 + (1+x^2) - 4x + \frac{4x^2}{(1+x^2)}\right\}dx$$

$$= \int_0^1 \left((x^2-1)(1-x)^4 + (1+x^2) - 4x + 4 - \frac{4}{1+x^2}\right)dx$$

$$= \int_0^1 \left(x^6 - 4x^5 + 5x^4 - 4x^2 + 4 - \frac{4}{1+x^2}\right)dx$$

$$= \left[\frac{x^7}{7} - \frac{4x^6}{6} + \frac{5x^5}{5} - \frac{4x^3}{3} + 4x - 4\tan^{-1}x\right]_0^1$$

$$= \frac{1}{7} - \frac{4}{6} + \frac{5}{5} - \frac{4}{3} + 4 - 4\left(\frac{\pi}{4} - 0\right) = \frac{22}{7} - \pi$$

90. Converting infinite series into definite integral

i.e. $\lim_{n\to\infty} \frac{h(n)}{n}$

$$\lim_{n\to\infty}\frac{1}{n}\sum_{r=g(n)}^{h(n)} f\left(\frac{r}{n}\right) = \int f(x)\,dx$$

$\lim_{n\to\infty}\frac{g(n)}{n}$, where, $\frac{r}{n}$ is replaced with x.

Σ is replaced with integral.

Here, $\lim_{n\to\infty}\frac{1^a + 2^a + \ldots + n^a}{(n+1)^{a-1}\{(na+1) + (na+2) + \ldots + (na+n)\}} = \frac{1}{60}$

$$\Rightarrow \quad \lim_{n\to\infty}\frac{\sum_{r=1}^{n} r^a}{(n+1)^{a-1}\cdot\left[n^2a + \frac{n(n+1)}{2}\right]} = \frac{1}{60}$$

$$\Rightarrow \quad \lim_{n\to\infty}\frac{2\sum_{r=1}^{n}\left(\frac{r}{n}\right)^a}{\left(1+\frac{1}{n}\right)^{a-1}\cdot(2na + n + 1)} = \frac{1}{60}$$

$$\Rightarrow \quad \lim_{n\to\infty}\frac{1}{n}\left(2\sum_{r=1}^{n}\left(\frac{r}{n}\right)^a\right)\cdot\lim_{n\to\infty}\frac{1}{\left(1+\frac{1}{n}\right)^{a-1}\cdot\left(2a+1+\frac{1}{n}\right)} = \frac{1}{60}$$

$$\Rightarrow \quad 2\int_0^1 (x^a)\,dx\cdot\frac{1}{1\cdot(2a+1)} = \frac{1}{60}$$

$$\Rightarrow \quad \frac{2\cdot[x^{a+1}]_0^1}{(2a+1)\cdot(a+1)} = \frac{1}{60}$$

$$\therefore \quad \frac{2}{(2a+1)(a+1)} = \frac{1}{60}$$

$$\Rightarrow \quad (2a+1)(a+1) = 120$$

$$\Rightarrow \quad 2a^2 + 3a + 1 - 120 = 0$$

$$\Rightarrow \quad 2a^2 + 3a - 119 = 0$$

$$\Rightarrow \quad (2a+17)(a-7) = 0$$

$$\Rightarrow \quad a = 7, \frac{-17}{2}$$

91. Here, $f(x) + 2x = (1-x)^2\cdot\sin^2 x + x^2 + 2x$ ...(i)

where, $P: f(x) + 2x = 2(1+x)^2$ ...(ii)

$$\therefore \quad 2(1+x^2) = (1-x)^2\sin^2 x + x^2 + 2x$$

$$\Rightarrow \quad (1-x)^2\sin^2 x = x^2 - 2x + 2$$

$$\Rightarrow \quad (1-x)^2\sin^2 x = (1-x)^2 + 1 \Rightarrow (1-x)^2\cos^2 x = -1$$

which is never possible.

$\therefore$ P is false.

Again, let $Q: h(x) = 2f(x) + 1 - 2x(1+x)$

where, $h(0) = 2f(0) + 1 - 0 = 1$

$h(1) = 2f(1) + 1 - 4 = -3$, as $h(0)\,h(1) < 0$

$\Rightarrow$ $h(x)$ must have a solution.

$\therefore$ Q is true.

92. Here, $f(x) = (1-x)^2\cdot\sin^2 x + x^2 \ge 0,\ \forall\, x.$

and $g(x) = \int_1^x\left(\frac{2(t-1)}{t+1} - \log t\right)f(t)\,dt$

$$\Rightarrow \quad g'(x) = \left\{\frac{2(x-1)}{(x+1)} - \log x\right\}\cdot\underbrace{f(x)}_{+\text{ ve}} \qquad \text{...(i)}$$

For $g'(x)$ to be increasing or decreasing,

let $\phi(x) = \frac{2(x-1)}{(x+1)} - \log x$

$$\phi'(x) = \frac{4}{(x+1)^2} - \frac{1}{x} = \frac{-(x-1)^2}{x(x+1)^2}$$

$\phi'(x) < 0$, for $x > 1 \Rightarrow \phi(x) < \phi(1) \Rightarrow \phi(x) < 0$ ...(ii)

From Eqs. (i) and (ii), we get

$g'(x) < 0$ for $x \in (1, \infty)$

$\therefore$ $g(x)$ is decreasing for $x \in (1, \infty)$.

93. Given, $f(x) = \begin{cases} x - [x], & \text{if } [x] \text{ is odd.} \\ 1 + [x] - x, & \text{if } [x] \text{ is even.} \end{cases}$

$f(x)$ and $\cos \pi x$ both are periodic with period 2 and both are even.

$$\therefore \int_{-10}^{10} f(x) \cos \pi x \, dx = 2 \int_0^{10} f(x) \cos \pi x \, dx$$

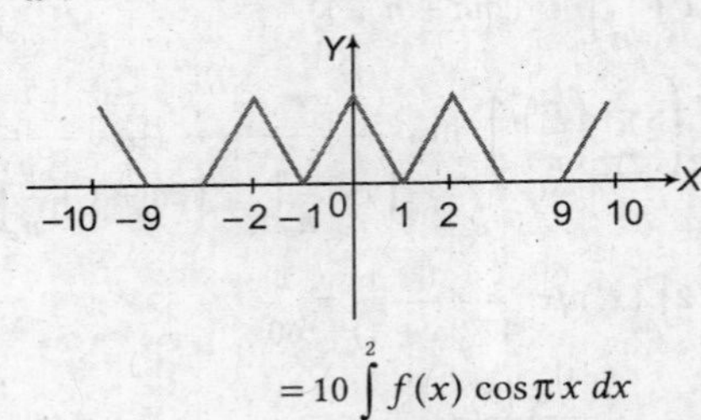

$$= 10 \int_0^2 f(x) \cos \pi x \, dx$$

Now, $\int_0^1 f(x) \cos \pi x \, dx = \int_0^1 (1-x) \cos \pi x \, dx = -\int_0^1 u \cos \pi u \, du$

and $\int_1^2 f(x) \cos \pi x \, dx = \int_1^2 (x-1) \cos \pi x \, dx = -\int_0^1 u \cos \pi u \, du$

$$\therefore \int_{-10}^{10} f(x) \cos \pi x \, dx = -20 \int_0^1 u \cos \pi u \, du = \frac{40}{\pi^2}$$

$$\Rightarrow \frac{\pi^2}{10} \int_{-10}^{10} f(x) \cos \pi x \, dx = 4$$

94. Given $\int_0^x \sqrt{1 - \{f'(t)\}^2} \, dt = \int_0^x f(t) dt, 0 \le x \le 1$

Differentiating both sides w.r.t. x by using Leibnitz's rule, we get

$$\sqrt{1 - \{f'(x)\}^2} = f(x) \Rightarrow f'(x) = \pm \sqrt{1 - \{f(x)\}^2}$$

$$\Rightarrow \int \frac{f'(x)}{\sqrt{1 - \{f(x)\}^2}} dx = \pm \int dx$$

$\Rightarrow \quad \sin^{-1} \{f(x)\} = \pm x + c$

Put $\quad x = 0 \Rightarrow \sin^{-1} \{f(0)\} = c$

$\Rightarrow \quad c = \sin^{-1}(0) = 0 \quad [\because f(0) = 0]$

$\therefore \quad f(x) = \pm \sin x$

but $\quad f(x) \ge 0, \forall x \in [0, 1]$

$\therefore \quad f(x) = \sin x$

As we know that,

$$\sin x < x, \forall x > 0$$

$$\therefore \sin\left(\frac{1}{2}\right) < \frac{1}{2} \text{ and } \sin\left(\frac{1}{3}\right) < \frac{1}{3}$$

$$\Rightarrow f\left(\frac{1}{2}\right) < \frac{1}{2} \text{ and } f\left(\frac{1}{3}\right) < \frac{1}{3}$$

95. Given $\quad I_n = \int_{-\pi}^{\pi} \frac{\sin nx}{(1 + \pi^x) \sin x} dx$ ...(i)

Using $\int_a^b f(x) \, dx = \int_a^b f(b + a - x) \, dx$, we get

$$I_n = \int_{-\pi}^{\pi} \frac{\pi^x \sin nx}{(1 + \pi^x) \sin x} dx \quad \text{...(ii)}$$

On adding Eqs. (i) and (ii), we have

$$2I_n = \int_{-\pi}^{\pi} \frac{\sin nx}{\sin x} dx = 2 \int_0^{\pi} \frac{\sin nx}{\sin x} dx$$

$\left[\because f(x) = \frac{\sin nx}{\sin x} \text{ is an even function}\right]$

$$\Rightarrow I_n = \int_0^{\pi} \frac{\sin nx}{\sin x} dx$$

Now, $\quad I_{n+2} - I_n = \int_0^{\pi} \frac{\sin (n+2)x - \sin nx}{\sin x} dx$

$$= \int_0^{\pi} \frac{2 \cos (n+1) x \cdot \sin x}{\sin x} dx$$

$$= 2 \int_0^{\pi} \cos (n+1)x \, dx = 2 \left[\frac{\sin (n+1) x}{(n+1)}\right]_0^{\pi} = 0$$

$\therefore \quad I_{n+2} = I_n$ ...(iii)

Since, $\quad I_n = \int_0^{\pi} \frac{\sin nx}{\sin x} dx \Rightarrow I_1 = \pi$ and $I_2 = 0$

From Eq. (iii) $\quad I_1 = I_3 = I_5 = \dots = \pi$ and $I_2 = I_4 = I_6 = \dots = 0$

$$\Rightarrow \sum_{m=1}^{10} I_{2m+1} = 10\pi \text{ and } \sum_{m=1}^{10} I_{2m} = 0$$

$\therefore$ Correct options are (a), (b), (c).

96. Given, $S_n = \sum_{k=0}^{n} \frac{n}{n^2 + kn + k^2}$

$$= \sum_{k=0}^{n} \frac{1}{n} \cdot \left(\frac{1}{1 + \frac{k}{n} + \frac{k^2}{n^2}}\right) < \lim_{n \to \infty} \sum_{k=0}^{n} \frac{1}{n} \left[\frac{1}{1 + \frac{k}{n} + \left(\frac{k}{n}\right)^2}\right]$$

$$= \int_0^1 \frac{1}{1 + x + x^2} dx = \left[\frac{2}{\sqrt{3}} \tan^{-1}\left(\frac{2}{\sqrt{3}}\left(x + \frac{1}{2}\right)\right)\right]_0^1$$

$$= \frac{2}{\sqrt{3}} \cdot \left(\frac{\pi}{3} - \frac{\pi}{6}\right) = \frac{\pi}{3\sqrt{3}} \text{ i.e. } S_n < \frac{\pi}{3\sqrt{3}}$$

Similarly, $T_n > \frac{\pi}{3\sqrt{3}}$

97. $\quad I = \int_{\pi/4}^{3\pi/4} \frac{dx}{1 + \cos x}$ ...(i)

$$I = \int_{\pi/4}^{3\pi/4} \frac{dx}{1 - \cos x} \quad \text{...(ii)}$$

Adding Eqs. (i) and (ii)

$$2I = \int_{\pi/4}^{3\pi/4} \frac{2}{\sin^2 x} dx \Rightarrow I = \int_{\pi/4}^{3\pi/4} \text{cosec}^2 x \, dx$$

$$I = -(\cot x)_{\pi/4}^{3\pi/4} = 2$$

98. $I_4 + I_6 = \int (\tan^4 x + \tan^6 x) \, dx = \int \tan^4 x \sec^2 x \, dx$

$$= \frac{1}{5} \tan^5 x + c \Rightarrow a = \frac{1}{5}, b = 0$$

99. (b) Let $l = \lim_{n\to\infty}\left[\frac{(n+1)\cdot(n+2)\ldots(3n)}{n^{2n}}\right]^{\frac{1}{n}}$

$$= \lim_{n\to\infty}\left[\frac{(n+1)\cdot(n+2)\ldots(n+2n)}{n^{2n}}\right]^{\frac{1}{n}}$$

$$= \lim_{n\to\infty}\left[\left(\frac{n+1}{n}\right)\left(\frac{n+2}{n}\right)\ldots\left(\frac{n+2n}{n}\right)\right]^{\frac{1}{n}}$$

Taking log on both sides, we get

$$\log l = \lim_{n\to\infty}\frac{1}{n}\left[\log\left\{\left(1+\frac{1}{n}\right)\left(1+\frac{2}{n}\right)\ldots\left(1+\frac{2n}{n}\right)\right\}\right]$$

$$\Rightarrow \log l = \lim_{n\to\infty}\frac{1}{n}\left[\log\left(1+\frac{1}{n}\right)+\log\left(1+\frac{2}{n}\right)+\ldots+\log\left(1+\frac{2n}{n}\right)\right]$$

$$\Rightarrow \log l = \lim_{n\to\infty}\frac{1}{n}\sum_{r=1}^{2n}\log\left(1+\frac{r}{n}\right)$$

$$\Rightarrow \log l = \int_0^2 \log(1+x)\,dx$$

$$\Rightarrow \log l = \left[\log(1+x)\cdot x - \int\frac{1}{1+x}\cdot x\,dx\right]_0^2$$

$$\Rightarrow \log l = [\log(1+x)\cdot x]_0^2 - \int_0^2\frac{x+1-1}{1+x}dx$$

$$\Rightarrow \log l = 2\cdot\log 3 - \int_0^2\left(1-\frac{1}{1+x}\right)dx$$

$$\Rightarrow \log l = 2\cdot\log 3 - \left[x-\log|1+x|\right]_0^2$$

$$\Rightarrow \log l = 2\cdot\log 3 - [2-\log 3]$$

$$\Rightarrow \log l = 3\cdot\log 3 - 2 \Rightarrow \log l = \log 27 - 2$$

$$\therefore \quad l = e^{\log 27 - 2} = 27\cdot e^{-2} = \frac{27}{e^2}$$

100. Central Idea Apply the property $\int_a^b f(x)dx = \int_a^b f(a+b-x)dx$ and then add. Let

$$I = \int_2^4\frac{\log x^2}{\log x^2 + \log(36-12x+x^2)}dx$$

$$= \int_2^4\frac{2\log x}{2\log x + \log(6-x)^2}dx$$

$$= \int_2^4\frac{2\log x\,dx}{2[\log x + \log(6-x)]}$$

$$\Rightarrow \quad I = \int_2^4\frac{\log x\,dx}{[\log x + \log(6-x)]} \quad \ldots\text{(i)}$$

$$\Rightarrow \quad I = \int_2^4\frac{\log(6-x)}{\log(6-x)+\log x}dx \quad \ldots\text{(ii)}$$

$$\left[\because \int_a^b f(x)dx = \int_a^b f(a+b-x)dx\right]$$

On adding Eqs. (i) and (ii), we get

$$2I = \int_2^4\frac{\log x + \log(6-x)}{\log x + \log(6-x)}dx$$

$$\Rightarrow \quad 2I = \int_2^4 dx = [x]_2^4$$

$$\Rightarrow \quad 2I = 2 \Rightarrow I = 1$$

101. Plan Use the formula, $|x-a| = \begin{cases} x-a, & x\ge a\\ -(x-a), & x<a\end{cases}$ to break given integral in two parts and then integrate separately.

$$\int_0^\pi\sqrt{\left(1-2\sin\frac{x}{2}\right)^2}dx = \int_0^\pi\left|1-2\sin\frac{x}{2}\right|dx$$

$$= \int_0^{\frac{\pi}{3}}\left(1-2\sin\frac{x}{2}\right)dx - \int_{\frac{\pi}{3}}^{\pi}\left(1-2\sin\frac{x}{2}\right)dx$$

$$= \left(x+4\cos\frac{x}{2}\right)_0^{\frac{\pi}{3}} - \left(x+4\cos\frac{x}{2}\right)_{\frac{\pi}{3}}^{\pi} = 4\sqrt{3}-4-\frac{\pi}{3}$$

102. Let $\quad I = \int_{\pi/6}^{\pi/3}\frac{dx}{1+\sqrt{\tan x}} \quad \ldots\text{(i)}$

$$\therefore \quad I = \int_{\pi/6}^{\pi/3}\frac{dx}{1+\sqrt{\tan\left(\frac{\pi}{2}-x\right)}} = \int_{\pi/6}^{\pi/3}\frac{dx}{1+\sqrt{\cot x}}$$

$$\Rightarrow \quad I = \int_{\pi/6}^{\pi/3}\frac{\sqrt{\tan x}\,dx}{1+\sqrt{\tan x}} \quad \ldots\text{(ii)}$$

On adding Eqs. (i) and (ii), we get

$$2I = \int_{\pi/6}^{\pi/3}dx \Rightarrow 2I = [x]_{\pi/6}^{\pi/3}dx$$

$$\Rightarrow \quad I = \frac{1}{2}\left[\frac{\pi}{3}-\frac{\pi}{6}\right] = \frac{\pi}{12}$$

Statement I is false.

But $\int_a^b f(x)dx = \int_a^b f(a+b-x)dx$ is a true statement by property of definite integrals.

103. Given, $y = \int_0^x |t|\,dt$

$$\therefore \quad \frac{dy}{dx} = |x|\cdot 1 - 0 = |x| \quad \text{[by Leibnitz's rule]}$$

$\because$ Tangent to the curve $y = \int_0^x |t|\,dt$, $x\in R$ are parallel to the line $y = 2x$

$\therefore$ Slope of both are equal $\Rightarrow x = \pm 2$

Points, $\quad y = \int_0^{\pm 2}|t|\,dt = \pm 2$

Equation of tangent is

$$y-2 = 2(x-2) \text{ and } y+2 = 2(x+2)$$

For x intercept put $y = 0$, we get

$$0-2 = 2(x-2) \text{ and } 0+2 = 2(x+2)$$

$$\Rightarrow \quad x = \pm 1$$

104. Given integral $g(x) = \int_0^x \cos 4t\,dt$

To find $g(x+\pi)$ in terms of $g(x)$ and $g(\pi)$.

$$g(x) = \int_0^x \cos 4t\,dt$$

$$\Rightarrow \quad g(x+\pi) = \int_{t=0}^{t=x+\pi}\cos 4t\,dt$$

$$= \int_0^x \cos 4t\,dt + \int_x^{x+\pi}\cos 4t\,dt$$

$$= g(x) + I_1 \quad \text{(say)}$$

$$I_1 = \int_x^{x+\pi}\cos 4t\,dt = \int_0^\pi \cos 4t\,dt \quad \text{(definite integral property)}$$

$$= g(\pi)$$

$\Rightarrow \quad g(x+\pi) = g(x) + g(\pi)$

But the value of I_1 is zero.

$$\Rightarrow \quad I_1 = \left[\frac{\sin 4t}{4}\right]_0^{\pi} = \left(\frac{\sin 4\pi}{4} - \frac{\sin 0}{4}\right) = 0$$

$\Rightarrow \quad g(x+\pi) = g(x) - g(\pi)$

In my opinion, the examiner has made this question keeping $g(x) + g(\pi)$ as the only answer in his/her mind. However, he/she did not realise that the value of the integral I_1 is actually zero. Hence, it does not matter whether you add to or subtract from $g(x)$.

105. $$I = \int_0^1 \frac{8\log(1+x)}{(1+x^2)}\,dx$$

Put $x = \tan\theta \Rightarrow dx = \sec^2\theta\, d\theta$

When $x = 0 \Rightarrow \tan\theta = 0$

$\therefore \theta = 0$

When $x = 1 = \tan\theta$

$\Rightarrow \theta = \frac{\pi}{4}$

$$\therefore \quad I = \int_0^{\pi/4} \frac{8\log[1+\tan\theta]}{1+\tan^2\theta}\cdot\sec^2\theta\, d\theta$$

$$I = 8\int_0^{\pi/4} \log(1+\tan\theta)\, d\theta \qquad \text{...(i)}$$

Using $\int_0^a f(x)\,dx = \int_0^a f(a-x)\,dx$, we get

$$I = 8\int_0^{\pi/4} \log\left\{1+\tan\left(\frac{\pi}{4}-\theta\right)\right\} d\theta$$

$$= 8\int_0^{\pi/4} \log\left\{1+\frac{1-\tan\theta}{1+\tan\theta}\right\} d\theta$$

$$= 8\int_0^{\pi/4} \log\left\{\frac{2}{1+\tan\theta}\right\} d\theta \qquad \text{...(ii)}$$

Adding Eqs. (i) and (ii), we get

$$2I = 8\int_0^{\pi/4}\left[\log\{1+\tan\theta\} + \log\left\{\frac{2}{1+\tan\theta}\right\}\right] d\theta$$

$$\Rightarrow \quad I = 4\int_0^{\pi/4} \log 2\, d\theta = 4\cdot\log 2(\theta)_0^{\pi/4}$$

$$= 4\log 2\cdot\left(\frac{\pi}{4} - 0\right) = \pi\log 2$$

106. If $\phi(x)$ and $\psi(x)$ are defined on $[a, b]$ and differentiable for every x and $f(t)$ is continuous, then

$$\frac{d}{dx}\left[\int_{\phi(x)}^{\psi(x)} f(t)dt\right] = f[\psi(x)]\cdot\frac{d}{dx}\psi(x) - f[\phi(x)]\frac{d}{dx}\phi(x)$$

Here, $f(x) = \int_0^x \sqrt{t}\sin t\, dt$, where $x \in \left(0, \frac{5\pi}{2}\right)$

$$f'(x) = \{\sqrt{x}\sin x - 0\} \qquad \text{...(i)}$$

(using Newton-Leibnitz formula)

$\therefore \quad f'(x) = \sqrt{x}\sin x = 0$

$\Rightarrow \quad \sin x = 0$

$\therefore \quad x = \pi, 2\pi$

$$f''(x) = \sqrt{x}\cos x + \frac{1}{2\sqrt{x}}\sin x$$

At $x = \pi$, $f''(\pi) = -\sqrt{\pi} < 0$

$\therefore$ Local maximum at $x = \pi$. At $x = 2\pi$, $f''(2\pi) = \sqrt{2\pi} > 0$

$\therefore$ Local minimum at $x = 2\pi$.

107. We have, $p'(x) = p'(1-x)$, $\forall\, x \in [0, 1]$, $p(0) = 1$, $p(1) = 41$

$\Rightarrow \quad p(x) = -p(1-x) + C$

$\Rightarrow \quad 1 = -41 + C$

$\Rightarrow \quad C = 42$

$\therefore \quad p(x) + p(1-x) = 42$

Now, $I = \int_0^1 p(x)dx = \int_0^1 p(1-x)dx$

$$\Rightarrow \quad 2I = \int_0^1 (p(x) + p(1-x))dx = \int_0^1 42\,dx = 42$$

$\Rightarrow \quad I = 21$

108. Let $I = \int_0^{\pi} [\cot x]\,dx \qquad \text{...(i)}$

$$\Rightarrow I = \int_0^{\pi} [\cot(\pi - x)]\,dx = \int_0^{\pi} [-\cot x]\,dx \qquad \text{...(ii)}$$

On adding Eqs. (i) and (ii),

$$2I = \int_0^{\pi} [\cot x]\,dx + \int_0^{\pi} [-\cot x]\,dx = \int_0^{\pi} (-1)\,dx$$

$[\because [x] + [-x] = -1, \text{ if } x \notin z \text{ and } 0, \text{ if } x \in z]$

$$= [-x]_0^{\pi} = -\pi$$

$$\therefore \quad I = -\frac{\pi}{2}$$

109. Since, $I = \int_0^1 \frac{\sin x}{\sqrt{x}}dx < \int_0^1 \frac{x}{\sqrt{x}}dx$,

because in $x \in (0,1), x > \sin x$.

$$I < \int_0^1 \sqrt{x}\,dx = \frac{2}{3}[x^{3/2}]_0^1 \Rightarrow I < \frac{2}{3}$$

and $$J = \int_0^1 \frac{\cos x}{\sqrt{x}}dx < \int_0^1 x^{-\frac{1}{2}}dx = 2$$

$$J < 2$$

CHAPTER

03

Area of Bounded Regions

Learning Part

Session 1

- Sketching of Some Common Curves
- Some More Curves which Occur Frequently in Mathematics in Standard Forms
- Asymptotes
- Areas of Curves Given by Cartesian Equations

Session 2

- Area Bounded by Two or More Curves

Practice Part

- JEE Type Examples
- Chapter Exercises

Arihant on Your Mobile !

Exercises with the symbol can be practised on your mobile. See inside cover page to activate for free.

Session 1

Sketching of Some Common Curves, Some More Curves which Occur Frequently in Mathematics in Standard Forms, Asymptotes, Areas of Curves Given by Cartesian Equations

Sketching of Some Common Curves

For finding the area of a given region, we require the knowledge of some standard curves.

(i) Straight Line

Every first degree equation in x, y represents a straight line. So, the general equation of a line is $ax + by + c = 0$. To draw a straight line find the points, where it meets with the coordinate axes by putting $y = 0$ and $x = 0$ respectively in its equation.

By joining these two points we get the sketch of the line. Sometimes the equation of a line is given in the form $y = mx$. This equation represents a line passing through the origin and inclined at an angle $\tan^{-1} m$ with the positive direction of X-axis. The equation of the form $x = a$ and $y = b$ represents straight lines parallel to Y-axis and X-axis, respectively.

Region Represented by a Linear Inequality

To find the region represented by linear inequality $ax + by \le c$ and $ax + by \ge c$, we proceed as follows

(i) Convert the inequality into equality to obtain a linear equation in x, y.

(ii) Draw the straight line represented by it.

(iii) The straight line obtained in (ii) divides the XY-plane in two parts.

To determine the region represented by the inequality choose some convenient points; e.g. origin or some points on the coordinate axes.

If the coordinates of a point satisfy the inequality, then region containing the points is the required region, otherwise the region not containing the point is required region.

Example 1 Mark the region represented by $3x + 4y \le 12$.

Sol. Converting the inequality into equation, we get $3x + 4y = 12$.

This line meets the coordinate axes at (4, 0) and (0, 3), respectively. Join these points to obtain straight line represented by $3x + 4y = 12$.

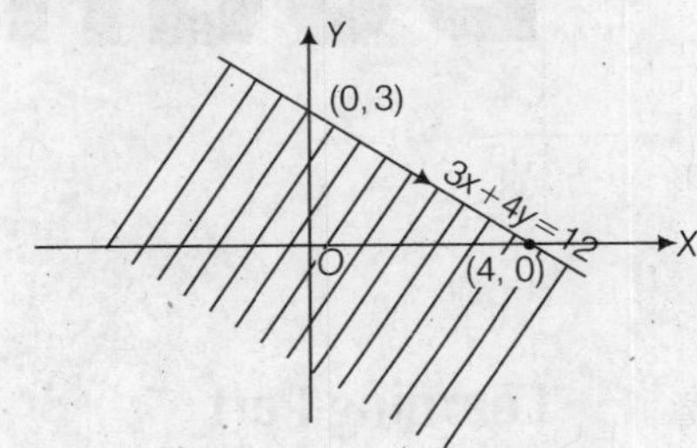

This straight line divides the plane in two parts. One part contains the origin and the other does not contains the origin. Clearly, (0, 0) satisfy the inequality $3x + 4y < 12$. So, the region represented by $3x + 4y < 12$ is region containing the origin as shown in the figure.

(ii) Circle

The general equation of a circle is

$$x^2 + y^2 + 2gx + 2fy + c = 0$$

$\therefore$ The second degree equation in x, y such that coeff. of x^2 = coeff. of y^2 and there is no term containing xy; it always represents a circle. To draw a sketch of a circle, we write the equation instandard form $(x - h)^2 + (y - k)^2 = r^2$, whose centre is (h, k) and radius is r.

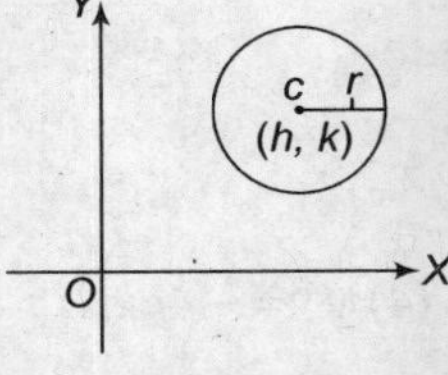

Figure 3.1

Remarks

1. The inequality $(x - a)^2 + (y - b)^2 < r^2$ represents the interior of a circle.
2. The inequality $(x - a)^2 + (y - b)^2 > r^2$ represents the exterior of a circle (i.e. region lying outside the circle).

(iii) Parabola

It is the locus of points such that its distance from a fixed point is equal to its distance from a fixed straight line.

Taking the fixed straight line $x = -a, a > 0$ and fixed point $(a, 0)$, we get the equation of parabola $y^2 = 4ax$.

Steps to Sketch the Curve

(i) It passes through (0, 0).

(ii) It is symmetrical about axis of X.

(iii) No part of the curve lies on the negative side of axis of X.

(iv) Curve turns at (0, 0) which is called the vertex of the curve.

(v) The curve extends to infinity. It is not a closed curve.

(1) $y^2 = 4ax$ (Standard equation of parabola)

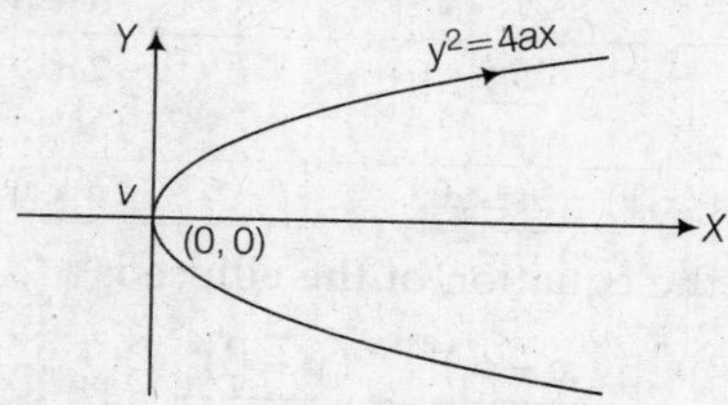

Figure 3.2

(2) $y^2 = 4a(x - h)$; where a and h are positive.

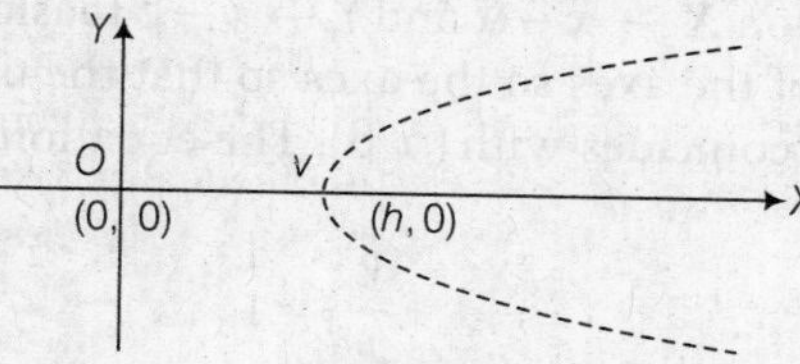

Figure 3.3

(3) $y^2 = 4a(x + h)$; where a and h are positive.

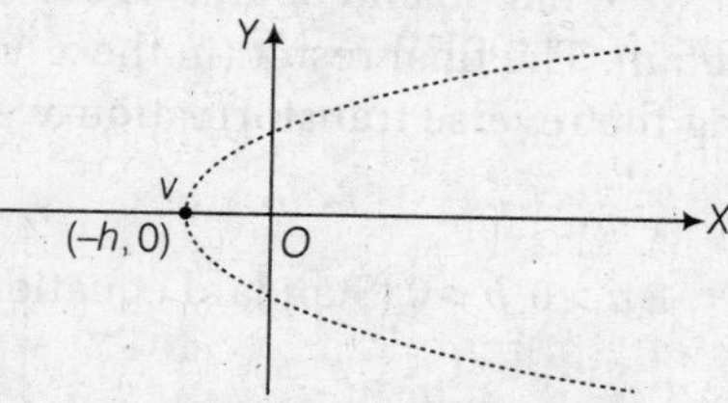

Figure 3.4

(4) $y^2 = -4ax; a > 0$

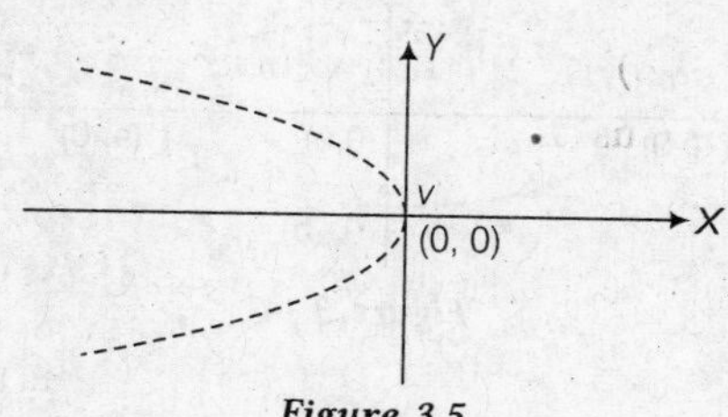

Figure 3.5

(5) $y^2 = -4a(x - h); a, h > 0$

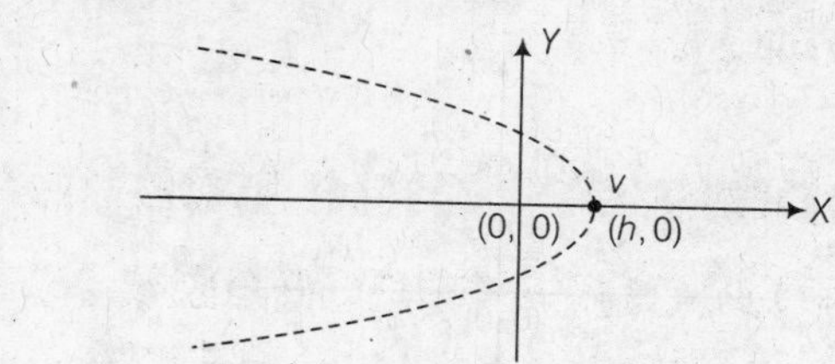

Figure 3.6

(6) $y^2 = -4a(x + h); a, h > 0$

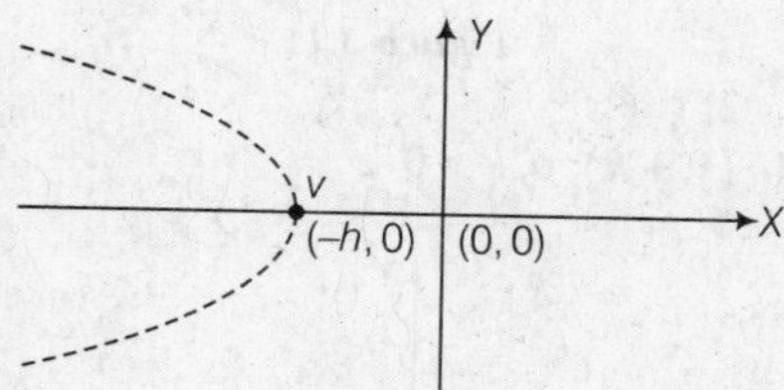

Figure 3.7

(7) $x^2 = 4ay; a > 0$

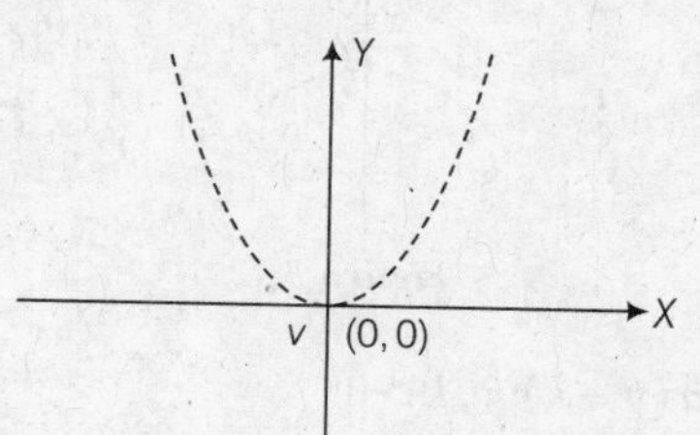

Figure 3.8

(8) $x^2 = 4a(y + k); a > 0, k > 0$

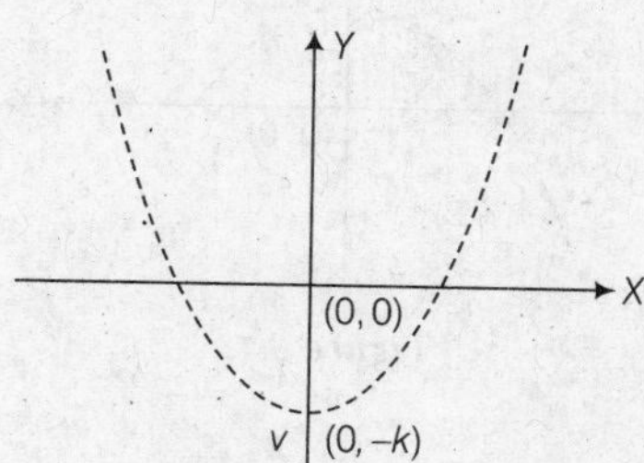

Figure 3.9

(9) $x^2 = 4a(y - k); a, k > 0$

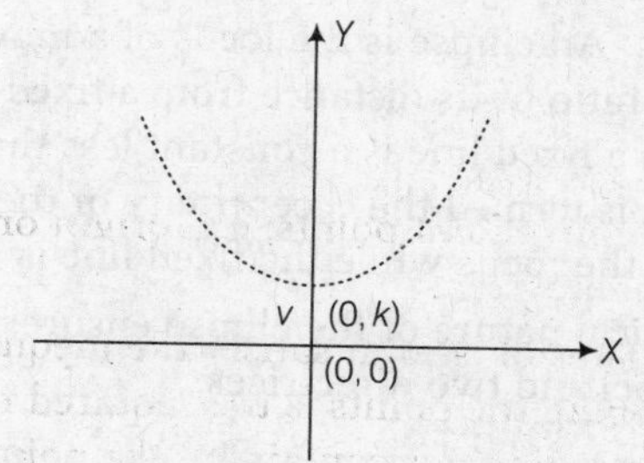

Figure 3.10

(10) $x^2 = -4ay;\ a > 0$

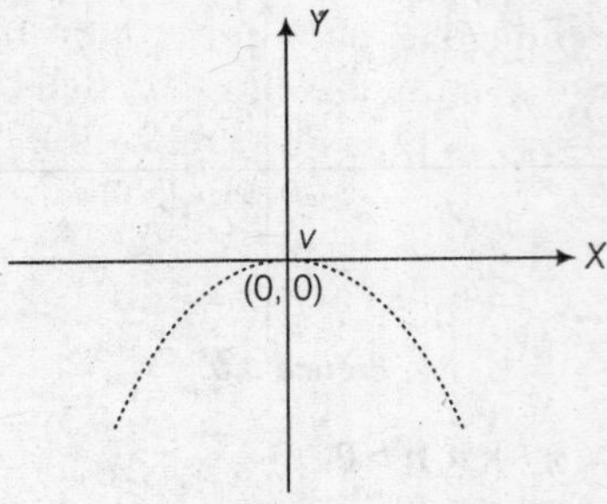

Figure 3.11

(11) $x^2 = -4a(y+k);\ a, k > 0$

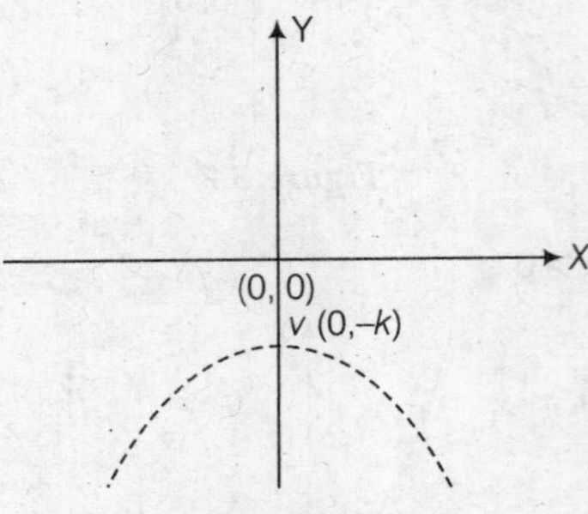

Figure 3.12

(12) $x^2 = -4a(y-k);\ a, k > 0$

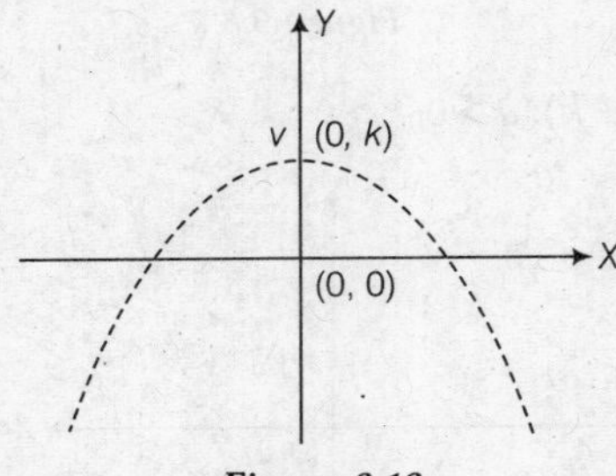

Figure 3.13

(iv) Ellipse

Basics of Ellipse

Definition 1. An ellipse is the locus of a moving point such that the ratio of its distance from a fixed point to its distance from a fixed line is a constant less than unity. This constant is termed the eccentricity of the ellipse. The fixed point is the focus while the fixed line is the directrix.

The symmetrical nature of the ellipse ensures that there will be two foci and two directrices.

Definition 2. An ellipse is the locus of a moving point such that the sum of the its distances from two fixed points is constant. The two fixed points are the two foci of the ellipse. To plot the ellipse, we can use the peg-and-thread method described earlier.

Stantard Equation

$$\frac{x^2}{a^2} + \frac{y^2}{b^2} = 1$$

	If $a > b$	**If $a < b$**
Vertices	$(a, 0)$ and $(-a, 0)$	$(0, b)$ and $(0, -b)$
Foci	$(ae, 0)$ and $(-ae, 0)$	$(0, be)$ and $(0, -be)$
Major axis	$2a$ (along x-axis)	$2b$ (along y-axis)
Minor axis	$2b$ (along y-axis)	$2a$ (along x-axis)
Directrices	$x = \frac{a}{e}$ and $x = -\frac{a}{e}$	$y = \frac{b}{e}$ and $y = -\frac{b}{e}$
Eccentricity e	$\sqrt{1 - \frac{b^2}{a^2}}$	$\sqrt{1 - \frac{a^2}{b^2}}$
Latus-rectum	$\frac{2b^2}{a}$	$\frac{2a^2}{b}$
Focal distances of (x, y)	$a \pm ex$	$b \pm ey$

And lastly, if the equation of the ellipse is

$$\frac{(x-\alpha)^2}{a^2} + \frac{(y-\beta)^2}{b^2} = 1$$

instead of the usual standard form, we can use the transformation $X \to x - \alpha$ and $Y \to y - \beta$ (basically a translation of the axes so the axes so that the origin of the new system coincides with (α, β). The equation then becomes

$$\frac{X^2}{a^2} + \frac{Y^2}{b^2} = 1$$

We can now work on this form, use all the standard formulae that we'd like to and obtain whatever it is that we wish to obtain. The final result (in the x-y system) is obtained using the reverse transformation $x \to X + \alpha$ and $y \to Y + \beta$.

(1) $\frac{x^2}{a^2} + \frac{y^2}{b^2} = 1;\ a > 0, b > 0$ (Standard equation of the ellipse)

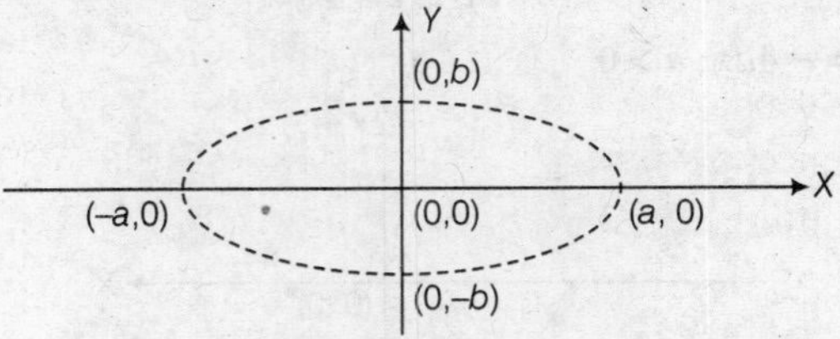

Figure 3.14

(2) $\dfrac{x^2}{a^2}+\dfrac{y^2}{b^2}=1;\ b>a>0$ (Conjugate ellipse)

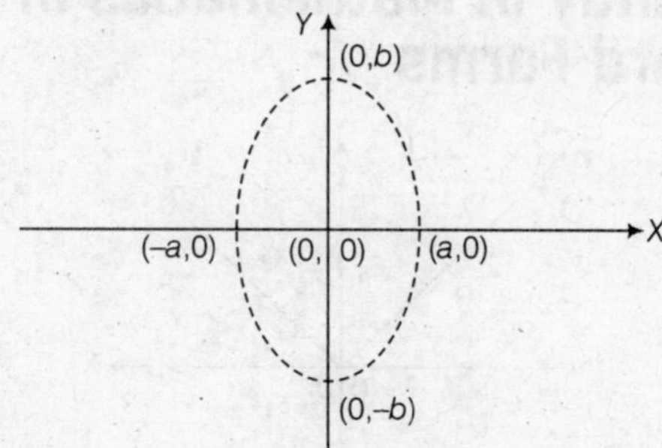

Figure 3.15

(3) $\dfrac{(x-h)^2}{a^2}+\dfrac{(y-k)^2}{b^2}=1;\ a>0, b>0$ and $a>b$

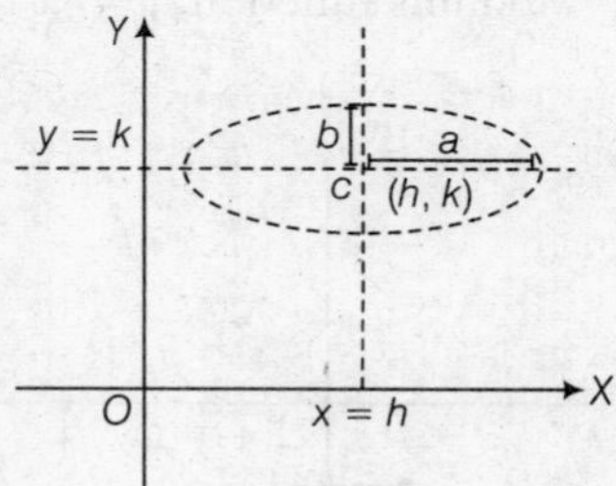

Figure 3.16

(4) $\dfrac{(x-h)^2}{a^2}+\dfrac{(y-k)^2}{b^2}=1$, where $a<b$

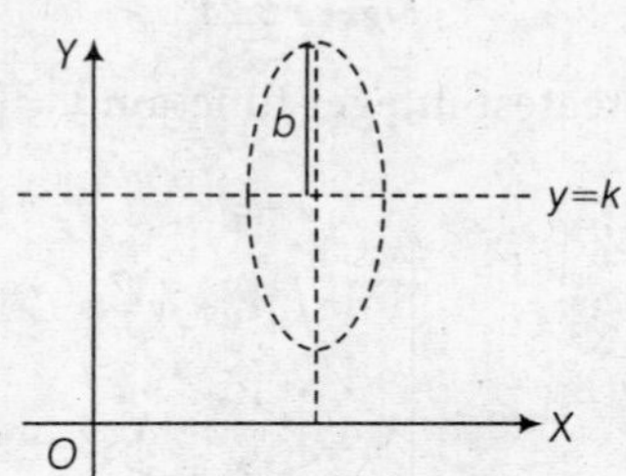

Figure 3.17

(v) Hyperbola

A hyperbola is the locus of a moving point such that the **difference** of its distances from two fixed points is always constant. The two fixed point are called the foci of the hyperbola. Constrast this with the definition of the ellipse where we had the sum of focal distances (instead of difference) as constant. As in the case of the ellipse, we have

Focal distance of $P(x, y)$

$$d_1 = e(PF) = e\left(x-\frac{a}{e}\right) = ex - a$$

$$d_2 = e(PF') = e\left(x+\frac{a}{e}\right) = ex + a$$

Latus-Rectum

The chord(s) of the hyperbola passing through the focus F (or F') and perpendicular to the transverse axis. The length of the latus-rectum can be evaluated by substituting $x=\pm ae$ in the equation for the hyperbola :

$$\frac{x^2}{a^2}-\frac{y^2}{a^2(e^2-1)}=1$$

$$\Rightarrow \quad e^2-\frac{y^2}{a^2(e^2-1)}=1$$

$$\Rightarrow \quad y^2=a^2(e^2-1)^2=\frac{a^2\cdot b^4}{a^4}=\frac{b^4}{a^2}$$

$$\Rightarrow \quad y=\pm\frac{b^2}{a}.$$

Thus, the length of the latus-rectum is $\dfrac{2b^2}{a}$.

We discussed in the unit of Ellipose that an ellipse with centre at (α, β) instead of the origin and the major and minor axis parallel to the coordinate axes will have the equation

$$\frac{(x-\alpha)^2}{a^2}+\frac{(y-\beta)}{b^2}=1 \text{ or } \frac{X^2}{a^2}+\frac{Y^2}{b^2}=1$$

where $X\to x-\alpha$ and $Y\to y-\beta$.

The same holds true for a hyperbola. Any hyperbola with centre at (α, β) and the transverse and conjugate axis parallel to the coordinate axes will have the form

$$\frac{(x-\alpha)^2}{a^2}-\frac{(y-\beta)^2}{b^2}=1$$

or

$$\frac{X^2}{a^2}-\frac{Y^2}{b^2}=1$$

where $X\to x-\alpha$ and $Y\to y-\beta$.

We can, using the definition of a hyperbola, write the equation of any hyperbola with an arbitrary focus and directrix, but we will rarely have the occassion to use it.

(1) $\dfrac{x^2}{a^2}-\dfrac{y^2}{b^2}=1$ (Standard equation of hyperbola)

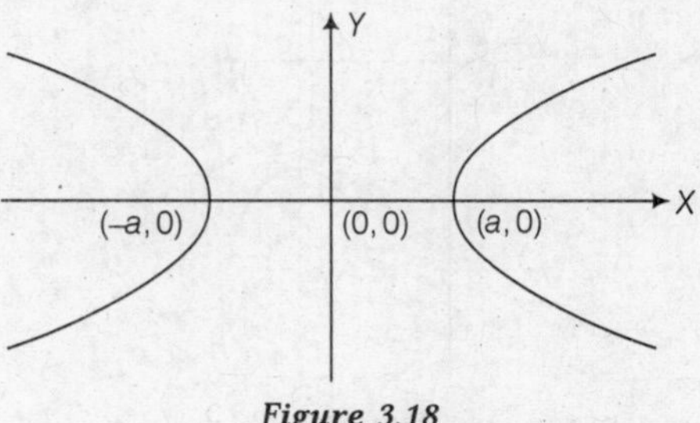

Figure 3.18

(2) $\dfrac{y^2}{b^2}-\dfrac{x^2}{a^2}=1$ (Conjugate hyperbola)

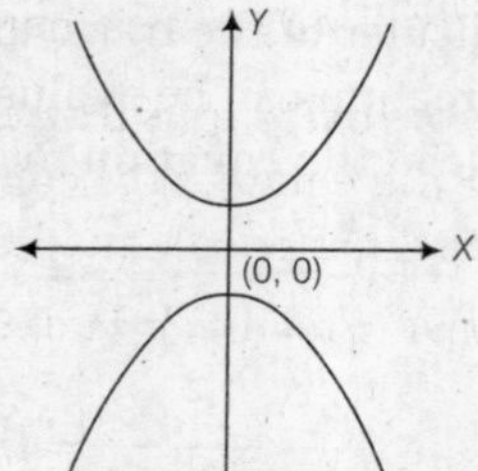

Figure 3.19

(3) $xy=c^2$ (Rectangular hyperbola)

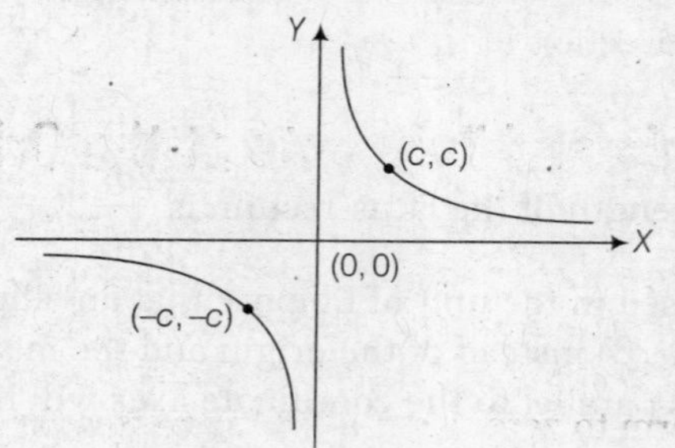

Figure 3.20

(4) $\dfrac{(x-h)^2}{a^2}-\dfrac{(y-k)^2}{b^2}=1;\ a>b>0$

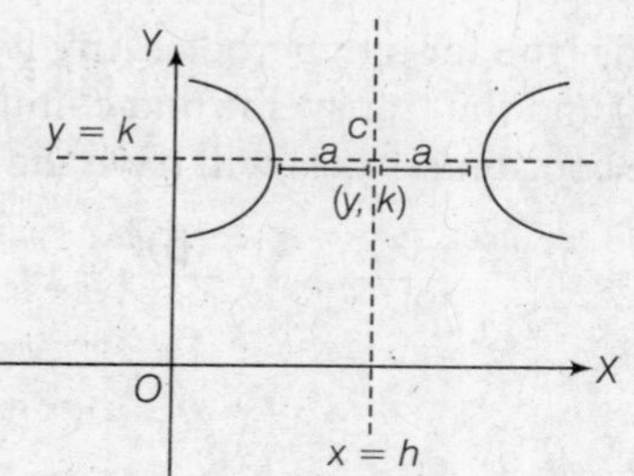

Figure 3.21

(5) $\dfrac{(x-h)^2}{a^2}-\dfrac{(y-k)^2}{b^2}=-1$

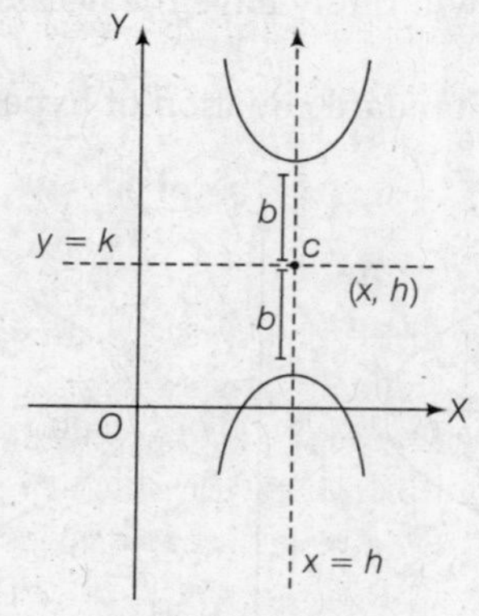

Figure 3.22

Some More Curves which Occur Frequently in Mathematics in Standard Forms

1.

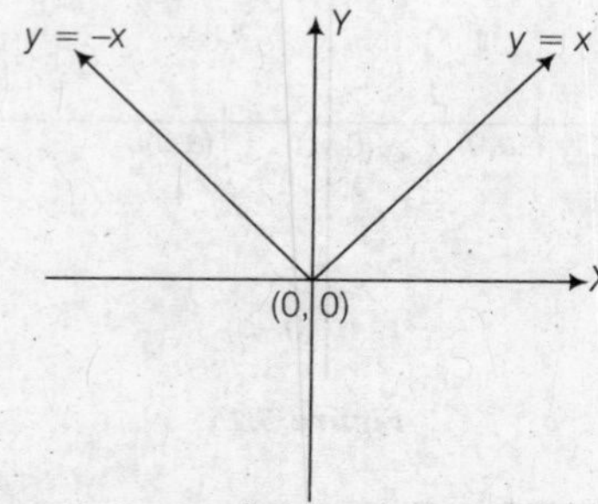

Figure 3.23

Modulus function, $y=|x|$

2.

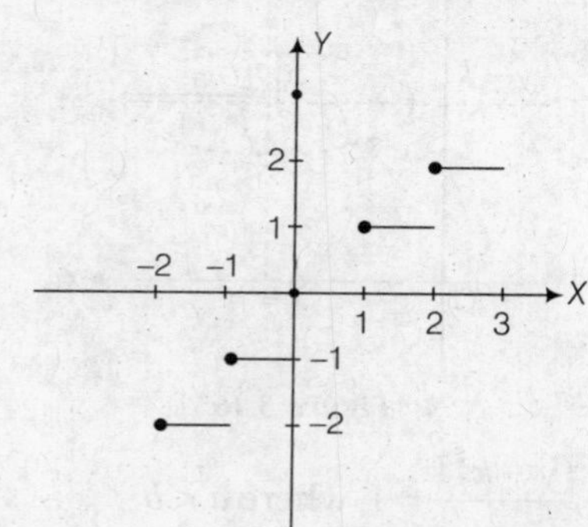

Figure 3.24

Greatest integer function $y=[x]$

3.

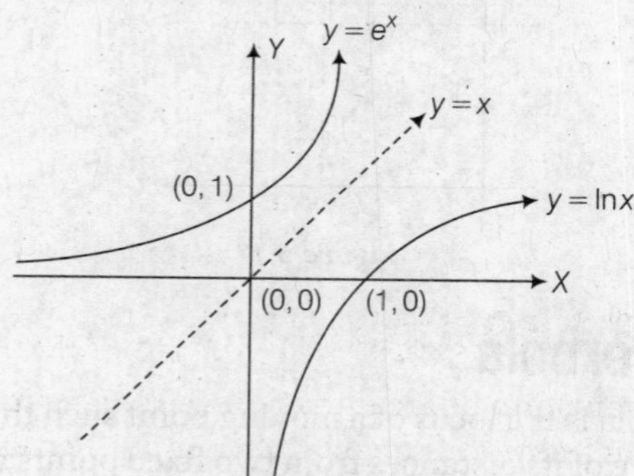

Figure 3.25

4.

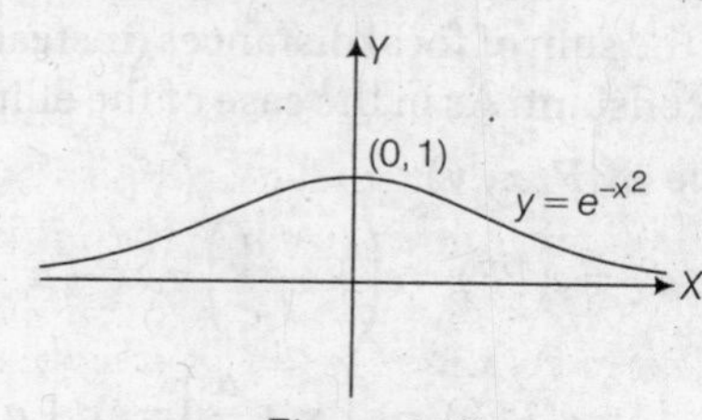

Figure 3.26

5.

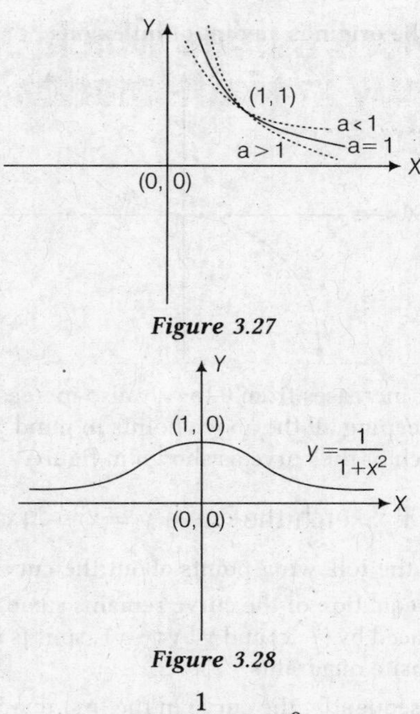

Figure 3.27

Figure 3.28

$$y=\frac{1}{x^{\alpha}}, \alpha>0$$

7. The Astroid

Its cartesian equation is $x^{2/3}+y^{2/3}=a^{2/3}$

Its parametric equation is $x=a\cos^3 t, y=a\sin^3 t$ and it could be plotted as

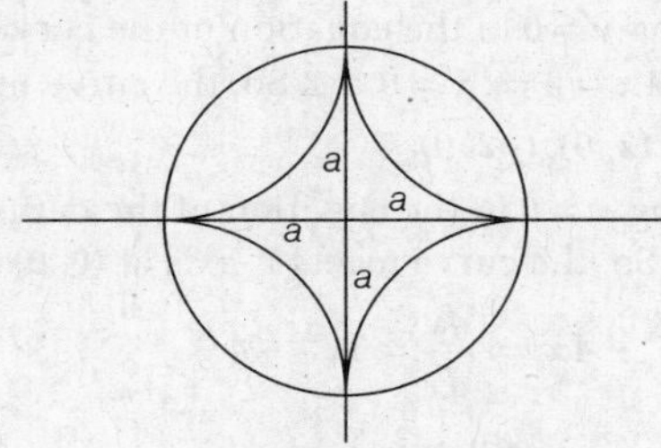

Figure 3.29

Curve Sketching

For the evaluation of area of bounded regions it is very essential to know the rough sketch of the curves. The following points are very useful to draw a rough sketch of a curve.

(i) Symmetry

(a) **Symmetry about X-axis** If all powers of y in the equation of the given curve are even, then it is symmetric about X-axis, i.e. the shape of the curve above X-axis is exactly identical to its shape below X-axis. **e.g.** $y^2=4ax$ is symmetric about X-axis.

(b) **Symmetry about Y-axis** If all powers of x in the equation of the given curve are even, then it is symmetric about Y-axis. **e.g.** $x^2=4ay$ is symmetric about Y-axis.

(c) **Symmetry in opposite quadrants** If by putting $-x$ for x and $-y$ for y, the equation of curve remains same, then it is symmetric in opposite quadrants.

e.g. $xy=c^2$, $x^2+y^2=a^2$ are symmetric in opposite quadrants.

(d) **Symmetric about the line $y=x$** If the equation of a given curve remains unaltered by interchanging x and y, then it is symmetric about the line $y=x$ which passes through the origin and makes an angle of 45° with positive direction of X-axis.

(ii) Origin and Tangents at the Origin

See whether the curve passes through origin or not. If the point (0, 0) satisfies the equation of the curve, then it passes through the origin and in such a case to find the equations of the tangents at the origin, equate the lowest degree term to zero. **e.g.** $y^2=4ax$ passes through the origin. The lowest degree term in this equation is $4ax$. Equating $4ax$ to zero, we get $x=0$.

So, $x=0$ i.e. Y-axis is tangent at the origin to $y^2=4ax$.

(iii) Points of Intersection of Curve with the Coordinate Axes

By putting $y=0$ in the equation of the given curve, find points where the curve crosses the X-axis. Similarly, by putting $x=0$ in the equation of the given curve we can find points where the curve crosses the Y-axis.

e.g. To find the points where the curve $xy^2=4a^2(2a-x)$ meets X-axis, we put $y=0$ in the equation which gives $4a^2(2a-x)=0$ or $x=2a$. So the curve $xy^2=4a^2(2a-x)$, meets X-axis at $(2a, 0)$. This curve does not intersect Y-axis, because by putting $x=0$ in the equation of the given curve get an absurd result.

(iv) Regions where the Curve Does Not Exist

Determine the regions in which the curve does not exist. For this, find the value of y in terms of x from the equation of the curve and find the value of x for which y is imaginary. Similarly, find the value of x in terms of y and determine the values of y for which x is imaginary. The curve does not exist for these values of x and y.

e.g. The values of y obtained from $y^2 = 4ax$ are imaginary for negative values of x. So, the curve does not exist on the left side of Y-axis. Similarly, the curve $a^2y^2 = x^2(a - x)$ does not exist for $x > a$ as the values of y are imaginary for $x > a$.

(v) Special Points

Find the points at which $\frac{dy}{dx} = 0$. At these points the tangent to the curve is parallel to X-axis.

Find the points at which $\frac{dx}{dy} = 0$. At these points the tangents to the curve is parallel to Y-axis.

(vi) Sign of dy/dx and Points of Maxima and Minima

Find the interval in which $\frac{dy}{dx} > 0$. In this interval, the function is monotonically increasing, find the interval in which $\frac{dy}{dx} < 0$. In this interval, the function is monotonically decreasing.

Put $\frac{dy}{dx} = 0$ and check the sign of $\frac{d^2y}{dx^2}$ at the points so obtained to find the points of maxima and minima.

Keeping the above facts in mind and plotting some points on the curve one can easily have a rough sketch of the curve. Following examples will clear the procedure.

Example 2 Sketch the curve $y = x^3$.

Sol. We observe the following points about the given curve

(i) The equation of the curve remains unchanged, if x is replaced by $-x$ and y by $-y$. So, it is symmetric in opposite quadrants. Consequently, the shape of the curve is similar in the first and the third quadrants.

(ii) The curve passes through origin. Equating lowest degree term y to zero, we get $y = 0$ i.e. X-axis is the tangent at the origin.

(iii) Putting $y = 0$ in the equation of the curve, we get $x = 0$. Similarly, when $x = 0$, we get $y = 0$. So, the curve meets the coordinate axes at (0, 0) only.

(iv) $y = x^3 \Rightarrow \frac{dy}{dx} = 3x^2, \frac{d^2y}{dx^2} = 6x$ and $\frac{d^3y}{dx^3} = 6$

Clearly, $\frac{dy}{dx} = 0 = \frac{d^2y}{dx^2}$ at the origin but $\frac{d^3y}{dx^3} \neq 0$.

So, the origin is a point of inflexion.

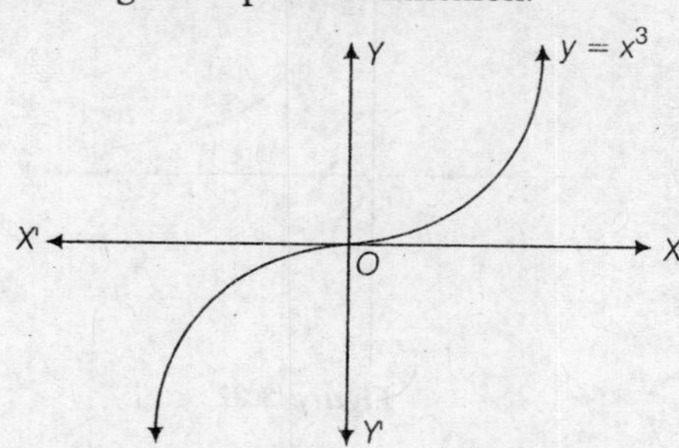

(v) As x increases from 0 to ∞, y also increases from 0 to ∞. Keeping all the above points in mind, we obtain a sketch of the curve as shown in figure.

Example 3 Sketch the curve $y = x^3 - 4x$.

Sol. We note the following points about the curve

(i) The equation of the curve remains same, if x is replaced by $(-x)$ and y by $(-y)$, so it is symmetric in opposite quadrants.

Consequently, the curve in the first quadrant is identical to the curve in third quadrant and the curve in second quadrant is similar to the curve in fourth quadrant.

(ii) The curve passes through the origin. Equating the lowest degree term $y + 4x$ to zero, we get $y + 4x = 0$ or $y = -4x$. So, $y = -4x$ is tangent to the curve at the origin.

(iii) Putting $y = 0$ in the equation of the curve, we obtain $x^3 - 4x = 0 \Rightarrow x = 0, \pm 2$. So, the curve meets X-axis at (0, 0), (2, 0), (−2, 0).

Putting $x = 0$ in the equation of the curve, we get $y = 0$. So, the curve meets Y-axis at (0, 0) only.

(iv) $y = x^3 - 4x \Rightarrow \frac{dy}{dx} = 3x^2 - 4$

Now, $\frac{dy}{dx} > 0 \Rightarrow 3x^2 - 4 > 0$

$\Rightarrow \left(x - \frac{2}{\sqrt{3}}\right)\left(x + \frac{2}{\sqrt{3}}\right) > 0$

$\Rightarrow x < -\frac{2}{\sqrt{3}}$ or $x > \frac{2}{\sqrt{3}}$ (using number line rule)

and $\frac{dy}{dx} < 0 \Rightarrow -\frac{2}{\sqrt{3}} < x < \frac{2}{\sqrt{3}}$

So, the curve is decreasing in the interval $(-2/\sqrt{3}, 2/\sqrt{3})$ and increasing for $x > \frac{2}{\sqrt{3}}$ or $x < -\frac{2}{\sqrt{3}}$.

$x = -\frac{2}{\sqrt{3}}$ is a point of local maximum and $x = \frac{2}{\sqrt{3}}$ is point of local minimum.

When $x = \frac{2}{\sqrt{3}}$, then $y = -\frac{16}{3\sqrt{3}}$

When $x = -\frac{2}{\sqrt{3}}$, then $y = \frac{16}{3\sqrt{3}}$

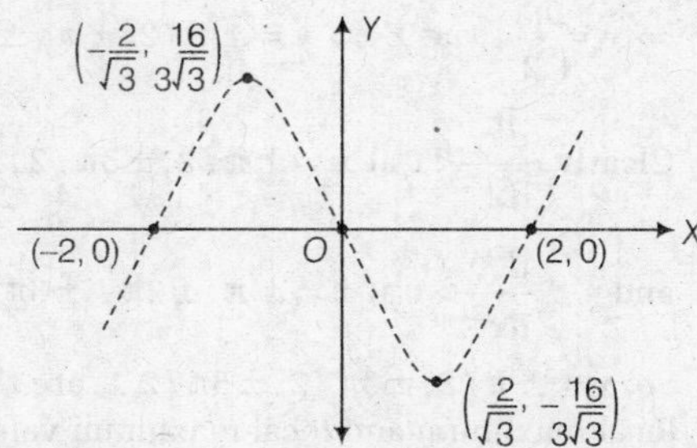

Keeping above points in mind, we sketch the curve as shown in figure.

Example 4 Sketch the curve $y = (x - 1)(x - 2)(x - 3)$.

Sol. We note the following points about the given curve

(i) The curve does not have any type of symmetry about the coordinate axes and also in opposite quadrants.

(ii) The curve does not pass through the origin.

(iii) Putting $y = 0$ in the equation of the curve, we get $(x - 1)(x - 2)(x - 3) = 0 \Rightarrow x = 1, 2, 3$. So, the curve meets X-axis at (1, 0), (2, 0) and (3, 0).

Putting $x = 0$ in the equation of the curve, we get $y = -6$. So, the curve crosses Y-axis at $(0, -6)$.

We observe that

$$x < 1 \quad \Rightarrow y < 0$$
$$1 < x < 2 \quad \Rightarrow y > 0$$
$$2 < x < 3 \quad \Rightarrow y < 0$$
and $$x > 3 \quad \Rightarrow y > 0$$

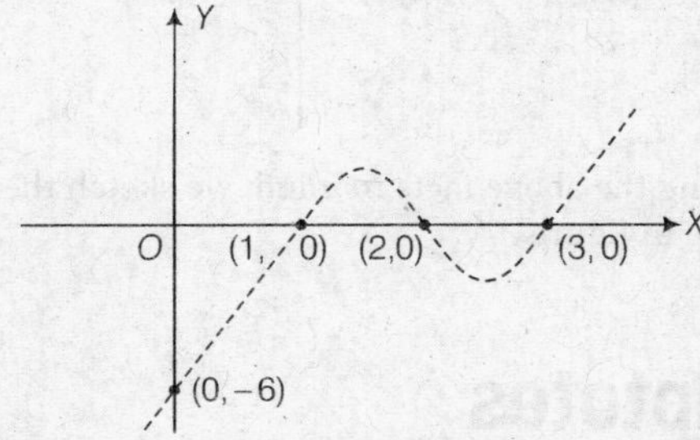

Clearly, y decreases as x decreases for all $x < 1$ and y increases as x increases for $x > 3$.

Keeping all the above points in mind, we sketch the curve as shown in figure.

Example 5 Sketch the graph for $y = x^2 - x$.

Sol. We note the following points about the curve

(i) The curve does not have any kind of symmetry.

(ii) The curve passes through the origin and the tangent at the origin is obtained by equating the lowest degree term to zero.

The lowest degree term is $x + y$. Equating it to zero, we get $x + y = 0$ as the equation of tangent at the origin.

(iii) Putting $y = 0$ in the equation of curve, we get $x^2 - x = 0 \Rightarrow x = 0, 1$. So, the curve crosses X-axis at (0, 0) and (1, 0).

Putting $x = 0$ in the equation of the curve, we obtain $y = 0$. So, the curve meets Y-axis at (0, 0) only.

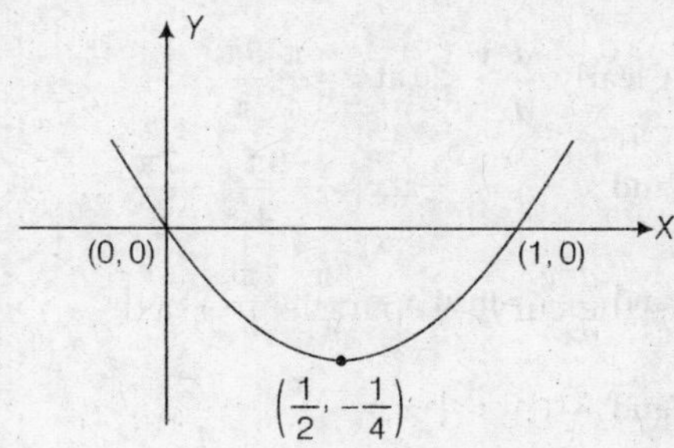

(iv) $y = x^2 - x \Rightarrow \frac{dy}{dx} = 2x - 1$ and $\frac{d^2y}{dx^2} = 2$

Now, $\frac{dy}{dx} = 0 \Rightarrow x = \frac{1}{2}$

At $x = \frac{1}{2}, \frac{d^2y}{dx^2} > 0$

So, $x = \frac{1}{2}$ is point of local minima.

(v) $\frac{dy}{dx} > 0 \Rightarrow 2x - 1 > 0 \Rightarrow x > \frac{1}{2}$

So, the curve increases for all $x > \frac{1}{2}$ and decreases for all $x < \frac{1}{2}$. Keeping above points in mind, we sketch the curve as shown in figure.

Example 6 Sketch the curve $y = \sin 2x$.

Sol. We note the following points about the curve

(i) The equation of the curve remains unchanged, if x is replaced by $(-x)$ and y by $(-y)$, so it is symmetric in opposite quadrants. Consequently, the shape of the curve is similar in opposite quadrants.

(ii) The curve passes through origin.

(iii) Putting $x = 0$ in the equation of the curve, we get $y = 0$. So, the curve crosses the Y-axis at (0, 0) only.

Putting $y = 0$ in the equation of the curve, we get

$$\sin 2x = 0 \Rightarrow 2x = n\pi, \; n \in Z$$

$$\Rightarrow \quad x = \frac{n\pi}{2}, n \in Z$$

So, the curve cuts the X-axis at the points

$$\ldots, (-\pi, 0), (-\pi/2, 0), (0, 0), (\pi/2, 0), (\pi, 0), \ldots$$

(iv) $y = \sin 2x \Rightarrow \frac{dy}{dx} = 2\cos 2x$ and $\frac{d^2y}{dx^2} = -4\sin 2x$

Now, $\frac{dy}{dx} = 0 \Rightarrow \cos 2x = 0$

$\Rightarrow \quad 2x = \pm\frac{\pi}{2}, \pm\frac{3\pi}{2}, \ldots$

$\Rightarrow \quad x = \pm\frac{\pi}{4}, \pm\frac{3\pi}{4}, \ldots$

Clearly, $\frac{d^2y}{dx^2} < 0$ at $x = \frac{\pi}{4}, \frac{5\pi}{4}, \ldots$

and at $x = -\frac{3\pi}{4}, -\frac{7\pi}{4}, \ldots$

and $\frac{d^2y}{dx^2} > 0$ at $x = \frac{3\pi}{4}, \frac{7\pi}{4}, \ldots$

and at $x = -\frac{\pi}{4}, -\frac{5\pi}{4}, \ldots$

So, the points $x = \frac{\pi}{4}, \frac{5\pi}{4}, \frac{7\pi}{4}, \ldots$

and $x = -\frac{3\pi}{4}, -\frac{7\pi}{4}, \ldots$ are points of local maximum and local maximum values at these points are 1.

Similarly, $x = -\frac{\pi}{4}, -\frac{5\pi}{4}, \ldots$ and $x = \frac{3\pi}{4}, \frac{7\pi}{4}, \ldots$ are points of local minimum and local minimum value at these points is (-1).

(v) $\sin 2(x + \pi) = \sin 2x$ for all x. So, the periodicity of the function is π. This means that the pattern of the curve repeats at intervals of length π.

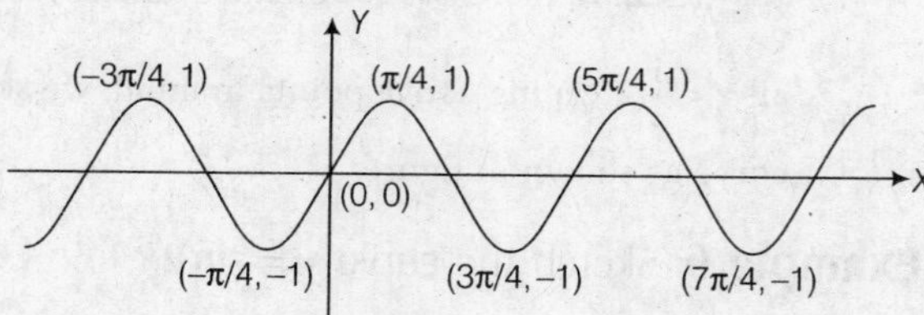

Thus, keeping in mind, we sketch the curve as shown in figure.

Example 7 Sketch the curve $y = \sin^2 x$.

Sol. We note the following points about the curve

(i) The equation of the curve remains same, if x is replaced by $(-x)$. So, the curve is symmetric about Y-axis, i.e. the curve on the left side of Y-axis is identical to the curve on its right side.

(ii) The curve meets the coordinate axes at the same points where $y = \sin x$ meets them.

(iii) $y = \sin^2 x \Rightarrow \frac{dy}{dx} = \sin 2x$ and $\frac{d^2y}{dx^2} = 2\cos 2x$

Now, $\frac{dy}{dx} = 0 \Rightarrow \sin 2x = 0 \Rightarrow 2x = n\pi, n \in Z$

$\Rightarrow x = \frac{n\pi}{2}, \; n \in Z \Rightarrow x = \pm\pi/2, \pm\pi, \pm 3\pi/2, \pm 2\pi, \ldots$

Clearly, $\frac{d^2y}{dx^2} < 0$ at $x = \pm\pi/2, \pm 3\pi/2, \pm 5\pi/2, \ldots$

and $\frac{d^2y}{dx^2} > 0$ at $x = \pm\pi, \pm 2\pi, \pm 3\pi \ldots$

So, $x = \pm\pi/2, \pm 3\pi/2, \pm 5\pi/2, \ldots$ are the points of local maximum and local maximum value at these points is 1. Points $x = \pm\pi, \pm 2\pi, \pm 3\pi, \ldots$ are points of local minimum and the local minimum value at these points is 0.

(iv) $y = \sin^2 x \Rightarrow \frac{dy}{dx} = \sin 2x$

Clearly, $\frac{dy}{dx} > 0$ when $0 < x < \frac{\pi}{2}$

and $\frac{dy}{dx} < 0$ when $\frac{\pi}{2} < x < \pi$.

So, the given curve is increasing in the interval $[0, \pi/2]$ and decreasing in $[\pi/2, \pi]$.

(v) $\sin^2(\pi + x) = \sin^2 x$ for all x. So, the periodicity of the function is π. This means that the shape of the curve repeats at the interval of length π.

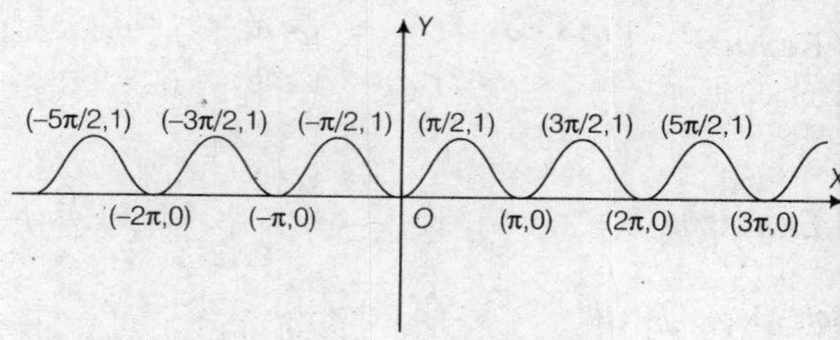

Keeping the above facts in mind, we sketch the curve as shown in figure.

Asymptotes

The straight line AB is called the asymptote of curve $y = f(x)$, if the distance MK from M a point on the curve $y = f(x)$ to the straight line AB tends to zero as M recedes infinity.

In other words, the straight line AB meets the curve $y = f(x)$ at infinity (K is a point on AB). Thus,

1. If $f(x) \to \pm\infty$ for $x \to a$, then the straight line $x = a$ is the asymptote of the curve $y = f(x)$.

2. If in the right hand member of the equation of the curve $y = f(x)$ it is possible to single out a linear part so that the remaining part tends to zero as $x \to \pm\infty$, i.e. if $y = f(x) = Kx + b + g(x)$ and $g(x) \to 0$ for $x \to \pm\infty$, then the straight line $y = Kx + b$ is the asymptote of the curve.

3. If there exist finite limits $\lim\limits_{x \to \pm\infty} \dfrac{f(x)}{x} = K$ and $\lim\limits_{x \to \pm\infty} [f(x) - Kx] = b$, then the straight line $y = Kx + b$ is the asymptote of the curve.

Methods to Sketch Curves

While constructing the graphs of functions, it is expedient to follow the procedure given below

(1) Find the domain of definition of the function.

(2) Determine the odd-even nature of the function.

(3) Find the period of the function if its periodic.

(4) Find the asymptotes of the function.

(5) Check the behaviour of the function for $x \to 0 \pm$

(6) Find the values of x, if possible for which $f(x) \to 0$.

(7) The interval of increase and decrease of the function in its range. Hence, determine the greatest and the least values of the function if any.

Remark

(5), (6) and (7) gives the points where the function cuts the coordinate axes.

Example 8 Construct the graph for $f(x) = \dfrac{x^2 - 1}{x^2 + 1}$.

Sol. Here, $f(x) = \dfrac{x^2 - 1}{x^2 + 1} = 1 - \dfrac{2}{x^2 + 1}$

(1) The function $f(x)$ is well defined for all real x.

$\Rightarrow$ Domain of $f(x) \in R$.

(2) $f(-x) = f(x)$, so it is an even function.

(3) Since, algebraic $\to$ non-periodic function.

$f(x) \to 1$ for $x \to \pm\infty$

and $f(x) \to -1$ for $x \to 0 \pm$

It may be observed that $f(x) < 1$ for any $x \in R$ and consequently its graph lies below the line $y = 1$ which is asymptote to the graph of the given function.

Again, $\dfrac{2}{x^2 + 1}$ decreases for $(0, \infty)$ and increases for $(-\infty, 0)$, thus $f(x)$ increases for $(0, \infty)$ and decreases for $(-\infty, 0)$ in its range.

(4) The greatest value $\to$ 1 for $x \to \pm\infty$ and the least value is -1 for $x = 0$.

Thus, its graph is as shown in figure

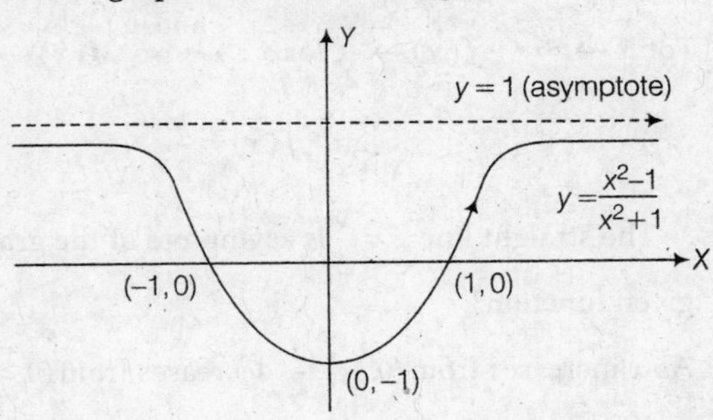

Example 9 Construct the graph for $f(x) = x + \dfrac{1}{x}$.

Sol. The function is defined for all x except for $x = 0$.

It is an odd function for $x \neq 0$.

It is not a periodic function.

For $x \to 0+$, $f(x) \to +\infty$; for $x \to 0-$, $f(x) \to -\infty$

For $x \to -\infty$, $f(x) \to -\infty$; for $x \to \infty$, $f(x) \to \infty$

$\therefore \lim\limits_{x \to \pm\infty} (f(x) - x) = 0$

$\therefore$ The straight lines $x = 0$ and $y = x$ are the asymptotes of the graph of the given function.

Now, consider $f(x_2) - f(x_1)$ (for $x_2 > x_1$)

$$= (x_2 - x_1) + \frac{1}{x_2} - \frac{1}{x_1}$$

$$= (x_2 - x_1)\left[1 - \frac{1}{x_1 x_2}\right] < 0 \text{ for } x_1 x_2 \in (0, 1]$$

and it is > 0 for $x_1 x_2 \in [1, \infty)$.

Thus, $f(x)$ increases for $x \in [1, \infty)$ and decreases for $x \in (0, 1]$.

Thus, the least value of the function is at $x = 1$ which is $f(1) = 2$. Thus, its graph can be drawn as

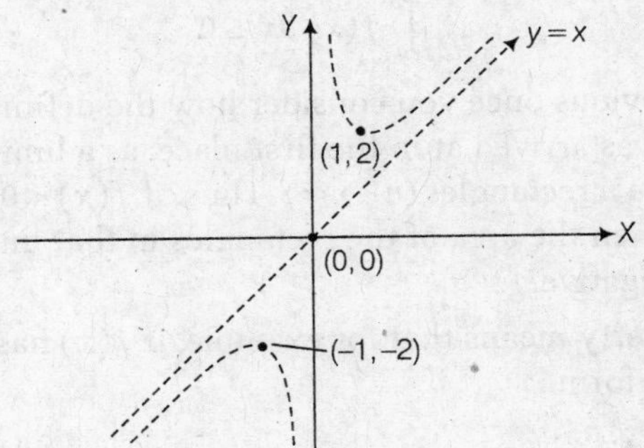

Example 10 Construct the graph for $f(x) = \dfrac{1}{1 + e^{1/x}}$.

Sol. The function is defined for all x except for $x = 0$. It is neither even nor an odd function. It is not a periodic function.

For $x \to 0+$ $\quad f(x) \to 0$; for $x \to 0-$, $\quad f(x) \to 1$

For $x \to \infty$ $\quad f(x) \to \frac{1}{2}$; for $x \to -\infty$, $\quad f(x) \to \frac{1}{2}$

$$\therefore \quad \lim_{x \to \pm\infty} f(x) = \frac{1}{2}$$

$\therefore$ The straight line $y = \frac{1}{2}$ is asymptote of the graph of the given function.

As x increases from $(0, \infty)$, $\frac{1}{x}$ decreases from $(0, \infty)$ and $e^{1/x}$ decreases from $(0, \infty)$. Thus, $(1 + e^{1/x})$ decreases from $(2, \infty)$.

$\therefore f(x)$ increases from $\left(0, \frac{1}{2}\right)$ for $x \in (0, \infty)$.

Similarly, $f(x)$ increases from $(1/2, 1)$ for $x \to (-\infty, 0)$.

i.e. $f(x)$ is an increasing function except for $x = 0$.

Thus, its graph can be drawn as shown in figure

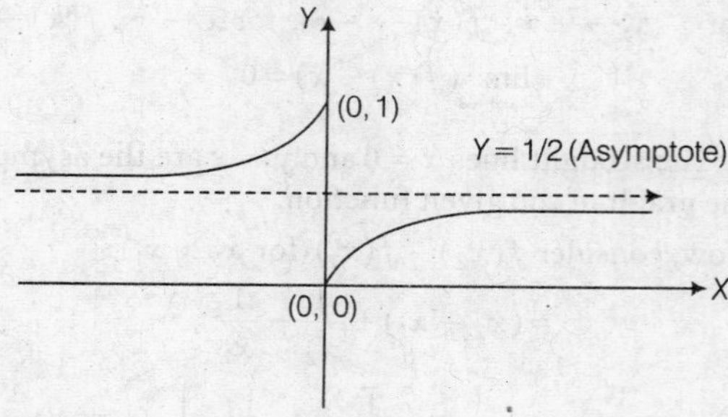

Areas of Curves

(1) Suppose that $f(x) < 0$ on some interval $[a, b]$. Then, the area under the curve $y = f(x)$ from $x = a$ to $x = b$ will be negative in sign, i.e.

$$\int_a^b f(x)\, dx \le 0$$

This is obvious once you consider how the definite integral was arrived at in the first place; as a limit of the sum of the n rectangles $(n \to \infty)$. Thus, if $f(x) < 0$ in some interval then the area of the rectangles in that interval will also be negative.

This property means that for example, if $f(x)$ has the following form

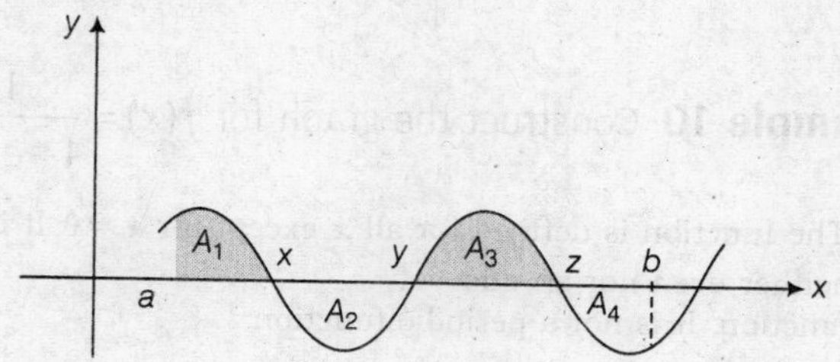

then $\int_a^b f(x)\, dx$ will equal $A_1 - A_2 + A_3 - A_4$ and not $A_1 + A_2 + A_3 + A_4$.

If we need to evaluate $A_1 + A_2 + A_3 + A_4$ (the magnitude of the bounded area), we will have to calculate

$$\int_a^x f(x)\, dx + \left|\int_x^y f(x)\, dx\right| \int_y^z f(x)\, dx + \left|\int_z^b f(x)\, dx\right|$$

From this, it should also be obvious that

$$\left|\int_a^b f(x)\, dx\right| \le \int_a^b |f(x)|\, dx$$

(2) The area under the curve $y = f(x)$ from $x = a$ to $x = b$ is equal in magnitude but opposite in sign to the area under the same curve from $x = b$ to $x = a$, i.e.

$$\int_a^b f(x)\, dx = -\int_b^a f(x)\, dx$$

This property is obvious if you consider the Newton-Leibnitz formula. If $g(x)$ is the anti-derivative of $x(f)$, then $\int_a^b f(x)\, dx$ is $g(b) - g(a)$ while $\int_a^b f(x)\, dx$ is $g(a) - g(b)$

(3) The area under the curve $y = f(x)$ from $x = a$ to $x = b$ can be written as the sum of the area under the curve from $x = a$ to $x = c$ and from $x = c$ to $x = b$, that is

$$\int_a^b f(x)\, dx = \int_a^c f(x)\, dx + \int_c^b f(x)\, dx$$

Let us consider an example of this. Let $c \in (a, b)$

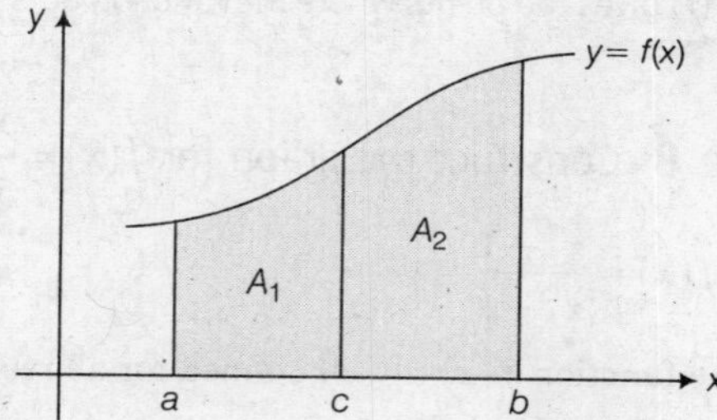

It is clear that the area under the curve from $x = a$ to $x = b$, A is $A_1 + A_2$.

Note that c need not lie between a and b for this relation to hold true. Suppose that $c > b$.

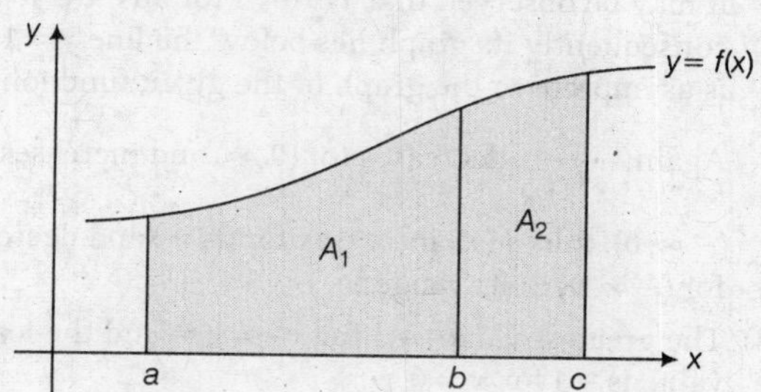

Observe that $A = \int_a^b f(x)\,dx = (A + A_1) - A_1$

$$= \int_a^c f(x)\,dx - \int_b^c f(x)\,dx$$

$$= \int_a^c f(x)\,dx + \int_a^b f(x)\,dx$$

Analytically, this relation can be proved easily using the Newton Leibnitz's formula.

(4) Let $f(x) > g(x)$ on the interval $[a, b]$. Then,

$$\int_a^b f(x)\,dx > \int_a^b g(x)\,dx$$

This is because the curve of $f(x)$ lies above the curve of $g(x)$, or equivalently, the curve of $f(x) - g(x)$ lies above the x-axis for $[a, b]$

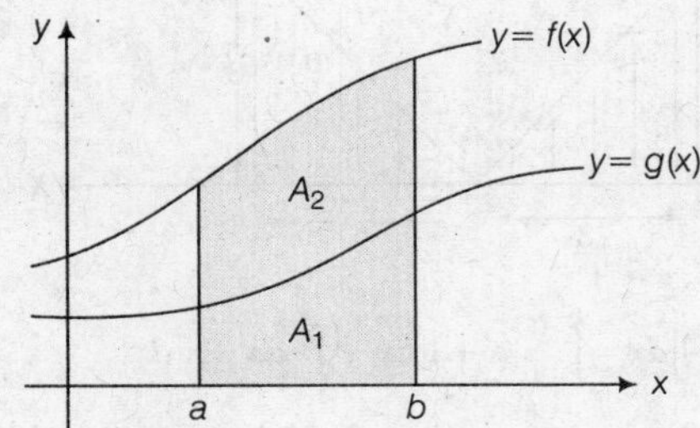

This is an example where $f(x) > g(x) > 0$.

$$\int_a^b f(x)\,dx = A_1 + A_2$$

while $$\int_a^b g(x)\,dx = A_1$$

Similarly, if $f(x) < g(x)$ on the interval $[a, b]$, then

$$\int_a^b f(x)\,dx < \int_a^b g(x)\,dx$$

(5) For the interval $[a, b]$, suppose $m < f(x) < M$. That is, m is a lower-bound for $f(x)$ while M is an upper bound.

Then $$m\,(b - a) < \int_a^b f(x)\,dx < M\,(b - a)$$

This is obvious once we consider the figure below :

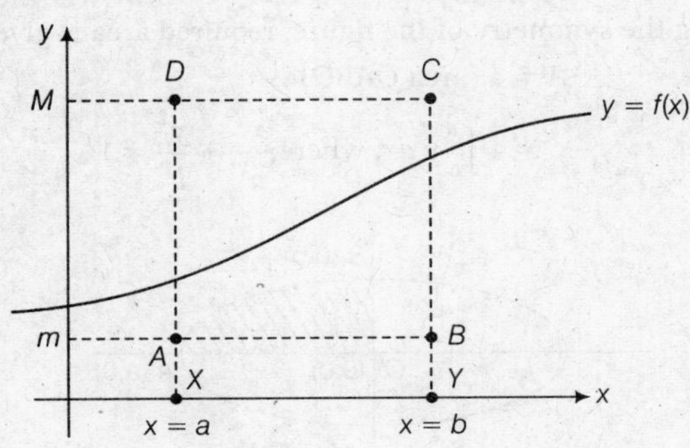

Observe that area (rect $AXYB$) $< \int_a^b f(x)\,dx <$ area (rect $DXYC$)

(6) Let us consider the integral of $f_1(x) + f_2(x)$ from $x = a$ to $x = b$. To evaluate the area under $f_1(x) + f_2(x)$, we can separately evaluate the area under $f_1(x)$ and the area under $f_2(x)$ and add the two area (algebraically).

Thus, $\int_a^b (f_1(x) + f_2(x))\,dx = \int_a^b f_1(x)\,dx + \int_a^b f_2(x)\,dx$

Now consider the integral of $kf(x)$ from $x = a$ to $x = b$. To evaluate the area under $kf(x)$, we can first evaluate the area under $f(x)$ and then multiply it by k, that is :

$$\int_a^b kf(x)\,dx = k\int_a^b f(x)\,dx$$

(7) Consider the odd function $f(x)$, i.e. $f(x) = -f(-x)$. This measn that the graph of $f(x)$ is symmetric about the origin.

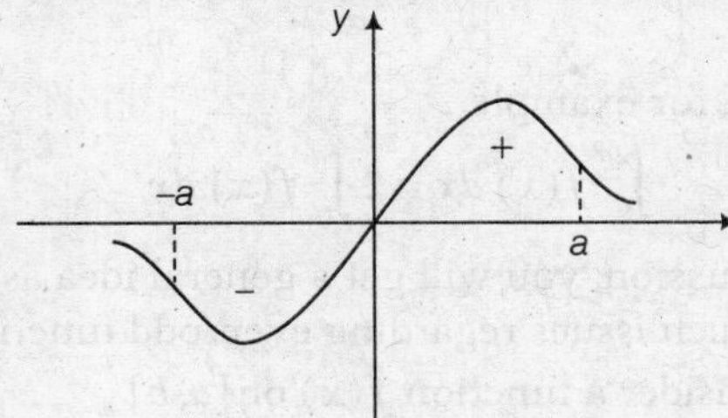

From the figure, it should be obvious that $\int_{-a}^a f(x)\,dx = 0$, because the area on the left side and that on the right algebraically add to 0.

Similarly, if $f(x)$ was even, i.e. $f(x) = f(-x)$

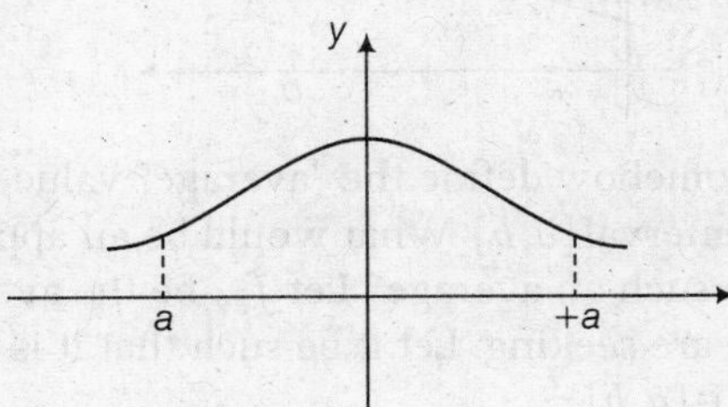

$\int_{-a}^a f(x)\,dx = 2\int_0^a f(x)\,dx$ because the graph is symmetrical about the y-axis. If you recall the discussion in the unit on functions, a function can also be even or odd about any arbitrary point $x = a$. Let us suppose that $f(x)$ is odd about $x = a$, i.e. $f(x) = -f(2a - x)$

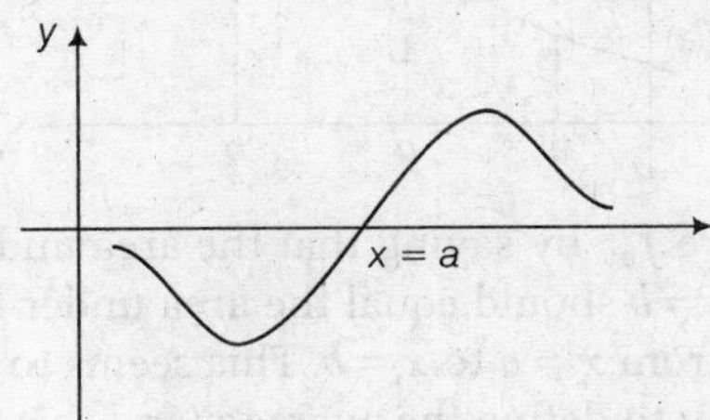

The points x and $2a - x$ lie equidistant from $x = a$ at either sides of it.

Suppose for example, that we need to calculate $\int_a^{2a} f(x)\,dx$.

It is obvious that this will be 0, since we are considering equal variation on either side of $x = a$, the area from $x = 0$ to $x = a$ and the area from $x = a$ to $x = 2a$ will add algebraically to 0.

Similarly, if $f(x)$ is even about $x = a$, i.e. $f(x) = f(2a - x)$

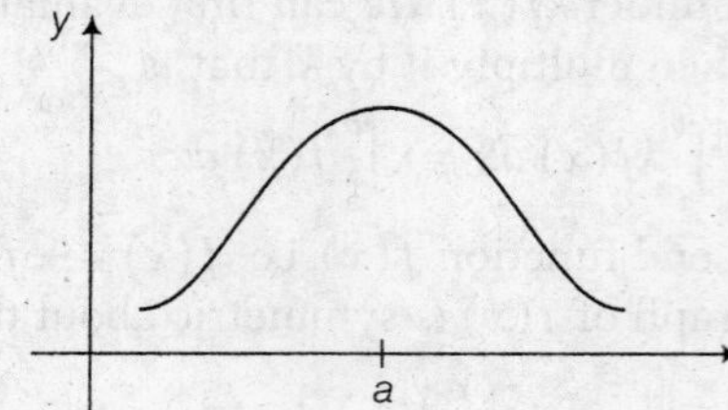

then we have, for example

$$\int_0^{2a} f(x)\,dx = 2\int_0^a f(x)\,dx$$

From the discussion, you will get a general idea as to how to approach such issues regarding even/odd functions.

(8) Let us consider a function $f(x)$ on $[a, b]$

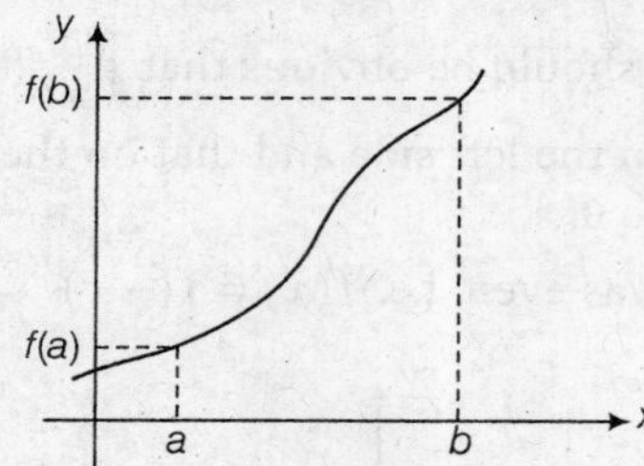

We want to somehow define the "average" value that $f(x)$ takes on the interval $[a, b]$. What would be an appropriate way to define such an average? Let f_{av} be the average value that we are seeking. Let it be such that it is obtained at some $x = c \in [a, b]$

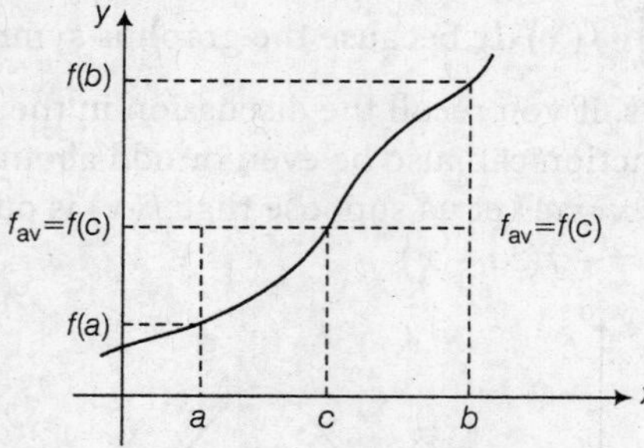

We can measure f_{av} by saying that the area under $f(x)$ from $x = a$ to $x = b$ should equal the area under the average value from $x = a$ to $x = b$. This seems to be the only logical way to define the average (and this is how it is actually defined!).

Thus $f_{av}(b - a) = \int_a^b f(x)\,dx \Rightarrow f_{av} = \frac{1}{b-a}\int_a^b f(x)\,dx$

This value is attained for at least one $c \in (a, b)$ (under the constraint that f is continuous, of course).

Example 11 Sketch the graph $y = |x+1|$. Evaluate $\int_{-4}^{2} |x+1|\,dx$. What does the value of this integral represents on the graph.

Sol. Here, $y = |x+1| = \begin{cases} (x+1), & \text{if } x \geq -1 \\ -(x+1), & \text{if } x \leq -1 \end{cases}$

which can be shown as

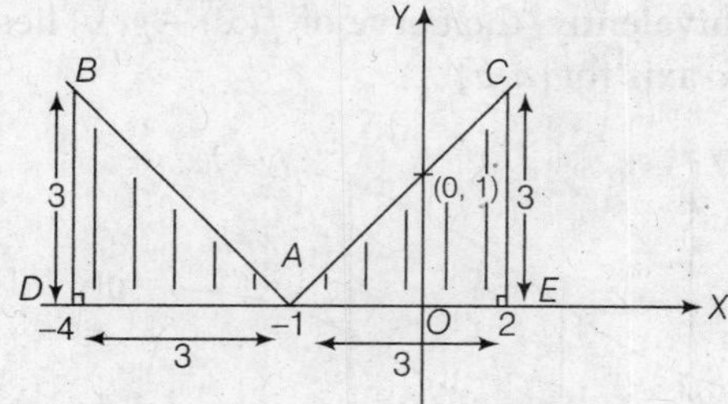

$$\therefore \int_{-4}^{2} |x+1|\,dx = \int_{-4}^{-1} |x+1|\,dx + \int_{-1}^{2} |x+1|\,dx$$

$$= \int_{-4}^{-1} -(x+1)\,dx + \int_{-1}^{2} |x+1|\,dx + \int_{-1}^{2} (x+1)\,dx$$

$$= -\left[\frac{x^2}{2} + x\right]_{-4}^{-1} + \left[\frac{x^2}{2} + x\right]_{-1}^{2} = 9$$

Representation of the value 9 of integral on graph.

$\therefore \int_{-4}^{2} |x+1|\,dx = 9$ represents the area bounded by the curve $y = |x+1|$. X-axis and the lines $x = -4$ and $x = 2$, i.e. if is equal to the sum of the ares of ΔABD and ACE,

i.e. $\frac{1}{2}(3)(3) + \frac{1}{3}(3)(3) = \frac{9}{2} + \frac{9}{2} = 9$

($\because$ area of triangle $= \frac{1}{2} \times$ base $\times$ height)

Example 12 Find the area of the ellipse $\frac{x^2}{a^2} + \frac{y^2}{b^2} = 1$.

Sol. Using the symmetry of the figure; required area is given by

$$A = 4\,(\text{area } OABO)$$

$$= 4\int_0^a y\,dx, \text{ where } \frac{x^2}{a^2} + \frac{y^2}{b^2} = 1$$

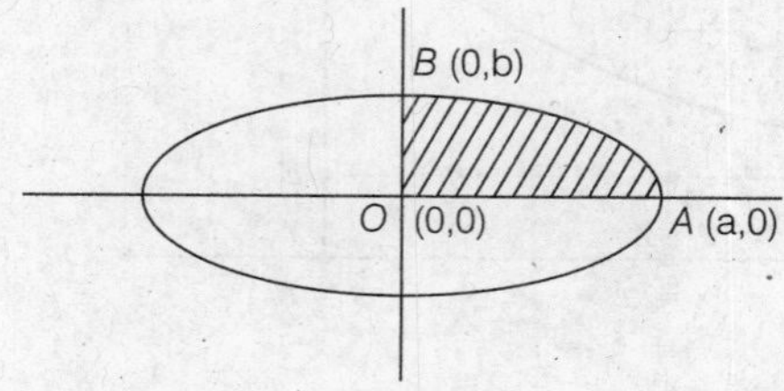

$\therefore \quad \dfrac{y^2}{b^2} = 1 - \dfrac{x^2}{a^2}$

$\Rightarrow \quad y^2 = \dfrac{b^2}{a^2}(a^2 - x^2)$

$\Rightarrow \quad y = \pm \dfrac{b}{a}\sqrt{a^2 - x^2}$

In the first quadrant,

$y = \dfrac{b}{a}\sqrt{a^2 - x^2}$

$A = 4\int_0^a \dfrac{b}{a}\sqrt{a^2 - x^2}\,dx = 4\dfrac{b}{a}\int_0^a \sqrt{a^2 - x^2}\,dx$

$= 4\dfrac{b}{a}\left\{\dfrac{x}{2}\sqrt{a^2 - x^2} + \dfrac{a^2}{2}\sin^{-1}\dfrac{x}{a}\right\}_0^a$

$= 4\dfrac{b}{a}\left[\left\{0 + \dfrac{a^2}{2}\sin^{-1}\dfrac{a}{a}\right\} - \{0+0\}\right] = \dfrac{4b}{a}\cdot\dfrac{a^2}{2}\sin^{-1}(1)$

$= 2ab\left(\dfrac{\pi}{2}\right)$

$A = \pi ab$ sq units

Example 13 Find the area bounded by the hyperbola $x^2 - y^2 = a^2$ between the straight lines $x = a$ and $x = 2a$.

Sol. We use the symmetry of figure.

Required area, $A = 2\int_a^{2a} y\,dx$, where $x^2 - y^2 = a^2$

i.e. $\quad x^2 - a^2 = y^2$

$\therefore \quad y = \pm\sqrt{x^2 - a^2}$

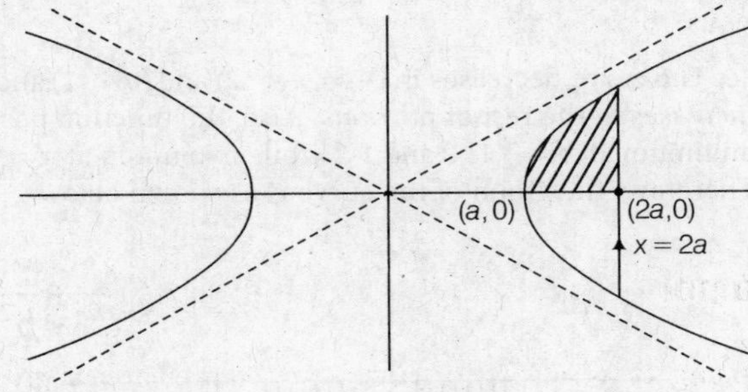

In the first quadrant; $y = +\sqrt{x^2 - a^2}$

$\therefore \; A = 2\int_a^{2a}\sqrt{x^2 - a^2}\,dx$

$= 2\left[\dfrac{x}{2}\sqrt{x^2 - a^2} - \dfrac{a^2}{2}\log(x + \sqrt{x^2 - a^2})\right]_a^{2a}$

$= 2\left[\left\{a\sqrt{4a^2 - a^2} - \dfrac{a^2}{2}\log(2a + \sqrt{4a^2 - a^2})\right\} - \left\{0 - \dfrac{a^2}{2}\log a\right\}\right]$

$= 2\left[a\sqrt{3a^2} - \dfrac{a^2}{2}\log(2a + a\sqrt{3}) + \dfrac{a^2}{2}\log a\right]$

$= 2\left[a^2\sqrt{3} - \dfrac{a^2}{2}\log\left(\dfrac{2a + a\sqrt{3}}{a}\right)\right]$

$= 2a^2\sqrt{3} - a^2\log(2 + \sqrt{3})$ sq units

Example 14 Find the area common to the parabola $5x^2 - y = 0$ and $2x^2 - y + 9 = 0$.

Sol. Given curves are $\quad y = 5x^2 \quad$ ...(i)

and $\quad y = 2x^2 + 9 \quad$ ...(ii)

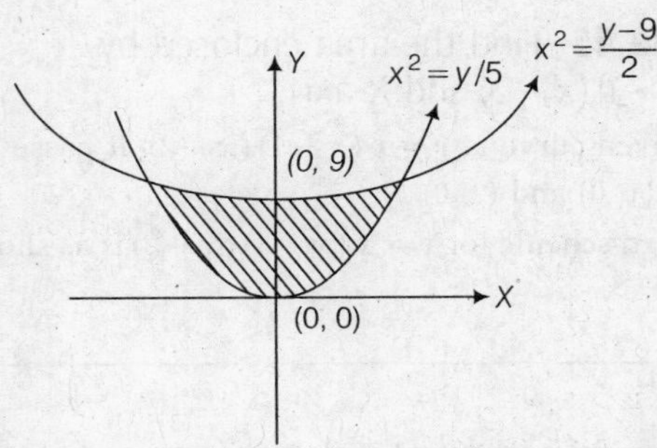

Remark

In such examples, figure is the most essential thing. Without figure it just becomes difficult to judge whether y_1 to be subtracted from y_2 or otherwise.

Let us solve Eqs. (i) and (ii) simultaneously,

$\therefore \quad 5x^2 = 2x^2 + 9$

$\Rightarrow \quad 3x^2 = 9 \Rightarrow x^2 = 3$

$\therefore \quad x = -\sqrt{3}$

or $\quad x = \sqrt{3}$

In the usual notations, the required area is given by

$$A = \int_{-\sqrt{3}}^{\sqrt{3}} (y_1 - y_2)\,dx$$

We have to find which curve is above and which is below w.r.t. X-axis in order to decide y_1 and y_2.

Take any point between $x = -\sqrt{3}$ and $x = \sqrt{3}$

Let us take $x = 0$, which lies between

$x = -\sqrt{3}$ and $x = \sqrt{3}$

When $x = 0$ from Eq. (i) $y = 0$

When $x = 0$ from Eq. (ii) $y = 9$

Now, $\quad 9 > 0$

$\therefore$ Parabola Eq. (ii) is above parabola Eq. (i) between

$x = -\sqrt{3}$

and $\quad x = \sqrt{3}$.

$\therefore$ y of the curve (ii) is to be taken as y_1 and y of the curve (i) is to be taken as y_2.

$$\therefore \quad \text{Area}(A) = \int_{-\sqrt{3}}^{\sqrt{3}} \{(2x^2+9) - 5x^2\}\, dx$$
$$= \int_{-\sqrt{3}}^{\sqrt{3}} (9-3x^2)\, dx$$
$$= 2\int_0^{\sqrt{3}} (9-3x^2)\, dx$$
$$= 2\,[9x - x^3]_0^{\sqrt{3}}$$
$$= 2\,[9\sqrt{3} - 3\sqrt{3}]$$
$$\text{Area} = 12\sqrt{3} \text{ sq units}$$

Example 15 Find the area enclosed by $y = x(x-1)(x-2)$ and X-axis.

Sol. The given curve is $y = x(x-1)(x-2)$. It passes through (0, 0), (1, 0) and (2, 0).

The sign scheme for $y = x(x-1)(x-2)$ is as shown in figure.

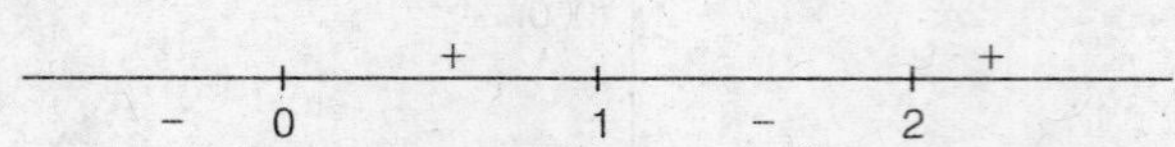

From the sign scheme it is clear that the curve is + ve when $0 < x < 1$ or $x > 2$, hence in these regions the curve lies above X-axis while in the rest regions the curve lies below X-axis.

Remark

Sometimes the discussion of monotonicity of function helps us in sketching polynomials. In the present case, $\frac{dy}{dx} = 3x^2 - 6x + 2$

When $\frac{dy}{dx} = 0$, then; $x = 1 \pm \frac{1}{\sqrt{3}}$. Sign scheme for $\frac{dy}{dx}$ is

$$\begin{array}{ccccc} + & & - & & + \\ & 1-\frac{1}{\sqrt{3}} & & 1+\frac{1}{\sqrt{3}} & \end{array}$$

Thus, it is clear that the curve increases in $\left(-\infty, 1-\frac{1}{\sqrt{3}}\right)$, decreases in $\left(1-\frac{1}{\sqrt{3}}, 1+\frac{1}{\sqrt{3}}\right)$ and again increases in $\left(1+\frac{1}{\sqrt{3}}, \infty\right)$. Therefore, the graph of the curve is as below

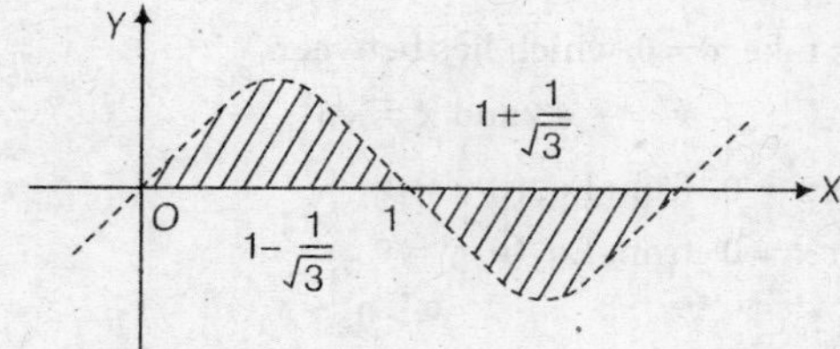

Hence, required area

$$= \int_0^1 x(x-1)(x-2)\, dx + \left| \int_1^2 x(x-1)(x-2)\, dx \right|$$
$$= \int_0^1 (x^3 - 3x^2 + 2x)\, dx + \left| \int_1^2 (x^3 - 3x^2 + 2x)\, dx \right|$$
$$= \left(\frac{x^4}{4} - x^3 + x^2\right)_0^1 + \left| \left(\frac{x^4}{4} - x^3 + x^2\right)_1^2 \right|$$
$$= \left(\frac{1}{4} - 1 + 1\right) + \left| (4 - 8 + 4) - \left(\frac{1}{4} - 1 + 1\right) \right|$$
$$= \frac{1}{4} + \frac{1}{4} = \frac{1}{2} \text{ sq unit}$$

Example 16 Find the area between the curves $y = 2x^4 - x^2$, the X-axis and the ordinates of two minima of the curve.

Sol. The given curve is $y = 2x^4 - x^2$.

When $y = 0$, then $x = 0, 0, \pm\frac{1}{\sqrt{2}}$

The sign scheme is as shown below

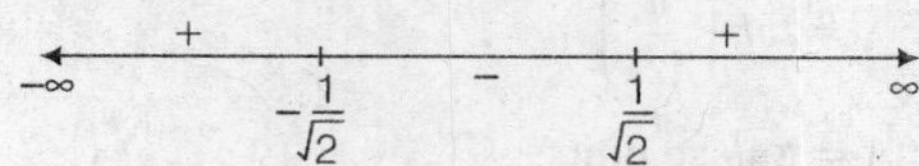

Therefore, it is clear that the curve cuts the X-axis at $x = -\frac{1}{\sqrt{2}}$, 0 and $\frac{1}{\sqrt{2}}$.

The curve is −ve in $\left(-\frac{1}{\sqrt{2}}, 0\right)$ and $\left(0, \frac{1}{\sqrt{2}}\right)$ while positive in the rest. Now, $\frac{dy}{dx} = 8x^3 - 2x$. The sign scheme for $\frac{dy}{dx}$ is as below

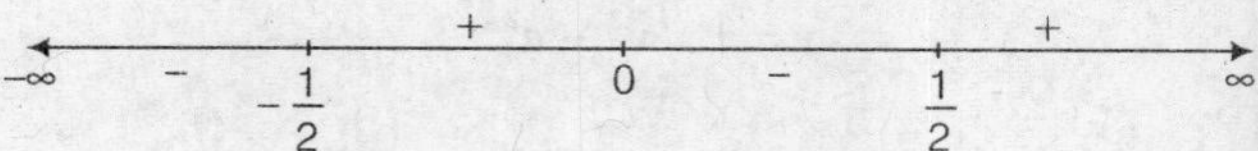

i.e. The curve decreases in $(-\infty, -1/2)$ and $(0, 1/2)$ and increases in the rest of portions. Also, the function possess minimum at $x = -1/2$ and $1/2$ while maximum at $x = 0$. Therefore, the graph of the curve is as shown below

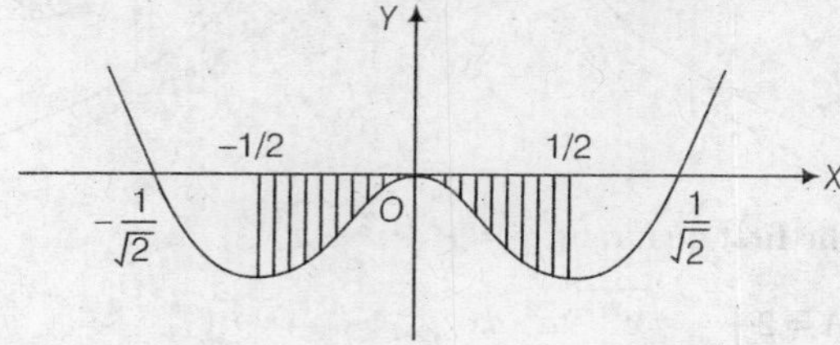

$$\therefore \text{ Required area} = 2\int_0^{1/2} |2x^4 - x^2|\, dx$$
$$= 2\int_0^{1/2} -(2x^4 - x^2)dx = -2\left[2\frac{x^5}{5} - \frac{x^3}{3}\right]_0^{1/2}$$
$$= \frac{7}{120} \text{ sq unit}$$

Exercise for Session 1

1. Draw a rough sketch of $y = \sin 2x$ and determine the area enclosed by the curve, X-axis and the lines $x = \pi / 4$ and $x = 3\pi / 4$.
2. Find the area under the curve $y = (x^2 + 2)^2 + 2x$ between the ordinates $x = 0$ and $x = 2$.
3. Find the area of the region bounded by the curve $y = 2x - x^2$ and the X-axis.
4. Find the area bounded by the curve $y^2 = 2y - x$ and the Y-axis.
5. Find the area bounded by the curve $y = 4 - x^2$ and the line $y = 0$ and $y = 3$.
6. Find the area bounded by $x = at^2$ and $y = 2at$ between the ordinates corresponding to $t = 1$ and $t = 2$.
7. Find the area of the parabola $y^2 = 4ax$ and the latusrectum.
8. Find the area bounded by $y = 1 + 2\sin^2 x$, X-axis, $x = 0$ and $x = \pi$.
9. Sketch the graph of $y = \sqrt{x} + 1$ in [0, 4] and determine the area of the region enclosed by the curve, the axis of X and the lines $x = 0$, $x = 4$.
10. Find the area of the region bounded by the curve $xy - 3x - 2y - 10 = 0$, X-axis and the lines $x = 3$, $x = 4$.

Session 2

Area Bounded by Two or More Curves

Area Bounded by Two or More Curves

Area bounded by the curves $y = f(x)$, $y = g(x)$ and the lines $x = a$ and $x = b$.

Let the curves $y = f(x)$ and $y = g(x)$ be represented by AB and CD, respectively. We assume that the two curves do not intersect each other in the interval $[a, b]$.

Thus, shaded area = Area of curvilinear trapezoid $APQB$ − Area of curvilinear trapezoid $CPQD$

$$= \int_a^b f(x)\,dx - \int_a^b g(x)\,dx = \int_a^b \{f(x) - g(x)\}\,dx$$

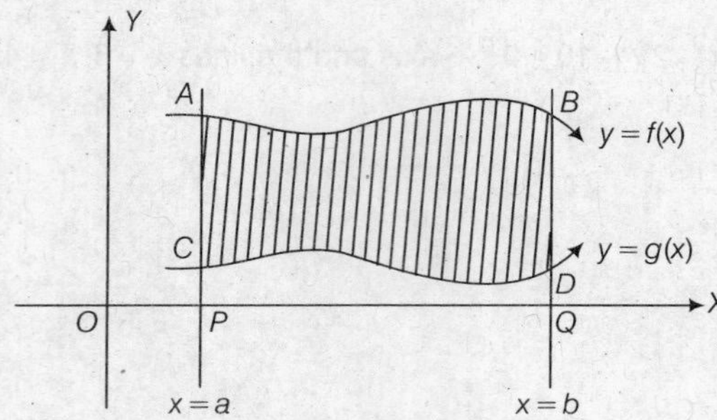

Figure 3.32

Now, consider the case when $f(x)$ and $g(x)$ intersect each other in the interval $[a, b]$.

First of all we should find the intersection point of $y = f(x)$ and $y = g(x)$. For that we solve $f(x) = g(x)$. Let the root is $x = c$. (We consider only one intersection point to illustrate the phenomenon).

Thus, required (shaded) area

$$= \int_a^c \{f(x) - g(x)\}dx + \int_c^b \{g(x) - f(x)\}\,dx$$

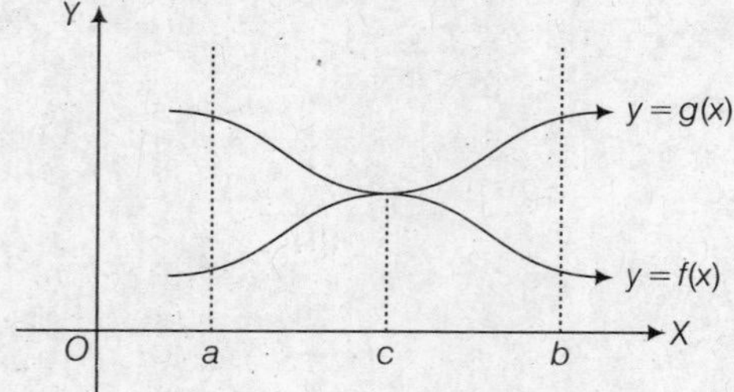

Figure 3.33

If confusion arises in such case evaluate $\int_a^b |f(x) - g(x)|\,dx$ which gives the required area.

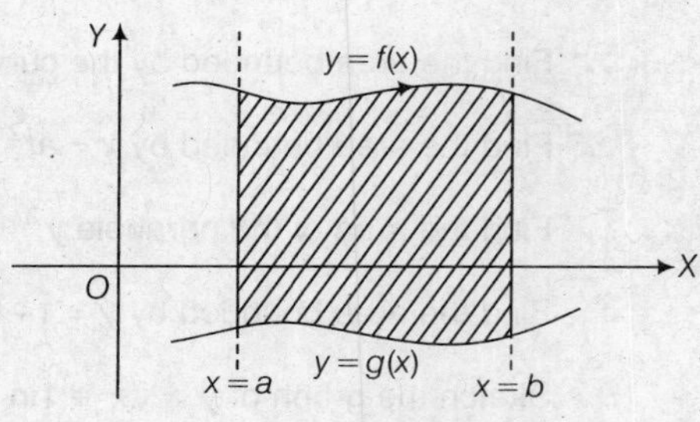

Figure 3.34

Area between two curves $y = f(x)$, $y = g(x)$ and the lines $x = a$ and $x = b$ is always given by $\int_a^b \{f(x) - g(x)\}\,dx$ provided $f(x) > g(x)$ in $[a, b]$; the position of the graph is immaterial. As shown in Fig. 3.34, Fig. 3.35, Fig. 3.36.

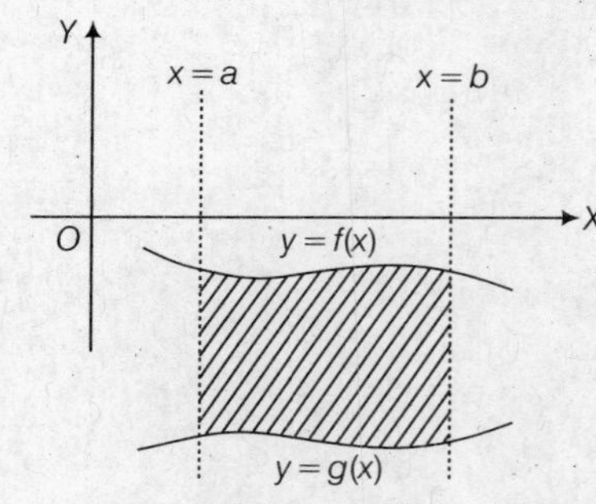

Figure 3.35

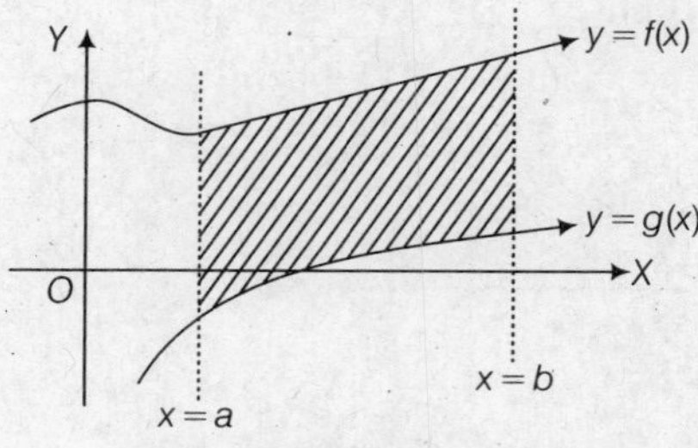

Figure 3.36

| Example 17 Sketch the curves and identify the region bounded by $x = 1/2$, $x = 2$, $y = \log_e x$ and $y = 2^x$. Find the area of this region. ***[IIT JEE 1991]***

Sol. The required area is the shaded portion in the following figure.

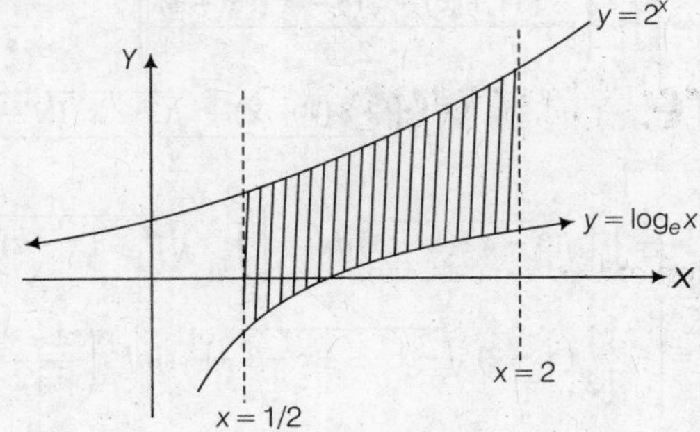

In the region $\frac{1}{2} \leq x \leq 2$; the curve $y = 2^x$ lies above as compared to $y = \log_e x$.

Hence, required area $= \int_{1/2}^{2} (2^x - \log x)\, dx$

$$= \left[\frac{2^x}{\log 2} - (x \log x - x) \right]_{1/2}^{2}$$

$$= \left(\frac{4 - \sqrt{2}}{\log 2} - \frac{5}{2} \log 2 + \frac{3}{2} \right) \text{sq units}$$

Example 18 Find the area given by $x + y \leq 6, x^2 + y^2 \leq 6y$ and $y^2 \leq 8x$.

Sol. Let us consider the curves

$$P \equiv y^2 - 8x = 0 \qquad \text{...(i)}$$

$$C \equiv x^2 + y^2 = 6y$$

i.e. $$x^2 + (y - 3)^2 - 9 = 0 \qquad \text{...(ii)}$$

and $$S \equiv x + y - 6 = 0 \qquad \text{...(iii)}$$

The intersection points of the curves (ii) and (iii) are given by

$$(6 - y)^2 + y^2 - 6y = 0$$

i.e. $$y = 3, 6$$

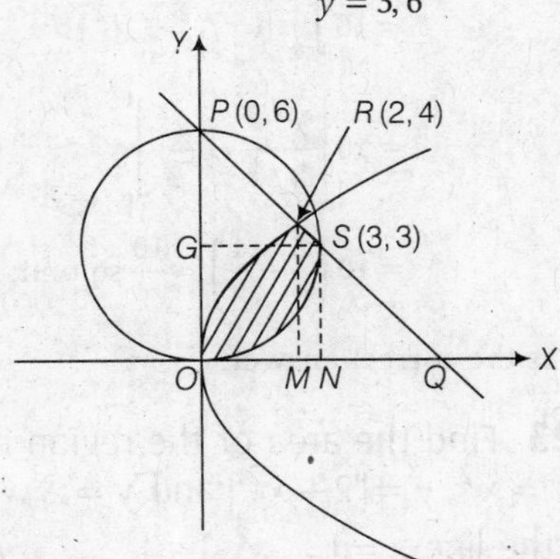

Therefore, the points are (0, 6) and (3, 3). The intersection points of the curves (i) and (iii) are given by

$$y^2 = 8(6 - y), \quad \text{i.e. } y = 4, -12$$

Therefore, the point of intersection in 1st quadrant is (2, 4).

Now, we know that

$C \leq 0$ denotes the region, inside the circle $C = 0$.

$P \leq 0$ denotes the region, inside the parabola $P = 0$.

$S \leq 0$ denotes the region, which is negative side of the line $S = 0$.

$\therefore$ Required area = Area of curvilinear $\Delta OMRO$

+ Area of trapezium $MNSR$ − Area of curvilinear $\Delta ONSO$

$$= \int_0^2 \sqrt{8x}\, dx + \frac{1}{2}(MR + NS) \cdot MN$$

$$- (\text{Area of square } ONSG - \text{Area of sector } OSGO)$$

$$= \int_0^2 \sqrt{8x}\, dx + \frac{1}{2}(4 + 3) \cdot 1 - \left(3^2 - \frac{\pi \cdot 3^2}{4} \right)$$

$$= \left(\frac{9\pi}{4} - \frac{1}{6} \right) \text{sq units}$$

Example 19 Find the area of the region $\{(x, y) : 0 \leq y \leq x^2 + 1, 0 \leq y \leq x + 1, 0 \leq x \leq 2\}$.

Sol. Let $R = \{(x, y) : 0 \leq y \leq x^2 + 1, 0 \leq y \leq x + 1, 0 \leq x \leq 2\}$

$$= \{(x, y) : 0 \leq y \leq x^2 + 1\} \cap \{(x, y) : 0 \leq y \leq x + 1\} \cap \{(x, y) : 0 \leq x \leq 2\}$$

$$= R_1 \cap R_2 \cap R_3$$

where, $R_1 = \{(x, y) : 0 \leq y \leq x^2 + 1\}$

$R_2 = \{(x, y) : 0 \leq y \leq x + 1\}$

and $R_3 = \{(x, y) : 0 \leq x \leq 2\}$

Thus, the sketch of R_1, R_2 and R_3 are

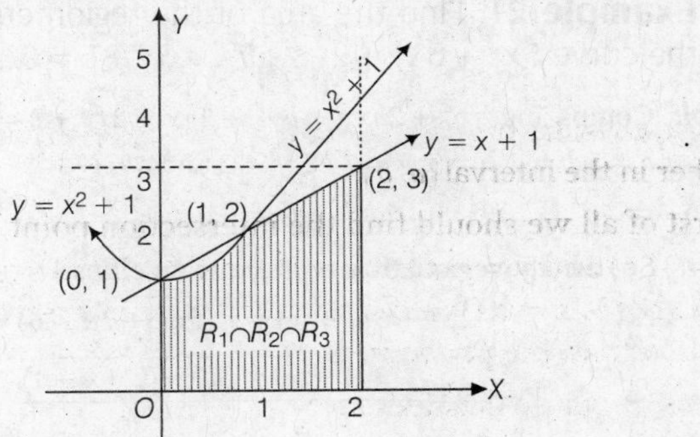

From the above figure,

$$\text{Required area} = \int_0^1 (x^2 + 1)\, dx + \int_1^2 (x + 1)\, dx$$

$$= \left(\frac{x^3}{3} + x \right)_0^1 + \left(\frac{x^2}{2} + x \right)_1^2 = \frac{23}{6} \text{ sq units}$$

Example 20 The area common to the region determined by $y \geq \sqrt{x}$ and $x^2 + y^2 < 2$ has the value

(a) π sq units

(b) $(2\pi - 1)$ sq units

(c) $\left(\frac{\pi}{4} - \frac{1}{6} \right)$ sq units

(d) None of these

Sol. The region formed by $y \geq \sqrt{x}$ is the outer region of the parabola $y^2 = x$, when $y \geq 0$ and $x \geq 0$ and $x^2 + y^2 < 2$ is the region inner to circle $x^2 + y^2 = 2$ shown as in figure.

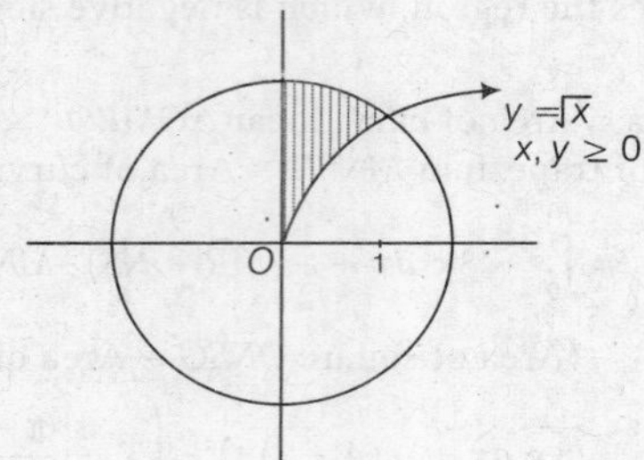

Now, to find the point of intersection put $y^2 = x$ in $x^2 + y^2 = 2$.

$$\Rightarrow \quad x^2 + x - 2 = 0$$

$$\Rightarrow \quad (x+2)(x-1) = 0$$

$$\Rightarrow \quad x = 1, \text{ as } x \geq 0$$

$$\therefore \text{ Required area} = \int_0^1 (\sqrt{2 - x^2} - \sqrt{x})\, dx$$

$$= \left[\frac{x\sqrt{2 - x^2}}{2} + \sin^{-1} \frac{x}{\sqrt{2}} - \frac{2}{\sqrt{3}} x^{3/2} \right]_0^1$$

$$= \frac{1}{2} + \frac{\pi}{4} - \frac{2}{3} = \left(\frac{\pi}{4} - \frac{1}{6} \right) \text{ sq units}$$

Hence, (c) is the correct answer.

Example 21 Find the area of the region enclosed by the curve $5x^2 + 6xy + 2y^2 + 7x + 6y + 6 = 0$.

Sol. Comparing $ax^2 + 2hxy + by^2 + 2gx + 2fy + c = 0$, we get $a = 5, b = 2, h = 3, g = 7/2, f = 3$ and $c = 6$

$$\Rightarrow \quad h^2 - ab = -1 < 0$$

So, the above equation represents an ellipse.

$$\therefore \quad 2y^2 + 6(1+x)y + (5x^2 + 7x + 6) = 0$$

$$\Rightarrow \quad y = \frac{-3(1+x) \pm \sqrt{(3-x)(x-1)}}{2}$$

Clearly, the values of y are real for all $x \in [1, 3]$. Thus, the graph is as shown below

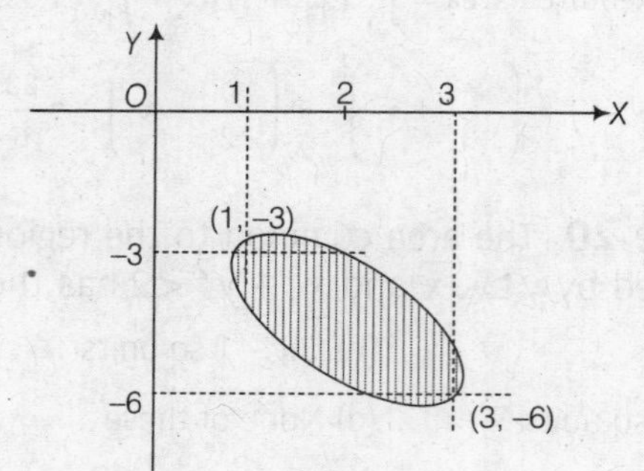

Thus, required area

$$= \left| \int_1^3 \left(\frac{-3(1+x) - \sqrt{(3-x)(x-1)}}{2} \right) - \left(\frac{-3(1+x) + \sqrt{(3-x)(x-1)}}{2} \right) dx \right|$$

$$= \left| -\int_1^3 \sqrt{(3-x)(x-1)}\, dx \right| = \left| \int_1^3 \sqrt{1^2 - (x-2)^2}\, dx \right|$$

$$= \left| -\left\{ \frac{1}{2}(x-2)\sqrt{-x^2 + 4x - 3} + \frac{1}{2}\sin^{-1}\left(\frac{x-2}{1} \right) \right\}_1^3 \right|$$

$$= \frac{\pi}{2} \text{ sq units}$$

Example 22 If $f(x) = \begin{cases} \sqrt{\{x\}}, & x \notin Z \\ 1, & x \in Z \end{cases}$ and $g(x) = \{x\}^2$ (where, {.} denotes fractional part of x), then the area bounded by $f(x)$ and $g(x)$ for $x \in [0, 10]$ is

(a) $\frac{5}{3}$ sq units (b) 5 sq units

(c) $\frac{10}{3}$ sq units (d) None of these

Sol. As, $f(x) = \begin{cases} \sqrt{\{x\}}, & x \notin z \\ 1, & x \in z \end{cases}$ and $g(x) = \{x\}^2$, where both $f(x)$ and $g(x)$ are periodic with period '1' shown as

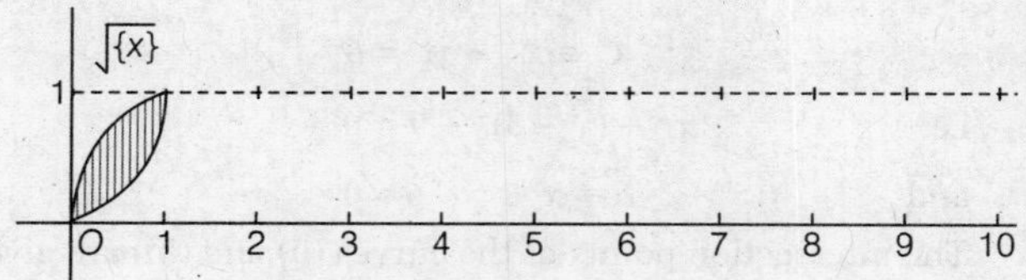

$$\text{Thus, required area} = 10 \int_0^1 [\sqrt{\{x\}} - \{x\}^2]\, dx$$

$$= 10 \int_0^1 [(x)^{1/2} - x^2]\, dx$$

$$= 10 \left[\frac{x^{3/2}}{3/2} - \frac{x^3}{3} \right]_0^1$$

$$= 10 \left(\frac{2}{3} - \frac{1}{3} \right) = \frac{10}{3} \text{ sq units}$$

Hence, (c) is the correct answer.

Example 23 Find the area of the region bounded by the curves $y = x^2$, $y = |2 - x^2|$ and $y = 2$, which lies to the right of the line $x = 1$. ***[IIT JEE 2002]***

Sol. The region bounded by given curves on the right side of $x = 1$ is shown as

$$\text{Required area} = \int_1^{\sqrt{2}} \{x^2 - (2 - x^2)\}\, dx + \int_{\sqrt{2}}^2 \{4 - x^2\}\, dx$$

$$= \int_1^{\sqrt{2}} (2x^2 - 2)\, dx + \int_{\sqrt{2}}^{2} (4 - x^2)\, dx$$

$$= \left(2 \cdot \frac{x^3}{3} - 2x\right)_1^{\sqrt{2}} + \left(4x - \frac{x^3}{3}\right)_{\sqrt{2}}^{2}$$

$$= \left(\frac{4\sqrt{2}}{3} - 2\sqrt{2}\right) - \left(\frac{2}{3} - 2\right) + \left(8 - \frac{8}{3}\right) - \left(4\sqrt{2} - \frac{2\sqrt{2}}{3}\right)$$

$$= \left(-4\sqrt{2} + \frac{20}{3}\right) = \left(\frac{20 - 12\sqrt{2}}{3}\right) \text{ sq units}$$

Example 24 The area enclosed by the curve $|y| = \sin 2x$, when $x \in [0, 2\pi]$ is

(a) 1 sq unit (b) 2 sq units

(c) 3 sq units (d) 4 sq units

Sol. As, we know $y = \sin 2x$ could be plotted as

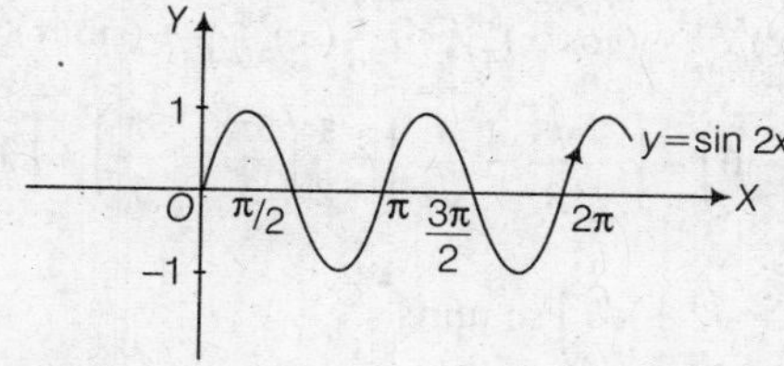

Thus, $|y| = \sin 2x$ is whenever positive, y can have both positive and negative values, i.e. the curve is symmetric about the axes.

$\sin 2x$ is positive only in $0 \le x \le \frac{\pi}{2}$ and $\pi \le x \le \frac{3\pi}{2}$. Thus, the curve consists of two loops one in $\left[0, \frac{\pi}{2}\right]$ and another in $\left[\pi, \frac{3\pi}{2}\right]$.

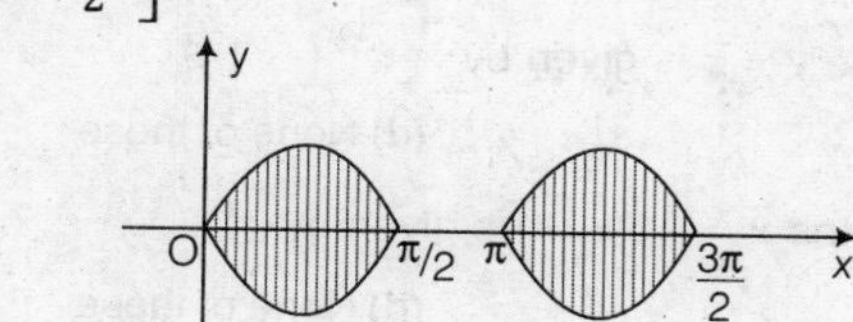

Thus, required area $= 4 \int_0^{\pi/2} (\sin 2x)\, dx$

$$= 4\left(-\frac{\cos 2x}{2}\right)_0^{\pi/2} = -2(\cos \pi - \cos 0)$$

$$= -2(-1 - 1) = 4 \text{ sq units}$$

Hence, (d) is the correct answer.

Example 25 Let $f(x) = x^2$, $g(x) = \cos x$ and $\alpha, \beta\ (\alpha < \beta)$ be the roots of the equation $18x^2 - 9\pi x + \pi^2 = 0$. Then, the area bounded by the curves $y = fog(x)$, the ordinates $x = \alpha$, $x = \beta$ and the X-axis is

(a) $\frac{1}{2}(\pi - 3)$ sq units (b) $\frac{\pi}{3}$ sq units

(c) $\frac{\pi}{4}$ sq units (d) $\frac{\pi}{12}$ sq units

Sol. Here, $y = fog(x) = f\{g(x)\} = (\cos x)^2 = \cos^2 x$

Also, $18x^2 - 9\pi x + \pi^2 = 0$

$\Rightarrow (3x - \pi)(6x - \pi) = 0$

$\Rightarrow x = \frac{\pi}{6}, \frac{\pi}{3}$ (as α, β)

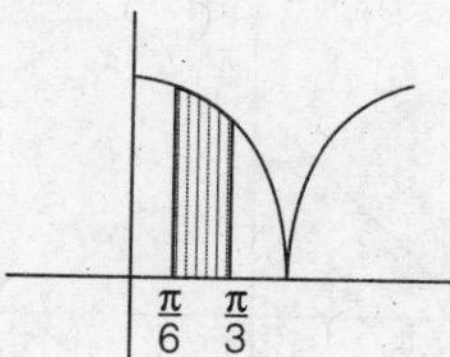

$\therefore$ Required area of curve

$$= \int_{\pi/6}^{\pi/3} \cos^2 x\, dx = \frac{1}{2} \int_{\pi/6}^{\pi/3} (1 + \cos 2x)\, dx$$

$$= \frac{1}{2}\left\{x + \frac{\sin 2x}{2}\right\}_{\pi/6}^{\pi/3} = \frac{1}{2}\left\{\left(\frac{\pi}{3} - \frac{\pi}{6}\right) + \frac{1}{2}\left(\sin \frac{2\pi}{3} - \sin \frac{2\pi}{6}\right)\right\}$$

$$= \frac{1}{2}\left\{\frac{\pi}{6} + \frac{1}{2}\left(\frac{\sqrt{3}}{2} - \frac{\sqrt{3}}{2}\right)\right\} = \frac{\pi}{12}$$

Hence, (d) is the correct answer.

Example 26 Find the area bounded by the curves $x^2 + y^2 = 25$, $4y = |4 - x^2|$ and $x = 0$ above the X-axis.

Sol. The 1st curve is a circle of radius 5 with centre at (0, 0).

The 2nd curve is $y = \left|\frac{4 - x^2}{4}\right| = \left|1 - \frac{x^2}{4}\right|$

which can be traced easily by graph transformation.

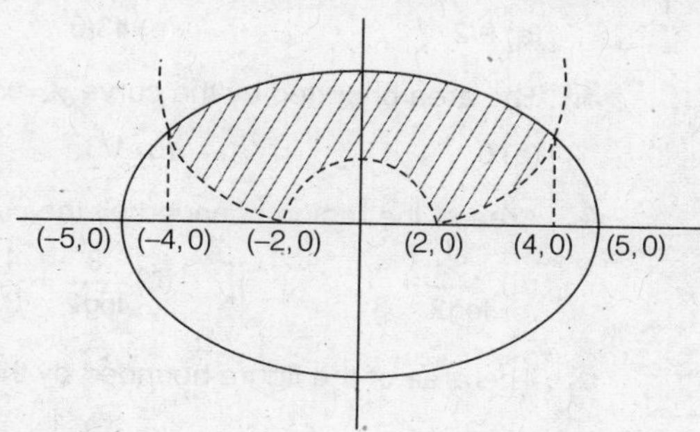

When the two curves intersect each other, then

$$x^2 + \left(1 - \frac{x^2}{4}\right)^2 = 25 \Rightarrow x = \pm 4$$

Hence, required area $= 2\int_0^4 \left(\sqrt{25 - x^2} - \left|1 - \frac{x^2}{4}\right|\right) dx$

$$= 2\left[\int_0^4 \sqrt{25 - x^2}\,dx - \int_0^2 \left(1 - \frac{x^2}{4}\right)dx + \int_2^4 \left(1 - \frac{x^2}{4}\right)dx\right]$$

$$= 2\left[6 + \frac{25}{2}\sin^{-1}\left(\frac{4}{5}\right) - \frac{4}{3} - \frac{8}{3}\right] = \left\{25\sin^{-1}\left(\frac{4}{5}\right) + 4\right\}$$

Example 27 Find the area enclosed by $|x| + |y| = 1$.

Sol. From the given equation, we have

$$|y| = 1 - |x| \geq 0 \qquad [\because |y| \geq 0]$$

$$\Rightarrow \qquad -1 \leq x \leq 1$$

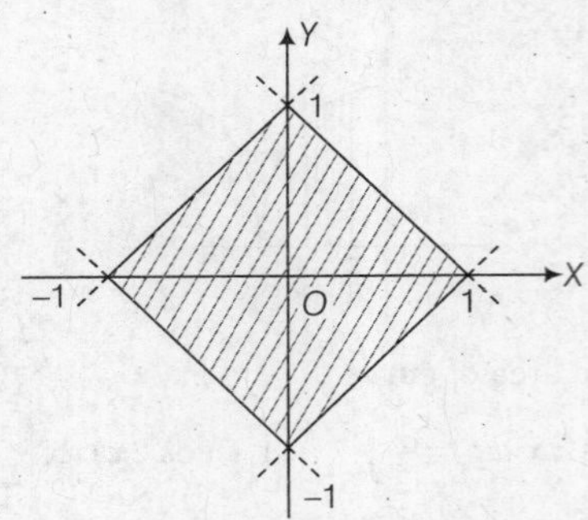

Therefore, the curve exists for $x \in [-1, 1]$ only

and for $-1 \leq x \leq 1$; $\quad y = \pm(1 - |x|)$ i.e. $y = \begin{cases} |x| - 1 \\ -(|x| - 1) \end{cases}$

Thus, the required graph is as given in figure.

$\therefore$ Required area $= (\sqrt{2})^2 = 2$ sq units

Example 28 Let $f(x) = \max\left\{\sin x, \cos x, \frac{1}{2}\right\}$, then determine the area of region bounded by the curves $y = f(x)$, X-axis, Y-axis and $x = 2\pi$.

Sol. We have, $f(x) = \max\left\{\sin x, \cos x, \frac{1}{2}\right\}$. Graphically, $f(x)$ could be drawn as

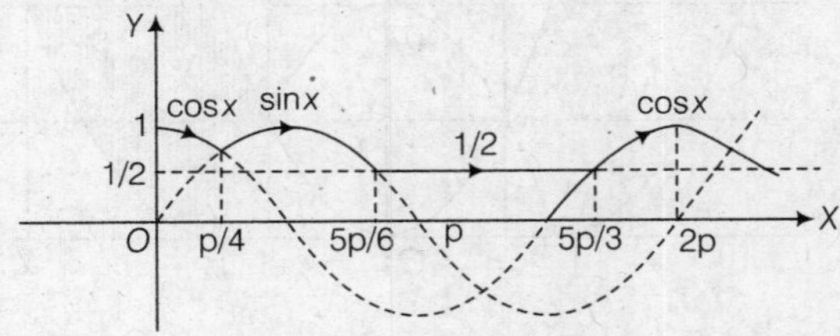

Here, the graph is plotted between 0 to 2π and between the points of intersection the maximum portion is included, thus the shaded part is required area

	Interval	Value of $f(x)$
i.e. for	$0 \leq x < \pi/4$	$\cos x$
for	$\pi/4 \leq x < 5\pi/6$	$\sin x$
for	$5\pi/6 \leq x < 5\pi/3$	$1/2$
for	$5\pi/3 \leq x < 2\pi$	$\cos x$

Hence, required area

$$I = \int_0^{\pi/4} \cos x\,dx + \int_{\pi/4}^{5\pi/6} \sin x\,dx + \int_{5\pi/6}^{5\pi/3} \frac{1}{2}\,dx + \int_{5\pi/3}^{2\pi} \cos x\,dx$$

$$= (\sin x)_0^{\pi/4} - (\cos x)_{\pi/4}^{5\pi/6} + \frac{1}{2}(x)_{5\pi/6}^{5\pi/3} + (\sin x)_{5\pi/3}^{2\pi}$$

$$= \left(\frac{1}{\sqrt{2}} - 0\right) - \left(-\frac{\sqrt{3}}{2} - \frac{1}{\sqrt{2}}\right) + \frac{1}{2}\left(\frac{5\pi}{3} - \frac{5\pi}{6}\right) + \left(0 + \frac{\sqrt{3}}{2}\right)$$

$$= \left(\frac{5\pi}{12} + \sqrt{2} + \sqrt{3}\right) \text{ sq units}$$

Exercise for Session 2

1. The area of the region bounded by $y^2 = 2x + 1$ and $x - y - 1 = 0$ is

(a) 2/3 (b) 4/3 (c) 8/3 (d) 16/3

2. The area bounded by the curve $y = 2x - x^2$ and the straight line $y = x$ is given by

(a) 9/2 (b) 43/6 (c) 35/6 (d) None of these

3. The area bounded by the curve $y = x|x|$, X-axis and the ordinates $x = -1$, $x = 1$ is given by

(a) 0 (b) 1/3 (c) 2/3 (d) None of these

4. Area of the region bounded by the curves $y = 2^x$, $y = 2x - x^2$, $x = 0$ and $x = 2$ is given by

(a) $\frac{3}{\log 2} - \frac{4}{3}$ (b) $\frac{3}{\log 2} + \frac{4}{3}$ (c) $3\log 2 - \frac{4}{3}$ (d) None of these

5. The area of the figure bounded by the cuves $y = e^x$, $y = e^{-x}$ and the straight line $x = 1$ is

(a) $e + \frac{1}{e}$ (b) $e - \frac{1}{e}$ (c) $e + \frac{1}{e} - 2$ (d) None of these

6. Area of the region bounded by the curve $y^2 = 4x$, Y-axis and the line $y = 3$ is

(a) 2 (b) 9/4 (c) $6\sqrt{3}$ (d) None of these

7. The area of the figure bounded by $y = \sin x$, $y = \cos x$ is the first quadrant is

(a) $2(\sqrt{2} - 1)$ (b) $\sqrt{3} + 1$ (c) $2(\sqrt{3} - 1)$ (d) None of these

8. The area bounded by the curves $y = xe^x$, $y = xe^{-x}$ and the line $x = 1$ is

(a) $\frac{2}{e}$ (b) $1 - \frac{2}{e}$ (c) $\frac{1}{e}$ (d) $1 - \frac{1}{e}$

9. The areas of the figure into which the curve $y^2 = 6x$ divides the circle $x^2 + y^2 = 16$ are in the ratio

(a) $\frac{2}{3}$ (b) $\frac{4\pi - \sqrt{3}}{8\pi + \sqrt{3}}$ (c) $\frac{4\pi + \sqrt{3}}{8\pi - \sqrt{3}}$ (d) None of these

10. The area bounded by the Y-axis, $y = \cos x$ and $y = \sin x$, $0 \geq x \leq \pi/2$ is

(a) $2(\sqrt{2} - 1)$ (b) $\sqrt{2} - 1$ (c) $(\sqrt{2} + 1)$ (d) $\sqrt{2}$

11. The area bounded by the curve $y = \frac{3}{|x|}$ and $y + |2 - x| = 2$ is

(a) $\frac{4 - \log 27}{3}$ (b) $2 - \log 3$ (c) $2 + \log 3$ (d) None of these

12. The area bounded by the curves $y = x^2 + 2$ and $y = 2|x| - \cos + x$ is

(a) 2/3 (b) 8/3 (c) 4/3 (d) 1/3

13. The are bounded by the curve $y^2 = 4x$ and the circle $x^2 + y^2 - 2x - 3 = 0$ is

(a) $2\pi + \frac{8}{3}$ (b) $4\pi + \frac{8}{3}$ (c) $\pi + \frac{8}{3}$ (d) $\pi - \frac{8}{3}$

14. A point P moves inside a triangle formed by $A(0, 0)$, $B\left(1, \frac{1}{\sqrt{3}}\right)$, $C(2, 0)$ such that $\min\{PA, PB, PC\} = 1$, then the area bounded by the curve traced by P, is

(a) $3\sqrt{3} - \frac{3\pi}{2}$ (b) $\sqrt{3} + \frac{\pi}{2}$ (c) $\sqrt{3} - \frac{\pi}{2}$ (d) $3\sqrt{3} + \frac{3\pi}{2}$

15. The graph of $y^2 + 2xy + 40|x| = 400$ divides the plane into regions. The area of the bounded region is

(a) 400 (b) 800 (c) 600 (c) None of these

16. The area of the region defined by $||x| - |y|| \leq 1$ and $x^2 + y^2 \leq 1$ in the xy plane is

(a) π (b) 2π (c) 3π (d) 1

17. The area of the region defined by $1 \leq |x - 2| + |y + 1| \leq 2$ is

(a) 2 (b) 4 (c) 6 (d) None of these

18. The area of the region enclosed by the curve $|y| = -(1 - |x|)^2 + 5$, is

(a) $\frac{8}{3}(7 + 5\sqrt{5})$ sq units (b) $\frac{2}{3}(7 + 5\sqrt{5})$ sq units (c) $\frac{2}{3}(5\sqrt{5} - 7)$ sq units (d) None of these

19. The area bounded by the curve $f(x) = ||\tan x + \cot x| - |\tan x - \cot x||$ between the lines $x = 0$, $x = \frac{\pi}{2}$ and the X-axis is

(a) $\log 4$ (b) $\log\sqrt{2}$ (c) $2\log 2$ (d) $\sqrt{2}\log 2$

20. If $f(x) = \max\left\{\sin x, \cos x, \frac{1}{2}\right\}$, then the area of the region bounded by the curves $y = f(x)$, X-axis, Y-axis and $x = \frac{5\pi}{3}$ is

(a) $\left(\sqrt{2} - \sqrt{3} + \frac{5\pi}{12}\right)$ sq units (b) $\left(\sqrt{2} + \sqrt{3} + \frac{5\pi}{2}\right)$ sq units

(c) $\left(\sqrt{2} + \sqrt{3} + \frac{5\pi}{2}\right)$ sq units (d) None of these

JEE Type Solved Examples : Single Option Correct Type Questions

● **Ex. 1** *If A denotes the area bounded by* $f(x)=\left|\dfrac{\sin x+\cos x}{x}\right|$, *X-axis,* $x=\pi$ *and* $x=3\pi$, *then*

(a) $1< A<2$ (b) $0< A<2$
(c) $2< A<3$ (d) None of these

Sol. $\dfrac{2\sqrt{2}}{2\pi}<\displaystyle\int_{\pi}^{2\pi}\frac{|\sin x+\cos x|}{x}\,dx<\frac{2\sqrt{2}}{2\pi}$

$$\left[\because \pi<x<2\pi \Rightarrow \frac{1}{2\pi}<\frac{1}{x}<\frac{1}{\pi}\right] \quad ...(i)$$

$$\frac{2\sqrt{2}}{3\pi}<\int_{2\pi}^{3\pi}\frac{|\sin x+\cos x|}{x}\,dx<\frac{2\sqrt{2}}{2\pi} \quad ...(ii)$$

On adding Eqs. (i) and (ii), we get

$$\frac{5\sqrt{2}}{3\pi}<A<\frac{3\sqrt{2}}{\pi}$$

$\Rightarrow$ $0.75 < A < 1.3$

Hence, (b) is the correct answer.

● **Ex. 2** *If* $f(x)\geq 0, \forall x\in(0,2)$ *and* $y=f(x)$ *makes positive intercepts of 2 and 1 unit on X and Y-axes respectively and encloses an area of 3/4 unit with axes, then* $\displaystyle\int_0^2 xf'(x)\,dx$ *is*

(a) $\dfrac{3}{4}$ (b) 1 (c) $\dfrac{5}{4}$ (d) $-\dfrac{3}{4}$

Sol. $I=xf(x)|_0^2-\displaystyle\int_0^2 f(x)\,dx=0-\frac{3}{4}=-\frac{3}{4}$

Hence, (d) is the correct answer.

● **Ex. 3** *The area of the region included between the regions satisfying* $\min(|x|,|y|)\geq 1$ *and* $x^2+y^2\leq 5$ *is*

(a) $\dfrac{5}{2}\left(\sin^{-1}\dfrac{2}{\sqrt{5}}-\sin^{-1}\dfrac{1}{\sqrt{5}}\right)-4$ (b) $10\left(\sin^{-1}\dfrac{2}{\sqrt{5}}-\sin^{-1}\dfrac{1}{\sqrt{5}}\right)-4$

(c) $\dfrac{2}{5}\left(\sin^{-1}\dfrac{2}{\sqrt{5}}-\sin^{-1}\dfrac{1}{\sqrt{5}}\right)-4$ (d) $15\left(\sin^{-1}\dfrac{2}{\sqrt{5}}-\sin^{-1}\dfrac{1}{\sqrt{5}}\right)-4$

Sol. Shaded region depicts $\min(|x|,|y|)\geq 1$

Required area $=4\displaystyle\int_1^2(\sqrt{5-x^2}-1)\,dx$

$$=10\left(\sin^{-1}\frac{2}{\sqrt{5}}-\sin^{-1}\frac{1}{\sqrt{5}}\right)-4$$

Hence, (b) is the correct answer.

● **Ex. 4** *The area of the region between the curves* $y=\sqrt{\dfrac{1+\sin x}{\cos x}}$ *and* $y=\sqrt{\dfrac{1-\sin x}{\cos x}}$ *and bounded by the lines* $x=0$ *and* $x=\dfrac{\pi}{4}$ *is* **[IIT JEE 2008]**

(a) $\displaystyle\int_0^{\sqrt{2}-1}\frac{t}{(1+t^2)\sqrt{1-t^2}}\,dt$

(b) $\displaystyle\int_0^{\sqrt{2}-1}\frac{4t}{(1+t^2)\sqrt{1-t^2}}\,dt$

(c) $\displaystyle\int_0^{\sqrt{2}+1}\frac{4t}{(1+t^2)\sqrt{1-t^2}}\,dt$

(d) $\displaystyle\int_0^{\sqrt{2}+1}\frac{t}{(1+t^2)\sqrt{1-t^2}}\,dt$

Sol. Required area $=\displaystyle\int_0^{\pi/4}\left(\sqrt{\frac{1+\sin x}{\cos x}}-\sqrt{\frac{1-\sin x}{\cos x}}\right)dx$

$$\left(\because \frac{1+\sin x}{\cos x}>\frac{1-\sin x}{\cos x}>0\right)$$

$$=\int_0^{\pi/4}\left(\sqrt{\frac{1+\dfrac{2\tan\frac{x}{2}}{1+\tan^2\frac{x}{2}}}{\dfrac{1-\tan^2\frac{x}{2}}{1+\tan^2\frac{x}{2}}}}-\sqrt{\frac{1-\dfrac{2\tan\frac{x}{2}}{1+\tan^2\frac{x}{2}}}{\dfrac{1-\tan^2\frac{x}{2}}{1+\tan^2\frac{x}{2}}}}\right)dx$$

$$=\int_0^{\pi/4}\left(\sqrt{\frac{1+\tan\frac{x}{2}}{1-\tan\frac{x}{2}}}-\sqrt{\frac{1-\tan\frac{x}{2}}{1+\tan\frac{x}{2}}}\right)dx$$

$$=\int_0^{\pi/4}\frac{1+\tan\frac{x}{2}-1+\tan\frac{x}{2}}{\sqrt{1-\tan^2\frac{x}{2}}}\,dx=\int_0^{\pi/4}\frac{2\tan\frac{x}{2}}{\sqrt{1-\tan^2\frac{x}{2}}}\,dx$$

Put $\tan\dfrac{x}{2}=t$

$\therefore$ Area $=\displaystyle\int_0^{\sqrt{2}-1}\frac{4t}{(1+t^2)\sqrt{1-t^2}}\,dt$

Hence, (b) is the correct answer.

JEE Type Solved Examples : More than One Correct Option Type Questions

- **Ex. 5** *Let T be the triangle with vertices $(0,0)$, $(0, c^2)$ and (c, c^2) and let R be the region between $y = cx$ and $y = x^2$, where $c > 0$, then*

(a) Area $(R) = \dfrac{c^3}{6}$ (b) Area of $R = \dfrac{c^3}{3}$

(c) $\lim\limits_{c\to 0^+} \dfrac{\text{Area }(T)}{\text{Area }(R)} = 3$ (d) $\lim\limits_{c\to 0^+} \dfrac{\text{Area }(T)}{\text{Area }(R)} = \dfrac{3}{2}$

Sol. Area $(T) = \dfrac{c\cdot c^2}{2} = \dfrac{c^3}{2}$

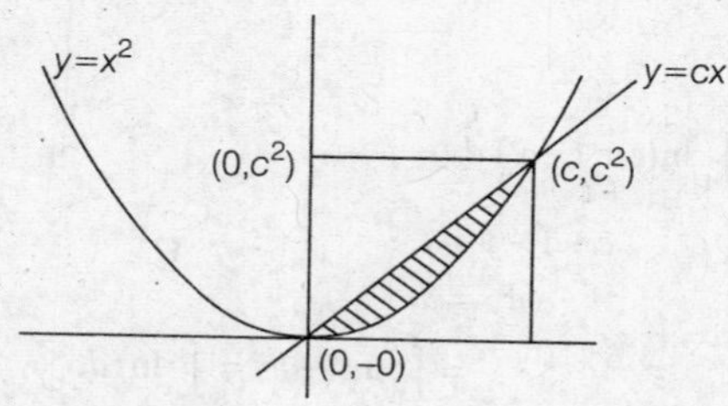

$$\text{Area }(R) = \frac{c^3}{2} - \int_0^c x^2\, dx = \frac{c^3}{2} - \frac{c^3}{3} = \frac{c^3}{6}$$

$$\therefore \quad \lim_{c\to 0^+} \frac{\text{Area}(T)}{\text{Area }(R)} = \lim_{c\to 0^+} \frac{c^3}{2}\cdot\frac{6}{c^3} = 3$$

Hence, (a) and (c) are the correct answers.

- **Ex. 6** *Suppose f is defined from $R \to [-1, 1]$ as $f(x) = \dfrac{x^2-1}{x^2+1}$ where R is the set of real number. Then, the statement which does not hold is*

(a) f is many-one onto

(b) f increases for $x > 0$ and decreases for $x < 0$

(c) minimum value is not attained even though f is bounded

(d) the area included by the curve $y = f(x)$ and the line $y = 1$ is π sq units

Sol. $y = f(x) = \dfrac{x^2-1}{x^2+1} = 1 - \dfrac{2}{x^2+1}$

$f'(x) = \dfrac{4x}{(x^2+1)^2}$ $x > 0$, f is increasing and $x < 0$ f is decreasing.

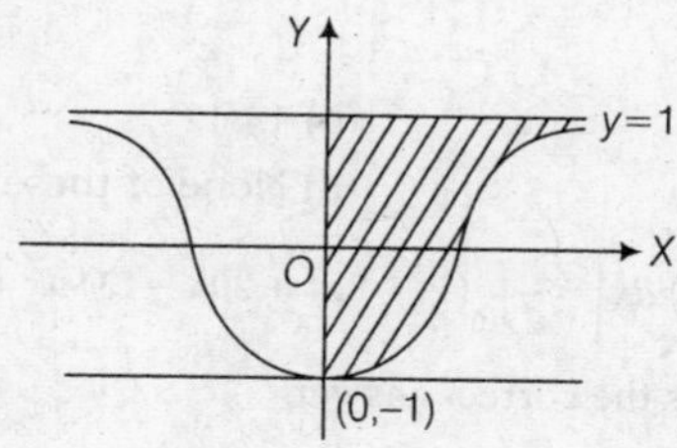

$\Rightarrow$ (b) is true; range is $[-1, 1)$ $\Rightarrow$ into $\Rightarrow$ (a) is false; minimum value occurs at $x = 0$ and $f(0) = -1$ $\Rightarrow$ (c) is false.

$$A = 2\int_0^\infty \left(1 - \frac{x^2-1}{x^2+1}\right) dx = 4\int_0^\infty \frac{dx}{x^2+1}$$

$$= [4\cdot \tan^{-1} x]_0^\infty = 4\cdot\frac{\pi}{2} = 2\pi \Rightarrow \text{(d) is false.}$$

Hence, (a), (c) and (d) are the correct answers.

- **Ex. 7** *Consider* $f(x) = \begin{cases} \cos x, & 0 \le x < \dfrac{\pi}{2} \\ \left(\dfrac{\pi}{2} - x\right)^2, & \dfrac{\pi}{2} \le x < \pi \end{cases}$ *such that f is periodic with period π, then*

(a) the range of f is $\left[0, \dfrac{\pi^2}{4}\right)$

(b) f is continuous for all real x, but not differentiable for some real x

(c) f is continuous for all real x

(d) the area bounded by $y = f(x)$ and the X-axis from $x = -n\pi$ to $x = n\pi$ is $2n\left(1 + \dfrac{\pi^2}{24}\right)$ for a given $n \in N$

Sol. Given, $f(x) = \begin{cases} \cos x, & 0 \le x < \dfrac{\pi}{2} \\ \left(\dfrac{\pi}{2} - x\right)^2, & \dfrac{\pi}{2} \le x < \pi \end{cases}$ and f is periodic with period π. Let us draw the graph of $y = f(x)$

From the graph, the range of the function is $\left[0, \dfrac{\pi^2}{4}\right)$.

It is discontinuous at $x = n\pi$, $n \in I$. It is not differentiable at $x = \dfrac{n\pi}{2}$, $n \in I$.

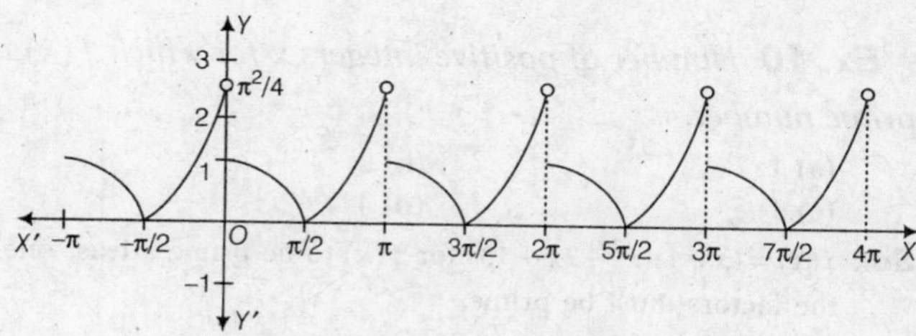

Area bounded by $y = f(x)$ and the X-axis from $-n\pi$ to $n\pi$ for $n \in N$

$$= 2n\int_0^\pi f(x)\,dx = 2n\left[\int_0^{\pi/2} \cos x\,dx + \int_{\pi/2}^{\pi} \left(\frac{\pi}{2} - x\right)^2 dx\right]$$

$$= 2n\left(1 + \frac{\pi^3}{24}\right)$$

Hence, (a) and (d) are the correct answers.

• **Ex. 8** *Consider the functions $f(x)$ and $g(x)$, both defined from $R \to R$ and are defined as $f(x) = 2x - x^2$ and $g(x) = x^n$ where $n \in N$. If the area between $f(x)$ and $g(x)$ is 1/2, then n is a divisor of*

(a) 12 (b) 15 (c) 20 (d) 30

Sol. Solving, $f(x) = 2x - x^2$ and $g(x) = x^n$ we have

$2x - x^2 = x^n \Rightarrow x = 0$ and $x = 1$

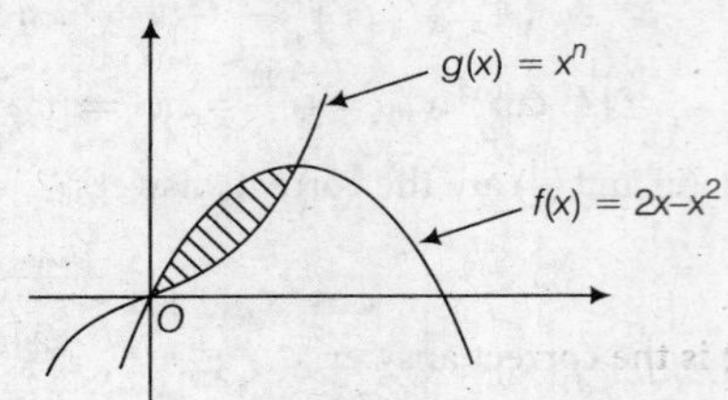

$$A = \int_0^1 (2x - x^2 - x^n)\, dx = \left[x^2 - \frac{x^3}{3} - \frac{x^{n+1}}{n+1}\right]_0^1$$

$$= 1 - \frac{1}{3} - \frac{1}{n+1} = \frac{2}{3} - \frac{1}{n+1}$$

Since, $\frac{2}{3} - \frac{1}{n+1} = \frac{1}{2} \Rightarrow \frac{2}{3} - \frac{1}{2} = \frac{1}{n+1}$

$\Rightarrow \frac{4-3}{6} = \frac{1}{n+1} \Rightarrow n + 1 = 6$

$\Rightarrow n = 5$

Thus, n is a divisor of 15, 20, 30.

Hence, (b), (c) and (d) are the correct answers.

• **Ex. 9** *Area of the region bounded by the curve $y = e^x$ and lines $x = 0$ and $y = e$ is* **[IIT JEE 2009]**

(a) $e - 1$ (b) $\int_1^e \ln(e + 1 - y)\, dy$

(c) $e - \int_0^1 e^x\, dx$ (d) $\int_1^e \ln y\, dy$

Sol. Shaded area $= e - \left(\int_0^1 e^x\, dx\right) = 1$

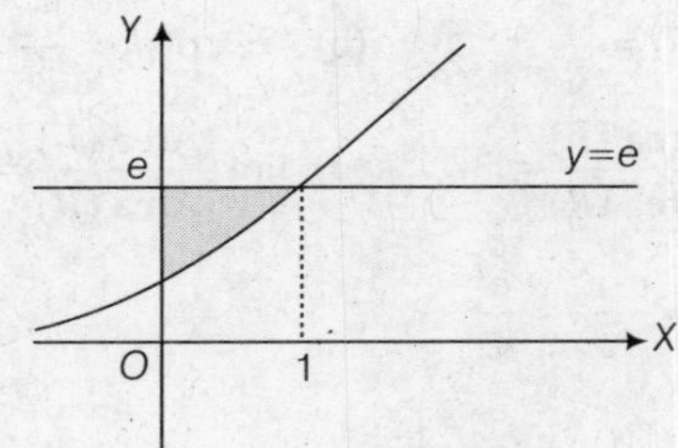

Also, $\int_1^e \ln(e + 1 - y)\, dy$

Put $e + 1 - y = t$

$\Rightarrow -dy = dt$

$$= \int_e^1 \ln t(-dt) = \int_1^e \ln t\, dt$$

$$= \int_1^e \ln y\, dy = 1$$

Hence, (b), (c) and (d) are the correct answers.

JEE Type Solved Examples : Passage Based Questions

Passage I

(Q. Nos. 10 to 12)

Consider the function $f(x) = x^3 - 8x^2 + 20x - 13$.

• **Ex. 10** *Number of positive integers x for which $f(x)$ is a prime number, is*

(a) 1 (b) 2

(c) 3 (d) 4

Sol. $f(x) = (x-1)(x^2 - 7x + 13)$ for $f(x)$ to be prime atleast one of the factors must be prime.

Therefore, $x - 1 = 1$

$\Rightarrow x = 2$

or $x^2 - 7x + 13 = 1$

$\Rightarrow x^2 - 7x + 12 = 0$

$\Rightarrow x = 3$ or 4

$\Rightarrow x = 2, 3, 4$

Hence, (c) is the correct answer.

• **Ex. 11** *The function $f(x)$ defined for $R \to R$*

(a) is one-one onto

(b) is many-one onto

(c) has 3 real roots

(d) is such that $f(x_1) \cdot f(x_2) < 0$ where x_1 and x_2 are the roots of $f'(x) = 0$

Sol. $f(x)$ is many-one as it increases and decreases, also range of $f(x) \in R \Rightarrow$ many-one onto.

Hence, (b) is the correct answer.

• **Ex. 12** *Area enclosed by $y = f(x)$ and the coordinate axes is*

(a) 65/12 (b) 13/12

(c) 71/12 (d) None of these

Sol. $A = \left|\int_0^1 f(x)\, dx\right| = -\int_0^1 (x^3 - 8x^2 + 20x - 13)\, dx = \frac{65}{12}$

Hence, (a) is the correct answer.

Passage II

(Q. Nos. 13 to 15)

Let $h(x) = f(x) - g(x)$, where $f(x) = \sin^4 \pi x$ and $g(x) = \ln x$. Let $x_0, x_1, x_2, \ldots, x_{n+1}$ be the roots of $f(x) = g(x)$ in increasing order.

Ex. 13 *The absolute area enclosed by $y = f(x)$ and $y = g(x)$ is given by*

(a) $\sum_{r=0}^{n} \int_{x_r}^{x_{r+1}} (-1)^r h(x)\, dx$ (b) $\sum_{r=0}^{n} \int_{x_r}^{x_{r+1}} (-1)^{r+1} h(x)\, dx$

(c) $2 \sum_{r=0}^{n} \int_{x_r}^{x_{r+1}} (-1)^r h(x)\, dx$ (d) $\frac{1}{2} \sum_{r=0}^{n} \int_{x_r}^{x_{r+1}} (-1)^{r+1} h(x)\, dx$

Sol.

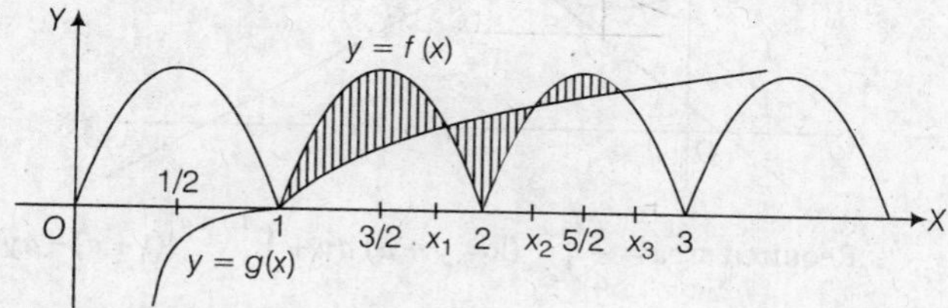

Hence, (a) is the correct answer.

Ex. 14 *In the above question, the value of n is*

(a) 1 (b) 2 (c) 3 (d) 4

Sol. $x_{n+1} = x_3 \Rightarrow n = 2.$

Hence, (b) is the correct answer.

Ex. 15 *The whole area bounded by $y = f(x)$, $y = g(x)$ and $x = 0$ is*

(a) $\frac{11}{8}$ (b) $\frac{8}{3}$ (c) 2 (d) $\frac{13}{3}$

Sol. Required area $= \int_0^1 \sin^4 \pi x\, dx - \int_0^1 \ln x\, dx = \frac{11}{8}$

Hence, (a) is the correct answer.

Passage III

(Q. Nos. 16 to 18)

Consider the function defined implicitly by the equation $y^3 - 3y + x = 0$ on various intervals in the real line. If $x \in (-\infty, -2) \cup (2, \infty)$, the equation implicitly defines a unique real-valued differentiable function $y = f(x)$. If $x \in (-2, 2)$, the equation implicitly defines a unique real-valued differentiable function $y = g(x)$ satisfying $g(0) = 0$. **[IIT JEE 2008]**

Ex. 16 *If $f(-10\sqrt{2}) = 2\sqrt{2}$, then $f''(-10\sqrt{2})$ is equal to*

(a) $\frac{4\sqrt{2}}{7^3 3^2}$ (b) $-\frac{4\sqrt{2}}{7^3 3^2}$ (c) $\frac{4\sqrt{2}}{7^3 3}$ (d) $-\frac{4\sqrt{2}}{7^3 3}$

Sol. $\therefore$ $y^3 - 3y + x = 0$

On differentiating, we get $3y^2 y' - 3y' - 1 = 0$

$$\Rightarrow \quad y' = \frac{1}{3(1 - y^2)}$$

$$\Rightarrow \quad y'(-10\sqrt{2}) = \frac{1}{3\{1 - (2\sqrt{2})^2\}} \quad \ldots\text{(i)}$$

$$\Rightarrow \quad y'(-10\sqrt{2}) = \frac{1}{3\{1 - (2\sqrt{2})^2\}} = \frac{1}{3(1-8)} = -\frac{1}{21}$$

Again differentiating Eq. (i), we get

$$y'' = \frac{6yy'^2}{3(1 - y^2)}$$

$$y''(-10\sqrt{2}) = \frac{6 \cdot 2\sqrt{2} \cdot \left(\frac{1}{21}\right)^2}{3(1-8)} = -\frac{4\sqrt{2}}{7^3 . 3^2}$$

Hence, (b) is the correct answer.

Ex. 17 *The area of the region bounded by the curve $y = f(x)$, the X-axis and the line $x = a$ and $x = b$, where $-\infty < a < b < -2$ is*

(a) $\int_a^b \frac{x}{3[\{f(x)\}^2 - 1]} dx + bf(b) - af(a)$

(b) $-\int_a^b \frac{x}{3[\{f(x)\}^2 - 1]} dx - bf(b) + af(a)$

(c) $\int_a^b \frac{x}{3[\{f(x)\}^2 - 1]} dx - bf(b) + af(a)$

(d) $-\int_a^b \frac{x}{3[\{f(x)\}^2 - 1]} dx - bf(b) + af(a)$

Sol. Required area $= \int_a^b f(x)\, dx = [xf(x)]_a^b - \int_a^b xf'(x)\, dx$

$$= bf(b) - af(a) + \int_a^b \frac{x}{3[\{f(x)\}^2 - 1]} dx$$

Hence, (a) is the correct answer.

Ex. 18 $\int_{-1}^{1} g'(x)\, dx$ *is equal to*

(a) $2g(-1)$ (b) 0 (c) $-2g(1)$ (d) $2g(1)$

Sol. $I = \int_{-1}^{1} g'(x)\, dx = [g(x)]_{-1}^{1} = g(1) - g(-1)$

Since, $y^3 - 3y + x = 0$ ...(i)

and $y = g(x)$

Since, $\{g(x)\}^3 - 3g(x) + x = 0$ [by Eq. (i)]

At $x = 1$, $\{g(1)\}^3 - 3g(1) + 1 = 0$ ...(ii)

At $x = -1$, $\{g(-1)\}^3 - 3g(-1) - 1 = 0$ ...(iii)

On adding Eqs. (i) and (ii), we get

$$\{g(1)\}^3 + \{g(-1)\}^3 - 3\{g(1) + g(-1)\} = 0$$

$$\{g(1) + g(-1)\}\{g(1)^2 + g(-1)^2 - g(1)g(-1) - 3\} = 0$$

$$\Rightarrow \quad g(1) + g(-1) = 0,\ g(1) = -g(-1)$$

$$\Rightarrow \quad I = g(1) - g(-1) = g(1) - (-g(1)) = 2g(1)$$

Hence, (d) is the correct answer.

Subjective Type Questions

● ***Ex. 19*** *Find the total area bounded by the curves* $y = \cos x - \cos^2 x$ *and* $y = x^2\left(x^2 - \frac{\pi^2}{4}\right)$.

Sol. Here, $y = \cos x - \cos^2 x$ and $y = x^2\left(x^2 - \frac{\pi^2}{4}\right)$ could be drawn as in figure.

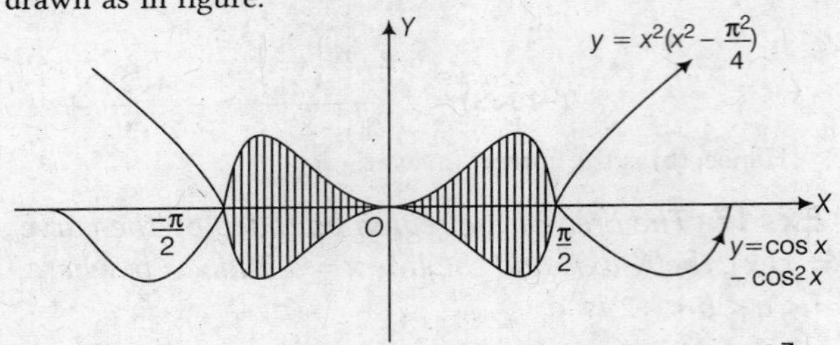

$$\text{Thus, the area} = 2\int_0^{\pi/2}\left[(\cos x - \cos^2 x) - \left\{x^2\left(x^2 - \frac{\pi^2}{4}\right)\right\}\right]dx$$

$$= 2\int_0^{\pi/2}\left(\cos x - \cos^2 x - x^4 + \frac{\pi^2}{4}x^2\right)dx$$

$$= 2\left[\sin x - \frac{x}{2} - \frac{\sin 2x}{4} - \frac{x^5}{5} + \frac{\pi^2 x^3}{12}\right]_0^{\pi/2}$$

$$= \left(2 - \frac{\pi}{2} + \frac{\pi^5}{120}\right)$$

● ***Ex. 20*** *A curve* $y = f(x)$ *passes through the point* $P(1, 1)$, *the normal to the curve at P is* $a(y-1) + (x-1) = 0$. *If the slope of the tangent at any point on the curve is proportional to the ordinate of that point, determine the equation of the curve. Also obtain the area bounded by the Y-axis, the curve and the normal to the curve at P.*

Sol. Here, slope of the normal at $P(x, y)$.

$\Rightarrow$ Slope of the line $a(y-1) + (x-1) = 0$ is $-\frac{1}{a}$

$\therefore$ Slope of the tangent at $P = a$,

$$\left(\frac{dy}{dx}\right)_P = a \qquad \text{...(i)}$$

It is given that the slope of the tangent at any point on the curve $y = f(x)$ is proportional to the ordinate of the point.

$$\therefore \quad \frac{dy}{dx} \propto y \Rightarrow \frac{dy}{dx} = \lambda y$$

$$\Rightarrow \quad \left(\frac{dy}{dx}\right)_{(1,1)} = \lambda \Rightarrow a = \lambda$$

$$\therefore \quad \frac{dy}{dx} = ay \quad \Rightarrow \quad \frac{dy}{y} = a\,dx$$

$$\Rightarrow \quad \log y = ax + \log c$$

$$\Rightarrow \quad y = ce^{ax}, \quad \text{which passes through } P(1, 1)$$

$$\therefore \quad c = e^{-a}$$

$$\Rightarrow \text{Curve is} \quad y = e^{-a}e^{ax} \Rightarrow y = e^{a(x-1)}$$

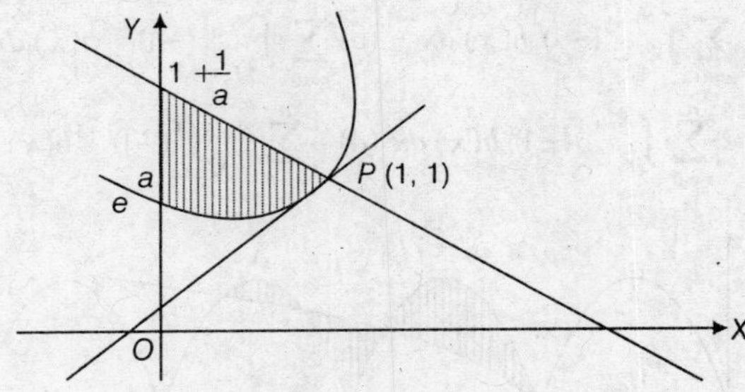

$$\therefore \text{Required area} = \frac{1}{a}\int_{e^{-a}}^{1}(\log y + a)\,dy + \int_1^{1+1/a}\{(1+a) - ay\}dy$$

$$= \frac{1}{a}\{y(\log y - 1) + ay\}_{e^{-a}}^{1} + \left\{(1+a)y - \frac{a}{2}y^2\right\}_1^{1+\frac{1}{a}}$$

$$= \frac{1}{a}\{(-1+a) - e^{-a}(-a-1) - ae^{-a}\} + \left[(1+a)\left(1 + \frac{1}{a} - 1\right) - \frac{a}{2}\left\{\left(1+\frac{1}{a}\right)^2 - 1^2\right\}\right]$$

$$= \frac{1}{a}[-1 + a + ae^{-a} + e^{-a} - ae^{-a}] + \left[\frac{1+a}{a} - \frac{a}{2}\left(2 + \frac{1}{a}\right)\frac{1}{a}\right]$$

$$= \frac{1}{a}(-1 + a + e^{-a}) + \left(\frac{1}{a} + 1 - 1 - \frac{1}{2a}\right) = \left(1 + \frac{e^{-a}}{a} - \frac{1}{2a}\right) \text{ sq units}$$

● ***Ex. 21*** *Sketch the region bounded by the curves* $y = x^2$ *and* $y = \frac{2}{1+x^2}$. *Find the area.*

Sol. For intersection point, $x^2 = \frac{2}{1+x^2}$

i.e. $\quad x^4 + x^2 - 2 = 0$

i.e. $\quad (x^2 + 2)(x^2 - 1) = 0$

i.e. $\quad x = \pm 1$

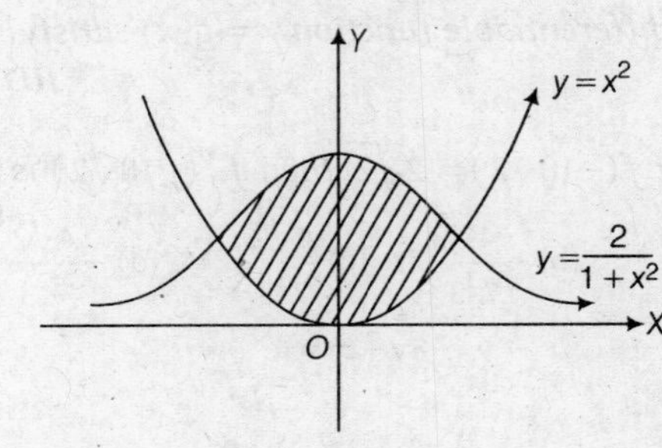

Hence, required area $= 2\int_0^1 \left(\frac{2}{1+x^2} - x^2\right) dx$

$$= 2\left[2\tan^{-1} x - \frac{x^3}{3}\right]_0^1 = 2\left(\frac{\pi}{2} - \frac{1}{3}\right)$$

• Ex. 22 *Find the area enclosed between the curves*

$$y = \log(x+e);\ x = \log_e\left(\frac{1}{y}\right) \text{ and X-axis.}$$

Sol. The given curves are $y = \log(x+e)$ and

$$x = \log_e\left(\frac{1}{y}\right) \Rightarrow \frac{1}{y} = e^x \Rightarrow y = e^{-x}$$

Using graph transformation we can sketch the curves.

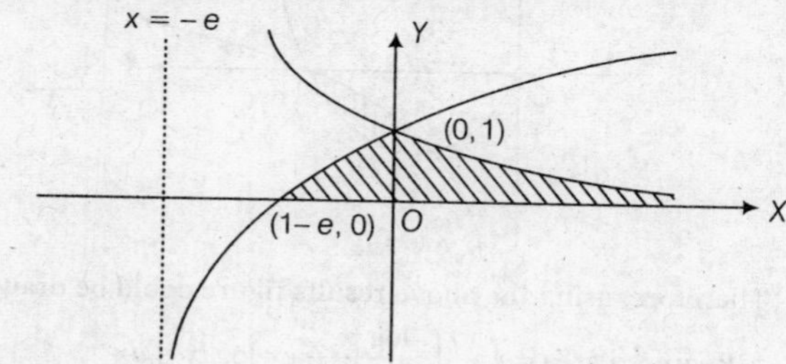

Hence, required area $= \int_{1-e}^{0} \log(x+e)\, dx + \int_0^\infty e^{-x}\, dx$

$$= \int_1^e \log(t)\, dt + \int_0^\infty e^{-x}\, dx$$

(putting $x + e = t$)

$$= [t\log t - t]_1^e - [e^{-x}]_0^\infty = 1 + 1 = 2$$

• Ex. 23 *Find the area of the region bounded by the curve $c : y = \tan x$, tangent drawn to c at $x = \pi/4$ and the X-axis.*

Sol. The given curve is $y = \tan x$

$$\therefore \quad \frac{dy}{dx} = \sec^2 x$$

$$\left(\frac{dy}{dx}\right)_{x=\pi/4} = \sec^2\frac{\pi}{4} = 2$$

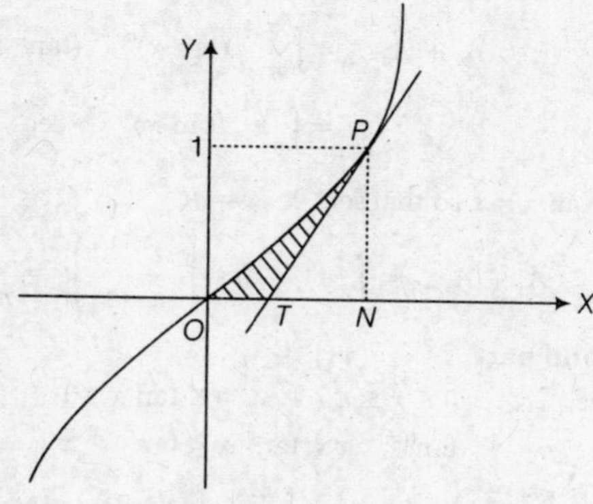

Also, at $x = \frac{\pi}{4}$; $y = 1$

$\therefore$ The equation of the tangent to the curve at the point $\left(\frac{\pi}{4}, 1\right)$ is $\quad y - 1 = 2\left(x - \frac{\pi}{4}\right)$

when $\quad y = 0;\ x = \frac{\pi}{4} - \frac{1}{2} = OT$

Now, the required area = Area of curvilinear ΔOPN – Area of ΔPTN

$$= \int_0^{\pi/4} (\tan x)\, dx - \frac{1}{2}\cdot NT \cdot PN$$

$$= [\log(\sec x)]_0^{\pi/4} - \frac{1}{2}\left(\frac{\pi}{4} - \frac{\pi}{4} + \frac{1}{2}\right)\cdot 1 = \frac{1}{2}\left(\log 2 - \frac{1}{2}\right)$$

• Ex. 24 *Find all the possible values of $b > 0$, so that the area of the bounded region enclosed between the parabolas $y = x - bx^2$ and $y = \frac{x^2}{b}$ is maximum.*

Sol. Eliminating y from $y = \frac{x^2}{b}$ and $y = x - bx^2$, we get

$$x^2 = bx - b^2x^2$$

$$\Rightarrow \quad x = 0, \frac{b}{1+b^2}$$

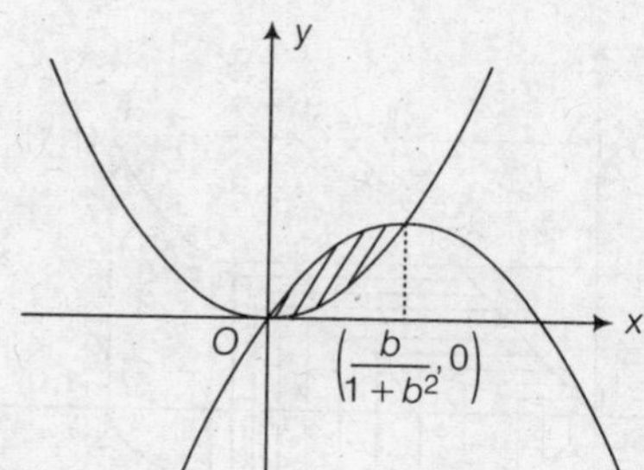

Thus, the area enclosed between the parabolas,

$$A = \int_0^{b/(1+b^2)} \left(x - bx^2 - \frac{x^2}{b}\right) dx$$

$$= \int_0^{b/1+b^2} \left\{x - x^2\left(\frac{1+b^2}{b}\right)\right\} dx$$

$$= \left(\frac{x^2}{2} - \frac{x^3}{3}\cdot\frac{1+b^2}{b}\right)_0^{b/1+b^2} = \frac{1}{6}\cdot\frac{b^2}{(1+b^2)^2}$$

For maximum value of A, $\frac{dA}{db} = 0$

But $\frac{dA}{db} = \frac{1}{6}\cdot\frac{(1+b^2)^2\cdot 2b - b^2\cdot 2(1+b^2)\cdot 2b}{(1+b^2)^4} = \frac{1}{3}\cdot\frac{b(1-b^2)}{(1+b^2)^3}$

Hence, $\frac{dA}{db} = 0$ gives $b = -1, 0, 1$ since $b > 0$

Therefore, we consider only $b = 1$

Sign scheme for $\frac{dA}{db}$ around $b = 1$ is as below

$0 \longleftarrow + \quad 1 \quad - \longrightarrow \infty$

From sign scheme it is clear that A is maximum.

Ex. 25 *Let C_1 and C_2 be the graphs of the function $y = x^2$ and $y = 2x, 0 \le x \le 1$, respectively. Let C_3 be the graph of a function $y = f(x); 0 \le x \le 1, f(0) = 0$. For a point P on C_1, let the lines through P parallel to the axes, meets C_2 and C_3 at Q and R respectively. If for every position of P on (C_1), the areas of the shaded region OPQ and ORP are equal, determine the function $f(x)$.* **[IIT JEE 1998]**

Sol. On the curve C_1, i.e. $y = x^2$.

Let P be (α, α^2). So, ordinate of point Q on C_2 is also α^2.

Now, C_2 ($y = 2x$) the abscissae of Q is given by $x = \frac{y}{2} = \frac{\alpha^2}{2}$.

$\therefore$ Q is $\left(\frac{\alpha^2}{2}, \alpha\right)$ and R on C_3 is $\{\alpha, f(x)\}$.

$$\text{Now, area of } \Delta OPQ = \int_0^{\alpha^2} (x_1 - x_2)\, dy = \int_0^{\alpha^2} \left(\sqrt{y} - \frac{y}{2}\right) dy$$

$$= \frac{2}{3}\alpha^3 - \frac{\alpha^4}{4} \quad \text{...(i)}$$

$$\text{Again, area of } \Delta ORP = \int_0^{\alpha} (y_1 - y_2) dx = \int_0^{\alpha^2} \{x^2 - f(x)\}\, dx \quad \text{...(ii)}$$

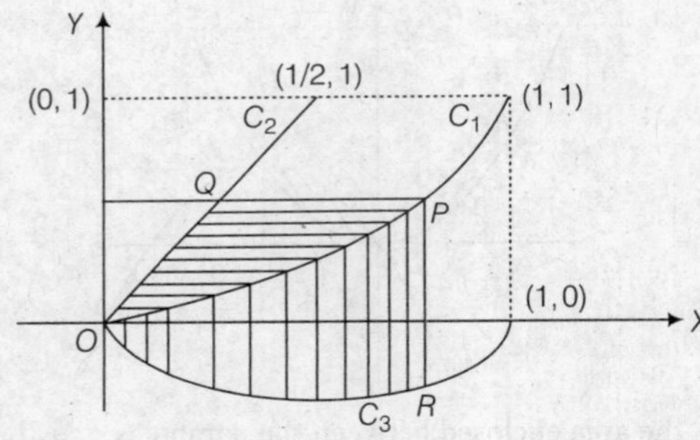

Thus, from Eqs. (i) and (ii), we get

$$\frac{2\alpha^3}{3} - \frac{\alpha^4}{4} = \int_0^{\alpha} \{x^2 - f(x)\}\, dx$$

Differentiating both the sides w.r.t. α, we get

$$2\alpha^2 - \alpha^3 = \alpha^2 - f(\alpha)$$

$$\Rightarrow \quad f(\alpha) = \alpha^3 - \alpha^2 \Rightarrow f(x) = x^3 - x^2$$

Ex. 26 *Find the area of the region bounded by the curves $y = ex \log x$ and $y = \frac{\log x}{ex}$.* **[IIT JEE 1990]**

Sol. Both the curves are defined for $x > 0$. Both are positive when $x > 1$ and negative when $0 < x < 1$.

We know that, $\lim_{x \to 0^+} \log x \to -\infty$

Therefore, $\lim_{x \to 0^+} \frac{\log x}{ex} \to -\infty$

Thus, Y-axis is asymptote of second curve.

and $\lim_{x \to 0^+} ex \log x$ [(0) $(-\infty)$ form]

$$= \lim_{x \to 0^+} \frac{e \log x}{1/x} \quad \left(-\frac{\infty}{\infty} \text{ form}\right)$$

$$= \lim_{x \to 0^+} \frac{e(1/x)}{(-1/x^2)} = 0 \quad \text{(using L'Hospital's rule)}$$

Thus, the first curve starts from (0, 0) but does not include (0, 0). Now, the given curves intersect therefore

$$ex \log x = \frac{\log x}{ex}$$

i.e. $\quad (e^2x^2 - 1) \log x = 0$

i.e. $\quad x = 1, \frac{1}{e} \quad (\because x > 0)$

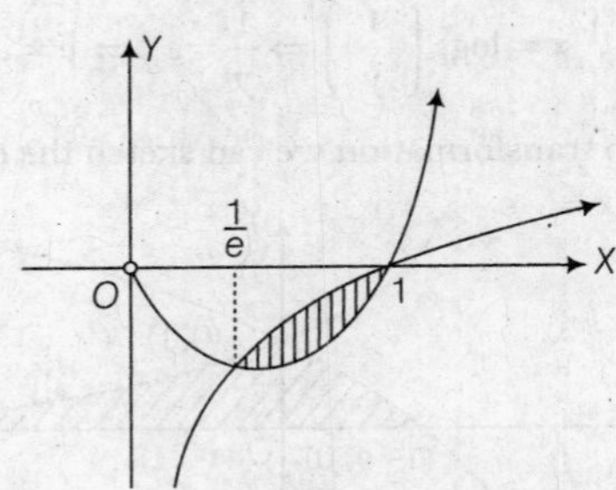

Therefore, using the above results figure could be drawn as

$$\therefore \text{Required area} = \int_{1/e}^{1} \left(\frac{\log x}{ex} - ex \log x\right) dx$$

$$= \frac{1}{e}\left[\frac{(\log x)^2}{2}\right]_{1/e}^{1} - e\left[\frac{x^2}{4}(2\log x - 1)\right]_{1/e}^{1} = \frac{e^2 - 5}{4e}$$

Ex. 27 *Let A_n be the area bounded by the curve $y = (\tan x)^n$ and the lines $x = 0, y = 0$ and $x = \frac{\pi}{4}$. Prove that for $n > 2$; $A_n + A_{n-2} = \frac{1}{n-1}$ and deduce that $\frac{1}{2n+2} < A_n < \frac{1}{2n-2}$.*

Sol. First part We have, $A_n = \int_0^{\pi/4} (\tan x)^n\, dx$

Hence, $\quad A_{n-2} = \int_0^{\pi/4} (\tan x)^{n-2}\, dx$

$$\therefore \quad A_n + A_{n-2} = \int_0^{\pi/4} (\tan x)^{n-2} (\tan^2 x + 1)\, dx$$

$$= \int_0^{\pi/4} (\tan x)^{n-2} \cdot \sec^2 x\, dx$$

Let $\tan x = t$, so that $\sec^2 x\, dx = dt$

$$\therefore \quad A_n + A_{n-2} = \int_0^1 t^{n-2}\, dt = \left(\frac{t^{n-1}}{n-1}\right)_0^1 = \frac{1}{n-1} \quad \text{...(i)}$$

Second part

Since, $\quad 0 \le x \le \pi/4 \therefore 0 \le \tan x \le 1$

$$\Rightarrow \quad \tan^{n+2} x < \tan^n x < \tan^{n-2} x$$

$$\Rightarrow \int_0^{\pi/4} \tan^{n+2} x\, dx < \int_0^{\pi/4} \tan^n x\, dx < \int_0^{\pi/4} \tan^{n-2} x\, dx$$

$$\Rightarrow \quad A_{n+2} < A_n < A_{n-2} \Rightarrow A_n + A_{n+2} < 2A_n < A_n + A_{n-2}$$

$\therefore \quad \dfrac{1}{n+1} < 2A_n < \dfrac{1}{n-1}$

$\Rightarrow \quad \dfrac{1}{2(n+1)} < A_n < \dfrac{1}{2(n-1)}$ [using Eq. (i)]

Ex. 28 *Consider a square with vertices at (1, 1) (−1, 1), (−1, −1) and (1, −1). Let S be the region consisting of all points inside the square which are nearer to the origin than to any edge. Sketch the region S and find its area.*

[IIT JEE 1995]

Sol. For the points lying in the ΔOAB the edge AB, i.e. $x = 1$ is the closest edge. Therefore, if the distance of a point $P(x, y)$ (lying in the ΔOAB) from origin is less than that of its distance from the edge $x = 1$ it will fall in the region S.

$\therefore \quad OP \le PQ$

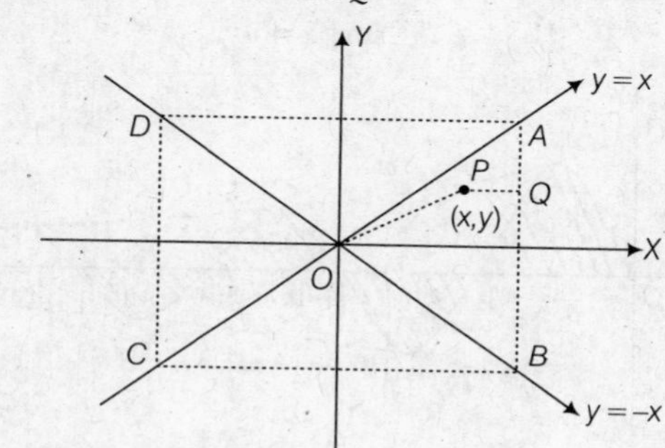

$\Rightarrow \quad \sqrt{x^2 + y^2} \le 1 - x$

$\Rightarrow \quad x^2 + y^2 \le x^2 - 2x + 1$

$\Rightarrow \quad y^2 \le 1 - 2x$

Similarly, for points lying in the ΔOAD the side $y = 1$ is the closest side and therefore the region S is determined by

$$x^2 \le 1 - 2y$$

Since, the edges are symmetric about the origin. Hence, by the above inequality and by symmetry, the required area will be the shaded portion in the figure given below

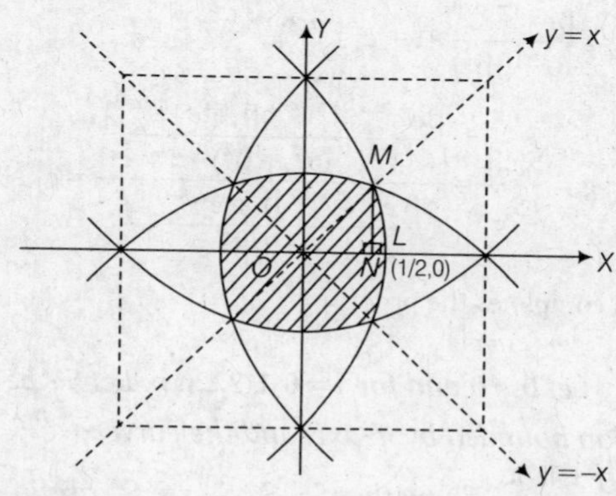

Now, when the curves $y^2 = 1 - 2x$ and $y = x$ intersect each other, then

$$x^2 = 1 - 2x \Rightarrow x^2 + 2x - 1 = 0$$

$\Rightarrow \quad x = \sqrt{2} - 1, -\sqrt{2} - 1$

Hence, the intersection points in the first quadrant is $(\sqrt{2} - 1, \sqrt{2} - 1)$.

$\therefore$ Required area = 8 [Area of curvilinear ΔOLM]

$$= 8\left[\frac{1}{2}(\sqrt{2}-1)(\sqrt{2}-1) + \int_{\sqrt{2}-1}^{1/2} \sqrt{1-2x}\, dx\right]$$

$$= 8\left[\frac{1}{2}(3 - 2\sqrt{2}) + \left(\frac{2(1-2x)^{3/2}}{3(-2)}\right)_{\sqrt{2}-1}^{1/2}\right]$$

$$= \frac{4}{3}(4\sqrt{2} - 5)$$

Ex. 29 *Sketch the region included between the curves $x^2 + y^2 = a^2$ and $\sqrt{|x|} + \sqrt{|y|} = \sqrt{a}\ (a > 0)$ and find its area.*

Sol. The graphs $|x| + |y| = a$ and $|x|^2 + |y|^2 = a^2$ are as shown in figure.

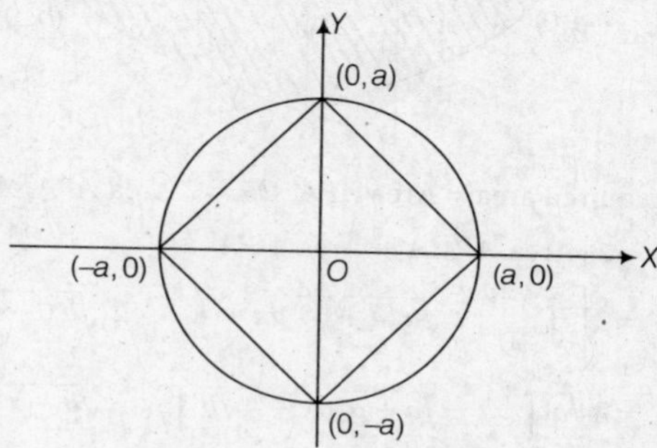

From the figure it can be concluded that when powers of $|x|$ and $|y|$ both is reduced to half the straight lines get stretched inside taking the shape as above.

Thus, required area = 4 [shaded area in the first quadrant]

$$= 4\left[\frac{\pi a^2}{4} - \int_0^a (\sqrt{a} - \sqrt{x})^2\, dx\right]$$

(since in 1st quadrant $x, y > 0$), hence

$$\sqrt{|x|} + \sqrt{|y|} = \sqrt{a}$$

$\Rightarrow \quad \sqrt{x} + \sqrt{y} = \sqrt{a}$

$\Rightarrow \quad y = (\sqrt{a} - \sqrt{x})^2$

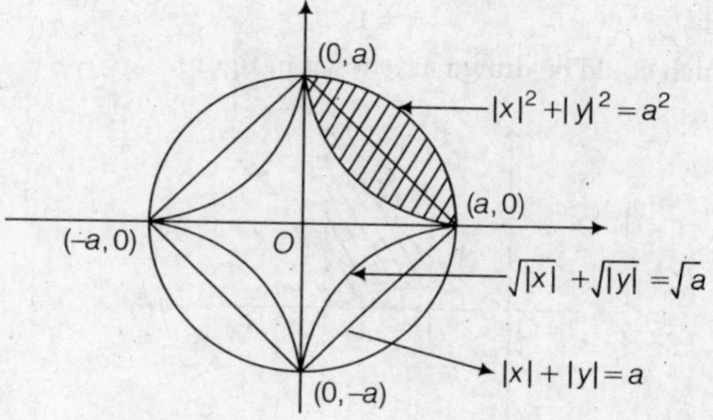

Hence, required the area $= \left(\pi - \dfrac{2}{3}\right)a^2$

Ex. 30 *Show that the area included between the parabolas $y^2 = 4a(x+a)$ and $y^2 = 4b(b-x)$ is $\frac{8}{3}(a+b)\sqrt{ab}$.*

Sol. Given parabolas are

$$y^2 = 4a(x+a) \qquad \text{...(i)}$$

and
$$y^2 = 4b(b-x) \qquad \text{...(ii)}$$

Solving Eqs. (i) and (ii), we get

$$x = (b-a) \quad \text{and} \quad y = \pm 2\sqrt{ab}$$

$\therefore$ P and Q are $(b-a, 2\sqrt{ab})$ and $(b-a, -2\sqrt{ab})$ respectively, and the points A and A' are $(-a, 0)$ and $(b, 0)$, respectively.

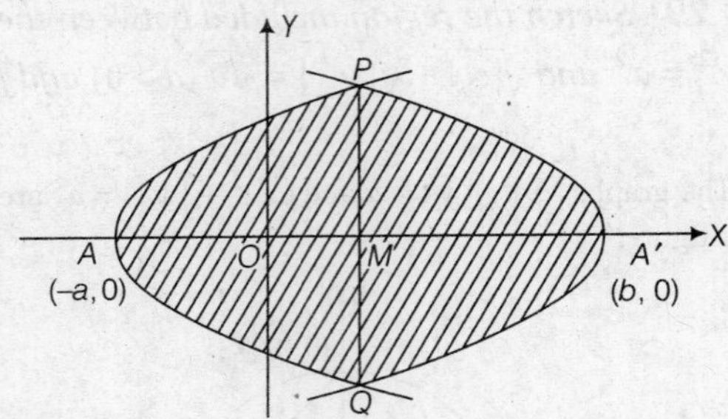

Now, required area = Area $APA'QA$ = 2 Area $APA'A$

$$= 2\,[\text{Area } APMA + \text{Area } MPA'M]$$

$$= 2\left[\int_{-a}^{b-a} 2\sqrt{a(a+x)}\,dx + \int_{b-a}^{b} 2\sqrt{b(b-x)}\,dx\right]$$

$$= 4\sqrt{a}\int_{-a}^{b-a}\sqrt{a+x}\,dx + 4\sqrt{b}\int_{b-a}^{b}\sqrt{b-x}\,dx$$

$$= 4\sqrt{a}\left[\frac{2}{3}(a+x)^{3/2}\right]_{-a}^{b-a} + 4\sqrt{b}\left[-\frac{2}{3}(b-x)^{3/2}\right]_{b-a}^{b}$$

$$= \frac{8}{3}\sqrt{a}\,(b)^{3/2} + \frac{8\sqrt{b}}{3}(a)^{3/2} = \frac{8}{3}\sqrt{ab}(a+b) \text{ sq units}$$

Ex. 31 *Determine the area of the figure bounded by two branches of the curve $(y-x)^2 = x^3$ and the straight line $x = 1$.*

Sol. Given curves are $(y-x)^2 = x^3$

$$y - x = \pm\, x\sqrt{x}$$

$$y = x + x\sqrt{x} \qquad \text{...(i)}$$

$$y = x - x\sqrt{x} \qquad \text{...(ii)}$$

and
$$x = 1 \qquad \text{...(iii)}$$

Which could be drawn as; shown in figure.

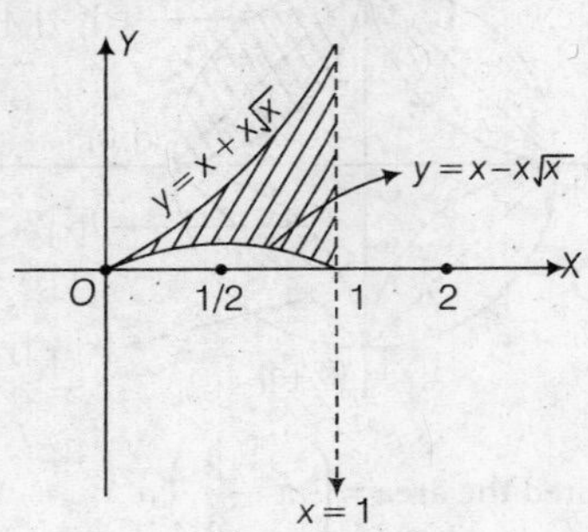

Hence, required area

$$= \int_0^1 \{(x + x\sqrt{x}) - (x - x\sqrt{x})\}\,dx$$

$$= \int_0^1 (2x\sqrt{x})\,dx$$

$$= 2\int_0^1 x^{3/2}\,dx = \frac{4}{5} \text{ sq unit}$$

Ex. 32 *Prove that the areas $S_0, S_1, S_2, \ldots$ bounded by the X-axis and half-waves of the curve $y = e^{-\alpha x}\sin\beta x$, $x\,|\,0$. form a geometric progression with the common ratio $g = e^{-\pi\alpha/\beta}$.*

Sol. The curve $y = e^{-\alpha x}\sin\beta x$ intersects the positive X-axis at the points where $y = 0$.

$$\therefore \qquad e^{-\alpha x}\sin\beta x = 0$$

$$\Rightarrow \qquad \sin\beta x = 0 \Rightarrow x_n = \frac{n\pi}{\beta},\ n = 0, 1, 2, \ldots$$

The function $y = e^{-\alpha x}\sin\beta x$ is positive in the interval (x_{2K}, x_{2K+1}) and negative in (x_{2K+1}, x_{2K+2}), i.e. the sign of the function in the interval (x_n, x_{n+1}), therefore

$$S_n = \left|\int_{n\pi/\beta}^{(n+1)\pi/\beta} e^{-\alpha x}\sin\beta x\,dx\right|$$

$$= \left|\left\{\frac{(-1)^{n+1}e^{-\alpha x}}{\alpha^2+\beta^2}(\alpha\sin\beta x + \beta\cos\beta x)\right\}_{n\pi/\beta}^{(n+1)\pi/\beta}\right|$$

$$= \frac{\beta e^{-n\pi\alpha/\beta}}{(\alpha^2+\beta^2)}\{1 + e^{-\pi\alpha/\beta}\}$$

Hence,
$$g = \frac{S_{n+1}}{S_n} = \frac{\dfrac{\beta e^{-(n+1)\pi\alpha/\beta}\{1+e^{-\pi\alpha/\beta}\}}{(\alpha^2+\beta^2)}}{\dfrac{\beta e^{-n\pi\alpha/\beta}\{1+e^{-\pi\alpha/\beta}\}}{\alpha^2+\beta^2}} = e^{-\pi\alpha/\beta}$$

which completes the proof.

Ex. 33 *Let $b \neq 0$ and for $j = 0, 1, 2, \ldots, n$. Let S_j be the area of the region bounded by Y-axis and the curve $x \cdot e^{ay} = \sin by$, $\frac{j\pi}{b} \leq y \leq \frac{(j+1)\pi}{b}$. Show that $S_0, S_1, S_2, \ldots, S_n$ are in geometric progression. Also, find their sum for $a = -1$ and $b = \pi$.*

Sol. Here, $S_j = \left|\int_{j\pi/b}^{(j+1)\pi/b} x\,dy\right| = \left|\int_{j\pi/b}^{(j+1)\pi/b} e^{-ay}\sin by\,dy\right|$

$$= \left| \left\{ \frac{e^{-ay}}{a^2+b^2}(-a\sin by - b\cos by) \right\}_{j\pi/b}^{(j+1)\pi/b} \right|$$

$$= \left| \frac{e^{-a(j+1)\pi/b}}{a^2+b^2} \times (-b)(-1)^{j+1} - \frac{e^{-aj\pi/b}}{a^2+b^2}(-b)(-1)^j \right|$$

$$= |b| \left\{ \frac{e^{-a(j+1)\pi/b}}{a^2+b^2} + \frac{e^{-aj\pi/b}}{a^2+b^2} \right\}$$

$$= |b| \frac{e^{-aj\pi/b}}{a^2+b^2}\{e^{-a\pi/b}+1\}; \{j = 0, 1, 2, \ldots, n\}$$

Now, $\frac{S_{j+1}}{S_j} = |b| \frac{e^{-a(j+1)\pi/b}}{a^2+b^2}\{e^{-a\pi/b}+1\} \Big/ |b| \frac{e^{-aj\pi/b}}{a^2+b^2}\{e^{-a\pi/b}+1\}$

$= e^{-a\pi/b}$ for all $j = 0, 1, 2, \ldots, n$

Hence, $S_0, S_1, S_2, \ldots, S_n$ are in GP with common ratio $e^{-a\pi/b}$.

For $a = -1$ and $b = \pi$, we have

$$S_j = \frac{e^j \pi (e+1)}{\pi^2+1}; \; j = 0, 1, 2, \ldots, n$$

$$\therefore \sum_{j=0}^{n} S_j = \sum_{j=0}^{n} \frac{e^{j\pi}(e+1)}{\pi^2+1} = \frac{(e+1)\pi}{\pi+1}\left\{\frac{e^{n+1}-1}{e-1}\right\}$$

Ex. 34 *For any real t, $x = 2 + \frac{e^t + e^{-t}}{2}$, $y = 2 + \frac{e^t - e^{-t}}{2}$ is a point on the hyperbola $x^2 - y^2 - 4x + 4y - 1 = 0$. Find the area bounded by the hyperbola and the lines joining the centre to the points corresponding to t_1 and $-t_1$.*

Sol. The points $x = 2 + \frac{e^t + e^{-t}}{2}$, $y = 2 + \frac{e^t - e^{-t}}{2}$ is on the curve

$(x-2)^2 - (y-2)^2 = 1$ or $x^2 - y^2 - 4x + 4y - 1 = 0$

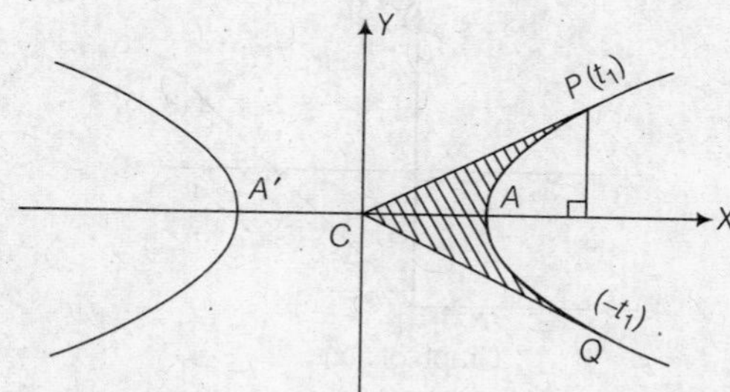

Put $(x-2) = x$, $(y-2) = y$

$$\therefore \quad x^2 - y^2 = 1 \text{ and } x = \frac{e^t + e^{-t}}{2}, y = \frac{e^t - e^{-t}}{2}$$

We have to find the area of the region bounded by the curve $x^2 - y^2 = 1$ and the lines joining the centre $x = 0$, $y = 0$ to the point (t_1) and $(-t_1)$.

$$\therefore \text{Required area} = 2\left[\text{Area of } \Delta PCN - \int_1^{\frac{e^{t_1}+e^{-t_1}}{2}} y\,dx\right]$$

$$= 2\left[\frac{1}{2}\left(\frac{e^{t_1}+e^{-t_1}}{2}\right)\left(\frac{e^{t_1}-e^{-t_1}}{2}\right) - \int_1^{t_1} y\frac{dx}{dt}dt\right]$$

$$= 2\left[\left(\frac{e^{2t_1}-e^{-2t_1}}{8}\right) - \int_0^{t_1}\left(\frac{e^t - e^{-t}}{2}\right)^2 dt\right]$$

$$= \frac{e^{2t_1}-e^{-2t_1}}{4} - \frac{1}{2}\int_0^{t_1}(e^{2t}+e^{-2t}-2)\,dt$$

$$= \frac{e^{2t_1}-e^{-2t_1}}{4} - \frac{1}{2}\left[\frac{e^{2t_1}}{2} - \frac{e^{-2t_1}}{2} - 2t_1\right]_0^{t_1}$$

$$= \frac{e^{2t_1}-e^{-2t_1}}{4} - \frac{1}{2}\left[\frac{e^{2t_1}}{2} - \frac{e^{-2t_1}}{2} - 2t_1\right] = t_1$$

Ex. 35 *Find the area enclosed by circle $x^2 + y^2 = 4$, parabola $y = x^2 + x + 1$, the curve $y = \left[\sin^2\frac{x}{4} + \cos\frac{x}{4}\right]$ and X-axis (where, [.] is the greatest integer function).*

Sol. $\because \quad y = \left[\sin^2\frac{x}{4} + \cos\frac{x}{4}\right]$

$\because \quad 1 < \sin^2\frac{x}{4} + \cos\frac{x}{4} < 2 \qquad$ for $x \in (-2, 2]$

$\therefore \quad y = \left[\sin^2\frac{x}{4} + \cos\frac{x}{4}\right] = 1$

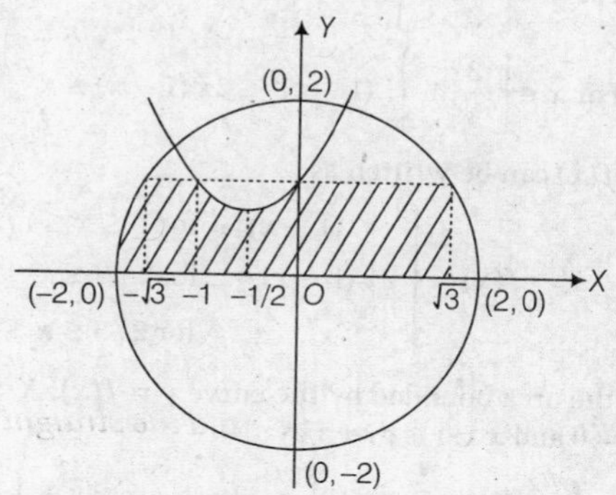

Now, we have to find out the area enclosed by the circle $x^2 + y^2 = 4$, parabola $\left(y - \frac{3}{4}\right) = \left(x + \frac{1}{2}\right)^2$, line $y = 1$ and X-axis. Required area is shaded area in the figure.

Hence, required area

$$= \sqrt{3} \times 1 + (\sqrt{3} - 1) \times 1 + \int_{-1}^{0}(x^2 + x + 1)\,dx + 2\int_{\sqrt{3}}^{2}(\sqrt{4 - x^2})\,dx$$

$$= (2\sqrt{3} - 1) + \left[\frac{x^3}{3} + \frac{x^2}{2} + x\right]_{-1}^{0} + 2\left[\frac{x}{2}\sqrt{4 - x^2} + 2\sin^{-1}\left(\frac{x}{2}\right)\right]_{\sqrt{3}}^{2}$$

$$= (2\sqrt{3} - 1) + \left[0 - \left(-\frac{1}{3} + \frac{1}{2} - 1\right)\right] + 2\left[(0 + \pi) - \left(\frac{\sqrt{3}}{2} + \frac{2\pi}{3}\right)\right]$$

$$= (2\sqrt{3} - 1) + \frac{5}{6} + \frac{2\pi}{3} - \sqrt{3} = \left(\frac{2\pi}{3} + \sqrt{3} - \frac{1}{6}\right) \text{ sq units}$$

● ***Ex. 36*** *Let $f(x) = \max\{x^2, (1-x)^2, 2x(1-x)\}$, where $0 \le x \le 1$. Determine the area of the region bounded by the curves $y = f(x)$, X-axis, $x = 0$ and $x = 1$.* **[IIT JEE 1997]**

Sol. We have, $f(x) = \max\{x^2, (1-x^2), 2x(1-x)\}$

Graphically it could be shown as;

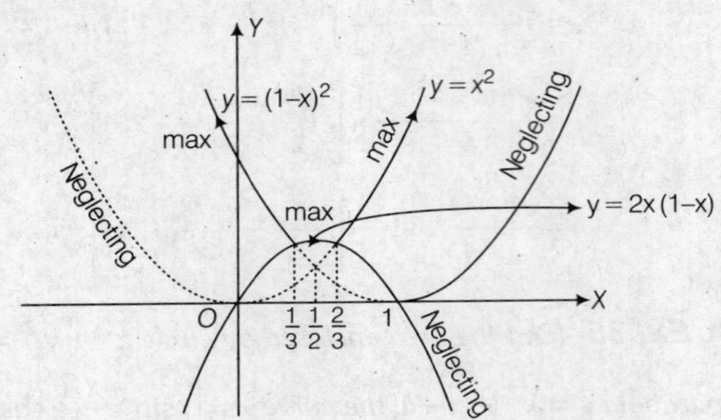

For figure it is clear that maximum graph (i.e. above max graph is considered and others are neglected).

$\therefore$ For $x \in \left[0, \frac{1}{3}\right]$, $x^2 \le 2x(1-x) \le (1-x)^2$

For $x \in \left[\frac{1}{3}, \frac{1}{2}\right]$, $x^2 \le (1-x)^2 \le 2x(1-x)$

For $x \in \left[\frac{1}{2}, \frac{2}{3}\right]$, $(1-x)^2 \le x^2 \le 2x(1-x)$

For $x \in \left[\frac{2}{3}, 1\right]$, $(1-x)^2 \le 2x(1-x) \le x^2$

Hence, $f(x)$ can be written as

$$f(x) = \begin{cases} (1-x)^2, & \text{for } 0 \le x \le 1/3 \\ 2x(1-x), & \text{for } 1/3 \le x \le 2/3 \\ x^2, & \text{for } 2/3 \le x \le 1 \end{cases}$$

Hence, the area bounded by the curve $y = f(x)$; X-axis and the lines $x = 0$ and $x = 1$ is given by

$$= \int_0^{1/3} (1-x)^2\,dx + \int_{1/3}^{2/3} 2x(1-x)\,dx + \int_{2/3}^{1} (x^2)\,dx$$

$$= \frac{17}{27} \text{ sq unit}$$

● ***Ex. 37*** *Find the ratio in which the curve, $y = [-0.01x^4 - 0.02x^2]$ [where, [·] denotes the greatest integer function) divides the ellipse $3x^2 + 4y^2 = 12$.*

Sol. Here, $y = [-0.01x^4 - 0.02x^2]$

i.e. $y = -1$, when $-2 < x < 2$

$y = -1$ cut the ellipse $3x^2 + 4y^2 = 12$

At $x^2 = \frac{8}{3}$ or $x = \pm\frac{2\sqrt{2}}{\sqrt{3}}$

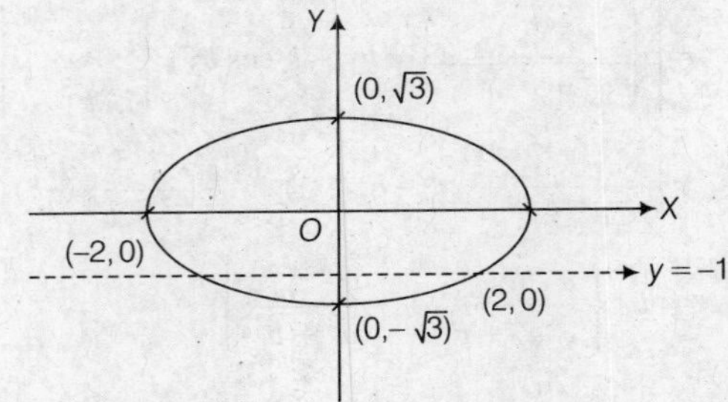

$$\text{Required area} = \int_{-2\sqrt{6}/3}^{2\sqrt{6}/3} \left\{\sqrt{\frac{12-3x^2}{4}} - 1\right\} dx$$

$$= \frac{\sqrt{3}}{2}\int_{-2\sqrt{6}/3}^{2\sqrt{6}/3} \sqrt{4-x^2}\,dx - \int_{-2\sqrt{6}/3}^{2\sqrt{6}/3} 1\,dx$$

$$= 2\sin^{-1}\sqrt{\frac{2}{3}} + \frac{2}{3} - \frac{4}{3}\sqrt{6}$$

● ***Ex. 38*** *Let $f(x) = \begin{cases} -2, -3 \le x \le 0 \\ x-2, 0 < x \le 3 \end{cases}$, where $g(x) = \min\{f(|x|) + |f(x)|, f(|x|) - |f(x)|\}$. Find the area bounded by the curve $g(x)$ and the X-axis between the ordinates at $x = 3$ and $x = -3$.*

Sol. Here, $f(|x|) = \begin{cases} -x-2, & -3 \le x \le 0 \\ x-2, & 0 < x \le 3 \end{cases}$

$$|f(x)| = \begin{cases} 2, & -3 \le x \le 0 \\ -x+2, & 0 < x \le 2 \\ x-2, & 2 < x \le 3 \end{cases}$$

$$\therefore f(|x|) - |f(x)| = \begin{cases} -x-4, & -3 \le x \le 0 \\ 2x-4, & 0 < x \le 2 \\ 0, & 2 < x \le 3 \end{cases}$$

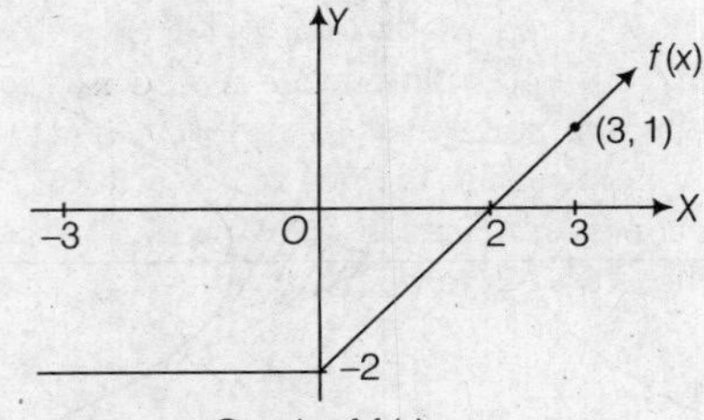

Graph of $f(x)$

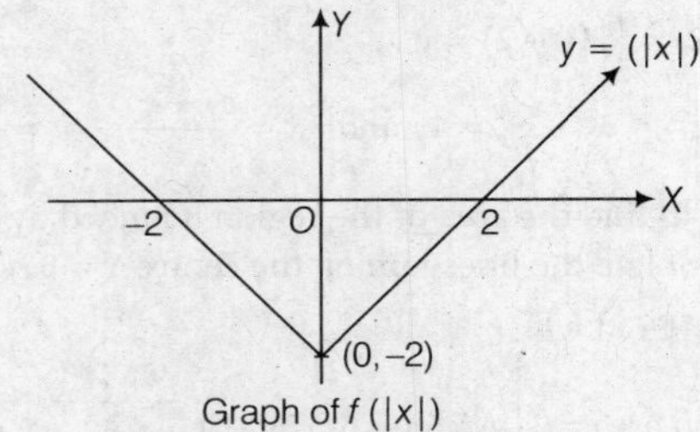

Graph of $f(|x|)$

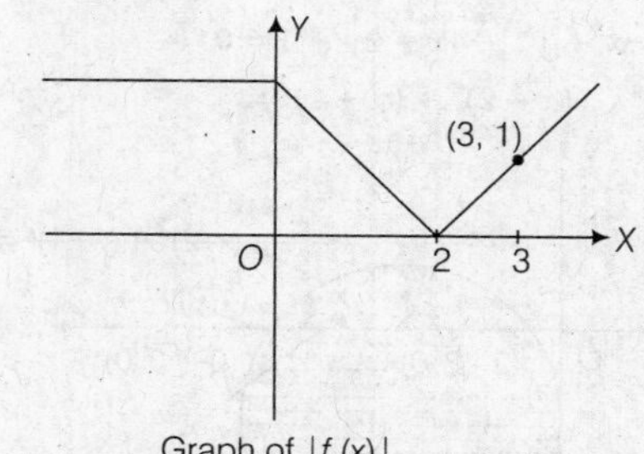

Graph of $|f(x)|$

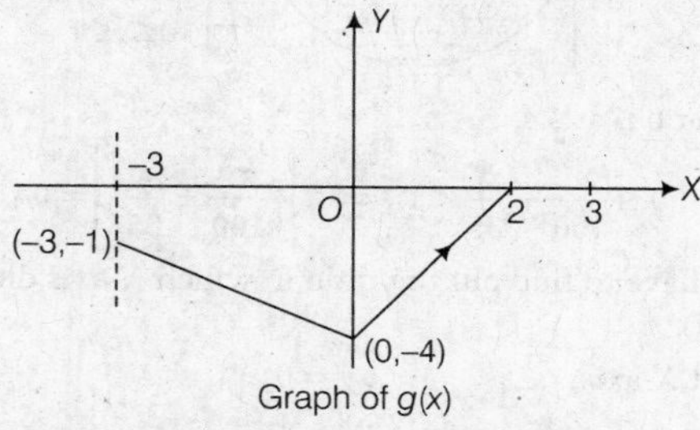

Graph of $g(x)$

Since, $|f(x)|$ is always positive.

$$g(x) = f(|x|) - |f(x)|$$

where the graphs could be drawn as shown in above figures.
From the graph, required area

$$= \frac{1}{2}(1+4) \times 3 + \left(\frac{1}{2} \times 2 \times 4\right) + 0 = \frac{23}{2} \text{ sq units}$$

● **Ex. 39** *Let ABC be a triangle with vertices $A \equiv (6, 2(\sqrt{3}+1))$, $B \equiv (4, 2)$ and $C \equiv (8, 2)$. Let R be the region consisting of all those points P inside Δ ABC which satisfy* $d(P, BC) \geq \max\{d(P, AB), d(P, AC)\}$, where $d(P, L)$ denotes the distance of the point P from the line L. Sketch the region R and find its area.

Sol. It is easy to see that ABC is an equilateral triangle with side of length 4. BD and CE are angle bisectors of angle B and C, respectively. Any point inside the $\Delta\, AEC$ is nearer to AC than BC and any point inside the $\Delta\, BDA$ is nearer to AB than BC. So any point inside the quadrilateral $AEGC$ will satisfy the given condition. Hence, shaded region is the required region, whose area is to be found, shown as in figure

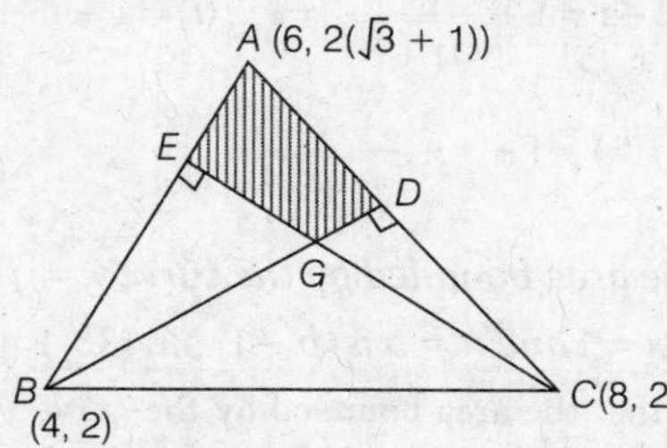

Thus, required area = 2 Area of $\Delta EAG = 2 \times \frac{1}{2}\, AE \times EG$

$$= \frac{1}{2}\, AB \times \frac{1}{3}\, CE = \frac{1}{6} \times 4 \times \sqrt{4^2 - 2^2}$$

$$= \frac{4\sqrt{3}}{3} \text{ sq units}$$

● **Ex. 40** *Let O (0, 0), A (2, 0) and B $\left(1, \frac{1}{\sqrt{3}}\right)$ be the vertices of a triangle. Let R be the region consisting of all those points P inside Δ OAB which satisfy $d(P, OA) \leq \min\{d(P, OB), d(P, AB)\}$, when 'd' denotes the distance from the point to the corresponding line. Sketch the region R and find its area.* **[IIT JEE 1997]**

Sol. Let the coordinate of P be (x, y).

Equation of line $OA \equiv y = 0$

Equation of line $OB \equiv \sqrt{3}y = x$

Equation of line $AB = \sqrt{3}y = 2 - x$

$d(P, OA)$ = Distance of P from line $OA = y$

$d(P, OB)$ = Distance of P from line $OB = \frac{|\sqrt{3}y - x|}{2}$

$d(P, AB)$ = Distance of P from line $AB = \frac{|\sqrt{3}y + x - 2|}{2}$

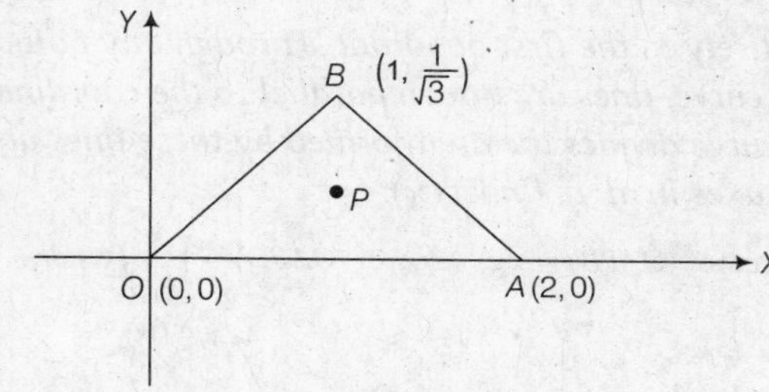

Given, $d(P, OA) \leq \min\{d(P, OB), d(P, AB)\}$

$$y \leq \min\left\{\frac{|\sqrt{3}y - x|}{2}, \frac{|\sqrt{3}y + x - 2|}{2}\right\}$$

$$\Rightarrow \quad y \leq \frac{|\sqrt{3}y - x|}{2} \quad \text{...(i)}$$

$$\text{and} \quad y \leq \frac{|\sqrt{3}y + x - 2|}{2} \quad \text{...(ii)}$$

Case I If $y \leq \frac{|\sqrt{3}y - x|}{2}$

$$\therefore \quad y \leq \frac{x - \sqrt{3}y}{2}, \text{ i.e. } x > \sqrt{3}y \qquad (\because \sqrt{3}y - x < 0)$$

$$\Rightarrow \quad (2+\sqrt{3})\, y \leq x$$

$$\Rightarrow \quad y \leq (2-\sqrt{3})\, x$$

$$\Rightarrow \quad y \leq x \tan 15° \quad \text{...(iii)}$$

($\because y = x \tan 15°$ is an acute angle bisector of $\angle AOB$)

Case II If $y \leq \frac{|\sqrt{3}y + x - 2|}{2}$

$$\Rightarrow \quad 2y \leq 2 - x - \sqrt{3}y \qquad (\text{i.e. } \sqrt{3}y + x - 2 < 0)$$

$$\Rightarrow \quad (2+\sqrt{3})\, y \leq 2 - x$$

$$\Rightarrow \quad y \leq -(2-\sqrt{3})(x-2)$$

$$\Rightarrow \quad y \leq -(\tan 15°)(x-2) \quad \text{...(iv)}$$

[$\because y = (x-2)\tan 15°$ is an acute angle bisector of CA]

From Eqs. (iii) and (iv), P moves inside the triangle as shown in figure.

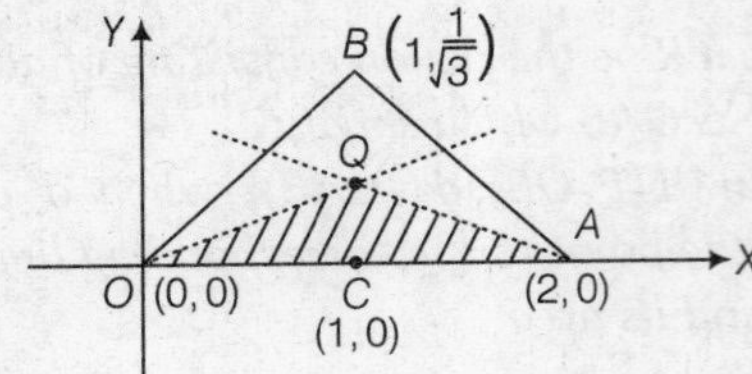

As $\angle QOB = \angle OBQ = 15°$, ΔOQB is an isosceles triangle

$\Rightarrow$ $OC = AC =$ unit

Area of shaded region = area of $\Delta OQA = \frac{1}{2}$ (base) × (height)

$$= \frac{1}{2}(2)(1 \tan 15°) = \tan 15°$$

$$= (2 - \sqrt{3}) \text{ sq units}$$

● ***Ex. 41*** *A curve $y = f(x)$ passes through the origin and lies entirely in the first quadrant. Through any point $P(x, y)$ on the curve, lines are drawn parallel to the coordinate axes. If the curve divides the area formed by these lines and coordinate axes in $m : n$, find $f(x)$.*

Sol. Area of $(OAPB) = xy$, Area of $(OAPO) = \int_0^x f(t)\, dt$

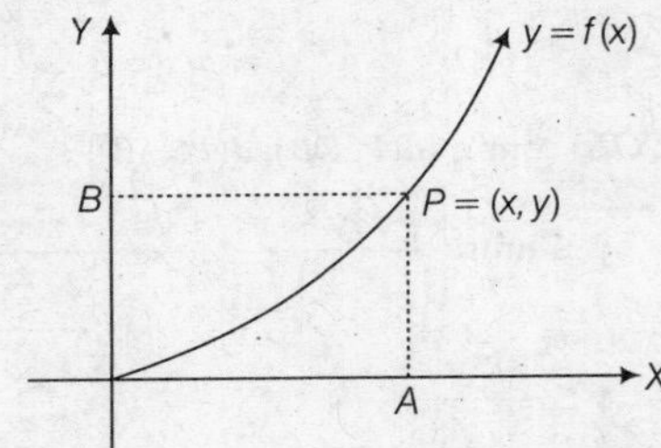

Therefore, area of $(OBPO) = xy - \int_0^x f(t)\, dt$

According to the given condition,

$$\frac{xy - \int_0^x f(t)\, dt}{\int_0^x f(t)\, dt} = \frac{m}{n}$$

$$\Rightarrow \quad n\, xy = (m+n) \int_0^x f(t)\, dt$$

Differentiating w.r.t. x, we get

$$n\left(x \frac{dy}{dx} + y\right) = (m+n)\, f(x) = (m+n)\, y, \text{ as } y = f(x)$$

$$\frac{m}{n} \cdot \frac{dx}{x} = \frac{dy}{y} \Rightarrow \frac{m}{n} \cdot (\log x) = \log y - \log c, \text{ where } c \text{ is a constant.}$$

$$\Rightarrow \quad y = cx^{m/n}$$

● ***Ex. 42*** *Find the ratio of the areas in which the curve $y = \left[\frac{x^3}{100} + \frac{x}{35}\right]$ divides the circle $x^2 + y^2 - 4x + 2y + 1 = 0$ (where, [.] denotes the greatest integer function).*

Sol. We have, $x^2 + y^2 - 4x + 2y + 1 = 0$

or $$(x-2)^2 + (y+1)^2 = 4 \quad \text{...(i)}$$

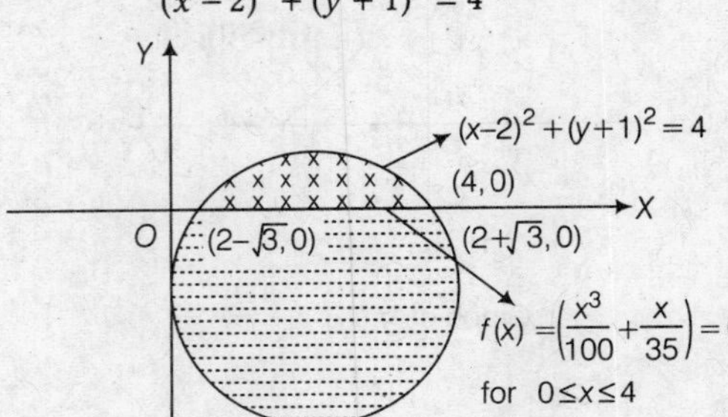

Now, for $0 \le x \le 4$,

$$0 \le \frac{x^3}{100} + \frac{x}{35} < 1 \Rightarrow \left[\frac{x^3}{100} + \frac{x}{35}\right] = 0$$

So, we have to find out the ratio in which X-axis divides the circle (i).

Now, at X-axis, $y = 0$

So, $(x-2)^2 = 3$

So, it cuts the X-axis at $(2 - \sqrt{3}, 0)$ and $(2 + \sqrt{3}, 0)$.

Therefore, required area, $A = \int_{2-\sqrt{3}}^{2+\sqrt{3}} \left(\sqrt{4 - (x-2)^2} - 1\right) dx$

$$= \frac{4\pi - 3\sqrt{3}}{3}$$

$\therefore$ $$\text{Required ratio} = \frac{A}{4\pi - A} = \frac{4\pi - 3\sqrt{3}}{8\pi + 3\sqrt{3}}$$

● ***Ex. 43*** *Area bounded by the line $y = x$, curve $y = f(x), (f(x) > x, \forall\, x > 1)$ and the lines $x = 1, x = t$ is $(t + \sqrt{1+t^2}) - (1 + \sqrt{2})$ for all $t > 1$. Find $f(x)$.*

Sol. The area bounded by $y = f(x)$ and $y = x$ between the lines $x = 1$ and $x = t$ is $\int_{+1}^{t} (f(x) - x)\, dx$. But it is equal to $(t + \sqrt{1+t^2}) - (1 + \sqrt{2})$.

So, $$\int_1^t (f(x) - x)\, dx = (t + \sqrt{1+t^2}) - (1 + \sqrt{2})$$

Differentiating both the sides w.r.t. t, we get

$$f(t) - t = 1 + \frac{t}{\sqrt{1+t^2}} \Rightarrow f(t) = 1 + t + \frac{t}{\sqrt{1+t^2}}$$

or $$f(x) = 1 + x + \frac{x}{\sqrt{1+x^2}}$$

● ***Ex. 44*** *The area bounded by the curve $y = f(x)$, X-axis and ordinates $x = 1$ and $x = b$ is $(b-1)\sin(3b+4)$, find $f(x)$.*

Sol. We know that the area bounded by the curve $y = f(x)$, X-axis and the ordinates $x = 1$ and $x = b$ is $\int_1^b f(x)\, dx$.

From the question; $\int_1^b f(x)\, dx = (b-1)\sin(3b+4)$

Differentiating w.r.t. b, we get

$$f(b) \cdot 1 = 3(b-1)\cos(3b+4) + \sin(3b+4)$$

$$\Rightarrow \quad f(x) = 3(x-1)\cos(3x+4) + \sin(3x+4)$$

Ex. 45 *Find the area of region enclosed by the curve* $\frac{(x-y)^2}{a^2}+\frac{(x+y)^2}{b^2}=2\ (a>b)$, *the line* $y=x$ *and the positive X-axis.*

Sol. The given curve $\frac{(x-y)^2}{a^2}+\frac{(x+y)^2}{b^2}=2$ is an ellipse major and minor axes are $x-y=0$ and $x+y=0$, respectively.
The required area is shown with shaded region.

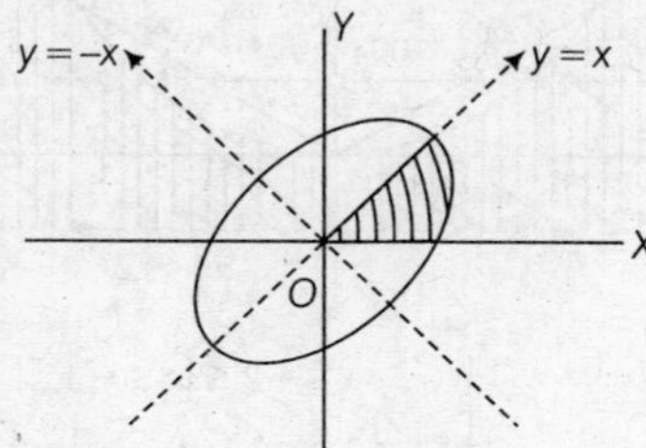

Instead of directly solving the problem we can solve equivalent problem with equivalent ellipse whose axes are $x=0$ and $y=0$.
The equivalent region is shown as $(OA'B'O)$ where the equation of ellipse is $\frac{x^2}{a^2}+\frac{y^2}{b^2}=1$.

$\therefore$ Required area = Area $(\Delta OA'A''+A'A''B')$

where, $A'=\left(\frac{ab}{\sqrt{a^2+b^2}},\frac{ab}{\sqrt{a^2+b^2}}\right)$

Area $\Delta OA'A''=\frac{1}{2}\times\frac{ab}{\sqrt{a^2+b^2}}\times\frac{ab}{\sqrt{a^2+b^2}}=\frac{1}{2}\left(\frac{a^2b^2}{a^2+b^2}\right)$ ...(i)

Area of $A'B'A''=\int_{\frac{ab}{\sqrt{a^2+b^2}}}^{a} b\sqrt{\left(1-\frac{x^2}{a^2}\right)}\,dx$

$$=\frac{b}{a}\cdot\int_{\frac{ab}{\sqrt{a^2+b^2}}}^{a}\sqrt{a^2-x^2}\,dx$$

$$=\frac{b}{a}\left[\frac{x}{2}\sqrt{a^2-x^2}+\frac{a^2}{2}\sin^{-1}\frac{x}{a}\right]_{ab/\sqrt{a^2+b^2}}^{a}$$

$$=\frac{b}{a}\left[0+\frac{a^2}{2}\cdot\frac{\pi}{2}-\frac{ab}{2\sqrt{a^2+b^2}}\cdot\sqrt{\left(a^2-\frac{a^2b^2}{a^2+b^2}\right)}-\frac{a^2}{2}\sin^{-1}\frac{b}{\sqrt{a^2+b^2}}\right]$$

$$=\frac{b}{a}\left[\frac{\pi a^2}{4}-\frac{a^2}{2}\sin^{-1}\left(\frac{b}{\sqrt{a^2+b^2}}\right)-\frac{a^3b}{2(a^2+b^2)}\right]$$

$$=\frac{\pi ab}{4}-\frac{ab}{2}\sin^{-1}\left(\frac{b}{\sqrt{a^2+b^2}}\right)-\frac{a^2b^2}{2(a^2+b^2)}\quad\text{...(ii)}$$

Hence, required area = Sum of Eqs. (i) and (ii)

$$=\frac{\pi ab}{4}-\frac{ab}{2}\sin^{-1}\left(\frac{b}{\sqrt{a^2+b^2}}\right)$$

Ex. 46 *Let* $f(x)$ *be a function which satisfy the equation* $f(xy)=f(x)+f(y)$ *for all* $x>0, y>0$ *such that* $f'(1)=2$. *Find the area of the region bounded by the curves* $y=f(x)$, $y=|x^3-6x^2+11x-6|$ *and* $x=0$.

Sol. Take $x=y=1\Rightarrow f(1)=0$

Now, $y=\frac{1}{x}$

$\Rightarrow\quad 0=f\left(x\cdot\frac{1}{x}\right)=f(x)+f\left(\frac{1}{x}\right)\Rightarrow f\left(\frac{1}{x}\right)=-f(x)$

$\therefore f\left(\frac{x}{y}\right)=f(x)+f\left(\frac{1}{y}\right)=f(x)-f(y)$ ...(i)

Now, $f'(x)=\lim_{h\to 0}\frac{f(x+h)-f(x)}{h}$

$=\lim_{h\to 0}\frac{f\left(\frac{x+h}{x}\right)}{h}$ [using Eq. (i)]

$=\lim_{h\to 0}\frac{f\left(1+\frac{h}{x}\right)-f(1)}{\frac{h}{x}\cdot x}=\frac{f'(1)}{x}$ $[\because f(1)=0]$

$f'(x)=\frac{2}{x}$

$\Rightarrow\quad f(x)=2\log x+c$ [since, $f(1)=0\Rightarrow c=0$]

$\Rightarrow\quad f(x)=2\log x$

Thus, $f(x)=2\log x$ and $y=|x^3-6x^2+11x-6|$ could be plotted as

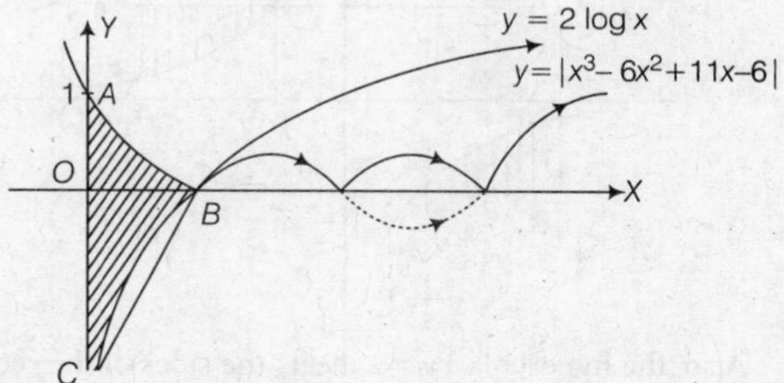

Hence, required area

$$=\int_0^1(x^3-6x^2+11x-6)\,dx+\int_{-\infty}^{0}e^{y/2}\,dy$$

$$=\left(\frac{x^4}{4}-\frac{6x^3}{3}+\frac{11x^2}{2}-6x\right)_0^1+2\,(e^{y/2})_{-\infty}^{0}$$

$$=\left(\frac{1}{4}-2+\frac{11}{2}-6\right)-(0)+2\,(e^0-e^{-\infty})$$

$$=\frac{1}{4}+\frac{11}{2}-8+2=-\frac{1}{4}\text{ sq unit}$$

Ex. 47 *Find the area of the region which contains all the points satisfying condition* $|x-2y|+|x+2y|\le 8$ *and* $xy\ge 2$.

Sol. The line $y=\pm\frac{x}{2}$ divide the xy plane in four parts

Region I $2y-x\le 0$ and $2y+x\ge 0$

So that, $|x-2y|+|x+2y|\le 8$

$\Rightarrow\quad (x-2y)+(x+2y)\le 8\Rightarrow 0\le x\le 4$

Region II $2y - x | 0$ and $2y + x \geq 0$

So that, $|x - 2y| + |x + 2y| \leq 8$

$\Rightarrow \quad -(x - 2y) + (x + 2y) \leq 8 \Rightarrow 0 \leq y \leq 2$

Region III $2y + x \leq 0, 2y - x \geq 0$

So that, $|x - 2y| + |x + 2y| \leq 8$

$\Rightarrow \quad -(x - 2y) - (x + 2y) \leq 8 \Rightarrow -4 \leq x \leq 0$

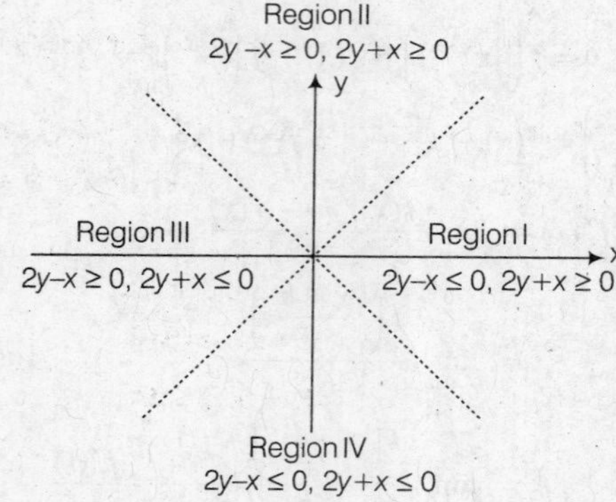

Region IV $2y + x \leq 0, 2y - x \leq 0$

So that, $|x - 2y| + |x + 2y| \leq 8 \Rightarrow -2 \leq y \leq 0$

Here, all the points lie in the rectangle.

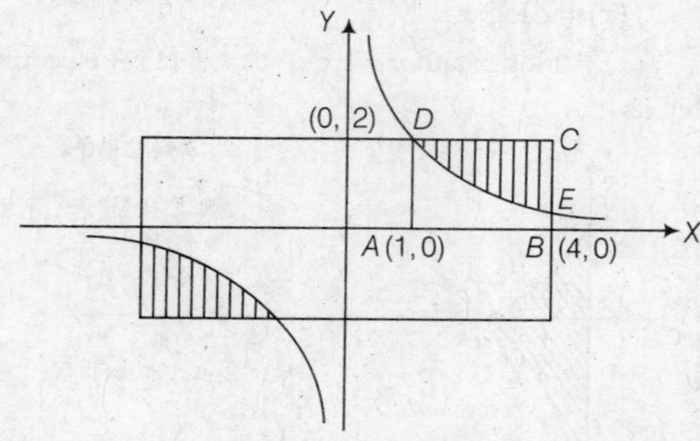

Also, the hyperbola $xy = 2$ meets the sides of the rectangle at the points $(1, 2)$ and $(4, 1/2)$ in the 1st quadrant graphically.

Hence, required area

$$= 2\,(\text{Area of rectangle } ABCD - \text{Area of } ABEDA)$$

$$= 2\left(3 \times 2 - \int_1^4 \frac{2}{x}\,dx\right) = 2\,(6 - 2\log 4) \text{ sq units}$$

• Ex. 48 *Consider the function*

$$f(x) = \begin{cases} x - [x] - \dfrac{1}{2}, & \text{if } x \notin I \\ 0, & \text{if } x \in I \end{cases}$$ *, where [.] denotes the greatest integer function and I is the set of integers. If* $g(x) = \max\{x^2, f(x), |x|\}, -2 \leq x \leq 2$*, then find the area bounded by* $g(x)$ *when* $-2 \leq x \leq 2$.

Sol. Here, $f(x) = \begin{cases} x - [x] - \dfrac{1}{2}, & \text{if } x \notin I \\ 0, & \text{if } x \in I \end{cases}$

$$= \begin{cases} \{x\} - \dfrac{1}{2}, & \text{if } x \notin I \\ 0, & \text{if } x \in I \end{cases}$$

Thus, $\quad g(x) = \max\{x^2, f(x), |x|\}$

which could be graphically expressed as

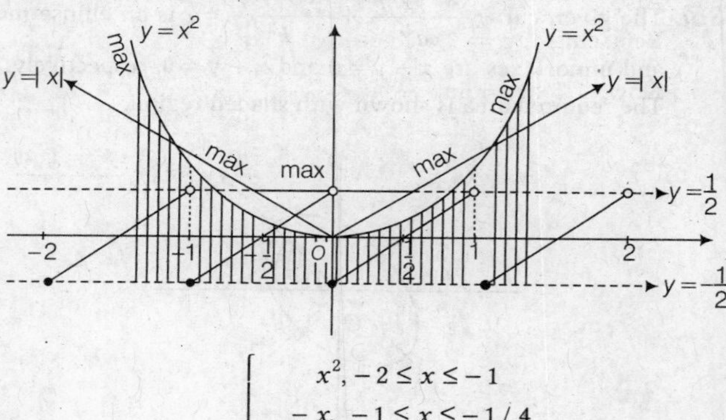

Clearly, $\quad g(x) = \begin{cases} x^2, & -2 \leq x \leq -1 \\ -x, & -1 \leq x \leq -1/4 \\ x + \dfrac{1}{2}, & -1/4 \leq x \leq 0 \\ x, & 0 \leq x \leq 1 \\ x^2, & 1 \leq x \leq 2 \end{cases}$

Hence, required area $= \int_{-2}^{2} g(x)\,dx$

$$= \int_{-2}^{-1} (x^2)\,dx + \int_{-1}^{-1/4} (-x)\,dx + \int_{-1/4}^{0} \left(x + \frac{1}{2}\right) dx + \int_0^1 x\,dx + \int_1^2 x^2\,dx$$

$$= \left(\frac{x^3}{3}\right)_{-2}^{-1} - \left(\frac{x^2}{2}\right)_{-1}^{-1/4} + \left(\frac{x^2}{2} + \frac{1}{2}x\right)_{-1/4}^{0} + \left(\frac{x^2}{2}\right)_0^1 + \left(\frac{x^3}{3}\right)_1^2 = \frac{275}{48} \text{ sq units}$$

• Ex. 49 *Find the area of the region bounded by* $y = f(x), y = |g(x)|$ *and the lines* $x = 0, x = 2$*, where f , g are continuous functions satisfying*

$$f(x + y) = f(x) + f(y) - 8xy, \; \forall\, x, y \in R$$

and $\quad g(x + y) = g(x) + g(y) + 3xy\,(x + y), \; \forall\, x, y \in R$

Also, $f'(0) = 8$ and $g'(0) = -4$.

Sol. Here, $f(x + y) = f(x) + f(y) - 8xy$

Replacing $x, y \to 0$, we get $f(0) = 0$

Now, $\quad f'(x) = \lim_{h \to 0} \dfrac{f(x + h) - f(x)}{h} = \lim_{y \to 0} \dfrac{f(x + y) - f(x)}{y}$

$$= \lim_{y \to 0} \frac{f(x) + f(y) - 8xy - f(x)}{y}$$

$$= \lim_{y \to 0} \left\{\frac{f(y)}{y} - \frac{8xy}{y}\right\}$$

$$= \lim_{y \to 0} \left(\frac{f'(y)}{1}\right) - 8x \text{ (using L'Hospital's rule)}$$

$$= f'(0) - 8x = 8 - 8x \qquad [\text{given, } f'(0) = 8]$$

$\Rightarrow \quad f'(x) = 8 - 8x$

Integrating both the sides, we get

$$f(x) = 8x - 4x^2 + c$$

As $\quad f(0) = 0 \Rightarrow c = 0$

$\Rightarrow \quad f(x) = 8x - 4x^2 \qquad \text{...(i)}$

Also, $\quad g(x + y) = g(x) + g(y) + 3xy\,(x + y)$

Replacing $x, y \Rightarrow 0$, we get $g(0) = 0$

Now, $\quad g'(x) = \lim_{y \to 0} \dfrac{g(x + y) - g(x)}{y}$

$$= \lim_{y \to 0} \frac{g(x) + g(y) + 3x^2 y + 3xy^2 - g(x)}{y}$$

$$= \lim_{y \to 0} \left[\frac{g(y)}{y} + \frac{y(3x^2 + 3xy)}{y} \right]$$

$$= \frac{g'(0)}{1} + 3x^2 = -4 + 3x^2$$

$\therefore \quad g'(x) = -4 + 3x^2$

$\Rightarrow \quad g(x) = x^3 - 4x \qquad$ [as $g(0) = 0$]...(ii)

Points where $f(x)$ and $g(x)$ meets, we have

$$f(x) = g(x) \quad \text{or} \quad 8x - 4x^2 = x^3 - 4x$$

$\Rightarrow \quad x = 0, 2, -6$

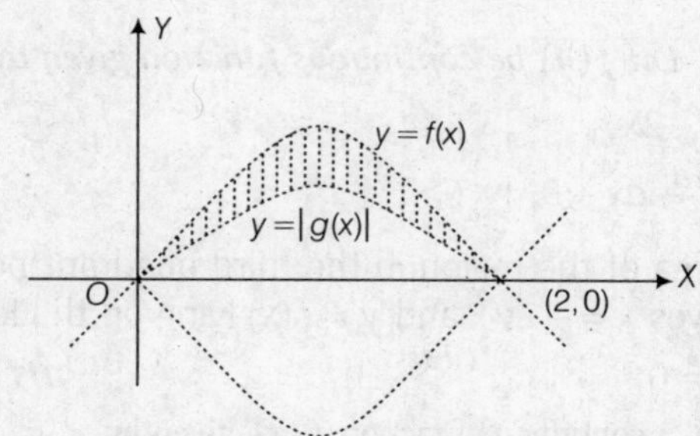

Now, $\quad | g(x) | = \begin{cases} x^3 - 4x, & x \in [-2, 0] \cup (2, \infty) \\ 4x - x^3, & x \in [-\infty, -2] \cup (0, 2) \end{cases}$

$\therefore$ Area bounded by $y = f(x)$ and $y = | g(x) |$ between $x = 0$ to $x = 2$

$$= \int_0^2 \{(8x - 4x^2) - (4x - x^3)\}\, dx$$

$$= \int_0^2 (x^3 - 4x^2 + 4x)\, dx = \frac{4}{3} \text{ sq units}$$

• Ex. 50 *Find the area of the region bounded by the curve $y = x^2$ and $y = \sec^{-1}[-\sin^2 x]$, where [.] denotes the greatest integer function.*

Sol. As we know, $[-\sin^2 x] = 0$ or -1. But $\sec^{-1}(0)$ is not defined.

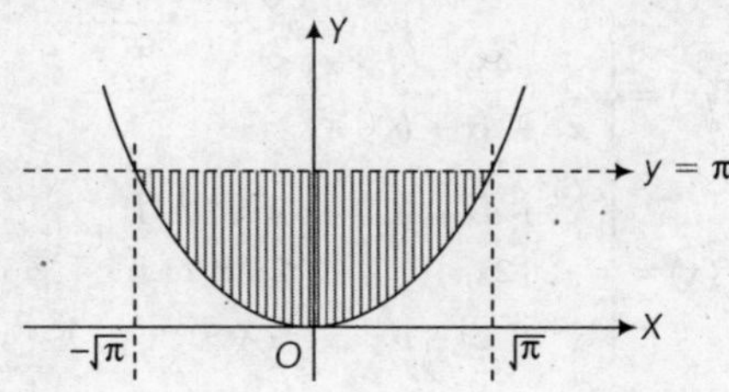

$\Rightarrow \quad \sec^{-1}[-\sin^2 x] = \sec^{-1}(-1) = \pi$

Thus, to find the area bounded between

$$y = x^2 \quad \text{and} \quad y = \pi$$

i.e. when $x^2 = \pi$ or $(x = -\sqrt{\pi}$ to $x = \sqrt{\pi})$

$\therefore$ Required area $= \displaystyle\int_{-\sqrt{\pi}}^{\sqrt{\pi}} (\pi - x^2)\, dx = \left(\pi x - \frac{x^3}{3} \right)_{-\sqrt{\pi}}^{\sqrt{\pi}}$

$$= \pi(\sqrt{\pi} + \sqrt{\pi}) - \frac{1}{3}(\pi\sqrt{\pi} + \pi\sqrt{\pi}) = \frac{4\pi}{3}\sqrt{\pi}$$

• Ex. 51 *Sketch the graph of $\cos^{-1}(4x^3 - 3x)$ and find the area enclosed between $y = 0$, $y = f(x)$ and $x \geq -1/2$.*

Sol. Here, $\quad f(x) = \cos^{-1}(4x^3 - 3x)$

Let $\quad x = \cos\theta$ and $0 \leq \theta \leq \pi$

$\Rightarrow \quad f(x) = \cos^{-1}(4\cos^3\theta - 3\cos\theta)$

$$= \cos^{-1}(\cos 3\theta);\ 0 \leq 3\theta \leq 3\pi$$

$\Rightarrow \quad f(x) = \begin{cases} 3\theta, & 0 \leq 3\theta \leq \pi \\ 2\pi - 3\theta, & \pi < 3\theta \leq 2\pi \\ 3\theta - 2\pi, & 2\pi < 3\theta \leq 3\pi \end{cases}$

$$= \begin{cases} 3\cos^{-1} x, & 1/2 \leq x \leq 1 \\ 2\pi - 3\cos^{-1} x, & -1/2 \leq x < 1 \\ 3\cos^{-1} x - 2\pi, & -1 \leq x < -1/2 \end{cases}$$

$\therefore \quad f'(x) = \begin{cases} -3/\sqrt{1 - x^2}, & 1/2 < x < 1 \\ 3/\sqrt{1 - x^2}, & -1/2 < x < 1/2 \\ -3/\sqrt{1 - x^2}, & -1 < x < -1/2 \end{cases}$

and $\quad f''(x) = \begin{cases} \dfrac{-3x}{(1 - x^2)^{3/2}}, & 1/2 < x < 1 \\ \dfrac{3x}{(1 - x^2)^{3/2}}, & -1/2 < x < 1/2 \\ \dfrac{-3x}{(1 - x^2)^{3/2}}, & -1 < x < -1/2 \end{cases}$

Thus, the graph for $f(x) = \cos^{-1}(4x^3 - 3x)$ is

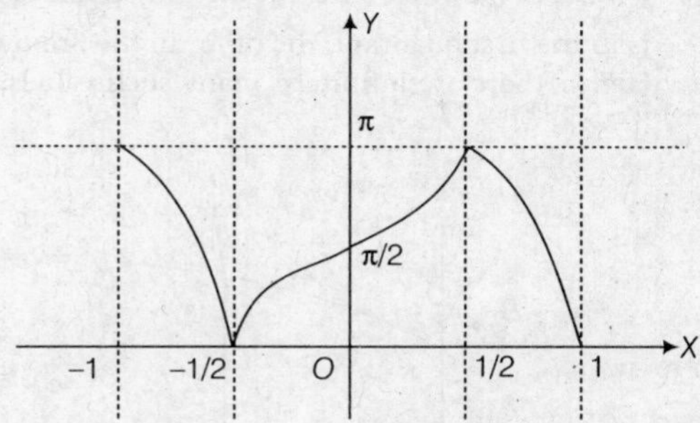

Thus, required area $= \displaystyle\int_{-1/2}^{1} f(x)\, dx$

$$= \int_{-1/2}^{1/2} (2\pi - 3\cos^{-1} x)\,dx + \int_{1/2}^{1} (3\cos^{-1} x)\,dx$$

$$= 2\pi - 3\int_{-1/2}^{1/2}\left(\frac{\pi}{2} - \sin^{-1} x\right)dx + 3\int_{1/2}^{1}(\cos^{-1} x)\,dx$$

$$= \frac{\pi}{2} + 3\int_{1/2}^{1}\cos^{-1} x\,dx \quad \left[\text{as } \int_{-1/2}^{1/2}\sin^{-1} x\,dx = 0\right]$$

$$= \frac{\pi}{2} + 3\left\{(x\cos^{-1} x)_{1/2}^{1} + \int_{1/2}^{1}\frac{x}{\sqrt{1-x^2}}dx\right\}$$

On solving, we get $= \dfrac{3\sqrt{3}}{2}$ sq units

Ex. 52 *Consider two curves $y^2 = 4a(x - \lambda)$ and $x^2 = 4a(y - \lambda)$, where $a > 0$ and λ is a parameter. Show that*

(i) there is a single positive value of λ for which the two curves have exactly one point of intersection in the 1st quadrant find it.

(ii) there are infinitely many negative values of λ for which the two curves have exactly one point of intersection in the 1st quadrant.

(iii) if $\lambda = -a$, then find the area of the bounded by the two curves and the axes in the 1st quadrant.

Sol. The two curves are inverse of each other. Hence, the two curves always meet along the line $y = x$.

Consider, $y^2 = 4a(x - \lambda)$ and put $x = y$

$$\Rightarrow \quad y^2 - 4ay + 4a\lambda = 0$$

$$\Rightarrow \quad y = \frac{4a \pm 4\sqrt{a^2 - a\lambda}}{2} = 2a \pm \sqrt{a^2 - a\lambda}$$

Since, y is real $\Rightarrow a^2 - a\lambda \mid 0$ or $\lambda \le a$

(i) If $0 < \lambda < a$, then there are two distinct values of y and both $2(a + \sqrt{a^2 - a\lambda})$ and $2(a - \sqrt{a^2 - a\lambda})$ are positive, i.e. both points lie in the first quadrant.

If $\lambda = a$, then $y = 2a$ only, i.e. only one point of intersection $(2a, 2a)$.

Hence, there is exactly one point of intersection in 1st quadrant for $\lambda = a$. It is infact the points of tangency of the two curves.

(ii) If $\lambda < 0$, then $y = 2(a + \sqrt{a^2 - a\lambda}) > 0$ and $y = 2(a - \sqrt{a^2 - a\lambda}) < 0$. i.e. the only point of intersection is in the first quadrant, the other in the 3rd quadrant. Hence, there are infinitely many such values.

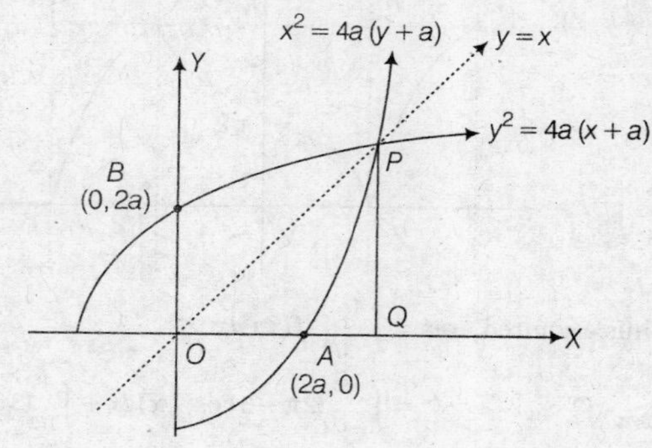

(iii) For $\lambda = -a$, we have $y^2 = 4a(x + a)$

$$x^2 = 4a(y + a)$$

The point of intersection in the 1st quadrant $P = ((2 + 2\sqrt{2})a, (2 + 2\sqrt{2})a)$

Required area = 2 (area of ΔOPQ − area $\overline{APQA}$)

of $\Delta OPQ = \frac{1}{2}\cdot(2 + 2\sqrt{2})^2 a^2 = 2(1 + \sqrt{2})^2 a^2$

$$\text{Area of } APQA = \int_{2a}^{(2+2\sqrt{2})a} y\,dx = \int_{2a}^{(2+2\sqrt{2})a}\left(\frac{x^2}{4a} - a\right)dx$$

$$= \frac{1}{4a}\left[\frac{x^3}{3}\right]_{2a}^{(2+2\sqrt{2})a} - a(x)_{2a}^{(2+2\sqrt{2})a}$$

$$= \frac{1}{12a}[(2 + 2\sqrt{2})^3\cdot a^3 - 8a^3] - 2\sqrt{2}a^2$$

$$= \left(\frac{4\sqrt{2} + 12}{3}\right)a^2$$

$$\therefore \text{ Required area} = 2\left(2(1 + \sqrt{2})^2 + \frac{4\sqrt{2} + 12}{3}\right)a^2$$

$$= \frac{4}{3}(15 + 8\sqrt{2})a^2$$

Ex. 53 *Let $f(x)$ be continuous function given by*

$$f(x) = \begin{cases} 2x, & |x| \le 1 \\ x^2 + ax + b, & |x| > 1 \end{cases}$$

Find the area of the region in the third quadrant bounded by the curves $x = -2y^2$ and $y = f(x)$ lying on the left of the line $8x + 1 = 0$. ***[IIT JEE 1999]***

Sol. Given, a continuous function $f(x)$, given by

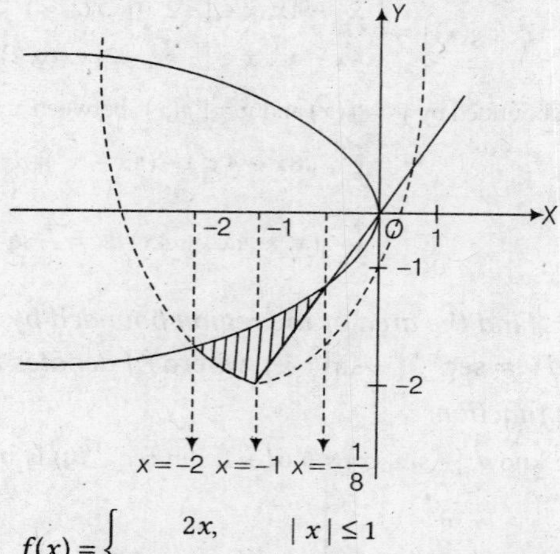

$$f(x) = \begin{cases} 2x, & |x| \le 1 \\ x^2 + ax + b, & |x| > 1 \end{cases}$$

i.e. $$f(x) = \begin{cases} x^2 + ax + b, & -\infty < x < -1 \\ 2x, & -1 \le x \le 1 \\ x^2 + ax + b, & 1 < x < \infty \end{cases}$$

$\because$ f is continuous.

$\therefore$ It is continuous at $x = -1$ and $x = 1$.

$\therefore \quad (-1)^2 + a(-1) + b = 2(-1)$

and $\quad (1)^2 + a(1) + b = 2(1)$

$\Rightarrow \quad 1 - a + b = -2$

and $\quad 1 + a + b = 2$

$\Rightarrow \quad -a + b = -3$

and $\quad a + b = 1$

$\Rightarrow \quad b = -1$ and $a = 2$

$$\therefore \quad f(x) = \begin{cases} x^2 + 2x - 1, & \text{when } -\infty < x < -1 \\ 2x, & \text{when } -1 \le x \le 1 \end{cases}$$

Now, $\quad y = x^2 + 2x - 1 = (x+1)^2 - 2$

or $\quad (y + 2) = (x + 1)^2$

We need the area of the region in third quadrant bounded by the curves $a = -2y^2$, $y = f(x)$ lying on the left of the line $8x + 1 = 0$.

$\Rightarrow \quad (y + 2) = (x + 1)^2$

Cuts the Y-axis at $(0, -1)$ and the X-axis at $(-1-\sqrt{2}, 0)$ and $(-1+\sqrt{2}, 0)$.

When $x = 1$ and $y = 2$

Solving $x = -2y^2$ and $(y + 2) = (x + 1)^2$, we get

$$(y + 2) = (-2y^2 + 1)^2$$

$\Rightarrow \quad 4y^4 - 4y^2 + 1 - y - 2 = 0$

$\Rightarrow \quad 4y^4 - 4y^2 - y - 1 = 0$

For $\quad y = -1,\ 4y^4 - 4y^2 - y - 1 = 0$

At $\quad y = -1, x = -2$

$$\therefore \quad \text{Required area} = \int_{-2}^{-1} \left\{ -\sqrt{-\frac{x}{2}} - (x+1)^2 + 2 \right\} dx + \int_{-1}^{-1/8} \left\{ -\sqrt{-\frac{x}{2}} - 2x \right\} dx$$

$$= \left[\frac{(-x/2)^{3/2}}{\frac{3}{2}(1/2)} - \frac{(x+1)^3}{3} + 2x \right]_{-2}^{-1} + \left[\frac{(-x/2)^{3/2}}{\frac{3}{2}(1/2)} - \frac{2x^2}{2} \right]_{-1}^{-1/8}$$

$$= \left[\frac{4}{3}\left(-\frac{x}{2}\right)^{3/2} - \frac{(x+1)^3}{3} + 2x \right]_{-2}^{-1} + \left[\frac{4}{3}\left(-\frac{x}{2}\right)^{3/2} - x^2 \right]_{-1}^{-1/8}$$

$$= \left\{ \frac{4}{3}\left(\frac{1}{2}\right)^{3/2} - 0 - 2 \right\} - \left\{ \frac{4}{3}(1)^{3/2} - \frac{(-1)^3}{3} - 4 \right\} - \left\{ \frac{4}{3}\left(\frac{1}{2}\right)^{3/2} - (-1)^2 \right\} + \left\{ \frac{4}{3}\left(\frac{1}{16}\right)^{3/2} - \frac{1}{64} \right\}$$

$$= \left\{ \frac{4}{3 \cdot 2\sqrt{2}} - 2 - \frac{4}{3} - \frac{1}{3} + 4 - \frac{4}{3 \cdot 2\sqrt{2}} + 1 + \frac{4}{3(64)} - \frac{1}{64} \right\}$$

$$= \frac{4}{3} + \frac{1}{3(64)} = \frac{257}{192} \text{ sq units}$$

● **Ex. 54** *Let $[x]$ denotes the greatest integer function. Draw a rough sketch of the portions of the curves $x^2 = 4[\sqrt{x}]\,y$ and $y^2 = 4[\sqrt{y}]\,x$ that lie within the square $\{(x, y) \mid 1 \le x \le 4, 1 \le y \le 4\}$. Find the area of the part of the square that is enclosed by the two curves and the line $x + y = 3$.*

Sol. We have, $\quad 1 \le x \le 4$ and $1 \le y \le 4$

$\Rightarrow \quad 1 \le \sqrt{x} \le 2$ and $1 \le \sqrt{y} \le 2$

$\Rightarrow [\sqrt{x}] = 1$ and $[\sqrt{y}] = 1$ for all (x, y) lying with in the square.

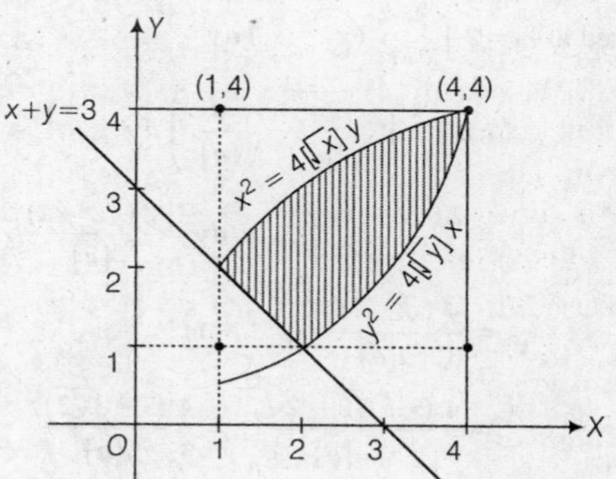

Thus, $\quad x^2 = 4[\sqrt{x}]\,y$ and $y^2 = 4[\sqrt{y}]\,x$

$\Rightarrow \quad x^2 = 4y$ and $y^2 = 4x$ when $1 \le x, y \le 4$ which could be plotted as;

Thus, required area

$$= \int_1^2 (2\sqrt{x} - 3 + x)\,dx + \int_2^4 \left(2\sqrt{x} - \frac{x^2}{4} \right) dx$$

$$= \left(\frac{4}{3}x^{3/2} - 3x + \frac{x^2}{2} \right)_1^2 + \left(\frac{4}{3}x^{3/2} - \frac{x^3}{12} \right)_2^4$$

$$= \left(\frac{8\sqrt{2}}{3} - 6 + 2 \right) - \left(\frac{4}{3} - 3 + \frac{1}{2} \right) + \left(\frac{32}{3} - \frac{64}{12} \right) - \left(\frac{8\sqrt{2}}{3} - \frac{8}{12} \right)$$

$$= \frac{19}{6} \text{ sq units}$$

● **Ex. 55** *Find all the values of the parameter a $(a \ge 1)$ for which the area of the figure bounded by pair of straight lines $y^2 - 3y + 2 = 0$ and the curves $y = [a]\,x^2$, $y = \frac{1}{2}[a]\,x^2$ is greatest, where [.] denotes the greatest integer function.*

Sol. The curves $y = [a]\,x^2$ and $y = \frac{1}{2}[a]\,x^2$ represent parabolas which are symmetric about Y-axis.

The equation $y^2 - 3y + 2 = 0$ gives a pair of straight lines $y = 1$, $y = 2$ which are parallel to X-axis.

Thus, the area bounded is shown as

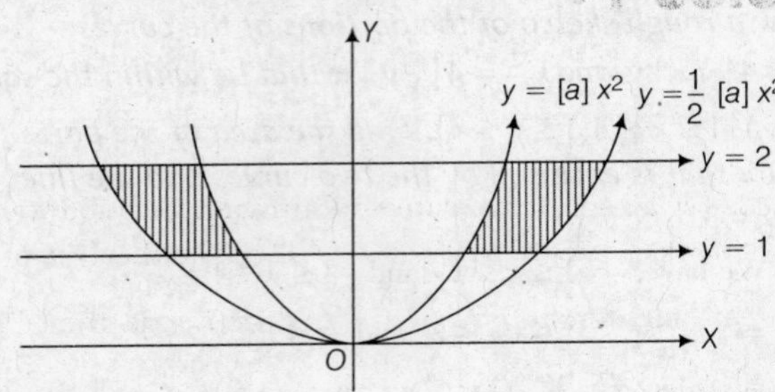

From the above figure,

$$\text{Required area} = 2\int_{y=1}^{y=2} (x_2 - x_1)\, dy$$

$$= 2\int_1^2 \left(\sqrt{\frac{2y}{[a]}} - \sqrt{\frac{y}{[a]}}\right) dy$$

$$= \frac{2(\sqrt{2}-1)}{[a]}\int_1^2 \sqrt{y}\, dy = \frac{2(\sqrt{2}-1)}{[a]}\,\frac{2}{3}\,(y^{3/2})_1^2$$

$$= \frac{4}{3}\,\frac{(\sqrt{2}-1)}{[a]}\cdot(2^{3/2}-1)$$

$$= \frac{4}{3}\,\frac{(5-\sqrt{2}-2\sqrt{2})}{[a]} = \frac{4}{3}\,\frac{(5-3\sqrt{2})}{[a]}$$

$\therefore$ Area is the greatest when $[a]$ is least, i.e. 1.

$\therefore$ Area is the greatest when $[a] = 1$

Hence, $a \in [1, 2)$

• Ex. 56 *Find the area in the first quadrant bounded by $[x] + [y] = n$, where $n \in N$ and $y = i$ (where, $i \in N\ \forall\ i \le n+1$), $[\cdot]$ denotes the greatest integer less than or equal to x.*

Sol. As we know, $[x] + [y] = n \Rightarrow [x] = n - [y]$

When $y = 0$, $[x] = n \Rightarrow n \le x < n+1$

When $y = 1$, $[x] = n-1 \Rightarrow n-1 \le x < n-2$

When $y = 2$, $[x] = n-2$

$\Rightarrow$ $n-2 \le x < n-3$. ... and so on.

When $y = n$, $[x] = 0 \Rightarrow 0 \le x < 1$

which could be shown as

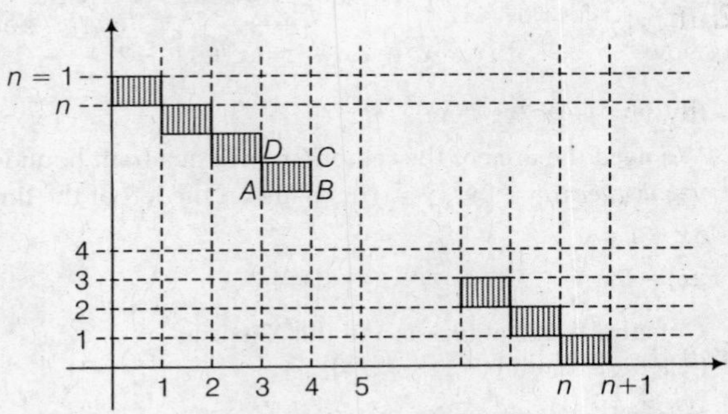

From the above figure,

$= (n+1)$ area of square $ABCD = (n+1)\cdot 1$

Required area $= (n+1)$ sq units

Area of Bounded Regions Exercise 1 : Single Option Correct Type Questions

1. A Point $P(x, y)$ moves such that $[x+y+1]=[x]$. (where $[\cdot]$ denotes greatest integer function) and $x \in (0, 2)$, then the area represented by all the possible positions of P, is

(a) $\sqrt{2}$ (b) $2\sqrt{2}$
(c) $4\sqrt{2}$ (d) 2

2. If $f:[-1,1] \to \left[-\frac{1}{2}, \frac{1}{2}\right]$, $f(x)=\frac{x}{1+x^2}$. The area bounded by $y=f^{-1}(x)$, X-axis, $x=\frac{1}{2}$, $x=-\frac{1}{2}$ is

(a) $\frac{1}{2}\log e$ (b) $\log\left(\frac{e}{2}\right)$
(c) $\frac{1}{2}\log\frac{e}{3}$ (d) $\frac{1}{2}\log\left(\frac{e}{2}\right)$

3. If the length of latusrectum of ellipse $E_1: 4(x+y-1)^2+2(x-y+3)^2=8$ and $E_2: \frac{x^2}{p}+\frac{y^2}{p^2}=1, (0<p<1)$ are equal, then area of ellipse E_2, is

(a) $\frac{\pi}{2}$ (b) $\frac{\pi}{\sqrt{2}}$
(c) $\frac{\pi}{2\sqrt{2}}$ (d) $\frac{\pi}{4}$

4. The area of bounded by the curve $4|x-2017^{2017}|+5|y-2017^{2017}| \le 20$, is

(a) 60 (b) 50
(c) 40 (d) 30

5. If the area bounded by the corve $y=x^2+1$, $y=x$ and the pair of lines $x^2+y^2+2xy-4x-4y+3=0$ is K units, then the area of the region bounded by the curve $y=x^2+1$, $y=\sqrt{x-1}$ and the pair of lines $(x+y-1)(x+y-3)=0$, is

(a) K (b) $2K$
(c) $\frac{K}{2}$ (d) None of these

6. Suppose $y=f(x)$ and $y=g(x)$ are two functions whose graphs intersect at the three points (0, 4), (2, 2) and (4, 0) with $f(x)>g(x)$ for $0<x<2$ and $f(x)<g(x)$ for $2<x<4$. If $\int_0^4 [f(x)-g(x)]\,dx=10$ and $\int_2^4 [g(x)-f(x)]\,dx=5$, then the area between two curves for $0<x<2$, is

(a) 5 (b) 10
(c) 15 (d) 20

7. Let 'a' be a positive constant number. Consider two curves $C_1: y=e^x$, $C_2: y=e^{a-x}$. Let S be the area of the part surrounding by C_1, C_2 and the Y-axis, then $\lim_{a\to 0}\frac{S}{a^2}$ equals

(a) 4 (b) 1/2
(c) 0 (d) 1/4

8. 3 points $O(0,0)$, $P(a,a^2)$, $Q(-b,b^2)$ $(a>0, b>0)$ are on the parabola $y=x^2$. Let S_1 be the area bounded by the line PQ and the parabola and let S_2 be the area of the ΔOPQ, the minimum value of S_1/S_2 is

(a) 4/3 (b) 5/3
(c) 2 (d) 7/3

9. Area enclosed by the graph of the function $y=\ln^2 x-1$ lying in the 4th quadrant is

(a) $\frac{2}{e}$ (b) $\frac{4}{e}$
(c) $2\left(e+\frac{1}{e}\right)$ (d) $4\left(e-\frac{1}{e}\right)$

10. The area bounded by $y=2-|2-x|$ and $y=\frac{3}{|x|}$ is

(a) $\frac{4+3\ln 3}{2}$ (b) $\frac{19}{8}-3\ln 2$
(c) $\frac{3}{2}+\ln 3$ (d) $\frac{1}{2}+\ln 3$

11. Suppose $g(x)=2x+1$ and $h(x)=4x^2+4x+5$ and $h(x)=(fog)(x)$. The area enclosed by the graph of the function $y=f(x)$ and the pair of tangents drawn to it from the origin, is

(a) 8/3 (b) 16/3
(c) 32/3 (d) None of these

12. The area bounded by the curves $y=-\sqrt{-x}$ and $x=-\sqrt{-y}$ where $x, y \le 0$

(a) cannot be determined
(b) is 1/3
(c) is 2/3
(d) is same as that of the figure bounded by the curves $y=\sqrt{-x};\ x\le 0$ and $x=\sqrt{-y};\ y\le 0$

13. $y=f(x)$ is a function which satisfies
(i) $f(0)=0$ (ii) $f''(x)=f'(x)$ and (iii) $f'(0)=1$
Then, the area bounded by the graph of $y=f(x)$, the lines $x=0$, $x-1=0$ and $y+1=0$, is

(a) e (b) $e-2$
(c) $e-1$ (d) $e+1$

14. Area of the region enclosed between the curves $x = y^2 - 1$ and $x = |y|\sqrt{1-y^2}$ is

(a) 1 (b) 4/3
(c) 2/3 (d) 2

15. The area bounded by the curve $y = xe^{-x}$; $xy = 0$ and $x = c$ where c is the x-coordinate of the curve's inflection point, is

(a) $1-3e^{-2}$ (b) $1-2e^{-2}$
(c) $1-e^{-2}$ (d) 1

16. If $(a, 0); a > 0$ is the point where the curve $y = \sin 2x - \sqrt{3} \sin x$ cuts the X-axis first, A is the area bounded by this part of the curve, the origin and the positive X-axis, then

(a) $4A + 8 \cos a = 7$ (b) $4A + 8 \sin a = 7$
(c) $4A - 8 \sin a = 7$ (d) $4A - 8 \cos a = 7$

17. The curve $y = ax^2 + bx + c$ passes through the point $(1, 2)$ and its tangent at origin is the line $y = x$. The area bounded by the curve, the ordinate of the curve at minima and the tangent line is

(a) $\frac{1}{24}$ (b) $\frac{1}{12}$ (c) $\frac{1}{8}$ (d) $\frac{1}{6}$

18. A function $y = f(x)$ satisfies the differential equation $\frac{dy}{dx} - y = \cos x - \sin x$, with initial condition that y is bounded when $x \to \infty$. The area enclosed by $y = f(x), y = \cos x$ and the Y-axis in the 1st quadrant

(a) $\sqrt{2} - 1$ (b) $\sqrt{2}$
(c) 1 (d) $1/\sqrt{2}$

19. If the area bounded between X-axis and the graph of $y = 6x - 3x^2$ between the ordinates $x = 1$ and $x = a$ is 19 sq units, then 'a' can take the value

(a) 4 or -2
(b) two values are in $(2, 3)$ and one in $(-1, 0)$
(c) two values one in $(3, 4)$ and one in $(-2, -1)$
(d) None of the above

20. Area bounded by $y = f^{-1}(x)$ and tangent and normal drawn to it at the points with abscissae π and 2π, where $f(x) = \sin x - x$ is

(a) $\frac{\pi^2}{2} - 1$ (b) $\frac{\pi^2}{2} - 2$
(c) $\frac{\pi^2}{2} - 4$ (d) $\frac{\pi^2}{2}$

21. If $f(x) = x - 1$ and $g(x) = |f(|x|) - 2|$, then the area bounded by $y = g(x)$ and the curve $x^2 - 4y + 8 = 0$ is equal to

(a) $\frac{4}{3}(4\sqrt{2} - 5)$ (b) $\frac{4}{3}(4\sqrt{2} - 3)$
(c) $\frac{8}{3}(4\sqrt{2} - 3)$ (d) $\frac{8}{3}(4\sqrt{2} - 5)$

22. Let $S = \left\{(x, y): \frac{y(3x-1)}{x(3x-2)} < 0\right\}$,
$S' = \{(x, y) \in A \times B: -1 \le A \le 1, -1 \le B \le 1\}$,
then the area of the region enclosed by all points in $S \cap S'$ is

(a) 1 (b) 2
(c) 3 (d) 4

23. The area of the region bounded between the curves $y = e||x|\ln|x||, x^2 + y^2 - 2(|x| + |y|) + 1 \ge 0$ and X-axis where $|x| \le 1$, if α is the x-coordinate of the point of intersection of curves in 1st quadrant, is

(a) $4\left[\int_0^\alpha ex \ln x \, dx + \int_\alpha^1 (1 - \sqrt{1-(x-1)^2}) dx\right]$

(b) $4\left[\int_0^\alpha ex \ln x \, dx + \int_1^\alpha (1 - \sqrt{1-(x-1)^2}) dx\right]$

(c) $4\left[-\int_0^\alpha ex \ln x \, dx + \int_\alpha^1 (1 - \sqrt{1-(x-1)^2}) dx\right]$

(d) $2\left[\int_0^\alpha ex \ln x \, dx + \int_1^\alpha (1 - \sqrt{1-(x-1)^2}) dx\right]$

24. A point P lying inside the curve $y = \sqrt{2ax - x^2}$ is moving such that its shortest distance from the curve at any position is greater than its distance from X-axis. The point P enclose a region whose area is equal to

(a) $\frac{\pi a^2}{2}$ (b) $\frac{a^2}{3}$
(c) $\frac{2a^2}{3}$ (d) $\left(\frac{3\pi - 4}{6}\right) a^2$

Area of Bounded Regions Exercise 2 : More than One Option Correct Type Questions

25. The triangle formed by the normal to the curve $f(x) = x^2 - ax + 2a$ at the point (2, 4) and the coordinate axes lies in second quadrant, if its area is 2 sq units, then a can be
(a) 2
(b) 17/4
(c) 5
(d) 19/4

26. Let f and g be continuous function on $a \le x \le b$ and set $p(x) = \max\{f(x), g(x)\}$ and $q(x) = \min\{f(x), g(x)\}$, then the area bounded by the curves $y = p(x)$, $y = q(x)$ and the ordinates $x = a$ and $x = b$ is given by
(a) $\int_a^b |f(x) - g(x)|\, dx$ (b) $\int_a^b |p(x) - q(x)|\, dx$
(c) $\int_a^b \{f(x) - g(x)\}\, dx$ (d) $\int_a^b \{p(x) - q(x)\}\, dx$

27. The area bounded by the parabola $y = x^2 - 7x + 10$ and X-axis equals
(a) area bounded by $y = -x^2 + 7x - 10$ and X-axis
(b) 1/6 sq units
(c) 5/6 sq units
(d) 9/2 sq units

28. Area bounded by the ellipse $\frac{x^2}{4} + \frac{y^2}{9} = 1$ is equal to
(a) 6π sq units
(b) 3π sq units
(c) 12π sq units
(d) area bounded by the ellipse $\frac{x^2}{9} + \frac{y^2}{4} = 1$

29. There is a curve in which the length of the perpendicular from the origin to tangent at any point is equal to abscissa of that point. Then,
(a) $x^2 + y^2 = 2$ is one such curve
(b) $y^2 = 4x$ is one such curve
(c) $x^2 + y^2 = 2cx$ (c parameters) are such curves
(d) there are no such curves

Area of Bounded Regions Exercise 3 : Statement I and II Type Questions

■ **Direction** (Q. No. 30-34) *For the following questions, choose the correct answers from the codes (a), (b), (c) and (d) defined as follows :*

(a) Statement I is true, Statement II is also true; Statement II is the correct explanation of Statement I
(b) Statement I is true, Statement II is also true; Statement II is not the correct explanation of Statement I
(c) Statement I is true, Statement II is false
(d) Statement I is false, Statement II is true

30. Statement I The area of the curve $y = \sin^2 x$ from 0 to π will be more than that of the curve $y = \sin x$ from 0 to π.

Statement II $x^2 > x$, if $x > 1$.

31. Statement I The area bounded by the curves $y = x^2 - 3$ and $y = kx + 2$ is least if $k = 0$.

Statement II The area bounded by the curves $y = x^2 - 3$ and $y = kx + 2$ is $\sqrt{k^2 + 20}$.

32. Statement I The area of region bounded parabola $y^2 = 4x$ and $x^2 = 4y$ is $\frac{32}{3}$ sq units.

Statement II The area of region bounded by parabola $y^2 = 4ax$ and $x^2 = 4by$ is $\frac{16}{3}ab$.

33. Statement I The area by region $|x + y| + |x - y| \le 2$ is 8 sq units.

Statement II Area enclosed by region $|x + y| + |x - y| \le 2$ is symmetric about X-axis.

34. Statement I Area bounded by $y = x(x - 1)$ and $y = x(1 - x)$ is $\frac{1}{3}$.

Statement II Area bounded by $y = f(x)$ and $y = g(x)$ is $\left|\int_a^b (f(x) - g(x))\, dx\right|$ is true when $f(x)$ and $g(x)$ lies above X-axis. (Where a and b are intersection of $y = f(x)$ and $y = g(x)$).

Area of Bounded Regions Exercise 4 : Passage Based Questions

Passage I

(Q. Nos. 35 to 37)

Let $f(x)=\dfrac{ax^2+bx+c}{x^2+1}$ such that $y=-2$ is an asymptote of the curve $y=f(x)$. The curve $y=f(x)$ is symmetric about Y-axis and its maximum values is 4. Let $h(x)=f(x)-g(x)$, where $f(x)=\sin^4 \pi x$ and $g(x)=\log_e x$. Let $x_0, x_1, x_2, \ldots, x_{n+1}$ be the roots of $f(x)=g(x)$ in increasing order.

35. Then, the absolute area enclosed by $y=f(x)$ and $y=g(x)$ is given by

(a) $\sum_{r=0}^{n} \int_{x_r}^{x_{r+1}} (-1)^r \cdot h(x)dx$

(b) $\sum_{r=0}^{n} \int_{x_r}^{x_{r+1}} (-1)^{r+1} \cdot h(x)dx$

(c) $2\sum_{r=0}^{n} \int_{x_r}^{x_{r+1}} (-1)^r \cdot h(x)dx$

(d) $\frac{1}{2}\cdot\sum_{r=0}^{n} \int_{x_r}^{x_{r+1}} (-1)^{r+1} h(x)dx$

36. In above inquestion the value of n, is

(a) 1 (b) 2
(c) 3 (d) 4

37. The whole area bounded by $y=f(x), y=g(x)$ $x=0$ is

(a) 11/8 (b) 8/3
(c) 2 (d) 13/3

Passage II

(Q. Nos. 38 to 40)

Consider the function $f:(-\infty,\infty)\to(-\infty,\infty)$ defined by $f(x)=\dfrac{x^2-ax+1}{x^2+ax+1}, 0< a< 2.$

38. Which of the following is true?

(a) $(2+a)^2 f''(1)+(2-a)^2 f''(-1)=0$

(b) $(2-a)^2 f''(1)-(2+a)^2 f''(-1)=0$

(c) $f'(1)f'(-1)=(2-a)^2$

(d) $f'(1)f'(-1)=-(2+a)^2$

39. Which of the following is true?

(a) $f(x)$ is decreasing on $(-1,1)$ and has a local minimum at $x=1$

(b) $f(x)$ is increasing on $(-1,1)$ and has a local maximum at $x=1$

(c) $f(x)$ is increasing on $(-1,1)$ but has neither a local maximum nor a local minimum at $x=1$

(d) $f(x)$ is decreasing on $(-1,1)$ but has neither a local maximum nor a local minimum at $x=1$

40. Let $g(x)=\int_0^{e^x} \frac{f'(t)}{1+t^2}dt$. Which of the following is true?

(a) $g'(x)$ is positive on $(-\infty,0)$ and negative on $(0,\infty)$

(b) $g'(x)$ is negative on $(-\infty,0)$ and positive on $(0,\infty)$

(c) $g'(x)$ change sign on both $(-\infty,0)$ and $(0,\infty)$

(d) $g'(x)$ does not change sign on $(-\infty,\infty)$

Passage III

(Q. Nos. 41 to 43)

Computing areas with parametrically represented boundaries : If the boundary of a figure is represented by parametric equations i.e. $x=x(t)$, $y=y(t)$, then the area of the figure is evaluated by one of the three formulas

$$S=-\int_\alpha^\beta y(t)\cdot x'(t)\,dt$$

$$S=\int_\alpha^\beta x(t)\cdot y'(t)\,dt$$

$$S=\frac{1}{2}\int_\alpha^\beta (xy'-yx')\,dt$$

where α and β are the values of the parameter 't' corresponding, respectively to the beginning and the end of the traversal of the curve corresponding to increasing 't'.

41. The area enclosed by the asteroid $\left(\frac{x}{a}\right)^{2/3}+\left(\frac{y}{a}\right)^{2/3}=1$ is

(a) $\frac{3}{4}a^2\pi$ (b) $\frac{3}{18}\pi a^2$
(c) $\frac{3}{8}\pi a^2$ (d) $\frac{3}{4}a\pi$

42. The area of the region bounded by an arc of the cycloid $x=a(t-\sin t), y=a(1-\cos t)$ and the X-axis is

(a) $6\pi a^2$ (b) $3\pi a^2$
(c) $4\pi a^2$ (d) None of these

43. Area of the loop described as $x=\frac{t}{3}(6-t), y=\frac{t^2}{8}(6-t)$ is

(a) $\frac{27}{5}$ (b) $\frac{24}{5}$
(c) $\frac{27}{6}$ (d) $\frac{21}{5}$

Area of Bounded Regions Exercise 5 : Matching Type Questions

44. Match the statements of Column I with values of Column II.

	Column I		Column II
(A)	The area bounded by the curve $y = x + \sin x$ and its inverse function between the ordinates $x = 0$ to $x = 2\pi$ is 4s. Then, the value of s is	(p)	2
(B)	The area bounded by $y = xe^{\lvert x\rvert}$ and lies $\lvert x\rvert = 1$, $y = 0$ is	(q)	1
(C)	The area bounded by the curves $y^2 = x^3$ and $\lvert y\rvert = 2x$ is	(r)	$\frac{16}{5}$
(D)	The smaller are included between the curves $\sqrt{\lvert x\rvert} + \sqrt{\lvert y\rvert} = 1$ and $\lvert x\rvert + \lvert y\rvert = 1$ is	(s)	$\frac{1}{3}$

45. Match the following :

	Column I		Column II
(A)	Area enclosed by $y = \lvert x\rvert$, $\lvert x\rvert = 1$ and $y = 0$ is	(p)	2
(B)	Area enclosed by the curve $y = \sin x$, $x = 0$, $x = \pi$ and $y = 0$ is	(q)	4
(C)	If the area of the region bounded by $x^2 \le y$ and $y \le x + 2$ is $\frac{k}{4}$, then k is equal to	(r)	27
(D)	Area of the quadrilateral formed by tangents at the ends of latusrectum of ellipse of ellipse $\frac{x^2}{9} + \frac{y^2}{5} = 1$ is	(s)	18

Area of Bounded Regions Exercise 6 : Single Integer Answer Type Questions

46. Consider $f(x) = x^2 - 3x + 2$. The area bounded by $\lvert y\rvert = \lvert f(\lvert x\rvert)\rvert$, $x \ge 1$ is A, then find the value of $3A + 2$.

47. The value of $c + 2$ for which the area of the figure bounded by the curve $y = 8x^2 - x^5$; the straight lines $x = 1$ and $x = c$ and X-axis is equal to $\frac{16}{3}$, is ....

48. The area bounded by $y = 2 - \lvert 2 - x\rvert$; $y = \frac{3}{\lvert x\rvert}$ is $\frac{k - 3\ln 3}{2}$, then k is equal to ....

49. The area of the ΔABC, coordinates of whose vertices are $A(2, 0)$, $B(4, 5)$ and $C(6, 3)$ is ....

50. A point P moves in XY-plane in such a way that $[\lvert x\rvert] + [\lvert y\rvert] = 1$, where $[\cdot]$ denotes the greatest integer function. Area of the region representing all possible of the point P is equal to ....

51. Let $f : [0, 1] \to \left[0, \frac{1}{2}\right]$ be a function such that $f(x)$ is a polynomial of 2nd degree, satisfy the following condition :

(a) $f(0) = 0$

(b) has a maximum value of $\frac{1}{2}$ at $x = 1$.

If A is the area bounded by $y = f(x)$; $y = f^{-1}(x)$ and the line $2x + 2y - 3 = 0$ in 1st quadrant, then the value of $24A$ is equal to ....

52. Let $f(x) = \min\left\{\sin^{-1} x, \cos^{-1} x, \frac{\pi}{6}\right\}$, $x \in [0, 1]$. If area bounded by $y = f(x)$ and X-axis, between the lines $x = 0$ and $x = 1$ is $\frac{a - X}{b(\sqrt{3} + 1)}$. Then, $(a - b)$ is ....

53. Let f be a real valued function satisfying $f\left(\frac{x}{y}\right) = f(x) - f(y)$ and $\lim_{x \to 0} \frac{f(1 + x)}{x} = 3$. Find the area bounded by the curve $y = f(x)$, the Y-axis and the line $y = 3$, where $x, y \in R^+$.

Area of Bounded Regions Exercise 7 : Subjective Type Questions

54. Find a continuous function 'f', $(x^4 - 4x^2) \leq f(x) \leq (2x^2 - x^3)$ such that the area bounded by $y = f(x)$, $y = x^4 - 4x^2$, the Y-axis and the line $x = t, (0 \leq t \leq 2)$ is k times the area bounded by $y = f(x)$, $y = 2x^2 - x^3$, Y-axis and line $x = t, (0 \leq t \leq 2)$.

55. Let $f(t) = |t-1| - |t| + |t+1|, \forall t \in R$ and $g(x) = \max\{f(t) : x+1 \leq t \leq x+2\}; \forall x \in R$. Find $g(x)$ and the area bounded by the curve $y = g(x)$, the X-axis and the lines $x = -3/2$ and $x = 5$.

56. Let $f(x) = \text{minimum}\{e^x, 3/2, 1+e^{-x}\}, 0 \leq x \leq 1$. Find the area bounded by $y = f(x)$, X-axis, Y-axis and the line $x = 1$.

57. Find the area bounded by $y = f(x)$ and the curve $y = \dfrac{2}{1+x^2}$, where f is a continuous function satisfying the conditions $f(x) \cdot f(y) = f(xy), \forall x, y \in R$ and $f'(1) = 2$, $f(1) = 1$.

58. Find out the area bounded by the curve $y = \int_{1/8}^{\sin^2 x} (\sin^{-1}\sqrt{t})\, dt + \int_{1/8}^{\cos^2 x} (\cos^{-1}\sqrt{t})\, dt \; (0 \leq x \leq \pi/2)$ and the curve satisfying the differential equation $y(x + y^3)\, dx = x(y^3 - x)\, dy$ passing through $(4, -2)$.

59. Let T be an acute triangle. Inscribe a pair R, S of rectangles in T as shown :

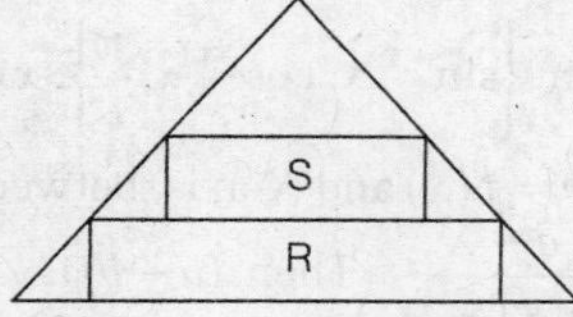

Let $A(x)$ denote the area of polygon X find the maximum value (or show that no maximum exists), of $\dfrac{A(R) + A(S)}{A(T)}$, where T ranges over all triangles and R, S over all rectangles as above.

60. Find the maximum area of the ellipse that can be inscribed in an isosceles triangles of area A and having one axis lying along the perpendicular from the vertex of the triangles to its base.

61. In the adjacent figure the graphs of two function $y = f(x)$ and $y = \sin x$ are given. $y = \sin x$ intersects, $y = f(x)$ at $A(a, f(a))$; $B(\pi, 0)$ and $C(2\pi, 0)$.

A_i $(i = 1, 2, 3)$ is the area bounded by the curves $y = f(x)$ and $y = \sin x$. between $x = 0$ and $x = a$; $i = 1$

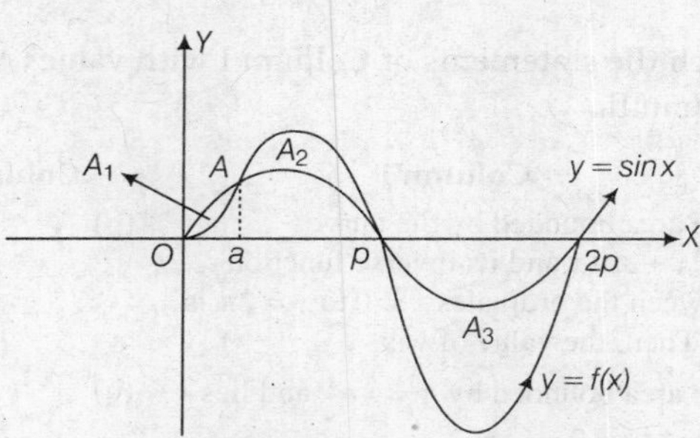

between $x = a$ and $x = \pi$; $i = 2$ between $x = \pi$ and $x = 2\pi$; $i = 3$. If $A_1 = 1 - \sin a + (a-1)\cos a$, determine the function $f(x)$. Hence, determine a and A_1. Also, calculate A_2 and A_3.

62. Find the area of the region bounded by curve $y = 25^x + 16$ and the curve $y = b \cdot 5^x + 4$, whose tangent at the point $x = 1$ make an angle $\tan^{-1}(40 \ln 5)$ with the X-axis.

63. If the circles of the maximum area inscribed in the region bounded by the curves $y = x^2 - x - 3$ and $y = 3 + 2x - x^2$, then the area of region $y - x^2 + 2x + 3 \leq 0$, $y + x^2 - 2x - 3 \leq 0$ and $s \leq 0$.

64. Find limit of the ratio of the area of the triangle formed by the origin and intersection points of the parabola $y = 4x^2$ and the line $y = a^2$, to the area between the parabola and the line as a approaches to zero.

65. Find the area of curve enclosed by : $|x + y| + |x - y| \leq 4$, $|x| \leq 1$, $y \geq \sqrt{x^2 - 2x + 1}$.

66. Calculate the area enclosed by the curve $4 \leq x^2 + y^2 \leq 2(|x| + |y|)$.

67. Find the area enclosed by the curve $[x] + [y] = 4$ in 1st quadrant (where [.] denotes greatest integer function).

68. Sketch the region and find the area bounded by the curves $|y + x| \leq 1$, $|y - x| \leq 1$ and $2x^2 + 2y^2 = 1$.

69. Find the area of the region bounded by the curve, $2^{|x|}|y| + 2^{|x|-1} \leq 1$, with in the square formed by the lines $|x| \leq 1/2$, $|y| \leq 1/2$.

70. Find all the values of the parameter $a\,(a \leq 1)$ for which the area of the figure bounded by the pair of straight lines $y^2 - 3y + 2 = 0$ and the curves $y = [a]x^2$, $y = \frac{1}{2}[a]x^2$ is the greatest, where [.] denotes greatest integer function.

71. If $f(x)$ is positive for all positive values of X and $f'(x) < 0$, $f''(x) > 0$, $\forall x \in R^+$, prove that $\frac{1}{2} f(1) + \int_1^n f(x)\, dx < \sum_{r=1}^{n} f(r) < \int_1^n f(x)\, dx + f(1)$.

Area of Bounded Regions Exercise 8 : Questions Asked in Previous 10 Years' Exams

(i) JEE Advanced & IIT-JEE

72. Area of the region $\{(x, y)\} \in R^2 : y \geq \sqrt{|x+3|}, 5y \leq (x+9) \leq 15\}$ is equal to **[Single Correct Option 2016]**

(a) $\frac{1}{6}$ (b) $\frac{4}{3}$ (c) $\frac{3}{2}$ (d) $\frac{5}{3}$

73. Let $F(x) = \int_x^{x^2 + \frac{\pi}{6}} 2\cos^2 t \, dt$ for all $x \in R$ and $f : \left[0, \frac{1}{2}\right] \to [0, \infty)$ be a continuous function. For $a \in \left[0, \frac{1}{2}\right]$, if $F'(a) + 2$ is the area of the region bounded by $x = 0, y = 0, y = f(x)$ and $x = a$, then $f(0)$ is **[Integer Answer Type 2015]**

74. The common tangents to the circle $x^2 + y^2 = 2$ and the parabola $y^2 = 8x$ touch the circle at the points P, Q and the parabola at the points R, S. Then, the area (in sq units) of the quadrilateral $PQRS$ is **[Single Correct Option 2014]**

(a) 3 (b) 6 (c) 9 (d) 15

75. The area enclosed by the curves $y = \sin x + \cos x$ and $y = |\cos x - \sin x|$ over the interval $\left[0, \frac{\pi}{2}\right]$ is **[Single Correct Option 2014]**

(a) $4(\sqrt{2}-1)$ (b) $2\sqrt{2}(\sqrt{2}-1)$

(c) $2(\sqrt{2}+1)$ (d) $2\sqrt{2}(\sqrt{2}+1)$

76. If S be the area of the region enclosed by $y = e^{-x^2}$, $y = 0$, $x = 0$ and $x = 1$. Then, **[More than One Option Correct 2012]**

(a) $S \geq \frac{1}{e}$ (b) $S \geq 1 - \frac{1}{e}$

(c) $S \leq \frac{1}{4}\left(1 + \frac{1}{\sqrt{e}}\right)$ (d) $S \leq \frac{1}{\sqrt{2}} + \frac{1}{\sqrt{e}}\left(1 - \frac{1}{\sqrt{2}}\right)$

77. Let $f : [-1, 2] \to [0, \infty)$ be a continuous function such that $f(x) = f(1-x), \forall x \in [-1, 2]$. If $R_1 = \int_{-1}^{2} x f(x)\, dx$ and R_2 are the area of the region bounded by $y = f(x)$, $x = -1, x = 2$ and the X-axis. Then, **[Single Correct Option 2011]**

(a) $R_1 = 2R_2$ (b) $R_1 = 3R_2$ (c) $2R_1 = R_2$ (d) $3R_1 = R_2$

78. If the straight line $x = b$ divide the area enclosed by $y = (1-x)^2, y = 0$ and $x = 0$ into two parts $R_1 (0 \leq x \leq b)$ and $R_2 (b \leq x \leq 1)$ such that $R_1 - R_2 = \frac{1}{4}$. Then, b equals to **[Single Correct Option 2011]**

(a) $\frac{3}{4}$ (b) $\frac{1}{2}$ (c) $\frac{1}{3}$ (d) $\frac{1}{4}$

79. Area of the region bounded by the curve $y = e^x$ and lines $x = 0$ and $y = e$ is **[More than One Option Correct 2009]**

(a) $e - 1$ (b) $\int_1^e \ln(e + 1 - y)\, dy$

(c) $e - \int_0^1 e^x\, dx$ (d) $\int_1^e \ln y\, dy$

80. The area of the region between the curves $y = \sqrt{\frac{1+\sin x}{\cos x}}$ and $y = \sqrt{\frac{1-\sin x}{\cos x}}$ and bounded by the lines $x = 0$ and $x = \frac{\pi}{4}$ is **[Single Correct Option 2008]**

(a) $\int_0^{\sqrt{2}-1} \frac{t}{(1+t^2)\sqrt{1-t^2}}\, dt$ (b) $\int_0^{\sqrt{2}-1} \frac{4t}{(1+t^2)\sqrt{1-t^2}}\, dt$

(c) $\int_0^{\sqrt{2}+1} \frac{4t}{(1+t^2)\sqrt{1-t^2}}\, dt$ (d) $\int_0^{\sqrt{2}+1} \frac{t}{(1+t^2)\sqrt{1-t^2}}\, dt$

■ **Directions** (Q. Nos. 81 to 83) Consider the functions defined implicity by the equation $y^3 - 3y + x = 0$ on various intervals in the real line. If $x \in (-\infty, -2) \cup (2, \infty)$, the equation implicitly defines a unique real-valued differentiable function $y = f(x)$. If $x \in (-2, 2)$, the equation implicitly defines a unique real-valued differentiable function $y = g(x)$, satisfying $g(0) = 0$. **[Passage Based Questions 2008]**

81. If $f(-10\sqrt{2}) = 2\sqrt{2}$, then $f''(-10\sqrt{2})$ is equal to

(a) $\frac{4\sqrt{2}}{7^3 3^2}$ (b) $-\frac{4\sqrt{2}}{7^3 3^2}$

(c) $\frac{4\sqrt{2}}{7^3 3}$ (d) $-\frac{4\sqrt{2}}{7^3 3}$

82. The area of the region bounded by the curve $y = f(x)$, the X-axis and the lines $x = a$ and $x = b$, where $-\infty < a < b < -2$, is

(a) $\int_a^b \frac{x}{3[\{f(x)\}^2 - 1]}\, dx + bf(b) - af(a)$

(b) $-\int_a^b \frac{x}{3[\{f(x)\}^2 - 1]}\, dx + bf(b) - af(a)$

(c) $\int_a^b \frac{x}{3[\{f(x)\}^2 - 1]}\, dx - bf(b) + af(a)$

(d) $-\int_a^b \frac{x}{3[\{f(x)\}^2 - 1]}\, dx - bf(b) + af(a)$

83. $\int_{-1}^{1} g'(x)\, dx$ is equal to

(a) $2g(-1)$ (b) 0 (c) $-2g(1)$ (d) $2g(1)$

(ii) JEE Main & AIEEE

84. The area (in sq. units) of the region $\{(x, y) : x \geq 0, x + y \leq 3, x^2 \leq 4y\}$ and $y \leq 1 + \sqrt{x}\}$ is **[2017 JEE Main]**

(a) $\frac{5}{2}$ (b) $\frac{59}{12}$ (c) $\frac{3}{2}$ (d) $\frac{7}{3}$

85. The area (in sq units) of the region $\{(x, y) : y^2 \geq 2x$ and $x^2 + y^2 \leq 4x, x \geq 0, y \geq 0\}$ is **[2016 JEE Main]**

(a) $\pi - \frac{4}{3}$ (b) $\pi - \frac{8}{3}$

(c) $\pi - \frac{4\sqrt{2}}{3}$ (d) $\frac{\pi}{2} - \frac{2\sqrt{2}}{3}$

86. The area (in sq units) of the region described by $\{(x, y) : y^2 \leq 2x$ and $y \geq 4x - 1\}$ is **[2015 JEE Main]**

(a) $\frac{7}{32}$ (b) $\frac{5}{64}$

(c) $\frac{15}{64}$ (d) $\frac{9}{32}$

87. The area (in sq units) of the quadrilateral formed by the tangents at the end points of the latusrectum to the ellipse $\frac{x^2}{9} + \frac{y^2}{5} = 1$ is **[2015 JEE Main]**

(a) $\frac{27}{4}$ (b) 18

(c) $\frac{27}{2}$ (d) 27

88. The area of the region described by $A = \{(x, y) : x^2 + y^2 \leq 1$ and $y^2 \leq 1 - x\}$ is **[2014 JEE Main]**

(a) $\frac{\pi}{2} + \frac{4}{3}$ (b) $\frac{\pi}{2} - \frac{4}{3}$

(c) $\frac{\pi}{2} - \frac{2}{3}$ (d) $\frac{\pi}{2} + \frac{2}{3}$

89. The area (in sq units) bounded by the curves $y = \sqrt{x}$, $2y - x + 3 = 0$, X-axis and lying in the first quadrant is **[2013 JEE Main]**

(a) 9 (b) 36

(c) 18 (d) $\frac{27}{4}$

90. The area bounded between the parabolas $x^2 = \frac{y}{4}$ and $x^2 = 9y$ and the straight line $y = 2$ is **[2012 AIEEE]**

(a) $20\sqrt{2}$ (b) $\frac{10\sqrt{2}}{3}$

(c) $\frac{20\sqrt{2}}{3}$ (d) $10\sqrt{2}$

91. The area of the region enclosed by the curves $y = x$, $x = e$, $y = \frac{1}{x}$ and the positive X-axis is **[2011 AIEEE]**

(a) 1 sq unit (b) $\frac{3}{2}$ sq units

(c) $\frac{5}{2}$ sq units (d) $\frac{1}{2}$ sq unit

92. The area bounded by the curves $y = \cos x$ and $y = \sin x$ between the ordinates $x = 0$ and $x = \frac{3\pi}{2}$ is **[2010 AIEEE]**

(a) $(4\sqrt{2} - 2)$ sq units (b) $(4\sqrt{2} + 2)$ sq units

(c) $(4\sqrt{2} - 1)$ sq units (d) $(4\sqrt{2} + 1)$ sq units

93. The area of the region bounded by the parabola $(y - 2)^2 = x - 1$, the tangent to the parabola at the point $(2, 3)$ and the X-axis is **[2009 AIEEE]**

(a) 6 sq units (b) 9 sq units

(c) 12 sq units (d) 3 sq units

94. The area of the plane region bounded by the curves $x + 2y^2 = 0$ and $x + 3y^2 = 1$ is equal to **[2008 AIEEE]**

(a) $\frac{5}{3}$ sq units (b) $\frac{1}{3}$ sq unit

(c) $\frac{2}{3}$ sq unit (d) $\frac{4}{3}$ sq units

Answers

Exercise for Session 1

1. 1 sq unit **2.** $\frac{436}{15}$ sq units **3.** $\frac{4}{3}$ sq units

4. $\frac{4}{3}$ sq units **5.** $\frac{28}{3}$ sq units **6.** $\frac{56}{3}a^2$ sq units

7. $\frac{8}{3}a^2$ sq units **8.** 2z sq units **9.** $\frac{28}{3}$ sq units

10. $3+16\log 2$ sq units

Exercise for Session 2

1. (d) **2.** (a) **3.** (c) **4.** (d) **5.** (a)
6. (b) **7.** (a) **8.** (a) **9.** (c) **10.** (b)
11. (d) **12.** (b) **13.** (a) **14.** (c) **15.** (b)
16. (a) **17.** (c) **18.** (a) **19.** (a) **20.** (b)

Chapter Exercises

1. (d) **2.** (b) **3.** (b) **4.** (c) **5.** (b)
6. (c) **7.** (d) **8.** (a) **9.** (b) **10.** (b)
11. (b) **12.** (b) **13.** (c) **14.** (d) **15.** (a)
16. (a) **17.** (a) **18.** (a) **19.** (c) **20.** (b)
21. (a) **22.** (b) **23.** (d) **24.** (c) **25.** (b, c)
26. (a, b, d) **27.** (a, d) **28.** (a, d) **29.** (a, c)
30. (d) **31.** (c) **32.** (d) **33.** (b) **34.** (c)
35. (a) **36.** (b) **37.** (a) **38.** (a) **39.** (a)
40. (b) **41.** (c) **42.** (b) **43.** (a)

44. (A) → (p); (B) → (p); (C) → (r); (D) → (s)

45. (A) → (p); (B) → (p); (C) → (r); (D) → (r)

46. (7) **47.** (1) **48.** (4) **49.** (7)
50. (8) **51.** (5) **52.** (3)

53. $3e$ sq units **54.** $f(x)=\frac{1}{k+1}[x^4-kx^3+(2k-4)x^2]$

55. $g(x)=\begin{cases}-x-1, & x\le -5/2\\ 4+x, & -5/2<x\le -2\\ 2, & -2<x\le -1\\ 1-x, & -1<x\le -1/2\\ 1+x, & x>-1/2\end{cases}$

and area $=\frac{101}{4}$ sq units

56. $\left[2+\log\left(\frac{4}{3\sqrt{3}}\right)-\frac{1}{e}\right]$ sq units

57. $\left(\pi-\frac{2}{3}\right)$ sq units **58.** $\frac{1}{8}\left(\frac{3\pi}{16}\right)^4$ sq units

59. Required maximum ratio $=\frac{2}{3}$

60. $(A)_{\max}=\frac{\sqrt{3}\,\pi A}{9}$ sq units

61. $A_1=1-\sin 1,\ A_2=\pi-1-\sin 1,\ A_3=3\pi-2$

62. $4\log_5\left(\frac{e^4}{27}\right)$ sq units

63. $4\left(\frac{16}{3}-4\pi\right)$ sq units

64. $\frac{3}{2}$ **65.** 2 sq units

66. 8 sq units **67.** 5 sq units

68. $\left(2-\frac{\pi}{2}\right)$ sq units

69. $\left[\frac{4}{\log 2}(1-2^{-1/2})-1\right]$ sq units

70. $a\in[1,2)$ **72.** (c) **73.** (3) **74.** (d) **75.** (b)
76. (b,d) **77.** (c) **78.** (b) **79.** (b,c,d) **80.** (b) **81.** (b)
82. (a) **83.** (d) **84.** (a) **85.** (b) **86.** (d) **87.** (d)
88. (a) **89.** (a) **90.** (c) **91.** (b) **92.** (a) **93.** (b)
94. (d)

Solutions

1. Here, $[x+y]=[x]-1$

when $x \in [0, 1) \Rightarrow [x+y] = -1$

$$-1 \le x+y < 0 \quad \text{...(i)}$$

when $x \in [1, 2) \Rightarrow [x+y] = 0$

$$\therefore \quad 0 \le x+y < 1 \quad \text{...(ii)}$$

which can be shown, as

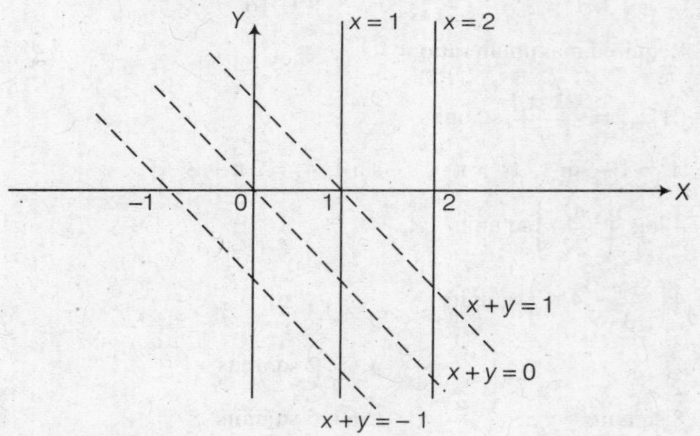

$\therefore$ Required area = 2

2. Required area $= 2\int_0^{1/2} f^{-1}(x)\,dx$

Let, $f^{-1}(x) = t \Rightarrow x = f(t)$

$dx = f'(t)dt$

$$\therefore \quad A = 2\int_0^1 (t \cdot f'(t))dt$$

$$= 2\left[\left(t \cdot f(t)\right)_0^1 - \int_0^1 1 \cdot f(t)dt\right]$$

$$= 2\left[f(1) - \int_0^1 \frac{t}{1+t^2}\,dt\right]$$

$$= 2\left[f(1) - \frac{1}{2}\left(\log(1+t^2)\right)_0^1\right]$$

$$= 2\left[f(1) - \frac{1}{2}\log 2\right]$$

$$= 2\left[\frac{1}{2} - \frac{1}{2}\log 2\right] = 1 - \log 2 = \log\left(\frac{e}{2}\right)$$

3. Here, $E_1 : \dfrac{\left(\dfrac{x+y-1}{\sqrt{2}}\right)^2}{12} + \dfrac{\left(\dfrac{x-y+3}{\sqrt{2}}\right)^2}{(\sqrt{2})^2} = 1$

Length of latusrectum $= 2\dfrac{a^2}{b} = \dfrac{2}{\sqrt{2}} = \sqrt{2}$

Now, $\dfrac{2p^2}{\sqrt{p}} = \sqrt{2} \Rightarrow p^{3/2} = 2^{-1//2}$

$$\Rightarrow \quad P = 2^{-1/3}$$

$$\therefore \quad E_2 : \frac{x^2}{2^{-1/3}} + \frac{y^2}{4^{-1/3}} = 1$$

Area of ellipse E_2, is

$$\pi \cdot \sqrt{p} \cdot p = \pi\, p^{3/2} = \frac{\pi}{\sqrt{2}}$$

4. Area of bounded region by $4|x - 2017^{2017}| + 5|y - 2017^{2017}| \le 20$, is same as area of the region bounded by $4|x| + 5|y| \le 20$.

$$\Rightarrow \quad 4 \times \frac{1}{2} \times 4 \times 5 = 40$$

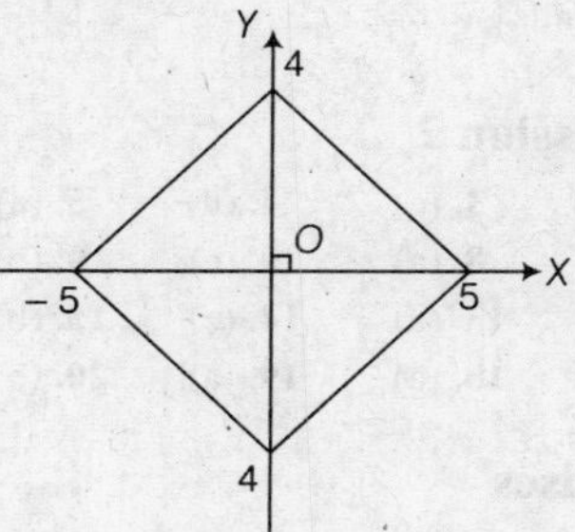

5. Here, $y = x^2 + 1$ and $y = \sqrt{x-1}$ are inverse of each other.

The shaded area is given K units

$\Rightarrow$ Area of the region bounded by $y = x^2 + 1$, $y = \sqrt{x-1}$ and $(x+y-1)(x+y-3) = 0$, is $2K$ units.

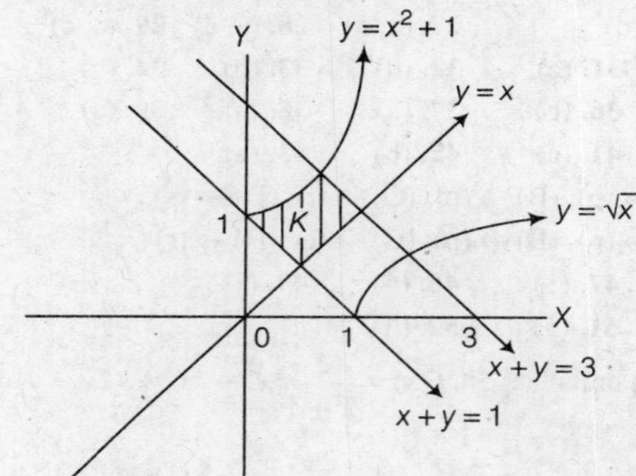

6. Given, $\int_0^4 f(x)\,dx - \int_0^4 g(x)\,dx = 10$

$$(A_1 + A_3 + A_4) - (A_2 + A_3 + A_4) = 10$$

$$A_1 - A_2 = 10 \quad \text{...(i)}$$

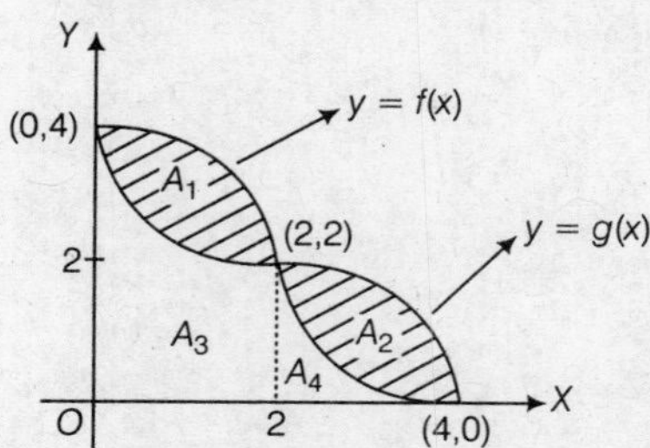

Again, $\int_2^4 g(x)\,dx - \int_2^4 f(x)\,dx = 5$

$$(A_2 + A_4) - A_4 = 5$$

$$A_2 = 5 \quad \text{...(ii)}$$

Adding Eqs. (i) and (ii),

$$A_1 = 15$$

7. Solving, $e^x = e^{a-x}$, we get $e^{2x} = e^a \Rightarrow x = \frac{a}{2}$

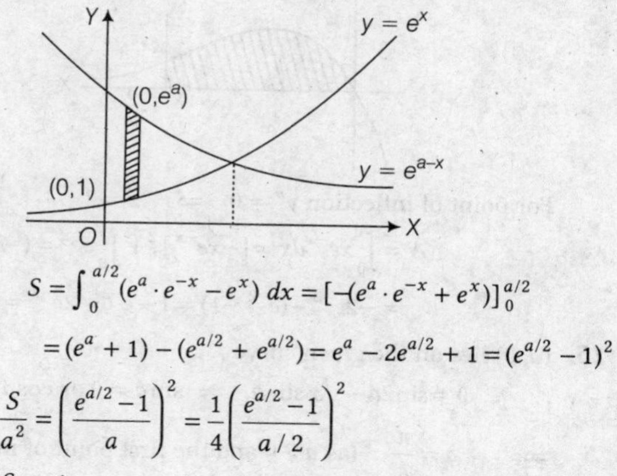

$$S = \int_0^{a/2} (e^a \cdot e^{-x} - e^x)\, dx = [-(e^a \cdot e^{-x} + e^x)]_0^{a/2}$$

$$= (e^a + 1) - (e^{a/2} + e^{a/2}) = e^a - 2e^{a/2} + 1 = (e^{a/2} - 1)^2$$

$$\therefore \quad \frac{S}{a^2} = \left(\frac{e^{a/2} - 1}{a}\right)^2 = \frac{1}{4}\left(\frac{e^{a/2} - 1}{a/2}\right)^2$$

$$\therefore \quad \lim_{a \to 0} \frac{S}{a^2} = \frac{1}{4}$$

8. $m_{PQ} = \frac{a^2 - b^2}{a + b} = a - b$ equation of PQ

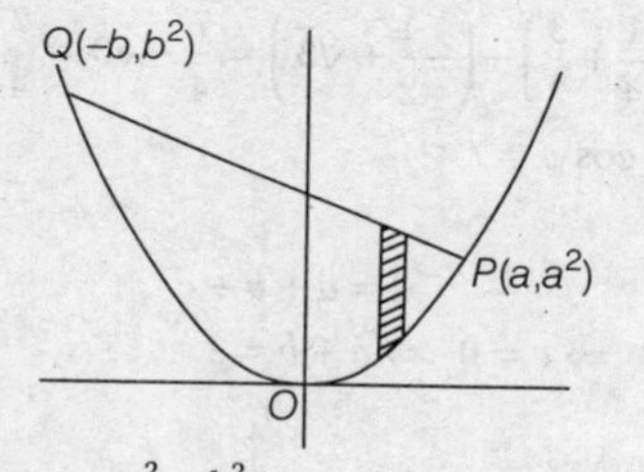

$$y - a^2 = \frac{a^2 - b^2}{a + b}(x - a) \quad \text{or} \quad y - a^2 = (a - b)(x - a)$$

$$y = a^2 + x(a - b) - a^2 + ab$$

$$y = (a - b)x + ab$$

$$\therefore \quad S_1 = \int_{-b}^{a} ((a - b)x + ab - x^2)\, dx$$

which simplifies to $\frac{(a + b)^3}{6}$. ...(i)

Also, $S_2 = \frac{1}{2}\begin{vmatrix} a & a^2 & 1 \\ -b & b^2 & 1 \\ 0 & 0 & 1 \end{vmatrix} = \frac{1}{2}[ab^2 + a^2 b] = \frac{1}{2} ab\,(a + b)$ ...(ii)

$$\therefore \quad \frac{S_1}{S_2} = \frac{(a + b)^3}{6} \cdot \frac{2}{ab\,(a + b)} = \frac{(a + b)^2}{3ab} = \frac{1}{3}\left[\frac{a}{b} + \frac{b}{a} + 2\right]$$

$$\therefore \quad \left.\frac{S_1}{S_2}\right|_{\min} = \frac{4}{3}$$

9. $y = \ln^2 x - 1 \Rightarrow y' = \frac{2 \ln x}{x} = 0 \quad \Rightarrow \quad x = 1$

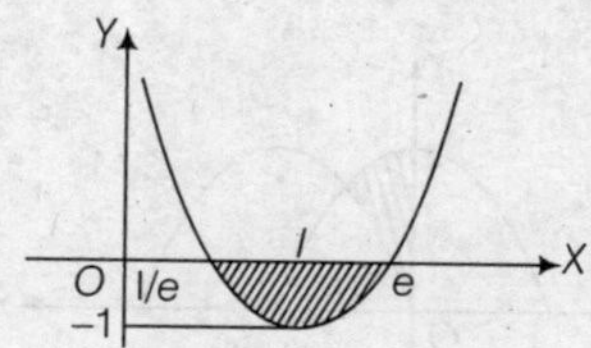

$x > 1$, y increasing and $0 < x < 1$, y is decreasing

$$A = \left| \int_{1/e}^{e} (\ln^2 x - 1)\, dx \right|$$

$$= \left| \int_{1/e}^{e} \ln^2 x\, dx - \int_{1/e}^{e} dx \right|$$

$$= \left| [x \ln^2 x]_{1/e}^{e} - 2\int_{1/e}^{e} \left(\frac{\ln x}{x}\right) \cdot x\, dx - \left(e - \frac{1}{e}\right) \right|$$

$$= \left| \left(e - \frac{1}{e}\right) - 2\int_{1/e}^{e} \left(\frac{\ln x}{x}\right) \cdot x\, dx - \left(e - \frac{1}{e}\right) \right|$$

$$= \left| -2\left[[x \ln x]_{1/e}^{e} - \int_{1/e}^{e} dx \right] \right|$$

$$= \left| -2\left[\left(e + \frac{1}{e}\right) - \left(e - \frac{1}{e}\right)\right] \right| = \left|\frac{4}{e}\right| = \frac{4}{e}$$

10. $y = \begin{cases} 2 - (2 - x), \text{ if } x \le 2 = x \\ 2 - (x - 2), \text{ if } x \ge 2 = 4 - x \end{cases} = \begin{cases} x, \text{ if } x \le 2 \\ 4 - x, \text{ if } x \ge 2 \end{cases}$

Also, $y = \begin{cases} \frac{3}{x}, \text{ if } x > 0 \\ -\frac{3}{x}, \text{ if } x < 0 \end{cases}$

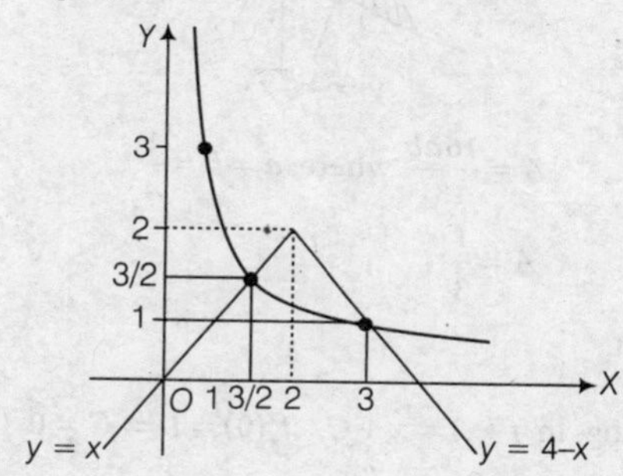

$$A = \int_{3/2}^{2} \left(x - \frac{3}{x}\right) dx + \int_{2}^{3} \left((4 - x) - \frac{3}{x}\right) dx$$

$$= \left[\frac{x^2}{2} - 3 \ln x\right]_{3/2}^{2} + \left[4x - \frac{x^2}{2} - 3 \ln x\right]_{2}^{3}$$

$$= \left[2 - 3 \ln 2 - \left(\frac{9}{8} - 3 \ln \frac{3}{2}\right)\right] + \left[12 - \frac{9}{2} - 3 \ln 3 - (8 - 2 - \ln 2)\right]$$

$$= \frac{7}{8} - 3 \ln 2 + 3 \ln 3 - 3 \ln 2 + \frac{3}{2} - 3 \ln 3 + 3 \ln 2 = \frac{19}{8} - 3 \ln 2$$

11. Given, $g(x) = 2x + 1$; $h(x) = (2x + 1)^2 + 4$

Now, $h(x) = f[g(x)]$

$$(2x + 1)^2 + 4 = f(2x + 1)$$

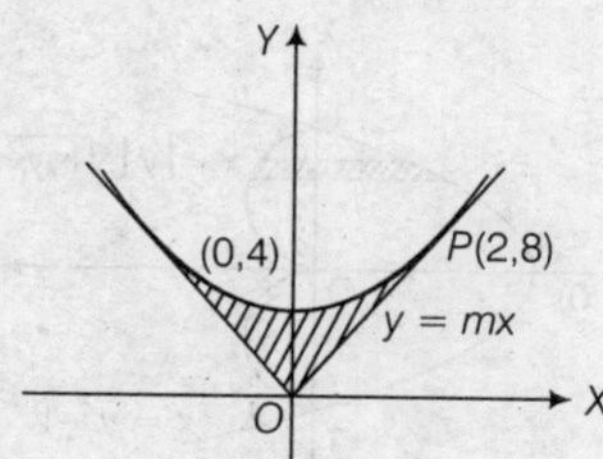

Let $2x+1=t \Rightarrow f(t)=t^2+4$

$\therefore \quad f(x)=x^2+4$ ...(i)

Solving, $y=mx$ and $y=x^2+4$

$x^2-mx+4=0$

Put $D=0$; $m^2=16 \Rightarrow m=\pm 4$

Tangents are $y=4x$ and $y=-4x$

$$A=2\int_0^2[(x^2+4)-4x]\,dx=2\int_0^2(x-2)^2dx$$

$$=\left[\frac{2}{3}(x-2)^3\right]_0^2=\frac{16}{3} \text{ sq units}$$

12. $y=-\sqrt{-x} \Rightarrow y^2=-x$, where x and y both negative

$x=-\sqrt{-y} \Rightarrow x^2=-y$, where x and y both negative

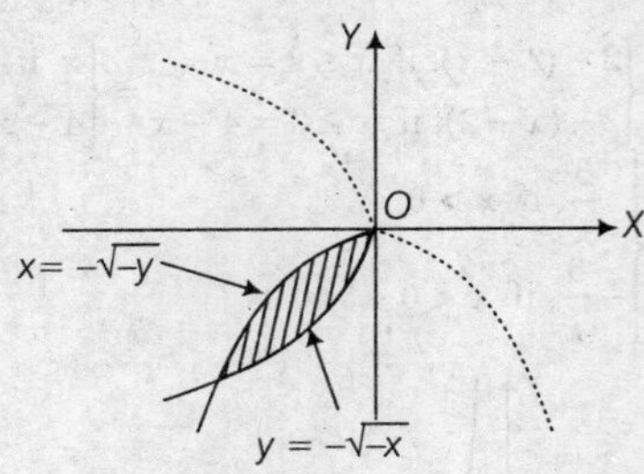

Since, $A=\dfrac{16ab}{3}$ where, $a=b=\dfrac{1}{4}$

$\therefore \quad A=\dfrac{1}{3}$

13. $\dfrac{f''(x)}{f'(x)}=1.$

Integrating, $\ln f'(x)=x+C,\ f'(0)=1 \Rightarrow C=0$

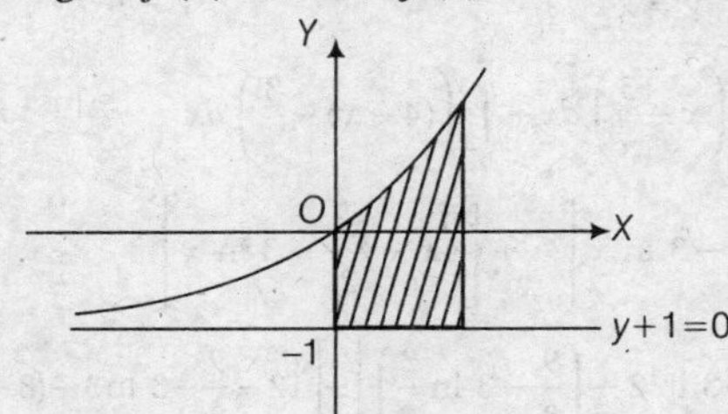

$f'(x)=e^x f(x)=e^x+k,\ f(0)=0 \Rightarrow k=-1$

$f(x)=e^x-1$

$$\text{Area}=\int_0^1(e^x-1+1)\,dx=[e^x]_0^1=e-1$$

14. $A=2\int_0^1[y\sqrt{1-y^2}-(y^2-1)]\,dy=2$

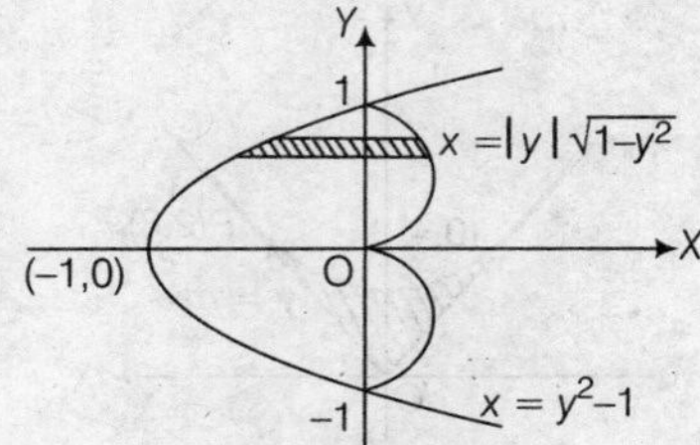

15. $y=xe^{-x}$

$y'=e^{-x}-xe^{-x}=(1-x)e^{-x}$ increasing for $x<1$

$y''=-e^x-[e^{-x}-xe^{-x}]=e^{-x}[-1-1+x]=(x-2)e^{-x}$

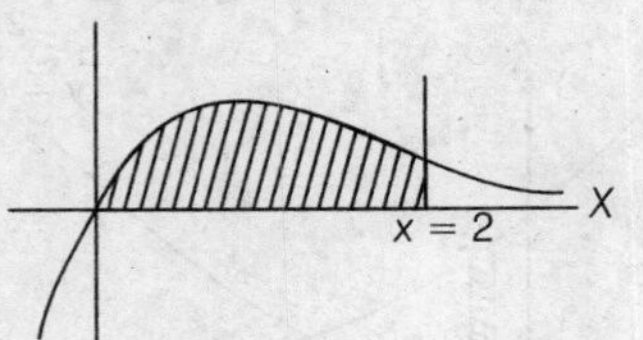

For point of inflection $y''=0 \Rightarrow x=2$

$$A=\int_0^2 xe^{-x}dx=[-xe^{-x}]_0^2+\int_0^2 e^{-x}=(-2e^{-2})-(e^{-x})_0^2$$

$$=-2e^{-2}-(e^{-2}-1)=1-e^{-2}-2e^{-2}=1-3e^{-2}$$

16. $(a, 0)$ lies on the given curve

$\therefore \quad 0=\sin 2a-\sqrt{3}\sin a \Rightarrow \sin a=0$ or $\cos a=\sqrt{3}/2$

$\Rightarrow \quad a=\dfrac{\pi}{6}$ (as $a>0$ and the first point of intersection with positive X-axis)

and $A=\displaystyle\int_0^{\pi/6}(\sin 2x-\sqrt{3}\sin x)\,dx=\left(-\frac{\cos 2x}{2}+\sqrt{3}\cos x\right)_0^{\pi/6}$

$$=\left(-\frac{1}{4}+\frac{3}{2}\right)-\left(-\frac{1}{2}+\sqrt{3}\right)=\frac{7}{4}-\sqrt{3}=\frac{7}{4}-2\cos a$$

$\Rightarrow \quad 4A+8\cos a=7$

17. $x=1;\ y=2$

$2=a+b+c$ ...(i)

$x=0,\ y=0 \Rightarrow c=0 \Rightarrow a+b=2$

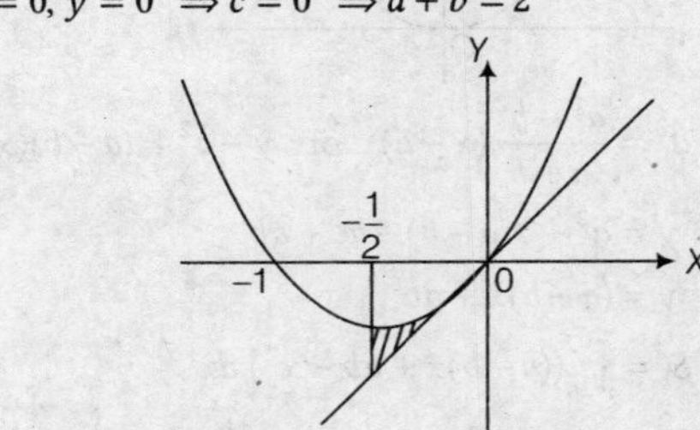

Now, $\left.\dfrac{dy}{dx}\right|_{(0,0)}=2a\,x+b=1$

$\therefore \quad b=1,\ a=1$

Hence, the curve is $y=x^2+x$

$$A=\int_{-\frac{1}{2}}^0(x^2+x-x)\,dx=\int_{-\frac{1}{2}}^0(x^2)\,dx=\frac{1}{24} \text{ sq units}$$

18. $\text{IF}=e^{-x}$

$\therefore\ ye^{-x}=\int e^{-x}(\cos x-\sin x)\,dx$. Put $-x=t$

$$=-\int e^t(\cos t+\sin t)\,dt=-e^t\sin t+C$$

$ye^{-x}=e^{-x}\sin x+C$

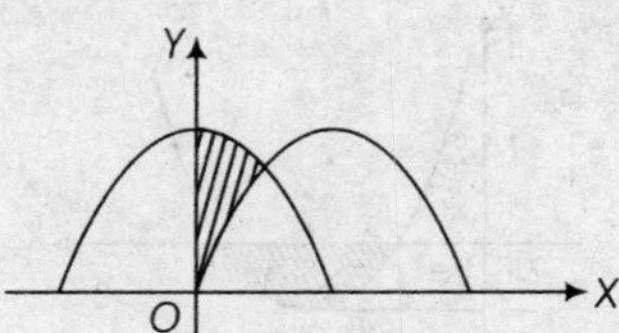

Since, y is bounded when $x\to\infty \Rightarrow C=0$

$\therefore \quad y = \sin x$

$$\text{Area} = \int_0^{\pi/4} (\cos x - \sin x)\, dx = \sqrt{2} - 1$$

19. $I = \int (6x - 3x^2)\, dx = \frac{6x^2}{2} - \frac{3x^3}{3} = 3x^2 - x^3 = x^2(3 - x)$

$A_1 = I(2) - I(1) = 4 - 2 = 2$ units

$A_2 = I(2) - I(3) = 4 - 0 = 4$ units

$A_3 = I(3) - I(4) = 0 - (-16) = 16$ units

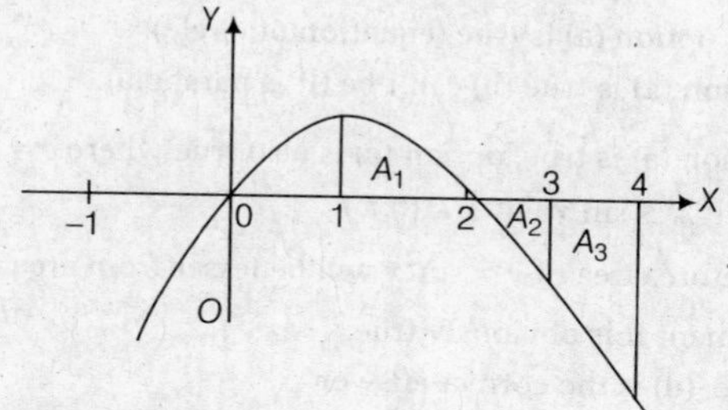

$\Rightarrow$ One value of a will lie in (3, 4).

Using symmetry, other will lie in (–2, –1).

20. Required area, $A = \int_{\pi}^{2\pi} ((\sin x - x) + 2\pi)\, dx$

$$= \frac{\pi^2}{2} - 2 \text{ sq units}$$

21. $g(x) = | f(|x|) - 2 | = || x | - 1 - 2 | = || x | - 3 |$

$$= \begin{cases} (|x| - 3), & x < -3 \\ -(|x| - 3), & -3 \le x < 3 \\ |x| - 3 & x \ge 3 \end{cases} = \begin{cases} -x - 3, & x < -3 \\ -(-x - 3), & -3 \le x < 0 \\ -(x - 3), & 0 \le x < 3 \\ x - 3, & x \ge 3 \end{cases}$$

$$= \begin{cases} -x - 3, & x < -3 \\ x + 3, & -3 \le x < 0 \\ -x + 3, & 0 \le x < 3 \\ x - 3, & x \ge 3 \end{cases}$$

Now, $\quad x^2 - 4y + 8 = 0$

$\Rightarrow \quad x^2 = 4(y - 2)$

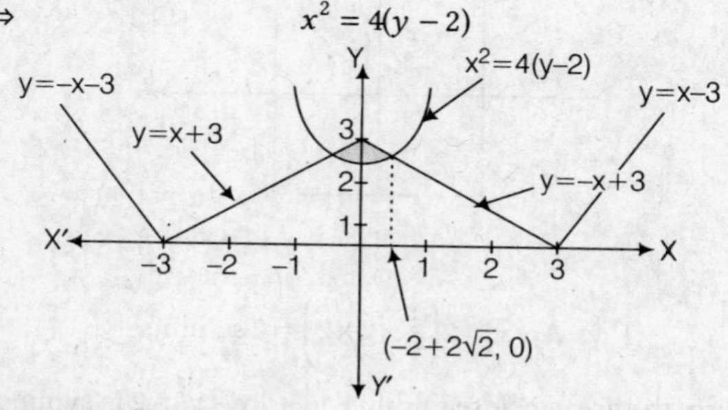

For point of intersection,

$$x^2 - 4(-x + 3) + 8 = 0$$

$\Rightarrow \quad x^2 + 4x - 4 = 0$

$\Rightarrow \quad x = \frac{-4 \pm \sqrt{16 + 16}}{2} = -2 \pm 2\sqrt{2}$

$\therefore$ Point of intersection is at $x = -2 + 2\sqrt{2}$

$\therefore$ Required area $= 2 \int_0^{-2+2\sqrt{2}} \left[(-x + 3) - \left(\frac{x^2 + 8}{4} \right) \right] dx$

$$= \frac{2}{4} \int_0^{-2+2\sqrt{2}} (4 - 4x - x^2)\, dx = \frac{1}{2} \left[4x - 2x^2 - \frac{x^3}{3} \right]_0^{-2+2\sqrt{2}}$$

$$= \frac{1}{6} [12x - 6x^2 - x^3]_0^{-2+2\sqrt{2}}$$

$$= \frac{1}{6} [12(-2 + 2\sqrt{2}) - 6(-2 + 2\sqrt{2})^2 - (-2 + 2\sqrt{2})^3]$$

$$= \frac{1}{6} [-24 + 24\sqrt{2} - 6(4 + 8 - 8\sqrt{2}) - (-8 + 16\sqrt{2}) + 24\sqrt{2} - 48]$$

$$= \frac{1}{6} [-24 + 24\sqrt{2} - 72 + 48\sqrt{2} + 56 - 40\sqrt{2}]$$

$$= \frac{1}{6} [32\sqrt{2} - 40] = \frac{8}{6} (4\sqrt{2} - 5) = \frac{4}{3} (4\sqrt{2} - 5)$$

22. Shaded region represents $S \cap S'$ clearly area enclosed is 2 sq units.

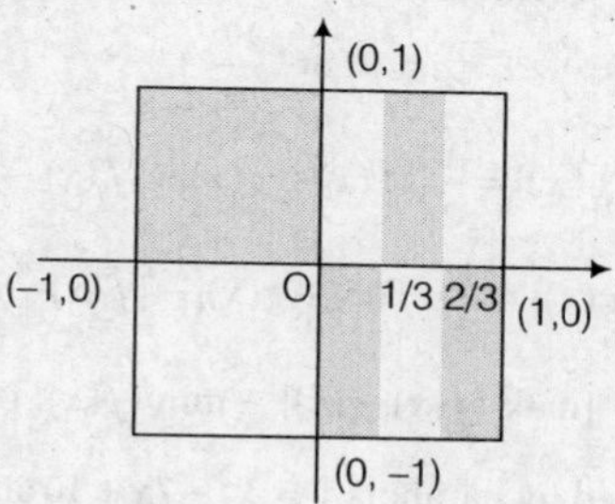

23. Required area is $2 \left[\int_0^{\alpha} ex \ln x\, dx + \int_1^{\alpha} (1 - \sqrt{1 - (x-1)^2})\, dx \right]$

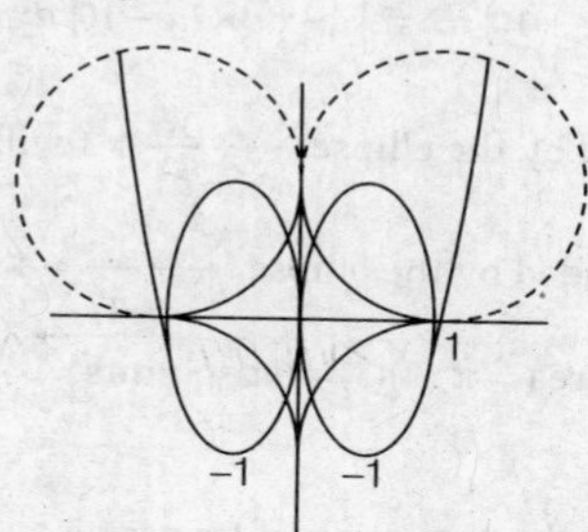

24. $y = \sqrt{2ax - x^2} \Rightarrow (x - a)^2 + y^2 = a^2$

Let $P(h, k)$ be a point, then $BP > PN$

For the bounded condition $BP = PN = k$

Now, $\quad AP = a - k = \sqrt{(h - a)^2 + k^2}$

$\Rightarrow \quad k = h - \frac{h^2}{2a}$

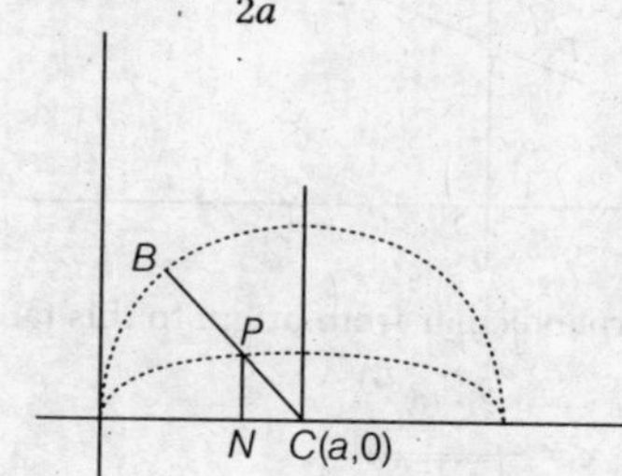

$\therefore$ Boundary of the region is $y = x - \frac{x^2}{2a}$

Required area $= 2\int_0^a \left(x - \frac{x^2}{2a}\right) dx = \frac{2a^2}{3}$

25. $f'(x) = 2x - a$. At (2, 4), $f'(x) = 4 - a$

Equation of normal at (2, 4) is $(y-4) = -\frac{1}{(4-a)}(x-2)$

Let point of intersection with X and Y-axes be A and B respectively, then

$$A \equiv (-4a + 18, 0)\ B \equiv \left(0, \frac{4a-18}{a-4}\right)$$

Since, $a > \frac{9}{2}$ as

$$\therefore \quad \text{Area of triangle} = \frac{1}{2}(4a-18)\frac{(4a-18)}{(a-4)} = 2$$

$$\Rightarrow \quad (4a-17)(a-5) = 0$$

$$\Rightarrow \quad a = 5 \text{ or } \frac{17}{4}$$

26. $\text{Max}\{f(x), g(x)\} = \frac{1}{2}[|f(x) + g(x)| + |f(x) - g(x)|]$

$\text{Min}\{f(x), g(x)\} = \frac{1}{2}[|f(x) + g(x)| - |f(x) - g(x)|]$

$\therefore$ Area $= \int_a^b [\max\{f(x), g(x)\} - \min\{f(x), g(x)\}]\, dx$

27. Area bounded by parabola $y = x^2 - 7x + 10$ and X-axis is given by

$$\int_2^5 |x^2 - 7x + 10|\, dx = \int_2^5 |-x^2 + 7x - 10|\, dx = \frac{9}{2} \text{ sq units}$$

28. Area bounded by the ellipse $\frac{x^2}{a^2} + \frac{y^2}{b^2} = 1$ will be the same as the area bounded by the ellipse $\frac{x^2}{b^2} + \frac{y^2}{a^2} = 1$ and πab

$\therefore$ Required area $= \pi(2)(3) = 6\pi$ sq units

29. $OP = x$

If slope is $\frac{dy}{dx}$, then equation of tangent is

$$Y - t = \frac{dy}{dx}(X - x)$$

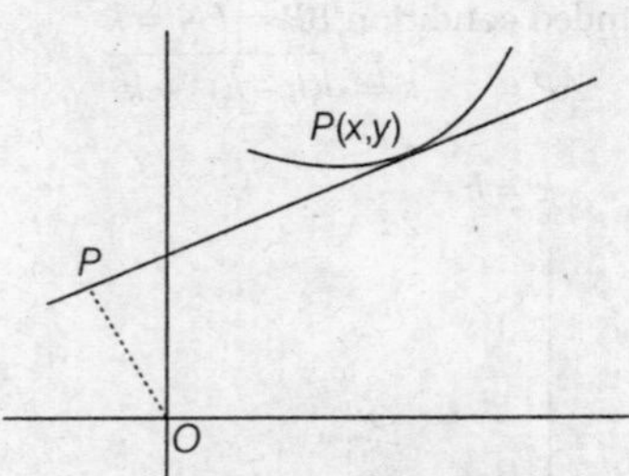

Length of perpendicular from origin to this tangent is

$$x = \frac{Y - x\frac{dy}{dx}}{\sqrt{1 + \left(\frac{dy}{x}\right)^2}}$$

$$x^2\left\{1 + \left(\frac{dy}{dx}\right)^2\right\} = y^2 + x^2\left(\frac{dy}{dx}\right)^2 = 2xy\frac{dy}{dx}$$

$$\Rightarrow \quad \frac{dy}{dx} = -\frac{x^2 - y^2}{2xy} \quad \text{[homogeneous form]}$$

$$\frac{dy}{dx} = \frac{1-x}{y} = \frac{x - x^2}{xy} = \frac{\left[\frac{x^2+y^2}{2}\right] - x^2}{xy} = \frac{y^2 - x^2}{2xy}$$

Since, option (a) is true (equation of circle).
If option (a) is true (b) can't be (It is parabola).

If option (a) is true, option (c) is also true where $c = 1$.

30. $\therefore \sin^2 x \le \sin x$, $\forall\, x \in (0, \pi)$

Therefore, area of $y = \sin^2 x$ will be lesser from area of $y = \sin x$.

Statement II is obviously true.

Hence, (d) is the correct answer.

31. Let the line $y = kx + 2$ cuts $y = x^2 - 3$ at $x = \alpha$ and $\alpha = \beta$, area bounded by the curves $= \int_\alpha^\beta (y_1 - y_2) = \int_\alpha^\beta \{(kx+2) - (x^2 - 3)\}\, dx$

$$\Rightarrow \quad f(x) = \frac{(k^2 + 20)^{3/2}}{6}$$

which clearly, shows the Statement II is false but $f(k)$ is least when $k = 0$.

Hence, (c) is the correct answer.

32. As of region bounded by parabola $y^2 = 4x$ and $x^2 = 4y$ is

$$\int_0^4 \left(2\sqrt{x} - \frac{x^2}{4}\right) dx = \left[\frac{4}{3}x^{3/2} - \frac{x^3}{12}\right]_0^4 = \frac{32}{3} - \frac{16}{3} = \frac{16}{3} \text{ sq units}$$

Hence, Statement I is false.

33. As the area enclosed by $|x| + |y| \le a$ is the area of square (i.e., $2a^2$).

$\therefore$ Area enclosed by $|x + y| + |x - y| \le 2$ is area of square shown as

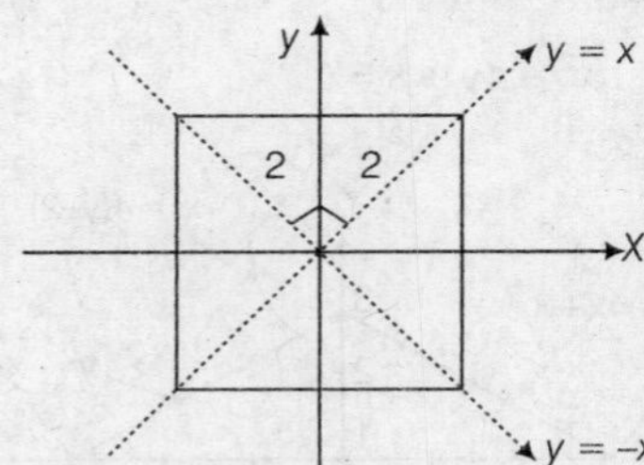

$$\therefore \quad \text{Area} = 4\left(\frac{1}{2} \times 2 \times 2\right) = 8 \text{ sq units}$$

Also, the area enclosed by $|x + y| + |x - y| \le 2$ is symmetric about X-axis, Y-axis, $y = x$ and $y = -x$.

$\therefore$ Both the Statements are true but Statement II is not the correct explanation of Statement I.

34. $\left|\int_a^b \{f(x) - g(x)\}\, dx\right|$ is true for all quadrants.

$\therefore$ Statement II is false.

The area bounded by $y = x(x-1)$ and $y = x(1-x)$.

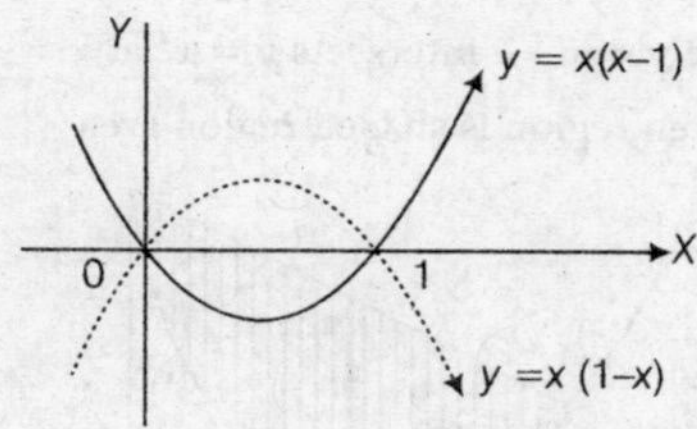

$\therefore$ Area enclosed $= 2\int_0^1 x(1-x)\,dx = 2\left\{\frac{x^2}{2}-\frac{x^3}{3}\right\}_0^1$

$$= 2\left(\frac{1}{2}-\frac{1}{3}\right) = 2\left(\frac{3-2}{6}\right) = \frac{1}{3}$$

35. Since, absolute area

$$= \int_{x_0}^{x_1} h(x)\,dx + \int_{x_1}^{x_2} -h(x)\,dx + \int_{x_2}^{x_3} h(x)\,dx$$

$$= \sum_{r=0}^{n} \int_{x_r}^{x_{r+1}} (-1)^r \cdot h(x)\,dx$$

36. Also, $x_{n+1} = x_3 \Rightarrow n = 2$

37. Required area $= \int_0^1 \sin^4 \pi x\,dx - \int_0^1 \log_e x\,dx = \frac{11}{8}$

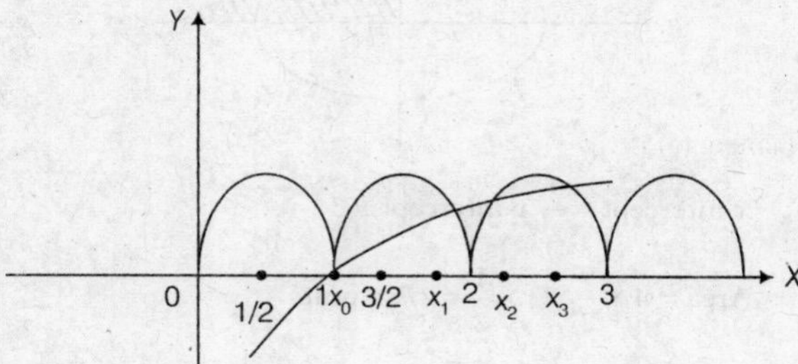

38. $f(x) = \dfrac{x^2 - ax + 1}{x^2 + ax + 1}$

For differentiation, better write $f(x)$ as

$$f(x) = 1 - \frac{2ax}{x^2 + ax + 1}$$

Now, on differentiation $f(x) = \dfrac{2a(x^2-1)}{(x^2+ax+1)^2}$ ...(i)

$$f'(1) = 0 = f'(-1)$$

Then, the options (b) and (d) are eliminated.

Again, for the differentiating Eq. (i) gives

$$(x^2+ax+1)^2 \cdot 2x - (x^2-1)$$

$$f''(x) = 2a \cdot \frac{2(x^2+ax+1)(2x+a)}{(x^2+ax+1)^4}$$

$$f''(-1) = -\frac{4a}{(2-a)^2},\ f''(1) = -\frac{4a}{(2+a)^2}$$

Combining both $f''(1)(2+a)^2 + f''(-1)(2-a)^2 = 0$

39. $f'(x) = 2a\dfrac{(x^2-1)}{(x^2+ax+1)^2} = 2a\dfrac{(x-1)(x+1)}{(x^2+ax+1)^2}$

If is easily seen that $f(x)$ decreases on $(-1,1)$ and has a local minimum at $x = 1$, because the derivatives changes its sign from negative to positive.

40. $\because$ $g'(x) = \dfrac{f'(e^x)e^x}{1+e^{2x}}$

Now, $f'(e^x) = \dfrac{2a\cdot(e^{2x}-1)}{(e^{2x}+ae^x+1)^2}$

It is seen from the above that $f'(e^x)$ and so $g'(x)$ is positive on $(0,\infty)$ and negative on $(-\infty, 0)$.

41. Clearly, $x = a\sin^3 t, y = a\cos^3 t, (0 \le t \le 2\pi)$

$$S = \int_0^{2\pi} a\sin^3 t \cdot a \cdot 3\sin^2 t(-\sin t)\,dt$$

$$= -3a^2 \times \int_0^{\pi/2} \sin^4 t\cos^2 t\,dt$$

$$= -3a^2 \times \frac{\overline{\left|\frac{5}{2}\right.}\,\overline{\left|\frac{3}{2}\right.}}{2\overline{\left|\frac{4+2+2}{2}\right.}} = -3a^2\,\frac{\frac{3}{2}\times\frac{1}{2}\sqrt{\pi}\times\frac{1}{2}\sqrt{\pi}}{2\times3\times2\times1}$$

$$= -\frac{3}{8}\pi a^2 = \frac{3}{8}\pi a^2 \quad \text{[absolute value]}$$

42. $S = -\int_0^{2\pi} a(1-\cos t)a(1-\cos t)\,dt$

$$= -a^2\int_0^{2\pi}(1-2\cos t+\cos^2 t)\,dt$$

$$= -a^2\int_0^{2\pi}\left(1-2\cos t+\left(\frac{1+\cos 2t}{2}\right)\right)dt$$

$$= -\frac{a^2}{2}\int_0^{2\pi}[3-4\cos t+\cos 2t]_0^{2\pi}$$

$$= -3\pi a^2 = 3\pi a^2 \quad \text{[absolute value]}$$

43. $x = \frac{t}{3}(6-t) = \frac{1}{3}(6t-t^2),\ y = \frac{t^2}{8}(6-t) = \frac{1}{8}(6t^2-t^3)$

$\therefore$ Area $= \int_0^6 \frac{t}{3}(6-t)\cdot\frac{1}{8}(12t-13t^2)dt$

$$= \frac{1}{8}\int_0^6 (t^4+24t^2-10t^3)\,dt = \frac{1}{8}\left[\frac{t^5}{5}+8t^3-\frac{5}{2}t^4\right]_0^6$$

$$= \frac{1}{8}\left[\frac{7776}{5}+1728-3240\right] = \frac{216}{5\times8} = \frac{27}{5}\text{ sq units}$$

44. (A) Required area = 4s

$$s = \int_0^{\pi}(x+\sin x)\,dx - \int_0^{\pi} x\,dx$$

$$= \frac{\pi^2}{2} - \cos\pi + \cos 0 - \frac{\pi^2}{2} = 2\text{ sq units}$$

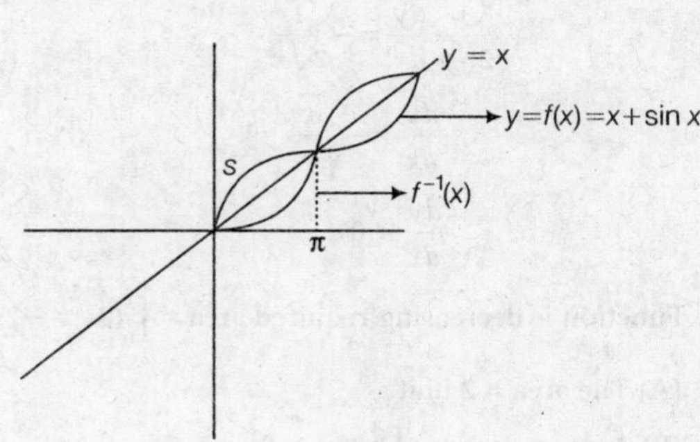

(B) Required area $= 2\int_0^1 xe^x \, dx = 2[xe^x - e^x]_0^1 = 2$

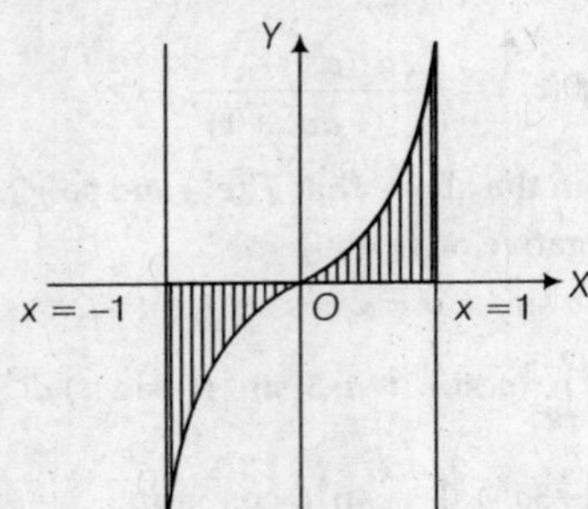

(C) $y^2 = x^3$ and $|y| = 2x$ both the curve are symmetric about Y-axis

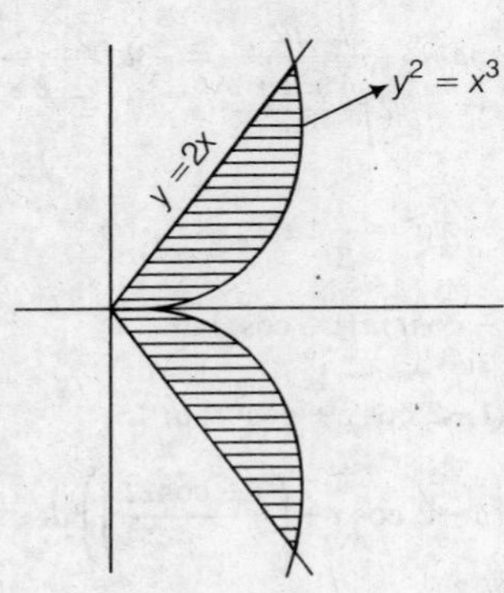

$$4x^2 = x^3 \Rightarrow x = 0, 4$$

Required area $= 2\int_0^4 (2x - x^{3/2}) \, dx = \frac{16}{5}$

(D) $\sqrt{x} + \sqrt{|y|} = 1$

Above curve is symmetric about X-axis

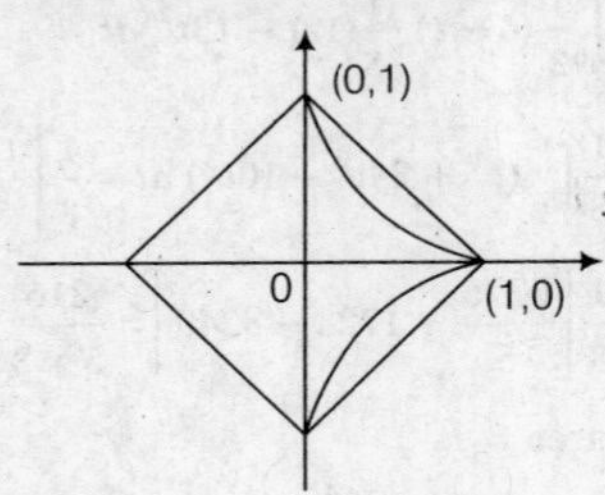

$$\sqrt{|y|} = 1 - \sqrt{x} \text{ and } \sqrt{x} = 1 - \sqrt{|y|}$$

$\Rightarrow$ for $x > 0, y > 0, \sqrt{y} = 1 - \sqrt{x}$

$$\frac{1}{2\sqrt{y}} \frac{dy}{dx} = -\frac{1}{2\sqrt{x}}$$

$$\frac{dy}{dx} = -\sqrt{\frac{x}{y}}$$

$$\frac{dy}{dx} < 0$$

Function is decreasing required area $= \int_0^1 (2\sqrt{x} - 2x) = \frac{1}{3}$.

45. (A) The area = 2 unit

(B) Area enclosed $= \int_0^{\pi} \sin x \, dx = 2$

(C) The line $y = x + 2$ intersects $y = x^2$ at $x = -1$ and $x = 2$

The given region is shaded region area

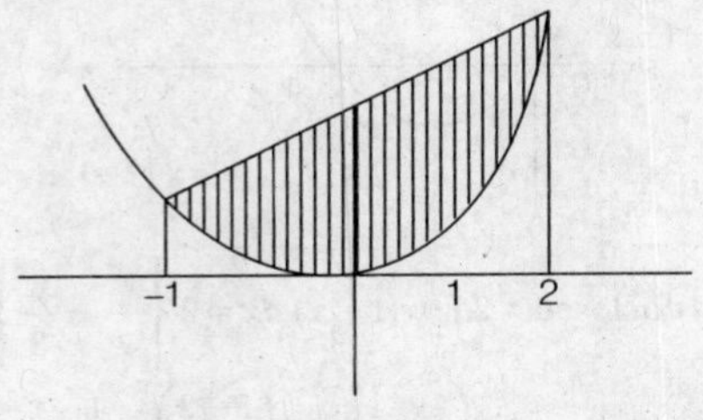

$$= \frac{15}{2} - \int_{-1}^{2} x^2 \, dx = \frac{9}{2}$$

(D) Here, $a^2 = 9, b^2 = 5, b^2 = a^2 (1 - e^2)$

$$\Rightarrow \quad e^2 = \frac{4}{9} \Rightarrow = \frac{2}{3}$$

Equation of tangent at $\left(2, \frac{5}{3}\right)$ is $\frac{2x}{9} + \frac{y}{3} = 1$

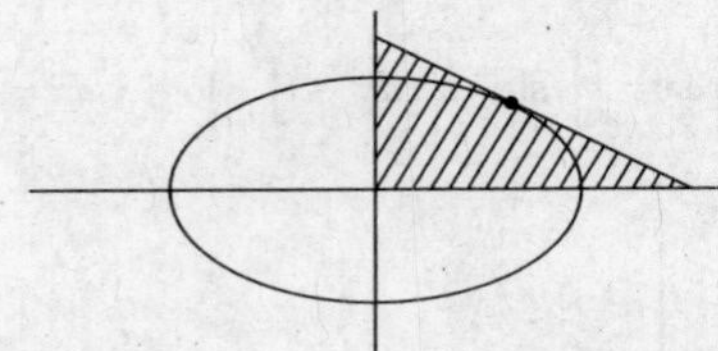

x-intercept $= \frac{9}{2}$, y-intercept $= 3$

Area $= 4 \times \frac{9}{2} \times 3 \times \frac{1}{2} = 27$ sq units

46.

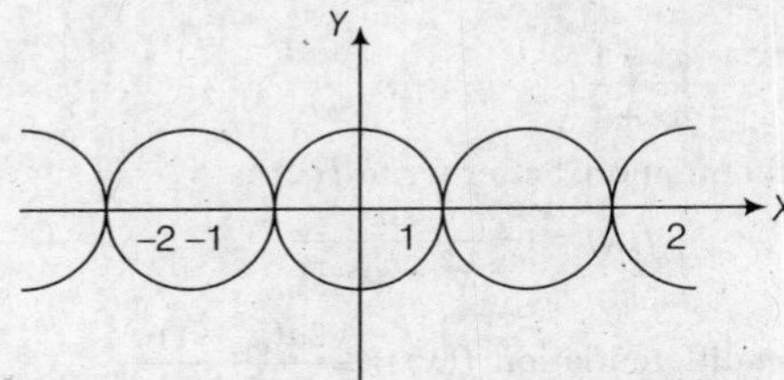

Area is given by $A = 2\int_0^1 (x^2 - 3x + 2) \, dx = \frac{5}{3}$

$$\Rightarrow \quad 3A + 2 = 3 \cdot \frac{5}{3} + 2 = 7$$

47. For $c < 1; \int_c^1 (8x^2 - x^5) \, dx = \frac{1}{3}$

$$\Rightarrow \quad \frac{8}{3} - \frac{1}{6} - \frac{8c^3}{3} - \frac{c^6}{6} = \frac{16}{6}$$

$$\Rightarrow \quad c^3\left[-\frac{8}{3} + \frac{c^3}{6}\right] = \frac{16}{3} - \frac{8}{3} + \frac{1}{6} = \frac{17}{6}$$

$$\Rightarrow \quad c = -1$$

Again, for $c \geq 1$ none of the values of c satisfy the required condition that

$$\int_1^c (8x^2 - x^5) \, dx = \frac{16}{3} \Rightarrow c + 2 = 1$$

48. $y = \begin{cases} x; & x < 2 \\ 4 - x; & x \geq 2 \end{cases}$ and $y = \begin{cases} 3/x; & x > 0 \\ -3/x & x < 2 \end{cases}$

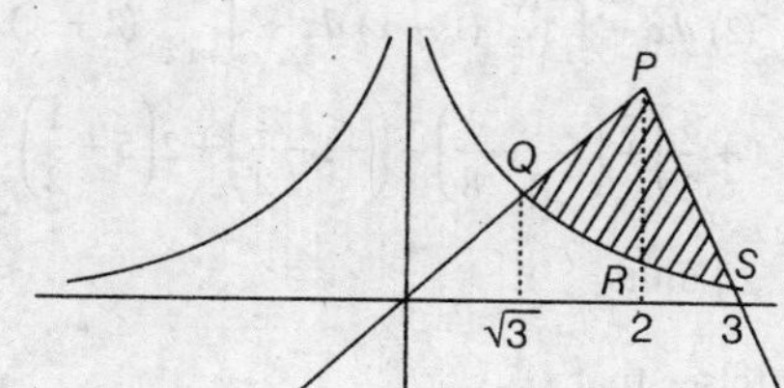

Required area = $PQRSP$ = Area $PQRP$ + Area $PRSP$

$$= \left| \int_{\sqrt{3}}^{2} \left(x - \frac{3}{x} \right) dx \right| + \left| \int_{2}^{3} \left((4 - x) - \frac{3}{x} \right) dx \right|$$

$$= \frac{4 - 3 \ln 3}{2} \text{ sq units}$$

49. Equation of AB $y = \frac{5}{2}(x - 2)$

Equation of BC $y - 5 = \frac{3 - 5}{6 - 4}(x - 4) \Rightarrow y = -x + 9$

Equation of CA $y - 3 = \frac{0 - 3}{2 - 6}(x - 6) \Rightarrow y = \frac{3}{4}(x - 2)$

Required area

$$= \frac{5}{2}\int_2^4 (x - 2)\, dx + \int_4^6 -(x - 9)\, dx - \frac{3}{4}\int_2^6 (x - 2)\, dx$$

$$= \frac{5}{2}\left[\frac{(x-2)^2}{2}\right]_2^4 - \left[\frac{(x-9)^2}{2}\right]_4^6 - \frac{3}{4}\left[\frac{(x-2)^2}{2}\right]_2^6$$

$$= \frac{5}{2}[2^2 - 0] - \frac{1}{2}[(-3)^2 - (-5)^2] - \frac{3}{8}[4^2 - 0]$$

$$= \frac{5}{4} \times 4 - \frac{1}{2}[9 - 25] - \frac{3}{8}[16 - 0]$$

$$= 5 - \frac{1}{2}[-16] - \frac{3}{8} \times 16 = 5 + 8 - 6 = 7 \text{ sq units}$$

50. If $[|x|] = 1$ and $[|y|] = 0$, then $1 \leq |x| < 2, 0 \leq |y| < 1$

$\Rightarrow$ $x \in (-2, -1] \cup [1, 2), y \in (-1, 1)$

If $[|x|] = 0, [|y|] = 1$

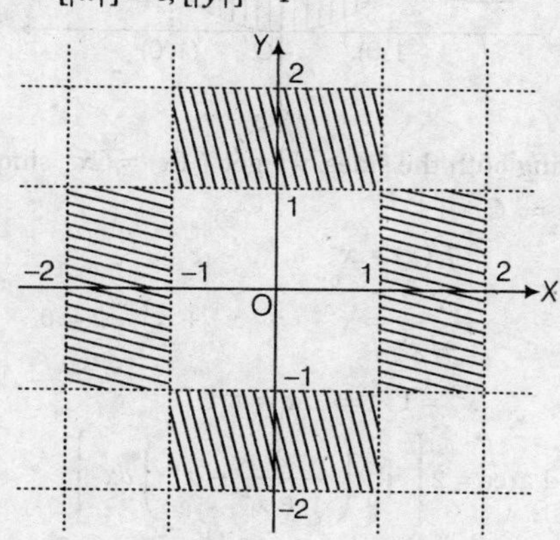

Then, $x \in (-1, 1), y \in (-2, -1] \cup [1, 2]$

Area of required region = $4(2 - 1)(1 - (-1)) = 8$ sq units

51. Clearly, $f(x) = \frac{2x - x^2}{2}$

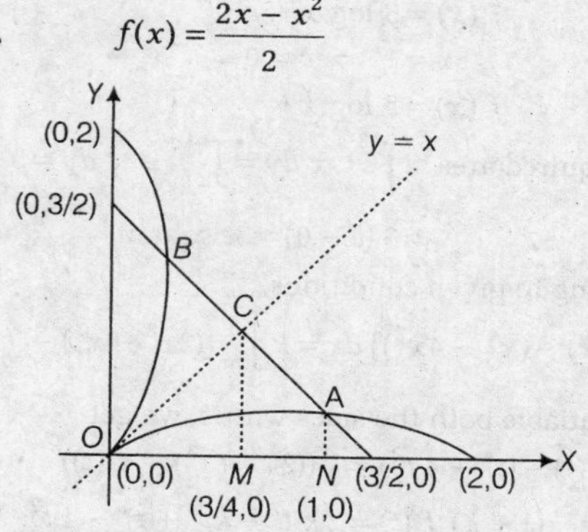

Since, $2x + 2y = 3$; passes through $A\left(1, \frac{1}{2}\right)$ and $B\left(\frac{1}{2}, 1\right)$

so bounded area A

= Area OAB = 2 [Area OCM + Area $CMNA$ – Area ONA]

$$= 2\left[\frac{1}{2} \times \frac{3}{4} \times \frac{3}{4} + \frac{1}{2}\left(\frac{3}{4} + \frac{1}{2}\right) \times \frac{1}{4} - \frac{1}{2}\int_0^1 (2x - x^2)\, dx\right] = \frac{5}{24}$$

$\Rightarrow$ $24A = 5$

52. $f(x) = \min\left\{\sin^{-1} x, \cos^{-1}, x \frac{\pi}{6}\right\}, x \in [0, 1]$

$$\therefore \text{ Area} = \int_0^{1/2} \sin^{-1} x, dx + \frac{1}{2}\left(\frac{\sqrt{3}}{2} - \frac{1}{2}\right) + \int_{\sqrt{3}/2}^{1} \cos^{-1} x\, dx$$

$$= (x \sin^{-1} x + \sqrt{1 - x^2})_0^{1/2} + \frac{\sqrt{3} - 1}{4} + (x \cos^{-1} x - \sqrt{1 - x^2})_{\sqrt{3}/2}$$

$$= \frac{\pi}{2}(1 - \sqrt{3}) + \frac{\sqrt{3} - 1}{2} + \frac{\sqrt{3} - 1}{2}$$

$$= (\sqrt{3} - 1)\left(\frac{3}{4} - \frac{\pi}{12}\right) = \frac{9 - \pi}{6(\sqrt{3} + 1)} = \frac{a - \pi}{b(\sqrt{3} + 1)}$$

$\therefore$ $a = 9, b = 6 \Rightarrow a - b = 3$

53. Given, $f\left(\frac{x}{y}\right) = f(x) - f(y)$ ...(i)

Putting, $x = y = 1$, $f(1) = 0$

Now, $f'(x) = \lim_{h \to 0} \frac{f(x + h) - f(x)}{h} = \lim_{h \to 0} \frac{f\left(1 + \frac{h}{x}\right)}{h}$ [from Eq. (i)]

$$= \lim_{h \to 0} \frac{f\left(1 + \frac{h}{x}\right)}{\frac{h}{x} \cdot x}$$

$\Rightarrow$ $f'(x) = \frac{3}{x}$ $\left[\text{since, } \lim_{x \to 0} \frac{f(1 + x)}{x} = 3\right]$

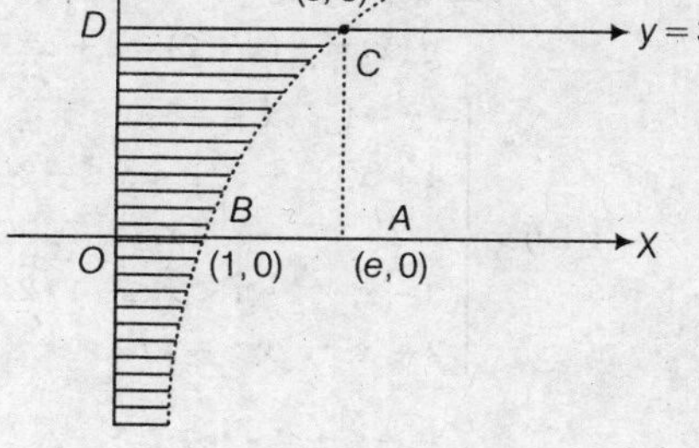

$\Rightarrow \quad f(x) = 3 \log x + c$

Putting $\quad x = 1 \Rightarrow c = 0$

$\Rightarrow \quad f(x) = 3 \log x = y$ [say]

$\therefore$ Required area $= \int_{-\infty}^{3} x\,dy = \int_{-\infty}^{3} e^{y/3}\,dy = 3\,[e^{y/3}]_{-\infty}^{3}$

$= 3(e - 0) = 3e$ sq units

54. According to given conditions,

$$\int_0^t [f(x) - (x^4 - 4x^2)]\,dx = k\int_0^t [(2x^2 - x^3) - f(x)]\,dx$$

Differentiable both the sides w.r.t. t, we get

$$f(t) - (t^4 - 4t^2) = k((2t^2 - t^3) - f(t))$$

or $\quad (1 + k) f(t) = 2k t^2 - kt^3 + t^4 - 4t^2.$

$$\Rightarrow \quad f(t) = \frac{1}{k+1}\{t^4 - kt^3 + (2k - 4)t^2\}$$

Hence, required f is given by;

$$f(x) = \frac{1}{k+1}[x^4 - kx^3 + (2k - 4)x^2]$$

55. $f(t) = |t - 1| = |t| + |t + 1|$

$$\Rightarrow \quad f(t) = \begin{cases} -t, & 1 \le -1 \\ 2 + t, & -1 < t \le 0 \\ 2 - t, & 0 < t \le 1 \\ t, & t > 1 \end{cases}$$

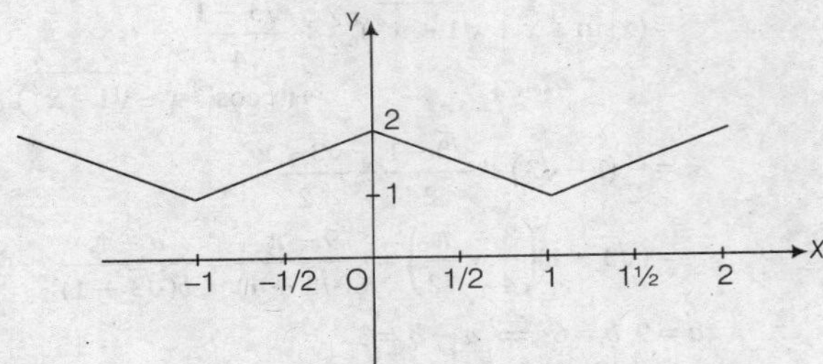

Case **I** $\quad x + 2 \le -\frac{1}{2} \Rightarrow x \le -\frac{5}{2}$

$g(x) = \max\{f(t) : x + 1 \le t \le x + 2\}$

$= f(x + 1) = -x - 1, x \le -5/2$

Case **II** $\quad -\frac{1}{2} < x + 2 \le 0 \Rightarrow -\frac{5}{2} < x \le -2$

$g(x) = f(x + 2) = 4 + x, -\frac{5}{2} < x \le -2$

Case **III** $\quad 0 < x + 2 \le 1 \Rightarrow -2 < x \le -1$

$g(x) = 2$

Case **IV** $\quad 1 < x + 2 \le 3/2 \Rightarrow -1 < x \le -1/2$

$g(x) = f(x + 1) = 1 - x$

Case **V** $\quad x + 2 > 3/2 \Rightarrow x > -1/2$

$g(x) = f(x + 2) = 2 + x$

$$\text{Hence,} \quad g(x) = \begin{cases} -x - 1, & x \le -5/2 \\ 4 + x, & -5/2 < x \le -2 \\ 2, & -2 < x \le -1 \\ 1 - x, & -1 < x \le -1/2 \\ 2 + x, & x > -1/2 \end{cases}$$

Now, required area $= \int_{-3/2}^{5} g(x)\,dx$

$= \int_{-3/2}^{-1} (2)\,dx + \int_{-1}^{-1/2} (1 - x)\,dx + \int_{-1/2}^{5} (2 + x)\,dx$

$= 2\left(-1 + \frac{3}{2}\right) + \left(-\frac{1}{2} - \frac{1}{8}\right) - \left(-1 - \frac{1}{2}\right) + 2\left(5 + \frac{1}{2}\right) + \frac{1}{2}\left(25 - \frac{1}{4}\right)$

$= \frac{101}{4}$ sq units

56. It is easy to see that,

$$f(x) = \begin{cases} e^x, & 0 \le x < \log(3/2) \\ 3/2, & \log(3/2) \le x < \log(2) \\ 1 + e^x, & \log(2) \le x \le 1 \end{cases}$$

Let A be the required area. Then,

$$A = \int_0^{(\log 3/2)} e^x\,dx + \int_{\log 3/2}^{\log 2} \frac{3}{2}\,dx + \int_{\log 2}^{1} (1 + e^{-x})\,dx$$

$= (e^x)_0^{\log 3/2} + \frac{3}{2}(x)_{\log 3/2}^{\log 2} + (x - e^{-x})_{\log 2}^{1}$

$= \left(\frac{3}{2} - 1\right) + \frac{3}{2}\left(\log 2 - \log\frac{3}{2}\right) + \left(1 - \frac{1}{e} - \log 2 + \frac{1}{2}\right)$

$= \left[2 + \log\left(\frac{4}{3\sqrt{3}}\right) - \frac{1}{e}\right]$ sq units

57. $f'(x) = \lim_{h \to 0} \frac{f(x + h) - f(x)}{h}$

$= \lim_{h \to 0} \frac{f(x(1 + h/x)) - f(x)}{h}$

$= \frac{f(x)}{x} \lim_{h \to 0} \frac{f(1 + h/x) - f(1)}{h/x} = \frac{f(x)}{x} \cdot f'(1)$

$\therefore f'(x) = \frac{2f(x)}{x}$ or $\frac{f'(x)}{f(x)} = \frac{2}{x}$

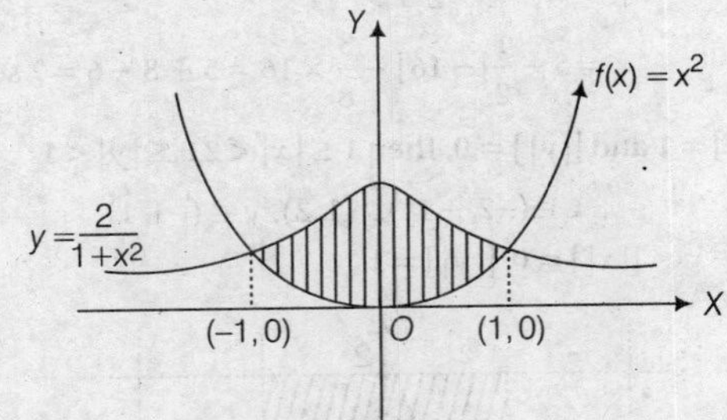

Integrating both the sides, we get $f(x) = Cx^2$, since $f(1) = 1 \Rightarrow C = 1$.

So, $\quad f(x) = x^2$

Now, $\quad \frac{2}{1 + x^2} = x^2 \Rightarrow x^4 + x^2 - 2 = 0$

$\Rightarrow \quad x^2 = 1 \Rightarrow x = \pm 1$

Required area $= 2\left[\int_0^1 \left(\frac{2}{1 + x^2} - x^2\right) dx\right]$

$= 2\left[2\tan^{-1} x - \frac{x^3}{3}\right]_0^1 = 2\left[\frac{\pi}{2} - \frac{1}{3}\right]$

$= \left(\pi - \frac{2}{3}\right)$ sq units

58. $y(x + y^3)\,dx = x(y^3 - x)\,dy$

$\Rightarrow \; xy\,dx + y^2\,dx = xy^3\,dy - x^2\,dy$

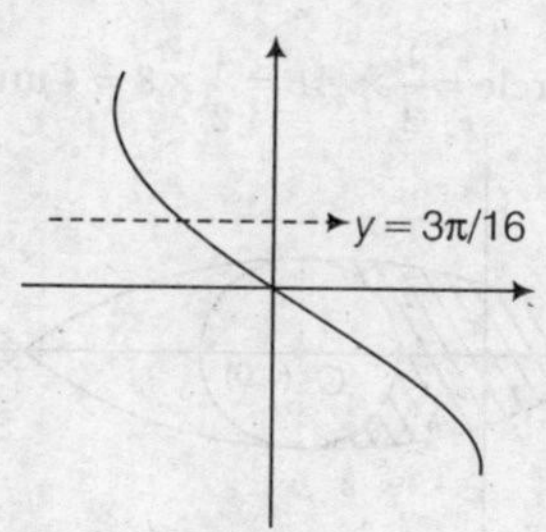

$$\Rightarrow \quad xd(xy) = x^2y^3\left(\frac{1}{x}dy - \frac{y}{x^2}dx\right)$$

$$\Rightarrow \quad \frac{d(xy)}{(xy)^2} = \frac{y}{x}\cdot d\left(\frac{y}{x}\right) \Rightarrow -\frac{1}{xy} = \frac{1}{2}\left(\frac{y}{x}\right)^2 + C$$

At, $x = 4,\ y = -2$

So, $\quad \frac{1}{8} = \frac{1}{2}\left(-\frac{1}{2}\right)^2 + C \Rightarrow C = 0$

Hence, $\quad y^3 + 2x = 0$

So, $\quad f(x) = (-2x)^{1/3}$

The second equation given is

$$y = \int_{1/8}^{\sin^2 x} \sin^{-1}\sqrt{t}\,dt + \int_{1/8}^{\cos^2 x} \cos^{-1}\sqrt{t}\,dt$$

$\Rightarrow \; y' = x\cdot 2\sin x\cos x + x\cdot 2\cos x(-\sin x) = 0$

So, y is constant.

Put $\sin x = \cos x = \frac{1}{\sqrt{2}}$

Hence, $y = \int_{1/8}^{1/2} (\sin^{-1}\sqrt{t} + \cos^{-1}\sqrt{t})\,dt$

$$= \int_{1/8}^{1/2}\left(\frac{\pi}{2}\right)dt = \frac{\pi}{2}\cdot\frac{3}{8} = \frac{3\pi}{16}, \text{ and } g(x) = \frac{3\pi}{16}$$

So, we must find the area between $y = f(x),\ y = \frac{3\pi}{16}$

At $y = \frac{3\pi}{16}$; $x = -\frac{1}{2}\left(\frac{3\pi}{16}\right)^3 = P$ (say)

Hence, $\quad$ area $= \int_P^0 \left(\frac{3\pi}{16} + (2x)^{1/3}\right)dx$

$$= \left(\frac{3\pi}{16}x + 2^{1/3}\cdot\frac{x^{4/3}}{4/3}\right)_P^0 = \frac{1}{8}\left(\frac{3\pi}{16}\right)^4 \text{ sq units}$$

59. As in the figure $\quad \frac{A(R) + A(S)}{A(T)} = \frac{ay + bz}{hx/2}$

where $h = a + b + c$, the altitude of T.

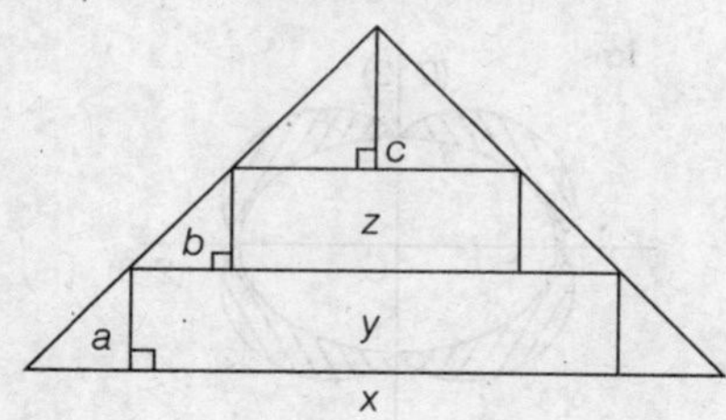

By similar triangles $\frac{x}{h} = \frac{y}{b+c} = \frac{z}{c}$,

$$\text{So, } \frac{A(R) + A(S)}{A(T)} = \frac{\frac{a(b+c)x}{h} + b\cdot\frac{cx}{h}}{hx/2}$$

$$= \frac{2}{h^2}(ab + ac + bc)$$

We need to maximize $(ab + bc + ca)$ subject to $a + b + c = h$. One way to do this is first to fix a, so $b + c = h - a$.

Then, $\quad (ab + bc + ac) = a(h - a) + bc$

and bc is maximized when $b = c$. We now wish to maximize $2ab + b^2$ subject to $a + 2b = h$. This is a straight forward calculus problem giving $a = b = c = 1/3$. Hence, the maximum ratio is 2/3 (independent of T).

60. Consider a coordinate system with vertex P of the isosceles ΔPQR at $(a, 0)$ and Q and R at $(0, b)$ and $(0, -b)$ respectively.

$$A = \frac{1}{2}a\cdot 2b = ab \quad \text{...(i)}$$

Let the centre of ellipse be $(\alpha, 0)$ and the axes be of lengths, 2α and 2β.

So, the equation of ellipse is $\frac{(x-\alpha)^2}{\alpha^2} + \frac{(y)^2}{\beta^2} = 1$

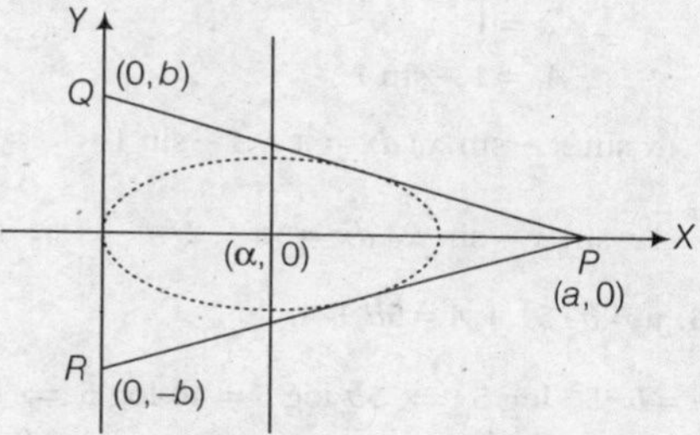

Now, the line PQ is tangent to the ellipse. To apply condition of tangency, let us take a new system $x'y'$ whose origin is at $(\alpha, 0)$.

Then, $x = x' + \alpha$ and $y = y'$.

So, the ellipse becomes $\frac{x'^2}{\alpha^2} + \frac{y'^2}{\beta^2} = 1$

and the line PQ becomes $\frac{x' + \alpha}{a} + \frac{y'}{b} = 1$

which can be written as $y' = -\frac{b}{a}x' + b\left(1 - \frac{\alpha}{a}\right)$

So, $\quad b^2\left(1 - \frac{\alpha}{a}\right)^2 = \alpha^2\left(-\frac{b}{a}\right)^2 + \beta^2$

$$\Rightarrow \quad \beta^2 = b^2\left(1 - \frac{2\alpha}{a}\right) \quad \text{...(ii)}$$

Now, area of ellipse $= \pi\alpha\beta \Rightarrow A^2 = \pi^2\alpha^2\beta^2$

Using Eq. (ii), $A^2 = \pi^2\alpha^2b^2\left(1 - \frac{2\alpha}{a}\right) = f(x) \quad$ (say)

$$f'(x) = \pi^2 b^2\left(2\alpha - \frac{6\alpha^2}{a}\right)$$

$$f'(\alpha) = 0 \Rightarrow 2\alpha = \frac{6\alpha^2}{a} \Rightarrow \alpha = \frac{a}{3}\ (\alpha \neq 0)$$

Since, $f''(\alpha) = \pi^2 b^2 \left(2 - \frac{12\alpha}{a}\right) = -2\pi^2 b^2 = (-\text{ve})$
(at $\alpha = a/3$)

So, $f\left(\frac{a}{3}\right) = \pi^2 \cdot \frac{a^2}{9} \cdot b^2 \left(1 - \frac{2}{3}\right) = \frac{\pi^2 A^2}{27}$ [using Eq. (i)]

Hence, $(A)_{\max} = \frac{\pi A}{3\sqrt{3}} = \frac{\sqrt{3}\pi A}{9}$ sq units

61. $A_1 = \int_0^a \{\sin x - f(x)\}\, dx = -[\cos x]_0^a - \int_0^a f(x)\, dx$

$= -(\cos a - 1) - \int_0^a f(x)\, dx = 1 - \sin a + (a-1)\cos a$ (given)

$\Rightarrow -\cos a - \int_0^a f(x)\, dx = -\sin a + (a-1)\cos a$

$\Rightarrow -\int_0^a f(x)\, dx = -\sin a + a\cos a$

$\Rightarrow \int_0^a f(x)\, dx = \sin a - a\cos a$

Differentiating w.r.t. a.

$f(a) = \cos a - (\cos a - a\sin a) = a\sin a$

$\therefore f(x) = x\sin x$

Now, $y = \sin x$ and $y = f(x)$ intersects at

$\Rightarrow a\sin a = \sin a \Rightarrow (a-1)\sin a = 0$

$\Rightarrow a = 1$ [as $\sin a = 0$]

Hence, $A_1 = 1 - \sin 1$

$A_2 = \int_1^{\pi} (x\sin x - \sin x)\, dx = \pi - 1 - \sin 1$

$A_3 = \int_{\pi}^{2\pi} |x\sin x - \sin x|\, dx = 3\pi - 2$

62. For $x = 1$, $y = b\cdot 5^x + 4 = 5b + 4$

and $\frac{dy}{dx} = b\cdot 5^x \log 5 \Rightarrow 5b\log 5 = 40\log 5 \Rightarrow b = 8$

The two curves intersects at points where

$8\cdot 5^x + 4 = 25^x + 16$

$\Rightarrow 5^{2x} - 8\cdot 5 + 12 = 0 \Rightarrow x = \log_5 \quad x = \log_5 6$

Hence, the area of the given region;

$= \int_{\log_5 2}^{\log_5 6} \{8\cdot 5^x + 4 - (25^x + 16)\}\, dx$

$= \int_{\log_5 2}^{\log_5 6} (8\cdot 5^x - 25^x - 12)\, dx$

$= \left[\frac{8\cdot 5^x}{\log_e 5} - 12x - \frac{25^x}{\log_e 25}\right]_{\log_5 2}^{\log_5 6}$

$= \frac{-5^{\log_5 36}}{\log_e 25} + \frac{8\cdot 5^{\log_5 6}}{\log_e 5} - 12(\log_5 6 - \log_5 2)$

$+ \frac{5^{\log_5 4}}{\log_e 25} - \frac{8\cdot 5^{\log_5 2}}{\log_e 5}$

$= \frac{-36}{2\log_e 5} + \frac{48}{\log_e 5} - 12[\log_5 3] + \frac{4}{2(\log_e 5)} - \frac{16}{(\log_e 5)}$

$= \frac{16}{\log_e 5} - 12\log_5 3 = 4\log_5 e^4 - 4\log_5 25$

$= 4\log_5 \left[\frac{e^4}{27}\right]$ sq units

63. By the symmetry of the figure circle(s) of maximum area will have the end point of diameter at the vertex of the two parabola.

$\Rightarrow$ Radius of circle $= \frac{1}{2} \times AB = \frac{1}{2} \times 8 = 4$ units

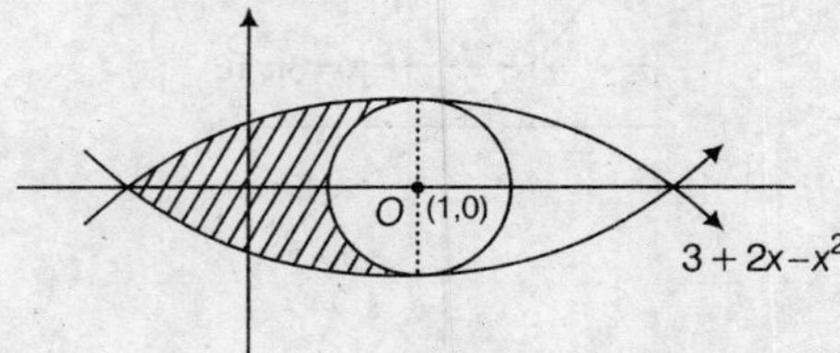

So, the area of shaded region $= 4 \times \left[\int_1^3 (3 + 2x - x^2)\, dx - \frac{1}{4}\right.$ area of circle$\left.\right] = 4\left(\frac{16}{3} - 4\pi\right)$ sq units

64. Area of $\Delta AOB = 2 \times \left(\frac{1}{2} \times \frac{a}{2} \times a^2\right) = \frac{a^3}{2}$

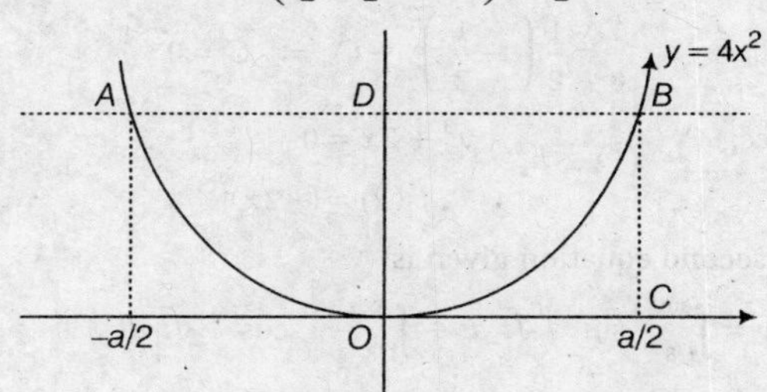

Area = Area $OCBD - \int_0^{a/2} 4x^2\, dx = \frac{a^3}{2} - \frac{a^3}{6} = \frac{a^3}{3}$

$= \lim_{x\to 0} \frac{\text{Area of triangle}}{\text{Area between the line and parabola}}$

$= \lim_{x\to 0} \frac{a^3/2}{a^3/3} = \frac{3}{2}$

65. Required area $= \frac{1}{2} \times 2 \times 2 = 2$ sq units

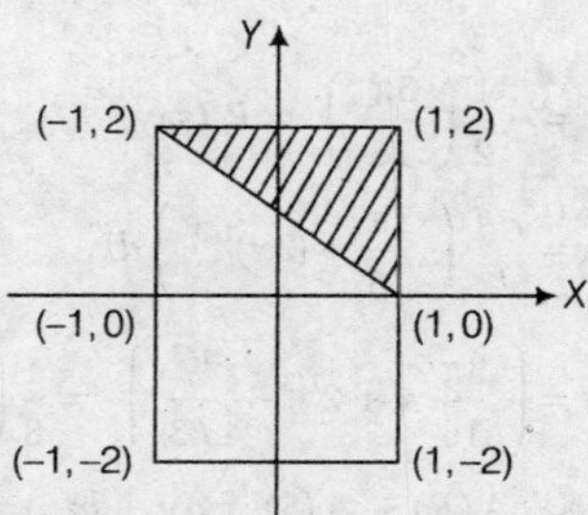

66. Required area $= 4 \times \left[\frac{\pi(\sqrt{2})^2}{2} - (\pi - 2)\right] = 8$ sq units

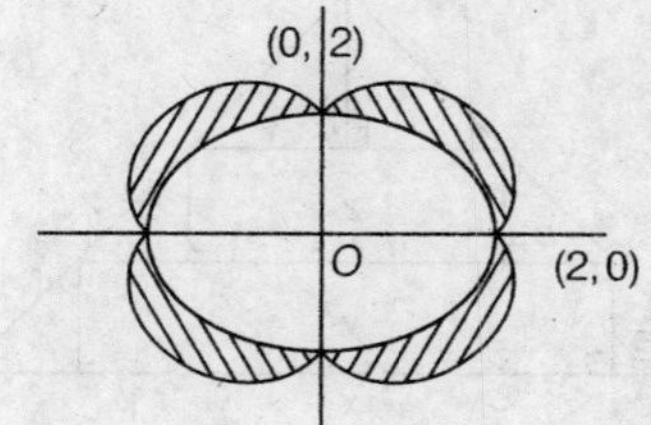

67. 5 sq units

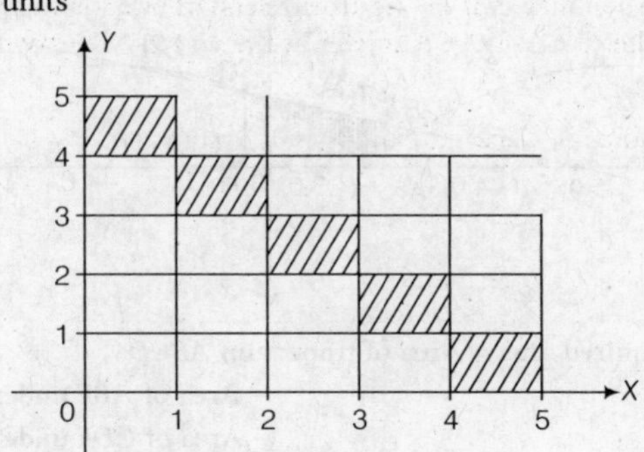

68. Area of the square $ABCD = 2$ sq units

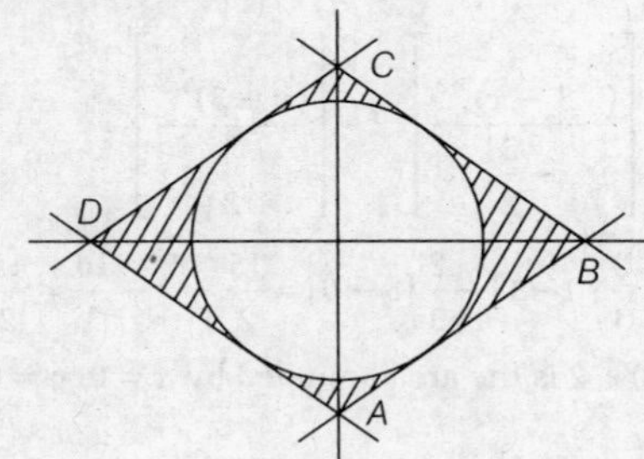

Area of the circle $= \pi \times \frac{1}{2} = \frac{\pi}{2}$ sq units.

Required area $= \left(2 - \frac{\pi}{2}\right)$ sq units

69. $$2^{|x|} \cdot |y| + 2^{|x|-1} \le 1 \quad \text{...(i)}$$

Clearly, this region is symmetrical about X and Y-axes.

Let $x < 0$, Eq. (i) gives,

$$2^x - y + 2^{x-1} \le 1$$

$$\Rightarrow \quad y \le \frac{1 - 2^{x-1}}{2^x} = 2^{-x} - \frac{1}{2}$$

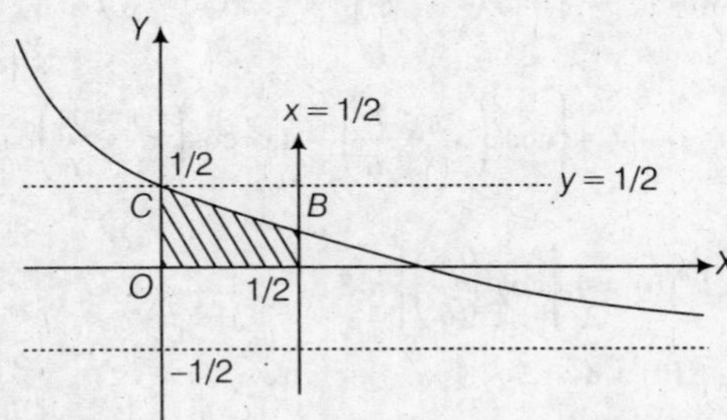

Clearly, bounded region in the first quadrant is $OABC$. The required area is 4 times the area of the region $OABC$.

$$\text{Required area} = 4\int_0^{1/2} \left(2^{-x} - \frac{1}{2}\right) dx = 4\left(-\frac{2^{-x}}{\ln 2} - \frac{x}{2}\right)_0^{1/2}$$

$$= \left[\frac{4}{\ln 2}(1 - 2^{-1/2}) - 1\right] \text{sq units}$$

70. Pair of lines $y^2 - 3y + 2 = 0$

$\Rightarrow$ Lines are $y = 2$, $y = 1$.

Let $\quad [a] = b$

Now, curves are $y = bx^2$ and $y = \frac{b}{2}x^2$

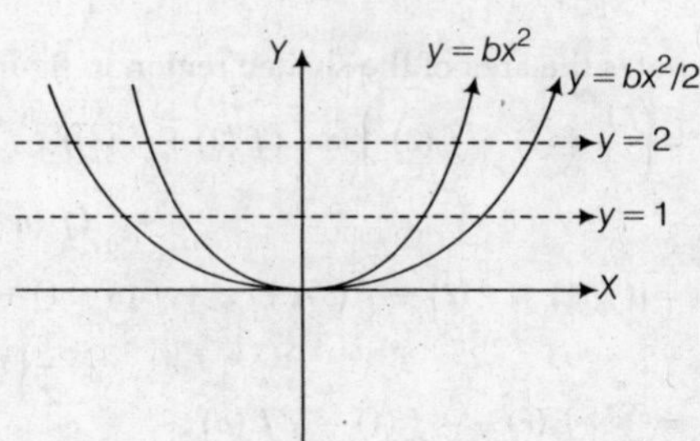

$$\text{Bounded area} = 2\left[\int_1^2 (x_2 - x_1)\, dy\right]$$

$$= 2\left[\int_1^2 \left(\sqrt{\frac{2y}{b}} - \sqrt{\frac{y}{b}}\right) dy\right]$$

$$= 2\left[\sqrt{\frac{2}{b}} \cdot \frac{y^{3/2}}{3/2} - \frac{1}{\sqrt{b}} \cdot \frac{y^{3/2}}{3/2}\right]_1^2$$

$$= \frac{4}{3\sqrt{b}}((\sqrt{2} - 1)\, y^{3/2})_1^2 = \frac{4}{3\sqrt{b}}(\sqrt{2} - 1)(2\sqrt{2} - 1)$$

Area will be maximum when $b = [a]$ is least.

As $a \ge 2 \Rightarrow [a]_{\text{least}} = 1 \Rightarrow 1 \le a < 2$

71. Since, $f'(x) < 0 \Rightarrow f(x)$ is a decreasing function and also $f''(x) > 0 \Rightarrow f(x)$ is concave upwards.

Hence, the graph of the function $y = f(x)$ is as follows :

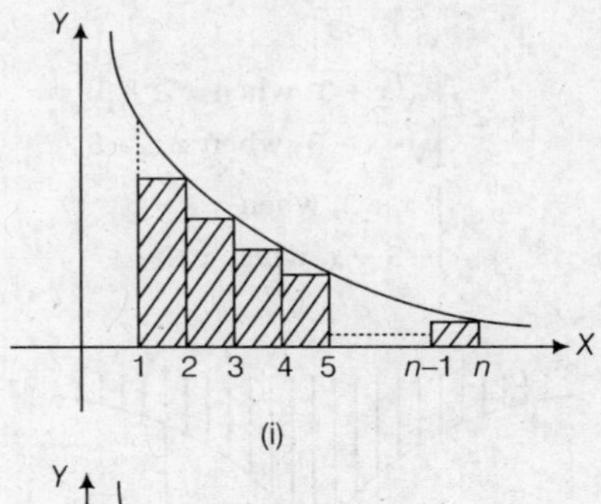

(i)

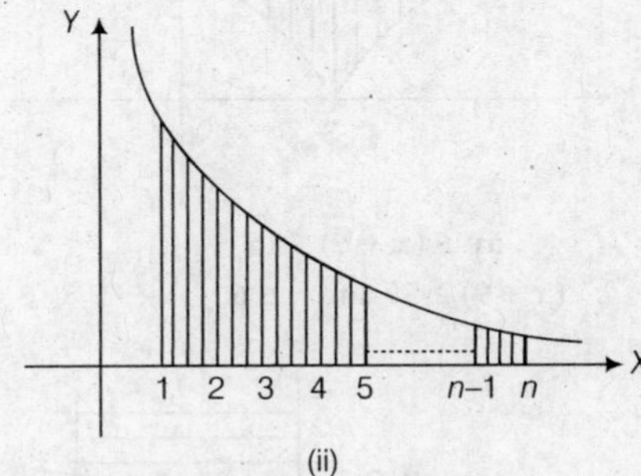

(ii)

Let S_L denotes the shaded area in figure (i).

$$\Rightarrow \quad S_L = f(2) + f(3) + \ldots + f(n) = \sum_{r=1}^{n} f(r) - f(1)$$

From the figure (i) it is clear that, $S_L < \int_1^n f(x)\, dx$

$$\Rightarrow \quad \sum_{r=1}^{n} f(r) - f(1) < \int_1^n f(x)\, dx$$

$$\Rightarrow \quad \sum_{r=1}^{n} f(r) < \int_1^n f(x)\,dx + f(1) \qquad \text{...(i)}$$

Let S_u denotes the area of the shaded region in figure (ii).

$$\Rightarrow \quad S_u = \left(\frac{1}{2} f(1) + f(2)\right) + \frac{1}{2}(f(2) + f(3)) + \ldots + \frac{1}{2}(f(n-1) + f(n))$$

$$= [(f(1) + f(2) + f(3)) + \ldots + f(n-1) + f(n)] - \frac{1}{2}(f(1) + f(n))$$

$$= \sum_{r=1}^{n} f(r) - \frac{1}{2} f(1) - \frac{1}{2} f(n)$$

From figure (ii) it is clear that;

$$S_u > \int_1^n f(x)\,dx$$

$$\Rightarrow \quad \sum_{r=1}^{n} f(r) - \frac{1}{2}(f(1) + f(n)) > \int_1^n f(x)\,dx$$

$$\Rightarrow \quad \sum_{r=1}^{n} f(r) > \int_1^n f(x)\,dx + \frac{1}{2}(f(1) + f(n))$$

$$> \int_1^n f(x)\,dx + 4 \cdot \frac{1}{2} f(1) \qquad \text{...(ii)}$$

From Eqs. (i) and (ii), we get

$$\frac{1}{2} f(1) + \int_1^n f(x)\,dx < \sum_{r=1}^{n} f(r) < \int_1^n f(x)\,dx + f(1).$$

72. Here, $\{(x, y) \in R^2 : y \ge \sqrt{|x+3|}, 5y \le (x+9) \le 15\}$

$$\therefore \quad y \ge \sqrt{|x+3|}$$

$$\Rightarrow \quad y \ge \begin{cases} \sqrt{x+3}, & \text{when } x \ge -3 \\ \sqrt{-x-3}, & \text{when } x \le -3 \end{cases}$$

or

$$y^2 \ge \begin{cases} x+3, & \text{when } x \ge -3 \\ -3-x, & \text{when } x \le -3 \end{cases}$$

Shown as

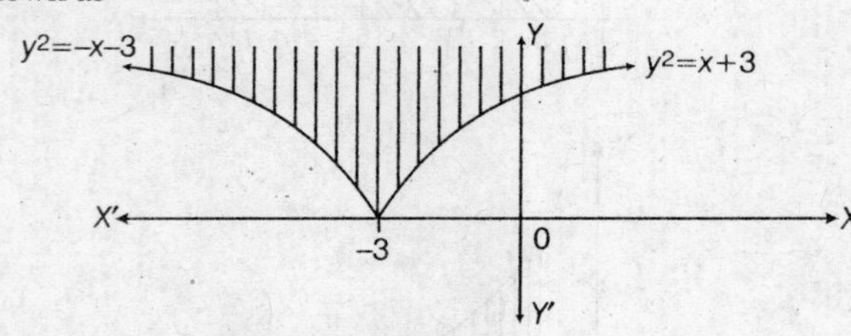

Also, $\quad 5y \le (x+9) \le 15$

$$\Rightarrow \quad (x+9) \ge 5y \text{ and } x \le 6$$

Shown as

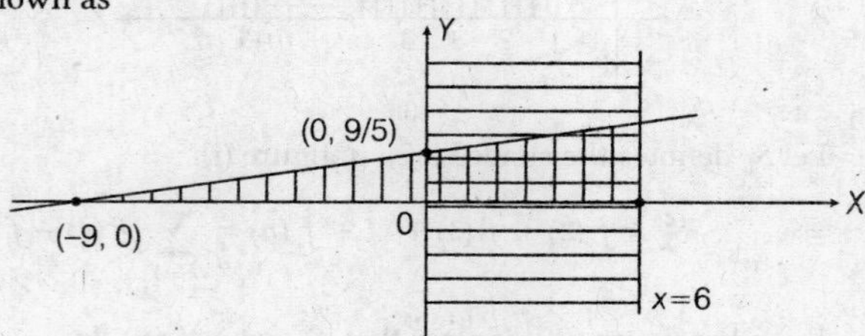

$$\therefore \quad \{(x, y) \in R^2 : y \ge \sqrt{|x+3|}, 5y \le (x+9) \le 15\}$$

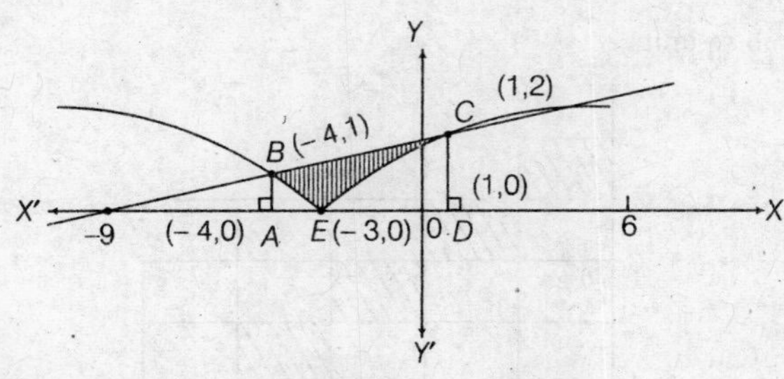

$\therefore$ Required area = Area of trapezium $ABCD$ – Area of ABE under parabola – Area of CDE under parabola

$$= \frac{1}{2}(1+2)(5) - \int_{-4}^{-3} \sqrt{-(x+3)}\,dx - \int_{-3}^{1} \sqrt{(x+3)}\,dx$$

$$= \frac{15}{2} - \left[\frac{(-3-x)^{3/2}}{-\frac{3}{2}}\right]_{-4}^{-3} - \left[\frac{(x+3)^{3/2}}{\frac{3}{2}}\right]_{-3}^{1}$$

$$= \frac{15}{2} + \frac{2}{3}[0-1] - \frac{2}{3}[8-0] = \frac{15}{2} - \frac{2}{3} - \frac{16}{3} = \frac{15}{2} - \frac{18}{3} = \frac{3}{2}$$

73. Since, $F'(a) + 2$ is the area bounded by $x = 0$, $y = 0$, $y = f(x)$ and $x = a$.

$$\therefore \quad \int_0^a f(x)\,dx = F'(a) + 2$$

Using Newton-Leibnitz formula,

$$f(a) = F''(a) \text{ and } f(0) = F''(0) \qquad \text{...(i)}$$

Given, $\quad F(x) = \int_x^{x^2 + \pi/6} 2\cos^2 t\,dt$

On differentiating,

$$F'(x) = 2\cos^2\left(x^2 + \frac{\pi}{6}\right) \cdot 2x - 2\cos^2 x \cdot 1$$

Again differentiating,

$$F''(x) = 4\left\{\cos^2\left(x^2 + \frac{\pi}{6}\right) - 2x\cos\left(x^2 + \frac{\pi}{6}\right)\sin\left(x^2 + \frac{\pi}{6}\right)2x\right\} + \{4\cos x \cdot \sin x\}$$

$$= 4\left\{\cos^2\left(x^2 + \frac{\pi}{6}\right) - 4x^2\cos\left(x^2 + \frac{\pi}{6}\right)\sin\left(x^2 + \frac{\pi}{6}\right)\right\} + 2\sin 2x$$

$$\therefore \quad F''(0) = 4\left\{\cos^2\left(\frac{\pi}{6}\right)\right\} = 3$$

$$\therefore \quad f(0) = 3$$

74. Let equation of tangent to parabola be $y = mx + \frac{2}{m}$

It also touches the circle $x^2 + y^2 = 2$.

$$\therefore \quad \left|\frac{2}{m\sqrt{1+m^2}}\right| = \sqrt{2}$$

$$\Rightarrow \quad m^4 + m^2 = 2 \Rightarrow m^4 + m^2 - 2 = 0$$

$$\Rightarrow \quad (m^2 - 1)(m^2 + 2) = 0$$

$$\Rightarrow \quad m = \pm 1, m^2 = -2 \qquad [\text{rejected } m^2 = -2]$$

So, tangents are $y = x + 2$, $y = -x - 2$.

They intersect at $(-2, 0)$.

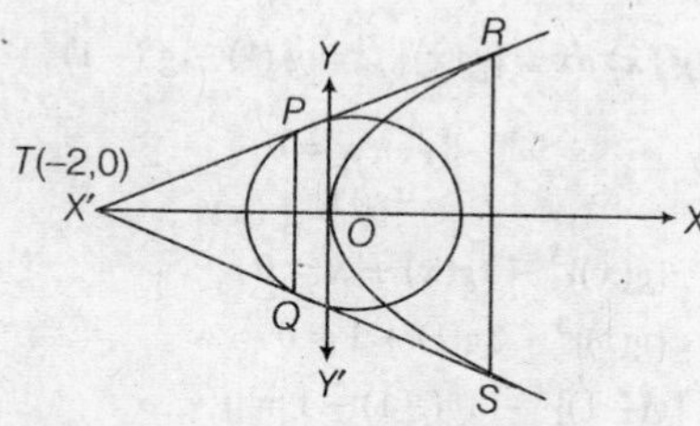

Equation of chord PQ is $-2x = 2 \Rightarrow x = -1$

Equation of chord RS is $0 = 4(x-2) \Rightarrow x = 2$

$\therefore$ Coordinates of P, Q, R, S are

$$P(-1, 1), Q(-1, -1), R(2, 4), S(2, -4)$$

$\therefore$ Area of quadrilateral $= \dfrac{(2+8)\times 3}{2} = 15$ sq units

75. To find the bounded area between $y = f(x)$ and $y = g(x)$ between $x = a$ to $x = b$.

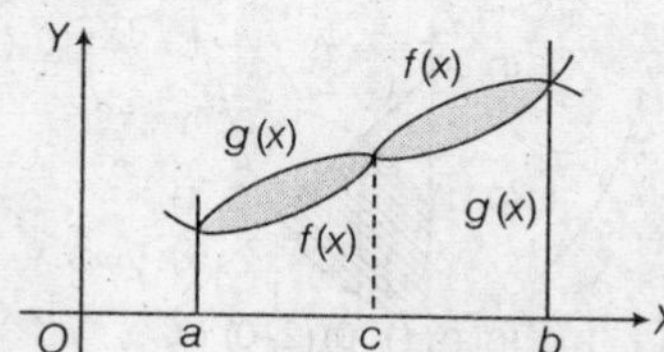

$\therefore$ Area bounded $= \int_a^c [g(x) - f(x)]dx + \int_c^b [f(x) - g(x)]dx$

$$= \int_a^b |f(x) - g(x)| dx$$

Here, $f(x) = y = \sin x + \cos x$, when $0 \le x \le \dfrac{\pi}{2}$

and $g(x) = y = |\cos x - \sin x| = \begin{cases} \cos x - \sin x, & 0 \le x \le \dfrac{\pi}{4} \\ \sin x - \cos x, & \dfrac{\pi}{4} \le x \le \dfrac{\pi}{2} \end{cases}$

could be shown as

$\therefore$ Area bounded $= \int_0^{\pi/4} \{(\sin x + \cos x) - (\cos x - \sin x)\} dx$

$$+ \int_{\pi/4}^{\pi/2} \{(\sin x + \cos x) - (\sin x - \cos x)\} dx$$

$$= \int_0^{\pi/4} 2\sin x\, dx + \int_{\pi/4}^{\pi/2} 2\cos x\, dx$$

$$= -2[\cos x]_0^{\pi/4} + 2[\sin x]_{\pi/4}^{\pi/2}$$

$$= 4 - 2\sqrt{2} = 2\sqrt{2}(\sqrt{2} - 1) \text{ sq units}$$

76. Graph for $y = e^{-x^2}$

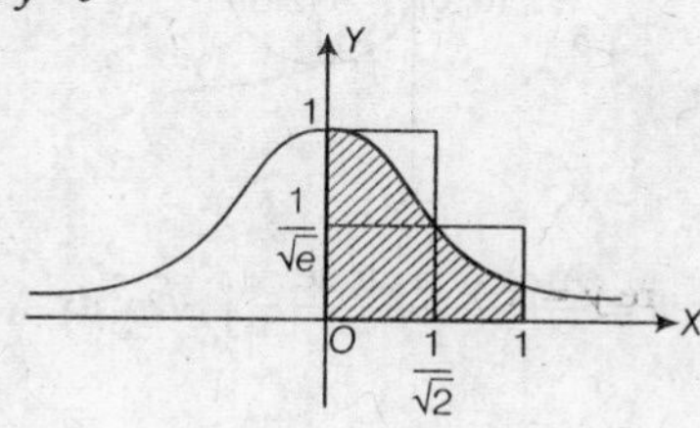

Since, $x^2 \le x$ when $x \in [0, 1]$

$$\Rightarrow \quad -x^2 \ge -x \text{ or } e^{-x^2} \ge e^{-x}$$

$$\therefore \quad \int_0^1 e^{-x^2} dx \ge \int_0^1 e^{-x} dx$$

$$\Rightarrow \quad S \ge -(e^{-x})_0^1 = 1 - \frac{1}{e} \quad \text{...(i)}$$

Also, $\int_0^1 e^{-x^2} dx \le$ Area of two rectangles

$$\le \left(1 \times \frac{1}{\sqrt{2}}\right) + \left(1 - \frac{1}{\sqrt{2}}\right) \times \frac{1}{\sqrt{e}}$$

$$\le \frac{1}{\sqrt{2}} + \frac{1}{\sqrt{e}}\left(1 - \frac{1}{\sqrt{2}}\right) \quad \text{...(ii)}$$

$$\therefore \quad \frac{1}{\sqrt{2}} + \frac{1}{\sqrt{e}}\left(1 - \frac{1}{\sqrt{2}}\right) \ge S \ge 1 - \frac{1}{e} \quad \text{[from Eqs. (i) and (ii)]}$$

77. $R_1 = \int_{-1}^2 x\, f(x)\, dx$ ...(i)

Using $\int_a^b f(x)\, dx = \int_a^b f(a + b - x)\, dx$

$$R_1 = \int_{-1}^2 (1-x)\, f(1-x)\, dx$$

$$\therefore \quad R_1 = \int_{-1}^2 (1-x)\, f(x)\, dx \quad \text{...(ii)}$$

[$f(x) = f(1-x)$, given]

Given, R_2 is area bounded by $f(x)$, $x = -1$ and $x = 2$.

$$\therefore \quad R_2 = \int_{-1}^2 f(x)\, dx \quad \text{...(iii)}$$

On adding Eqs. (i) and (ii), we get

$$2R_1 = \int_{-1}^2 f(x)\, dx \quad \text{...(iv)}$$

From Eqs. (iii) and (iv), we get

$$2R_1 = R_2$$

78. Here, area between 0 to b is R_1 and b to 1 is R_2.

$$\therefore \quad \int_0^b (1-x)^2\, dx - \int_b^1 (1-x)^2\, dx = \frac{1}{4}$$

$$\Rightarrow \quad \left[\frac{(1-x)^3}{-3}\right]_0^b - \left[\frac{(1-x)^3}{-3}\right]_b^1 = \frac{1}{4}$$

$$\Rightarrow -\frac{1}{3}[(1-b)^3 - 1] + \frac{1}{3}[0 - (1-b)^3] = \frac{1}{4}$$

$$\Rightarrow \quad -\frac{2}{3}(1-b)^3 = -\frac{1}{3} + \frac{1}{4} = -\frac{1}{12}$$

$$\Rightarrow \quad (1-b)^3 = \frac{1}{8}$$

$$\Rightarrow \quad (1-b) = \frac{1}{2} \Rightarrow b = \frac{1}{2}$$

79. Shaded area $= e - \left(\int_0^1 e^x\, dx\right) = 1$

Also, $\int_1^e \ln(e + 1 - y)\, dy$ [put $e + 1 - y = t \Rightarrow -dy = dt$]

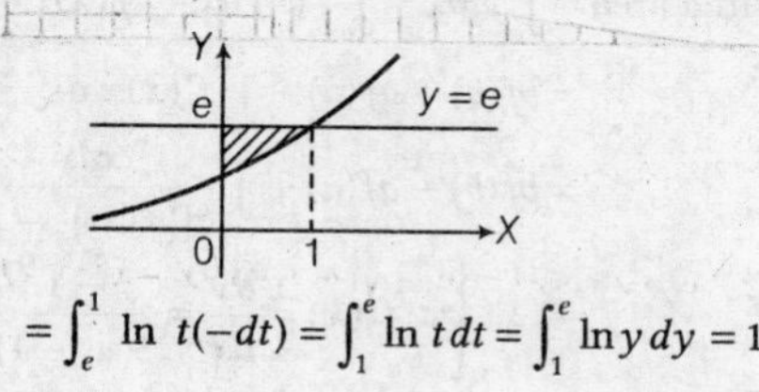

$$= \int_e^1 \ln\, t(-dt) = \int_1^e \ln t\, dt = \int_1^e \ln y\, dy = 1$$

80. Required area $= \int_0^{\pi/4} \left(\sqrt{\frac{1+\sin x}{\cos x}} - \sqrt{\frac{1-\sin x}{\cos x}} \right) dx$

$$\left[\because \frac{1+\sin x}{\cos x} > \frac{1-\sin x}{\cos x} > 0 \right]$$

$$= \int_0^{\pi/4} \left(\sqrt{\frac{1+\frac{2\tan\frac{x}{2}}{1+\tan^2\frac{x}{2}}}{\frac{1-\tan^2\frac{x}{2}}{1+\tan^2\frac{x}{2}}}} - \sqrt{\frac{1-\frac{2\tan\frac{x}{2}}{1+\tan^2\frac{x}{2}}}{\frac{1-\tan^2\frac{x}{2}}{1+\tan^2\frac{x}{2}}}} \right) dx$$

$$= \int_0^{\pi/4} \left(\sqrt{\frac{1+\tan\frac{x}{2}}{1-\tan\frac{x}{2}}} - \sqrt{\frac{1-\tan\frac{x}{2}}{1+\tan\frac{x}{2}}} \right) dx$$

$$= \int_0^{\pi/4} \frac{1+\tan\frac{x}{2} - 1 + \tan\frac{x}{2}}{\sqrt{1-\tan^2\frac{x}{2}}} dx = \int_0^{\pi/4} \frac{2\tan\frac{x}{2}}{\sqrt{1-\tan^2\frac{x}{2}}} dx$$

Put $\tan\frac{x}{2} = t \Rightarrow \frac{1}{2}\sec^2\frac{x}{2}\, dx = dt$

$$= \int_0^{\tan\frac{\pi}{8}} \frac{4t\, dt}{(1+t^2)\sqrt{1-t^2}}$$

As $\int_0^{\sqrt{2}-1} \frac{4t\, dt}{(1+t^2)\sqrt{1-t^2}}$ $\left[\because \tan\frac{\pi}{8} = \sqrt{2}-1\right]$

81. Given, $y^3 - 3y + x = 0$

$$\Rightarrow 3y^2\frac{dy}{dx} - 3\frac{dy}{dx} + 1 = 0 \quad \text{...(i)}$$

$$\Rightarrow 3y^2\left(\frac{d^2y}{dx^2}\right) + 6y\left(\frac{dy}{dx}\right)^2 - 3\frac{d^2y}{dx^2} = 0 \quad \text{...(ii)}$$

At $x = -10\sqrt{2},\ y = 2\sqrt{2}$

On substituting in Eq. (i) we get

$$3(2\sqrt{2})^2 \cdot \frac{dy}{dx} - 3\cdot\frac{dy}{dx} + 1 = 0 \Rightarrow \frac{dy}{dx} = -\frac{1}{21}$$

Again, substituting in Eq. (ii), we get

$$3(2\sqrt{2})^2\frac{d^2y}{dx^2} + 6(2\sqrt{2})\cdot\left(-\frac{1}{21}\right)^2 - 3\cdot\frac{d^2y}{dx^2} = 0$$

$$\Rightarrow 21\cdot\frac{d^2y}{dx^2} = -\frac{12\sqrt{2}}{(21)^2}$$

$$\Rightarrow \frac{d^2y}{dx^2} = \frac{-12\sqrt{2}}{(21)^3} = \frac{-4\sqrt{2}}{7^3\cdot 3^2}$$

82. Required area $= \int_a^b y\, dx = \int_a^b f(x)\, dx = [f(x)\cdot x]_a^b - \int_a^b f'(x) x\, dx$

$$= bf(b) - af(a) - \int_a^b f'(x) x\, dx$$

$$= bf(b) - af(a) + \int_a^b \frac{x dx}{3[\{f(x)\}^2 - 1]}$$

$$\left[\because f'(x) = \frac{dy}{dx} = \frac{-1}{3(y^2-1)} = \frac{-1}{3[\{f(x)\}^2-1]}\right]$$

83. Let $I = \int_{-1}^1 g'(x)\, dx = [g(x)]_{-1}^1 = g(1) - g(-1)$

Since, $y^3 - 3y + x = 0$ ...(i)

and $y = g(x)$

$\therefore$ $\{g(x)\}^3 - 3g(x) + x = 0$ [from Eq. (i)]

At $x = 1$, $\{g(1)\}^3 - 3g(1) + 1 = 0$ ...(ii)

At $x = -1$, $\{g(-1)\}^3 - 3g(-1) - 1 = 0$ ...(iii)

On adding Eqs. (i) and (ii), we get

$\{g(1)\}^3 + \{g(-1)\}^3 - 3\{g(1) + g(-1)\} = 0$

$\Rightarrow [g(1) + g(-1)][\{g(1)\}^2 + \{g(-1)\}^2 - g(1)g(-1) - 3] = 0$

$\Rightarrow g(1) + g(-1) = 0$

$\Rightarrow g(1) = -g(-1)$

$\therefore I = g(1) - g(-1) = g(1) - \{-g(1)\} = 2g(1)$

84. Required area $= \int_0^1 (1+\sqrt{x})dx + \int_1^2 (3-x)dx - \int_0^2 \frac{x^2}{4} dx$

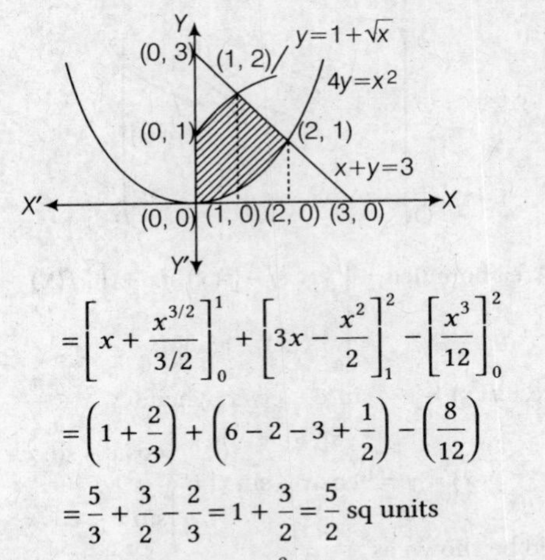

$$= \left[x + \frac{x^{3/2}}{3/2}\right]_0^1 + \left[3x - \frac{x^2}{2}\right]_1^2 - \left[\frac{x^3}{12}\right]_0^2$$

$$= \left(1 + \frac{2}{3}\right) + \left(6 - 2 - 3 + \frac{1}{2}\right) - \left(\frac{8}{12}\right)$$

$$= \frac{5}{3} + \frac{3}{2} - \frac{2}{3} = 1 + \frac{3}{2} = \frac{5}{2} \text{ sq units}$$

85. Given equations of curves are $y^2 = 2x$, ...(i)

which is a parabola with vertex (0, 0) and axis parallel to X-axis.

And $x^2 + y^2 = 4x$ ...(ii)

which is a circle with centre (2, 0) and radius = 2

On substituting $y^2 = 2x$ in Eq. (ii), we get

$$x^2 + 2x = 4x \Rightarrow x^2 = 2x$$

$\Rightarrow$ $x = 0$ or $x = 2$

$\Rightarrow$ $y = 0$ or $y = \pm 2$ [using Eq. (i)]

Now, the required area is the area of shaded region, i.e.

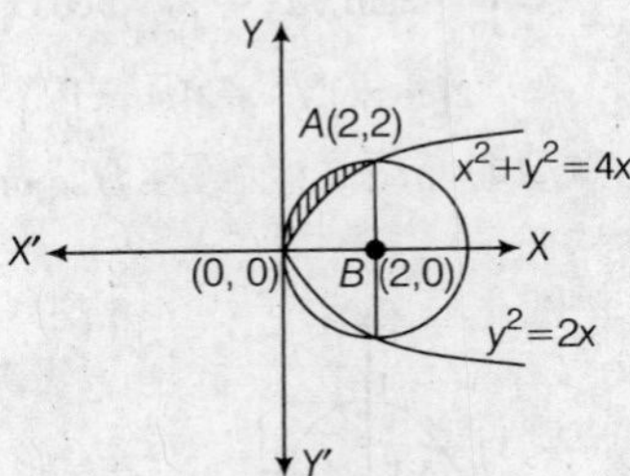

Required area $= \frac{\text{Area of a circle}}{4} - \int_0^2 \sqrt{2x}\, dx$

$$= \frac{\pi(2)^2}{4} - \sqrt{2}\int_0^2 x^{1/2}dx = \pi - \sqrt{2}\left[\frac{x^{3/2}}{3/2}\right]_0^2$$

$$= \pi - \frac{2\sqrt{2}}{3}[2\sqrt{2} - 0] = \left(\pi - \frac{8}{3}\right) \text{ sq units}$$

86. Given region is $\{(x, y) : y^2 \le 2x \text{ and } y \ge 4x - 1\}$

$y^2 \le 2x$ represents a region inside the parabola

$$y^2 = 2x \quad \text{...(i)}$$

and $y \ge 4x - 1$ represents a region to the left of the line

$$y = 4x - 1 \quad \text{...(ii)}$$

The point of intersection of the curve (i) and (ii) is

$$(4x - 1)^2 = 2x$$

$$\Rightarrow \quad 16x^2 + 1 - 8x = 2x$$

$$\Rightarrow \quad 16x^2 - 10x + 1 = 0$$

$$\Rightarrow \quad x = \frac{1}{2}, \frac{1}{8}$$

$\therefore$ The points where these curves intersect, are $\left(\frac{1}{2}, 1\right)$ and $\left(\frac{1}{8}, -\frac{1}{2}\right)$.

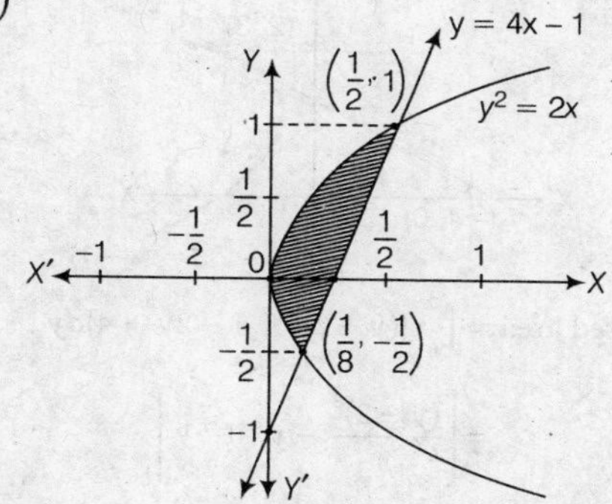

Hence, required area $= \int_{-1/2}^{1}\left(\frac{y+1}{4} - \frac{y^2}{2}\right)dy$

$$= \frac{1}{4}\left(\frac{y^2}{2} + y\right)_{-1/2}^{1} - \frac{1}{6}(y^3)_{-1/2}^{1}$$

$$= \frac{1}{4}\left\{\left(\frac{1}{2} + 1\right) - \left(\frac{1}{8} - \frac{1}{2}\right)\right\} - \frac{1}{6}\left\{1 + \frac{1}{8}\right\}$$

$$= \frac{1}{4}\left\{\frac{3}{2} + \frac{3}{8}\right\} - \frac{1}{6}\left\{\frac{9}{8}\right\} = \frac{1}{4} \times \frac{15}{8} - \frac{3}{16} = \frac{9}{32}$$

87. Given equation of ellipse is

$$\frac{x^2}{9} + \frac{y^2}{5} = 1 \quad \text{...(i)}$$

$$\therefore \quad a^2 = 9, b^2 = 5 \quad \Rightarrow \quad a = 3, b = \sqrt{5}$$

Now, $\quad e = \sqrt{1 - \frac{b^2}{a^2}} = \sqrt{1 - \frac{5}{9}} = \frac{2}{3}$

Foci $= (\pm ae, 0) = (\pm 2, 0)$ and $\frac{b^2}{a} = \frac{5}{3}$

$\therefore$ Extremities of one of latusrectum are $\left(2, \frac{5}{3}\right)$ and $\left(2, \frac{-5}{3}\right)$.

$\therefore$ Equation of tangent at $\left(2, \frac{5}{3}\right)$ is,

$$\frac{x(2)}{9} + \frac{y(5/3)}{5} = 1$$

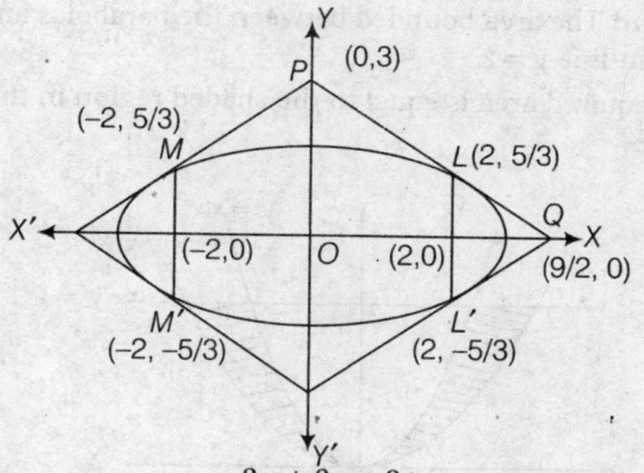

or $\quad 2x + 3y = 9 \quad \text{...(ii)}$

Eq.(ii) intersects X and Y-axes at $\left(\frac{9}{2}, 0\right)$ and $(0, 3)$, respectively.

$\therefore$ Area of quadrilateral $= 4 \times$ Area of ΔPOQ

$$= 4 \times \left(\frac{1}{2} \times \frac{9}{2} \times 3\right) = 27 \text{ sq units}$$

88. Given, $A = \{(x, y) : x^2 + y^2 \le 1 \text{ and } y^2 \le 1 - x\}$

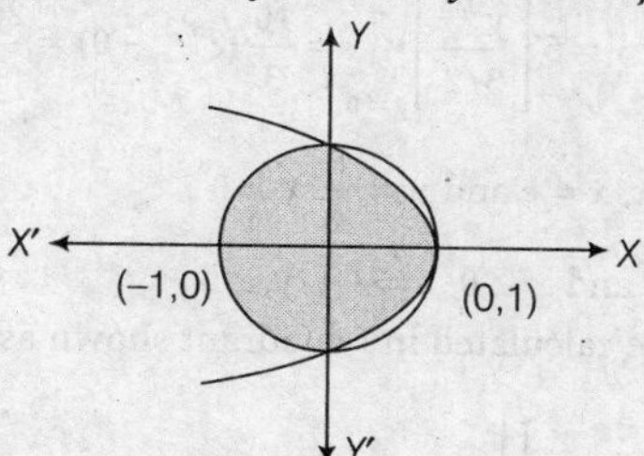

Required area $= \frac{1}{2}\pi r^2 + 2\int_0^1 (1 - y^2)dy = \frac{1}{2}\pi(1)^2 + 2\left(y - \frac{y^3}{3}\right)_0^1$

$$= \frac{\pi}{2} + \frac{4}{3}$$

89. Given curves are $y = \sqrt{x}$ ...(i)

and $\quad 2y - x + 3 = 0$ ...(ii)

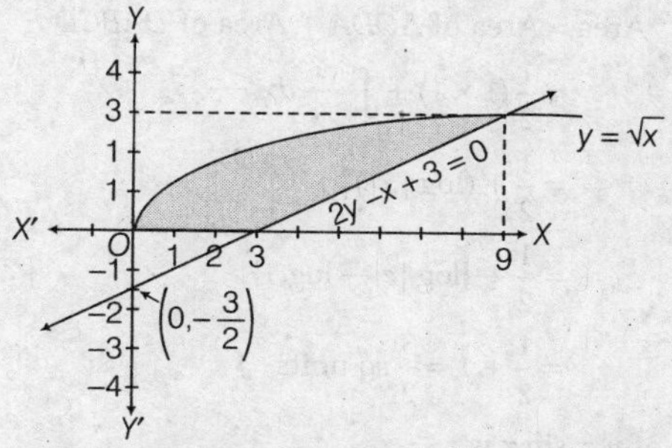

On solving Eqs. (i) and (ii), we get $2\sqrt{x} - (\sqrt{x})^2 + 3 = 0$

$$\Rightarrow \quad (\sqrt{x})^2 - 2\sqrt{x} - 3 = 0$$

$$\Rightarrow \quad (\sqrt{x} - 3)(\sqrt{x} + 1) = 0$$

$$\Rightarrow \quad \sqrt{x} = 3 \quad [\because \sqrt{x} = -1 \text{ is not possible}]$$

$$\Rightarrow \quad y = 3$$

$\therefore$ Required area $= \int_0^3 (\text{ line} - \text{curve})\, dy = \int_0^3 \{(2y + 3) - y^2\}\, dy$

$$= \left[y^2 + 3y - \frac{y^3}{3}\right]_0^3 = 9 + 9 - 9 = 9$$

90. **Given** Two parabolas $x^2 = \frac{y}{4}$ and $x^2 = 9y$

To find The area bounded between the parabolas and the straight line $y = 2$.

The required area is equal to the shaded region in the drawn figure.

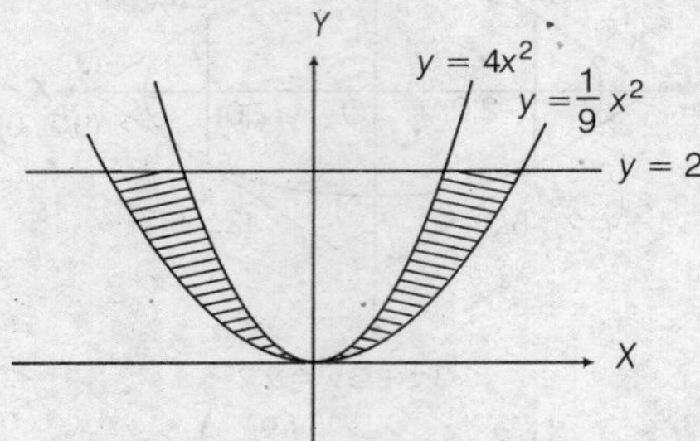

The area of the shaded region (which can be very easily found by using integration) is twice the area shaded in first quadrant.

$$\text{Required area} = 2\int_0^2 \left(3\sqrt{y} - \frac{\sqrt{y}}{2}\right) dy = 2\int_0^2 \left(\frac{5}{2}\sqrt{y}\right) dy$$

$$= 5\left[\frac{y^{3/2}}{3/2}\right]_{y=0}^{y=2} = \frac{10}{3}(2^{3/2} - 0) = \frac{20\sqrt{2}}{3}$$

91. Given, $y = x$, $x = e$ and $y = \frac{1}{x}$, $x \ge 0$

Since, $y = x$ and $x \ge 0 \Rightarrow y \ge 0$

$\therefore$ Area to be calculated in I quadrant shown as

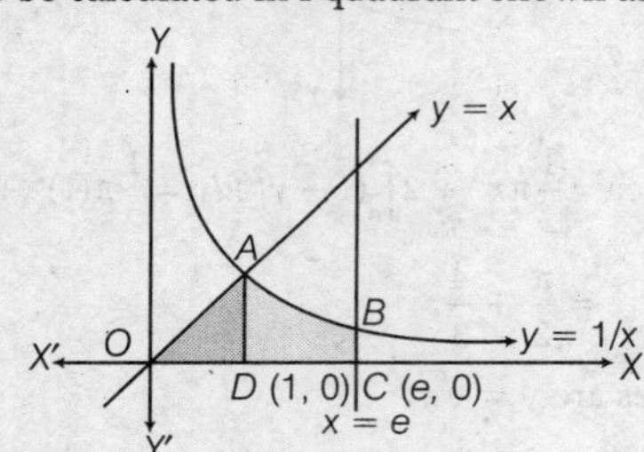

$\therefore$ Area = Area of ΔODA + Area of $DABCD$

$$= \frac{1}{2}(1 \times 1) + \int_1^e \frac{1}{x}\, dx$$

$$= \frac{1}{2} + (\log|x|)_1^e$$

$$= \frac{1}{2} + \{\log|e| - \log 1\} \qquad [\because \log|e| = 1]$$

$$= \frac{1}{2} + 1 = \frac{3}{2} \text{ sq units}$$

92. Graph of $y = \sin x$ is

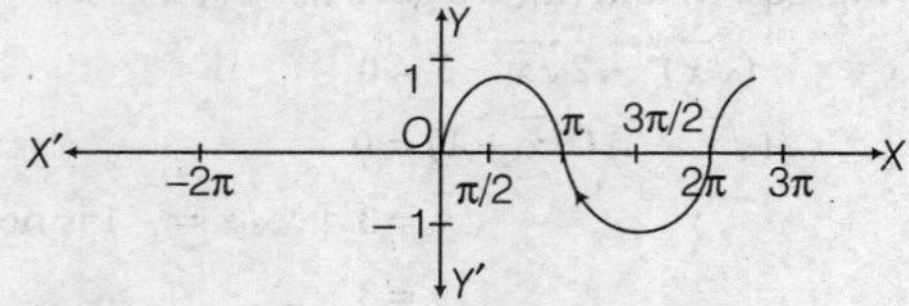

and graph of $y = \cos x$ is

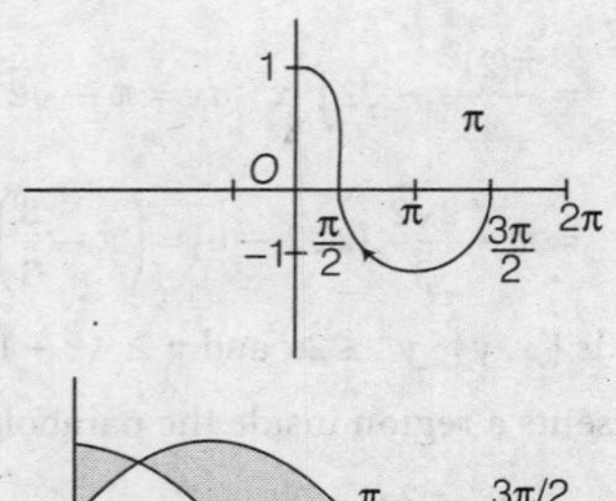

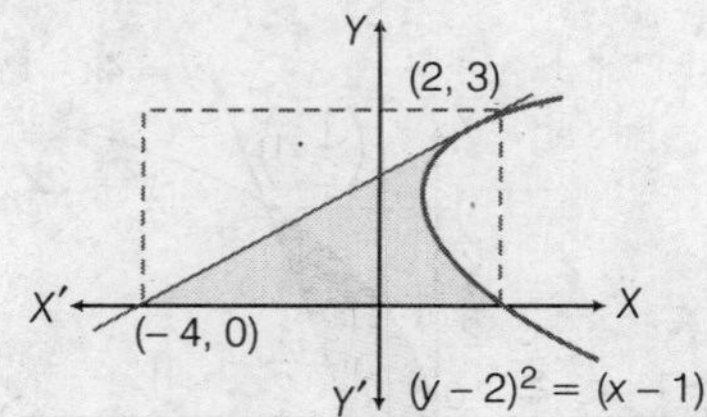

$$\text{Required area} = \int_0^{\pi/4} (\cos x - \sin x)\, dx + \int_{\pi/4}^{5\pi/4} (\sin x - \cos x)\, dx + \int_{5\pi/4}^{3\pi/2} (\cos x - \sin x)\, dx$$

$$= [\sin x + \cos x]_0^{\pi/4} + [-\cos x - \sin x]_{\pi/4}^{5\pi/4} + [\sin x + \cos x]_{5\pi/4}^{3\pi/2}$$

$$= (4\sqrt{2} - 2) \text{ sq units}$$

93. The equation of tangent at (2, 3) to the given parabola is $x = 2y - 4$

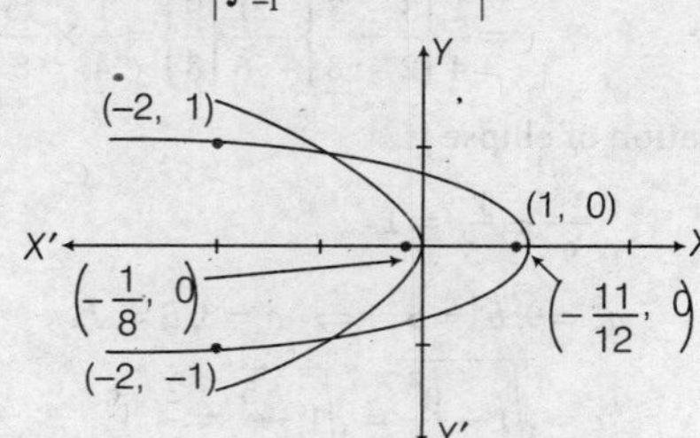

$$\therefore \text{Required area} = \int_0^3 \{(y-2)^2 + 1 - 2y + 4\} dy$$

$$= \left[\frac{(y-2)^3}{3} - y^2 + 5y\right]_0^3$$

$$= \frac{1}{3} - 9 + 15 + \frac{8}{3} = 9 \text{ sq units}$$

94. Given, equations of curves are $x + 3y^2 = 1$ ... (i)

and $x + 2y^2 = 0$ ... (ii)

On solving Eqs. (i) and (ii), we get

$y = \pm 1$ and $x = -2$

$$\therefore \text{Required area} = \left|\int_{-1}^{1} (x_1 - x_2)\, dy\right|$$

$$= \left|\int_{-1}^{1} (1 - 3y^2 + 2y^2)\, dy\right| = \left|\int_{-1}^{1} (1 - y^2)\, dy\right|$$

$$= \left|2\int_0^1 (1 - y^2)\, dy\right| = \left|2\left[y - \frac{y^3}{3}\right]_0^1\right| = \left|2\left(1 - \frac{1}{3}\right)\right| = \frac{4}{3} \text{ sq units}$$

CHAPTER

04

Differential Equations

Learning Part

Session 1

- Solution of a Differential Equation

Session 2

- Solving of Varibale Seperable Form
- Homogeneous Differential Equation

Session 3

- Solving of Linear Differential Equations
- Bernoulli's Equation
- Orthogonal Trajectory

Session 4

- Exact Differential Equations

Session 5

- Solving of First Order and Higher Degrees
- Application of Differential Equations
- Application of First Order Differential Equations

Practice Part

- JEE Type Examples
- Chapter Exercises

A differential equation can simply be said to be an equation involving derivatives of an unknown function. For example, consider the equation

$$\frac{dy}{dx} + xy = x^2$$

This is a differential equation since it involves the derivative of the funtion $y(x)$ which we may wish to determine. We must first understand why and how differnetial equations arise and why we need them at all. In general, we can say that a differential equation describes the behaviour of some continuously varying quantity.

Scenario 1 : A Freely Falling Body

A body is release at rest from a heigh h. How do we described the motion of this body?

The height x of the body is a function of time. Since the acceleration of the body is g, we have $\frac{d^2x}{dt^2} = g$

This is the differential equation describing the motion of the body. Along with the initial condition $x(0) = h$, it completely describes the motion of the body at all instants after the body starts falling.

Scenario 2 : Radioactive disintegration

Experimental evidence shows that the rate of decay of any ratioactive substance is proportional to the amount of the substance present,

i.e. $$\frac{dm}{dt} = -\lambda m$$

where m is the mass of the radioactive substance and a function of t. If we know $m(0)$, the initial mass, we can use this differential equation to determine the mass of the substance remaining at any later time instant.

Scenario 3 : Population Growth

The growth of population (of say, a biological culture) in a closed environment is dependent on the birth and death rates. The birth rate will contribute to increaseing the population while the death rate will contribute to its decrease. It has been found that for low populations, the birth rate is the dominant influence in population growth and the growth rate is linearly dependent on the current population. For high populations, there is a competition among the population for the limited resources available, and thus death rate becomes dominant. Also, the death rate shows a quadratic dependence on the current population.

Thus, if $N(t)$ represents the population at time t, the different equation describing the population variation is of the form

$$\frac{dN}{dt} = \lambda_1 N - \lambda_2 N^2$$

where λ_1 and λ_2 are constants.

Along with the initial population $N(0)$, this equation can tell us the population at any later time instant.

Session 1

Solution of a Differential Equation

These three examples should be sufficient for you to realise why and how differential equations arise and why they are important.

In all the three equations mentioned above, there is only independent variable (the time t in all the three cases). Such equations are termed **ordinary differential equations.** We might have equations involving more than one independent variable :

$$\frac{\partial f}{\partial x} + x\frac{\partial f}{\partial y} = x^2$$

where the notation $\frac{\partial}{\partial x}$ stands for the partial derivative, i.e. the term $\frac{\partial f}{\partial x}$ would imply that we differentiate the function f with respect to the independent variable x as the variable (while treating the other independent variable y as a constant). A similar interpretation can be attached to $\frac{\partial}{\partial y}$.

Such equations are termed **partial differential equations** but we shall not be concerned with them in this chapter.

Consider the ordinary differnetial equation

$$\frac{d^2y}{dx^2} + x\frac{dy}{dx} + x^2 = c$$

The order of the highest derivative present in this equation is two; thus we shall call it a second order differential equation (*DE*, for convenience).

The **order** of a *DE* is the order of the highest derivative that occurs in the equation

Again, consider the *DE*

$$\frac{d^2y}{dx^3}+\frac{dy}{dx}=x^2y^2$$

The degree of the highest order derivative in this DE is two, so this is a DE of degree two (and order three).

The degree of a DE is the degree of the highest order derivative that occurs in the equation, **when all the derivatives in the equation are made of free of fractional powers.**

$$\sqrt{\left(\frac{dy}{dx}\right)^2-1+x\left(\frac{d^2y}{dx^2}\right)}=k$$

is not of degree two. When we make this equation free of fractional powers, by the following rearrangement,

$$\left(\frac{dy}{dx}\right)^2-1+\left\{k-x\left(\frac{d^2y}{dx^2}\right)^2\right\}^2$$

we see that the degree of the highest order derivative will become four. Thus, this is a DE of degree four (and order two).

Finally, an nth **linear DE** (degree one) is an equation of the form

$$a_0\frac{d^ny}{dx^n}+a_1\frac{d^{n-1}}{dx^{n-1}}+\ldots+a_{n-1}\frac{dy}{dx}+a_ny=b$$

where the a_i's and b are functions of x.

Solving an nth order DE to evaluate the unknown function will essentially consists of doing n integrations on the DE. Each integration step will introduce an arbitrary constant. Thus, you can expect in general that the **solution of an nth order DE will contain n independnet arbitrary constants.**

By n independent constants, we mean to say that the most general solution of the DE cannot be expressed in fewer that n constants. As an example, the second order DE

$$\frac{d^y}{dx^2}+y=0$$

has its most general solution of the form

$$y=A\cos x+B\sin x. \quad \ldots(1)$$

(verify that this is a solution by explicit substitution).

Thus, two arbitrary and independent constants must be included in the general solution. We cannot reduce (1) to a relation containing only one arbitrary constant. On the other hand, it can be verified that the function

$$y=ae^{x+b}$$

is a solution to the second-order DE

$$\frac{d^2y}{dx^2}=y$$

but even through it (seems to) contain two arbitrary constants, it is not the general solution to this DE. This is because it can be reduced to a relation involving only one arbitrary constant :

$$y=ae^{x+b}=ae^x.e^b=ce^x \quad (\text{where } c=a\cdot e^b)$$

Let us summarise what we have seen till now : the most general solution of an nth order DE will consist of n orbitrary constants; conversely, from a functional relation involving n arbitrary constants, an nth order DE can be generated (we shall soon see how to do this). We are generally interested in solutions of the DE satisfying some particular constraints (say, some initial values). Since the most general solution of the DE involves n arbitrary constant, we see that the maximum member of independent conditions which can be imposed on a solution of the DE is n. As a first example, consider the functional relation

$$y=x^2+c_1e^{2x}+c_2e^{3x} \quad \ldots(i)$$

This curve's equation contains two arbitrary constants; as we vary c_1 and c_2, we obtain different curves; those curves constitute a family of curves. All members of this family will satisfy the DE that we can generate from this general relation; this DE will be second order since the relation contains two arbitrary constants.

We now see how to generate the DE. Differentiate the given relation twice to obtain

$$y'=2x+2c_1e^{2x}+3c_2e^{3x} \quad \ldots(ii)$$

$$y''=2+4c_1e^{2x}+9c_2e^{3x} \quad \ldots(iii)$$

From Eqs. (i), (ii) and (iii), c_1 and c_2 can be eliminated to obtain

$$\begin{vmatrix} e^{2x} & e^{3x} & x^2-y \\ 2e^{2x} & 3e^{3x} & 2x-y' \\ 4e^{2x} & 9e^{3x} & 2-y'' \end{vmatrix}$$

$$\Rightarrow \quad \begin{vmatrix} 1 & 1 & x^2-y \\ 2 & 3 & 2x-y' \\ 4 & 9 & 2-y'' \end{vmatrix}$$

$$\Rightarrow 6-3''-18x+9y'+8x-4y'-4+2y''+7x^2-6y=0$$

$$\Rightarrow \quad y''-5y'+6y=6x^2-10x+2 \quad \ldots(iv)$$

This is the required DE; it corresponds to the family of curves given by Eq. (i). Differently put, the most general solution of this DE is given by Eq. (i).

As an exercise for the reader, show that the DE corrersponding to the general equation

$$y = Ae^{2x} + Be^{x} + C$$

where A, B, C are arbitrary constants, is

$$y''' - 3y'' + 2y' = 0$$

By expected, the three arbitrary constants cause the DE to the third order.

Example 1 Find the order and degree (if defined) of the following differential equations :

(i) $y = 1 + \left(\frac{dy}{dx}\right) + \frac{1}{2!}\left(\frac{dy}{dx}\right)^2 + \frac{1}{3!}\left(\frac{dy}{dx}\right)^3 + \dots$

(ii) $\left(\frac{d^3y}{dx^3}\right)^{2/3} = \frac{dy}{dx} + 2$ (iii) $\frac{d^2y}{dx^2} = x \ln\left(\frac{dy}{dx}\right)$

Sol. (i) The given differential equation can be rewritten as

$$y = e^{dy/dx}$$

$$\Rightarrow \quad \frac{dy}{dx} = \ln y.$$

Hence, its order is 1 and degree 1.

(ii) The given differential equation can be rewritten as

$$\left(\frac{d^3y}{dx^3}\right)^2 = \left(\frac{dy}{dx} + 2\right)^3.$$

Hence, its order is 3 and degree 2.

(iii) Its order is obviously 2.

Since, the given differential equation cannot be written as a polynomial in all the differential coefficients, the degree of the equation is not defined.

Example 2 Find the order and degree (if defined) of the following differential equations :

(i) $\sqrt{\frac{d^2y}{dx^2}} = \sqrt[3]{\frac{dy}{dx} + 3}$ (ii) $\frac{d^2y}{dx^2} = \sin\left(\frac{dy}{dx}\right)$

(iii) $\frac{dy}{dx} = \sqrt{3x + 5}$

Sol. (i) The given differential equation can be rewritten as

$$\left(\frac{d^2y}{dx^2}\right)^3 = \left(\frac{dy}{dx} + 3\right)^2$$

Hence, order is 2 and degree is 3.

(ii) The given differential equation has the order 2. Since, the given differential equation cannot be written as a polynomial in the differential coefficients, the degree of the equation is not defined.

(iii) Its order is obviously 1 and degree 1.

Linear and Non-linear Differential Equation

A differential equation is a linear differential equation if it is expressible in the form

$$a_0 \frac{d^ny}{dx^n} + a_1 \frac{d^{n-1}y}{dx^{n-1}} + a_2 \frac{d^{n-2}y}{dx^{n-2}} + \dots + a_{n-1}\frac{dy}{dx} + any = Q$$

where $a_0, a_1, a_2, \dots, a_n$ and Q are either constants or functions of independent variable x.

Thus, if a differential equation when expressed in the form of a polynomial involves the derivatives and dependent variable in the first power and there ae no product of these, and also the coefficient of the various terms are either constants or functions of the independent variable, then it is said to be linear differential equation. otherwise, it i a non-linear differential equation.

The differentiable equation $\left(\frac{d^3y}{dx^3}\right)^2 - 6\left(\frac{d^2y}{dx^2}\right) - 4y = 0$, is a non-linear differential equation, because its degree is 2, more than one.

e.g. The differential equation, $\left(\frac{d^3y}{dx^3}\right) + 2\left(\frac{dy}{dx}\right)^2 + 9y = x$, is non-linear differential equation, because differential coefficient $\frac{dy}{dx}$ has exponent 2.

e.g. The differential equation $(x^2 + y^2)\,dx - 2xydy = 0$ is a non-linear differential equation, because the exponent of dependent variable y is 2 and it involves the product of y and $\frac{dy}{dx}$. e.g. Consider the differential equation

$$\left(\frac{d^2y}{dx^2}\right) - 5\left(\frac{dy}{dx}\right) + 6y = \sin x$$

This is a linear differential equation of order 2 and degree.

Formation of Differential Equations

If an equation in independent and dependent variables involving some arbitrary constants is given, then a differential equation is obtained as follows :

(i) Differentiate the given equation w.r.t. the independent variable (say x) as many times as the number of arbitrary constants in it.

(ii) Eliminate the arbitrary constants.

(iii) The eliminant is the required differential equation. i.e. If we have an equation $f(x, y, c_1, c_2, \dots, c_n) = 0$

Containing n arbitrary constants $c_1, c_2, c_3, \ldots, c_n$, then by differentiating this n times, we shall get n-equations.

Now, among these n-equations and the given equation, in all $(n+1)$ equations, if the n arbitrary constants $c_1, c_2, c_3, \ldots, c_n$ are eliminated, we shall evidently get a differential equation of the nth order. For there being n differentiation, the resulting equation must contain a derivative of the nth order.

Algorithm for Formation of Differential Equations

Step I Write the given equation involving independent variable x (say), dependent variable y (say) and the arbitrary constant.

Step II Obtain the number of arbitrary constants in Step I. Let there be n arbitrary constants.

Step III Differentiate the relation in step I, n times with respect to x.

Step IV Eliminate arbitrary consstants with the help of n equations involving differential coefficients obtained in step III and an equation in step I.

The equation so obtained is the desired differential equation. The following examples will illustrate the above procedure.

Example 3 Form the differential equation, if $y^2 = 4a(x+b)$, where a, b are arbitrary constants.

Sol. Differentiating $y^2 = 4a(x+b)$ w.r.t. x,

$$2y \cdot \frac{dy}{dx} = 4a \quad \text{i.e.} \quad y\frac{dy}{dx} = 2a$$

Again, differentiating w.r.t. x, we get

$$y\frac{d^2y}{dx^2} + \left(\frac{dy}{dx}\right)^2 = 0$$

which is the required differential equation. Thus, the elimination of arbitrary leads to the formation of a differential equation.

Example 4 Find the differential equation whose solution represents the family $xy = ae^x + be^{-x}$.

Sol.
$$xy = ae^x + be^{-x} \quad \ldots\text{(i)}$$

Differentiating Eq. (i) w.r.t. x, we get

$$x\frac{dy}{dx} + y = ae^x - be^{-x} \quad \ldots\text{(ii)}$$

Differentiating Eq. (ii) w.r.t. x, we get

$$x\frac{d^2y}{dx^2} + \frac{dy}{dx} \cdot 1 + \frac{dy}{dx} = ae^x + be^{-x} \quad \ldots\text{(iii)}$$

Using Eqs. (i) and (iii), we get

$$x\frac{d^2y}{dx^2} + 2\frac{dy}{dx} = xy$$

Which is the required differential equation.

Example 5 Find the differential equation whose solution represents the family $c(y+c)^2 = x^3$.

Sol. Differentiating $c(y+c)^2 = x^3$ ...(i)

We get $c[2(y+c)]\frac{dy}{dx} = 3x^2$ but from Eq. (i), we have

$$\frac{2x^3}{(y+c)^2}(y+c)\frac{dy}{dx} = 3x^2$$

$$\Rightarrow \frac{2x^3}{y+c} \cdot \frac{dy}{dx} = 3x^2 \quad \text{i.e.} \quad \frac{2x}{y+c} \cdot \frac{dy}{dx} = 3$$

$$\Rightarrow \frac{2x}{3}\left[\frac{dy}{dx}\right] = y + c \quad \therefore \quad c = \frac{2x}{3}\left[\frac{dy}{dx}\right] - y$$

Substituting c in Eq. (i), we get

$$\left[\frac{2x}{3}\left(\frac{dy}{dx}\right) - y\right]\left[\frac{2x}{3}\frac{dy}{dx}\right]^2 = x^3$$

Which is the required differential equation.

Example 6 Find the differential equation whose solution represents the family $y = ae^{3x} + be^x$.

Sol.
$$y = ae^{3x} + be^x \quad \ldots\text{(i)}$$

Differentiating the given equation twice, we get

$$\frac{dy}{dx} = 3ae^{3x} + be^x \quad \text{and} \quad \frac{d^2y}{dx^2} = 9ae^{3x} + be^x$$

From the three equations by eliminating a and b, we obtain

$$\frac{d^2y}{dx^2} - \frac{4dy}{dx} + 3y = 0$$

Remark

The order of the differential equation will be equal to number of independent parameters and is not equal to the number of all the parameters in the family of curves.

Example 7 Find the order of the family of curves $y = (c_1 + c_2)e^x + c_3 e^{x+c_4}$.

Sol. Here, the number of arbitrary parameters is 4 but the order of the corresponding differential equation will not be 4 as it can be rewritten as, $y = (c_1 + c_2 + c_3 e^{c_4})e^x$, which is of the form $y = Ae^x$. Hence, the corresponding differential equation will be of order 1.

Example 8 The differential equation of all non-horizontal lines in a plane is given by

(a) $\frac{d^2y}{dx^2} = 0$ (b) $\frac{d^2x}{dy^2} = 0$

(c) $\frac{d^2y}{dx^2} = 0$ and $\frac{d^2x}{dy^2} = 0$ (d) All of these

Sol. The equation of the family of all non-horizontal lines in a plane is given by,

$$ax + by = 1 \qquad \text{(where } a \neq 0) \quad ...(i)$$

Differentiating w.r.t. y, we get

$$a\frac{dx}{dy} + b = 0 \qquad \text{(as } a \neq 0 \text{ and } b \in R)$$

Again, differentiating w.r.t. y, we get

$$a\frac{d^2x}{dy^2} = 0 \qquad \text{(as } a \neq 0 \text{ and } b \in R)$$

$$\Rightarrow \frac{d^2x}{dy^2} = 0 \qquad \text{(as } a \neq 0)$$

$\therefore$ Differential equation of all non-horizontal lines in a plane is $\frac{d^2x}{dy^2} = 0$. Hence, (b) is the correct answer.

| Example 9 The differential equation of all non-vertical lines in a plane is given by

(a) $\frac{d^2y}{dx^2} = 0$ (b) $\frac{d^2x}{dy^2} = 0$

(c) $\frac{d^2x}{dy^2} = 0$ and $\frac{d^2y}{dx^2} = 0$ (d) All of these

Sol. The equation of the family of all non-vertical lines in a plane is given by $ax + by = 1$, where $b \neq 0$ and $a \in R$.

Differentiating both the sides w.r.t. x, we get

$$a + b\frac{dy}{dx} = 0 \qquad \text{(as } b \neq 0 \text{ and } a \in R)$$

Again, differentiating both the sides w.r.t. x, we get

$$b\frac{d^2y}{dx^2} = 0 \qquad \text{(as } b \neq 0 \text{ and } a \in R)$$

$$\Rightarrow \frac{d^2y}{dx^2} = 0 \qquad \text{(as } b \neq 0)$$

$\therefore$ Differential equation of all non-vertical lines in a plane.

$$\Rightarrow \frac{d^2y}{dx^2} = 0$$

Hence, (a) is the correct answer.

| Example 10 The differential equation of all straight lines which are at a constant distance p from the origin, is

(a) $(y + xy_1)^2 = p^2(1 + y_1^2)$ (b) $(y - xy_1^2) = p^2(1 + y_1)^2$

(c) $(y - xy_1)^2 = p^2(1 + y_1^2)$ (d) None of these

Sol. As, we know $x\cos\alpha + y\sin\alpha = p$ ...(i)

Represents the family of straight lines which are at a constant distance p from origin. Differentiating Eq. (i) w.r.t. x, we get

$$\cos\alpha + \sin\alpha \cdot \frac{dy}{dx} = 0$$

$$\Rightarrow \tan\alpha = -\frac{1}{y_1} \text{ or } \sin\alpha = \frac{1}{\sqrt{1 + y_1^2}}$$

and $$\cos\alpha = -\frac{y_1}{\sqrt{1 + y_1^2}} \quad ...(ii)$$

From Eqs. (i) and (ii), we get

$$\frac{-xy_1}{\sqrt{1 + y_1^2}} + \frac{y}{\sqrt{1 + y_1^2}} = p$$

$\Rightarrow (y - xy_1)^2 = p^2(1 + y_1^2)$ is required differential equations.

Hence, (c) is the correct answer.

| Example 11 The differential equation of all circles of radius r, is given by

(a) $\{1 + (y_1)^2\}^2 = r^2 y_2^3$ (b) $\{1 + (y_1)^2\}^3 = r^2 y_2^3$

(c) $\{1 + (y_1)^2\}^3 = r^2 y_2^2$ (d) None of these

Sol. Equation of circle of radius r,

$$(x - a)^2 + (y - b)^2 = r^2 \quad ...(i)$$

(Here, a, b are two arbitrary constants)

Differentiating Eq. (i), we get

$$2(x - a) + 2(y - b)y_1 = 0 \quad ...(ii)$$

Again, differentiating Eq. (ii), we get

$$1 + (y - b)y_2 + y_1^2 = 0$$

$$\Rightarrow (y - b) = -\left(\frac{1 + y_1^2}{y_2}\right) \quad ...(iii)$$

Putting $(y - b)$ in Eq. (ii), we get

$$(x - a) = \frac{(1 + y_1^2)y_1}{y_2} \quad ...(iv)$$

From Eqs. (i), (iii) and (iv), we get

$$\frac{(1 + y_1^2)^2 \cdot y_1^2}{y_2^2} + \frac{(1 + y_1^2)^2}{y_2^2} = r^2$$

$$\Rightarrow (1 + (y_1)^2)^3 = r^2 y_2^2$$

Hence, (c) is the correct answer.

| Example 12 The differential equations of all circles touching the x-axis at origin is

(a) $(y^2 - x^2) = 2xy\left(\frac{dy}{dx}\right)$

(b) $(x^2 - y^2)\frac{dy}{dx} = 2xy$

(c) $(x^2 - y^2) = 2xy\left(\frac{dy}{dx}\right)$

(d) None of the above

Sol. The equation of circle touches x-axis at origin.

$$\Rightarrow (x - 0)^2 + (y - a)^2 = a^2$$

or $$x^2 + y^2 - 2ay = 0 \quad ...(i)$$

Differentiating w.r.t. x, we get

$$2x + 2y\frac{dy}{dx} - 2a\frac{dy}{dx} = 0$$

$$\Rightarrow \quad \frac{dy}{dx}(a - y) = x$$

$$\Rightarrow \quad a = \frac{x + y\left(\frac{dy}{dx}\right)}{\left(\frac{dy}{dx}\right)} \quad \text{...(ii)}$$

From Eqs. (i) and (ii), we get

$$x^2 + y^2 - 2y\left[\frac{x + y\left(\frac{dy}{dx}\right)}{\left(\frac{dy}{dx}\right)}\right] = 0$$

or $$(x^2 - y^2)\frac{dy}{dx} = 2xy$$

Hence, (b) is the correct answer.

Example 13 The differential equation of all circles in the first quadrant which touch the coordinate axes is

(a) $(x - y)^2 (1 + (y')^2) = (x + yy')^2$

(b) $(x + y)^2 (1 + (y')^2) = (x + y')^2$

(c) $(x - y)^2 (1 + y') = (x + yy')^2$

(d) None of these

Sol. Equation of circles touching coordinate axes is

$$(x - a)^2 + (y - a)^2 = a^2 \quad \text{...(i)}$$

Differentiating, we get

$$2(x - a) + 2(y - a)y' = 0$$

$$\Rightarrow \quad a = \frac{x + yy'}{1 + y'}; \text{ where } y' = \frac{dy}{dx} \quad \text{...(ii)}$$

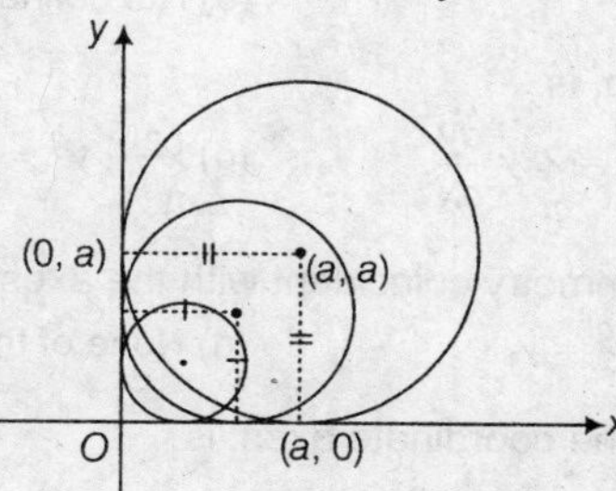

From Eqs. (i) and (ii),

$$\left(x - \frac{x + yy'}{1 + y'}\right)^2 + \left(y - \frac{x + yy'}{1 + y'}\right)^2 = \left(\frac{x + yy'}{1 + y'}\right)^2$$

$$\Rightarrow \quad \left(\frac{xy' - yy'}{1 + y'}\right)^2 + \left(\frac{y - x}{1 + y'}\right)^2 = \left(\frac{x + yy'}{1 + y'}\right)^2$$

$$\Rightarrow \quad (x - y)^2 (y')^2 + (y - x)^2 = (x + yy')^2$$

$$\Rightarrow \quad (x - y)^2 (1 + (y')^2) = (x + yy')^2$$

Hence, (a) is the correct answer.

Example 14 The differential equation satisfying the curve $\frac{x^2}{a^2 + \lambda} + \frac{y^2}{b^2 + \lambda} = 1$, where λ being arbitrary unknown, is

(a) $(x + yy_1)(xy_1 - y) = (a^2 - b^2)y_1$

(b) $(x + yy_1)(x - yy_1) = y_1$

(c) $(x - yy_1)(xy_1 + y) = (a^2 - b^2)y_1$

(d) None of these

Sol. Here, $$\frac{x^2}{a^2 + \lambda} + \frac{y^2}{b^2 + \lambda} = 1 \quad \text{...(i)}$$

Differentiating both the sides, we get

$$\frac{2x}{a^2 + \lambda} + \frac{2y}{b^2 + \lambda} \cdot \frac{dy}{dx} = 0$$

$$\Rightarrow \quad x(b^2 + \lambda) + y(a^2 + \lambda)y_1 = 0$$

$$\Rightarrow \quad \lambda = -\left(\frac{xb^2 + a^2yy_1}{x + yy_1}\right)$$

$$\therefore \quad a^2 + \lambda = a^2 - \frac{xb^2 + a^2yy_1}{x + yy_1}$$

$$\Rightarrow \quad a^2 + \lambda = \frac{(a^2 - b^2)x}{x + yy_1} \quad \text{...(ii)}$$

Also, $$b^2 + \lambda = \frac{(a^2 - b^2)yy_1}{x + yy_1} \quad \text{...(iii)}$$

From Eqs. (i), (ii) and (iii), we get

$$\frac{x^2(x + yy_1)}{(a^2 - b^2)x} + \frac{y^2(x + yy_1)}{(a^2 - b^2)yy_1} = 1$$

$$\Rightarrow \quad (x + yy_1)(xy_1 - y) = (a^2 - b^2)y_1$$

Hence, (a) is the correct answer.

Example 15 The differential equation of all conics whose centre lies at origin, is given by

(a) $(3xy_2 + x^2y_3)(y - xy_1) = 3xy_2(y - xy_1 - x^2y_2)$

(b) $(3xy_1 + x^2y_2)(y_1 - xy_3) = 3xy_1(y - xy_2 - x^2y_3)$

(c) $(3xy_2 + x^2y_3)(y_1 - xy) = 3xy_1(y - xy_1 - x^2y_2)$

(d) None of the above

Sol. Equation of all conics whose centre lies at origin, is

$$ax^2 + 2hxy + by^2 = 1 \quad \text{...(i)}$$

Differentiating Eq. (i) w.r.t. x, we get

$$2ax + 2hxy_1 + 2hy + 2byy_1 = 0$$

$$\Rightarrow \quad ax + h(y + xy_1) + byy_1 = 0$$

Multiplying by x equation becomes,

$$ax^2 + h(xy + x^2y_1) + bxyy_1 = 0 \quad \text{...(ii)}$$

Subtracting Eqs. (i) and (ii), we get

$$h(xy - x^2y_1) + b(y^2 - xyy_1) = 1$$

$$\Rightarrow \quad (hx + by)\, y - xy_1 (hx + by) = 1$$

$$\Rightarrow \quad (hx + by)(y - xy_1) = 1$$

$$\Rightarrow \quad hx + by = \frac{1}{y - xy_1} \quad \text{...(iii)}$$

Again, differentiating w.r.t. x, we get

$$h + by_1 = -\frac{(y_1 - xy_2 - y_1)}{(y - xy_1)^2}$$

or
$$h + by_1 = \frac{xy_2}{(y - xy_1)^2} \quad \text{...(iv)}$$

From Eqs. (iii) and (iv), we get

$$b(y - xy_1) = \frac{y - xy_1 - x^2 y_2}{(y - xy_1)^2}$$

$$\Rightarrow \quad b = \frac{y - xy_1 - x^2 y_2}{(y - xy_1)^3} \quad \text{...(v)}$$

Again, differentiating both the sides w.r.t. x, we get

$$0 = \frac{y_1 - y_1 - 3xy_2 - x^2 y_3}{(y - xy_1)^3} + \frac{3(y - xy_1 - x^2 y_2)\, xy_2}{(y - xy_1)^4}$$

$$\Rightarrow \quad (3xy_2 + x^2 y_3)(y - xy_1) = 3xy_2 (y - xy_1 - x^2 y_2)$$

Hence, (a) is the correct answer.

Exercise for Session 1

1. The differential equation of all parabolas whose axis of symmetry is along X-axis is of order.
(a) 2 (b) 3 (c) 1 (d) None of these

2. The order and degree of the differential equation of all tangent lines to the parabola $x^2 = 4y$ is
(a) 1, 2 (b) 2, 2 (c) 3, 1 (d) 4, 1

3. The degree of the differential equation $\frac{d^2y}{dx^2} + 3\left(\frac{dy}{dx}\right)^2 = x^2 \log\left(\frac{d^2y}{dx^2}\right)$ is
(a) 1 (b) 2 (c) 3 (d) Not defined

4. The degree of the defferential equation satisfying the relation $\sqrt{1+x^2} + \sqrt{1+y^2} = \lambda(x\sqrt{1+y^2} - y\sqrt{1+x^2})$ is
(a) 1 (b) 2 (c) 3 (d) 4

5. The degree of the differential equation $\left(\frac{d^2y}{dx^2}\right)^2 + \left(\frac{dy}{dx}\right)^2 = x \sin\left(\frac{d^2y}{dx^2}\right)$ is
(a) 1 (b) 2 (c) 3 (d) Not defined

6. The differential equation of all circles touching the y-axis at origin, is
(a) $y^2 - x^2 = 2xy\frac{dy}{dx}$ (b) $y^2 - x^2 = 2xy\frac{dx}{dy}$ (c) $x^2 - y^2 = 2xy\frac{dy}{dx}$ (d) $x^2 - y^2 = 2xy\frac{dx}{dy}$

7. The differential equation of all parabolas having their axes of symmetry coincident with the axes of x, is
(a) $yy_2 + y_1^2 = y + y_1$ (b) $yy_2 + y_1^2 = 0$ (c) $yy_2 + y_1^2 = y_1$ (d) None of these

8. The differential equation of all conics whose axes coincide with the coordinate axes, is
(a) $xyy_2 + xy_1^2 - yy_1 = 0$
(b) $yy_2 + y_1^2 - yy_1 = 0$
(c) $xyy_2 + (x - y)\, y_1 = 0$
(d) None of these

9. The differential equation having $y = (\sin^{-1} x)^2 + A(\cos^{-1} x) + B$, where A and B are arbitrary constant, is
(a) $(1 - x^2)\, y_2 - xy_1 = 2$
(b) $(1 - x^2)\, y_2 + yy_1 = 0$
(c) $(1 - x)\, y_2 + xy_1 = 0$
(d) None of these

10. The differential equation of circles passing through the points of intersection of unit circle with centre at the origin and the line bisecting the first quadrant, is
(a) $y_1 (x^2 + y^2 - 1) + (x + yy_1) = 0$
(b) $(y_1 - 1)(x^2 + y^2 - 1) + (x + yy_1)\, 2(x - y) = 0$
(c) $(x^2 + y^2 - 1) + yy_2 = 0$
(d) None of these

Session 2

Solving of Variable Seperable Form, Homogeneous Differential Equation

Solving of Variable Seperable Form

Solution of a Differential Equation

The solution of the differential equation is a relation between the variables of the equation not containing the derivatives, but satisfying the given differential equation (i.e from which the given differential equation can be derived).

Thus, the solution of $\frac{dy}{dx} = e^x$ could be obtained by simply integrating both the sides, i.e. $y = e^x + C$ and that of, $\frac{dy}{dx} = px + q$ is $y = p\frac{x^2}{2} + qx + C$, where C is arbitrary constant.

(i) **A general solution or an integral** of a differential equation is a relation between the variables (not involving the derivatives) which contains the same number of the arbitrary constants as the order of the differential equation. For example, a general solution of the differential equation $\frac{d^2x}{dt^2} = -4x$ is $x = A\cos 2t + B\sin 2t$, where A and B are the arbitrary constants.

(ii) **Particular solution or particular integral** is that solution of the differential equation obtained from the general solution by assigning particular values to the arbitrary constant in the general solution.
For example, $x = 10\cot 2t + 5\sin 2t$ is a particular solution of differential equation $\frac{d^2x}{dt^2} = -4x$.

Differential Equations of the First Order and First Degree

In this section we shall discuss the differential equations which are of first order and first degree only.

A differential equation of first order and first degree is of the form $\frac{dy}{dx} = f(x, y)$.

Remark

All the differential equations, even of first order and first degree, cannot be solved. However, if they belong to any of the standard forms which we are going to discuss, in the subsequent articles they can be solved.

Equations in Which the Variables are Separable

The equation $\frac{dy}{dx} = f(x, y)$ is said to be in variables separable form, if we can express it in the form $f(x)\,dx = g(y)\,dy$.
By integrating this, solution of the equation is obtained which is, $\int f(x)\,dx = \int g(y)\,dy + C$

Example 16 Solve

$$\sec^2 x \tan y\,dx + \sec^2 y \tan x\,dy = 0.$$

Sol. Dividing the given equation by $\tan x \tan y$, we get

$$\frac{\sec^2 x}{\tan x}dx + \frac{\sec^2 y}{\tan y}dy = 0$$

This is variable-separable type

Integrating, $\int \frac{\sec^2 x}{\tan x}dx + \int \frac{\sec^2 y}{\tan y}dy = C'$

$$\ln|\tan x| + \ln|\tan y| = \ln C; \text{ where } C' = \ln C$$

or $\quad \ln|\tan x \cdot \tan y| = \ln C;\ (C > 0)$

$\Rightarrow \quad |\tan x \cdot \tan y| = C$

This is the general solution.

Example 17 Solve $\frac{dy}{dx} = e^{x-y} + x^2 e^{-y}$.

Sol. Here, $\frac{dy}{dx} = \frac{e^x}{e^y} + \frac{x^2}{e^y} \Rightarrow e^y\,dy = (x^2 + e^x)\,dx$

This is variable-separable form,

$\therefore$ Integrating both the sides,

$$\int e^y\,dy = \int (x^2 + e^x)\,dx \Rightarrow e^y = \frac{x^3}{3} + e^x + C$$

Which is the general solution of the given differential equation, where C is an arbitrary constant.

Example 18 Solve $\sqrt{1+x^2+y^2+x^2y^2} + xy\dfrac{dy}{dx} = 0.$

Sol. The given differential equation can be written as

$$\sqrt{(1+y^2)(1+x^2)} = -xy\frac{dy}{dx}$$

$$\Rightarrow \quad -\frac{\sqrt{1+x^2}\,dx}{x} = \frac{y\,dy}{\sqrt{1+y^2}}$$

This is the variable-separable form.

$\therefore$ Integrating both the sides, we get

$$-\int \frac{\sqrt{1+x^2}}{x}\,dx = \int \frac{y}{\sqrt{1+y^2}}\,dy$$

$$\Rightarrow -\left[\sqrt{1+x^2} + \frac{1}{2}\log\left(\frac{\sqrt{1+x^2}-1}{\sqrt{1+x^2}+1}\right)\right] = \sqrt{1+y^2} + C$$

This is the general solution to the given differential equation.

Example 19 Solve $y - x\dfrac{dy}{dx} = a\left(y^2 + \dfrac{dy}{dx}\right).$

Sol. Rewriting the given equation as

$$y - ay^2 = (x+a)\frac{dy}{dx}$$

$$\Rightarrow \quad \frac{dy}{y(1-ay)} = \frac{dx}{(x+a)}$$

This is the variable-separable form.

Integrating both the sides, we get

$$\int \frac{dy}{y(1-ay)} = \int \frac{dx}{(x+a)}$$

$$\Rightarrow \quad \int\left(\frac{1}{y} + \frac{a}{1-ay}\right)dy = \int \frac{dx}{x+a}$$

$$\Rightarrow \quad \ln y - \frac{a}{a}\ln(1-ay) + \ln C = \ln(a+x)$$

$$\Rightarrow \quad \ln\left(\frac{(a+x)(1-ay)}{y}\right) = \ln(C)$$

or $\quad Cy = (a+x)(1-ay)$ is the general solution.

Example 20 Solve $e^{dy/dx} = x+1$, given that when $x = 0, y = 3$.

Sol. This is an Example of particular solution.

$$e^{(dy/dx)} = x+1$$

$$\therefore \quad \frac{dy}{dx} = \ln(x+1)$$

$$\therefore \quad \int dy = \int \ln(x+1)\,dx \qquad \text{(integration by parts)}$$

i.e. $\quad y = x\ln(x+1) - \displaystyle\int \frac{x}{x+1}\,dx$

i.e. $\quad y = x\ln(x+1) - x + \ln(x+1) + C$

This is the general solution.

To find the particular solution, put $x = 0$, $y = 3$ in the general equation.

$\therefore \quad 3 = 0 - 0 + 0 + C$

$\therefore \quad C = 3$

$\therefore$ The required particular solution is,

$$y = (x+1)\ln(x+1) - x + 3$$

Differential Equations Reducible to the Separable Variable Type

Sometimes differential equation of the first order cannot be solved directly by variable separation but by some substitution we can reduce it to a differential equation with separable variable. "A differential equation of the form $\dfrac{dy}{dx} = f(ax+by+c)$ is solved by writing $ax+by+c = t$."

Example 21 Solve $\dfrac{dy}{dx} = \sin^2(x+3y) + 5.$

Sol. Let $x + 3y = t$, so that $1 + \dfrac{3dy}{dx} = \dfrac{dt}{dx}$

The given differential equation becomes,

$$\frac{1}{3}\left(\frac{dt}{dx} - 1\right) = \sin^2(t) + 5 \Rightarrow \frac{dt}{dx} = 3\sin^2 t + 16$$

$$\Rightarrow \quad \int \frac{dt}{3\sin^2 t + 16} = \int dx$$

$$\Rightarrow \quad \int \frac{\sec^2 t\,dt}{3\tan^2 t + 16\sec^2 t} = x + C$$

$$\Rightarrow \quad \int \frac{\sec^2 t\,dt}{19\tan^2 t + 16} = x + C$$

$$\Rightarrow \quad \int \frac{du}{19u^2 + 16} = x + C; \text{ where } \tan t = u$$

$$\Rightarrow \quad \sec^2 t\,dt = du$$

$$\Rightarrow \quad \frac{1}{19}\int \frac{du}{u^2 + \frac{16}{19}} \Rightarrow \frac{1}{19}\cdot\frac{\sqrt{19}}{4}\tan^{-1}\left(\frac{\sqrt{19}u}{4}\right) + C$$

$$\Rightarrow \quad \frac{1}{4\sqrt{19}}\left\{\tan^{-1}\left(\frac{\sqrt{19}}{4}\tan(3y+x)\right)\right\} + C$$

Example 22 Solve $(x+y)^2 \dfrac{dy}{dx} = a^2$.

Sol. $$(x+y)^2 \frac{dy}{dx} = a^2 \quad \text{...(i)}$$

Put $x + y = t \Rightarrow 1 + \dfrac{dy}{dx} = \dfrac{dt}{dx}$ or $\dfrac{dy}{dx} = \left(\dfrac{dt}{dx} - 1\right)$

$\therefore$ Eq. (i) reduces to $t^2 \left\{\dfrac{dt}{dx} - 1\right\} = a^2$

i.e. $t^2 \dfrac{dt}{dx} = a^2 + t^2$, separating the variable and integrating.

$$\int dx = \int \frac{t^2}{a^2 + t^2}\, dt = \int \left(1 - \frac{a^2}{a^2 + t^2}\right) dt$$

$\therefore$ $$x = t - a \tan^{-1}\left(\frac{t}{a}\right) + C$$

i.e. $$x = x + y - a \tan^{-1}\left(\frac{x+y}{a}\right) + C$$

i.e. $y = a \tan^{-1}\left(\dfrac{x+y}{a}\right) - C$ is the required general solution.

Example 23 Solve
$(2x + 3y - 1)\, dx + (4x + 6y - 5)\, dy = 0.$

Sol. $(2x + 3y - 1)\, dx + (4x + 6y - 5)\, dy = 0$ ...(i)

Substitute $u = 2x + 3y - 1$

$\therefore$ $$\frac{du}{dx} = 2 + \frac{3dy}{dx} \quad \text{or} \quad \frac{dy}{dx} = \frac{1}{3}\left(\frac{du}{dx} - 2\right)$$

$\therefore$ Eq. (i) reduces to

$$u + (2u - 3)\frac{1}{3}\left(\frac{du}{dx} - 2\right) = 0$$

i.e. $$u - \frac{2}{3}(2u - 3) + \frac{1}{3}(2u - 3)\frac{du}{dx} = 0$$

i.e. $$\frac{-u + 6}{3} + \frac{1}{3}(2u - 3)\frac{du}{dx} = 0$$

Writing this in the variable-separable form

$$\left(\frac{2u - 3}{u - 6}\right) du = dx$$

$\therefore$ $$\int dx = \int \frac{2u - 3}{u - 6}\, du$$

$\therefore$ $$x + C = \int \frac{2(u - 6) + 9}{(u - 6)}\, du$$

$\therefore$ $$x + C = 2u + 9 \ln |u - 6|$$

$\therefore$ $$x + C = 2(2x + 3y - 1) + 9 \ln |2x + 3y - 7|$$

$3x + 6y - 2 + 9 \ln |2x + 3y - 7| = C$ is the general solution.

Remarks

Sometimes transformation to the polar coordinates facilitates separation of varibales. It is convenient to remember the following differentials.

1. $x\, dx + y\, dy = r\, dr$ **2.** $x\, dy - y\, dx = r^2\, d\theta$

3. $dx^2 + dy^2 = dr^2 + r^2 d\,\theta^2$

Example 24 Solve $\dfrac{x\,dx + y\,dy}{x\,dy - y\,dx} = \sqrt{\dfrac{a^2 - x^2 - y^2}{x^2 + y^2}}$.

Sol. Let $x = r\cos\theta$, $y = r\sin\theta$

So that $$x^2 + y^2 = r^2 \quad \text{...(i)}$$

and $$\tan\theta = \frac{y}{x} \quad \text{...(ii)}$$

From Eq. (i), we have $d(x^2 + y^2) = d(r^2)$

i.e. $$x\,dx + y\,dy = r\,dr \quad \text{...(iii)}$$

From Eq. (ii), we have $d\left(\dfrac{y}{x}\right) = d(\tan\theta)$

i.e. $$\frac{x\,dy - y\,dx}{x^2} = \sec^2\theta\, d\theta$$

i.e. $x\,dy - y\,dx = x^2 \sec^2\theta\, d\theta = r^2\cos^2\theta \sec^2\theta\, d\theta$ ...(iv)

Using Eqs. (iii) and (iv) in the given equation, we get

$$\frac{r\,dr}{r^2\,d\theta} = \sqrt{\frac{a^2 - r^2}{r^2}} \quad \text{i.e.} \quad \frac{dr}{\sqrt{a^2 - r^2}} = d\theta$$

i.e. $$\sin^{-1}\left(\frac{r}{a}\right) = \theta + C \quad \text{or} \quad r = a\sin(\theta + C)$$

or $$\sqrt{x^2 + y^2} = a\sin\{C + \tan^{-1}(y/x)\}$$

It is advised to remember the results (iii) and (iv).

Homogeneous Differential Equation

By definition, a homogeneouos function $f(x, y)$ of degree n satisfies the property

$$f(\lambda x, \lambda y) = \lambda^n f(x, y)$$

For example, the functions

$$f_1(x, y) = x^3 + y^3$$
$$f_2(x, y) = x^2 + xy + y^2$$
$$f_3(x, y) = x^3 e^{x/y} + xy^2$$

are all homogeneous functions, of degrees three, two and three respectively (verify this assertion).

Observe that any homogeneous function $f(x, y)$ of degree n can be equivalnetly written as follows :

$$f(x, y) = x^n f\left(\frac{y}{x}\right) = y^n f\left(\frac{x}{y}\right)$$

For example, $f_{(x,}\ y) = x^3 + y^3$

$$= x^3\left(1 + \left(\frac{y}{x}\right)^3\right) = y^3\left(1 + \left(\frac{x}{y}\right)^3\right)$$

Having seen homogeneous functions we define homogeneous DEs as follows :

Any DE of the form $M(x, y)\, dx + N(x, y) dy = 0$ or $\frac{dy}{dx} = -\frac{M(x, y)}{N(x, y)}$ is called homogeneous if $M(x, y)$ and $N(x, y)$ are homogeneous functions of the same degree.

What is so special about homogeneous DEs? Well, it turns out that they areextremely simple to solve. To see how, we express both $M(x, y)$ and $N(x, y)$ as, say $x^n M\left(\frac{y}{x}\right)$ and $x^n N\left(\frac{y}{x}\right)$. This can be done sicne $M(x, y)$ and $N(x, y)$ are both homogeneous function of degree n. Doing this reduces our DE to

$$\frac{dy}{dx} = -\frac{M(x, y)}{N(x, y)} = \frac{x^n M\left(\frac{y}{x}\right)}{x^n N\left(\frac{y}{x}\right)} = -\frac{M\left(\frac{y}{x}\right)}{N\left(\frac{y}{x}\right)} = P\left(\frac{y}{x}\right)$$

(The function $P(t)$ stands for $\frac{-M(t)}{N(t)}$)

Now, the simple substitution $y = vx$ reduces this DE to a VS form

$$y = vx$$

$$\Rightarrow \quad \frac{dy}{dx} = v + x\frac{dy}{dx}$$

Thus, $\frac{dy}{dx} = p\left(\frac{y}{x}\right)$ transforms to

$$v + x\frac{dv}{dx} = P(v)$$

$$\Rightarrow \quad \frac{dv}{P(v) - v} = \frac{dx}{x}$$

This can now be integraed directly since it is in VS form. Let us see some examples of solving homogeneous DEs.

Alogorithm for Solving Homogeneous Differential Equation

***Step* I** Put the differential equation in the form

$$\frac{dy}{dx} = \frac{\phi(x, y)}{\psi(x, y)}$$

***Step* II** Put $y = vx$ and $\frac{dy}{dx} = v + x\frac{dv}{dx}$ in the equation in step I and can out x from the right hand side. The equation reduces to the form $v + x\frac{dv}{dx} = f(v)$.

***Step* III** Shift v on R.H.S and seperate the variables in v and x.

***Step* IV** Integrate both sides to obtain the solution in terms of v and x.

***Step* V** Replace v by $\frac{y}{x}$ in the solution obtained in step IV to obtain the solution in terms of x and y.

Following examples illustrate the procedure.

Example 25 Solve $y\, dx + (2\sqrt{xy} - x)\, dy = 0$.

Sol.

$$y\, dx + (2\sqrt{xy} - x)\, dy = 0 \qquad \text{...(i)}$$

This is homogeneous type. Substitute $y = ux$

$$\therefore \quad \frac{dy}{dx} = u + \frac{x\, du}{dx}$$

$\therefore$ Equation $ux\, dx + (2\sqrt{x^2 u} - x)(u\, dx + x\, du) = 0$

i.e. $x \cdot \{ udx + (2\sqrt{u} - 1)\, u\, dx + x\, du\, (2\sqrt{u} - 1)\} = 0$

i.e. $dx\, (2u^{3/2} - u + u) + x\, du\, (2\sqrt{u} - 1) = 0$

Separating the variables, $\frac{dx}{x} + \left(\frac{2\sqrt{u} - 1}{2u^{3/2}}\right) du = 0$

Integrating both the sides $\ln|x| + \ln|u| + \frac{1}{\sqrt{u}} = C$

or $\ln|xu| + \frac{1}{\sqrt{u}} = C$ or $\ln|y| + \sqrt{\frac{x}{y}} = C \quad \left(\because u = \frac{y}{x}\right)$

Which is the general solution.

Example 26 Solve $(x^2 + y^2)\, dx - 2xy\, dy = 0$.

Sol. Here, $\frac{dy}{dx} = \frac{x^2 + y^2}{2xy} = \frac{1}{2}\left[\frac{x}{y} + \frac{y}{x}\right]$

With $y = ux$, $\frac{dy}{dx} = u + x\frac{du}{dx}$, so that the differential equation becomes

$$u + x\frac{du}{dx} = \frac{1}{2}\left(\frac{1}{u} + u\right)$$

$$\Rightarrow \quad \frac{x\, du}{dx} = \frac{1 + u^2}{2u} - u$$

$$\Rightarrow \quad \frac{x\, du}{dx} = \frac{1 - u^2}{2u}$$

$$\Rightarrow \quad \int \frac{2u}{1 - u^2}\, du = \int \frac{dx}{x}$$

$$\Rightarrow \quad -\log|1 - u^2| = \log|x| - \log|C|$$

$$\Rightarrow \quad x(1 - u^2) = C$$

$$\Rightarrow \quad \frac{x^2 - y^2}{x} = C \qquad \left(\because u = \frac{y}{x}\right)$$

Hence, $x^2 - y^2 = xC$, is the required solution.

| Example 27 Solve $\frac{2\,dy}{dx} = \frac{y}{x} + \frac{y^2}{x^2}$.

Sol. The above equation is homogeneous so that we put $y = ux$.

$$\Rightarrow \quad 2\left[u + x\frac{du}{dx}\right] = u + u^2 \Rightarrow 2u + 2x\frac{du}{dx} = u + u^2$$

$$\Rightarrow \quad 2x\frac{du}{dx} = u^2 - u \Rightarrow \frac{du}{u^2 - u} = \frac{dx}{2x}$$

$$\Rightarrow \quad \int \frac{du}{u(u-1)} = \frac{1}{2}\int \frac{dx}{x}$$

$$\Rightarrow \quad \int \frac{1}{u-1}\,du - \int \frac{1}{u}\,du = \frac{1}{2}\int \frac{dx}{x}$$

$$\Rightarrow \quad \log|u-1| - \log|u| = \frac{1}{2}\log|x| + \log|C|$$

$$\Rightarrow \quad \log\left|\frac{u-1}{u}\right| = \log|C\sqrt{x}|$$

$$\Rightarrow \quad \frac{u-1}{u} = C\sqrt{x} \Rightarrow \frac{y-x}{y} = C\sqrt{x}$$

$$\Rightarrow \quad y - x = C\sqrt{x}\cdot y$$

Which is the required solution.

| Example 28 Solve
$(1 + 2e^{x/y})\,dx + 2e^{x/y}(1 - x/y)\,dy = 0.$

Sol. The appearance of x/y in the equation suggests the substitution $x = vy$ or $dx = v\,dy + y\,dv$.

$\therefore$ The given equation is

$$(1 + 2e^v)(v\,dy + y\,dv) + 2e^v(1 - v)\,dy = 0$$

i.e. $$y(1 + 2e^v)\,dv + (v + 2e^v)\,dy = 0$$

i.e. $$\frac{1 + 2e^v}{v + 2e^v}\,dv + \frac{dy}{y} = 0$$

Integrating, $$\int \frac{1 + 2e^v}{v + 2e^v}\,dv + \int \frac{dy}{y} = 0$$

$$\log|v + 2e^v| + \log|y| = \log|C|$$

$$\Rightarrow \quad (v + 2e^v)\,y = C \qquad \left(v = \frac{x}{y}\right)$$

$$\Rightarrow \quad \left(\frac{x}{y} + 2e^{x/y}\right)y = C$$

$$\Rightarrow \quad (x + 2ye^{x/y}) = C,$$ is required solution.

| Example 29 Show that any equation of the form
$y\,f(xy)\,dx + x\,g(xy)\,dy = 0$
can be converted to variable separable form by substituting $xy = v$.

Sol. Since, $xy = v$, $y = \frac{v}{x}$ and $d(xy) = dv$

i.e. $$x\,dy + y\,dx = dv$$

and $$dy = d\left(\frac{v}{x}\right) = \frac{x\,dv - v\,dx}{x^2}$$

i.e. $$x\,dy = dv - \frac{v}{x}\,dx$$

$$\therefore \quad \frac{v}{x}f(v)\,dx + g(v)\left\{dv - \frac{v}{x}\,dx\right\} = 0$$

$$\therefore \quad \frac{v\{f(v) - g(v)\}}{x}\,dx + g(v)\,dv = 0$$

i.e. $$\frac{dx}{x} + \frac{g(v)\,dv}{v\{f(v) - g(v)\}} = 0$$

Which is in variables separable form.

Reducible to Homogeneous Form

Type I

Many a times, the DE specified may not be homogeneous but some suibtale manipulation might reduce it to a homogeneous form. Generally, such equations involve a function of a rational expression whose numerator and denominator are linear functions of the variable, i.e., of the form

$$\frac{dy}{dx} = f\left(\frac{ax + by + c}{dx + cy + f}\right) \qquad \text{...(i)}$$

Note that the presence of the constant c and f causes this DE to be non-homogeneous.

To make it homogeneous, we use the substitutions

$$x \to X + h$$
$$y \to Y + k$$

and select h and k so that

$$\left.\begin{aligned} ah + bk + c &= 0 \\ dh + ek + f &= 0 \end{aligned}\right\} \qquad \text{...(ii)}$$

This can always be done $\left(\text{if } \frac{a}{b} \neq \frac{d}{e}\right)$. The RHS of the DE in (i) now reduces to $= f\left(\frac{a(X+h) + b(Y+k) + c}{d(X+h) + e(Y+k+f)}\right)$

$$= f\left(\frac{aX + bY}{dX + eY}\right) \qquad \text{(Using Eq. (ii))}$$

This expression is clearly homogeneous! The LHS of Eq. (i) is $\frac{dy}{dx}$ which equals $\frac{dy}{dY}\cdot\frac{dY}{dX}\cdot\frac{dX}{dx}$. Since $\frac{dy}{dY}\cdot\frac{dx}{dX} = 1$, the LHS $\frac{dy}{dx}$ equals $\frac{dY}{dX}$. Thus, our equation becomes

$$\frac{dY}{dX} = f\left(\frac{aX + bY}{dX + eY}\right) \quad \text{...(iii)}$$

We have thus succeeded in transforming the non-homogeneous DE in Eq. (i) to the homogeneous DE in Eq. (iii). This can now be solved as described earlier.

Example 30 Solve the DE $\frac{dy}{dx} = \frac{2y - x - 4}{y - 3x + 3}$.

Sol. We substitute $x \to X + h$ and $y \to Y + k$ where h, k need to be determined

$$\frac{dy}{dx} = \frac{dY}{dX} = \frac{(2Y - X) + (2k - h - 4)}{(Y - 3X) + (k - 3h + 3)}$$

h and k must be chosen so that

$$2k - h - 4 = 0$$

$$k - 3h + 3 = 0$$

This gives $h = 2$ and $k = 3$. Thus,

$$x = X + 2$$

$$y = Y + 3$$

Our DE now reduces to

$$\frac{dY}{dX} = \frac{2Y - X}{Y - 3X}$$

Using the substitution $Y = vX$, and simplifying, we have (verify),

$$\frac{v - 3}{v^2 \;\; 5v + 1} dv = \frac{-dX}{X}$$

We now integrate this DE which is VS; the left-hand side can be integrated by the techniques described in the unit of Indefinite Integration.

Finally, we substitute $v = \frac{Y}{X}$ and

$$X = x - 2$$

$$Y = y - 3$$

to obtain the general solution.

Type II

Suppose our DE is of the form

$$\frac{dy}{dx} = f\left(\frac{ax + by + c}{dx + ey + f}\right)$$

We try to find h, k so that

$$ah + bk + c = 0$$

$$dh + ek + f = 0$$

What if this system does not yield a solution? Recall that this will happen if $\frac{a}{b} = \frac{d}{e}$. How do we reduce the DE to a homogeneous one in such a case?

Let $\frac{a}{d} = \frac{b}{e} = \lambda$ (say).

Thus,

$$\frac{ax + by + c}{dx + ey + f} = \frac{\lambda(dx + ey) + c}{dx + ey + f}$$

This suggests the substitution $dx + ey = v$, which will give

$$d + e\frac{dy}{dx} = \frac{dv}{dx}$$

$$\Rightarrow \quad \frac{dy}{dx} = \frac{1}{e}\left(\frac{dv}{dx} - d\right)$$

Thus, our DE reduces to

$$\frac{1}{e}\left(\frac{dv}{dx} - d\right) = \frac{\lambda v + c}{v + f}$$

$$\Rightarrow \quad \frac{dv}{dx} = \frac{\lambda ev + ec}{v + f} + d$$

$$= \frac{(\lambda e + d)v + (ec + d)}{v + f}$$

$$\Rightarrow \quad \frac{(v + f)}{(\lambda e + d)\, v + ec + df} dv = dx$$

which is in VS form and hence can be solved.

Example 31 Solve the DE $\frac{dy}{dx} = \frac{x + 2y - 1}{x + 2y + 1}$.

Sol. Note that h, k do not exist in this case which can reduce this DE to homogeneous form. Thus, we use the substitution

$$x + 2y = v$$

$$\Rightarrow \quad 1 + 2\frac{dy}{dx} = \frac{dv}{dx}$$

Thus, our DE becomes

$$\frac{1}{2}\left(\frac{dv}{dx} - 1\right) = \frac{v - 1}{v + 1}$$

$$\Rightarrow \quad \frac{dv}{dx} = \frac{2v - 2}{v + 1} + 1 = \frac{3v - 1}{v + 1}$$

$$\Rightarrow \quad \frac{v + 1}{3v - 1} dv = dx$$

$$\Rightarrow \quad \frac{1}{3}\left(1 + \frac{4}{3v - 1}\right) dv = dx$$

Integrating, we have

$$\frac{1}{3}\left(v + \frac{4}{3}\ln(3v - 1)\right) = x + C_1$$

Substituting $v = x + 2y$, we have

$$x + 2y + \frac{4}{3}\ln(3x + 6y - 1) = 3x + C_2$$

$$\Rightarrow \quad y - x + \frac{2}{3}\ln(3x + 6y - 1) = C$$

Example 32 The solution of the differential equation $\dfrac{dy}{dx} = \dfrac{\sin y + x}{\sin 2y - x\cos y}$ is

(a) $\sin^2 y = x\sin y + \dfrac{x^2}{2} + C$

(b) $\sin^2 y = x\sin y - \dfrac{x^2}{2} + C$

(c) $\sin^2 y = x + \sin y + \dfrac{x^2}{2} + C$

(d) $\sin^2 y = x - \sin y + \dfrac{x^2}{2} + C$

Sol. Here, $\dfrac{dy}{dx} = \dfrac{\sin y + x}{\sin 2y - x\cos y}$

$\Rightarrow \cos y \dfrac{dy}{dx} = \dfrac{\sin y + x}{2\sin y - x}$, put $\sin y = t$

$\Rightarrow \dfrac{dt}{dx} = \dfrac{t + x}{2t - x}$, put $t = vx$

$$\frac{x\,dv}{dx} + v = \frac{vx + x}{2vx - x} = \frac{v+1}{2v-1}$$

$\therefore \quad x\dfrac{dv}{dx} = \dfrac{v+1}{2v-1} - v = \dfrac{v + 1 - 2v^2 + v}{2v - 1}$

or $\quad \dfrac{2v^2 - v}{-2v^2 + 2v + 1}dv = \dfrac{dx}{x}$

On solving, we get

$$\sin^2 y = x\sin y + \frac{x^2}{2} + C$$

Hence, (a) is the correct answer.

Example 33 The equation of curve passing through (1, 0) and satisfying $\left(y\dfrac{dy}{dx} + 2x\right)^2 = (y^2 + 2x^2)\left(1 + \left(\dfrac{dy}{dx}\right)^2\right)$, is given by

(a) $\sqrt{2}\,x^{\pm\frac{1}{\sqrt{2}}} = \dfrac{y + \sqrt{y^2 + 2x^2}}{x}$

(b) $\sqrt{2}x^{\pm\sqrt{2}} = \dfrac{y + \sqrt{y^2 + \sqrt{2}\,x^2}}{x}$

(c) $\sqrt{2}\,y^{\pm\frac{1}{\sqrt{2}}} = \dfrac{y + \sqrt{x^2 + 2y^2}}{x}$

(d) None of the above

Sol. The given differential equation can be written as

$$y^2\left(\frac{dy}{dx}\right)^2 + 4x^2 + 4xy\cdot\frac{dy}{dx} = (y^2 + 2x^2)\left(1 + \left(\frac{dy}{dx}\right)^2\right)$$

$$\Rightarrow \quad \frac{dy}{dx} = \frac{y}{x} \pm \sqrt{\frac{1}{2}\left(\frac{y}{x}\right)^2 + 1} \quad \text{...(i)}$$

Let $y = vx$

$$\Rightarrow \quad v + x\frac{dv}{dx} = \frac{dy}{dx}$$

$\therefore$ Eq. (i) becomes

$$v + x\frac{dv}{dx} = v \pm \sqrt{\frac{1}{2}v^2 + 1}$$

or $\quad \displaystyle\int \frac{dv}{\sqrt{\frac{1}{2}v^2 + 1}} = \int \frac{dx}{x}$

$$\Rightarrow \quad \sqrt{2}\log|v + \sqrt{v^2 + 2}| = \log|xC|$$

$$\Rightarrow \sqrt{2}\log\left|\frac{y + \sqrt{y^2 + 2x^2}}{x}\right| = \log|xC|,$$

putting $x = 1$ and $y = 0$

$$\Rightarrow \quad C = (\sqrt{2})^{\sqrt{2}}$$

$\therefore$ Curves are given by $\dfrac{y + \sqrt{y^2 + 2x^2}}{x} = \sqrt{2}\,x^{\pm\frac{1}{\sqrt{2}}}$

Hence, (a) is the correct answer.

Exercise for Session 2

1. The solution of $\frac{dy}{dx}=\frac{(x+y)^2}{(x+2)(y-2)}$, is given by

(a) $(x+2)^4\left(1+\frac{2y}{x}\right)=ke^{2y/x}$

(b) $(x+2)^4\left(1+\frac{2(y-2)}{(x+2)}\right)=k\,e^{\frac{2(y-2)}{(x+2)}}$

(c) $(x+2)^3\left(1+2\frac{(y-2)}{x+2}\right)=ke^{\frac{2(y-2)}{x+2}}$

(d) None of these

2. If $(y^3-2x^2y)\,dx+(2xy^2-x^3)\,dy=0$, then the value of $xy\sqrt{y^2-x^2}$, is

(a) y^2+x

(b) xy^2

(c) any constant

(d) None of these

3. The solution of $dy/dx=\cos(x+y)+\sin(x+y)$, is given by

(a) $\log\left|1+\tan\left(\frac{x+y}{2}\right)\right|=x+C$

(b) $\log|1+\tan(x+y)|=x+C$

(c) $\log|1-\tan(x+y)|=x+C$

(d) None of these

4. The solution of $\frac{dy}{dx}=(x+y-1)+\frac{x+y}{\log(x+y)}$, is given by

(a) $\{1+\log(x+y)\}-\log\{1+\log(x+y)\}=x+C$

(b) $\{1-\log(x+y)\}-\log\{1-\log(x+y)\}=x+C$

(c) $\{1+\log(x+y)\}^2-\log\{1+\log(x+y)\}=x+C$

(d) None of these

5. The solution of $(2x^2+3y^2-7)\,xdx-(3x^2+2y^2-8)\,ydy=0$, is given by

(a) $(x^2+y^2-1)=(x^2+y^2-3)^5\,C$

(b) $(x^2+y^2-1)^2=(x^2+y^2-3)^5\,C$

(c) $(x^2+y^2-3)=(x^2+y^2-1)^5\,C$

(d) None of these

6. The solution of $\frac{dy}{dx}=\frac{(x-1)^2+(y-2)^2\tan^{-1}\left(\frac{y-2}{x-1}\right)}{(xy-2x-y+2)\tan^{-1}\left(\frac{y-2}{x-1}\right)}$, is equal to

(a) $\{(x-1)^2+(y-1)^2\}\tan^{-1}\left(\frac{y-2}{x-1}\right)-2(x-1)(y-2)=2(x-1)^2\log C(x-1)$

(b) $\{(x-1)^2+(y-1)^2\}-2(x-1)(y-2)\tan^{-1}\left(\frac{y-2}{x-1}\right)=2(x-1)^2\log C$

(c) $\{(x-1)^2+(y-1)^2\}\tan^{-1}\left(\frac{y-2}{x-1}\right)-2(x-1)(y-2)=\log C(x-1)$

(d) None of the above

7. The solution of $\frac{dy}{dx}=\left(\frac{x+2y-3}{2x+y+3}\right)^2$, is

(a) $(x+3)^3-(y-3)^3=C(x-y+6)^4$

(b) $(x+3)^3-(y-3)^3=C$

(c) $(x+3)^4+(y-3)^4=C$ (d) None of these

8. The solution of $\frac{dy}{dx}=\frac{-\cos x\,(3\cos y-7\sin x-3)}{\sin y\,(3\sin x-7\cos y+7)}$, is

(a) $(\cos y-\sin x-1)^2(\sin x+\cos y-1)^5=C$

(b) $(\cos y-\sin x-1)^2(\sin x+\cos y-1)^3=C$

(c) $(\cos y-\sin x-1)^2(\sin x+\cos y-1)^7=C$

(d) None of these

9. A curve C has the property that if the tangent drawn at any point P on C meets. The coordinate axes at A and B, then P is the mid point of AB. The curve passes through the point (1, 1). Then the equation of curve is

(a) $xy = 1$
(b) $\frac{x}{y} = 1$
(c) $2x = xy - 1$
(d) None of these

10. The family of curves whose tangent form an angle $\frac{\pi}{4}$ with the hyperbola $xy = 1$, is

(a) $y = x - 2\tan^{-1}(x) + K$
(b) $y = x + 2\tan^{-1}(x) + K$
(c) $y = 2x - \tan^{-1}(x) + K$
(d) $y = 2x + \tan^{-1}(x) + K$

11. A and B are two separate reservoires of mater capacity of reservoir are filled completely with water their inlets are closed and then the water is released simultaneously from both the reservoirs. The rate of flow of water out of each reservoir at any instant of time is proportional to the quantity of water in the reservoir at that time. One hour after the water is released, the quantity of water in the reservoir A is $1\frac{1}{2}$ times the quantity of the water in reservoir B. The time after which do both the reservoirs have the same quantity of water, is

(a) $\log_{3/4}(2)$
(b) $\log_{3/4}\left(\frac{1}{2}\right)$
(c) $\log_{1/2}\left(\frac{1}{2}\right)$
(d) None of these

12. A curve passes through (2, 1) and is such that the square of the ordinate is twice the rectangle contained by the abscissa and the intercept of the normal. Then the equation of curve is

(a) $x^2 + y^2 = 9x$
(b) $4x^2 + y^2 = 9x$
(c) $4x^2 + 2y^2 = 9x$
(d) None of these

13. A normal at $P(x, y)$ on a curve neets the X-axis at Q and N is the foot of the ordinate at P. If $NQ = \frac{x(1+y^2)}{(1+x^2)}$. Then the equation of curve passing through (3, 1) is

(a) $5(1+y^2) = (1+x^2)$
(b) $(1+y^2) = 5(1+x^2)$
(c) $(1+x^2) = (1+y^2).x$
(d) None of these

14. The curve for which the ratio of the length of the segment intercepted by any tangent on the Y-axis to the length of the radius vector is constant (k), is

(a) $(y + \sqrt{x^2 - y^2})x^{k-1} = c$
(b) $(y + \sqrt{x^2 + y^2})x^{k-1} = c$
(c) $(y - \sqrt{x^2 - y^2})x^{k-1} = c$
(d) $(y - \sqrt{x^2 + y^2})x^{k-1} = c$

15. A point $P(x, y)$ nores on the curve $x^{2/3} + y^{2/3} = a^{2/3}, a > 0$ for each position (x, y) of p, perpendiculars are drawn from origin upon the tangent and normal at P, the length (absolute valve) of them being $P_1(x)$ and $P_2(x)$ brespectively, then

(a) $\frac{dp_1}{dx}.\frac{dp_2}{dx} < 0$
(b) $\frac{dp_1}{dx}.\frac{dp_2}{dx} \leq 0$
(c) $\frac{dp_1}{dx}.\frac{dp_2}{dx} > 0$
(d) $\frac{dp_1}{dx}.\frac{dp_2}{dx} \geq 0$

Session 3

Solving of Linear Differential Equations, Bernoulli's Equation, Orthogonal Trajectory

Solving of Linear Differential Equations

First Order Linear Differential Equations

A differential equation is said to be linear if an unknown variable and its derivative occur only in the first degree.

An equation of the form

$$\frac{dy}{dx} + P(x) \cdot y = Q(x).$$

Where $P(x)$ and $Q(x)$ are functions of x only or constant is called a linear equation of the first order.

To get the general solution of the above equation we proceeds as follows. By multiplying both the sides of the above equation by $e^{\int Pdx}$, we get

$$e^{\int Pdx} \cdot \frac{dy}{dx} + yP \cdot e^{\int Pdx} = Q\, e^{\int Pdx}$$

i.e. $$e^{\int Pdx} \cdot \frac{dy}{dx} + y \frac{d}{dx}(e^{\int Pdx}) = Q\, e^{\int Pdx}$$

i.e. $$\frac{d}{dx}(y\, e^{\int Pdx}) = Q \cdot e^{\int Pdx}$$

$\therefore$ Integrating, we get $y\, e^{\int Pdx} = \int Q\, e^{\int Pdx} dx + C$

Here, the term $e^{\int Pdx}$ which converts the left hand expression of the equation into a perfect differential is called an Integrating factor. In short it is written as IF. Thus, we remember the solution of the above equation as

$$y\text{ (IF)} = \int Q \text{ (IF) } dx + C.$$

Algoritm for Solving A Linear Differential Equation

Step I Write the differential equation in the form $dy / dx + Py = Q$ and obtain P and Q.

Step II Find integrating factor (I.F.) given by I.F. $= e^{\int Pdx}$.

Step III Multiply both sides of equation in Step I by I.F.

Step IV Integrate both sides of the equation obtained in step III. w.r.t x to obtain y (I.F.) $= \int Q.(\text{I.F.})\, dx + C$

This gives the required solution following examples illustrate the procedure.

Example 34 Solve $\frac{dy}{dx} + 2y = \cos x$.

Sol. It is a linear equation of the form

$$\frac{dy}{dx} + Py = Q(x)$$

where $P = 2$ and $Q = \cos x$

Then $$\text{IF} = e^{\int Pdx} = e^{\int 2dx} = e^{2x}$$

Hence, the general solution is $y\text{ (IF)} = \int Q\text{ (IF) } dx$

i.e. $$y \cdot e^{2x} = \int e^{2x} \cos x \, dx + C$$

$$y \cdot e^{2x} = \frac{e^{2x}}{5}[2 \cos x + \sin x] + C$$

Example 35 Solve $\frac{dy}{dx} + \frac{y}{x} = \log x$.

Sol. It is a linear differential equation of the form

$$\frac{dy}{dx} + Py = Q(x)$$

Here, $$P = \frac{1}{x}, Q = \log x$$

Then $$\text{IF} = e^{\int Pdx} = e^{\int 1/x\, dx} = e^{\log x} = x$$

Hence, the general solution is

$$y\text{ (IF)} = \int Q\text{ (IF) } dx + C$$

i.e. $$yx = \int (\log x)\, x\, dx + C$$

i.e. $$yx = (\log x) \cdot \frac{x^2}{2} - \int \frac{1}{x} \cdot \frac{x^2}{2} + C$$

i.e. $$yx = \frac{x^2}{2}(\log x) - \frac{x^2}{4} + C$$

Example 36 Solve $\dfrac{dy}{dx}=\dfrac{y}{2y\ln y+y-x}$.

Sol. The equation can be written as

$$\frac{dx}{dy}=\frac{2y\ln y+y-x}{y}=(2\ln y+1)-\frac{x}{y}$$

i.e. $$\frac{dx}{dy}+\frac{1}{y}\cdot x=(2\ln y+1)$$

In this equation it is clear that $P=\dfrac{1}{y}$ and $Q=(2\ln y+1)$.

Which are function of y only because equation contains derivatives of x with respect to y.

$$\text{IF}=e^{\int P dy}=e^{\int 1/y\, dy}=e^{\ln y}=y$$

$\therefore$ The solution is; $x\,(\text{IF})=\int(2\ln y+1)\,(\text{IF})\,dy$

i.e. $$xy=\int(2\ln y+1)\cdot y\,dy=y^2\ln y+C$$

i.e. $$x=y\ln y+\frac{C}{y}$$

Note In some cases a linear differential equation may be of the form $\dfrac{dx}{dy}+P_1x=Q_1$, where P_1 and Q_1 are function of y alone. In such a case the integrating factor is $e^{\int P_1\,dy}$.

Example 37 Solve $\cos^2 x\dfrac{dy}{dx}-y\tan 2x=\cos^4 x$, where $|x|<\dfrac{\pi}{4}$ and $y\left(\dfrac{\pi}{6}\right)=\dfrac{3\sqrt{3}}{8}$.

Sol. The given equation can be written as

$$\frac{dy}{dx}-\sec^2 x\cdot\tan 2x\cdot y=\cos^2 x$$

$$\text{IF}=e^{\int-\tan 2x\cdot\sec^2 x\,dx}=e^{\int+\frac{2\tan x}{\tan^2 x-1}\sec^2 x\,dx}$$

$$=e^{\int\frac{dt}{t}},\text{ where } t=\tan^2 x-1$$

$$=e^{\ln|t|}=|t|=|\tan^2 x-1|$$

It is given that $|x|<\dfrac{\pi}{4}$ and for this region $\tan^2 x<1$.

$\therefore$ $$\text{IF}=(1-\tan^2 x)$$

$\therefore$ The solution is

$$y(1-\tan^2 x)=\int\cos^2 x(1-\tan^2 x)\,dx$$
$$=\int(\cos^2 x-\sin^2 x)\,dx$$
$$=\int(\cos 2x)\,dx=\frac{\sin 2x}{2}+C$$

Now, when $x=\dfrac{\pi}{6},\ y=\dfrac{3\sqrt{3}}{8}$

$\therefore$ $$\frac{3\sqrt{3}}{8}\left(1-\frac{1}{3}\right)=\frac{1}{2}\cdot\frac{\sqrt{3}}{2}+C\ \Rightarrow\ C=0$$

$\therefore$ $$y=\frac{\sin 2x}{2(1-\tan^2 x)}$$

Example 38 Solve $\dfrac{dy}{dx}+y\,\phi'(x)=\phi(x)\cdot\phi'(x)$, where $\phi(x)$ is a given function.

Sol. Here, $P=\phi'(x)$ and $Q=\phi(x)\,\phi'(x)$

$$\text{IF}=e^{\int\phi'(x)\,dx}=e^{\phi(x)}$$

$\therefore$ The solution is

$$y\,e^{\phi(x)}=\int\phi(x)\cdot\phi'(x)\cdot e^{\phi(x)}\,dx=\int t\cdot e^t\,dt,$$

where $\phi(x)=t$

$$y\,e^{\phi(x)}=e^t(t-1)+C$$

i.e. $$ye^{\phi(x)}=\{\phi(x)-1\}\,e^{\phi(x)}+C$$

Bernoulli's Equation

Sometimes a differential equation is not linear but it can be converted into a linear differential equation by a suitable substitution. An equation of the form

$$\frac{dy}{dx}+Py=Q\,y^n.\qquad(n\neq 0,1)$$

Where P and Q are functions of x only, is known as Bernoulli's equation (for $n=0$ the equation is linear.)

It is easy to reduce the above equation into linear form as below :

Dividing both the sides by y^n, we get

$$y^{-n}\frac{dy}{dx}+P\,y^{1-n}=Q$$

Putting $y^{1-n}=z$ and hence, $(1-n)\,y^{-n}\dfrac{dy}{dx}=\dfrac{dz}{dx}$ the equation becomes $\dfrac{dz}{dx}+(1-n)\,Pz=(1-n)\,Q$ which is linear in z.

Here, $$\text{IF}=e^{\int(1-n)\,P\,dx}$$

$\therefore$ The solution is,

$$z\,e^{\int(1-n)\,Pdx}=\int\{(1-n)\cdot Q\cdot e^{\int(1-n)\,Pdx}\}\,dx$$

Example 39 Solve $(y \log x - 1)\, y\, dx = x\, dy$.

Sol. The given differential equation can be written as

$$x\frac{dy}{dx} + y = y^2 \log x \quad \text{...(i)}$$

Dividing by xy^2, hence

$$\frac{1}{y^2}\cdot\frac{dy}{dx} + \frac{1}{xy} = \frac{1}{x}\log x$$

Let $\frac{1}{y} = v \Rightarrow -\frac{1}{y^2}\cdot\frac{dy}{dx} = \frac{dv}{dx}$

So that $\frac{dv}{dx} - \frac{1}{x}v = -\frac{1}{x}\log x$

Which is the standard linear differential equations, with

$$P = -\frac{1}{x},\; Q = -\frac{1}{x}\log x$$

$$\text{IF} = e^{\int -1/x\, dx} = e^{-\ln x} = e^{\ln x^{-1}} = \frac{1}{x}$$

The solution is given by

$$v\cdot\frac{1}{x} = \int\frac{1}{x}\left(-\frac{1}{x}\log x\right)dx = -\int\frac{\log x}{x^2}\,dx$$

$$= \frac{\log x}{x} - \int\frac{1}{x}\,\frac{1}{x}\,dx = \frac{\log x}{x} + \frac{1}{x} + C$$

$$\Rightarrow \quad v = 1 + \log x + Cx = \log(ex) + Cx$$

or $\frac{1}{y} = \log(ex) + Cx$ or $y\{\log(ex) + Cx\} = 1$

Example 40 Solve $\frac{dy}{dx} + xy = xy^2$.

Sol. Dividing by y^2, we get

$$y^{-2}\frac{dy}{dx} + \frac{1}{y}\cdot x = x$$

Let $\frac{1}{y} = z$

So that $-\frac{1}{y^2}\cdot\frac{dy}{dx} = \frac{dz}{dx}$

$\therefore$ The given equation reduces to

$$\frac{dz}{dx} - xz = -x$$

$$\text{IF} = e^{\int -x\, dx} = e^{-x^2/2}$$

$\therefore$ The solution is

$$z\, e^{-x^2/2} = \int -x\cdot e^{-x^2/2}\,dx = e^{-x^2/2} + C$$

i.e. $\frac{1}{y} = 1 + Ce^{x^2/2}$

Example 41 Solve $\frac{dy}{dx} = \frac{y\,\phi'(x) - y^2}{\phi(x)}$, where $\phi(x)$ is a given function.

Sol. The equation can be written as

$$\frac{dy}{dx} - \frac{\phi'(x)}{\phi(x)}y = -\frac{y^2}{\phi(x)}$$

i.e. $-y^{-2}\frac{dy}{dx} + \frac{\phi'(x)}{\phi(x)}\cdot\frac{1}{y} = \frac{1}{\phi(x)}$

Let $\frac{1}{y} = z$. So that, $-\frac{1}{y^2}\frac{dy}{dx} = \frac{dz}{dx}$

$$\therefore \quad \frac{dz}{dx} + \frac{\phi'(x)}{\phi(x)}\cdot z = \frac{1}{\phi(x)}$$

$$\text{IF} = e^{\int\frac{\phi'(x)}{\phi(x)}dx} = e^{\ln\phi(x)} = \phi(x)$$

$\therefore$ The solution is $z\cdot\phi(x) = \int\frac{1}{\phi(x)}\cdot\phi(x)\,dx = x + C$

i.e. $\frac{\phi(x)}{y} = x + C$ *ie,* $\frac{\phi(x)}{x + C} = y$

Remark

Another type of equation which is reducible to the linear form is

$$f'(y)\frac{dy}{dx} + P(x)\cdot f(y) = Q(x)$$

An equation of this type can be easily reduced the linear form by taking $z = f(y)$.

Example 42 Solve $\sec^2 y\frac{dy}{dx} + 2x\tan y = x^3$.

Sol. Let $\tan y = z$ so that $\sec^2 y\cdot\frac{dy}{dx} = \frac{dz}{dx}$

Thus, the given equation reduces to

$$\frac{dz}{dx} + 2x\cdot z = x^3$$

$$\text{IF} = e^{\int 2x\, dx} = e^{x^2}$$

$\therefore$ The solution is, $z\cdot e^{x^2} = \int x^3\cdot e^{x^2}dx$

i.e. $\tan y\cdot e^{x^2} = \frac{1}{2}\int x^2 e^{x^2}\cdot(2x)\,dx = \frac{1}{2}\int t\cdot e^t\,dt$, where $t = x^2$

$$\tan y\cdot e^{x^2} = \frac{1}{2}(t\cdot e^t - e^t) + C$$

i.e. $\tan y = Ce^{-x^2} + \frac{e^{-x^2}}{2}\cdot e^{x^2}(x^2 - 1)$

$$\tan y = Ce^{-x^2} + \frac{1}{2}(x^2 - 1)$$

Example 43 Solve $\frac{dy}{dx} + x(x+y) = x^3(x+y)^3 - 1$.

Sol. The given equation can be written as

$$\left(\frac{dy}{dx}+1\right) + x(x+y) = x^3(x+y)^3$$

i.e. $$\frac{d(x+y)}{dx} + x(x+y) = x^3(x+y)^3$$

i.e. $$(x+y)^{-3}\cdot\frac{d(x+y)}{dx} + x(x+y)^{-2} = x^3$$

Let $(x+y)^{-2} = z$ so that $-2(x+y)^{-3}\frac{d(x+y)}{dx} = \frac{dz}{dx}$

The given equation reduces to

$$-\frac{1}{2}\frac{dz}{dx} + xz = x^3$$

i.e. $$\frac{dz}{dx} - 2xz = -2x^3$$

$$\text{IF} = e^{\int -2x\,dx} = e^{-x^2}$$

$\therefore$ The solution is

$$z\cdot e^{-x^2} = \int -2x^3\cdot e^{-x^2}\,dx = (x^2+1)e^{-x^2} + C$$

$$\frac{1}{(x+y)^2} = Ce^{x^2} + x^2 + 1$$

Example 44 Solve $\sin y\cdot\frac{dy}{dx} = \cos y(1 - x\cos y)$.

Sol. The given differential equation is

$$\sin y\,\frac{dy}{dx} = \cos y\,(1 - x\cos y)$$

or $$\sin y\,\frac{dy}{dx} - \cos y = -x\cos^2 y$$

Dividing by $\cos^2 y$, we get

$$\tan y\cdot\sec y\cdot\frac{dy}{dx} - \sec y = -x$$

Let $\sec y = v \Rightarrow \sec y\tan y\cdot\frac{dy}{dx} = \frac{dv}{dx}$

So that $$\frac{dv}{dx} - v = -x$$

Which is linear differential equation with $P = -1, Q = -x$

$$\text{IF} = e^{\int P dx} = e^{\int -1\,dx} = e^{-x}$$

The solution is given by

$$v\cdot e^{-x} = \int -x\cdot e^{-x}\,dx = xe^{-x} + e^{-x} + C$$

$$= e^{-x}(x+1) + C$$

or $$v = (1+x) + Ce^x$$

or $$\sec y = (1+x) + Ce^x$$

Orthogonal Trajectory

Any curve, which cuts every member of a given family of curves at right angles, is called an orthogonal trajectory of the family. For example, each straight line passing through the origin, *ie*, $y = kx$ is an orthogonal trajectory of the family of the circles $x^2 + y^2 = a^2$.

Procedure for Finding the Orthogonal Trajectory

(i) Let $f(x, y, c) = 0$ be the equation of the given family of curves, where c is an arbitrary parameter.

(ii) Differentiate $f = 0$; w.r.t. 'x' and eliminate 'c', i.e. form a differential equation.

(iii) Substitute $-\frac{dx}{dy}$ for $\frac{dy}{dx}$ in the above differential equation. This will give the differential equation of the orthogonal trajectories.

(iv) By solving this differential equation, we get the required orthogonal trajectories.

Example 45 Find the orthogonal trajectories of the hyperbola $xy = C$.

Sol. The equation of the given family of curves is $xy = c$ ...(i)

Differentiating Eq. (i) w.r.t. x, we get

$$\frac{x\,dy}{dx} + y = 0 \quad \text{...(ii)}$$

Substitute $-\frac{dx}{dy}$ for $\frac{dy}{dx}$ in Eq. (ii), we get

$$-\frac{x\,dx}{dy} + y = 0 \quad \text{...(iii)}$$

This is the differential equation for the orthogonal trajectory of given family of hyperbola. Eq. (iii) can be rewritten as $x\,dx = y\,dy$, which on integration gives

$$x^2 - y^2 = C.$$

This is the family of required orthogonal trajectories.

Example 46 Find the orthogonal trajectories of the curves $y = cx^2$.

Sol. Here, $$y = cx^2 \quad \text{...(i)}$$

Differentiating w.r.t. x, we get

$$\frac{dy}{dx} = 2cx \quad \text{...(ii)}$$

Eliminating c from Eqs. (i) and (ii),

$$y = \left(\frac{1}{2x}\frac{dy}{dx}\right)x^2$$

$$\Rightarrow \quad 2y = x\frac{dy}{dx} \quad \text{...(iii)}$$

This is the differential equation of the family of curves given in Eq. (i).

Now, to obtain orthogonal trajectory replace $\frac{dy}{dx}$ by $-\frac{dx}{dy}$ in Eq. (iii).

$$\Rightarrow \quad 2y = -x\frac{dx}{dy}$$

or $$2y\,dy = -x\,dx$$

Integrating both the sides, we get

$$y^2 = -\frac{x^2}{2} + C_1$$

$\Rightarrow x^2 + 2y^2 = C_1$, is the required family of orthogonal trajectory.

| Example 47 Find the equation of all possible curves that will cut each member of the family of circles $x^2 + y^2 - 2cx = 0$ at right angle.

Sol. Here, $$x^2 + y^2 - 2cx = 0 \quad \text{...(i)}$$

Differentiating w.r.t. x, we get

$$2x + 2yy_1 - 2c = 0$$

$$\Rightarrow \quad c = x + yy_1 \quad \text{...(ii)}$$

From Eqs. (i) and (ii), we eliminate c

$$\Rightarrow \quad x^2 + y^2 - 2(x + yy_1)x = 0$$

or $$-x^2 + y^2 - 2xy\frac{dy}{dx} = 0$$

This is the differential equation representing the given family of circles. To find differential equation of the orthogonal trajectories, we replace $\frac{dy}{dx}$ by $-\frac{dx}{dy}$.

$$\Rightarrow \quad y^2 - x^2 = -2xy\frac{dx}{dy}$$

$$\Rightarrow \quad y^2\,dy = x^2\,dy - 2xy\,dx$$

$$\Rightarrow \quad -dy = \frac{yd(x^2) - x^2\,dy}{y^2}$$

$$\Rightarrow \quad -dy = d\left(\frac{x^2}{y}\right)$$

Integrating both the sides, we get

$$-y = \frac{x^2}{y} + C \Rightarrow x^2 + y^2 + Cy = 0$$

Represents family of orthogonal trajectory.

| Example 48 Find the orthogonal trajectory of the circles

$$x^2 + y^2 - ay = 0.$$

Sol. Here, $$x^2 + y^2 - ay = 0 \quad \text{...(i)}$$

Differentiating, we get

$$2x + 2yy_1 - ay_1 = 0$$

$$\Rightarrow \quad a = \frac{2(x + yy_1)}{y_1} \quad \text{...(ii)}$$

Substituting 'a' in Eq. (i), we get

$$x^2 + y^2 - \frac{2(x + yy_1)}{y_1}y = 0$$

$$\Rightarrow \quad (x^2 - y^2)y_1 - 2xy = 0$$

This is the differential equation of the family of circles given in Eq. (i).

$\therefore$ The differential representing the orthogonal trajectory is obtained by replacing $\frac{dy}{dx}$ by $-\frac{dy}{dx}$.

i.e. $$-(x^2 - y^2)\frac{dx}{dy} - 2xy = 0$$

$$\Rightarrow \quad 2xy\,dy - y^2\,dx = -x^2\,dx$$

$$\Rightarrow \quad \frac{x\,d(y^2) - y^2\,dx}{x^2} = -dx$$

$$\Rightarrow \quad d\left(\frac{y^2}{x}\right) = -dx$$

Integrating both the sides, we get

$y^2 + x^2 = Cx$, is required family of orthogonal trajectories.

Exercise for Session 3

1. The solution of $(1+x^2)\dfrac{dy}{dx}+y=e^{\tan^{-1}x}$, is given by

(a) $2ye^{\tan^{-1}x}=e^{2\tan^{-1}x}+C$
(b) $ye^{\tan^{-1}y}=e^{2\tan^{-1}x}+C$
(c) $2ye^{\tan^{-1}y}=e^{2\tan^{-1}y}+C$
(d) None of these

2. The solution of $\dfrac{dy}{dx}+\dfrac{x}{1-x^2}y=x\sqrt{y}$, is given by

(a) $3\sqrt{y}+(1-x^2)=C(1-x^2)^{1/4}$
(b) $\dfrac{3}{2}\sqrt{y}+(1-x^2)=C(1-x^2)^{3/2}$
(c) $3\sqrt{y}-(1-x^2)=C(1-x^2)^{3/2}$
(d) None of these

3. The solution of $\dfrac{dy}{dx}+x\sin 2y=x^3\cos^2 y$, is

(a) $e^{x^2}=(x^2-1)e^{x^2}\tan y+C$
(b) $e^{x^2}\tan y=\dfrac{1}{2}(x^2-1)e^{x^2}+C$
(c) $e^{x^2}\tan y=(x^2-1)\tan y+C$
(d) None of these

4. The solution of $3x(1-x^2)y^2\,dy/dx+(2x^2-1)y^3=ax^3$ is

(a) $y^3=ax+C\sqrt{1-x^2}$
(b) $y^3=ax+Cx\sqrt{1-x^2}$
(c) $y^2=ax+C\sqrt{1-x^2}$
(d) None of these

5. The solution of $\dfrac{dy}{dx}+\dfrac{y}{x}\log y=\dfrac{y}{x^2}(\log y)^2$, is

(a) $x=\dfrac{1}{2x}\log y+C$
(b) $x^2+\log y=C$
(c) $\dfrac{1}{x\log y}=\dfrac{1}{2x^2}+C$
(d) None of these

6. The solution of $\dfrac{dy}{dx}+y\,f'(x)-f(x)\cdot f'(x)=0,\ y\neq f(x)$ is

(a) $y=f(x)+1+ce^{-f(x)}$
(b) $y-ce^{-f(x)}$
(c) $y=f(x)-1+ce^{-f(x)}$
(d) None of these

7. The solution of $(x^{2-1})\,dy/dx\cdot\sin y-2x\cdot\cos y=2x-2x^3$, is

(a) $(x^2-1)\cos y=\dfrac{x^4}{2}-x^2+C$
(b) $(x^2-1)\sin y=\dfrac{x^4}{2}-x^2+C$
(c) $(x^2-1)\cos y=\dfrac{x^4}{4}-\dfrac{x^2}{2}+C$
(d) $(x^2-1)\sin y=\dfrac{x^4}{4}-\dfrac{x^2}{2}+C$

8. The Curve possessing the property text the intercept made by the tangent at any point of the curve on the y-axis is equal to square of the abscissa of the point of tangency, is given by

(a) $y^2=x+C$
(b) $y=2x^2+cx$
(c) $y=-x^2+cx$
(d) None of these

9. The tangent at a point P of a curve meets the y-axis at A, and the line parallel to y-axis at A, and the line parallel to y-axis through P meets the x-axis at B. If area of ΔOAB is constant (O being the origin), Then the curve is

(a) $cx^2-xy+k=0$
(b) $x^2+y^2=cx$
(c) $3x^2+4y^2=k$
(d) $xy-x^2y^2+kx=0$

10. The value of k such that the family of parabolas $y=cx^2+k$ is the orthogonal trajectory of the family of ellipse $x^2+2y^2-y=C$, is

(a) y_2
(b) y_3
(c) y_4
(d) y_5

Session 4

Exact Differential Equations

Exact Differential Equations

A differential equation of the form $M(x, y)\,dx + N(x, y)\,dy = 0$ is said to be exact (or total) if its left hand expression is the exact differential of some function $u(x, y)$.

i.e. $$du = M \cdot dx + N \cdot dy$$

Hence, its solution is $u(x, y) = c$ (where c is an arbitrary constant). But then there is a question that how do we confirm whether the above mentioned equation is exact. The answer to this question is the following theorem.

Theorem The necessary and sufficient condition for the differential equation $M\,dx + N\,dy = 0$ to be exact is $\dfrac{\partial M}{\partial y} = \dfrac{\partial N}{\partial x}$.

The solution of $M\,dx + N\,dy = 0$ is ,

$$\int_{y-\text{constant}} M\,dx + \int (\text{terms of } N \text{ not containing } x)\,dy = C$$

provided $\dfrac{\partial M}{\partial y} = \dfrac{\partial N}{\partial x}$.

| Example 49 Solve $(x^2 - ay)\,dx + (y^2 - ax)\,dy = 0$.

Sol. Here, we have $M = x^2 - ay$ and $N = y^2 - ax$

$$\therefore \quad \frac{\partial M}{\partial y} = -a = \frac{\partial N}{\partial x}$$

Thus, the equation is exact.

$\therefore$ The solution is, $\displaystyle\int_{y-\text{constant}} (x^2 - ay)\,dx + \int y^2\,dy = C$

$$\Rightarrow \quad \frac{x^3}{3} - axy + \frac{y^3}{3} = C$$

| Example 50 Solve $(2x \log y)\,dx + \left(\dfrac{x^2}{y} + 3y^2\right)dy = 0$.

Sol. Here, we have $M = 2x \log y$ and $N = \dfrac{x^2}{y} + 3y^2$

$$\therefore \quad \frac{\partial M}{\partial y} = \frac{2x}{y}$$

and $\dfrac{\partial N}{\partial x} = \dfrac{2x}{y}$ and hence the equation is exact.

$\therefore$ The solution is,

$$\int_{y-\text{constant}} (2x \log y)\,dx + \int 3y^2\,dy = C$$

$$\Rightarrow \quad x^2 \log y + y^3 = C$$

Equations Reducible to the Exact Form

Sometimes a differential equation of the form $M\,dx + N\,dy = 0$ which is not exact can be reduced to an exact form by multiplying by a suitable function $f(x, y)$ which is not identically zero. This function $f(x, y)$ which then multiplied to a non-exact differential equation makes it exact is known as integrating factor.

One can find integrating factors by inspection but for that some experience and practice is required.

For finding the integrating factors by inspection, the following identities must be remembered.

1. $x\,dy + y\,dx = d\,(xy)$
2. $x\,dx + y\,dy = \dfrac{1}{2}\,d\,(x^2 + y^2)$
3. $\dfrac{x\,dy - y\,dx}{x^2} = d\left(\dfrac{y}{x}\right)$
4. $\dfrac{y\,dx - x\,dy}{y^2} = d\left(\dfrac{x}{y}\right)$
5. $\dfrac{x\,dy - y\,dx}{xy} = \dfrac{dy}{y} - \dfrac{dx}{x} = d\left[\log\left(\dfrac{y}{x}\right)\right]$
6. $\dfrac{y\,dx - x\,dy}{xy} = d\left[\log\left(\dfrac{x}{y}\right)\right]$
7. $\dfrac{x\,dy - y\,dx}{x^2 + y^2} = \dfrac{\dfrac{x\,dy - y\,dx}{x^2}}{1 + \dfrac{y^2}{x^2}} = \dfrac{d\left(\dfrac{y}{x}\right)}{1 + \left(\dfrac{y}{x}\right)^2} = d\left[\tan^{-1}\left(\dfrac{y}{x}\right)\right]$
8. $\dfrac{dx + dy}{x + y} = d\,[\ln(x + y)]$
9. $d\,(\ln(xy)) = \dfrac{x\,dy + y\,dx}{xy}$
10. $d\left(\dfrac{1}{2}\ln(x^2 + y^2)\right) = \dfrac{x\,dx + y\,dy}{x^2 + y^2}$

11. $d\left(-\dfrac{1}{xy}\right)=\dfrac{x\,dy+y\,dx}{x^2y^2}$

12. $d\left(\dfrac{e^y}{x}\right)=\dfrac{x\,e^y\,dy-e^y\,dx}{x^2}$

13. $d\left(\dfrac{e^x}{y}\right)=\dfrac{ye^x dx-e^x dy}{y^2}$

14. $d\,(x^m\,y^n)=x^{m-1}\,y^{n-1}\,(my\,dx+nx\,dy)$

15. $\dfrac{d\,[f(x,y)]^{1-n}}{1-n}=\dfrac{f'(x,y)}{(f(x,y))^n}$

Example 51 Solve $(x^2-ay)\,dx+(y^2-ax)\,dy=0$.

Sol. The given differential equation is

$$x^2dx+y^2dy-a\,(y\,dx+x\,dy)=0$$

$$\Rightarrow \quad d\left(\frac{x^3}{3}\right)+d\left(\frac{y^3}{3}\right)-ad\,(xy)=0$$

Integrating, we get $\dfrac{x^3}{3}+\dfrac{y^3}{3}-a\,xy=k$

$$\Rightarrow \quad x^3+y^3-3axy=3k=C$$

Example 52 Solve $(2x\log y)\,dx+\left(\dfrac{x^2}{y}+3y^2\right)dy=0$.

Sol. The given differential equation is

$$(\log y)\,2x\,dx+\frac{x^2}{y}\,dy+3y^2\,dy=0$$

$$\Rightarrow \quad (\log y)\,d\,(x^2)+x^2\,d\,(\log y)+d\,(y^3)=0$$

$$\Rightarrow \quad d\,(x^2\log y)+d\,(y^3)=0$$

$$\Rightarrow \quad x^2\log y+y^3=C$$

(integrating both the sides)

Example 53 Solve $x\,dx+y\,dy=x\,dy-y\,dx$.

Sol. The given equation can be written as

$$\frac{1}{2}\,d\,(x^2+y^2)=x^2\,d\left(\frac{y}{x}\right)$$

$$\Rightarrow \quad \frac{d\,(x^2+y^2)}{x^2+y^2}=\frac{2x^2\,d\left(\frac{y}{x}\right)}{x^2+y^2}$$

$$\Rightarrow \quad \frac{d\,(x^2+y^2)}{x^2+y^2}=\frac{2d\,(y/x)}{1+(y/x)^2}$$

$$\Rightarrow \quad \log\,(x^2+y^2)=2\tan^{-1}\left(\frac{y}{x}\right)+C$$

Example 54 Solve

$$\frac{y+\sin x\cos^2(xy)}{\cos^2(xy)}\,dx+\left(\frac{x}{\cos^2(xy)}+\sin y\right)dy=0.$$

Sol. The given differential equation can be written as

$$\frac{y\,dx+x\,dy}{\cos^2(xy)}+\sin x\,dx+\sin y\,dy=0$$

$$\Rightarrow \quad \sec^2(xy)\,d\,(xy)+\sin x\,dx+\sin y\,dy=0$$

$$d\,(\tan(xy))+d\,(-\cos x)+d\,(-\cos y)=0$$

$$\Rightarrow \quad \tan(xy)-\cos x-\cos y=C$$

Example 55 Solve $\dfrac{x+y\dfrac{dy}{dx}}{y-x\dfrac{dy}{dx}}=x^2+2y^2+\dfrac{y^4}{x^2}$.

Sol. The given equation can be written as

$$\frac{x\,dx+y\,dy}{(x^2+y^2)^2}=\frac{y\,dx-x\,dy}{y^2}\cdot\frac{y^2}{x^2}$$

$$\Rightarrow \quad \int\frac{d\,(x^2+y^2)}{(x^2+y^2)^2}=2\int\frac{1}{x^2/y^2}\,d\left(\frac{x}{y}\right)$$

Integrating both the sides, we get

$$-\frac{1}{(x^2+y^2)}=-\frac{1}{(x/y)}+C$$

$$\Rightarrow \quad \frac{y}{x}-\frac{1}{x^2+y^2}=C$$

Example 56 The solution of

$e^{x\frac{(y^2-1)}{y}}\{xy^2\,dy+y^3dx\}+\{ydx-xdy\}=0$, is

(a) $e^{xy}+e^{x/y}+C=0$ (b) $e^{xy}-e^{x/y}+C=0$

(c) $e^{xy}+e^{y/x}+C=0$ (d) $e^{xy}-e^{y/x}+C=0$

Sol. Here, $e^{x\frac{(y^2-1)}{y}}\cdot y^2\,\{xdy+ydx\}+\{ydx-xdy\}=0$

$$\Rightarrow \quad e^{xy}\cdot y^2\cdot\{xdy+ydx\}+e^{x/y}\,\{ydx-xdy\}=0$$

or $$e^{xy}\cdot\{xdy+ydx\}+e^{x/y}\,\frac{\{ydx-xdy\}}{y^2}=0$$

or $$e^{xy}\cdot d\,(xy)+e^{x/y}\cdot d\left(\frac{x}{y}\right)=0$$

or $$d\,(e^{xy})+d\,(e^{x/y})=0$$

Integrating both the sides, we get

$$e^{xy}+e^{x/y}+C=0$$

Hence, (a) is the correct answer.

Example 57 The solution of $x^2dy - y^2dx + xy^2(x-y)\,dy = 0$, is

(a) $\log\left|\dfrac{x-y}{xy}\right| = \dfrac{y^2}{2} + C$ (b) $\log\left|\dfrac{xy}{x-y}\right| = \dfrac{x^2}{2} + C$

(c) $\log\left|\dfrac{x-y}{xy}\right| = \dfrac{x^2}{2} + C$ (d) $\log\left|\dfrac{x-y}{xy}\right| = x + C$

Sol. Here, $x^2y^2\left(\dfrac{dy}{y^2} - \dfrac{dx}{x^2}\right) + x^2y^3\left(\dfrac{1}{y} - \dfrac{1}{x}\right)dy = 0$

$$\Rightarrow \quad -d\left(\frac{1}{y} - \frac{1}{x}\right) + y\left(\frac{1}{y} - \frac{1}{x}\right)dy = 0$$

$$\Rightarrow \quad -\frac{d\left(\frac{1}{y} - \frac{1}{x}\right)}{\left(\frac{1}{y} - \frac{1}{x}\right)} + y\,dy = 0 \text{ or } \frac{d\left(\frac{1}{y} - \frac{1}{x}\right)}{\left(\frac{1}{y} - \frac{1}{x}\right)} = d\left(\frac{y^2}{2}\right)$$

Integrating both the sides, we get

$$\log\left|\frac{1}{x} - \frac{1}{y}\right| = \frac{y^2}{2} + C$$

Hence, (a) is the correct answer.

Example 58 The solution of the differential equation $y\,dx - x\,dy + xy^2\,dx = 0$, is

(a) $\dfrac{x}{y} + x^2 = \lambda$ (b) $\dfrac{x}{y} + \dfrac{x^2}{2} = \lambda$

(c) $\dfrac{x}{2y^2} + \dfrac{x^2}{4} = \lambda$ (d) None of these

Sol. Given equation is, $y\,dx - x\,dy + xy^2\,dx = 0$

Which could be converted into exact form

i.e. $\dfrac{y\,dx - x\,dy}{y^2} + x\,dx = 0$

$$\Rightarrow \quad d\left(\frac{x}{y}\right) + d\left(\frac{x^2}{2}\right) = 0$$

Integrating both the sides, we get

$$\frac{x}{y} + \frac{x^2}{2} = \text{constant}$$

or $\dfrac{x}{y} + \dfrac{x^2}{2} = \lambda$

Hence, (b) is the correct answer.

Example 59 The solution of differential equation $x\,dy\,(y^2e^{xy} + e^{x/y}) = y\,dx\,(e^{x/y} - y^2e^{xy})$, is

(a) $xy = \log(e^x + \lambda)$ (b) $x^2/y = \log(e^{x/y} + \lambda)$

(c) $xy = \log(e^{x/y} + \lambda)$ (d) $xy^2 = \log(e^{x/y} + \lambda)$

Sol. The given equation is

$$(xy^2e^{xy})\,dy + (xe^{x/y})\,dy = (ye^{x/y})\,dx - (y^3e^{xy})\,dx$$

$$\Rightarrow \quad y^2e^{xy}(x\,dy + y\,dx) = e^{x/y}(y\,dx - x\,dy)$$

$$\Rightarrow \quad e^{xy}(d(xy)) = e^{x/y}\cdot\left(\frac{y\,dx - x\,dy}{y^2}\right)$$

$$\Rightarrow \quad e^{xy}(d(xy)) = e^{x/y}\cdot d\left(\frac{x}{y}\right)$$

$$\Rightarrow \quad d(e^{xy}) = d(e^{x/y})$$

Integrating both the sides, we get

$$e^{xy} = e^{x/y} + \lambda$$

$$\Rightarrow \quad xy = \log(e^{x/y} + \lambda)$$

Hence, (c) is the correct answer.

Example 60 The solution of the differential equation $(y + x\sqrt{xy}\,(x+y))\,dx + (y\sqrt{xy}\,(x+y) - x)\,dy = 0$, is

(a) $\dfrac{x^2+y^2}{2} + 2\tan^{-1}\sqrt{\dfrac{x}{2y}} = C$

(b) $\dfrac{x^2+y^2}{2} + 2\tan^{-1}\sqrt{\dfrac{x}{y}} = C$

(c) $\dfrac{x^2+y^2}{\sqrt{2}} + 2\tan^{-1}\sqrt{\dfrac{x}{y}} = C$

(d) None of these

Sol. The given equation can be written as

$$(y\,dx - x\,dy) + x\sqrt{xy}\,(x+y)\,dx + y\sqrt{xy}\,(x+y)\,dy = 0$$

$$\Rightarrow \quad (y\,dx - x\,dy) + (x+y)\sqrt{xy}\,(x\,dx + y\,dy) = 0$$

$$\Rightarrow \quad \frac{y\,dx - x\,dy}{y^2} + \left(\frac{x}{y} + 1\right)\cdot\sqrt{\frac{x}{y}}\,d\left(\frac{x^2+y^2}{2}\right) = 0$$

$$\Rightarrow \quad d\left(\frac{x}{y}\right) + d\left(\frac{x^2+y^2}{2}\right)\left(\frac{x}{y} + 1\right)\sqrt{\frac{x}{y}} = 0$$

$$\Rightarrow \quad d\left(\frac{x^2+y^2}{2}\right) + \frac{d\left(\frac{x}{y}\right)}{\left(\frac{x}{y} + 1\right)\cdot\sqrt{\frac{x}{y}}} = 0$$

or $$d\left(\frac{x^2+y^2}{2}\right) + 2d\left(\tan^{-1}\left(\sqrt{\frac{x}{y}}\right)\right) = 0$$

Integrating both the sides, we get

$$\Rightarrow \quad \frac{x^2+y^2}{2} + 2\tan^{-1}\sqrt{\frac{x}{y}} = C$$

Hence, (b) is the correct answer.

Exercise for Session 4

1. The solution of $xdy + ydx + 2x^3dx = 0$, is

(a) $xy + x^4 = C$ (b) $xy + \frac{1}{2}x^4 = C$ (c) $\frac{x^2}{y} + \frac{x^4}{4} = C$ (d) None of these

2. The solution of, $ydx - xdy + (1 + x^2)\,dx + x^2 \sin y\,dy = 0$, is given by

(a) $x + 1 - y^2 + \cos y + C = 0$ (b) $y + 1 - x^2 + x\cos y + C = 0$

(c) $\frac{x}{y} + \frac{1}{y} - y + \cos y + C = 0$ (d) $\frac{y}{x} + \frac{1}{x} - x + \cos y + C = 0$

3. The solution of $(1 + x\sqrt{x^2 + y^2})\,dx + (-1 + \sqrt{x^2 + y^2})\,ydy = 0$, is

(a) $2x - y^2 + \frac{2}{3}(x^2 + y^2)^{3/2} = C$ (b) $2x - y + \frac{2}{3}(x^2 + y^2)^{3/2} = C$

(c) $2y - x^2 + \frac{2}{3}(x^2 + y^2)^{3/2} = C$ (d) None of these

4. The solution of, $\frac{xdy}{x^2 + y^2} = \left(\frac{y}{x^2 + y^2} - 1\right)dx$, is given by

(a) $\tan^{-1}\left(\frac{x}{y}\right) + x = C$ (b) $\tan^{-1}\left(\frac{y}{x}\right) + x = C$ (c) $\tan^{-1}\left(\frac{y}{x}\right) + xy = C$ (d) $\tan^{-1}\left(\frac{y}{x}\right) + x^2 = C$

5. The solution of $ye^{x/y}\,dx = (xe^{x/y} + y^2 \sin y)\,dy$, is given by

(a) $e^{x/y} = -\cos y + C$ (b) $e^{x/y} + 2\cos y = C$ (c) $e^{x/y} = x\cos y + C$ (d) $e^{x/y} = 2\cos y\, e^{x/y} + C$

6. The solution of $x\sin\left(\frac{y}{x}\right)dy = \left\{y\sin\left(\frac{y}{x}\right) - x\right\}dx$, is given by

(a) $\log x - \cos\left(\frac{y}{x}\right) = \log C$ (b) $\log x - \sin\left(\frac{y}{x}\right) = C$ (c) $\log\left(\frac{x}{y}\right) - \cos\left(\frac{y}{x}\right) = \log C$ (d) None of these

7. The solution of $\frac{xdx + ydy}{xdy - ydx} = \sqrt{\frac{a^2 - x^2 - y^2}{x^2 + y^2}}$, is given by

(a) $\sin^{-1}(\sqrt{x^2 + y^2}) = a\tan^{-1}\left(\frac{y}{x}\right) + C$ (b) $\sin^{-1}(\sqrt{x^2 + y^2}) = \frac{1}{a}\tan^{-1}\left(\frac{y}{x}\right) + C$

(c) $\sin^{-1}\left(\frac{\sqrt{x^2 + y^2}}{a}\right) = \tan^{-1}\left(\frac{y}{x}\right) + C$ (d) None of the above

8. The solution of $(1 + e^{x/y})\,dx + e^{x/y}\left(1 - \frac{x}{y}\right)dy = 0$, is given by

(a) $x - ye^{x/y} = C$ (b) $x + ye^{x/y} = C$ (c) $y - \frac{x}{y}e^{x/y} = C$ (d) None of these

9. The solution of $\frac{x + y\,dy/dx}{y - x\,dy/dx} = \frac{x\sin^2(x^2 + y^2)}{y^3}$, is given by

(a) $-\cot(x^2 + y^2) = \left(\frac{x}{y}\right)^2 + C$ (b) $\tan(x^2 + y^2) = x^2y^2 + C$

(c) $\cot(x^2 + y^2) = \frac{x}{y} + C$ (d) None of these

10. The solution of $\frac{dy}{dx} + \frac{y}{x} = \frac{1}{(1 + \log x + \log y)^2}$, is given by

(a) $xy\,(1 + \log(xy)) = C$ (b) $xy^2\,(1 + \log(xy)) = C$ (c) $xy\,(1 + \log(xy))^2 = C$ (d) $xy\,(1 + (\log xy)^2) = C$

Session 5

Solving of First Order and Higher Degrees, Application of Differential Equations, Application of First Order Differential Equations

Solving of First Order and Higher Degrees

Differential Equation of First Order and Higher Degrees

A differential equation of first order is of the form $f(x, y, P)$ where $P = dy / dx$. If in the equation degree of P is greater than one, then the equation is of first order and higher degree.

The differential equation of first order and higher degree can be written in the form

$$P^n + F_1(x, y) P^{n-1} + \ldots + F_{n-1}(x, y) P + F_n(x, y) = 0$$

The differential equations of these category can be solved by one or more of the following methods :

(i) Equations solvable for P.

(ii) Equations solvable for y.

(iii) Equations solvable for x.

(iv) Clairaut's equations.

Now, we shall discuss these cases.

(i) Equations Solvable For P

If the equation

$$P^n + F_1(x, y) P^{n-1} + \ldots + F_{n-1}(x, y) P + F_n(x, y) = 0,$$

is solvable for P, then LHS expression can be resolved into n linear factors and hence can be put in the form

$$(P - f_1(x, y))(P - f_2(x, y)) \ldots (P - f_n(x, y)) = 0.$$

Equating each of these factors to zero, we get n differential equations of the first order and first degree.

$$\frac{dy}{dx} = f_1(x, y), \frac{dy}{dx} = f_2(x, y), \ldots, \frac{dy}{dx} = f_n(x, y)$$

Let the solutions of these obtained equations are

$$\phi_1(x, y, c_1) = 0, \phi_2(x, y, c_2) = 0, \ldots, \phi_n(x, y, c_n) = 0$$

respectively.

Hence, the general solution is given by

$$\phi_1(x, y, c), \phi_2(x, y, c), \ldots, \phi_n(x, y, c) = 0$$

Here, the arbitrary constant $c_1, c_2, \ldots, c_n$ are replaced by a single arbitrary constant c because every first order equation has only one arbitrary constant in its solution.

| Example 61 Solve $(p - x)(p - e^x)(p - 1/y) = 0$; where $p = \dfrac{dy}{dx}$.

Sol. The component linear equations are $p = x, p = e^x, p = \dfrac{1}{y}$

If $\dfrac{dy}{dx} = x$, then $dy = x\,dx \Rightarrow y = \dfrac{x^2}{2} + C_1$

If $\dfrac{dy}{dx} = e^x$, then $dy = e^x\,dx \Rightarrow y = e^x + C_2$

If $\dfrac{dy}{dx} = \dfrac{1}{y}$, then $y\,dy = dx \Rightarrow \dfrac{y^2}{2} = x + C_3$

$\therefore$ The required solution is

$$\left(y - \frac{x^2}{2} + C\right)(y - e^x + C)\left(\frac{y^2}{2} - x + C\right) = 0$$

| Example 62 Solve $x^2p^2 + xyp - 6y^2 = 0$.

Sol. The given equation is

$$x^2p^2 + xyp - 6y^2 = 0$$

Solving as a quadratic in p, we get

$$p = \frac{(-xy \pm \sqrt{x^2y^2 + 24x^2y^2})}{2x^2} = \frac{2y}{x}, -\frac{3y}{x}$$

If $p = \dfrac{2y}{x}$, then $\dfrac{dy}{dx} = \dfrac{2y}{x} \Rightarrow \dfrac{dy}{y} = \dfrac{2dx}{x}$

$$\Rightarrow \quad \log\left|\frac{y}{x^2}\right| = k \Rightarrow y = C_1 x^2$$

If $p = -\dfrac{3y}{x}$, then $\dfrac{dy}{dx} = -\dfrac{3y}{x} \Rightarrow \dfrac{dy}{y} = -\dfrac{3dx}{x}$

$$\Rightarrow \quad x^3y = C_2$$

$\therefore$ The required solution is $(y - Cx^2)(x^3y - C) = 0$.

Example 63 Solve $xy^2(p^2+2)=2py^3+x^3$.

Sol. The given equation can be written as

$$(xy^2p^2-x^3)+2(xy^2-py^3)=0$$

$$\Rightarrow \quad x(y^2p^2-x^2)+2y^2(x-py)=0$$

$$\Rightarrow \quad (py-x)\{x(py+x)-2y^2\}=0$$

If $py-x=0$, then $y\,dy-x\,dx=0 \Rightarrow y^2-x^2=C_1$

If $xyp+x^2-2y^2=0$, then $2y\dfrac{dy}{dx}-\dfrac{4y^2}{x}=-2x$

$$\Rightarrow \quad \frac{dt}{dx}-\frac{4}{x}t=-2x,$$

where $t=y^2$ $\quad$ IF $=e^{-\int \frac{4}{x}dx}=e^{-4\ln x}=\dfrac{1}{x^4}$

Its solution is $t\left(\dfrac{1}{x^4}\right)=\displaystyle\int -2x\cdot\frac{1}{x^4}\,dx$

i.e. $\dfrac{t}{x^4}=\dfrac{1}{x^2}+C_2$ i.e. $y^2=x^2+C_2x^4$

Hence, the required solution is

$$(y^2-x^2-C)(y^2-x^2-Cx^4)=0$$

(ii) Equations Solvable For y

Equation that comes under this category, can be expressed in the form

$$y=g(x,p)$$

(i.e. an explicit function y in term of x and p)...(i)

Differentiating Eq. (i) w.r.t. x, we get

$$\frac{dy}{dx}=p=F\left(x,p,\frac{dp}{dx}\right)$$

Which is a differential equation of the first order containing x and p. Let us suppose that its solution is

$$\phi(x,p,c)=0 \quad \text{...(ii)}$$

Then, the solution is obtained by eliminating p between $y=g(x,p)$ and $\phi(x,p,c)=0$. However, if eliminating of p is difficult express x and y as a function of the parameter p.

Example 64 Solve $xp^2-2yp+ax=0$.

Sol. The given equation can be written as,

$$y=\frac{xp}{2}+\frac{ax}{2p} \quad \text{...(i)}$$

$$\frac{dy}{dx}=\frac{p}{2}+\frac{x}{2}\cdot\frac{dp}{dx}+\frac{a}{2p}-\frac{ax}{2p^2}\cdot\frac{dp}{dx}$$

$$\Rightarrow \quad p(p^2-a)=x(p^2-a)\cdot\frac{dp}{dx}$$

$$\Rightarrow \quad \frac{dp}{dx}=\frac{p}{x}\Rightarrow p=Cx$$

(The equation $p^2-a=0$ gives us singular solution in which we are not interested).

The substitute p in Eq. (i), we get the required solution

$$2y=Cx^2+\frac{a}{C}$$

Example 65 Solve $y=2px-p^2$.

Sol. Differentiating the given equation w.r.t. x, we get

$$\frac{dy}{dx}=2p+2x\frac{dp}{dx}-2p\frac{dp}{dx}$$

or $\quad 2(x-p)\dfrac{dp}{dx}+p=0$

or $\quad \dfrac{dx}{dp}+\dfrac{2}{p}x=2$

It is a linear equation in x and p.

$$\text{IF}=e^{\int \frac{2}{p}dx}=e^{2\log p}=p^2$$

$\therefore$ The solution is $xp^2=\displaystyle\int p^2\cdot 2\,dp=\frac{2}{3}p^3+C$

Thus, the solution of the given equation is

$$x=\frac{2}{3}p+Cp^{-2}\text{, where } p \text{ is parameter.}$$

(iii) Equations Solvable For x

This type of equation can be put in the form

$$x=g(y,p) \quad \text{...(i)}$$

Differentiating w.r.t. y, we get

$$\frac{1}{p}=\frac{dx}{dy}=G\left(x,p,\frac{dp}{dx}\right)$$

which is a differential equation of 1st order containing y and p and its solution is

$$\phi(y,p,c)=0$$

Then, the solution is obtained by eliminating p between $x=g(y,p)$ and $\phi(y,p,c)=0$. However, if eliminating of p is difficult express x and y as a function of the parameter p.

Example 66 Solve $y=2px+y^2p^3$.

Sol. Solving for x, we get

$$x=\frac{y}{2p}-\frac{y^2p^2}{2} \quad \text{...(i)}$$

Differentiating Eq. (i) w.r.t. y, we get

$$\frac{dx}{dy}=\frac{1}{2p}-\frac{y}{2p^2}\cdot\frac{dp}{dy}-yp^2-y^2p\cdot\frac{dp}{dy}$$

or $$\frac{1}{p}-\frac{1}{2p}+yp^2=-y\left(\frac{1}{2p^2}+yp\right)\cdot\frac{dp}{dy}$$

or $$(1+2yp^3)\,p=-y\,(1+2p^3y)\cdot\frac{dp}{dy}$$

or $$\frac{dp}{p}+\frac{dy}{y}=0\Rightarrow py=C\Rightarrow p=\frac{C}{y}$$

Substituting this in the Eq. (i), we get

$$x=\frac{y^2}{2C}-\frac{C^2}{2}\Rightarrow y^2=2Cx+C^2$$

(iv) Clairaut's Equation

The differential equation $y=px+f(p)$ is known as Clairaut's equation. The solution of equation of this type is given by $y=cx+f(c)$.

Which is obtained by replacing p by c in the given equation.

Remark

Some equations can be reduced to Clairaut's form by suitable substitution.

Example 67 Solve $y=px+\dfrac{p}{\sqrt{1+p^2}}$.

Sol. Its solution is, $y=cx+\dfrac{c}{\sqrt{1+c^2}}$

Example 68 Solve $\sqrt{1+p^2}=\tan(px-y)$.

Sol. The given equation is

$$\sqrt{1+p^2}=\tan(px-y)$$

or $$px-y=\tan^{-1}(\sqrt{1+p^2})$$

or $$y=px-\tan^{-1}(\sqrt{1+p^2})$$

Its solution is, $$y=cx-\tan^{-1}(\sqrt{1+c^2})$$

Example 69 Solve $y^2\log y=pxy+p^2$.

Sol. Let $\log y=t$. Then $\dfrac{1}{y}\dfrac{dy}{dx}=\dfrac{dt}{dx}$

So, if $\dfrac{dt}{dx}=p$, then $\dfrac{p}{y}=p$

Substituting these in the given equation, we have

$$y^2t=y\cdot p\,xy+p^2y^2\quad\text{or}\quad t=px+p^2$$

Which is in Clairaut's form.

Thus, the required solution is

$$t=cx+c^2\quad\text{or}\quad\log y=cx+c^2$$

(c being an arbitrary constant.)

Application of Differential Equations

Differential Equation of First Order But not of First Degree

1. The most general form of a first order and higher degree differential equation is $p^n+P_1\,p^{n-1}+P_2\,p^{n-2}+\ldots\ldots+P_n=0$ where $P_1,P_2,$ ......, P_n are function of x, y and $p=dy/dx$. If a 1st order any degree equation can be resolved into differential equation (involving p) of first degree and 1st order, in such case we say that the equation is solvable for p.

   Let their solution be $g_1(x,y,c_1)\times g_2(x,y,c_2)\times\ldots\times g_n(x,y,c_n)=0$, (where $c_1,c_2,\ldots\ldots\ldots,c_n$, are arbitrary constant) we take $c_1=c_2=\ldots..=c_n=c$ because the differential equation of 1st order 1st degree contain only one arbitrary constant. So solution is

   $$g_1(x,y,c)\times g_2(x,y,c)\times\ldots\times g_n(x,y,c)=0$$

2. The most general form of a first order and higher degree differential equation is $p^n+P_1\,p^{n-1}+P_2\,p^{n-2}+\ldots+P_n=0$, where $P_1,P_2,$ ......, P_n are function of x, y and $p=dy/dx$. If differential equation is expressible in the form $y=f(x,p)$, then

   ***Step* 1** Differentiate w.r.t. x, we get $p\dfrac{dy}{dx}=f\left(x,p,\dfrac{dp}{dx}\right)$.

   ***Step* 2** Solving this we obtain $\phi(x,p,c)=0$.

   ***Step* 3** The solution of differential equation is obtained by eliminating p.

Application of First Order Differential Equations

Growth and Decay Problems

Let $N(t)$ denotes the amount of substance (or population) that is either growing or decaying. If we assume that dN/dt, the time rate of change of this amount of substance, is proportional to the amount of substance present, then

$$\frac{dN}{dt}=kN\quad\text{or}\quad\frac{dN}{dt}-kN=0\qquad\ldots\text{(i)}$$

Where k is the constant of proportionality. We are assuming that $N(t)$ is a differentiable, hence continuous, function of time.

Example 70 The population of a certain country is known to increase at a rate proportional to the number of people presently living in the country. If after two years the population has doubled and after three years the population is 20000, estimate the number of people initially living in the country.

Sol. Let N denotes the number of people living in the country at any time t, and let N_0 denote the number of people initially living in the country. Then, from Eq. (i)

$$\frac{dN}{dt} - kN = 0$$

Which has the solution $N = Ce^{kt}$ ...(i)

At $t = 0$, $N = N_0$; hence, it follows from Eq. (i) that $N_0 = Ce^{k(0)}$ or that $C = N_0$.

Thus, $$N = N_0 e^{kt} \quad \text{...(ii)}$$

At $t = 2$, $N = 2N_0$. Substituting these values into Eq. (ii), we have

$$2N_0 = N_0 e^{2k} \text{ from which } k = \frac{1}{2} \ln 2 = 0.347$$

Substituting this value into Eq. (i) gives

$$N = N_0 e^{(0.347)\,t} \quad \text{...(iii)}$$

At $t = 3$, $N = 20000$. Substituting these values into Eq. (iii), we obtain

$$20000 = N_0 e^{(0.347)(3)}$$

Example 71 A certain radioactive material is known to decay at a rate proportional to the amount present. If initially there is 50 mg of the material present and after two hours it is observed that the material has lost 10% of its original mass, find (a) and expression for the mass of the material remaining at any time t, (b) the mass of the material after four hours, and (c) the time at which the material has decayed to one half of its initial mass.

Sol. (a) Let N denotes the amount of material present at time t. Then, from Eq. (i)

$$\frac{dN}{dt} - kN = 0$$

This differential equation is separable and linear, its solution is

$$N = Ce^{kt} \quad \text{...(i)}$$

At $t = 0$, we are given that $N = 50$. Therefore, from Eq. (i), $50 = Ce^{k(0)}$ or $C = 50$.

Thus, $$N = 50\, e^{kt} \quad \text{...(ii)}$$

At $t = 2$, 10% of the original mass of 50 mg or 5 mg has decayed. Hence, at $t = 2$, $N = 50 - 5 = 45$. Substituting these values into Eq. (ii) and solving for k, we have

$$45 = 50e^{2k} \quad \text{or} \quad k = \frac{1}{2} \ln \frac{45}{50} = -0.053$$

Substituting this value into Eq. (ii), we obtain the amount of mass present at any time t as

$$N = 50e^{-0.053\,t} \quad \text{...(iii)}$$

Where t is measured in hours.

(b) We require N at $t = 4$. Substituting $t = 4$ into Eq. (iii) and then solving for N, we find $N = 50e^{(-0.053)\,(4)}$

(c) We require t when $N = 50/2 = 25$. Substituting $N = 25$ into Eq. (iii) and solving for t, we find $25 = 50e^{-0.053t}$

or $$-0.053\, t = \ln \frac{1}{2} \quad \text{or} \quad t = 13\text{ h}$$

Example 72 Five mice in a stable population of 500 are intentionally infected with a contagious disease to test a theory of epidemic spread that postulates the rate of change in the infected population is proportional to the product of the number of mice who have the disease with the number that are disease free. Assuming the theory is correct, how long will it take half the population to contract the disease?

Sol. Let $N(t)$ denotes the number of mice with the disease at time t. We are given that $N(0) = 5$, and it follows that $500 - N(t)$ is the number of mice without the disease at time t. The theory predicts that

$$\frac{dN}{dt} = kN\,(500 - N) \quad \text{...(i)}$$

Where k is a constant of proportionality. This equation is different from Eq. (i) because the rate of change is no longer proportional to just the number of mice who have the disease. Eq. (i) has the differential form

$$\frac{dN}{N(500 - N)} - kdt = 0 \quad \text{...(ii)}$$

Which is separable. Using partial fraction decomposition, we have

$$\frac{1}{N(500 - N)} = \frac{1/500}{N} + \frac{1/500}{500 - N}$$

Hence, Eq. (ii) may be rewritten as

$$\frac{1}{500}\left(\frac{1}{N} + \frac{1}{500 - N}\right) dN - kdt = 0$$

It solution is $$\frac{1}{500}\int\left(\frac{1}{N} + \frac{1}{500 - N}\right) dN - \int kdt = C$$

or $$\frac{1}{500}(\ln |N| - \ln|500 - N|) - kt = C$$

Which may be rewritten as

$$\ln \left|\frac{N}{500 - N}\right| = 500\,(C + kt)$$

$$\frac{N}{500-N} = e^{500(C+kt)} \qquad \text{...(iii)}$$

But $e^{500(C+kt)} = e^{500}\, e^{kt}$. Setting $C_1 = e^{500C}$, we can write Eq. (iii) as

$$\frac{N}{500-N} = C_1 e^{500kt} \qquad \text{...(iv)}$$

At $t = 0$, $N = 5$. Substituting these values into Eq. (iv), we find

$$\frac{4}{495} = C_1\, e^{500k(0)} = C_1$$

So, $C_1 = 1/99$ and Eq. (iv) becomes

$$\frac{N}{500-N} = \frac{1}{99}\, e^{500kt} \qquad \text{...(v)}$$

We could solve Eq. (v) for N, but this is not necessary. We seek a value of t when $N = 250$, one half the population. Substituting $N = 250$ into Eq. (v) and solving for t, we obtain

$$1 = \frac{1}{99}\, e^{500kt}; \qquad \ln 99 = 500kt$$

or $t = 0.0091/k$ time units. Without additional information, we cannot obtain a numerical value for the constant of proportionality k or be more definitive about t.

Geometrical Applications

Let $P(x_1, y_1)$ be any point on the curve $y = f(x)$, then slope of the tangent at $P\,(= \tan\psi) = \left(\frac{dy}{dx}\right)_{(x_1, y_1)}$ and hence we find the following facts.

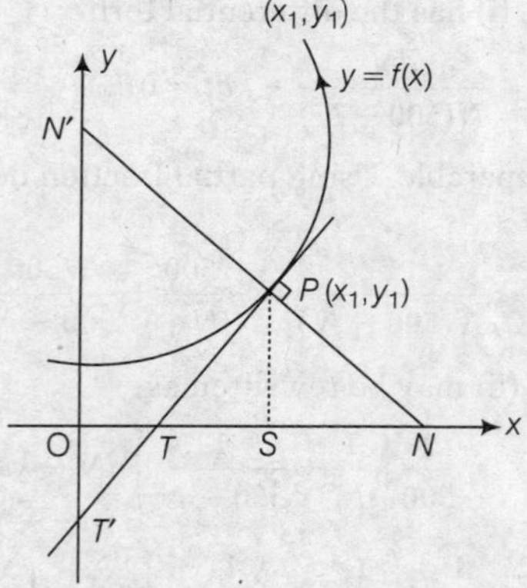

Fig. 4.2

(i) The equation of the tangent at P is,

$y - y_1 = \frac{dy}{dx}(x - x_1)$ when it cuts x-axis, $y = 0$.

$\therefore$ x-intercept of the tangent $= x_1 - y_1 \left(\frac{dx}{dy}\right)$

y-intercept of the tangent $= y_1 - x_1 \frac{dy}{dx}$

(ii) The equation of normal at P is,

$y - y_1 = -\frac{1}{(dy/dx)}(x - x_1)$ x and y-intercepts of normal are; $x_1 + y_1 \frac{dy}{dx}$ and $y_1 + x_1 \frac{dx}{dy}$

(iii) Length of tangent $= PT = |y_1| \sqrt{1 + (dx/dy)^2_{(x_1, y_1)}}$

(iv) Length of normal $= PN = |y_1| \sqrt{1 + (dy/dx)^2_{(x_1, y_1)}}$

(v) Length of subtangent $= ST = \left| y_1 \left(\frac{dx}{dy}\right)_{(x_1, y_1)} \right|$

(vi) Length of subnormal $= SN = \left| y_1 \left(\frac{dy}{dx}\right)_{(x_1, y_1)} \right|$

(vii) Length of radius vector $= \sqrt{x_1^2 + y_1^2}$

Example 73 Find the curve for which the area of the triangle formed by the x-axis tangent drawn at any point on the curve and radius vector of the point of tangency is constant equal to a^2.

Sol. Tangent drawn at any point (x, y) is

$$Y - y = \frac{dy}{dx}(X - x)$$

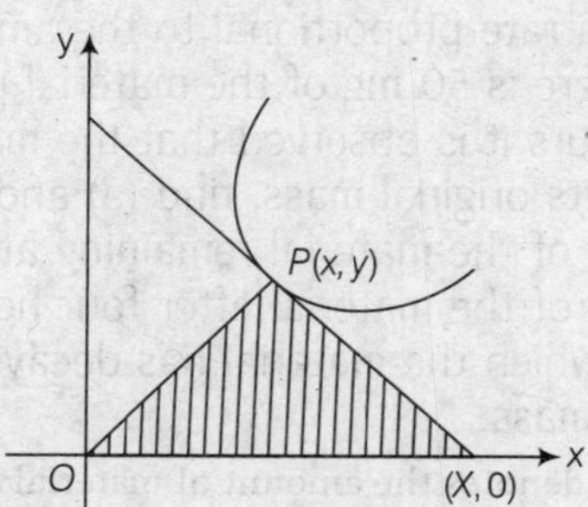

When $\quad Y = 0,\ X = x - y\frac{dx}{dy}$

Area of $\Delta = 2a^2$ (given)

i.e. $\quad \left|\frac{1}{2} \cdot X \cdot Y\right| = 2a^2$

i.e. $\quad \left| xy - y^2 \frac{dx}{dy} \right| = 2a^2$

i.e. $\quad xy - y^2 \frac{dx}{dy} = \pm\, 2a^2$

i.e. $\quad \frac{dx}{dy} - \frac{x}{y} = \pm\, \frac{2a^2}{y^2}$

$$\text{IF} = e^{\int -\frac{1}{y} dy} = \frac{1}{y}$$

$\therefore$ The solution is $x \cdot \frac{1}{y} = \int \pm \frac{2a^2}{y^2} \cdot \frac{1}{y} dy$

$$\frac{x}{y} = \pm \frac{2a^2 \cdot y^{-2}}{-2} + C, \text{ i.e. } x = Cy + \frac{a^2}{y}$$

Example 74 Find the curve for which the intercept cut off by any tangent on y-axis is proportional to the square of the ordinate of the point of tangency.

Sol. The equation of tangent at any point (x, y) is

$$Y - y = \frac{dy}{dx}(X - x)$$

When $X = 0; Y = y - x\frac{dy}{dx} = y\text{-intercept}$

It is given $Y \propto y^2$. i.e. $Y = ky^2$

(k being constant of proportionality)

i.e. $$y - x\frac{dy}{dx} = ky^2$$

i.e. $$\frac{dy}{dx} - \frac{1}{x}y = -\frac{ky^2}{x}$$

i.e. $$-y^{-2}\frac{dy}{dx} + \frac{1}{x}\cdot\frac{1}{y} = \frac{k}{x}$$

Let $\frac{1}{y} = z$ so that, $-\frac{1}{y^2}\cdot\frac{dy}{dx} = \frac{dz}{dx}$ $\therefore$ $\frac{dz}{dx} + \frac{z}{x} = \frac{k}{x}$

$$\text{IF} = e^{\int \frac{1}{x} dx} = e^{\log x} = x$$

$\therefore$ The solution is $zx = \int \frac{kx}{x} dx = kx + C$

$\Rightarrow$ $\frac{x}{y} = kx + C$

$\Rightarrow$ $x = kxy + Cy$

$\Rightarrow$ $x - Cy = kxy \Rightarrow \frac{1}{ky} + \frac{-C}{k}\cdot\frac{1}{x} = 1$

$\Rightarrow$ $\frac{C_1}{x} + \frac{C_2}{y} = 1$ $\left(\text{where } \frac{1}{k} = C_2 \text{ and } -\frac{C}{k} = C_1\right)$

Example 75 For any differential function $y = f(x)$, the value of $\frac{d^2y}{dx^2} + \left(\frac{dy}{dx}\right)^3 \cdot \frac{d^2x}{dy^2}$ is equal to

(a) $2y\frac{dy}{dx}$ (b) $y^2\frac{dy}{dx}$

(c) $y\frac{dy}{dx} + \left(\frac{d^2x}{dy^2}\right)^2$ (d) None of these

Sol. We know, $\frac{dy}{dx} = \left(\frac{dx}{dy}\right)^{-1}$, differentiating both the sides

or $$\frac{d^2y}{dx^2} = -\left(\frac{dx}{dy}\right)^{-2} \cdot \frac{d}{dy}\left(\frac{dx}{dy}\right)\cdot\frac{dy}{dx}$$

$$= -\left(\frac{dx}{dy}\right)^{-2} \cdot \frac{d^2x}{dy^2}\cdot\frac{dy}{dx}$$

$\Rightarrow$ $$\frac{d^2y}{dx^2} = -\frac{d^2x}{dy^2}\cdot\left(\frac{dy}{dx}\right)^3$$

or $$\frac{d^2y}{dx^2} + \left(\frac{dy}{dx}\right)^3 \cdot \frac{d^2x}{dy^2} = 0$$

Hence, (d) is the correct answer.

Example 76 The solution of $y = x\frac{dy}{dx} + \frac{dy}{dx} - \left(\frac{dy}{dx}\right)^2$, is

(a) $y = (x-1)^2$ (b) $4y = (x+1)^2$

(c) $(y-1)^2 = 4x$ (d) None of these

Sol. The given equation can be written as

$$y = xp + p - p^2; \quad \text{where } p = \frac{dy}{dx} \quad \text{...(i)}$$

Differentiating both the sides w.r.t. x, we get

$$p = p + \frac{xdp}{dx} + \frac{dp}{dx} - 2p\frac{dp}{dx}$$

$\therefore$ $$\frac{dp}{dx}(x + 1 - 2p) = 0$$

$\therefore$ Either $\frac{dp}{dx} = 0$ i.e. $p = C$ ...(ii)

or $x + 1 - 2p = 0$ *ie*, $p = \frac{1}{2}(x+1)$ ...(iii)

Eliminating p between Eqs. (i) and (ii), we get

$$y = Cx + C - C^2$$

As the complete solution and eliminating p between Eqs. (i) and (iii)

$$y = \frac{1}{2}(x+1)x + \frac{1}{2}(x+1) - \frac{1}{4}(x+1)^2$$

ie, $4y = (x+1)^2$ as the singular solution.

Hence, (b) is the correct answer.

Example 77 The solution of $\left(\frac{dy}{dx}\right)^2 + (2x + y)\frac{dy}{dx} + 2xy = 0$, is

(a) $(y + x^2 - C_1)(x + \log y + y^2 + C_2) = 0$

(b) $(y + x^2 - C_1)(x - \log y - C_2) = 0$

(c) $(y + x^2 - C_1)(x + \log y - C_2) = 0$

(d) None of the above

Sol. The given equation can be written as

$$p^2 + (2x + y)p + 2xy = 0, \text{ where } p = \frac{dy}{dx}$$

i.e. $$(p + 2x)(p + y) = 0$$

$\therefore$ $$p + 2x = 0, \text{ otherwise } p + y = 0$$

$$\Rightarrow \quad \frac{dy}{dx} + 2x = 0 \quad \text{or} \quad \frac{dy}{dx} + y = 0$$

$$\Rightarrow \quad \int dy + 2\int x\,dx = C_1 \quad \text{or} \quad \int \frac{dy}{y} + \int dx = C_2$$

$$\Rightarrow \quad y + x^2 = C_1 \quad \text{or} \quad \log y + x = C_2$$

$$\therefore \quad (y + x^2 - C_1) = 0$$

or $$(x + \log y - C_2) = 0$$

$$\Rightarrow \quad (y + x^2 - C_1)(x + \log y - C_2) = 0$$

is the required solution.

Hence, (c) is the correct answer.

Example 78 A curve $y = f(x)$ passes through the origin. Through any point (x, y) on the curve, lines are drawn parallel to the coordinate axes. If the curve divides the area formed by these lines and coordinate axes in the ratio $m : n$. Then the equation of curve is

(a) $y = Cx^{m/n}$ (b) $my^2 = Cx^{m/n}$

(c) $y^3 = Cx^{m/n}$ (d) None of these

Sol. $$\frac{\text{Area of } OBPO}{\text{Area of } OPAO} = \frac{m}{n}$$

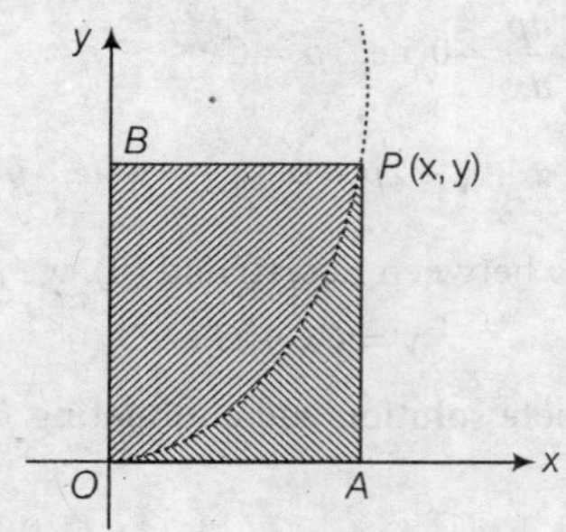

$$\Rightarrow \quad \frac{xy - \int_0^x y\,dx}{\int_0^x y\,dx} = \frac{m}{n} \Rightarrow nxy = (m + n)\int_0^x y\,dx$$

Differentiating w.r.t. x, we get

$$n\left(x\frac{dy}{dx} + y\right) = (m + n)\,y$$

$$\Rightarrow \quad nx\frac{dy}{dx} = my$$

$$\Rightarrow \quad \frac{m}{n}\cdot\frac{dx}{x} = \frac{dy}{y}, \text{ integrating both the sides}$$

$$y = Cx^{m/n}$$

Hence, (a) is the correct answer.

Example 79 The equation of the curve passing through the points $(3a, a)$ $(a > 0)$ in the form $x = f(y)$ which satisfy the differential equation;

$\frac{a^2}{xy}\cdot\frac{dx}{dy} = \frac{x}{y} + \frac{y}{x} - 2$, is

(a) $x = y + a\left(\frac{1 + e^{y-k}}{1 - 2e^{y-k}}\right)$ (b) $x = y + a\left(\frac{1 + e^{y-k}}{1 - e^{y-k}}\right)$

(c) $y = x + a\left(\frac{1 + e^{y-k}}{1 - e^{y-k}}\right)$ (d) None of these

Sol. Here, $$\frac{a^2}{xy}\cdot\frac{dx}{dy} = \frac{x}{y} + \frac{y}{x} - 2$$

$$\Rightarrow \quad a^2 = \frac{dy}{dx}(x^2 + y^2 - 2xy)$$

$$\Rightarrow \quad (x - y)^2\cdot\frac{dy}{dx} = a^2, \text{ put } x - y = v \therefore 1 - \frac{dy}{dx} = \frac{dv}{dx}$$

$$\Rightarrow \quad v^2\left(1 - \frac{dv}{dx}\right) = a^2$$

$$\Rightarrow \quad v^2 - a^2 = v^2\frac{dv}{dx} \Rightarrow \frac{v^2 dv}{v^2 - a^2} = dx$$

$$\Rightarrow \quad \left(1 + \frac{a^2}{v^2 - a^2}\right)dv = dx$$

Integrating both the sides, we get

$$v + \frac{a}{2}\log\left|\frac{v - a}{v + a}\right| = x + C$$

$$\Rightarrow \quad (x - y) + \frac{a}{2}\log\left(\frac{x - y - a}{x - y + a}\right) = x + C$$

$$\Rightarrow \quad y + C = \frac{a}{2}\log\left(\frac{x - y - a}{x - y + a}\right) \quad \text{...(i)}$$

It passes through $(3a, a)$

$$\Rightarrow \quad a + C = \frac{a}{2}\log\left(\frac{1}{3}\right)$$

$$\Rightarrow \quad C = -a + \frac{a}{2}\log\left(\frac{1}{3}\right)$$

$$\Rightarrow \quad C = -a\left(\frac{2 + \log 3}{2}\right)$$

$$\therefore \quad y = \frac{a}{2}(2 + \log 3) + \log\left(\frac{x - y - a}{x - y + a}\right)$$

$$\Rightarrow \quad \frac{x - y - a}{x - y + a} = e^{y-k}, \text{ where } k = \frac{a}{2}(2 + \log 3)$$

$$\therefore \quad \frac{x - y}{a} = \frac{1 + e^{y-k}}{1 - e^{y-k}}$$

$$\Rightarrow \quad x = y + a\left(\frac{1 + e^{y-k}}{1 - e^{y-k}}\right), \text{ where } k = \frac{a}{2}(2 + \log 3)$$

Which is required equation of curve.

Hence, (b) is the correct answer.

Example 80 The family of curves, the subtangent at any point of which is the arithmetic mean of the coordinates of the point of tangency, is given by

(a) $(x-y)^2 = Cy$ (b) $(y-x)^2 = Cx$

(c) $(x-y)^2 = Cxy$ (d) None of these

Sol. Let the family of curves be $y = f(x)$

$$\tan\theta = \frac{l(PP')}{l(TP')}$$

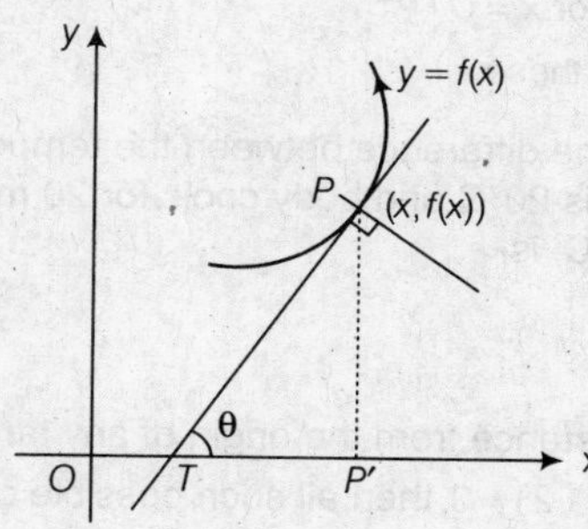

$$\tan\theta = \frac{l(PP')}{l(TP')}$$

$$\therefore \quad l\,(\text{subtangent}) = \frac{f(x)}{f'(x)}$$

$$\therefore \quad \frac{y}{y'} = \frac{x+y}{2} \text{ (given)}$$

$$\therefore \quad y' = \frac{2y}{x+y}$$

$$\Rightarrow \quad \frac{dy}{dx} = \frac{2y}{x+y} \quad \therefore \quad \frac{dx}{dy} = \frac{x+y}{2xy} \quad \text{...(i)}$$

It is a homogeneous differential equation.

$\therefore$ Put $x = vy$

Differentiating w.r.t. y, we get

$$\frac{dx}{dy} = v + y\frac{dv}{dy} \quad \text{...(ii)}$$

In Eq. (i) replacing $\frac{dx}{dy}$ by Eq. (ii), we get

$$v + y\frac{dv}{dy} = \frac{vy+y}{2y} = \frac{1+v}{2}$$

$$\Rightarrow \quad y\frac{dv}{dy} = \frac{1+v}{2} - v = \frac{1+v-2v}{2} = \frac{1-v}{2}$$

$$\Rightarrow \quad \frac{2}{1-v}dv = \frac{dy}{y}$$

Integrating, $\frac{2\log|1-v|}{-1} = \log|y| + \log C_1 \; (C_1 > 0)$

$$\therefore \quad -2\log|y-x| + 2\log|y| = \log|y| + \log C_1$$

$$\Rightarrow \quad \log|y-x|^2 = \log|y| - \log C_1$$

$$\Rightarrow \quad \log|y-x|^2 = \log|y| + \log C,$$

where $\log C = -\log C_1$

$$\Rightarrow \quad \log|y-x|^2 = \log|yC|$$

$\Rightarrow (x-y)^2 = Cy$, is the required equation of family of curves.

Hence, (a) is the correct answer.

Exercise for Session 5

1. The equation of curve for which the normal at every point passes through a fixed point, is
   (a) a circle
   (b) an ellipse
   (c) a hyperbola
   (d) None of these

2. If the tangent at any point P of a curve meets the axis of x in T. Then the curve for which $OP = PT$, O being the origin is
   (a) $x = Cy^2$
   (b) $x = Cy^2$ or $x = C/y^2$
   (c) $x = Cy$ or $x = C/y$
   (d) None of these

3. According to Newton's law, the rate of cooling is proportional to the difference between the temperature of the body and the temperature of the air. If the temperature of the air is 20°C and body cools for 20 min from 100°C to 60°C, then the time it will take for it temperature to drop to 30°C, is
   (a) 30 min
   (b) 40 min
   (c) 60 min
   (d) 80 min

4. Let $f(x, y)$ be a curve in the x-y plane having the property that distance from the origin of any tangent to the curve is equal to distance of point of contact from the y-axis. If $f(1, 2) = 0$, then all such possible curves are
   (a) $x^2 + y^2 = 5x$
   (b) $x^2 - y^2 = 5x$
   (c) $x^2y^2 = 5x$
   (d) All of these

5. Given the curves $y = f(x)$ passing through the point (0, 1) and $y = \int_{-\infty}^{x} f(t)$ passing through the point $\left(0, \frac{1}{2}\right)$. The tangents drawn to both the curves at the points with equal abscissae intersect on the x-axis. Then the curve $y = f(x)$, is
   (a) $f(x) = x^2 + x + 1$
   (b) $f(x) = \frac{x^2}{e^x}$
   (c) $f(x) = e^{2x}$
   (d) $f(x) = x - e^x$

6. A curve passing through (1, 0) is such that the ratio of the square of the intercept cut by any tangent on the y-axis to the Sub-normal is equal to the ratio of the product of the Coordinates of the point of tangency to the product of square of the slope of the tangent and the subtangent at the same point, is given by
   (a) $x = e^{\pm 2\sqrt{y/x}}$
   (b) $x = e^{\pm\sqrt{y/x}}$
   (c) $y = e^{\pm\sqrt{y/x}} - 1$
   (d) $xy + e^{y/x} - 1 = 0$

7. Consider a curve $y = f(x)$ in xy-plane. The curve passes through (0, 0) and has the property that a segment of tangent drawn at any point $P(x, f(x))$ and the line $y = 3$ gets bisected by the line $x + y = 1$ then the equation of curve, is
   (a) $y^2 = 9(x - y)$
   (b) $(y - 3)^2 = 9(1 - x - y)$
   (c) $(y + 3)^2 = 9(1 - x - y)$
   (d) $(y - 3)^2 - 9(1 + x + y)$

8. Consider the curved mirror $y = f(x)$ passing through (0, 6) having the property that all light rays emerging from origin, after getting reflected from the mirror becomes parallel to x-axis, then the equation of curve, is
   (a) $y^2 = 4(x - y)$ or $y^2 = 36(9 + x)$
   (b) $y^2 = 4(1 - x)$ or $y^2 = 36(9 - x)$
   (c) $y^2 = 4(1 + x)$ or $y^2 = 36(9 - x)$
   (d) None of these

JEE Type Solved Examples : Single Option Correct Type Questions

Ex. 1 *The order of the differential equation of family of curves $y = C_1 \sin^{-1} x + C_2 \cos^{-1} x + C_3 \tan^{-1} x + C_4 \cot^{-1} x$ (where C_1, C_2, C_3 and C_4 are arbitrary constants) is*

(a) 2 (b) 3
(c) 4 (d) None of these

Sol. Here, $y = C_1 \sin^{-1} x + C_2 \cos^{-1} x + C_3 \tan^{-1} x + C_4 \cot^{-1} x$

$$\Rightarrow y = C_1 \sin^{-1} x + C_2\left(\frac{\pi}{2} - \sin^{-1} x\right) + C_3 \tan^{-1} x + C_4\left(\frac{\pi}{2} - \tan^{-1} x\right)$$

$$= (C_1 - C_2)\sin^{-1} x + (C_3 - C_4)\tan^{-1} x + (C_3 - C_4)\frac{\pi}{2}$$

There are only two independent arbitrary constant order of the differential equation is 2.

Hence, (c) is the correct answer.

Ex. 2 *The solution of the differential equation $\frac{dy}{dx} = \frac{1}{xy(x^2 \sin y^2 + 1)}$ is*

(a) $x^2(\cos y^2 - \sin y^2 - 2ce^{-y^2}) = 2$

(b) $y^2(\sin x^2 - \cos y^2 - 2ce^{-y^2}) = 2$

(c) $x^2(\cos y^2 - \sin y^2 - e^{-y^2}) = 4c$

(d) None of the above

Sol. Here, $\frac{dx}{dy} = xy(x^2 \sin y^2 + 1)$

$$\Rightarrow \frac{1}{x^3}\frac{dx}{dy} - \frac{1}{x^2} y = y \sin y^2$$

Let, $-\frac{1}{x^2} = t \Rightarrow \frac{2}{x^3}\frac{dx}{dy} = \frac{dt}{dy}$

$$\Rightarrow \frac{dt}{dy} + 2t \cdot y = y \cdot \sin y^2, \text{I.F.} = e^{\int 2y\, dy} = e^{+y^2}$$

So, required solution is

$$t \cdot e^{y^2} = \int 2y \sin y^2 \times e^{y^2} dy = \frac{1}{2} e^{y^2}(\sin y^2 - \cos y^2) + C$$

$$\Rightarrow 2t = (\sin y^2 - \cos y^2) + 2C e^{-y^2}$$

$$\Rightarrow 2 = -x^2(\sin y^2 - \cos y^2 + 2ce^{-y^2})$$

$$\Rightarrow x^2(\cos y^2 - \sin y^2 - 2ce^{-y^2}) = 2$$

Ex. 3 *The curve satisfying the differential equation $\frac{dy}{dx} = \frac{y(x+y^3)}{x(y^3 - x)}$ and passing through $(4, -2)$ is*

(a) $y^2 = -2x$ (b) $y = -2x$
(c) $y^3 = -2x$ (d) None of these

Sol. Here, $(xy^3 - x^2)dy = (xy + y^4)dx$

$$\Rightarrow y^3(xdy - ydx) - x(xdy + ydx = 0)$$

$$\Rightarrow x^2y^3 d\left(\frac{y}{x}\right) - x\, d(xy) = 0$$

dividing by x^3y^2, we get

$$\Rightarrow \frac{y}{x} d\left(\frac{y}{x}\right) - \frac{1}{x^2y^2} \cdot d\left(\frac{x}{y}\right) = 0$$

$$\Rightarrow \frac{1}{2} d\left(\frac{y}{x}\right)^2 + d\left(\frac{1}{xy}\right) = 0$$

Now integrating, we get

$$\frac{1}{2}\left(\frac{y}{x}\right)^2 + \frac{1}{xy} = c$$

It passes through $(4, -2)$

$$\Rightarrow \frac{1}{8} - \frac{1}{8} = c \Rightarrow C = 0$$

$\therefore y^3 = -2x$ is required curve.

Ex. 4 *Spherical rain drop evaporates at a rate proportional to its surface area. The differential equation corresponding to the rate of change of the radius of the rain drop, if the constant of proportionality is $K > 0$, is*

(a) $\frac{dr}{dt} + K = 0$ (b) $\frac{dr}{dt} - K = 0$

(c) $\frac{dr}{dt} = Kr$ (d) None of these

Sol. $$\frac{dV}{dt} = -k4\pi r^2 \quad \text{...(i)}$$

But $$V = \frac{4}{3}\pi r^3$$

$$\Rightarrow \frac{dV}{dt} = 4\pi r^2 \frac{dr}{dt} \quad \text{...(ii)}$$

Therefore, $$\frac{dr}{dt} = -K$$

Hence, (a) is the correct answer.

Ex. 5 *A function $y = f(x)$ satisfies the differential equation $f(x) \cdot \sin 2x - \cos x + (1 + \sin^2 x) f'(x) = 0$ with initial condition $y(0) = 0$. The value of $f(\pi/6)$ is equal to*

(a) 1/5 (b) 3/5
(c) 4/5 (d) 2/5

Sol. $y \sin 2x - \cos x + (1 + \sin^2 x)\frac{dy}{dx} = 0$ where $y = f(x)$

$$\frac{dy}{dx} + \left(\frac{\sin 2x}{1 + \sin^2 x}\right) y = \frac{\cos x}{1 + \sin^2 x}$$

$$\text{IF} = e^{\int \frac{\sin 2x}{1+\sin^2 x}dx} = e^{\int \frac{dt}{t}} = e^{\ln(1+\sin^2 x)}$$

$$= 1 + \sin^2 x \text{ (by putting } 1 + \sin^2 x = t)$$

$$y(1 + \sin^2 x) = \int \cos x \, dx$$

$$y(1 + \sin^2 x) = \sin x + C; \; y(0) = 0 \Rightarrow C = 0$$

Therefore, $$y = \frac{\sin x}{1 + \sin^2 x}; \; y\left(\frac{\pi}{6}\right) = \frac{2}{5}$$

Hence, (d) is the correct answer.

Ex. 6 *The general solution of the differential equation $\frac{dy}{dx} = \frac{1-x}{y}$ is a family of curves which looks most like which of the following?*

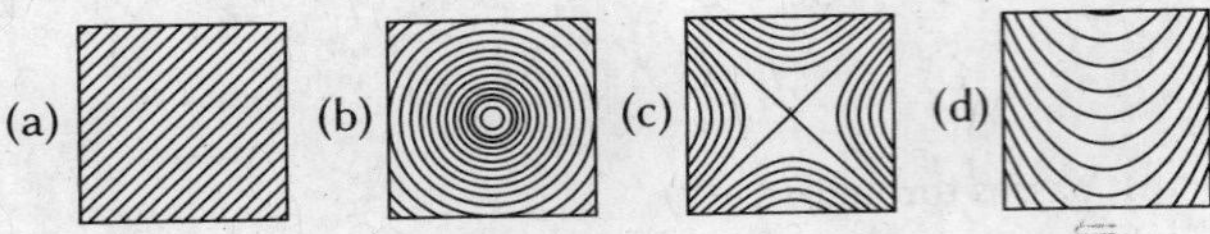

Sol. $$\int y\,dy = \int (1 - x)\,dx$$

$$\frac{y^2}{2} = x - \frac{x^2}{2} + C$$

$$x^2 + y^2 - 2x = C$$

$$(x - 1)^2 + y^2 = C + 1 = C$$

Hence, (b) is the correct answer.

Remark

Family of concentric circles with (1, 0) as the centre and variable radius.

Ex. 7 *Water is drained from a vertical cylindrical tank by opening a valve at the base of the tank. It is known that the rate at which the water level drops is proportional to the square root of water depth y, where the constant of proportionality $k > 0$ depends on the acceleration due to gravity and the geometry of the hole. If t is measured in minutes and $k = \frac{1}{15}$, then the time to drain the tank, if the water is 4 m deep to start with is*

(a) 30 min (b) 45 min (c) 60 min (d) 80 min

Sol. $\frac{dy}{dt} = -k\sqrt{y}$; when $t = 0$; $y = 4$

$$\int_4^0 \frac{dy}{\sqrt{y}} = -k\int_0^t dt$$

$$[2\sqrt{y}]_4^0 = -kt = -\frac{t}{15}$$

$$0 - 4 = -\frac{t}{15}$$

$$\Rightarrow \quad t = 60 \text{ min}$$

Hence, (c) is the correct answer.

Ex. 8 *Number of straight lines which satisfy the differential equation $\frac{dy}{dx} + x\left(\frac{dy}{dx}\right)^2 - y = 0$ is*

(a) 1 (b) 2 (c) 3 (d) 4

Sol. $$y = kx + b; \; \frac{dy}{dx} = k$$

$$\Rightarrow \quad kx + b \equiv k + xk^2 \quad \Rightarrow k = k^2 \text{ and } b = k$$

$$k = 0 \text{ or } k = 1$$

Hence, (b) is the correct answer.

Ex. 9 *Consider the two statements :*

Statement I *$y = \sin kt$ satisfy the differential equation $y'' + 9y = 0$.*

Statement II *$y = e^{kt}$ satisfy the differential equation $y'' + y' - 6y = 0$.*

The value of k for which both the statements are correct is

(a) −3 (b) 0 (c) 2 (d) 3

Sol. Statement I $y = \sin kt$, $y' = k\cos kt$; $y'' = -k^2 \sin kt$

$$\therefore \quad -k^2 \sin kt + 9\sin kt = 0$$

$$\sin kt\,[9 - k^2] = 0 \Rightarrow k = 0, k = 3, k = -3$$

Statement II $y = e^{kt}$, $y' = ke^{kt}$; $y'' = k^2 e^{kt}$

$$\therefore \quad k^2 e^{kt} + ke^{kt} - 6e^{kt} = 0$$

$$e^{kt}[k^2 + k - 6] = 0$$

$$(k + 3)(k - 2) = 0$$

$$k = -3 \text{ or } 2$$

Common value is $k = -3$.

Hence, (a) is the correct answer.

Ex. 10 *If $y = \frac{x}{\ln|cx|}$ (where c is an arbitrary constant) is the general solution of the differential equation $\frac{dy}{dx} = \frac{y}{x} + \phi\left(\frac{x}{y}\right)$, then the function $\phi\left(\frac{x}{y}\right)$ is*

(a) $\frac{x^2}{y^2}$ (b) $-\frac{x^2}{y^2}$ (c) $\frac{y^2}{x^2}$ (d) $-\frac{y^2}{x^2}$

Sol. $\ln c + \ln|x| = \frac{x}{y}$

Differentiating w.r.t. x, $\frac{1}{x} = \frac{y - xy_1}{y^2}$

$$\frac{y^2}{x} = y - x\frac{dy}{dx}$$

$$\frac{dy}{dx} = \frac{y}{x} - \frac{y^2}{x^2} \Rightarrow \phi\left(\frac{x}{y}\right) = -\frac{y^2}{x^2}$$

Hence, (d) is the correct answer.

• Ex. 11 *If $\int_a^x ty(t)\,dt = x^2 + y(x)$, then y as a function of x is*

(a) $y = 2-(2+a^2)e^{\frac{x^2-a^2}{2}}$ (b) $y = 1-(2+a^2)e^{\frac{x^2-a^2}{2}}$

(c) $y = 2-(1+a^2)e^{\frac{x^2-a^2}{2}}$ (d) None of these

Sol. Differentiating both the sides, we get

$$xy(x) = 2x - y'(x)$$

Hence, $\frac{dy}{dx} - xy = -2x$ $\left[y'(x) = \frac{dy}{dx};\ y(x) = y\right]$

$$\text{IF} = e^{\int -x\,dx} = e^{\frac{-x^2}{2}}$$

$$ye^{\frac{-x^2}{2}} = \int -2xe^{\frac{-x^2}{2}}\,dx$$

Let $e^{\frac{-x^2}{2}} = t \Rightarrow -xe^{\frac{-x^2}{2}}\,dx = dt$

$$I = \int 2dt$$

$$ye^{-\frac{x^2}{2}} = 2e^{-\frac{x^2}{2}} + C$$

$$y = 2 + Ce^{\frac{x^2}{2}}$$

If $x = a \Rightarrow a^2 + y = 0 \Rightarrow y = -a^2$ (from the given equation)

Hence, $-a^2 = 2 + Ce^{\frac{a^2}{2}};\ Ce^{\frac{a^2}{2}} = -(2+a^2)$

$$C = -(2+a^2)e^{-\frac{a^2}{2}};\ y = 2-(2+a^2)e^{\frac{x^2-a^2}{2}}$$

Hence, (a) is the correct answer.

• Ex. 12 *The differential equation $\frac{dy}{dx} = \frac{\sqrt{1-y^2}}{y}$ determines a family of circles with* **[IIT JEE 2007]**

(a) variable radii and a fixed centre at (0, 1)

(b) variable radii and fixed centre at (0, –1)

(c) fixed radius 1 and variable centres along the x-axis

(d) fixed radius 1 and variable centres along the y-axis

Sol. $\because \frac{dy}{dx} = \frac{\sqrt{1-y^2}}{y}$

$\Rightarrow \int \frac{y}{\sqrt{1-y^2}}\,dy = \int dx \Rightarrow -\frac{1}{2}\cdot 2\sqrt{1-y^2} = x + C$

$\Rightarrow -\sqrt{1-y^2} = x + C \Rightarrow 1 - y^2 = (x+C)^2$

$\Rightarrow (x+C)^2 + y^2 = 1$

Therefore, the differential equation represents a circle of fixed radius 1 and variable centres along the x-axis. Hence, (c) is the correct answer.

JEE Type Solved Examples : More than One Correct Option Type Questions

• Ex. 13 *A curve $y = f(x)$ has the property that the perpendicular distance of the origin from the normal at any point P of the curve is equal to the distance of the point P from the x-axis. Then the differential equation of the curve*

(a) is homogeneous

(b) can be converted into linear differential equation with some suitable substitution

(c) is the family of circles touching the x-axis at the origin

(d) the family of circles touching the y-axis at the origin

Sol. Equation of normal

$$Y - y = -\frac{1}{m}(X - x) \Rightarrow -my + my = X - x$$

$$X + my - (x + my) = 0$$

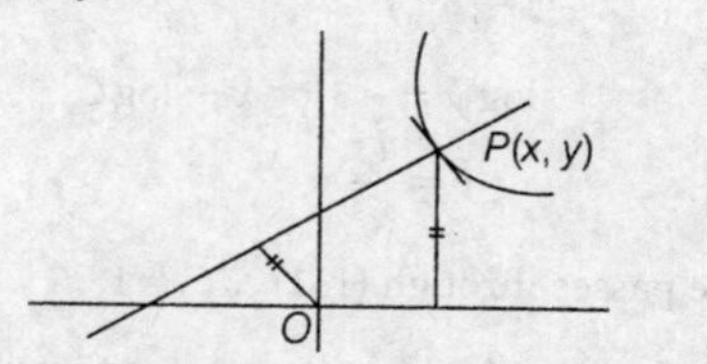

Perpendicular from (0, 0) $= \left|\frac{x+my}{\sqrt{1+m^2}}\right| = y \Rightarrow x^2 + 2xym = y^2$

$$\frac{dy}{dx} = \frac{y^2-x^2}{2xy} \Rightarrow \text{homogeneous}$$

Also, $x\cdot 2y\cdot\frac{dy}{dx} - x^2 = y^2$

Put $y^2 = t$; $2y\frac{dy}{dx} = \frac{dt}{dx};\ x\cdot\frac{dt}{dx} + x^2 = t$

$\frac{dt}{dx} - \frac{1}{x}t = -x$ which is linear differential equation.

Hence, (a), (b) and (d) are the correct answers.

• Ex. 14 *A differentiable function satisfies $f(x) = \int_0^x \{f(t)\cos t - \cos(t-x)\}\,dt$. Which is of the following hold good?*

(a) $f(x)$ has a minimum value $1-e$

(b) $f(x)$ has a maximum value $1-e^{-1}$

(c) $f''\left(\frac{\pi}{2}\right) = e$ (d) $f'(0) = 1$

Sol. $f(x) = \int_0^x \{f(t)\cos t - \cos(t-x)\}\,dx$

$$= \int_0^x f(t)\cos t\,dt - \int_0^x \cos(-t)\,dt \left[\int_0^a f(x)dx = \int_0^a f(a-x)\,dx\right]$$

$$f(x) = \int_0^x f(t) \cos t \, dt - \sin x$$

Differentiating both the sides, we get

$$f'(x) = f(x) \cos x - \cos x$$

Let $\quad f(x) = y;\ f'(x) = \dfrac{dy}{dx}$

$$\frac{dy}{dx} - y \cos x = -\cos x \qquad \text{(L.D.E.)}$$

$$\text{IF} = e^{-\int \cos x \, dx} = e^{-\sin x}$$

Therefore, $\quad y \cdot e^{-\sin x} = -\int e^{-\sin x} \cos x \, dx;$

$$y \cdot e^{-\sin x} = C + e^{-\sin x};\ y = Ce^{\sin x} + 1$$

If $x = 0;\quad y = 0$ (from the given relation)

$\Rightarrow \quad C = -1$

Therefore, $\quad f(x) = 1 - e^{\sin x}$

Now, minimum value $= 1 - e$ (when $x = \pi/2$)

Maximum value $= 1 - e^{-1}$ (when $x = -\pi/2$)

$$f'(x) = -e^{\sin x} \cos x$$

Therefore, $\quad f'(0) = -1$

$$f''(x) = -[\cos^2 x \cdot e^{\sin x} - e^{\sin x} \cdot \sin x]$$

$$f''\left(\frac{\pi}{2}\right) = e$$

Hence, (a), (b) and (c) are the correct answers.

• Ex. 15 *Let $\dfrac{dy}{dx} + y = f(x)$ where y is a continuous function of x with $y(0) = 1$ and $f(x) = \begin{cases} e^{-x}, & \text{if } 0 \le x \le 2 \\ e^{-2}, & \text{if } x > 2 \end{cases}$. Which is of the following hold(s) good?*

(a) $y(1) = 2e^{-1}$ (b) $y'(1) = -e^{-1}$

(c) $y(3) = -2e^{-3}$ (d) $y'(3) = -2e^{-3}$

Sol. $\quad \dfrac{dy}{dx} + y = f(x) \Rightarrow \text{IF} = e^x$

$$ye^x = \int e^x f(x) \, dx + C$$

Now, if $0 \le x \le 2$, then $ye^x = \int e^x e^{-x} \, dx + C$

$\Rightarrow \quad ye^x = x + C$

$x = 0,\ y(0) = 1,\ C = 1$

$\therefore \quad ye^x = x + 1 \qquad \text{...(i)}$

$$y = \frac{x+1}{e^x};\ y(1) = \frac{2}{e} \Rightarrow y' = \frac{e^x - (x+1)e^x}{e^{2x}}$$

$$y'(1) = \frac{e - 2e}{e^2} = \frac{-e}{e^2} = -\frac{1}{e}$$

If $x > 2,\quad ye^x = \int e^{x-2} \, dx$

$$ye^x = e^{x-2} + C$$

$$y = e^{-2} + Ce^{-x}$$

As y is continuous.

$\therefore \quad \lim\limits_{x \to 2} \dfrac{x+1}{e^x} = \lim\limits_{x \to 2} (e^{-2} + Ce^{-x})$

$$3e^{-2} = e^{-2} + Ce^{-2} \Rightarrow C = 2$$

$\therefore$ for $x > 2$

$$y = e^{-2} + 2e^{-x}$$

Hence, $\quad y(3) = 2e^{-3} + e^{-2} = e^{-2}(2e^{-1} + 1)$

$$y' = -2e^{-x}$$

$$y'(3) = -2e^{-3}$$

Hence, (a), (b) and (d) are the correct answers.

• Ex. 16 *A curve $y = f(x)$ passes through (1, 1) and tangent at $P(x, y)$ cuts the x-axis and y-axis at A and B respectively such that $BP : AP = 3 : 1$, then* **[IIT JEE 2006]**

(a) equation of curve is $xy' - 3y = 0$

(b) normal at (1, 1) is $x + 3y = 4$

(c) curve passes through $\left(2, \dfrac{1}{8}\right)$

(d) equation of curve is $xy' + 3y = 0$

Sol. Equation of the tangent to the curve $y = f(x)$ at (x, y) is

$$Y - y = \frac{dy}{dx}(X - x)$$

$\because$ Thus, cuts the x-axis at A and y-axis at B.

$\therefore \quad A\left(\dfrac{x\dfrac{dy}{dx} - y}{\dfrac{dy}{dx}}, 0\right)$ and $B\left(0, -x\dfrac{dy}{dx} + y\right)$

$\because \quad BP : PA = 3 : 1$

$\Rightarrow \quad x = \dfrac{\dfrac{3\left(x\dfrac{dy}{dx} - y\right)}{(dy/dx)} + 1 \times 0}{4}$

$\Rightarrow \quad x\dfrac{dy}{dx} + 3y = 0$

$\Rightarrow \quad \displaystyle\int \frac{dy}{y} = \int -3\frac{dx}{x}$

$\Rightarrow \quad \log y = -3 \log x + \log C$

$\Rightarrow \quad y = \dfrac{C}{x^3}$

$\because$ Curve passes through (1, 1) $\therefore C = 1$

$\therefore$ Curve is $x^3 y = 1$ which also passes through $\left(2, \dfrac{1}{8}\right)$.

Hence, (c) and (d) are the correct answers.

JEE Type Solved Examples : Statement I and II Type Questions

- **Ex. 17** *Let a solution $y = y(x)$ of the differential equation $x\sqrt{x^2-1}\,dy - y\sqrt{y^2-1}\,dx = 0$ satisfy $y(2) = \frac{2}{\sqrt{3}}$.*

[IIT JEE 2008]

Statement I $y(x) = \sec\left(\sec^{-1} x - \frac{\pi}{6}\right)$.

Statement II *$y(x)$ is given by* $\frac{1}{y} = \frac{2\sqrt{3}}{x} - \sqrt{1 - \frac{1}{x^2}}$.

(a) Statement I is true, Statement II is also true; Statement II is the correct explanation of Statement I.
(b) Statement I is true, Statement II is also true; Statement II is not the correct explanation of Statement I.
(c) Statement I is true, Statement II is false.
(d) Statement I is false, Statement II is true.

Sol. $\because$ $x\sqrt{x^2-1}\,dy - y\sqrt{y^2-1}\,dx = 0$

Which can be rewritten as $\frac{dx}{x\sqrt{x^2-1}} = \frac{dy}{y\sqrt{y^2-1}}$

Integration yields, $\int \frac{dx}{x\sqrt{x^2-1}} = \int \frac{dy}{y\sqrt{y^2-1}}$

$\Rightarrow$ $\sec^{-1} x = \sec^{-1} y + C$

$\Rightarrow$ $\sec^{-1}(2) = \sec^{-1}(2/\sqrt{3}) + C$

$\Rightarrow$ $\frac{\pi}{3} = \frac{\pi}{6} + C \Rightarrow C = \frac{\pi}{6}$

Thus, $\sec^{-1} x = \sec^{-1} y + \frac{\pi}{6}$

$\Rightarrow$ $y = \sec\left(\sec^{-1} x - \frac{\pi}{6}\right)$

$$= \frac{1}{\cos\left(\cos^{-1}\frac{1}{x} - \frac{\pi}{6}\right)} = \frac{1}{\frac{1}{x}\cdot\frac{\sqrt{3}}{2} + \sqrt{1-\frac{1}{x^2}}\cdot\frac{1}{2}}$$

$\Rightarrow$ $\frac{1}{y} = \frac{\sqrt{3}}{2x} + \frac{\sqrt{1-\frac{1}{x^2}}}{2}$

Hence, (c) is the correct answer.

JEE Type Solved Examples : Passage Based Questions

Passage

(Q. Nos. 18 to 20)

A curve $y = f(x)$ satisfies the differential equation $(1+x^2)\frac{dy}{dx} + 2yx = 4x^2$ and passes through the origin.

18 The function $y = f(x)$
(a) is strictly increasing, $\forall x \in R$
(b) is such that it has a minima but no maxima
(c) is such that it has a maxima but no minima
(d) has no inflection point

19 The area enclosed by $y = f^{-1}(x)$, the x-axis and the ordinate at $x = 2/3$ is
(a) $2\ln 2$ (b) $\frac{4}{3}\ln 2$ (c) $\frac{2}{3}\ln 2$ (d) $\frac{1}{3}\ln 2$

20 For the function $y = f(x)$ which one of the following does not hold good?
(a) $f(x)$ is a rational function
(b) $f(x)$ has the same domain and same rage
(c) $f(x)$ is a transcendental function
(d) $y = f(x)$ is a bijective mapping

Sol. (Q. Nos. 18 to 20)

$$\frac{dy}{dx} + \left(\frac{2x}{1+x^2}\right)y = \frac{4x^2}{1+x^2}$$

$$\text{IF} = e^{\int \frac{2x}{1+x^2}dx} = e^{\ln(1+x^2)} = (1+x^2)$$

$\therefore$ $y(1+x^2) = \int 4x^2\,dx = \frac{4x^3}{3} + C$

Passing through (0, 0) $\Rightarrow C = 0$

$\therefore$ $y = \frac{4x^3}{3(1+x^2)}$

$$\frac{dy}{dx} = \frac{4}{3}\left[\frac{(1+x^2)\,3x^2 - x^3\cdot 2x}{(1+x^2)^2}\right]$$

$$= \frac{4}{3}\left[\frac{3x^2 + x^4}{(1+x^2)^2}\right] = \frac{4x^2(3+x^2)}{3(1+x^2)^2}$$

Hence, $\frac{dy}{dx} > 0, \forall x \neq 0; \frac{dy}{dx} = 0$ at $x = 0$

and it does not change sign $\Rightarrow x = 0$ is the point of inflection $y = f(x)$ is increasing for all $x \in R$.

$x \to \infty;\ y \to \infty;\ x \to -\infty;\ y \to -\infty$

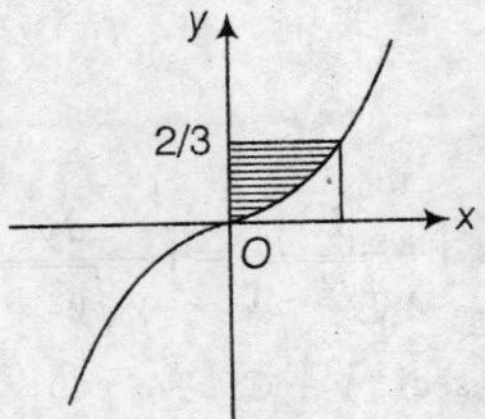

Area enclosed by $y = f^{-1}(x)$, x-axis and ordinate at $x = \frac{2}{3}$

$$A = \frac{2}{3} - \frac{4}{3}\int_0^1 \frac{x^3}{1+x^2}\,dx$$

Put $1 + x^2 = t \Rightarrow 2x\,dx = dt$

$$A = \frac{2}{3} - \frac{2}{3}\int_1^2 \frac{(t-1)}{t}\,dt$$

$$= \frac{2}{3} - \frac{2}{3}\int_1^2 \left(1 - \frac{1}{t}\right) dt$$

$$= \frac{2}{3} - \frac{2}{3}[t - \ln t]_1^2 = \frac{2}{3} - \frac{2}{3}[(2 - \ln 2) - 1]$$

$$= \frac{2}{3} - \frac{2}{3}[1 - \ln 2] = \frac{2}{3}\ln 2$$

JEE Type Solved Examples : Single Integer Answer Type Questions

- ***Ex. 21*** *Let $y = f(x)$ be a curve passing through $(4, 3)$ such that slope of normal at any point lying in the first quadrant is negative and the normal and tangent at any point P cuts the Y-axis at A and B respectively such that the mid-point of AB is origin, then the number of solutions of $y = f(x)$ and $y = |5 - |x||$, is*

Sol. Equation of tangent at any point (x_1, y_1) of curve $y = f(x)$ is $(y - y_1) = f'(x_1)(x - x_1)$, so $B\,(0, y_1 - x_1 f'(x_1))$

Equation of normal at (x_1, y_1) is $(y, y_1) = -\frac{1}{f'(x_1)}(x, x_1)$ so,

$A = \left(0, y_1 + \frac{x_1}{f'(x_1)}\right)$ mid point of AB is origin, so

$$2y_1 - x_1\left(f'(x_1) - \frac{1}{f'(x_1)}\right) = 0$$

Thus differential equation of curve $y = f(x)$, is

$$x\left(\frac{dy}{dx}\right)^2 - 2y\frac{dy}{dx} - x = 0$$

Thus, $$\frac{dy}{dx} = \frac{y \pm \sqrt{x^2 + y^2}}{x}$$

In first quadrant, $x > 0, y > 0, \frac{dy}{dx} > 0,$

So $$\frac{dy}{dx} = \frac{y + \sqrt{x^2 + y^2}}{x}, \text{ put } y = vx$$

$$\Rightarrow \quad v + x\frac{dv}{dx} = \frac{vx + x\sqrt{1 + v^2}}{x}$$

$$\Rightarrow \quad \int \frac{dv}{\sqrt{1 + v^2}} = \int \frac{dx}{x}$$

on solving we get $y = \frac{x^2}{4} - 1$

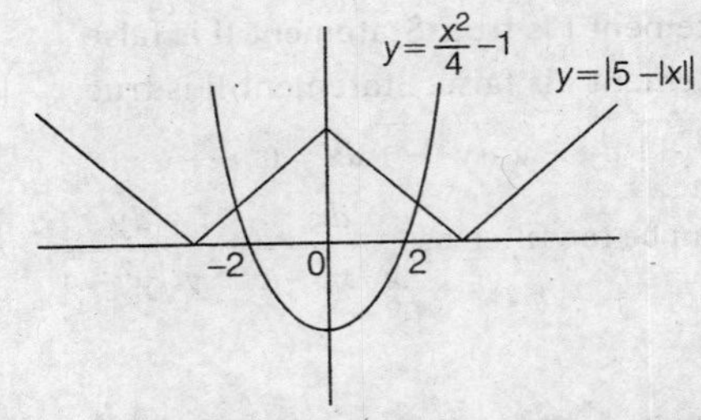

$\therefore$ number of solutions for $y = f(x)$ and $y = |5 - |x||$

$\therefore$ number of solutions are 2.

- ***Ex. 22*** *A real valued function, $f(x)$, $f : \left(0, \frac{\pi}{2}\right) \to R^+$ satisfies the differential equation $xf'(x) = 1 + f(x)\{x^2 f(x)^{-1}\}$ and $f\left(\frac{\pi}{4}\right) = \frac{4}{\pi}$, then $\lim_{x \to 0} f(x)$, is*

Sol. Here, $xf'(x) = 1 + x^2 f^2(x) - f(x)$

$$\Rightarrow \quad \frac{x f'(x) + f(x)}{1 + x^2 f^2(x)} = 1$$

Integrating both sides

$$\int \frac{(x f'(x) + f(x))dx}{1 + (x f(x))^2} = x + C$$

$$\Rightarrow \quad \tan^{-1}(xf(x)) = x + C, \text{ as } f\left(\frac{\pi}{4}\right) = \frac{4}{\pi}.$$

$$\Rightarrow \quad \tan^{-1} 1 = \frac{\pi}{4} + C$$

$$\Rightarrow \quad C = 0$$

$$\therefore \quad x f(x) = \tan x$$

$$\Rightarrow \quad f(x) = \frac{\tan x}{x}$$

and $$\lim_{x \to 0} f(x) = \lim_{x \to 0} \frac{\tan x}{x} = 1$$

● **Ex. 23** *If the area bounded by $y = f(x)$, $x = \frac{1}{2}$, $x = \frac{\sqrt{3}}{2}$ and the X-axis is A sq units where $f(x) = x + \frac{2}{3}x^3 + \frac{2}{3}\cdot\frac{4}{5}x^5 + \frac{2}{3}\cdot\frac{4}{5}\cdot\frac{6}{7}x^7 + \ldots \infty, |x| < 1$, Then the value of $[4A]$ is (where $[\cdot]$ is G.I.F)*

Sol. Here, $f'(x) = 1 + 2x^2 + \frac{2}{3}\cdot 4x^4 + \frac{2}{3}\cdot\frac{4}{5}\cdot 6x^6 + \ldots \infty$

$$= 1 + x\left(\frac{d}{dx}(xf(x))\right)$$

$$\Rightarrow \quad f'(x) = 1 + x\,|xf'(x) + f(x)|$$

$$\Rightarrow (1 - x^2)f'(x) = 1 + xf(x)$$

$$\Rightarrow \quad \frac{dy}{dx} - \frac{x}{1 - x^2}\cdot y = \frac{1}{x^2}, \text{ I.F.} = e^{\int \frac{-x}{1-x^2}dx} = e^{\frac{1}{2}\log|1-x^2|} = \sqrt{1-x^2}$$

$$\therefore \quad y\cdot\sqrt{1-x^2} = \int \frac{1}{1-x^2}\cdot\sqrt{1-x^2} + C$$

$$\Rightarrow \quad y\sqrt{1-x^2} = \sin^{-1}x + C, \text{ as } f(0) = 0 \Rightarrow C = 0$$

$$\Rightarrow \quad y = \frac{\sin^{-1}x}{\sqrt{1-x^2}}$$

$$\Rightarrow A = \int_{1/2}^{\sqrt{3}/2} \frac{\sin^{-1}x}{\sqrt{1-x^2}}dx = \int_{\pi/6}^{\pi/3} t\,dt = \left(\frac{t^2}{2}\right)_{\frac{\pi}{6}}^{\frac{\pi}{2}} = \frac{1}{2}\left[\frac{\pi^2}{4} - \frac{\pi^2}{36}\right]$$

$$\therefore \quad [4A] = 1$$

Subjective Type Questions

● **Ex. 24** *For a certain curve $y = f(x)$ satisfying $\frac{d^2y}{dx^2} = 6x - 4$; $f(x)$ has a local minimum value 5 when $x = 1$. Find the equation of the curve and also the global maximum and global minimum values of $f(x)$ given that $0 \le x \le 2$.*

Sol. Integrating, $\frac{d^2y}{dx^2} = 6x - 4$, we get $\frac{dy}{dx} = 3x^2 - 4x + C$

when $x = 1$, $\frac{dy}{dx} = 0$. So that $C = 1$

Hence, $\frac{dy}{dx} = 3x^2 - 4x + 1$ ...(i)

Integrating, we get

$y = x^3 - 2x^2 + x + C_1$, when $x = 1$, $y = 5$,

so that $C_1 = 5$

Thus, we have $y = x^3 - 2x^2 + x + 5$

Form Eq. (i), we get the critical points $x = \frac{1}{3}$, $x = 1$

At the critical point $x = \frac{1}{3}$, $\frac{d^2y}{dx^2}$ is (–ve).

Therefore, at $x = \frac{1}{3}$, y has a local maximum.

At $x = 1$, $\frac{d^2y}{dx^2}$ is (+ ve).

Therefore, at $x = 1$, y has a local minimum.

Also, $f(1) = 5$

$$\Rightarrow \quad f\left(\frac{1}{3}\right) = \frac{139}{27}$$

$$f(0) = 5, f(2) = 7$$

Hence, the global maximum value = 7, the global minimum value = 5.

● **Ex. 25** *If $\phi(x)$ is a differentiable real-valued function satisfying $\phi'(x) + 2\phi(x) \le 1$, prove that $\phi(x) - \frac{1}{2}$ is a non-increasing function of x.*

Sol.

$$\phi'(x) + 2\phi(x) \le 1$$

$$\Rightarrow \quad e^{2x}\phi'(x) + 2\phi(x)e^{2x} \le e^{2x}$$

$$\Rightarrow \quad \frac{d}{dx}\left(e^{2x}\phi(x) - \frac{1}{2}e^{2x}\right) \le 0$$

$\Rightarrow e^{2x}\left(\phi(x) - \frac{1}{2}\right)$ is a non-increasing function of x.

$\Rightarrow \phi(x) - \frac{1}{2}$ is a non-increasing function of x.

● **Ex. 26** *Determine all curve for which the ratios of the length of the segment intercepted by any tangent on the y-axis to the length of the radius vector is a constant.*

Sol. Let $y = f(x)$ be the equation of the required curve.

Given that $\frac{\left|y - x\frac{dy}{dx}\right|}{\sqrt{x^2 + y^2}} = k$ (a constant)

$$\Rightarrow \quad \frac{dy}{dx} = \frac{y}{x} \pm k\sqrt{1 + \left(\frac{y}{x}\right)^2}$$

Let $y = vx$, then $v + x\frac{dv}{dx} = v \pm k\sqrt{1 + v^2}$

$$\Rightarrow \quad \frac{dv}{\sqrt{1+v^2}} = \pm k\frac{dx}{x}, \text{ integrating we get}$$

$$\Rightarrow \quad \log\left|v + \sqrt{1+v^2}\right| = \pm k\ln x + C$$

$$\Rightarrow \quad \log\left|\frac{xy + \sqrt{x^2+y^2}}{x}\right| = \pm k\ln x + C$$

Which are the equations of the required curves.

Ex. 27 *Let $u(x)$ and $v(x)$ satisfy the differential equations $\frac{du}{dx} + p(x)\,u = f(x)$ and $\frac{dv}{dx} + p(x)\,v = g(x)$, where $p(x)$, $f(x)$ and $g(x)$ are continuous functions.*
If $u(x_1) > v(x_1)$ for some x_1 and $f(x) > g(x)$, for all $x > x_1$, prove that any point (x, y), where $x > x_1$, does not satisfy the equation $y = u(x)$ and $y = v(x)$. **[IIT JEE 1997]**

Sol. Given that

$$\frac{du}{dx} + p(x)\cdot u = f(x) \text{ and } \frac{dv}{dx} + p(x)\cdot v = g(x)$$

Subtracting, we get

$$\frac{d(u-v)}{dx} + p(x)\cdot(u-v) = f(x) - g(x)$$

Multiplying by $e^{\int p(x)\,dx}$, we get

$$e^{\int p(x)\,dx}\cdot\frac{d(u-v)}{dx} + (u-v)\cdot p(x)\cdot e^{\int p(x)\,dx}$$

$$= \{f(x) - g(x)\}\cdot e^{\int p(x)\,dx}$$

i.e. $$\frac{d}{dx}\{(u-v)\,e^{\int p dx}\} = \{f(x) - g(x)\}\,e^{\int p(x)\,dx}$$

Since, exponential function takes only positive values and $f(x) > g(x)$ for all $x > x_1$, RHS is + ve; $x > x_1$

$\therefore$ $$\frac{d}{dx}\{(u-v)\cdot e^{\int p(x)\,dx}\} = 0$$

ie, $(u-v)\cdot e^{\int p(x)\,dx}$ is increasing function.

Hence, if $e^{\int p(x)\,dx} = \phi(x)$, then for $x > x_1$

We have, $\{u(x) - v(x)\}\,\phi(x) > \{u(x_1) - v(x_1)\}\,\phi(x_1)$

i.e. $$u(x) - v(x) > \frac{\{u(x_1) - v(x_1)\}\cdot\phi(x_1)}{\phi(x)} > 0\ [\because u(x_1) > v(x_1)]$$

Thus, $u(x) > v(x),\ \forall\ x > x_1$

i.e. $u(x) \neq v(x),\ \forall\ x > x_1$

Hence, no point (x, y) such that $x > x_1$ can satisfy the equations $y = u(x)$ and $y = v(x)$.

Ex. 28 *A normal is drawn at a point $P(x, y)$ of a curve. It meets the x-axis at Q. If PQ is of constant length k, then show that the differential equation describing such curves is, $y\frac{dy}{dx} = \pm\sqrt{k^2 - y^2}$ and the equation of such a curve passing through $(0, k)$.* **[IIT JEE 1994]**

Sol. Let $y = f(x)$ be the curve such that the normal at $P(x, y)$ to this curve meets x-axis at Q. Then,

PQ = length of the normal at P

$$= y\sqrt{1 + \left(\frac{dy}{dx}\right)^2}$$

But $PQ = k$

$\therefore$ $$y\sqrt{1 + \left(\frac{dy}{dx}\right)^2} = k$$

$\Rightarrow$ $$y^2 + y^2\left(\frac{dy}{dx}\right)^2 = k^2 \text{ or } y\frac{dy}{dx} = \pm\sqrt{k^2 - y^2}$$

$\Rightarrow$ $$\frac{y\,dy}{\sqrt{k^2 - y^2}} = \pm\,dx$$

Integrating both the sides, we get

$-\sqrt{k^2 - y^2} = \pm\,x + C$, since it passes through $(0, k) \rightarrow C = 0$.

$\therefore$ $$-\sqrt{k^2 - y^2} = \pm\,x$$

or $$k^2 - y^2 = x^2$$

$\Rightarrow$ $x^2 + y^2 = k^2$, is required equation of the curve.

Ex. 29 *A curve passing through the point (1, 1) has the property that the perpendicular distance of the normal at any point P on the curve from the origin is equal to the distance of P from x-axis. Determine the equation of the curve.* **[IIT JEE 1999]**

Sol. Let $P(x, y)$ be any point on the curve $y = f(x)$. Then, the equation of the normal at P is,

$$Y - y = -\frac{1}{(dy/dx)}(X - x)$$

or $$X + Y\frac{dy}{dx} - \left(y\frac{dy}{dx} + x\right) = 0 \quad \text{...(i)}$$

It is given that distance of Eq. (i) from origin = Distance from x-axis (i.e. y)

i.e. $$\left|\frac{0 - \left(y\frac{dy}{dx} + x\right)}{\sqrt{1 + \left(\frac{dy}{dx}\right)^2}}\right| = y$$

$\Rightarrow$ $$\left(y\frac{dy}{dx} + x\right)^2 = y^2\left[1 + \left(\frac{dy}{dx}\right)^2\right]$$

$\Rightarrow$ $$x^2 + 2xy\frac{dy}{dx} = y^2$$

or $$\frac{dy}{dx} = \frac{y^2 - x^2}{2xy}$$

which is homogeneous differential equation and we can solve by homogeneous or by total differential.

Here, using total differential,

$$2xy\,dy - y^2\,dx = -x^2\,dx$$

$\Rightarrow$ $$\frac{x\,d(y^2) - y^2\,dx}{x^2} = -\,dx$$

$\Rightarrow$ $$d\left(\frac{y^2}{x}\right) = -\,dx$$

Integrating both the sides, we get

$\Rightarrow$ $$\frac{y^2}{x} = -x + C \quad \text{...(ii)}$$

It passes through (1, 1) $\Rightarrow C = 2$

$\therefore$ $$\frac{y^2}{x} = -x + 2 \text{ or } y^2 = -x^2 + 2x$$

$\Rightarrow$ $x^2 + y^2 - 2x = 0$, is required equation of curve.

Ex. 30 *A country has a food deficit of 10%. Its population grows continuously at a rate of 3% per year. Its annual food production every year is 4% more than that of the last year. Assuming that the average food requirement per person remains constant, prove that the country will become self-sufficient in food after n years, where n is the smallest integer bigger than or equal to* $\dfrac{\log_e 10 - \log_e 9}{(\log_e 1.04) - 0.03}$ **[IIT JEE 2000]**

Sol. Let P_0 be the initial population, Q_0 be its initial food production.

Let P be the population of the country in year t and Q be its food production in year t.

$$\Rightarrow \quad \frac{dP}{dt} = \frac{3P}{100} \text{ or } \frac{dP}{P} = \frac{3}{100}\,dt$$

Integrating, we get

$$\log P = \frac{3}{100}t + C$$

At $t = 0$, we have $P = P_0$

$$\Rightarrow \quad C = \log P_0$$

$$\Rightarrow \quad P = P_0\, e^{0.03t} \qquad \text{...(i)}$$

It is given that the annual food production every year is 4% more than that of last year.

$$\Rightarrow \quad Q = Q_0\left(1 + \frac{4}{100}\right)^t$$

Let the average consumption per person be k units.

$$\Rightarrow \quad Q_0 = kP_0\left(\frac{90}{100}\right) = 0.9\,kP_0$$

$$\therefore \quad Q = 0.9\,kP_0\,(1.04)^t \qquad \text{...(ii)}$$

This gives quantity of food available in year t. The population in year t is,

$$P = P_0\,e^{0.03t} \qquad \text{[from Eq. (i)]}$$

$\therefore$ Consumption in year, $t = kP_0e^{0.03t}$ ...(iii)

The country will be self sufficient, if

$$Q \ge P$$

$$\Rightarrow \quad 0.9k\,P_0\,(1.04)^t \ge kP_0e^{0.03t}$$

$$\Rightarrow \quad \frac{9}{10}(1.04)^t \ge e^{0.03t}$$

$$\Rightarrow \quad (1.04)^t e^{-0.03t} \ge \frac{10}{9}$$

$$\Rightarrow \quad t\log(1.04) - 0.03\,t \ge \log\left(\frac{10}{9}\right)$$

$$\Rightarrow \quad t\,\{\log(1.04) - 0.03\} \ge \log\left(\frac{10}{9}\right)$$

$$\Rightarrow \quad t \ge \frac{\log 10 - \log 9}{\log(1.04) - 0.03}$$

Thus, the least number of year in which country becomes self sufficient.

$$\Rightarrow \quad t = \frac{\log 10 - \log 9}{\log(1.04) - 0.03}$$

Ex. 31 *A right circular cone with radius R and height H contains a liquid which evaporates at a rate proportional to its surface area in contact with air (proportionality constant = k > 0), find the time after which the cone is empty.* **[IIT JEE 2003]**

Sol. Let the semi-vertical angle of the cone be θ and let the height of the liquid at time 't' be 'h' from the vertex V and radius of the liquid cone be r. Let V be the volume at time t. Then,

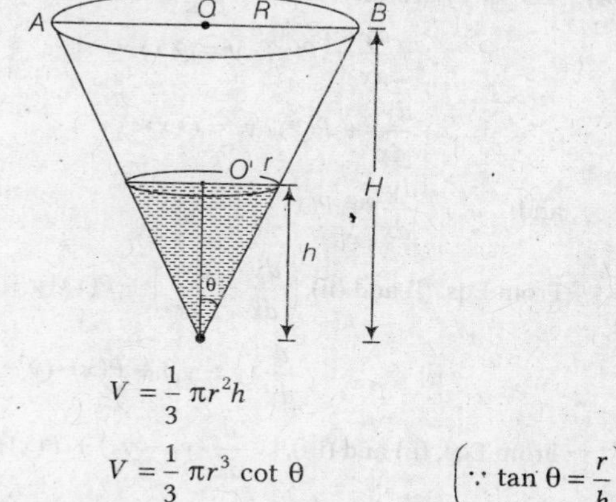

$$V = \frac{1}{3}\pi r^2 h$$

$$\Rightarrow \quad V = \frac{1}{3}\pi r^3 \cot\theta \qquad \left(\because \tan\theta = \frac{r}{h}\right)$$

Let S be the surface area of the liquid in contact with air at time t.

Then, $S = \pi r^2$

$$\Rightarrow \quad \frac{dV}{dt} \propto S$$

$\Rightarrow \quad \dfrac{dV}{dt} = -kS$, k is constant of proportionality.

$$\Rightarrow \quad \frac{d}{dt}\left(\frac{1}{3}\pi r^3 \cot\theta\right) = -k\pi r^2$$

$$\Rightarrow \quad \pi r^2 \frac{dr}{dt}\cot\theta = -k\pi r^2 \Rightarrow \cot\theta\, dr = -k\,dt$$

On integrating, we get $\cot\theta \displaystyle\int_R^0 dr = -k\int_0^T dt$

$\Rightarrow$ $R\cot\theta = +kT$, where T is required time.

$$\Rightarrow \quad T = H/k \qquad \text{(as } \tan\theta = R/H\text{)}$$

Ex. 32 *Solve the equation*

$$x\int_0^x y(t)\,dt = (x+1)\int_0^x t\,y(t)\,dt,\ x > 0.$$

Sol. Differentiating the equation w.r.t. x, we get

$$xy(x) + 1\cdot\int_0^x y(t)\,dt = (x+1)\,xy(x) + 1\cdot\int_0^x t\,y(t)\,dt$$

i.e. $$\int_0^x y(t)\,dt = x^2\,y(x) + \int_0^x t\,y(t)\,dt$$

Again, differentiating w.r.t. x, we get

$$y(x) = x^2\,y'(x) + 2xy(x) + xy(x)$$

i.e. $$(1-3x)\,y(x) = \frac{x^2\,dy(x)}{dx}$$

i.e. $$\frac{(1-3x)\,dx}{x^2} = \frac{dy(x)}{y(x)}$$

Integrating, we get $y = \dfrac{C}{x^3}e^{-1/x}$

• Ex. 33 *If (y_1, y_2) are two solutions of the differential equation* $\frac{dy}{dx} + P(x) \cdot y = Q(x)$

Then prove that $y = y_1 + C(y_1 - y_2)$ is the general solution of the equation where C is any constant. For what relation between the constant α, β will the linear combination $\alpha y_1 + \beta y_2$ also be a solution.

Sol. As y_1, y_2 are the solutions of the differential equation;

$$\frac{dy}{dx} + P(x) \cdot y = Q(x) \quad \text{...(i)}$$

$$\therefore \quad \frac{dy_1}{dx} + P(x) \cdot y_1 = Q(x) \quad \text{...(ii)}$$

and $$\frac{dy_2}{dx} + P(x) \cdot y_2 = Q(x) \quad \text{...(iii)}$$

From Eqs. (i) and (ii), $\left(\frac{dy}{dx} - \frac{dy_1}{dx}\right) + P(x)(y - y_1) = 0$

$$\therefore \quad \frac{d}{dx}(y - y_1) + P(x) \cdot (y - y_1) = 0 \quad \text{...(iv)}$$

From Eqs. (ii) and (iii), $\frac{d}{dx}(y_1 - y_2) + P(x)(y_1 - y_2) = 0$ ...(v)

From Eqs. (iv) and (v), $\frac{\frac{d}{dx}(y - y_1)}{\frac{d}{dx}(y_1 - y_2)} = \frac{y - y_1}{y_1 - y_2}$

$$\Rightarrow \quad \frac{\frac{d}{dx}(y - y_1)}{y - y_1} = \frac{\frac{d}{dx}(y_1 - y_2)}{y_1 - y_2}$$

Integrating both the sides, we get

$$\log(y - y_1) = \log(y_1 - y_2)$$

$$\therefore \quad y = y_1 + C(y_1 - y_2)$$

Now, $y = \alpha y_1 + \beta y_2$ will be a solutions, if

$$\frac{d}{dx}(\alpha y_1 + \beta y_2) + P(x)(\alpha y_1 + \beta y_2) = Q(x)$$

or $$\alpha\left(\frac{dy_1}{dx} + P(x) y_1\right) + \beta\left(\frac{dy_2}{dx} + P(x) y_2\right) = Q(x)$$

or $$\alpha Q(x) + \beta Q(x) = Q(x) \quad \text{[using Eqs. (ii) and (iii)]}$$

$$\therefore \quad (\alpha + \beta) Q(x) = Q(x)$$

Hence, $$\alpha + \beta = 1$$

• Ex. 34 *Find a pair of curves such that*

(a) the tangents drawn at points with equal abscissae intersect on the y-axis.

(b) the normal drawn at points with equal abscissae intersect on x-axis.

(c) one curve passes through (1, 1) and other passes through (2, 3).

Sol. Let the curve be $y = f_1(x)$ and $y = f_2(x)$ equation of tangents with equal abscissa, x are

$$(y - f_1(x)) = f'_1(x)(X - x)$$

and $$Y - f_2(x) = f'_2(x)(X - x)$$

These tangent intersect at y-axis,

$$\Rightarrow \quad -x f'_1(x) + f_1(x) = -x f'_2(x) + f_2(x)$$

$$\Rightarrow \quad f_1(x) - f_2(x) = x(f'_1(x) - f'_2(x))$$

Integrating both the sides, we get

$$\Rightarrow \quad \ln|f_1(x) - f_2(x)| = \ln|x| + C$$

$$\Rightarrow \quad f_1(x) - f_2(x) = \pm C_1 x \quad \text{...(i)}$$

Now, equations of normal with equal abscissa x, are

$$y - f_1(x) = -\frac{1}{f'_1(x)}(X - x)$$

and $$(y - f_2(x)) = -\frac{1}{f'_2(x)}(X - x)$$

As these normal intersect on the x-axis,

$$x + f_1(x) \cdot f'_1(x) = x + f_2(x) \cdot f'_2(x)$$

$$\Rightarrow \quad f_1(x) \cdot f_1'(x) = f_2(x) \cdot f_2'(x) \text{ Integrating}$$

$$\Rightarrow \quad f'^2_1(x) - f_2^2(x) = C_2$$

$$\Rightarrow \quad f_1(x) + f_2(x) = \frac{C_2}{f_1(x) - f_2(x)} = \pm \frac{C_2}{C_1 x} = \pm \frac{\lambda_2}{x}$$

[using Eq. (i)] ...(ii)

From Eqs. (i) and (ii), we get

$$2f_1(x) = \pm\left(\frac{\lambda_2}{x} + C_1 x\right), 2f_2(x) = \pm\left(\frac{\lambda_2}{x} - C_1 x\right)$$

We have, $f_1(1) = 1$ and $f_2(2) = 3$

$$\Rightarrow \quad f_1(x) = \frac{2}{x} - x \text{ and } f_2(x) = \frac{2}{x} + x$$

• Ex. 35 *Given two curves $y = f(x)$ passing through (0, 1) and $y = \int_{-\infty}^{x} f(t)\,dt$ passing through (0, / n). The tangents drawn to both the curves at the points with equal abscissae intersect on the x-axis find the curve $y = f(x)$.*

Sol. Equation of the tangent to the curve; $y = f(x)$ is

$$(Y - y) = f'(x)(X - x)$$

Equation of tangent to the curve $g(x) = y_1 = \int_{-\infty}^{x} f(t)\,dt$ is

$$(Y - y_1) = g'(x)(X - x) = f(x)(X - x)$$

Given that tangent with equal abscissas intersect on the x-axis.

$$\Rightarrow \quad x - \frac{y}{f'(x)} = x - \frac{y_1}{f(x)}$$

$$\Rightarrow \quad \frac{f(x)}{f'(x)} = \frac{y_1}{f(x)} \quad [\because y = f(x)]$$

$$\Rightarrow \quad \frac{f(x)}{y_1} = \frac{f'(x)}{f(x)} \Rightarrow \frac{g'(x)}{g(x)} = \frac{f'(x)}{f(x)}$$

$$\Rightarrow \quad \frac{g'(x)}{g(x)} = k \Rightarrow g(x) = Ce^{kx}$$

$$\Rightarrow \quad g'(x) = k\,Ce^{kx} \Rightarrow f(x) = k\,Ce^{kx}$$

$y = f(x)$ passes through $(0, 1) \Rightarrow kC = 1$

$y_1 = g(x)$ passes through

$$(0, 1/n) \Rightarrow C = \frac{1}{n} \Rightarrow k = n$$

$$\Rightarrow \quad f(x) = e^{nx}$$

• Ex. 36 *A normal is drawn at a point $P(x, y)$ of a curve. It meets the x-axis and the y-axis in point A and B, respectively, such that $\frac{1}{OA}+\frac{1}{OB}=1$, where O is the origin, find the equation of such a curve passing through (5, 4).*

Sol. The equation of the normal at (x, y) is

$$(X-x)+(Y-y)\frac{dy}{dx}=0$$

$$\Rightarrow \quad \frac{X}{x+y\frac{dy}{dx}}+\frac{Y}{\frac{(x+y\,dy/dx)}{dy/dx}}=1$$

$$\Rightarrow \quad OA=x+y\frac{dy}{dx},\ OB=\frac{\left(x+y\frac{dy}{dx}\right)}{\frac{dy}{dx}}$$

Also, $\frac{1}{OA}+\frac{1}{OB}=1 \Rightarrow 1+\frac{dy}{dx}=x+y\frac{dy}{dx}$

$$\Rightarrow \quad (y-1)\frac{dy}{dx}+(x-1)=0$$

Integrating, we get

$$(y-1)^2+(x-1)^2=C$$

Since, the curve passes through (5, 4), $C=25$.

Hence, the curve is $(x-1)^2+(y-1)^2=25$.

• Ex. 37 *A line is drawn from a point $P(x, y)$ on curve $y=f(x)$, making an angle with the x-axis which is supplementary to the one made by the tangent to the curve at $P(x, y)$. The line meets the x-axis at A. Another line perpendicular to the first, is drawn from $P(x, y)$ meeting the y-axis at B. If $OA=OB$, where O is origin, find all curve which passes through (1, 1).*

Sol. The equation of the line through $P(x, y)$ making an angle with the x-axis which is supplementary to the angle made by the tangent at $P(x, y)$ is

$$Y-y=-\frac{dy}{dx}(X-x) \quad \text{...(i)}$$

where it meets the x-axis.

$$Y=0,\quad X=x+\frac{y}{dy/dx} \Rightarrow OA=x+y\frac{dx}{dy} \quad \text{...(ii)}$$

The line through $P(x, y)$ and perpendicular to Eq. (i) is

$$Y-y=\frac{dx}{dy}(X-x)$$

where it meets the y-axis.

$$X=0,\ Y=y-x\frac{dx}{dy} \Rightarrow OB=y-x\frac{dx}{dy} \quad \text{...(iii)}$$

Since, $OA=OB$

$$\Rightarrow \quad x+y\frac{dx}{dy}=y-x\frac{dx}{dy}$$

or $$(y-x)=(y+x)\frac{dx}{dy}$$

or $$\frac{dy}{dx}=\frac{y+x}{y-x},\ \text{put } y=vx$$

$$\Rightarrow \quad x\frac{dv}{dx}=\frac{1+2v-v^2}{v-1}$$

$$\Rightarrow \quad \frac{(1-v)\,dv}{1+2v-v^2}+\frac{dx}{x}=0$$

$$\Rightarrow \quad \log(1+2v-v^2)+\log x=C_1$$

$$\Rightarrow \quad x^2+2xy-y^2=C$$

where $C_1=\log\sqrt{C}$

Since, curve passes through (1, 1) $\rightarrow C=2$

$\therefore$ Required curve, $\quad x^2-y^2+2xy=2$

• Ex. 38 *The tangent and a normal to a curve at any point P meet the x and y axes at A, B, C and D respectively. Find the equation of the curve passing through (1, 0) if the centre of circle through O, C, P and B lies on the line $y=x$ (where O is origin).*

Sol. Let $P(x, y)$ be a point on the curve.

$$\Rightarrow \quad C\equiv\left(x+y\frac{dy}{dx},0\right)$$

$$B\equiv\left(0,\ y-x\frac{dy}{dx}\right)$$

Circle passing through O, C, P and B has its centre at mid-point of BC.

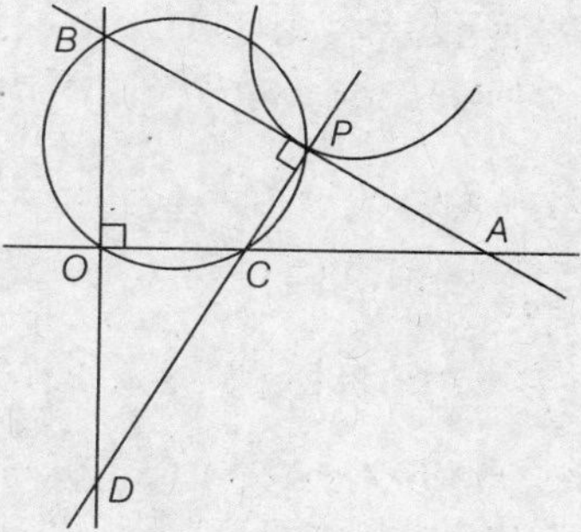

Let the centre of the circle be (α, β).

$$\Rightarrow \quad 2\alpha=x+y\frac{dy}{dx}$$

and $$2\beta=y-x\frac{dy}{dx}$$

and since $\beta=\alpha$, $y-x\frac{dy}{dx}=x+y\frac{dy}{dx}$

$$\Rightarrow \quad \frac{dy}{dx}=\frac{y-x}{y+x}$$

Let $y=vx \Rightarrow x\frac{dv}{dx}=-\frac{(1+v^2)}{1+v}$

$$\Rightarrow \quad \frac{1+v}{v^2+1}dv=-\frac{dx}{x}$$

Integrating both the sides, we get

$$\int \frac{1+v}{v^2+1}\,dv = -\int \frac{dx}{x}$$

$$\Rightarrow \quad \frac{1}{2}\int \frac{2v}{v^2+1}\,dv + \int \frac{dv}{v^2+1} = -\int \frac{dx}{x}$$

$$\Rightarrow \quad \frac{1}{2}\log|v^2+1| + \tan^{-1}|v| = -\log x + C$$

$$\Rightarrow \quad \log\{(\sqrt{v^2+1})\,x\} + \tan^{-1} v = C$$

$$\Rightarrow \quad \log\sqrt{x^2+y^2} + \tan^{-1}\frac{y}{x} = C$$

As $x = 1$ and $y = 0$,

$$\log 1 + \tan^{-1} 0 = C \Rightarrow C = 0$$

$\therefore$ Required curve, $(\log\sqrt{x^2+y^2}) + \tan^{-1}\left(\frac{y}{x}\right) = 0$

● **Ex. 39** *If $f(x)$ be a positive, continuous and differentiable on the interval (a, b). If $\lim_{x \to a^+} f(x) = 1$ and $\lim_{x \to b^-} f(x) = 3^{1/4}$. Also, $f'(x) \ge f^3(x) + \frac{1}{f(x)}$, then*

(a) $b - a \ge \pi/4$ (b) $b - a \le \pi/4$

(c) $b - a \le \pi/24$ (d) None of these

Sol. Since,

$$f'(x) \ge f^3(x) + \frac{1}{f(x)}$$

$$\Rightarrow \quad f'(x)\,f(x) \ge 1 + f^4(x)$$

$$\Rightarrow \quad \frac{f(x)\,f'(x)}{1+f^4(x)} \ge 1$$

On integrating w.r.t. 'x' from $x = a$ to $x = b$.

$$\frac{1}{2}(\tan^{-1}(f^2(x)))_a^b \ge (b-a)$$

or $$(b-a) \le \frac{1}{2}\left\{\lim_{x \to b^-}(\tan^{-1}(f^2(x))) - \lim_{x \to a^+}(\tan^{-1}(f^2(x)))\right\}$$

or $$(b-a) \le \pi/24$$

Hence, (c) is the correct answer.

Differential Equations Exercise 1 : Single Option Correct Type Questions

1. If the differential equation of the family of curve given by $y = Ax + Be^{2x}$, where A and B are arbitrary constants, is of the form $(1-2x)\frac{d}{dx}\left(\frac{dy}{dx}+ly\right)+k\left(\frac{dy}{dx}+ly\right)=0$, then the ordered pair (k, l) is

(a) $(2, -2)$ (b) $(-2, 2)$
(c) $(2, 2)$ (d) $(-2, -2)$

2. A curve passes through the point $\left(1, \frac{\pi}{4}\right)$ and its slope at any point is given by $\frac{y}{x} - \cos^2\left(\frac{y}{x}\right)$. Then, the curve has the equation

(a) $y = x\tan^{-1}\left(\ln\frac{e}{x}\right)$ (b) $y = x\tan^{-1}(\ln 2)$
(c) $y = \frac{1}{x}\tan^{-1}\left(\ln\frac{e}{x}\right)$ (d) None of these

3. The x-intercept of the tangent to a curve is equal to the ordinate of the point of contact. The equation of the curve through the point (1, 1) is

(a) $ye^{\frac{x}{y}} = e$ (b) $xe^{\frac{x}{y}} = e$
(c) $xe^{\frac{y}{x}} = e$ (d) $ye^{\frac{y}{x}} = e$

4. A function $y = f(x)$ satisfies the condition $f'(x)\sin x + f(x)\cos x = 1$, $f(x)$ being bounded when $x \to 0$. If $I = \int_0^{\pi/2} f(x)\,dx$, then

(a) $\frac{\pi}{2} < I < \frac{\pi^2}{4}$ (b) $\frac{\pi}{4} < I < \frac{\pi^2}{2}$
(c) $1 < I < \frac{\pi}{2}$ (d) $0 < I < 1$

5. A curve is such that the area of the region bounded by the coordinate axes, the curve and the ordinate of any point on it is equal to the cube of that ordinate. The curve represents

(a) a pair of straight lines (b) a circle
(c) a parabola (d) an ellipse

6. The value of the constant 'm' and 'c' for which $y = mx + c$ is a solution of the differential equation $D^2y - 3Dy - 4y = -4x$.

(a) is $m = -1; c = 3/4$ (b) is $m = 1; c = -3/4$
(c) no such real m, c (d) is $m = 1; c = 3/4$

7. The real value of m for which the substitution, $y = u^m$ will transform the differential equation, $2x^4y\frac{dy}{dx} + y^4 = 4x^6$ into a homogeneous equation is

(a) $m = 0$ (b) $m = 1$
(c) $m = 3/2$ (d) No value of m

8. The solution of the differential equation,

$$x^2\frac{dy}{dx}\cdot\cos\frac{1}{x} - y\sin\frac{1}{x} = -1,$$

where $y \to -1$ as $x \to \infty$ is

(a) $y = \sin\frac{1}{x} - \cos\frac{1}{x}$ (b) $y = \frac{x+1}{x\sin\frac{1}{x}}$
(c) $y = \sin\frac{1}{x} + \cos\frac{1}{x}$ (d) $y = \frac{x+1}{x\cos\frac{1}{x}}$

9. A wet porous substance in the open air loses its moisture at a rate proportional to the moisture content. If a sheet hung in the wind loses half its moisture during the first hour, then the time when it would have lost 99.9% of its moisture is (weather conditions remaining same)

(a) more than 100 h
(b) more than 10 h
(c) approximately 10 h
(d) approximately 9 h

10. A curve C passes through origin and has the property that at each point (x, y) on it, the normal line at that point passes through (1, 0). The equation of a common tangent to the curve C and the parabola $y^2 = 4x$ is

(a) $x = 0$ (b) $y = 0$
(c) $y = x + 1$ (d) $x + y + 1 = 0$

11. A function $y = f(x)$ satisfies

$$(x+1)\cdot f'(x) - 2(x^2+x)f(x) = \frac{e^{x^2}}{(x+1)}, \forall\, x > -1.$$

If $f(0) = 5$, then $f(x)$ is

(a) $\left(\frac{3x+5}{x+1}\right)\cdot e^{x^2}$ (b) $\left(\frac{6x+5}{x+1}\right)\cdot e^{x^2}$
(c) $\left(\frac{6x+5}{(x+1)^2}\right)\cdot e^{x^2}$ (d) $\left(\frac{5-6x}{x+1}\right)\cdot e^{x^2}$

12. The curve, with the property that the projection of the ordinate on the normal is constant and has a length equal to 'a', is

(a) $x - a\ln(\sqrt{y^2 - a^2} + y) = C$
(b) $x + \sqrt{a^2 - y^2} = C$
(c) $(y - a)^2 = Cx$
(d) $ay = \tan^{-1}(x + C)$

13. The differential equation corresponding to the family of curves $y = e^x (ax + b)$ is

(a) $\frac{d^2y}{dx^2} + 2\frac{dy}{dx} - y = 0$ (b) $\frac{d^2y}{dx^2} - 2\frac{dy}{dx} + y = 0$
(c) $\frac{d^2y}{dx^2} + 2\frac{dy}{dx} + y = 0$ (d) $\frac{d^2y}{dx^2} - 2\frac{dy}{dx} - y = 0$

14. The equation to the orthogonal trajectories of the system of parabolas $y = ax^2$ is

(a) $\frac{x^2}{2} + y^2 = C$ (b) $x^2 + \frac{y^2}{2} = C$
(c) $\frac{x^2}{2} - y^2 = C$ (d) $x^2 - \frac{y^2}{2} = C$

15. A function $f(x)$ satisfying $\int_0^1 f(tx)\,dt = n\,f(x)$, where $x > 0$, is

(a) $f(x) = C \cdot x^{\frac{1-n}{n}}$ (b) $f(x) = C \cdot x^{\frac{n}{n-1}}$
(c) $f(x) = C \cdot x^{\frac{1}{n}}$ (d) $f(x) = C \cdot x^{(1-n)}$

16. The substitution $y = z^\alpha$ transforms the differential equation $(x^2y^2 - 1)\,dy + 2xy^3\,dx = 0$ into a homogeneous differential equation for

(a) $\alpha = -1$ (b) 0
(c) $\alpha = 1$ (d) No value of α

17. A curve passing through (2, 3) and satisfying the differential equation $\int_0^x t y(t)\,dt = x^2 y(x), (x > 0)$ is

(a) $x^2 + y^2 = 13$ (b) $y^2 = \frac{9}{2}x$
(c) $\frac{x^2}{8} + \frac{y^2}{18} = 1$ (d) $xy = 6$

18. Which one of the following curves represents the solution of the initial value problem $Dy = 100 - y$, where $y(0) = 50$?

(a)
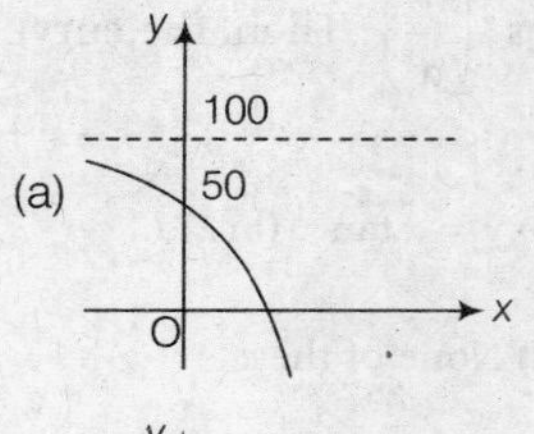

(b)
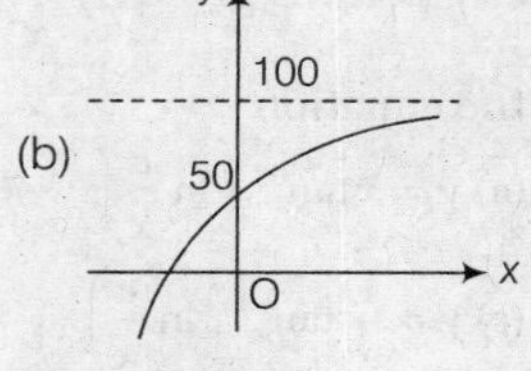

(c)
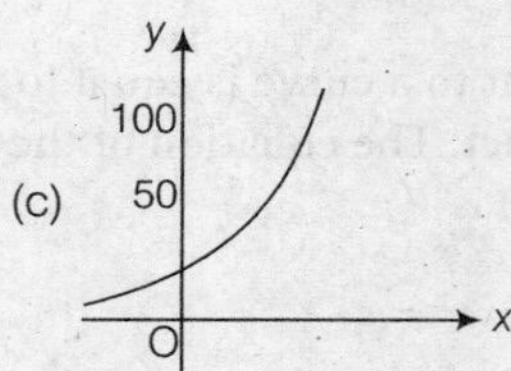

(d)
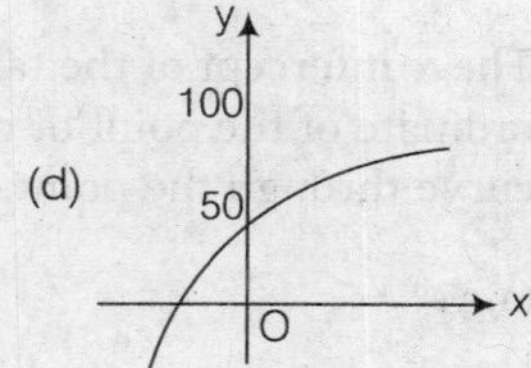

Differential Equations Exercise 2 :
More than One Option Correct Type Questions

19. The differential equation $x\frac{dy}{dx} + \frac{3}{\frac{dy}{dx}} = y^2$

(a) is of order 1 (b) is of degree 2
(c) is linear (d) is non-linear

20. The function $f(x)$ satisfying the equation $f^2(x) + 4f'(x)\cdot f(x) + [f'(x)]^2 = 0$.

(a) $f(x) = C \cdot e^{(2-\sqrt{3})x}$
(b) $f(x) = C \cdot e^{(2+\sqrt{3})x}$
(c) $f(x) = C \cdot e^{(\sqrt{3}-2)x}$
(d) $f(x) = C \cdot e^{-(2+\sqrt{3})x}$

where C is an arbitrary constant.

21. Which of the following pair(s) is/are orthogonal?

(a) $16x^2 + y^2 = C$ and $y^{16} = kx$
(b) $y = x + Ce^{-x}$ and $x + 2 = y + ke^{-y}$
(c) $y = Cx^2$ and $x^2 + 2y^2 = k$
(d) $x^2 - y^2 = C$ and $xy = k$

22. Family of curves whose tangent at a point with its intersection with the curve $xy = c^2$ form an angle of $\frac{\pi}{4}$ is

(a) $y^2 - 2xy - x^2 = k$
(b) $y^2 + 2xy - x^2 = k$
(c) $y = x - 2c\tan^{-1}\left(\frac{x}{c}\right) + k$
(d) $y = c\ln\left|\frac{c + x}{c - x}\right| - x + k$

23. The general solution of the differential equation, $x\left(\frac{dy}{dx}\right) = y \cdot \log\left(\frac{y}{x}\right)$ is

(a) $y = xe^{1-Cx}$

(b) $y = xe^{1+Cx}$

(c) $y = ex \cdot e^{Cx}$

(d) $y = xe^{Cx}$

where C is an arbitrary constant.

24. Which of the following equation(s) is/are linear?

(a) $\frac{dy}{dx} + \frac{y}{x} = \ln x$

(b) $y\left(\frac{dy}{dx}\right) + 4x = 0$

(c) $dx + dy = 0$

(d) $\frac{d^2y}{dx^2} = \cos x$

25. The equation of the curve passing through (3, 4) and satisfying the differential equation,

$$y\left(\frac{dy}{dx}\right)^2 + (x - y)\frac{dy}{dx} - x = 0$$

can be

(a) $x - y + 1 = 0$

(b) $x^2 + y^2 = 25$

(c) $x^2 + y^2 - 5x - 10 = 0$

(d) $x + y - 7 = 0$

26. Identify the statement(s) which is/are true?

(a) $f(x, y) = e^{y/x} + \tan\frac{y}{x}$ is homogeneous of degree zero.

(b) $x \cdot \log\frac{y}{x}\, dx + \frac{y^2}{x}\sin^{-1}\frac{y}{x}\, dy = 0$ is homogeneous differential equation.

(c) $f(x, y) = x^2 + \sin x \cdot \cos y$ is not homogeneous.

(d) $(x^2 + y^2)\, dx - (xy^2 - y^3)\, dy = 0$ is a homogeneous differential equation.

27. The graph of the function $y = f(x)$ passing through the point $(0, -1)$ and satisfying the differential equation $\frac{dy}{dx} + y\cos x = \cos x$ is such that

(a) it is a constant function

(b) it is periodic

(c) it is neither an even nor an odd function

(d) it is continuous and differentiable for all x

28. A function $y = f(x)$ satisfying the differential equation $\frac{dy}{dx} \cdot \sin x - y\cos x + \frac{\sin^2 x}{x^2} = 0$ is such that, $y \to 0$ as $x \to \infty$, then the statement which is correct?

(a) $\lim_{x \to 0} f(x) = 1$

(b) $\int_0^{\pi/2} f(x)\, dx$ is less than $\frac{\pi}{2}$

(c) $\int_0^{\pi/2} f(x)\, dx$ is greater than unity

(d) $f(x)$ is an odd function

29. Identify the statement(s) which is/are true?

(a) The order of differential equation $\sqrt{1 + \frac{d^2y}{dx^2}} = x$ is 1.

(b) Solution of the differential equation $xdy - ydx = \sqrt{x^2 + y^2}\, dx$ is $y + \sqrt{x^2 + y^2} = Cx^2$.

(c) $\frac{d^2y}{dx^2} = 2\left(\frac{dy}{dx} - y\right)$ is differential equation of family of curves $y = e^x(A\cos x + B\sin x)$.

(d) The solution of differential equation $(1 + y^2) + (x - 2e^{\tan^{-1} y})\frac{dy}{dx} = 0$ is $xe^{\tan^{-1} y} = e^{2\tan^{-1} y} + k$.

30. Let $y = (A + Bx)e^{3x}$ is a solution of the differential equation $\frac{d^2y}{dx^2} + m\frac{dy}{dx} + ny = 0$, $m, n \in I$, then

(a) $m = -6$

(b) $n = -6$

(c) $m = 9$

(d) $n = 9$

Differential Equations Exercise 3 : Statement I and II Type Questions

Directions

(Q. Nos. 31 to 40)

For the following questions, choose the correct answers from the codes (a), (b), (c) and (d) defined as follows :

(a) Statement I is true, Statement II is true and Statement II is the correct explanation for Statement I.
(b) Statement I is true, Statement II is true and Statement II is not the correct explanation for Statement I.
(c) Statement I is true, Statement II is false.
(d) Statement I is false, Statement II is true.

31. A curve C has the property that its initial ordinate of any tangent drawn is less than the abscissa of the point of tangency by unity.

Statement I Differential equation satisfying the curve is linear.

Statement II Degree of differential equation is one.

32. Statement I Differential equation corresponding to all lines, $ax + by + c = 0$ has the order 3.

Statement II General solution of a differential equation of nth order contains n independent arbitrary constants.

33. Statement I Integral curves denoted by the first order linear differential equation $\frac{dy}{dx} - \frac{1}{x}y = -x$ are family of parabolas passing through the origin.

Statement II Every differential equation geometrically represents a family of curve having some common property.

34. Statement I The solution of $(y\,dx - x\,dy)\cot\left(\frac{x}{y}\right) = ny^2\,dx$ is $\sin\left(\frac{x}{y}\right) = Ce^{nx}$

Statement II Such type of differential equations can only be solved by the substitution $x = vy$.

35. Statement I The order of the differential equation whose general solution is $y = c_1\cos 2x + c_2\sin^2 x + c_4e^{2x} + c_5e^{2x + c_6}$ is 3.

Statement II Total number of arbitrary parameters in the given general solution in the Statement I is 6.

36. Consider differential equation $(x^2 + 1)\cdot\frac{d^2y}{dx^2} = 2x\cdot\frac{dy}{dx}$

Statement I For any member of this family $y \to \infty$ as $x \to \infty$.

Statement II Any solution of this differential equation is a polynomial of odd degree with positive coefficient of maximum power.

37. Statement I Order of differential equation of family of parallel whose axis is parallel to Y-axis and latusrectum is fixed is 2.

Statement II Order of first equation is same as actual number of arbitrary constant present in differential equation.

38. Statement I The differential equation of all non-vertical lines in a plane is $\frac{d^2x}{dy^2} = 0$.

Statement II The general equation of all non-vertical lines in a plane is $ax + by = 1$, where $b \neq 0$.

39. Statement I The order of differential equation of all conics whose centre lies at origin is, 2.

Statement II The order of differential equation is same as number of arbitrary unknowns in the given curve.

40. Statement I $y = a\sin x + b\cos x$ is general solution of $y'' + y = 0$.

Statement II $y = a\sin x + b\cos x$ is a trigonometric function.

Differential Equations Exercise 4 :
Passage Based Questions

Passage I
(Q. Nos. 41 to 43)

Let $y = f(x)$ satisfies the equation
$f(x) = (e^{-x} + e^{x})\cos x - 2x - \int_0^x (x - t) f'(t) dt.$

41. y satisfies the differential equation

(a) $\frac{dy}{dx} + y = e^x(\cos x - \sin x) - e^{-x}(\cos x + \sin x)$

(b) $\frac{dy}{dx} - y = e^x(\cos x - \sin x) + e^{-x}(\cos x + \sin x)$

(c) $\frac{dy}{dx} + y = e^x(\cos x + \sin x) - e^{-x}(\cos x - \sin x)$

(d) $\frac{dy}{dx} - y = e^x(\cos x - \sin x) + e^{-x}(\cos x - \sin x)$

42. The value of $f'(0) + f''(0)$ equals to

(a) −1 (b) 2
(c) 1 (d) 0

43. $f(x)$ as a function of x equals to

(a) $e^{-x}(\cos x - \sin x) + \frac{e^x}{5}(3\cos x + \sin x) + \frac{2}{5}e^{-x}$

(b) $e^{-x}(\cos x + \sin x) + \frac{e^x}{5}(3\cos x - \sin x) - \frac{2}{5}e^{-x}$

(c) $e^{-x}(\cos x - \sin x) + \frac{e^x}{5}(3\cos x - \sin x) + \frac{2}{5}e^{-x}$

(d) $e^{-x}(\cos x + \sin x) + \frac{e^x}{5}(3\cos x - \sin x) - \frac{2}{5}e^{-x}$

Passage II
(Q. Nos. 44 to 46)

For certain curves $y = f(x)$ satisfying $\frac{d^2y}{dx^2} = 6x - 4$, $f(x)$ has local minimum value 5 when $x = 1$

44. Number of critical point for $y = f(x)$ for $x \in [0, 2]$

(a) 0 (b) 1
(c) 2 (d) 3

45. Global minimum value of $y = f(x)$ for $x \in [0, 2]$ is

(a) 5 (b) 7
(c) 8 (d) 9

46. Global maximum value of $y = f(x)$ for $x \in [0, 2]$ is

(a) 5 (b) 7
(c) 8 (d) 9

Passage III
(Q. Nos. 47 to 49)

If any differential equation in the form
$f(f_1(x, y))\, d(f_1(x, y)) + \phi(f_2(x, y))\, d(f_2(x, y)) + \ldots = 0$
then each term can be integrated separately.
For example,

$$\int \sin xy\, d(xy) + \int \left(\frac{x}{y}\right) d\left(\frac{x}{y}\right) = -\cos xy + \frac{1}{2}\left(\frac{x}{y}\right)^2 + C$$

47. The solution of the differential equation $x dy - y\, dx = \sqrt{x^2 - y^2}\, dx$ is

(a) $Cx = e^{\sin^{-1}\frac{y}{x}}$ (b) $xe^{\sin^{-1}\frac{y}{x}} = C$
(c) $x + e^{\sin^{-1}\frac{y}{x}} = C$ (d) None of these

48. The solution of the differential equation $(xy^4 + y)\, dx - x dy = 0$ is

(a) $\frac{x^3}{4} + \frac{1}{2}\left(\frac{x}{y}\right)^2 = C$ (b) $\frac{x^4}{4} + \frac{1}{3}\left(\frac{x}{y}\right)^3 = C$
(c) $\frac{x^4}{4} - \frac{1}{2}\left(\frac{x}{y}\right)^3 = C$ (d) $\frac{x^3}{4} - \frac{1}{2}\left(\frac{x}{y}\right)^2 = C$

49. Solution of differential equation $(2x\cos y + y^2\cos x)\, dx + (2y\sin x - x^2\sin y)\, dy = 0$ is

(a) $x^2\cos y + y^2\sin x = C$
(b) $x\cos y - y\sin x = C$
(c) $x^2\cos^2 y + y^2\sin^2 x = C$
(d) None of the above

Passage IV
(Q. Nos. 50 to 52)

Differential equation $\frac{dy}{dx} = f(x)\,g(x)$ can be solved by separating variable $\frac{dy}{g(y)} = f(x)\, dx.$

50. The equation of the curve to the point (1, 0) which satisfies the differential equation $(1 + y^2)\, dx - xy\, dy = 0$ is

(a) $x^2 + y^2 = 1$ (b) $x^2 - y^2 = 1$
(c) $x^2 + y^2 = 2$ (d) $x^2 - y^2 = 2$

51. Solution of the differential equation $\frac{dy}{dx}+\frac{1+y^2}{\sqrt{1-x^2}}=0$ is

(a) $\tan^{-1} y+\sin^{-1} x=C$
(b) $\tan^{-1} x+\sin^{-1} y=C$
(c) $\tan^{-1} y\cdot\sin^{-1} x=C$
(d) $\tan^{-1} y-\sin^{-1} x=C$

52. If $\frac{dy}{dx}=1+x+y+xy$ and $y(-1)=0$, then y is equal to

(a) $e^{\frac{(1-x)^2}{2}}$
(b) $e^{\frac{(1+x)^2}{2}}-1$
(c) $\ln(1+x)-1$
(d) $1+x$

Passage V
(Q. Nos. 53 to 55)

Let C be the set of curves having the property that the point of intersection of tangent with y-axis is equidistant from the point of tangency and origin (0, 0)

53. If $C_1, C_2 \in C$

C_1: Curve is passing through (1, 0)

C_2: Curve is passing through (−1,0)

The number of common tangents for C_1 and C_2 is

(a) 1
(b) 2
(c) 3
(d) None of these

54. If $C_3 \in C$

C_3: is passing through (2, 4). If $\frac{x}{a}+\frac{y}{b}=1$. is tangent to C_3, then

(a) $25a+10b^2-ab^2=0$
(b) $25a+10b-13ab=0$
(c) $13a+25b-16ab=0$
(d) $29a+b+13ab=0$

55. If common tangents of C_1 and C_2 form an equilateral triangle, where $C_1, C_2 \in C$ and C_1: Curve passes through (2, 0), then C_2 may passes through

(a) $(-1/3, 1/3)$
(b) $(-1/3, 1)$
(c) $(-2/3, 4)$
(d) $(-2/3, 2)$

Differential Equations Exercise 5 : Matching Type Questions

56. Match the following :

	Column I		Column II
(A)	$\frac{xdx+ydy}{xdy-ydx}=\sqrt{\frac{a^2-x^2-y^2}{x^2+y^2}}$	(p)	$y=\frac{C}{x^3}e^{-1/x}$
(B)	Solution of $\cos^2 x\frac{dy}{dx}-\tan 2x\cdot y=\cos^4 x$, where $\lvert x\rvert<\frac{\pi}{4}$ and $y\left(\frac{\pi}{6}\right)=\frac{3\sqrt{3}}{8}$	(q)	$\sqrt{x^2+y^2}=a\sin\left\{C+\tan^{-1}\left(\frac{y}{x}\right)\right\}$
(C)	The equation of all possible curves that will cut each member of the family of circles $x^2+y^2-2cx=0$ at right angle	(r)	$x^2+y^2+Cy=0$
(D)	Solution of the equation $x\int_0^x y(t)\,dt=(x+1)\int_0^x ty(t)\,dt,\ x>0$ is	(s)	$y=\frac{\sin 2x}{2(1-\tan^2 x)}$

57. Match the following :

	Column I		Column II
(A)	Circular plate is expanded by heat from radius 5 cm to 5.06 cm. Approximate increase in area is	(p)	4
(B)	Side of cube increasing by 1%, then percentage increase in volume is	(q)	0.6π
(C)	If the rate of decrease of $\frac{x^2}{2}-2x+5$ is twice the rate of decrease of x, then x is equal to	(r)	3
(D)	Rate of increase in area of equilateral triangle of side 15 cm, when each side is increasing at the rate of 0.1 cm/s; is	(s)	$\frac{3\sqrt{3}}{4}$

58. Match the following :

Column I		Column II
(A) The differential equation of the family of curves $y = e^x (A\cos x + B\sin x)$, where A, B are arbitrary constants, has the degree n and order m. Then, the values of n and m are, respectively	(p)	2, 1
(B) The degree and order of the differential equation of the family of all parabolas whose axis is the x-axis, are respectively	(q)	1, 1
(C) The order and degree of the differential equations of the family of circles touching the x-axis at the origin, are respectively	(r)	2, 2
(D) The degree and order of the differential equation of the family of ellipse having the same foci, are respectively.	(s)	1, 2

Differential Equations Exercise 6 :
Single Integer Answer Type Questions

59. Find the constant of integration by the general solution of the differential equation $(2x^2 y - 2y^4)\, dx + (2x^3 + 3xy^3)\, dy = 0$ if curve passes through (1, 1).

60. A tank initially contains 50 gallons of fresh water. Brine contains 2 pounds per gallon of salt, flows into the tank at the rate of 2 gallons per minutes and the mixture kept uniform by stirring, runs out at the same rate. If it will take for the quantity of salt in the tank to increase from 40 to 80 pounds (in seconds) is 206λ, then find λ.

61. If $f : R - \{-1\} \rightarrow$ and f is differentiable function which satisfies :
$f\{x + f(y) + xf(y)) = y + f(x) + yf(x) \,\forall\, x, y \in R - \{-1\}$,
then find the value of 2010 $[1 + f(2009)]$.

62. If $\phi(x)$ is a differential real-valued function satisfying $\phi'(x) + 2\phi(x) \le 1$, then the value of $2\phi(x)$ is always less than or equal to ....

63. The degree of the differential equation satisfied by the curves $\sqrt{1+x} - a\sqrt{1+y} = 1$, is ....

64. Let $f(x)$ be a twice differentiable bounded function satisfayi $2f^5(x) \cdot f'(x) + 2(f'(x))^3 \cdot f^5(x) = f''(x)$. If $f(x)$ is bounded in between $y = k$, and $y = k_2$, Then the number of integers between k_1 and k_2 is/are (where $f(0) = f'(0) = 0$).

65. Let $y(x)$ be a function satisfying $d^2y/dx^2 - dy/dx + e^{2x} = 0$, $y(0) = 2$ and $y'(0) = 1$. If maximum value of $y(x)$ is $y(\alpha)$, Then Integral part of (2α) is ....

Differential Equations Exercise 7 :
Subjective Type Questions

66. Find the time required for a cylindrical tank of radius r and height H to empty through a round hole of area 'a' at the bottom. The flow through a hole is according to the law $U(t) = u\sqrt{2gh(t)}$ where $v(t)$ and $h(t)$ are respectively the velocity of flow through the hole and the height of the water level above the hole at time t and g is the acceleration due to gravity.

67. The hemispherical tank of radius 2 m is initially full of water and has an outlet of 12 cm^2 cross-sectional area at the bottom. The outlet is opened at some instant. The flow through the outlet is according to the law $v(t) = 0 \cdot 6\sqrt{2gh(t)}$, where $v(t)$ and $h(t)$ are respectively velocity of the flow through the outlet and the height of water level above the outlet at time t and g is the acceleration due to gravity. Find the time it takes to empty the tank.

68. Let $f : R^+ \to R$ satisfies the functional equation $f(xy) = e^{xy-x-y}(e^y f(x) + e^x f(y)) \forall x, y \in R^+$. If $f'(1) = e$, determine $f(x)$.

69. Let $y = f(x)$ be curve passing through $(1, \sqrt{3})$ such that tangent at any point P on the curve lying in the first quadrant has positive slope and the tangent and the normal at the point P cut the x-axis at A and B respectively so that the mid-point of AB is origin. Find the differential equation of the curve and hence determine $f(x)$.

70. If y_1 and y_2 are the solution of differential equation $dy/dx + Py = Q$, where P and Q are function of x alone and $y_2 = y_1 z$, then prove that $z = 1 + c \cdot e^{-\int \frac{Q}{y_1} dx}$, where c is an arbitrary constant.

71. Let $y = f(x)$ be a differentiable function $\forall x \in R$ and satisfies :

$f(x) = x + \int_0^1 x^2 z f(z)\, dz + \int_0^1 x z^2 f(z)\, dz.$

Determine the function.

72. If $f : R - \{-1\} \to R$ and f is differentiable function satisfies :

$f((x) + f(y) + x f(y)) = y + f(x) + yf(x) \forall x, y \in R - \{-1\}$ Find $f(x)$.

Differential Equations Exercise 8 : Questions Asked in Previous 10 Years' Exams

(i) JEE Advanced & IIT-JEE

73. A solution curve of the differential equation $(x^2 + xy + 4x + 2y + 4)\frac{dy}{dx} - y^2 = 0, x > 0$, passes through the point (1, 3). Then, the solution curve **[More than One Correct 2016]**

(a) intersects $y = x + 2$ exactly at one point
(b) intersects $y = x + 2$ exactly at two points
(c) intersects $y = (x + 2)^2$
(d) does not intersect $y = (x + 3)^2$

74. Let $f : (0, \infty) \to R$ be a differentiable function such that $f'(x) = 2 - \frac{f(x)}{x}$ for all $x \in (0, \infty)$ and $f(1) \neq 1$. Then **[More than One Correct 2016]**

(a) $\lim_{x \to 0+} f'\left(\frac{1}{x}\right) = 1$
(b) $\lim_{x \to 0+} x f\left(\frac{1}{x}\right) = 2$
(c) $\lim_{x \to 0+} x^2 f'(x) = 0$
(d) $|f(x)| \leq 2$ for all $x \in (0, 2)$

75. Let $y(x)$ be a solution of the differential equation $(1 + e^x)y' + ye^x = 1$. If $y(0) = 2$, then which of the following statement(s) is/are true? **[More than One Correct 2015]**

(a) $y(-4) = 0$
(b) $y(-2) = 0$
(c) $y(x)$ has a critical point in the interval $(-1, 0)$
(d) $y(x)$ has no critical point in the interval $(-1, 0)$

76. Consider the family of all circles whose centres lie on the straight line $y = x$. If this family of circles is represented by the differential equation $Py'' + Qy' + 1 = 0$, where P, Q are the functions of x, y and y' (here, $y' = \frac{dy}{dx}, y'' = \frac{d^2y}{dx^2}$), then which of the following statement(s) is/are true? **[More than One correct 2015]**

(a) $P = y + x$
(b) $P = y - x$
(c) $P + Q = 1 - x + y + y' + (y')^2$
(d) $P - Q = x + y - y' - (y')^2$

77. The function $y = f(x)$ is the solution of the differential equation $\frac{dy}{dx} + \frac{xy}{x^2 - 1} = \frac{x^4 + 2x}{\sqrt{1 - x^2}}$ in $(-1, 1)$ satisfying $f(0) = 0$. Then, $\int_{-\frac{\sqrt{3}}{2}}^{\sqrt{3}/2} f(x)\, dx$ is **[Only One correct 2014]**

(a) $\frac{\pi}{3} - \frac{\sqrt{3}}{2}$ (b) $\frac{\pi}{3} - \frac{\sqrt{3}}{4}$ (c) $\frac{\pi}{6} - \frac{\sqrt{3}}{4}$ (d) $\frac{\pi}{6} - \frac{\sqrt{3}}{2}$

78. Let $f : [1/2, 1] \to R$ (the set of all real numbers) be a positive, non-constant and differentiable function such that $f'(x) < 2f(x)$ and $f(1/2) = 1$. Then, the value of $\int_{1/2}^1 f(x)\, dx$ lies in the interval **[Only One Correct 2013]**

(a) $(2e - 1, 2e)$ (b) $(e - 1, 2e - 1)$
(c) $\left(\frac{e-1}{2}, e - 1\right)$ (d) $\left(0, \frac{e-1}{2}\right)$

79. A curve passes through the point $\left(1, \frac{\pi}{6}\right)$. Let the slope of the curve at each point (x, y) be $\frac{y}{x} + \sec\left(\frac{y}{x}\right), x > 0$. Then, the equation of the curve is **[Only One Correct 2013]**

(a) $\sin\left(\frac{y}{x}\right) = \log x + \frac{1}{2}$ (b) $\text{cosec}\left(\frac{y}{x}\right) = \log x + 2$

(c) $\sec\left(\frac{2y}{x}\right) = \log x + 2$ (d) $\cos\left(\frac{2y}{x}\right) = \log x + \frac{1}{2}$

- **Directions** (Q. Nos. 80 to 83) Let $f : [0, 1] \to R$ (the set of all real numbers) be a function. Suppose the function f is twice differentiable, $f(0) = f(1) = 0$ and satisfies $f''(x) - 2f'(x) + f(x) \geq e^x$, $x \in [0, 1]$ **[Passage Based Questions 2013]**

80. If the function $e^{-x} f(x)$ assumes its minimum in interval $[0, 1]$ at $x = 1/4$, then which of the following is true?

(a) $f'(x) < f(x), \frac{1}{4} < x < \frac{3}{4}$ (b) $f'(x) > f(x), 0 < x < \frac{1}{4}$

(c) $f'(x) < f(x), 0 < x < \frac{1}{4}$ (d) $f'(x) < f(x), \frac{3}{4} < x < 1$

81. Which of the following is true?

(a) $0 < f(x) < \infty$ (b) $-\frac{1}{2} < f(x) < \frac{1}{2}$

(c) $-\frac{1}{4} < f(x) < 1$ (d) $-\infty < f(x) < 0$

82. Which of the following is true?

(a) g is increasing on $(1, \infty)$
(b) g is decreasing on $(1, \infty)$
(c) g is increasing on $(1, 2)$ and decreasing on $(2, \infty)$
(d) g is decreasing on $(1, 2)$ and increasing on $(2, \infty)$

83. Consider the statements.

I. There exists some $x \in R$ such that, $f(x) + 2x = 2(1 + x^2)$

II. There exists some $x \in R$ such that, $2f(x) + 1 = 2x(1 + x)$

(a) Both I and II are true (b) I is true and II is false
(c) I is false and II is true (d) Both I and II are false

84. If $y(x)$ satisfies the differential equation $y' - y \tan x = 2x \sec x$ and $y(0)$, then **[More than One Correct 2016]**

(a) $y\left(\frac{\pi}{4}\right) = \frac{\pi^2}{8\sqrt{2}}$ (b) $y'\left(\frac{\pi}{4}\right) = \frac{\pi^2}{18}$

(c) $y\left(\frac{\pi}{3}\right) = \frac{\pi^2}{9}$ (d) $y'\left(\frac{\pi}{3}\right) = \frac{4\pi}{3} + \frac{2\pi^2}{3\sqrt{3}}$

85. Let $y'(x) + y(x)g'(x) = g(x)g'(x)$, $y(0) = 0$, $x \in R$, where $f'(x)$ denotes $\frac{d\,f(x)}{dx}$ and $g(x)$ is a given non-constant differentiable function on R with $g(0) = g(2) = 0$. Then, the value of $y(2)$ is ...... **[Integer Type 2011]**

86. Let $f : R \to R$ be a continuous function, which satisfies $f(x) = \int_0^x f(t)\, dt$. Then, the value of $f(\ln 5)$ is .... **[Integer Type 2009]**

- **Direction** For the following question, choose the correct answer from the codes (a), (b), (c) and (d) defined as follows

(a) Statement I is true, Statement II is also true; Statement II is the correct explanation of Statement I.
(b) Statement I is true, Statement II is also true; Statement II is not the correct explanation of Statement I.
(c) Statement I is true; Statement II is false.
(d) Statement I is false; Statement II is true.

87. Let a solution $y = y(x)$ of the differential equation $x\sqrt{x^2 - 1}\, dy - y\sqrt{y^2 - 1}\, dx = 0$ satisfy $y(2) = \frac{2}{\sqrt{3}}$

Statement I $y(x) = \sec\left(\sec^{-1} x - \frac{\pi}{6}\right)$ and

Statement II $y(x)$ is given by $\frac{1}{y} = \frac{2\sqrt{3}}{x} - \sqrt{1 - \frac{1}{x^2}}$

[Statement Based Questions 2008]

(ii) JEE Main & AIEEE

88. If a curve $y = f(x)$ passes through the point $(1, -1)$ and satisfies the differential equation, $y(1 + xy)dx = x\,dy$, then $f\left(-\frac{1}{2}\right)$ is equal to **[2016 JEE Main]**

(a) $-\frac{2}{5}$ (b) $-\frac{4}{5}$ (c) $\frac{2}{5}$ (d) $\frac{4}{5}$

89. Let $y(x)$ be the solution of the differential equation $(x \log x)\frac{dy}{dx} + y = 2x \log x, (x \geq 1)$. Then, $y(e)$ is equal to **[2015 JEE Main]**

(a) e (b) 0 (c) 2 (d) $2e$

90. Let the population of rabbits surviving at a time t be governed by the differential equation $\frac{dp(t)}{dt} = \frac{1}{2}p(t) - 200$. If $p(0) = 100$, then $p(t)$ is equal to **[2014 JEE Main]**

(a) $400 - 300e^{\frac{t}{2}}$

(b) $300 - 200e^{-\frac{t}{2}}$

(c) $600 - 500e^{\frac{t}{2}}$

(d) $400 - 300e^{-\frac{t}{2}}$

91. At present, a firm is manufacturing 2000 items. It is estimated that the rate of change of production P with respect to additional number of workers x is given by $\frac{dP}{dx} = 100 - 12\sqrt{x}$. If the firm employees 25 more workers, then the new level of production of items is **[2013 JEE Main]**

(a) 2500 (b) 3000
(c) 3500 (d) 4500

92. The population $p(t)$ at time t of a certain mouse species satisfies the differential equation $\frac{dp(t)}{dt} = 0.5(t) - 450$. If $p(0) = 850$, then the time at which the population becomes zero is **[2012 AIEEE]**

(a) 2 log 18 (b) log 9
(c) $\frac{1}{2}$ log 18 (d) log 18

93. If $\frac{dy}{dx} = y + 3 > 0$ and $y(0) = 2$, then $y(\log 2)$ is equal to **[2011 JEE Main]**

(a) 5 (b) 13
(c) −2 (d) 7

94. Let I be the purchase value of an equipment and $V(t)$ be the value after it has been used for t years. The value $V(t)$ depreciates at a rate given by differential equation $\frac{dV(t)}{dt} = -k(T - t)$, where $k > 0$ is a constant and T is the total life in years of the equipment. Then, the scrap value $V(T)$ of the equipment is **[2010 AIEEE]**

(a) $I - \frac{kT^2}{2}$ (b) $I - \frac{k(T-t)^2}{2}$
(c) e^{-kT} (d) $T^2 - \frac{1}{k}$

95. Solution of the differential equation

$$\cos x\, dy = y(\sin x - y)\, dx,\ 0 < x < \frac{\pi}{2}, \text{ is}$$ **[2010 AIEEE]**

(a) $\sec x = (\tan x + C)y$
(b) $y \sec x = \tan x + C$
(c) $y \tan x = \sec x + C$
(d) $\tan x = (\sec x + C)y$

96. The differential equation which represents the family of curves $y = c_1 e^{c_2 x}$, where c_1 and c_2 are arbitrary constants, is **[2009 AIEEE]**

(a) $y' = y^2$ (b) $y'' = y'y$
(c) $yy'' = y'$ (d) $yy'' = (y')^2$

97. The differential equation of the family of circles with fixed radius 5 units and centre on the line $y = 2$ is **[AIEEE 2008]**

(a) $(x-2)y'^2 = 25 - (y-2)^2$
(b) $(y-2)y'^2 = 25 - (y-2)^2$
(c) $(y-2)^2 y'^2 = 25 - (y-2)^2$
(d) $(x-2)^2 y'^2 = 25 - (y-2)^2$

Answers

Exercise for Session 1

1. (a) **2.** (a) **3.** (d) **4.** (a) **5.** (d)
6. (a) **7.** (b) **8.** (a) **9.** (a) **10.** (b)

Exercise for Session 2

1. (b) **2.** (c) **3.** (a) **4.** (a) **5.** (c)
6. (a) **7.** (a) **8.** (a) **9.** (a) **10.** (a)
11. (b) **12.** (c) **13.** (a) **14.** (b) **15.** (b)

Exercise for Session 3

1. (a) **2.** (a) **3.** (b) **4.** (b) **5.** (c)
6. (c) **7.** (a) **8.** (c) **9.** (a) **10.** (c)

Exercise for Session 4

1. (b) **2.** (d) **3.** (a) **4.** (b) **5.** (a)
6. (a) **7.** (c) **8.** (b) **9.** (a) **10.** (d)

Exercise for Session 5

1. (a) **2.** (c) **3.** (c) **4.** (a) **5.** (c)
6. (a) **7.** (b) **8.** (c)

Chapter Exercises

1. (a) **2.** (a) **3.** (a) **4.** (a) **5.** (c)
6. (b) **7.** (c) **8.** (a) **9.** (c) **10.** (a)
11. (b) **12.** (a) **13.** (b) **14.** (a) **15.** (a)
16. (a) **17.** (d) **18.** (b) **19.** (a,b,d)
20. (c,d) **21.** (a,b,c,d) **22.** (b,c,d)
23. (a,b,c) **24.** (a,c,d) **25.** (a,b)
26. (a,b,c) **27.** (a,b,d) **28.** (a,b,c)
29. (b,c,d) **30.** (a,d) **31.** (b)
32. (d) **33.** (d) **34.** (c) **35.** (c) **36.** (a)
37. (b) **38.** (d) **39.** (d) **40.** (b) **41.** (a)
42. (d) **43.** (c) **44.** (c) **45.** (a) **46.** (b)
47. (a) **48.** (b) **49.** (a) **50.** (b) **51.** (a)
52. (b) **53.** (c) **54.** (a) **55.** (a)
56. (A) → (q), (B) → (s), (C) → (r), (D) → (p)
57. (A) → (q), (B) → (r), (C) → (p), (D) → (s)
58. (A) → (s), (B) → (s), (C) → (q), (D) → (p)
59. (1) **60.** (8) **61.** (1) **62.** (1) **63.** (1)
64. (3) **65.** (1)
66. $t = \dfrac{\pi r^2}{\mu a}\sqrt{\dfrac{2H}{g}}$
67. $t = \dfrac{7\pi \times 10^5}{135\sqrt{g}}$
68. $f(x) = e^x \log x$
69. $x + f(x)f'(x) = \sqrt{x^2 + f^2(x)}$ and $f^2(x) = 1 + 2x$
71. $f(x) = \dfrac{20x}{119}(4 + 9x)$
72. $f(x) = \dfrac{-x}{1 + x}$
73. (a, d) **74.** (a,d) **75.** (a, c) **76.** (b, e) **77.** (b)
78. (d) **79.** (a) **80.** (c) **81.** (d) **82.** (b)
83. (c) **84.** (d) **85.** (0) **86.** (0) **87.** (c)
88. (d) **89.** (c) **90.** (a) **91.** (c) **92.** (a)
93. (d) **94.** (a) **95.** (a) **96.** (d) **97.** (c)

Solutions

1. $y \cdot e^{-2x} = Ax\, e^{-2x} + B$

$e^{-2x} \cdot y_1 - 2ye^{-2x} = A(e^{-2x} - 2x\, e^{-2x})$

Cancelling e^{-2x} throughout

$$y_1 - 2y = A(1 - 2x) \quad \text{...(i)}$$

Differentiating again $y_2 - 2y_1 = -2A$

$$\Rightarrow \quad A = \frac{2y_1 - y_2}{2}$$

On substituting A in Eq. (i)

$$2(y_2 - 2y) = (2y_1 - y_2)(1 - 2x)$$

$$2y_1 - 4y = 2y_1(1 - 2x) - (1 - 2x)y_2$$

$$(1 - 2x)\frac{d}{dx}\left(\frac{dy}{dx} - 2y\right) + 2\left(\frac{dy}{dx} - 2y\right) = 0$$

Hence, $\quad k = 2$ and $l = -2$

$\Rightarrow$ Ordered pair $(k, l) \equiv (2, -2)$

2. $\dfrac{dy}{dx} = \dfrac{y}{x} - \cos^2\dfrac{y}{x} \quad y = vx$

$$v + x\frac{dv}{dx} = v - \cos^2 v$$

$$\int \frac{dv}{\cos^2 v} + \int \frac{dx}{x} = C \Rightarrow \tan v + \ln x = C$$

$$\tan\frac{y}{x} + \ln x = C$$

If $x = 1, y = \dfrac{\pi}{4} \Rightarrow C = 1 \Rightarrow \tan\dfrac{y}{x} = 1 - \ln x = \ln\dfrac{e}{x}$

$$y = x\tan^{-1}\left(\ln\frac{e}{x}\right)$$

3. $Y - y = m(X - x)$. For X-intercept $Y = 0$

$$X = x - \frac{y}{m}$$

Therefore, $x - \dfrac{y}{m} = y$

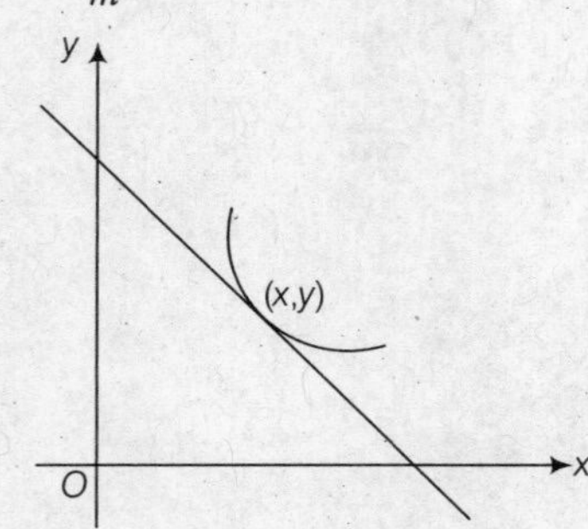

or $\quad \dfrac{dy}{dx} = \dfrac{y}{x - y}$

Put $y = vx \quad v + x\dfrac{dv}{dx} = \dfrac{v}{1 - v}$

$$x\frac{dv}{dx} = \frac{v}{1 - v} - v = \frac{v - v + v^2}{1 - v}$$

$$\int \frac{1 - v}{v^2}\, dv = \int \frac{dx}{x}$$

$$-\frac{1}{v} - \ln v = \ln x + C$$

$$-\frac{x}{y} - \ln\frac{y}{x} = \ln x + C \Rightarrow -\frac{x}{y} = \ln y + C$$

$x = 1, y = 1 \Rightarrow C = -1$

$$1 - \frac{x}{y} = \ln y \Rightarrow y = e \cdot e^{-x/y}$$

$$e^{-x/y} = \frac{e}{y} \Rightarrow ye^{x/y} = e$$

4. $\sin x\dfrac{dy}{dx} + y\cos x = 1$

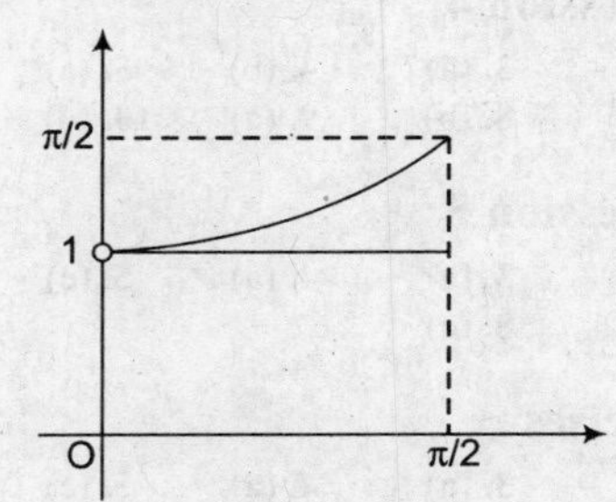

$$\frac{dy}{dx} + y\cot x = \operatorname{cosec} x$$

$$\text{IF} = e^{\int \cot x\, dx} = e^{\ln(\sin x)} = \sin x$$

$$y\sin x = \int \operatorname{cosec} x \cdot \sin x\, dx$$

$$y\sin x = x + C$$

If $x = 0$, y is finite $\therefore \quad C = 0$

$$y = x(\operatorname{cosec} x) = \frac{x}{\sin x}$$

Now, $\quad I < \dfrac{\pi^2}{4}$ and $I > \dfrac{\pi}{2}$

Hence, $\quad \dfrac{\pi}{2} < I < \dfrac{\pi^2}{4}$

5. $\int_0^x f(x)\, dx = y^3$. Differentiating $f(x) = 3y^2 \cdot \dfrac{dy}{dx}$

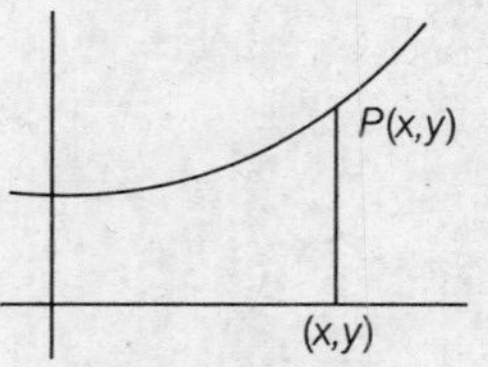

$$y = 3y^2\frac{dy}{dx} \Rightarrow y = 0 \quad \text{(rejected)}$$

or $\quad 3y\, dy = dx$

$$\frac{3y^2}{2} = x + C \Rightarrow \text{Parabola}$$

6. $y = mx + c; \dfrac{dy}{dx} = m; \dfrac{d^2y}{dx^2} = 0$

Substituting in $\dfrac{d^2y}{dx^2} - 3\dfrac{dy}{dx} - 4y = -4x$

$$0 - 3m - 4(mx + c) = -4x$$
$$-3m - 4c - 4mx = -4x$$
$$-(3m + 4c) = 4x(m - 1) \quad \text{...(i)}$$

Eq. (i) is true for all real x, if $m = +1$ and $c = -3/4$.

7. $y = u^m \Rightarrow \dfrac{dy}{dx} = mu^{m-1}\dfrac{dy}{dx}$

Since, $2x^4 \cdot u^m \cdot mu^{m-1} \cdot \dfrac{du}{dx} + u^{4m} = 4x^6$

$$\frac{du}{dx} = \frac{4x^6 - u^{4m}}{2m\,x^4\,u^{2m-1}}$$

$\Rightarrow \quad 4m = 6 \Rightarrow m = \dfrac{3}{2}$

and $\quad 2m - 1 = 2 \Rightarrow m = \dfrac{3}{2}$

8. $\dfrac{dy}{dx} - \dfrac{y}{x^2}\tan\dfrac{1}{x} = -\sec\dfrac{1}{x}\cdot\dfrac{1}{x^2}$

$\text{IF} = e^{-\int \frac{1}{x^2}\tan\frac{1}{x}dx} = \sec\dfrac{1}{x} \Rightarrow y\cdot\sec\dfrac{1}{x}$

$$= -\int \sec^2\left(\frac{1}{x}\right)\frac{1}{x^2}\,dx = \tan\frac{1}{x} + C$$

If $y \to -1$, then $x \to \infty$

$\Rightarrow \quad C = -1 \Rightarrow y = \sin\dfrac{1}{x} - \cos\dfrac{1}{x}$

9. $\dfrac{dM}{dt} = -KM \Rightarrow M = Ce^{-kt}$ when $t = 0$; $M = M_0$

$\Rightarrow \quad C = M_0$

$\Rightarrow \quad M = M_0e^{-kt}$

when $t = 1$, $M = \dfrac{M_0}{2}$

$\Rightarrow \quad k = \ln 2$

Therefore, $M = M_0e^{-t\ln 2}$

when $\quad M = \dfrac{M_0}{1000}$, then $t = \log_2 1000 = 9.98$

$= 10\,\text{h}$ approximately

10. Slope of the normal $= -\dfrac{y}{x-1}$

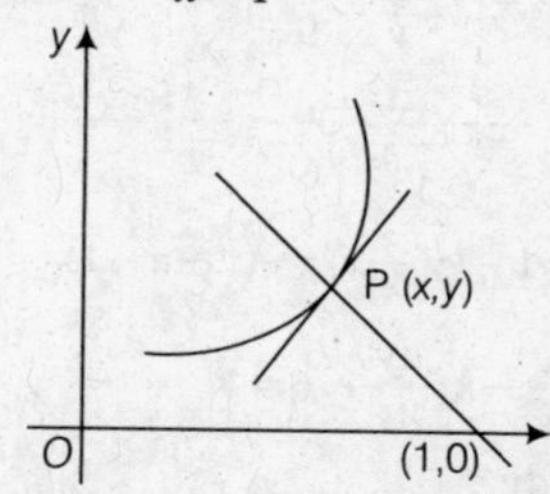

$\therefore \quad \dfrac{dy}{dx} = \dfrac{1-x}{y}$

$$\frac{y^2}{2} = x - \frac{x^2}{2} + C \quad \text{...(ii)}$$

Eq. (ii) passes through (0, 0).
Thus, $C = 0$

$$x^2 + y^2 - 2x = 0$$

Now, tangent to $y^2 = 4x$

$$y = mx + \frac{1}{m} \quad \text{...(iii)}$$

If it touches the circle

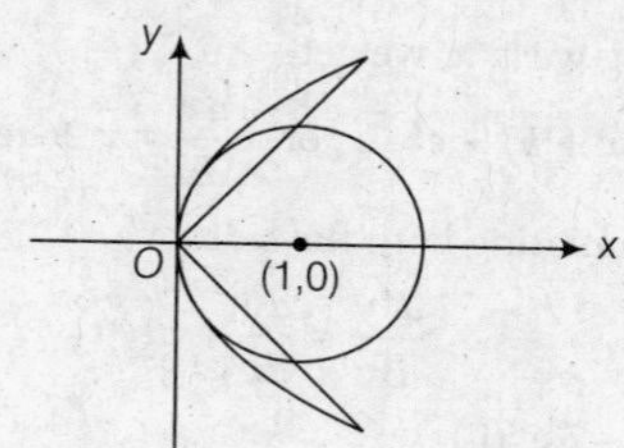

$$x^2 + y^2 - 2x = 0$$

Then, $\quad \left|\dfrac{m + (1/m)}{\sqrt{1+m^2}}\right| = 1$

$\Rightarrow \quad 1 + m^2 = m^2$

$\Rightarrow \quad m \to \infty$

Hence, tangent is y-axis *ie*, $x = 0$.

11. $f'(x) - \dfrac{2x(x+1)}{x+1}f(x) = \dfrac{e^{x^2}}{(x+1)^2}$

$$\text{IF} = e^{\int -2x\,dx} = e^{-x^2}$$

$\therefore \quad f(x)\cdot e^{-x^2} = \displaystyle\int \frac{dx}{(x+1)^2}$

$\Rightarrow \quad f(x)\cdot e^{-x^2} = -\dfrac{1}{x+1} + C$

At $x = 0$, $f(0) = 5 \Rightarrow C = 6$

$\therefore \quad f(x) = \left(\dfrac{6x+5}{x+1}\right)\cdot e^{x^2}$

12. Ordinate $= PM$. Let $P \equiv (x, y)$

Projection of ordinate on normal $= PN$

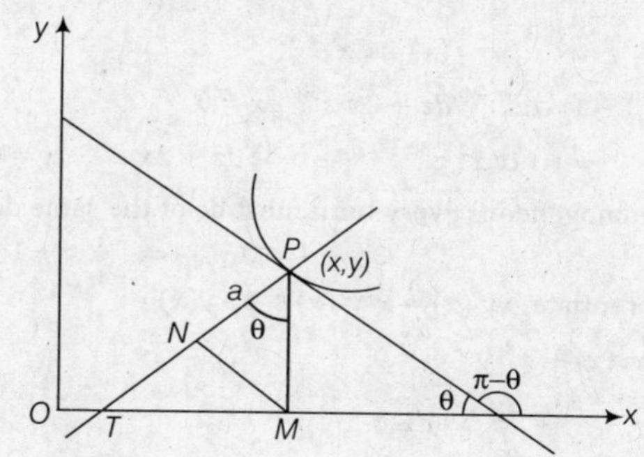

$\therefore \quad PN = PN \cos\theta = a$ (given)

$\therefore \quad \dfrac{y}{\sqrt{1+\tan^2\theta}} = a$

$\Rightarrow \quad y = a\sqrt{1+(y_1)^2}$

$\Rightarrow \quad \dfrac{dy}{dx} = \dfrac{\sqrt{y^2-a^2}}{a}$

$\Rightarrow \quad \int \dfrac{a\,dy}{\sqrt{y^2-a^2}} = \int dx$

$\Rightarrow \quad a\ln|y+\sqrt{y^2-a^2}| = x + C$

13. $y = e^x(ax+b)$ ...(i)

Differentiating w.r.t. x, we get

$\dfrac{dy}{dx} = e^x(ax+b) + e^x\cdot a$ or $\dfrac{dy}{dx} = y + ae^x$ ...(ii)

Again, differentiating both the sides

$\dfrac{d^2y}{dx^2} = \dfrac{dy}{dx} + ae^x$ ...(iii)

From Eq. (iii) – Eq. (ii)

$$\frac{d^2y}{dx^2} - \frac{2dy}{dx} + y = 0$$

is required differential equation.

14. $\dfrac{dy}{dx} = 2ax = 2x\cdot\dfrac{y}{x^2}$; $\dfrac{dy}{dx} = \dfrac{2y}{x}$;

Now, $\quad m\dfrac{dy}{dx} = -1 \Rightarrow m = -\dfrac{x}{2y} \Rightarrow \dfrac{dy}{dx} = -\dfrac{x}{2y}$

$$y^2 = -\frac{x^2}{2} + C$$

15. $\int_0^1 f(tx)\,dt = n\cdot f(x)$

Put, $x = y \Rightarrow dt = \dfrac{1}{x}dy$

$\therefore \quad \dfrac{1}{x}\int_0^x f(y)\,dy = nf(x)$

$\therefore \quad \int_0^x f(y)\,dy = x\cdot n\cdot f(x)$

Differentiating, $\quad f(x) = n[f(x) + xf'(x)]$

$f(x)(1-n) = nx\,f'(x)$

$\therefore \quad \dfrac{f'(x)}{f(x)} = \dfrac{1-n}{nx}$

Integrating, $\ln f(x) = \left(\dfrac{1-n}{n}\right)\ln Cx = \ln (Cx)^{\frac{1-n}{n}}$;

$\therefore \quad f(x) = Cx^{\frac{1-n}{n}}$

16. $(x^2z^{2\alpha}-1)\,\alpha z^{\alpha-1}\,dz + 2x\,z^{3\alpha}\,dx = 0$

or $\quad \alpha(x^2z^{3\alpha-1} - z^{\alpha-1})\,dz + 2x\,z^{3\alpha}\,dx = 0$

for homogeneous every term must be of the same degree,

$$3\alpha + 1 = \alpha - 1 \Rightarrow \alpha = -1$$

17. Differentiate, $xy(x) = x^2y'(x) + 2\,xy(x)$

or $\quad xy(x) + x^2\,y'(x) = 0$

$$x\frac{dy}{dx} + y = 0$$

$\ln y + \ln x = \ln C$

$xy = C$

At point (2, 3),

$2\times 3 = C \Rightarrow C = 6$

$\therefore \quad xy = 6$

18. $\int \dfrac{dy}{100-y} = \int dx$

$-\ln(100-y) = x + C$

$\ln(100-y) = -x + C$

Also $\quad x = 0,\ y = 50$

$\therefore \quad C = \ln 50$

$x = \ln 50 - \ln(100-y)$

$\Rightarrow \quad \ln\dfrac{50}{100-y} = x$

$\Rightarrow \quad \dfrac{50}{100-y} = e^x$

$\Rightarrow \quad 100 - y = 50e^{-x}$

$\Rightarrow \quad y = 100 - 50e^{-x}$

19. Here, $x\left(\dfrac{dy}{dx}\right)^2 - 3y^2\left(\dfrac{dy}{dx}\right) + 3 = 0$

has order 1, degree 2 and non-linear.

20. Here, $(f'(x))^2 + 4f'(x)\cdot f(x) + (f(x))^2 = 0$

$\Rightarrow \quad \left(\dfrac{f'(x)}{f(x)}\right)^2 + 4\left(\dfrac{f'(x)}{f(x)}\right) + 1 = 0$

$\Rightarrow \quad \dfrac{f'(x)}{f(x)} = \dfrac{-4\pm\sqrt{16-4}}{2}$

$\Rightarrow \quad \dfrac{f'(x)}{f(x)} = -2\pm\sqrt{3}$

Integrating both the sides

$\log|f(x)| = (-2\pm\sqrt{3})\,x + C_1$

$\Rightarrow \quad f(x) = e^{(-2\pm\sqrt{3})x}\cdot C$

21. (a) $32x + 2y\dfrac{dy}{dx} = 0$

$\Rightarrow \quad \dfrac{dy}{dx} = m_1 = -\dfrac{16x}{y}$

and $\quad 16y^{15}\dfrac{dy}{dx} = k$

$\Rightarrow \quad \dfrac{dy}{dx} = m_2 = \dfrac{k}{16y^{15}}$

$m_1m_2 = -\dfrac{16x}{y}\cdot\dfrac{k}{16y^{15}} = -\dfrac{x}{y^{16}}\cdot k$

$= -\dfrac{x}{y^{16}}\cdot\dfrac{y^{16}}{x} = -1$

(b) $\dfrac{dy}{dx} = 1 - ce^{-x} = 1-(y-x) = -(y-x-1)$ [using $ce^{-x} = y - x$]

and $\quad \dfrac{dy}{dx} - k\cdot\dfrac{dy}{dx}e^{-y} = 1$

$\dfrac{dy}{dx}[1-ke^{-y}] = 1$

or $\quad [1-(x+2-y)]\dfrac{dy}{dx}=1 \qquad [\text{using } ke^{-y}=x-y+2]$

$$\frac{dy}{dx}=m_2=\frac{1}{y-x-1}$$

$$\Rightarrow \qquad m_1m_2=-1$$

(c) $\dfrac{dy}{dx}=2cx=2x\cdot\dfrac{y}{x^2}=\dfrac{2y}{x}=m_1$

Also, $\quad 2x+4y\dfrac{dy}{dx}=0 \Rightarrow \dfrac{dy}{dx}=-\dfrac{x}{2y}=m_2$

Hence, $\quad m_1m_2=-1$

(d) $\quad x^2-y^2=c$

$$2x-2y\frac{dy}{dx}=0 \Rightarrow \frac{dy}{dx}=\frac{x}{y}=m_1$$

$$xy=k$$

$$x\frac{dy}{dx}+y=0 \Rightarrow \frac{dy}{dx}=-\frac{y}{x}=m_2$$

$$\therefore \qquad m_1m_2=-1$$

Hence, (a), (b), (c) and (d) are all correct.

22. Let $m=\dfrac{dy}{dx}$ be the slope of tangent (x, y) to the required curve.

m_1 = slope of the tangent at $xy=c^2$

$$=-\frac{c^2}{x^2}=-\frac{y}{x}$$

Hence, $\quad \dfrac{m+\dfrac{c^2}{x^2}}{1-\dfrac{c^2}{x^2}m}=\pm 1$ or $\dfrac{m+\dfrac{y}{x}}{1-\dfrac{y}{x}m}=\pm 1 \qquad$ ...(i)

Consider $\quad y^2-2xy-x^2=k$

$$\Rightarrow 2y\frac{dy}{dx}-2\left(y+x\frac{dy}{dx}\right)-2x=0$$

$$\Rightarrow \frac{dy}{dx}(y-x)=x+y$$

$$\Rightarrow \frac{dy}{dx}=\frac{x+y}{y-x}=m \qquad \text{(say)}$$

From Eq. (i)

$$\text{LHS}=\frac{\dfrac{x+y}{y-x}+\dfrac{y}{x}}{1-\dfrac{y}{x}\left(\dfrac{x+y}{y-x}\right)}$$

$$=\frac{x^2+y^2}{x^2+y^2}=1 \text{ RHS}$$

Similarly option, (b), (c) and (d) safisfy

23. $x\dfrac{dy}{dx}=y\log\left(\dfrac{y}{x}\right)\ \dfrac{dy}{dx}=\dfrac{y}{x}\log\left(\dfrac{y}{x}\right)$, put $y=vx$

$$\Rightarrow \frac{dy}{dx}=v+x\frac{dv}{dx}$$

$$\therefore \qquad v+x\frac{dv}{dx}=v\log v \Rightarrow x\frac{dv}{dx}=v(\log v-1)$$

$$\Rightarrow \int\frac{dv}{v(\log v-1)}=\int\frac{dx}{x} \Rightarrow \int\frac{dt}{t-1}=\int\frac{dx}{x},$$

let $\log v=t$

$$\Rightarrow \log(t-1)=\log(x)+\log C$$

$$\Rightarrow \log(t-1)=\log(xC)$$

$$\Rightarrow t=1+xC$$

$$\Rightarrow \log\frac{y}{x}=1+xC$$

$$\Rightarrow y=x\cdot e^{1+Cx}$$

or $\quad y=x\cdot e^{1-Cx}$

and $\quad \log\dfrac{y}{x}=\log e+Cx$

$$\Rightarrow y=ex\cdot e^{Cx}$$

24. Clearly, (a) and (c) are of the form $\dfrac{dy}{dx}+Py=Q$, which is linear in y.

Also, (d) is $\dfrac{d^2y}{dx^2}=\cos x$, on integrating $\dfrac{dy}{dx}=\sin x+C$ which is also linear in y.

25. $\dfrac{dy}{dx}=\dfrac{(y-x)\pm\sqrt{(x-y)^2+4xy}}{2y}$

$$\Rightarrow \frac{dy}{dx}=1 \text{ or } \frac{dy}{dx}=-\frac{x}{y}$$

$$\Rightarrow x-y+1=0 \text{ and } x^2+y^2=25$$

26. (a) $f(x, tx)=e^t+\tan^{-1}(t)$, independent of x.

$\Rightarrow$ Homogeneous differential equation.

(b) $\log\left(\dfrac{y}{x}\right)dx+\dfrac{y^2}{x^2}\sin^{-1}\dfrac{y}{x}\cdot dy=0$

$$\Rightarrow \frac{dy}{dx}=\frac{\log\left(\dfrac{y}{x}\right)}{\dfrac{y^2}{x^2}\sin^{-1}\left(\dfrac{y}{x}\right)}$$

$$f(x,y)=\frac{\log\left(\dfrac{y}{x}\right)}{\dfrac{y^2}{x^2}\sin^{-1}\left(\dfrac{y}{x}\right)}$$

$\therefore \quad f(x, tx)=\dfrac{\log(t)}{t^2\sin^{-1}(t)}$, independent of x

$\Rightarrow$ Homogeneous differential equation.

(c) $f(x,y)=x^2+\sin x\cdot\cos y$

$f(x, tx)=x^2+\sin x\cdot\cos(tx)$, not independent of x.

$\Rightarrow$ Not homogeneous differential equation.

(d) $f(x,y)=\dfrac{x^2+y^2}{xy^2-y^3}$

$\Rightarrow f(x, tx)$ is not independent of x.

$\Rightarrow$ Not homogeneous differential equation.

27. Integrating Factor $= e^{\int \cos x\, dx} = e^{\sin x}$

or $\quad y \cdot e^{\sin x} = \int e^{+\sin x} \cos x = -e^{+\sin x} + C$

At point (0, −1),

$$-1\, e^0 = -e^0 + C \Rightarrow 0$$

$$\therefore \quad ye^{\sin x} = -e^{\sin x}$$

$$y = -1$$

28. $\dfrac{dy}{dx} - y \cot x = -\dfrac{\sin x}{x^2}$

Integrating Factor $= e^{\int -\cot x\, dx} = e^{-\log \sin x} = \dfrac{1}{\sin x}$

$\therefore$ Required solution is $y \cdot \dfrac{1}{\sin x} = \int -\dfrac{\sin x}{x^2} \cdot \dfrac{1}{\sin x}\, dx + C$

$$y \cdot \frac{1}{\sin x} = \frac{1}{x} + C$$

As $x \to \infty, y \to 0 \Rightarrow C = 0$

$$\therefore \quad y = \frac{\sin x}{x} \Rightarrow \lim_{x \to 0} f(x) = 1 \qquad \text{...(i)}$$

$$\therefore \quad I = \int_0^{\pi/2} \frac{\sin x}{x}\, dx$$

Since, $\dfrac{\sin x}{x}$ is decreasing, when $x > 0$

$$\Rightarrow \quad f(x) < f(0)$$

$$\Rightarrow \quad \int_0^{\pi/2} f(x) < \frac{\pi}{2} \text{ and } x < \frac{\pi}{2}$$

$$\Rightarrow \quad f(x) > \int \left(\frac{\pi}{2}\right) \Rightarrow \int_0^{\pi/2} f(x)\, dx > 1$$

29. (a) Order of the differential equation is 2.

(b) $\quad \dfrac{xdy - ydx}{\sqrt{x^2 + y^2}} = dx \Rightarrow \dfrac{\dfrac{xdy - ydx}{x^2}}{\sqrt{\left(1 + \dfrac{y^2}{x^2}\right)}} = \dfrac{dx}{x}$

$$\therefore \quad \ln \left| \frac{y}{x} + \sqrt{1 + \frac{y^2}{x^2}} \right| = \ln |Cx|$$

$$\therefore \quad \frac{y}{x} + \frac{\sqrt{x^2 + y^2}}{x} = Cx$$

i.e. $\quad y + \sqrt{x^2 + y^2} = Cx^2$

(c) $\; y = e^x (A \cos x + B \sin x)$

$$\frac{dy}{dx} = e^x (A \cos x + B \sin x) + e^x(-A \sin x + B \cos x)$$

$$= y + e^x (-A \sin x + B \cos x)$$

$$\therefore \quad \frac{d^2y}{dx^2} = \frac{dy}{dx} + e^x (-A \sin x + B \cos x)$$

$$+ e^x (-A \cos x - B \sin x)$$

$$\therefore \quad \frac{d^2y}{dx^2} = \frac{dy}{dx} + e^x (-A \sin x + B \cos x) - y$$

$$\frac{dy}{dx} + \frac{dy}{dx} - y - y = 2\left(\frac{dy}{dx} - y\right)$$

(d) $(1 + y^2) \dfrac{dy}{dx} + x = 2e^{\tan^{-1} y}$

$$\Rightarrow \quad \frac{dx}{dy} + \frac{1}{1 + y^2} x = \frac{e^{\tan^{-1} y}}{1 + y^2}$$

$$\text{IF} = e^{\int \frac{1}{1 + y^2}} = e^{\tan^{-1} y}$$

$$\Rightarrow \quad xe^{\tan^{-1} y} = 2 \int e^{\tan^{-1} y} \cdot \frac{e^{\tan^{1} y}}{1 + y^2}\, dy$$

$$\Rightarrow \quad xe^{\tan^{-1} y} = e^{2 \tan^{-1} y} + k$$

30. $\dfrac{dy}{dx} = 3(A + Bx)\, e^{3x} = Be^{3x}$

$$\Rightarrow \quad \frac{dy}{dx} + my = (3 + m)(A + Bx)\, e^{3x} + Be^{3x}$$

$$\Rightarrow \quad \frac{d^2y}{dx^2} + m \frac{dy}{dx} + ny = (9 + 3m + n)(A + Bx)\, e^{3x}$$

$$+ B(6 + m)\, e^{3x} = 0$$

$$\Rightarrow \quad 3m + n + 9 = 0 \text{ and } m + 6 = 0$$

$$\Rightarrow \quad m = -6 \text{ and } n = 9$$

31. Equation of tangent

$$Y - y = m(X - x)$$

Put $X = 0$, $\quad Y = y - mx$

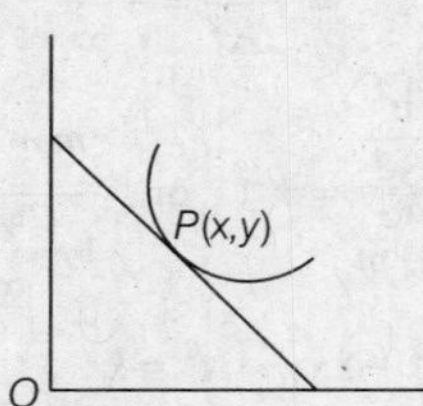

Since, initial ordinate is

$$y - mx = x - 1$$

$$\Rightarrow \quad mx - y = 1 - x$$

$\dfrac{dy}{dx} - \dfrac{1}{x} y = \dfrac{1 - x}{x}$ which is a linear differential equation.

Hence, Statement I is correct and its degree is 1.

⇒ Statement II is also correct. Since, every 1st degree differential equation need not be linear, hence Statement II is not the correct explanation of Statement I.

32. **Statement I** The order of differential equation is 2.

∴ Statement I is false.

33. Integral curves are $y = cx - x^2$

The differential equation does not represent all the parabolas passing through origin but it represents all parabolas through origin with axis of symmetry parallel to y-axis and coefficient of x^2 as −1, hence Statement I is false.

Statement II is universally true.

34. $\quad \dfrac{ydx - xdy}{y^2} \cdot \cot \dfrac{x}{y} = x\, dx$

or $\quad \int \cot \dfrac{x}{y} \cdot d\left(\dfrac{x}{y}\right) = \int x\, dx$

or $\int \cot t \, dx = nx + C$

$$\ln(\sin t) = nx + C; \sin\frac{x}{y} = Ce^{nx}$$

35. $y = c_1 \cos 2x + c_2 \sin^2 x + c_3 \cos^2 x + c_4 e^{2x} + c_5$

$$e^{2x+c_6} = c_1 \cos 2x + c_2\left[\frac{1-\cos 2x}{2}\right] + c_3\left[\frac{\cos 2x + 1}{2}\right] + c_4 e^{2x} + c_5 e^{2x} \cdot e^{c_6}$$

$$= \left(c_1 - \frac{c_2}{2} + \frac{c_3}{2}\right)\cos 2x + \left(\frac{c_2}{2} + \frac{c_3}{2}\right) + (c_4 + c'_5)\, e^{2x}$$

$$= \lambda_1 \cos 2x + \lambda_2 e^{2x} + \lambda_3$$

$\Rightarrow$ Total number of independent parameters in the given general solution is 3.

36. The given differential equation is

$$\frac{d\left(\frac{dy}{dx}\right)}{\frac{dy}{dx}} = \frac{2x}{x^2+1}\, dx$$

$$\Rightarrow \quad \ln\left(\frac{dy}{dx}\right) = \ln(x^2+1) + \ln C, C > 0$$

$$\Rightarrow \quad \frac{dy}{dx} = C(x^2+1)$$

$$\Rightarrow \quad y = C\left(\frac{x^3}{3} + x\right) + C', C' \in R$$

Obviously $y \to \infty$, as $x \to \infty$; as $C > 0$

37. $(x-h)^2 = 4b(y-k)$ here b is constant and h, k are parameters.

38. The general equation of all non-vertical lines in a plane is $ax + by = 1$, where $b \neq 0$.

Now, $\quad ax + by = 1$

$$\Rightarrow \quad a + b\frac{dy}{dx} = 0 \quad \text{(differentiating w.r.t. } x)$$

$$\Rightarrow \quad b\frac{d^2y}{dx^2} = 0 \quad \text{(differentiating w.r.t. } x)$$

$$\Rightarrow \quad \frac{d^2y}{dx^2} = 0 \quad (\text{as } b \neq 0)$$

Hence, the differential equation is $\frac{d^2y}{dx^2} = 0$.

39. The equation $ax^2 + 2hxy + by^2 = 1$ represents the family of all conics whose centre lies at the origin for different values of a, h, b.

$\therefore$ Order is 3.

Thus, Statement I is false and Statement II is true.

Hence, option (d) is the correct answer.

40. $y = a \sin x + b \cos x$

$$\frac{dy}{dx} = a\cos x - b\sin x$$

$$\Rightarrow \quad \frac{d^2y}{dx^2} = -a\cos x - b\sin x = -y$$

$$\Rightarrow \quad \frac{d^2y}{dx^2} + y = 0$$

But Statement II is not the correct explanation of the Statement I.

41. $f(0) = 2$

$$f(x) = (e^x + e^{-x})\cos x - 2x - \left[x\int_0^x f'(t)\,dt - \int_0^x \underbrace{t}_{\text{I}}\,\underbrace{f'(t)}_{\text{II}}\,dt\right]$$

$$f(x) = (e^x + e^{-x})\cos x - 2x - [x(f(x) - f(0)) - \{t \cdot f(t)|_0^x - \int_0^x f(t)dt\}]$$

$$f(x) = (e^x + e^{-x})\cos x - 2x - xf(x) + 2x + \left[x\, f(x) - \int_0^x f(t)\,dt\right]$$

$$f(x) = (e^x + e^{-x})\cos x - \int_0^x f(t)\,dt \quad \text{...(i)}$$

On differentiating Eq. (i)

$$f'(x) + f(x) = \cos x\,(e^x - e^{-x}) - (e^x + e^{-x})\sin x \quad \text{...(ii)}$$

Hence, $\frac{dy}{dx} + y = e^x(\cos x - \sin x) - e^x(\cos x + \sin x)$

42. $f'(0) + f(0) = 0 - 2 \cdot 0 = 0$

43. IF of Eq. (i) is e^x

$$y \cdot e^x = \int e^{2x}(\cos x - \sin x)\,dx - \int(\cos x + \sin x)\,dx$$

$$y \cdot e^x = \int e^{2x}(\cos x - \sin x)\,dx - (\sin x - \cos x) + C$$

Let $\quad I = \int e^{2x}(\cos x - \sin x)\,dx = e^{2x}(A\cos x + B\sin x)$

Solving, $\quad A = 3/5$ and $B = -1/5$ and $C = 2/5$

$$\therefore \quad y = e^x\left(\frac{3}{5}\cos x - \frac{1}{5}\sin x\right) - (\sin x - \cos x)\,e^{-x} + \frac{2}{5}e^{-x}$$

Solutions (Q. Nos. 44 to 46)

Integrating, $\frac{d^2y}{dx^2} = 6x - 4$,

we get $\frac{dy}{dx} = 3x^2 - 4x + A$

When $x = 1$, $\frac{dy}{dx} = 0$ so that $A = 1$.

Hence, $\quad \frac{dy}{dx} = 3x^2 - 4x + 1 \quad$ ...(i)

Integrating, we get $y = x^3 - 2x^2 + x + B$.

When $x = 1$, $y = 5$, so that $B = 5$

Thus, we have $y = x^3 - 2x^2 + x + 5$

From Eq. (i), we get the critical points $x = \frac{1}{3}$, $x = 1$

At the critical point $x = \frac{1}{3}$, $\frac{d^2y}{dx^2}$ is negative.

Therefore, at $x = \frac{1}{3}$, y has a local maximum.

At $x = 1$, $\frac{d^2y}{dx^2}$ is positive. Therefore, at $x = 1$, y has a local minimum.

Also, $\quad f(1) = 5$, $f\left(\frac{1}{3}\right) = \frac{157}{27}$, $f(0) = 5$, $f(2) = 7$

Hence, the global maximum value = 7.

and the global minimum value = 5.

47. $xdy - ydx = \sqrt{x^2 - y^2}\, dx$

$\Rightarrow \quad d\left(\frac{y}{x}\right) = \frac{\sqrt{1-(y/x)^2}}{x}\, dx \Rightarrow \int \frac{d(y/x)}{\sqrt{1-(y/x)^2}} = \int \frac{dx}{x}$

$\Rightarrow \sin^{-1}\frac{y}{x} = \ln x = \ln C$ or $Cx = e^{\sin^{-1} y/x}$

48. $$(xy^4 + y)\, dx - x\, dy = 0$$

$$\Rightarrow \quad xy^4 dx + y\, dx - x\, dy = 0$$

$$\Rightarrow \quad \int x^3\, dx - \int \left(\frac{x}{y}\right)^2 d\left(\frac{x}{y}\right) = 0$$

$$\Rightarrow \quad \frac{x^4}{4} + \frac{1}{3}\left(\frac{x}{y}\right)^3 = C$$

49. $2x\cos y\, dx - x^2 \sin y\, dy + y^2 \cos x\, dx + 2y\sin x\, dy = 0$

$$\Rightarrow \quad \int d(x^2 \cos y) + \int d(y^2 \sin x) = 0$$

$$\Rightarrow \quad x^2 \cos y + y^2 \sin x = C$$

50. $$\frac{dx}{x} = \frac{ydy}{1+y^2}$$

$$\Rightarrow \quad \ln x = \frac{1}{2}\cdot \ln(1+y^2) + C$$

From the given condition, $C = 0$

$$\therefore \quad x^2 - y^2 = 1$$

51. $$\frac{dy}{dx} + \frac{1+y^2}{\sqrt{1-x^2}} = 0$$

$$\Rightarrow \quad \frac{dy}{1+y^2} + \frac{dx}{\sqrt{1-x^2}} = 0$$

$$\Rightarrow \quad \tan^{-1} y + \sin^{-1} x = C$$

52. $\frac{dy}{dx} = (1+x)\cdot(1+y)$ gives $y = e^{\frac{(1+x)^2}{2}} - 1$

53. Tangent at point $P(x,y)$, is $y - y = f'(x)(x - x)$

$Q:(0, y - x f'(x))$

Then, $\quad PQ = OQ$

$\Rightarrow x^2 + x^2(f'(x))^2 = y^2 + x^2(f'(x))^2 - 2xy(f'(x))$

$\Rightarrow x^2 = y^2 - 2xy \cdot f'(x)$

or $dy/dx = \frac{y^2 - x^2}{2xy}$, put $y = tx$

$$\Rightarrow \quad t + x\frac{dt}{dx} = \frac{dy}{dx}$$

$$\therefore \quad t + x\frac{dt}{dx} = \frac{t^2 - 1}{2t}$$

$$\Rightarrow \quad x\frac{dt}{dx} = \frac{-(1+t^2)}{2t} \Rightarrow \int \frac{2t}{1+t^2}dt = -\int \frac{dx}{x}$$

$$\Rightarrow \quad \frac{c}{x} = 1 + \frac{y^2}{x^2} \Rightarrow x^2 + y^2 - cx = 0$$

$$\therefore \quad C_1 : x^2 + y^2 - x = 0$$

$$C_2 : x^2 + y^2 + x = 0$$

C_1 and C_2 touch externally $\Rightarrow$ number of common tangents = 3.

54. $C_3 : (x-5)^2 + y^2 = 5^2$

Tangent, $bx + ay - ab = 0$, length of perpendicular to tangent from centre = radius.

$$\Rightarrow \quad |5b - ab| = 5\sqrt{a^2 + b^2}$$

$$\Rightarrow \quad a^2b^2 - 10ab^2 = 25a^2$$

$$\Rightarrow \quad ab^2 - 10b^2 = 25a$$

55. $C_1 : x^2 + y^2 - 2x = 0$

$C_2 : x^2 + y^2 - Cx = 0$

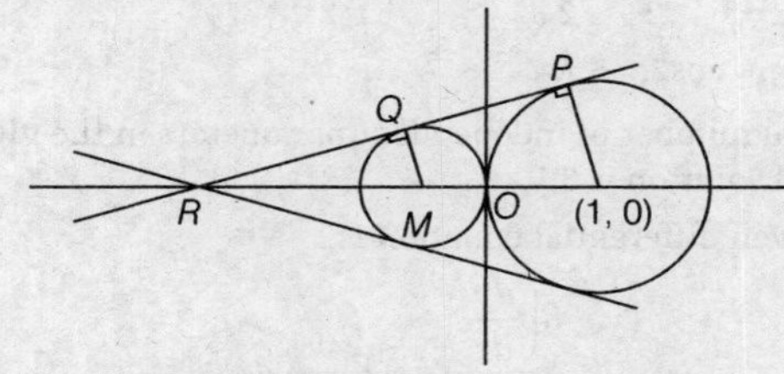

$$\angle QRM = 30°$$

$$\sin 30° = \frac{1}{1 + OR} \Rightarrow OR = 1$$

$$\sin 30° = \frac{QM}{1 - QM} \Rightarrow QM = 1/3$$

radius of $C_2 = 1/3 \Rightarrow C = -2/3, C_2 : x^2 + y^2 + \frac{2}{3}x = 0$

Point $(-1/3, 1/3)$ will satisfy C_2.

56. (A) Let $x = r\cos\theta$, $y = r\sin\theta$

$$\therefore \quad x^2 + y^2 = r^2(\sin^2\theta + \cos^2\theta) = r^2 \quad \text{...(i)}$$

and $$\tan\theta = \frac{y}{x} \quad \text{...(ii)}$$

$$\therefore \quad d(x^2 + y^2) = d(r^2)$$

From Eq. (i), $x\, dx + y\, dy = rdr$ ...(iii)

From Eq. (ii),

$$d\left(\frac{y}{x}\right) = d(\tan\theta)$$

$$\Rightarrow \quad \frac{xdy - ydx}{x^2} = \sec^2\theta\, d\theta$$

$$\therefore \quad x\, dy - y\, dx = x^2 \sec^2\theta\, d\theta$$

$$= r^2\cos^2\theta \sec^2\theta\, d\theta = r^2 d\theta \quad \text{...(iv)}$$

From Eqs. (iii) and (iv)

$$\frac{rdr}{r^2 d\theta} = \sqrt{\frac{a^2 - r^2}{r^2}}$$

or $$\frac{dr}{\sqrt{a^2 - r^2}} = d\theta$$

$$\sin^{-1}\left(\frac{r}{a}\right) = \theta + C$$

$$\Rightarrow \quad r = a\sin(\theta + C)$$

$$\Rightarrow \quad \sqrt{x^2 + y^2} = a\sin\left\{C + \tan^{-1}\left(\frac{y}{x}\right)\right\}$$

(B) $\frac{dy}{dx} - \sec^2 x \tan 2xy = \cos^2 x$

$$\text{IF} = e^{\int \tan 2x \sec^2 x\, dx} = e^{\int \frac{2\tan x}{\tan^2 x - 1} \times \sec^2 x\, dx}$$

$$= e^{\int \frac{dt}{t}}, \text{ where } t = \tan^2 x - 1$$

$$= e^{\ln|t|} = |t| = |\tan^2 x - 1|$$

Given that, $|x| < \frac{\pi}{4}$

$\therefore \quad \tan^2 x < 1$

$\therefore \quad \text{IF} = 1 - \tan^2 x$

Solution is $y(1 - \tan^2 x) = \int \cos^2 x (1 - \tan^2 x)\, dx$

$$= \int (\cos^2 x - \sin^2 x)\, dx$$

$$= \int \cos 2x\, dx = \frac{\sin 2x}{2} + C$$

when $x = \frac{\pi}{6}, y = \frac{3\sqrt{3}}{8}$

$\therefore \quad \frac{3\sqrt{3}}{8}\left(1 - \frac{1}{3}\right) = \frac{1}{2} \times \frac{\sqrt{3}}{2} + C$

$\therefore \quad C = 0 \Rightarrow y = \frac{\sin 2x}{2(1 - \tan^2 x)}$

(C) $\quad x^2 + y^2 - 2cx = 0 \quad$ ...(i)

$\therefore \quad 2x + 2y\frac{dy}{dx} - 2c = 0$

or $\quad C = x + \frac{ydy}{dx} \quad$ ...(ii)

From Eqs. (i) and (ii), $x^2 + y^2 - 2\left(x + \frac{ydy}{dx}\right)x = 0$

or $-x^2 + y^2 - 2xy\frac{dy}{dx} = 0$ is the differential equation representing the given family of circles. To find the orthogonal trajectories.

$$y^2 - x^2 = -2xy\frac{dx}{dy}$$

or $\quad y^2\, dy = x^2\, dy - 2xy\, dx$

or $\quad -dy = \frac{yd(x^2) - x^2\, dy}{y^2}$

or $\quad -dy = d\left(\frac{x^2}{y}\right)$

or $\quad -y = \frac{x^2}{y} + C$

$\Rightarrow \quad x^2 + y^2 + Cy = 0$

$\Rightarrow$ Orthogonal trajectory.

(D) Differentiating the equation w.r.t. x, we get

$$xy(x) + 1\int_0^x y(t)\, dt = (x+1)\, xy(x) + 1\int_0^x ty(t)\, dt$$

Again, differentiating, w.r.t. x, we get

$$y(x) = x^2 y'(x) + 2xy(x) + xy(x)$$

or $\quad (1 - 3x)\, y(x) = \frac{x^2 dy(x)}{dx}$

or $\quad \frac{(1-3x)\, dx}{x^2} = \frac{dy(x)}{y(x)}$ or $y = \frac{C}{x^3} e^{-1/x}$

57. (A) $r = 5$ cm, $\delta r = 0.06$, $A = \pi r^2$

$$\delta A = 2\pi r\, \delta r = 10\pi \times 0.06 = 0.6\pi$$

(B) $v = x^3$

$$\delta v = 3x^2\, \delta x$$

$$\frac{\delta v}{v} \times 100 = 3\frac{\delta x}{x} \times 100 = 3 \times 1 = 3$$

(C) $(x - 2)\frac{dx}{dt} = 2\frac{dx}{dt} \Rightarrow x = 4$

(D) $\quad A = \frac{\sqrt{3}}{4}x^2$

$$\frac{dA}{dt} = \frac{\sqrt{3}}{2}x\frac{dx}{dt} = \frac{\sqrt{3}}{2}\cdot 15 \cdot \frac{1}{10} = \frac{3\sqrt{3}}{4}$$

58. (A) $\frac{dy}{dx} = e^x(A\cos x + B\sin x) + e^x(-A\sin x + B\cos x)$

$$= y + e^x(-A\sin x + B\cos x)$$

$\therefore \quad \frac{d^2y}{dx^2} = \frac{dy}{dx} + e^x(-A\sin x + B\cos x) + e^x(-A\cos x - B\sin x)$

$$= \frac{dy}{dx} + \left(\frac{dy}{dx} - y\right) - y = 2\left(\frac{dy}{dx} - y\right)$$

So, degree = 1 and order = 2

(B) The equation of the family is $y^2 = 4a(x - b)$ where a, b are arbitrary constants.

$\therefore \quad 2y\frac{dy}{dx} = 4a$ or $\left(\frac{dy}{dx}\right)^2 + y\frac{d^2y}{dx^2} = 0$

So, degree = 1 and order = 2

(C) The equation of the family is

$$(x - c)^2 + y^2 = c^2$$

or $\quad x^2 + y^2 - 2cx = 0$ or $\frac{x^2 + y^2}{x} = 2c$

$\Rightarrow \quad \frac{\left(2x + 2y\frac{dy}{dx}\right)x - (x^2 + y^2)\cdot 1}{x^2} = 0$

So, degree = 1 and order = 1

(D) The equation of the family is $\frac{x^2}{a^2 + \lambda} + \frac{y^2}{b^2 + \lambda} = 1$ because they have the same foci $(\pm\sqrt{a^2 - b^2}, 0)$.

On differentiating, $\frac{2x}{d^2 + \lambda} + \frac{2y}{b^2 + \lambda}\cdot\frac{dy}{dx} = 0$

or $\quad \frac{x}{a^2 + \lambda} + \frac{yp}{b^2 + \lambda} = 0 \quad \left(\text{Let } p = \frac{dy}{dx}\right)$

or $\quad x(b^2 + \lambda) + yp(a^2 + \lambda) = 0$

$$\Rightarrow \qquad \lambda = \frac{-b^2x - a^2yp}{x + yp}$$

$\therefore$ The differential equation is

$$\frac{x^2}{a^2 + \dfrac{-b^2x - a^2yp}{x + yp}} + \frac{y^2}{b^2 + \dfrac{-b^2x - a^2yp}{x + yp}} = 1$$

or $$\frac{x(x + yp)}{a^2 - b^2} + \frac{y(x + yp)}{(b^2 - a^2)p} = 1$$

So, order = 1 and degree = 2

59. $2x^2y\,dx - 2y^4\,dx + 2x^3dy + 3xy^3\,dy = 0$

Dividing throughout by x^3y, we get

$$2\frac{dx}{x} - \frac{2y^3}{x^3}dx + 2\cdot\frac{dy}{y} + \frac{3y^2}{x^2}dy = 0$$

$$\Rightarrow \qquad 2\frac{dx}{x} + 2\frac{dy}{y} + \frac{3y^2x^4\,dy - 2y^3x^3dx}{x^6} = 0$$

$$\Rightarrow \qquad 2\frac{dx}{x} + 2\frac{dy}{y} + \frac{3y^2x^2\,dy - 2y^3x\,dx}{x^4} = 0$$

$$\Rightarrow \qquad 2d(\ln x) + 2d(\ln y) + d\left(\frac{y^3}{x^2}\right) = 0$$

$$\Rightarrow \qquad 2\ln|x| + 2\ln|y| + \frac{y^3}{x^2} = C$$

when $x = 1, y = 1$. So, $C = 1$

60. Let the salt content at time 't' be u lb, so that its rate of change is du/dt.

$$= 2\text{ gal} \times 2\text{ lb} = 4\text{ lb / min}$$

If c be the concentration of the brine at time t, the rate at which the salt content decreases due to the out flow

$$= 2\text{ gal} \times c\text{ lb / min}$$
$$= 2c\text{ lb / min}$$

$$\therefore \qquad \frac{du}{dt} = 4 - 2c \qquad \text{...(i)}$$

Also, since there is no increase in the volume of the liquid, the concentrations $c = \dfrac{u}{50}$

$\therefore$ Eq. (i) becomes $\dfrac{du}{dt} = 4 - \dfrac{2u}{50}$

Separating the variables and integrating, we have

$$\int dt = 25\int\frac{du}{100 - u}$$

or $$t = -25\ln(100 - u) + K \qquad \text{...(ii)}$$

Initially when $t = 0, u = 0$

$$0 = -25\ln 100 + K \qquad \text{...(iii)}$$

Eliminating 'K' from Eqs. (ii) and (iii), we get

$$t = 25\ln\left(\frac{100}{100 - u}\right).$$

Taking $t = t_1$ when $u = 40$ and $t = t_2$ when $u = 80$, we have

$$t_1 = 25\ln\left(\frac{100}{60}\right) \text{ and } t_2 = 25\ln\left(\frac{100}{20}\right)$$

$\therefore$ The required time $(t_2 - t_1) = 25\left(\ln 5 - \ln\dfrac{5}{3}\right) = 25\ln 3$

$$= 25 \times 1.0986 = 26\text{ min }28\text{ s}$$
$$= 1648\text{ s} = 206 \times 8 = 206 \times \lambda$$

$$\therefore \qquad \lambda = 8$$

61. $f(x + f(y) + xf(y)) = y + f(x) + yf(x)$ ...(i)

Differentiating w.r.t. x and y is constant

$$f'(x + f(y) + xf(y))(1 + f(y)) = f'(x) + yf'(x) \qquad \text{...(ii)}$$

From Eq. (i) again differentiating w.r.t. y as x is constant

$$f'(x + f(y) + xf(y))(1 + x)f'(y) = 1 + f(x) \qquad \text{...(iii)}$$

From Eqs. (ii) and (iii)

$$\frac{1 + f(y)}{(1 + x)f'(y)} = \frac{(1 + y)f'(x)}{1 + f(x)}$$

$$\frac{(1 + y)f'(y)}{1 + f(y)} = \frac{1 + f(x)}{(1 + x)f'(x)} = \lambda$$

$$\therefore \qquad f'(y) = \frac{1 + f(y)}{1 + y}\lambda \text{ and } f'(x) = \frac{1 + f(x)}{\lambda(1 + x)}$$

$$\therefore \qquad \lambda = \frac{1}{\lambda} \Rightarrow \lambda = \pm 1 \therefore \frac{f'(x)}{1 + f(x)} = \pm\frac{1}{1 + x}$$

Integrating both the sides $f(x) = C(1 + x)^{\pm 1} - 1$

From Eq. (i) put $x = y = 0$

$$f(f(0)) = f(0)$$

From Eq. (ii), $f(0) = C - 1$

So, $$f(C - 1) = C - 1$$

$$\therefore \qquad C = 0, 1 \qquad \text{(taking +ve sign)}$$

So, $f(x) = -1$ and $f(x) = (1 + x) - 1 = x$ and $C = 1$

$$\therefore \qquad f(x) = (1 + x)^{-1} - 1 = \frac{-x}{1 + x}$$

$$1 + f(x) = \frac{1}{1 + x}$$

$$\therefore \qquad 1 + f(2009) = \frac{1}{2010} \quad \therefore (2010)(1 + f(2009)) = 1$$

62. $$\phi'(x) + 2\phi(x) \le 1$$

$$e^{2x}\phi'(x) + 2\phi(x)e^{2x} \le e^{2x}$$

$$\frac{d}{dx}\left(e^{2x}\phi(x) - \frac{1}{2}e^{2x}\right) \le 0$$

$\therefore$ $\left(e^{2x}\phi(x) - \dfrac{1}{2}\right)$ is a non-increasing function of x.

$\Rightarrow \phi(x) - \dfrac{1}{2}$ is a non-increasing function of x.

$\therefore$ $2\phi(x)$ is always less than or equal to 1.

63. $\dfrac{1}{2}(1 + x)^{-1/2} - \dfrac{a}{2}(1 + y)^{-1/2}\dfrac{dy}{dx} = 0$

$$\Rightarrow \qquad \frac{1}{\sqrt{1 + x}} = \frac{a}{\sqrt{1 + y}}\cdot\frac{dy}{dx} \Rightarrow a = \frac{\sqrt{1 + y}}{\sqrt{1 + x}}\cdot\frac{1}{dy/dx}$$

Putting this value in the given equation,

$$\frac{dy}{dx}\sqrt{1 + x} - \frac{1 + y}{\sqrt{1 + x}} = \frac{dy}{dx}$$

$$\Rightarrow \quad (1+x)\frac{dy}{dx} = 1 + y + \sqrt{1+x}\,\frac{dy}{dx}$$

$$\Rightarrow (1 + x - \sqrt{1+x})\frac{dy}{dx} = 1 + y$$

$\therefore$ Degree of the given equation is 1.

64. Here, $2f^5(x)\cdot f'(x)\cdot|1+(f'(x))^2| = f''(x)$

$$\Rightarrow \quad f^4(x)d(f^2(x)) = \frac{f''(x)}{1+(f'(x))^2}$$

$$\Rightarrow \quad |f^4(x)d(f^2(x))| = \int d(\tan^{-1}(f'(x)))$$

$$\Rightarrow \frac{f^6(x)}{3} + C = \tan^{-1}(f'(x)), \text{ as } f(0) = f'(0) = 0 \Rightarrow c = 0$$

$$\Rightarrow \quad \frac{f^6(x)}{3} = \tan^{-1}(f'(x))$$

$$\Rightarrow \quad -\frac{\pi}{2} < \frac{f^6(x)}{3} < \frac{\pi}{2}$$

$$\therefore \quad -\left(\frac{3\pi}{2}\right)^{1/6} < f(x) < \left(\frac{3\pi}{2}\right)^{1/6}$$

$\Rightarrow$ Number of integers between k_1 and k_2 are 3.

65. Put, $dy / dx = t$

$\therefore \quad dt / dx - t + e^{2x} = 0$, I.F. $= e^{\int -dx = e^{-x}}$

$\therefore \quad$ Solution is, $t\cdot e^{-x} = \int -e^{2x}\cdot e^{-x}\,dx + C$

$\Rightarrow te^{-x} = -e^x + C\; y'(0) = 1 \Rightarrow C = 2$

$\therefore \quad dy / dx = \dfrac{2-e^x}{e-x} \int dy = \int (2e^x - e^{2x})dx$

$\Rightarrow y = 2^{ex} - \dfrac{e^{2x}}{2} + C^1, y(0) = 2 \Rightarrow C^1 = 1/2$

$\therefore \quad y(x) = 2e^x - \dfrac{e^{2x}}{2} + \dfrac{1}{2} \Rightarrow \quad y(x) \le \dfrac{5}{2}$ for $x = \log 2$

$\therefore \quad [2x] = [2\log 2] = [\log 4] = 1$

66. Let in time dt the decrease in water level in the tank is dh, then amount of water flown out in time $dt = \pi r^2\cdot dh$

Now, through the hole the amount of water flown = (Volume of cylinder of cross sectional area 'a' and length vdt).

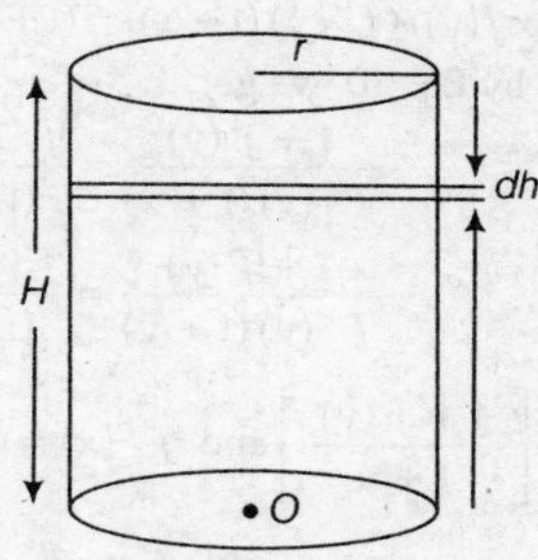

$$= a\cdot v\cdot dt = a\,\mu\,\sqrt{2gh}\,dt$$

Hence, $\quad \mu a\sqrt{2gh}\,dt = -\pi r^2 dh$

$$\Rightarrow \quad dt = \frac{-\pi r^2}{\mu a\sqrt{2g}}\cdot h^{-1/2}\,dh$$

Now, when $t = 0$, $h = H$ and when $t = t$, $h = 0$

Thus, $\quad \displaystyle\int_0^t dt = \frac{-\pi r^2}{\mu a\sqrt{2g}}\int_H^0 h^{-1/2}\,dh$

$$\Rightarrow \quad t = \frac{-\pi r^2}{\mu a\sqrt{2g}}\cdot 2(\sqrt{h})_H^0$$

$$\Rightarrow \quad t = \frac{\pi r^2}{\mu a}\cdot\sqrt{\frac{2H}{g}}$$

67. Let at time t the depth of water is h; the radius of water surface is r.

Then, $\quad r^2 = R^2 - (R-h)^2$

$$\Rightarrow \quad r^2 = 2Rh - h^2$$

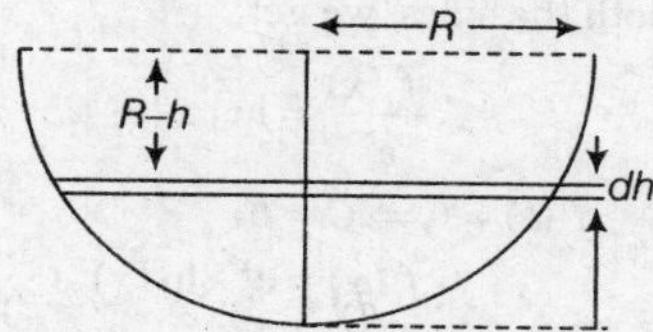

Now, if in time dt the decrease in water level is dh, then

$$-\pi r^2\,dh = 0.6\sqrt{2gh}\cdot a\,dt$$

(a is cross-sectional area of the outlet)

$$\Rightarrow \quad \frac{-\pi}{(0.6)\,a\sqrt{2g}}(2Rh - h^2)\frac{dh}{\sqrt{h}} = dt$$

$$\Rightarrow \quad \frac{\pi}{(0.6)\,a\sqrt{2g}}\int_R^0 (h^{3/2} - 2R\,h^{1/2})\,dh = \int_0^t dt$$

$$\Rightarrow \quad \frac{\pi}{(0.6)\,a\sqrt{2g}}\left[\frac{2}{5}h^{5/2} - \frac{4}{3}Rh^{3/2}\right]_R^0 = t$$

$$\Rightarrow \quad t = \frac{\pi}{(0.6)\,a\sqrt{2g}}\left[0 - R^{5/2}\left(\frac{2}{5} - \frac{4}{3}\right)\right] = \frac{7\pi\times 10^5}{135\sqrt{g}}$$

68. We have been given,

$f(xy) = e^{xy-x-y}\{e^y f(x) + e^x f(y)\},\ \forall\ x, y \in R^+$ ...(i)

Replacing $x = 1$, $y = 1$ in Eq. (i), we get

$$f(1) = e^{1-1-1}\{e\,f(1) + e\,f(1)\} \Rightarrow f(1) = 0$$

Now, $\quad f'(x) = \displaystyle\lim_{h\to 0}\frac{f(x+h) - f(x)}{h}$

$$= \lim_{h\to 0}\frac{f\left(x\left(1+\frac{h}{x}\right)\right) - f(x)}{h}$$

$$= \lim_{h\to 0}\frac{e^{x+h-x-1-\frac{h}{x}}(e^{1+h/x}\cdot f(x) + e^x\cdot f(1+h/x)) - f(x)}{h}$$

$$= \lim_{h\to 0}\frac{e^h f(x) + e^{h-1-\frac{h}{x}+x}\cdot f\left(1+\frac{h}{x}\right) - f(x)}{h}$$

$$= \lim_{h\to 0}\frac{f(x)(e^h - 1) + e^{h-1-\frac{h}{x}+x}\cdot\left(f\left(1+\frac{h}{x}\right) - f(1)\right)}{h}$$

$$= \lim_{h\to 0}\frac{f(x)(e^h-1)}{h} + \lim_{h\to 0}\frac{e^{h-1-\frac{h}{x}+x}\left(f\left(1+\frac{h}{x}\right)-f(1)\right)}{\frac{h}{x}\cdot x}$$

$$= f(x) + \frac{e^{x-1}\cdot f'(1)}{x} = f(x) + \frac{e^x}{x}$$

$$\Rightarrow \quad f'(x) - f(x) = \frac{e^x}{x}$$

$$\Rightarrow \quad \frac{e^x f'(x) - f(x)e^x}{e^{2x}} = \frac{1}{x}$$

$$\Rightarrow \quad \frac{d}{dx}\left(\frac{f(x)}{e^x}\right) = \frac{1}{x}$$

Integrating both the sides, we get

$$\frac{f(x)}{e^x} = \ln|x| + C$$

Since, $f(1) = 0 \Rightarrow C = 0$

Thus, $f(x) = e^x \cdot \ln(x)$

69. Let $P(x, f(x))$ be a point lying on the curve in first quadrant. Equation of normal and tangent at P are

$$(Y - f(x)) = -\frac{1}{f'(x)}(X - x) \text{ and}$$

$(Y - f(x)) = f'(x)(X - x)$ respectively.

$$\Rightarrow A \equiv \left(x - \frac{f(x)}{f'(x)}, 0\right), B \equiv (x + f(x) f'(x), 0)$$

Since, the mid-point of segment AB is origin.

$$\Rightarrow \quad 2x - \frac{f(x)}{f'(x)} + f(x)\cdot f'(x) = 0$$

$$\Rightarrow \quad f(x)(f'(x))^2 + 2x f'(x) - f(x) = 0$$

$$\Rightarrow \quad f'(x) = \frac{-2x \pm \sqrt{4x^2 + 4f^2(x)}}{2f(x)} = \frac{-x + \sqrt{x^2 + f^2(x)}}{f(x)}$$

Negative sign been neglected as $f'(x) > 0$

Thus, we have, $x + f(x)\cdot f'(x) = \sqrt{x^2 + f^2(x)}$

$$\Rightarrow \quad \frac{d}{2dx}(x^2 + f^2(x)) = \sqrt{x^2 + f^2(x)}$$

$$\Rightarrow \quad \frac{d(x^2 + f^2(x))}{2\sqrt{x^2 + f^2(x)}} = dx$$

Integrating both the sides, we get $\sqrt{x^2 + f^2(x)} = x + \lambda$

It passes through $(1, \sqrt{3})$.

Hence, $\lambda + 1 = 2 \Rightarrow \lambda = 1$

$\therefore$ Curve is $x^2 + f^2(x) = (x+1)^2$ or $y^2 = 1 + 2x$

70. We have been given,

$$\frac{dy_1}{dx} + Py_1 = Q, \frac{dy_2}{dx} + Py_2 = Q$$

Now, $y_2 = y_1 z \Rightarrow \frac{dy_2}{dx} = y_1\frac{dz}{dx} + z\frac{dy_1}{dx}$

$$\Rightarrow y_1\frac{dz}{dx} + z\frac{dy_1}{dx} + Py_1 z = Q$$

$$\Rightarrow y_1\cdot\frac{dz}{dx} + z\left(\frac{dy_1}{dx} + py_1\right) = Q$$

$$\Rightarrow \quad y_1\cdot\frac{dz}{dx} + zQ = Q$$

$$\Rightarrow \quad y_1\frac{dz}{dx} = Q(1 - z)$$

$$\Rightarrow \quad \frac{dz}{1-z} = \int\frac{Q}{y_1}dx$$

$\Rightarrow \ln|z - 1| = -\int\frac{Q}{y_1}dx + \lambda$, '$\lambda$' being constant of integration

$$\Rightarrow \quad z = 1 + ce^{\int -\frac{Q}{y_1}dx}$$

71. We have, $f(x) = x + x^2\int_0^1 z f(z)\,dz + x\int_0^1 z^2 f(z)\,dz$

$$f(x) = x + x^2\lambda_1 + x\lambda_2 \quad \text{(say)}$$

Now, $\lambda_1 = \int_0^1 z f(z)\,dz = \int_0^1 ((1+\lambda_2)z + z^2\lambda_1)z\,dz$

$$= \frac{1+\lambda_2}{3} + \frac{\lambda_1}{4}$$

$$\Rightarrow \quad 9\lambda_1 - 4\lambda_2 = 4 \quad \text{...(i)}$$

Also, $\lambda_2 = \int_0^1 z^2 f(z)\,dz$

$$= \int_0^1 ((1+\lambda_2)z^3 + z^4\lambda_1)\,dz$$

$$= \frac{(1+\lambda_2)}{4} + \frac{\lambda_1}{5}$$

$$\Rightarrow \quad 15\lambda_2 - 4\lambda_1 = 5 \quad \text{...(ii)}$$

From Eqs. (i) and (ii),

$$\lambda_1 = \frac{80}{119} \text{ and } \lambda_2 = \frac{61}{119}$$

$$\Rightarrow \quad f(x) = x + \frac{80}{119}x^2 + \frac{61}{119}x = \frac{20x}{119}(4 + 9x)$$

72. $f(x + f(y) + x f(y)) = y + f(x) + y f(x)$

Keep y constant and differentiating the expression w.r.t. 'x', we get

$$f'(x + f(y) + x(y))(1 + f(y)) = f'(x)(1 + y) \quad \text{...(i)}$$

Similarly, differentiate the expression w.r.t. 'y' and keep x constant, we get

$$f'(x + f(y) + x f(y))(f'(y)(1 + x)) = (1 + f(x)) \quad \text{...(ii)}$$

Dividing Eq. (i) by Eq. (ii), we get

$$\frac{1 + f(y)}{f'(y)(1+x)} = \frac{f'(x)(1+y)}{(1+f(x))}$$

$$\Rightarrow \quad \frac{1 + f(y)}{f'(y)(1+y)} = \frac{f'(x)(1+x)}{(1+f(x))} = C$$

$$\Rightarrow f'(y) = \frac{1}{C}\left[\frac{1 + f(y)}{1 + y}\right] \text{ and } f'(x) = C\frac{1 + f(x)}{(1+x)}$$

$$\Rightarrow \quad C = \frac{1}{C} \Rightarrow C = \pm 1$$

$$\therefore \quad \frac{f'(x)}{1 + f(x)} = \pm\frac{1}{1+x}$$

$$\Rightarrow \quad f(x) = \lambda_1(1+x)^{\pm 1} - 1$$

Replacing $x, y \to 0$ in the Eq. (i), we get

$$f(f(0)) = f(0)$$

Now, $f(x) = \lambda_1 (1 + x)^{\pm 1} - 1 \Rightarrow f(0) = \lambda_1 - 1$

and $f(f(0)) = f(\lambda_1 - 1) = \lambda_1 \lambda_1^{\pm 1} - 1$

Since, $f(f(0)) = f(0), \lambda_1 \lambda_1^{\pm 1} - 1 = \lambda_1 - 1$

$\Rightarrow \quad \lambda_1^{1 \pm 1} = \lambda_1$

By taking +ve sign, we get $\lambda_1 = 0, 1$

$\Rightarrow \quad f(x) = -1 \quad \text{or} \quad f(x) = x$

By taking – ve sign, we get $\lambda_1 = 1$

$$\Rightarrow \quad f(x) = \frac{1}{1+x} - 1 = -\frac{x}{1+x}$$

73. Given, $(x^2 + xy + 4x + 2y + 4)\dfrac{dy}{dx} - y^2 = 0$

$$\Rightarrow \quad [(x^2 + 4x + 4) + y(x+2)]\frac{dy}{dx} - y^2 = 0$$

$$\Rightarrow \quad [(x+2)^2 + y(x+2)]\frac{dy}{dx} - y^2 = 0$$

Put $x + 2 = X$ and $y = Y$, then

$$(X^2 + XY)\frac{dY}{dX} - Y^2 = 0$$

$$\Rightarrow \quad X^2 dY + XYdY - Y^2 dX = 0$$

$$\Rightarrow \quad X^2 dY + Y(XdY - YdX) = 0$$

$$\Rightarrow \quad -\frac{dY}{Y} = \frac{XdY - YdX}{X^2}$$

$$\Rightarrow \quad -d(\log|Y|) = d\left(\frac{Y}{X}\right)$$

On integrating both sides, we get

$$-\log|Y| = \frac{Y}{X} + C, \text{ where } x + 2 = X \text{ and } y = Y$$

$$\Rightarrow \quad -\log|y| = \frac{y}{x+2} + C \quad \text{...(i)}$$

Since, it passes through the point (1, 3).

$\therefore \quad -\log 3 = 1 + C$

$\Rightarrow \quad C = -1 - \log 3 = -(\log e + \log 3)$

$\quad = -\log 3e$

$\therefore$ Eq. (i) becomes

$$\log|y| + \frac{y}{x+2} - \log(3e) = 0$$

$$\Rightarrow \quad \log\left(\frac{|y|}{3e}\right) + \frac{y}{x+2} = 0 \quad \text{...(ii)}$$

Now, to check option (a), $y = x + 2$ intersects the curve.

$$\Rightarrow \quad \log\left(\frac{|x+2|}{3e}\right) + \frac{x+2}{x+2} = 0$$

$$\Rightarrow \quad \log\left(\frac{|x+2|}{3e}\right) = -1$$

$$\Rightarrow \quad \frac{|x+2|}{3e} = e^{-1} = \frac{1}{e}$$

$\Rightarrow \quad |x+2| = 3 \quad \text{or} \quad x + 2 = \pm 3$

$\therefore \quad x = 1, -5$ (rejected), as $x > 0$ [given]

$\therefore$ $x = 1$ only one solution.

Thus, (a) is the correct answer.

To check option (c), we have $\quad y = (x+2)^2$

and $\quad \log\left(\dfrac{|y|}{3e}\right) + \dfrac{y}{x+2} = 0$

$$\Rightarrow \quad \log\left[\frac{|x+2|^2}{3e}\right] + \frac{(x+2)^2}{x+2} = 0$$

$$\Rightarrow \quad \log\left[\frac{|x+2|^2}{3e}\right] = -(x+2)$$

$$\Rightarrow \quad \frac{(x+2)^2}{3e} = e^{-(x+2)} \text{ or } (x+2)^2 \cdot e^{x+2} = 3e$$

$$\Rightarrow \quad e^{x+2} = \frac{3e}{(x+2)^2}$$

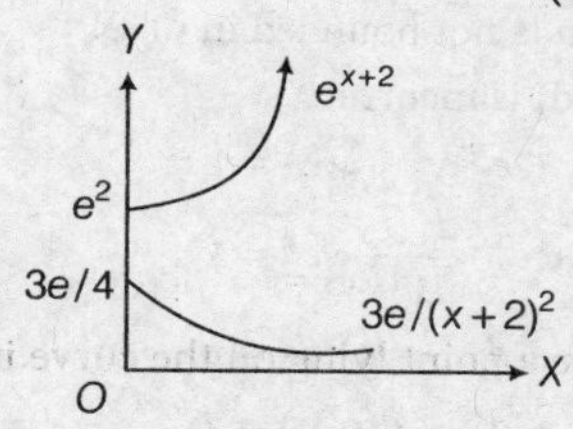

Clearly, they have no solution.

To check option (d), $y = (x+3)^2$

i.e. $\quad \log\left[\dfrac{|x+3|^2}{3e}\right] + \dfrac{(x+3)^2}{(x+2)} = 0$

To check the number of solutions.

Let $\quad g(x) = 2\log(x+3) + \dfrac{(x+3)^2}{(x+2)} - \log(3e)$

$$\therefore \quad g'(x) = \frac{2}{x+3} + \left(\frac{(x+2)\cdot 2(x+3) - (x+3)^2 \cdot 1}{(x+2)^2}\right) - 0$$

$$= \frac{2}{x+3} + \frac{(x+3)(x+1)}{(x+2)^2}$$

Clearly, when $x > 0$, then, $g'(x) > 0$

$\therefore \quad g(x)$ is increasing, when $x > 0$.

Thus, when $x > 0$, then $g(x) > g(0)$

$$g(x) > \log\left(\frac{3}{e}\right) + \frac{9}{4} > 0$$

Hence, there is no solution.

Thus, option (d) is true.

74. Here, $f'(x) = 2 - \dfrac{f(x)}{x}$

or $\quad \dfrac{dy}{dx} + \dfrac{y}{x} = 2 \quad$ [i.e. linear differential equation in y]

Integrating Factor, $\text{IF} = e^{\int \frac{1}{x} dx} = e^{\log x} = x$

$\therefore$ Required solution is $y \cdot (\text{IF}) = \int Q(\text{IF})dx + C$

$$\Rightarrow \quad y(x) = \int 2(x)\, dx + C$$

$$\Rightarrow \quad yx = x^2 + C$$

$$\therefore \quad y = x + \frac{C}{x} \quad [\because C \neq 0, \text{ as } f(1) \neq 1]$$

(a) $\lim_{x \to 0^+} f'\left(\frac{1}{x}\right) = \lim_{x \to 0^+} (1 - Cx^2) = 1$

$\therefore$ Option (a) is correct.

(b) $\lim_{x \to 0^+} x f\left(\frac{1}{x}\right) = \lim_{x \to 0^+} (1 + Cx^2) = 1$

$\therefore$ Option (b) is incorrect.

(c) $\lim_{x \to 0^+} x^2 f'(x) = \lim_{x \to 0^+} (x^2 - C) = -C \neq 0$

$\therefore$ Option (c) is incorrect.

(d) $f(x) = x + \frac{C}{x}, C \neq 0$

For $C > 0$, $\lim_{x \to 0^+} f(x) = \infty$

$\therefore$ Function is not bounded in (0, 2).

$\therefore$ Option (d) is incorrect.

75. Here, $(1 + e^x)y' + ye^x = 1$

$\Rightarrow \frac{dy}{dx} + e^x \cdot \frac{dy}{dx} + ye^x = 1$

$\Rightarrow dy + e^x dy + ye^x\, dx = dx$

$\Rightarrow dy + d(e^x y) = dx$

On integrating both sides, we get

$$y + e^x y = x + C$$

Given, $y(0) = 2$

$\Rightarrow 2 + e^0 \cdot 2 = 0 + C$

$\Rightarrow C = 4$

$\therefore y(1 + e^x) = x + 4$

$\Rightarrow y = \frac{x + 4}{1 + e^x}$

Now at $x = -4$, $y = \frac{-4 + 4}{1 + e^{-4}} = 0$

$\therefore y(-4) = 0$ ...(i)

For critical points, $\frac{dy}{dx} = 0$

i.e. $\frac{dy}{dx} = \frac{(1 + e^x) \cdot 1 - (x + 4)e^x}{(1 + e^x)^2} = 0$

$\Rightarrow e^x (x + 3) - 1 = 0$

or $e^{-x} = (x + 3)$

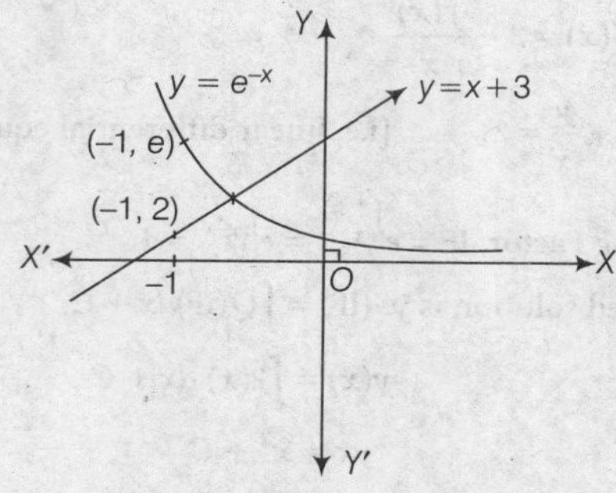

Clearly, the intersection point lies between (− 1, 0).

$\therefore y(x)$ has a critical point in the interval (− 1, 0).

76. Since, centre lies on $y = x$.

$\therefore$ Equation of circle is $x^2 + y^2 - 2ax - 2ay + c = 0$

On differentiating, we get

$$2x + 2yy' - 2a - 2ay' = 0$$

$\Rightarrow x + yy' - a - ay' = 0$

$\Rightarrow a = \frac{x + yy'}{1 + y'}$

Again differentiating, we get

$$0 = \frac{(1 + y')[1 + yy'' + (y')^2] - (x + yy') \cdot (y'')}{(1 + y')^2}$$

$\Rightarrow (1 + y')[1 + (y')^2 + yy''] - (x + yy')(y'') = 0$

$\Rightarrow 1 + y'[(y')^2 + y' + 1] + y''(y - x) = 0$

On comparing with $Py'' + Qy' + 1 = 0$, we get

$$P = y - x$$

and $Q = (y')^2 + y' + 1$

77. (i) Solution of the differential equation $\frac{dy}{dx} + Py = Q$ is

$$y \cdot (\text{IF}) = \int Q \cdot (\text{IF})\, dx + c$$

where, $\text{IF} = e^{\int P\, dx}$

(ii) $\int_{-a}^{a} f(x)\, dx = 2 \int_0^a f(x)\, dx$, if $f(-x) = f(x)$

Given differential equation

$$\frac{dy}{dx} + \frac{x}{x^2 - 1} y = \frac{x^4 + 2x}{\sqrt{1 - x^2}}$$

This is a linear differential equation.

$$\text{IF} = e^{\int \frac{x}{x^2 - 1} dx} = e^{\frac{1}{2} \ln|x^2 - 1|} = \sqrt{1 - x^2}$$

$\Rightarrow$ Solution is

$$y\sqrt{1 - x^2} = \int \frac{x(x^3 + 2)}{\sqrt{1 - x^2}} \cdot \sqrt{1 - x^2}\, dx$$

or $y\sqrt{1 - x^2} = \int (x^4 + 2x)\, dx = \frac{x^5}{5} + x^2 + c$

$$f(0) = 0 \Rightarrow c = 0$$

$\Rightarrow f(x)\sqrt{1 - x^2} = \frac{x^5}{5} + x^2$

Now, $\int_{-\sqrt{3}/2}^{\sqrt{3}/2} f(x)\, dx = \int_{-\sqrt{3}/2}^{\sqrt{3}/2} \frac{x^2}{\sqrt{1 - x^2}}\, dx$ [using property]

$= 2\int_0^{\sqrt{3}/2} \frac{x^2}{\sqrt{1 - x^2}}\, dx$

$= 2\int_0^{\pi/3} \frac{\sin^2\theta}{\cos\theta} \cos\theta\, d\theta$ [taking $x = \sin\theta$]

$= 2\int_0^{\pi/3} \sin^2\theta\, d\theta = \int_0^{\pi/3} (1 - \cos 2\theta)\, d\theta$

$= \left(\theta - \frac{\sin 2\theta}{2}\right)_0^{\pi/3} = \frac{\pi}{3} - \frac{\sin 2\pi/3}{2} = \frac{\pi}{3} - \frac{\sqrt{3}}{4}$

78. Whenever we have linear differential equation containing inequality, we should always check for increasing or decreasing,

i.e. for $\frac{dy}{dx} + Py < 0 \Rightarrow \frac{dy}{dx} + Py > 0$

Multiply by integrating factor, i.e. $e^{\int P dx}$ and convert into total differential equation.

Here, $f'(x) < 2f(x)$, multiplying by $e^{-\int 2dx}$

$$f'(x) \cdot e^{-2x} - 2e^{-2x} f(x) < 0 \Rightarrow \frac{d}{dx}(f(x) \cdot e^{-2x}) < 0$$

$\therefore$ $\phi(x) = f(x)e^{-2x}$ is decreasing for $x \in \left[\frac{1}{2}, 1\right]$

Thus, when $x > \frac{1}{2}$

$$\phi(x) < \phi\left(\frac{1}{2}\right) \Rightarrow e^{-2x} f(x) < e^{-1} \cdot f\left(\frac{1}{2}\right)$$

$$\Rightarrow \quad f(x) < e^{2x-1} \cdot 1, \text{ given } f\left(\frac{1}{2}\right) = 1$$

$$\Rightarrow \quad 0 < \int_{1/2}^{1} f(x)dx < \int_{1/2}^{1} e^{2x-1} dx$$

$$\Rightarrow \quad 0 < \int_{1/2}^{1} f(x)dx < \left(\frac{e^{2x-1}}{2}\right)_{1/2}^{1}$$

$$\Rightarrow \quad 0 < \int_{1/2}^{1} f(x)dx < \frac{e-1}{2}$$

79. To solve homogeneous differential equation, i.e. substitute $\frac{y}{x} = v$

$$\therefore \quad y = vx \Rightarrow \frac{dy}{dx} = v + x\frac{dv}{dx}$$

Here, slope of the curve at (x, y) is

$$\frac{dy}{dx} = \frac{y}{x} + \sec\left(\frac{y}{x}\right)$$

Put $\frac{y}{x} = v$

$$\therefore \quad v + x\frac{dv}{dx} = v + \sec(v)$$

$$\Rightarrow \quad x\frac{dv}{dx} = \sec(v) \Rightarrow \int \frac{dv}{\sec v} = \int \frac{dx}{x}$$

$$\Rightarrow \quad \int \cos v \, dv = \int \frac{dx}{x} \Rightarrow \sin v = \log x + \log c$$

$$\Rightarrow \quad \sin\left(\frac{y}{x}\right) = \log(cx)$$

As it passes through $\left(1, \frac{\pi}{6}\right) \Rightarrow \sin\left(\frac{\pi}{6}\right) = \log c$

$$\Rightarrow \quad \log c = \frac{1}{2}$$

$$\therefore \quad \sin\left(\frac{y}{x}\right) = \log x + \frac{1}{2}$$

80. Let $\phi(x) = e^{-x} f(x)$

Here, $\phi'(x) < 0, x \in \left(0, \frac{1}{4}\right)$

and $\phi'(x) > 0, x \in \left(\frac{1}{4}, 1\right)$

$$\Rightarrow e^{-x} f'(x) - e^{-x} f(x) < 0, x \in \left(0, \frac{1}{4}\right)$$

$$\Rightarrow f'(x) < f(x), 0 < x < \frac{1}{4}$$

81. Here, $f''(x) - 2f'(x) + f(x) \geq e^x$

$$\Rightarrow f''(x)e^{-x} - f'(x)e^{-x} - f'(x)e^{-x} + f(x)e^{-x} \geq 0$$

$$\Rightarrow \quad \frac{d}{dx}\{f'(x)e^{-x}\} - \frac{d}{dx}\{f(x)e^{-x}\} \geq 1$$

$$\Rightarrow \quad \frac{d}{dx}\{f'(x)e^{-x} - f(x)e^{-x}\} \geq 1$$

$$\Rightarrow \quad \frac{d^2}{dx^2}\{e^{-x} f(x)\} \geq 1, \forall x \in [0, 1]$$

$\therefore$ $\phi(x) = e^{-x} f(x)$ is concave function.

$$f(0) = f(1) = 0$$

$$\Rightarrow \quad \phi(0) = 0 = f(1)$$

$$\Rightarrow \quad \phi(x) < 0$$

$$\Rightarrow \quad e^{-x} f(x) < 0$$

$$\therefore \quad f(x) < 0$$

82. Here, $f(x) = (1-x)^2 \cdot \sin^2 x + x^2 \geq 0, \forall x$

and $g(x) = \int_1^x \left(\frac{2(t-1)}{t+1} - \log t\right) f(t) dt$

$$\Rightarrow \quad g'(x) = \left\{\frac{2(x-1)}{(x+1)} - \log x\right\} \cdot \underbrace{f(x)}_{+\text{ve}} \quad \text{...(i)}$$

For $g'(x)$ to be increasing or decreasing.

Let $\phi(x) = \frac{2(x-1)}{x+1} - \log x$

$$\phi'(x) = \frac{4}{(x+1)^2} - \frac{1}{x} = \frac{-(x-1)}{x(x+1)^2}$$

$$\phi'(x) < 0, \forall x > 1$$

$$\Rightarrow \quad \phi(x) < \phi(1) \Rightarrow \phi(x) < 0 \quad \text{...(ii)}$$

From Eqs. (i) and (ii), $g'(x) < 0, x \in (1, \infty)$

$\therefore g(x)$ is decreasing on $x \in (1, \infty)$.

83. Here, $f(x) + 2x = (1-x)^2 \cdot \sin^2 x + x^2 + 2x$ ...(i)

where, I: $f(x) + 2x = 2(1+x)^2$ ...(ii)

$$\therefore \quad 2(1+x^2) = (1-x)^2 \sin^2 x + x^2 + 2x$$

$$\Rightarrow \quad (1-x)^2 \sin^2 x = x^2 - 2x + 2$$

$$\Rightarrow \quad (1-x)^2 \sin^2 x = (1-x)^2 + 1$$

$$\Rightarrow \quad (1-x)^2 \cos^2 x = -1$$

which is never possible.

$\therefore$ I is false.

Again, let $h(x) = 2f(x) + 1 - 2x(1+x)$

where, $h(0) = 2f(0) + 1 - 0 = 1$

$h(1) = 2(1) + 1 - 4 = -3$ as $[h(0)h(1) < 0]$

$\Rightarrow h(x)$ must have a solution.

$\therefore$ II is true.

84. Linear differential equation under one variable.

$$\frac{dy}{dx}+Py=Q;\quad \text{IF}=e^{\int P\,dx}$$

$\therefore$ Solution is, $y\,(\text{IF})=\int Q\cdot(\text{IF})dx+C$

$$y'-y\tan x=2x\sec x \text{ and } y(0)=0$$

$$\Rightarrow \quad \frac{dy}{dx}-y\tan x=2x\sec x$$

$$\therefore \quad \text{IF}=\int e^{-\tan x}\,dx=e^{\log|\cos x|}=\cos x$$

Solution is $y\cdot\cos x=\int 2x\sec x\cdot\cos x\,dx+C$

$$\Rightarrow \quad y\cdot\cos x=x^2+C$$

As $\quad y(0)=0$

$\Rightarrow \quad C=0$

$\therefore \quad y=x^2\sec x$

Now, $\quad y\left(\frac{\pi}{4}\right)=\frac{\pi^2}{8\sqrt{2}}$

$$\Rightarrow \quad y'\left(\frac{\pi}{4}\right)=\frac{\pi}{\sqrt{2}}+\frac{\pi^2}{8\sqrt{2}} \Rightarrow y\left(\frac{\pi}{3}\right)=\frac{2\pi^2}{9}$$

$$\Rightarrow \quad y'\left(\frac{\pi}{3}\right)=\frac{4\pi}{3}+\frac{2\pi^2}{3\sqrt{3}}$$

85. $\frac{dy}{dx}+y\cdot g'(x)=g(x)\,g'(x)$

$$\text{IF}=e^{\int g'(x)\,dx}=e^{g(x)}$$

$\therefore$ Solution is $y\,(e^{g(x)})=\int g(x)\cdot g'(x)\cdot e^{g(x)}\,dx+C$

Put $\quad g(x)=t,\ g'(x)\,dx=dt$

$$y(e^{g(x)})=\int t\cdot e^t\,dt+C=t\cdot e^t-\int 1\cdot e^t\,dt+C$$

$$=t\cdot e^t-e^t+C$$

$$y\,e^{g(x)}=(g(x)-1)\,e^{g(x)}+C \quad \text{...(i)}$$

Given, $\quad y(0)=0,\ g(0)=g(2)=0$

$\therefore$ Eq. (i) becomes,

$$y(0)\cdot e^{g(0)}=(g(0)-1)\cdot e^{g(0)}+C$$

$$\Rightarrow \quad 0=(-1)\cdot 1+C \Rightarrow C=1$$

$$\therefore \quad y(x)\cdot e^{g(x)}=(g(x)-1)\,e^{g(x)}+1$$

$$\Rightarrow \quad y(2)\cdot e^{g(2)}=(g(2)-1)\,e^{g(2)}+1, \text{ where } g(2)=0$$

$$\Rightarrow \quad y(2)\cdot 1=(-1)\cdot 1+1$$

$$y(2)=0$$

86. From given integral equation, $f(0)=0$.

Also, differentiating the given integral equation w.r.t. x

$$f'(x)=f(x)$$

If $\quad f(x)\neq 0$

$$\Rightarrow \quad \frac{f'(x)}{f(x)}=1 \Rightarrow \log f(x)=x+c$$

$$\Rightarrow \quad f(x)=e^c e^x$$

$$\because \quad f(0)=0 \Rightarrow e^c=0, \text{ a contradiction}$$

$$\therefore \quad f(x)=0,\ \forall\ x\in R \Rightarrow f(\ln 5)=0$$

Alter

Given, $\quad f(x)=\int_0^x f(t)\,dt$

$\Rightarrow \quad f(0)=0$ and $f'(x)=f(x)$

If $f(x)\neq 0$

$$\Rightarrow \quad \frac{f'(x)}{f(x)}=1 \Rightarrow \ln f(x)=x+c$$

$$\Rightarrow \quad f(x)=e^c\cdot e^x$$

$$\because \quad f(0)=0$$

$\Rightarrow e^c=0$, a contradiction

$$\therefore \quad f(x)=0,\ \forall\ x\in R \Rightarrow f(\ln 5)=0$$

87. Given, $\quad \frac{dy}{dx}=\frac{y\sqrt{y^2-1}}{x\sqrt{x^2-1}}$

$$\int\frac{dy}{y\sqrt{y^2-1}}=\int\frac{dx}{x\sqrt{x^2-1}}$$

$$\Rightarrow \quad \sec^{-1} y=\sec^{-1} x+c$$

At $x=2$, $y=\frac{2}{\sqrt{3}}$; $\frac{\pi}{6}=\frac{\pi}{3}+c \Rightarrow c=-\frac{\pi}{6}$

Now, $y=\sec\left(\sec^{-1} x-\frac{\pi}{6}\right)=\cos\left[\cos^{-1}\frac{1}{x}-\cos^{-1}\frac{\sqrt{3}}{2}\right]$

$$=\cos\left[\cos^{-1}\left(\frac{\sqrt{3}}{2x}+\sqrt{1-\frac{1}{x^2}}\sqrt{1-\frac{3}{4}}\right)\right]$$

$$y=\frac{\sqrt{3}}{2x}+\frac{1}{2}\sqrt{1-\frac{1}{x^2}}$$

88. Given differential equation is

$$y(1+xy)\,dx=x\,dy$$

$$\Rightarrow \quad y\,dx+xy^2\,dx=x\,dy$$

$$\Rightarrow \quad \frac{x\,dy-y\,dx}{y^2}=x\,dx$$

$$\Rightarrow \quad -\frac{(y\,dx-x\,dy)}{y^2}=x\,dx \Rightarrow -d\left(\frac{x}{y}\right)=x\,dx$$

On integrating both sides, we get

$$-\frac{x}{y}=\frac{x^2}{2}+C \quad \text{...(i)}$$

$\because$ It passes through $(1,-1)$.

$$\therefore \quad 1=\frac{1}{2}+C \Rightarrow C=\frac{1}{2}$$

Now, from Eq. (i) $\quad -\frac{x}{y}=\frac{x^2}{2}+\frac{1}{2}$

$$\Rightarrow \quad x^2+1=-\frac{2x}{y} \Rightarrow y=-\frac{2x}{x^2+1}$$

$$\therefore \quad f\left(-\frac{1}{2}\right)=\frac{4}{5}$$

89. Given differential equation is

$$(x\log x)\frac{dy}{dx}+y=2x\log x, \quad (x\geq 1)$$

$$\Rightarrow \quad \frac{dy}{dx}+\frac{y}{x\log x}=2$$

This is a linear differential equation.

$\therefore \quad \text{IF} = e^{\int \frac{1}{x \log x} dx} = e^{\log(\log x)} = \log x$

Now, the solution of given differential equation is given by

$$y \cdot \log x = \int \log x \cdot 2dx$$

$$\Rightarrow \quad y \cdot \log x = 2\int \log x \, dx$$

$$\Rightarrow \quad y \cdot \log x = 2[x \log x - x] + c$$

At $\quad x = 1, c = 2$

$$\Rightarrow \quad y \cdot \log x = 2[x \log x - x] + 2$$

At $\quad x = e,$

$$y = 2(e - e) + 2$$

$$\Rightarrow \quad y = 2$$

90. Given differential equation $\frac{dp}{dt} - \frac{1}{2}p(t) = -200$ is a linear differential equation.

Here, $\quad p(t) = \frac{-1}{2}, Q(t) = -200$

$$\text{IF} = e^{\int -\left(\frac{1}{2}\right)dt} = e^{-\frac{t}{2}}$$

Hence, solution is

$$p(t).\text{IF} = \int Q(t)\,\text{IF}\, dt$$

$$p(t) \cdot e^{-\frac{t}{2}} = \int -200 \cdot e^{-\frac{t}{2}} dt$$

$$p(t) \cdot e^{-\frac{t}{2}} = 400 e^{-\frac{t}{2}} + K$$

$$\Rightarrow \quad p(t) = 400 + ke^{-1/2}$$

If $p(0) = 100$, then $k = -300$

$$\Rightarrow \quad p(t) = 400 - 300 e^{\frac{t}{2}}$$

91. Given, $\frac{dP}{dx} = (100 - 12\sqrt{x})$

$$\Rightarrow \quad dP = (100 - 12\sqrt{x})\, dx$$

On integrating both sides, we get

$$\int dP = \int (100 - 12\sqrt{x})\, dx$$

$$P = 100x - 8x^{3/2} + C$$

When $x = 0$, then $P = 2000$

$$\Rightarrow \quad C = 2000$$

Now, when $x = 25$, then

$$P = 100 \times 25 - 8 \times (25)^{3/2} + 2000$$

$$= 2500 - 8 \times 125 + 2000$$

$$= 4500 - 1000 = 3500$$

92. Given

(i) The population of mouse at time 't' satisfies the differential equation $p'(t) = \frac{dp(t)}{dt} = 0.5p(t) - 450$

(ii) Population of mouse at time $t = 0$ is

$$p(0) = 850$$

To find The time at which the population of the mouse will become zero, i.e. to find the value of 't' at which $p(t) = 0$.

Let's solve the differential equation first

$$p'(t) = \frac{dp(t)}{dt} = 0.5\, p(t) - 450$$

$$\Rightarrow \quad \frac{2dp(t)}{p(t) - 900} = dt$$

$$\Rightarrow \quad \int \frac{2dp(t)}{p(t) - 900} = \int dt$$

$\Rightarrow 2\log|p(t) - 900| = t + C$, where C is the constant of integration.

To find the value of 'C', let's substitute $t = 0$.

$$\Rightarrow \quad 2\log|p(0) - 900| = 0 + C$$

$$\Rightarrow \quad C = 2\log|850 - 900|$$

$$\Rightarrow \quad C = 2\log 50$$

Now, substituting the value of C back in the solution, we get

$$2\log|p(t) - 900| = t + 2\log 50$$

Here, since we want to find the value of t at which $p(t) = 0$, hence substituting $p(t) = 0$, we get

$$2\log|0 - 900| = t + 2\log 50$$

$$\Rightarrow \quad t = 2\log\left|\frac{900}{50}\right|$$

$$\Rightarrow \quad t = 2\log 18$$

93. Here, $\frac{dy}{dx} = y + 3 > 0$ and $y(0) = 2$

$$\Rightarrow \quad \int \frac{dy}{y + 3} = \int dx$$

$$\Rightarrow \quad \log|y + 3| = x + C$$

Since, $\quad y(0) = 2$

$$\Rightarrow \quad \log_e|2 + 3| = 0 + C$$

$$\therefore \quad C = \log_e 5$$

$$\Rightarrow \quad \log_e|y + 3| = x + \log_e 5$$

When $\quad x = \log_e 2$

$$\Rightarrow \quad \log_e|y + 3| = \log_e 2 + \log_e 5 = \log_e 10$$

$$\Rightarrow \quad y + 3 = 10$$

$$\Rightarrow \quad y = 7$$

94. Given, $\quad \frac{d\{V(t)\}}{dt} = -k(T - t)$

$$\therefore \quad d\{V(t)\} = -k(T - t)\, dt$$

On integrating both sides, we get

$$V(t) = -k\frac{(T - t)^2}{2(-1)} + C$$

$$\Rightarrow \quad V(t) = \frac{k}{2}(T - t)^2 + C$$

$\because \quad$ At $t = 0$, $V(t) = I$

$$\therefore \quad I = \frac{k}{2}(T - 0)^2 + C$$

$$\Rightarrow \quad C = I - \frac{k}{2}T^2$$

$$\therefore \quad V(t) = \frac{k}{2}(T-t)^2 + I - \frac{k}{2}T^2$$

Now, $\quad V(T) = I - \frac{k}{2}T^2$

95. Since, $\cos x\, dy = y \sin x\, dx - y^2\, dx$

$$\Rightarrow \quad \frac{1}{y^2}\frac{dy}{dx} - \frac{1}{y}\tan x = -\sec x$$

Put $-\frac{1}{y} = z$

$$\Rightarrow \quad \frac{1}{y^2}\frac{dy}{dx} = \frac{dz}{dx}$$

$$\Rightarrow \quad \frac{dz}{dx} + (\tan x)z = -\sec x$$

This is a linear differential equation.

Therefore,

$$\text{IF} = e^{\int \tan x\, dx} = e^{\log \sec x} = \sec x$$

Hence, the solution is

$$z \cdot (\sec x) = \int -\sec x \cdot \sec x\, dx + C_1$$

$$\Rightarrow \quad -\frac{1}{y}\sec x = -\tan x + C_1$$

$$\Rightarrow \quad \sec x = y(\tan x + C)$$

96. Given, $\quad y = c_1 e^{c_2 x}$

$$\Rightarrow \quad y' = c_2 c_1 e^{c_2 x}$$

$$\Rightarrow \quad y' = c_2 y \quad \ldots(\text{i})$$

$$\Rightarrow \quad y'' = c_2 y' \quad \ldots(\text{ii})$$

$$\Rightarrow \quad y'' = \frac{(y')^2}{y} \quad \left[\text{from Eq. (i), } c_2 = \frac{y'}{y}\right]$$

$$\Rightarrow \quad yy'' = (y')^2$$

97. Equation of circle having centre (h, k) and radius a is $(x-h)^2 + (y-k)^2 = a^2$.

The equation of family of circles with centre on $y = 2$ and of radius 5 is

$$(x-\alpha)^2 + (y-2)^2 = 5^2 \quad \ldots(\text{i})$$

$$\Rightarrow \quad x^2 + \alpha^2 - 2\alpha x + y^2 + 4 - 4y = 25$$

On differentiating w.r.t. x, we get

$$2x - 2\alpha + 2y\frac{dy}{dx} - 4\frac{dy}{dx} = 0$$

$$\Rightarrow \quad \alpha = x + \frac{dy}{dx}(y-2)$$

On putting the value of α in Eq. (i), we get

$$\left[x - x - \frac{dy}{dx}(y-2)\right]^2 + (y-2)^2 = 5^2$$

$$\Rightarrow \quad \left(\frac{dy}{dx}\right)^2 (y-2)^2 = 25 - (y-2)^2$$

$$\Rightarrow \quad y'^2 (y-2)^2 = 25 - (y-2)^2$$

Previous Years' Questions
JEE Main and Advanced (2021-18)

Indefinite Integral

1. The integral $\int \frac{1}{\sqrt[4]{(x-1)^3 (x+2)^5}} dx$ is equal to (where C is a constant of integration) **[JEE Main 2021]**

(a) $\frac{3}{4}\left(\frac{x+2}{x-1}\right)^{1/4} + C$ (b) $\frac{3}{4}\left(\frac{x+2}{x-1}\right)^{5/4} + C$

(c) $\frac{4}{3}\left(\frac{x-1}{x+2}\right)^{1/4} + C$ (d) $\frac{4}{3}\left(\frac{x-1}{x+2}\right)^{5/4} + C$

2. If $\int \frac{\sin x}{\sin^3 x + \cos^3 x} dx = \alpha \log_e |1 + \tan x| + \beta \log_e |1 - \tan x + \tan^2 x| + \gamma \tan^{-1}\left(\frac{2\tan x - 1}{\sqrt{3}}\right) + C$, when C is constant of integration, then the value of $18(\alpha + \beta + \gamma^2)$ is **[JEE Main 2021]**

3. If $\int \frac{dx}{(x^2 + x + 1)^2} = a \tan^{-1}\left(\frac{2x+1}{\sqrt{3}}\right) + b\left(\frac{2x+1}{x^2 + x + 1}\right) + C, x > 0$ where C is the constant of integration, then the value of $9(\sqrt{3}a + b)$ is equal to **[JEE Main 2021]**

4. If $\int \frac{2e^x + 3e^{-x}}{4e^x + 7e^{-x}} dx = \frac{1}{14}(ux + v \log_e (4e^x + 7e^{-x})) + C$, where C is a constant of integration, then $u + v$ is equal to **[JEE Main 2021]**

5. Let $f : [3,5] \to R$ be a twice differentiable function on $(3, 5)$ such that $f(x) = e^{-x} \int_3^x [3t^2 + 2t + 4f'(t)]\, dt$.

If $f'(4) = \frac{\alpha e^\beta - 224}{(e^\beta - 4)^2}$, then $\alpha + \beta$ is equal to .... **[JEE Main 2021]**

6. If $\int_0^\pi (\sin^3 x) e^{-\sin^2 x} dx = \alpha - \frac{\beta}{e} \int_0^1 \sqrt{t}\, e^t dt$, then $(\alpha + \beta)$ is equal to .... **[JEE Main 2021]**

7. The integral $\int \frac{(2x-1)\cos\sqrt{(2x-1)^2 + 5}}{\sqrt{4x^2 - 4x + 6}} dx$ is equal to (where, c is a constant of integration) **[JEE Main 2021]**

(a) $\frac{1}{2}\sin\sqrt{(2x-1)^2 + 5} + c$ (b) $\frac{1}{2}\cos\sqrt{(2x+1)^2 + 5} + c$

(c) $\frac{1}{2}\cos\sqrt{(2x-1)^2 + 5} + c$ (d) $\frac{1}{2}\sin\sqrt{(2x+1)^2 + 5} + c$

8. If $f(x) = \int \frac{5x^8 + 7x^6}{(x^2 + 1 + 2x^7)^2} dx, (x \geq 0), f(0) = 0$ and $f(1) = \frac{1}{K}$, then the value of K is .... **[JEE Main 2021]**

9. For real numbers α, β, γ and δ, if

$$\int \frac{(x^2 - 1) + \tan^{-1}\left(\frac{x^2+1}{x}\right)}{(x^4 + 3x^2 + 1)\tan^{-1}\left(\frac{x^2+1}{x}\right)} dx = \alpha \log_e\left[\tan^{-1}\left(\frac{x^2+1}{x}\right)\right] + \beta \tan^{-1}\left(\frac{\gamma(x^2-1)}{x}\right) + \delta \tan^{-1}\left(\frac{x^2+1}{x}\right) + C$$

where C is an arbitrary constant, then the value of $10(\alpha + \beta\gamma + \delta)$ is equal to......... . **[JEE Main 2021]**

10. The integral $\int \frac{e^{3\log_e 2x} + 5e^{2\log_e 2x}}{e^{4\log_e x} + 5e^{3\log_e x} - 7e^{2\log_e x}} dx, x > 0$, is equal to (where, c is a constant of integration) **[JEE Main 2021]**

(a) $\log_e |x^2 + 5x - 7| + c$

(b) $4 \log_e |x^2 + 5x - 7| + c$

(c) $\frac{1}{4}\log_e |x^2 + 5x - 7| + c$

(d) $\log_e \sqrt{x^2 + 5x - 7} + c$

11. The value of the integral

$$\int \left[\frac{\sin\theta \cdot \sin 2\theta (\sin^6\theta + \sin^4\theta + \sin^2\theta)\sqrt{2\sin^4\theta + 3\sin^2\theta + 6}}{1 - \cos 2\theta}\right] d\theta$$

is (where, c is a constant of integration) **[JEE Main 2021]**

(a) $\frac{1}{18}[11 - 18\sin^2\theta + 9\sin^4\theta - 2\sin^6\theta]^{\frac{3}{2}} + c$

(b) $\frac{1}{18}[9 - 2\cos^6\theta \;\; 3\cos^4\theta - 6\cos^2\theta]^{\frac{3}{2}} + c$

(c) $\frac{1}{18}[9 - 2\sin^6\theta - 3\sin^4\theta - 6\sin^2\theta]^{\frac{3}{2}} + c$

(d) $\frac{1}{18}[11 - 18\cos^2\theta + 9\cos^4\theta - 2\cos^6\theta]^{\frac{3}{2}} + c$

12. If $\int \frac{\cos x - \sin x}{\sqrt{8 - \sin 2x}} dx = a \sin^{-1}\left(\frac{\sin x + \cos x}{b}\right) + c$, where c is a constant of integration, then the ordered pair (a, b) is equal to **[JEE Main 2021]**

(a) (3, 1) (b) (1, 3) (c) (– 1, 3) (d) (1, – 3)

13. If $\int \sin^{-1}\left(\sqrt{\frac{x}{1+x}}\right) dx = A(x)\tan^{-1}(\sqrt{x}) + B(x) + C$, where C is a constant of integration, then the ordered pair $(A(x), B(x))$ can be **[JEE Main 2020]**

(a) $(x - 1, \sqrt{x})$ (b) $(x + 1, \sqrt{x})$
(c) $(x + 1, -\sqrt{x})$ (d) $(x - 1, -\sqrt{x})$

14. The integral $\int \left(\frac{x}{x\sin x + \cos x}\right)^2 dx$ is equal to (where C is a constant of integration) **[JEE Main 2020]**

(a) $\sec x - \frac{x\tan x}{x\sin x + \cos x} + C$ (b) $\sec x + \frac{x\tan x}{x\sin x + \cos x} + C$

(c) $\tan x - \frac{x\sec x}{x\sin x + \cos x} + C$ (d) $\tan x + \frac{x\sec x}{x\sin x + \cos x} + C$

15 Let $f(x) = \int \frac{\sqrt{x}}{(1+x)^2} dx \ (x \geq 0)$. Then $f(3) - f(1)$ is equal to **[JEE Main 2020]**

(a) $-\frac{\pi}{6} + \frac{1}{2} + \frac{\sqrt{3}}{4}$ (b) $-\frac{\pi}{12} + \frac{1}{2} + \frac{\sqrt{3}}{4}$

(c) $\frac{\pi}{6} + \frac{1}{2} - \frac{\sqrt{3}}{4}$ (d) $\frac{\pi}{12} + \frac{1}{2} - \frac{\sqrt{3}}{4}$

16. If $\int (e^{2x} + 2e^x - e^{-x} - 1)e^{(e^x + e^{-x})} dx = g(x)e^{(e^x + e^{-x})} + c$, where c is a constant of integration, then $g(0)$ is equal to **[JEE Main 2020]**

(a) 2 (b) e^2 (c) e (d) 1

17. If $\int \frac{\cos\theta}{5 + 7\sin\theta - 2\cos^2\theta} d\theta = A\log_e|B(\theta)| + C$, where C is a constant of integration, then $\frac{B(\theta)}{A}$ can be **[JEE Main 2020]**

(a) $\frac{2\sin\theta + 1}{\sin\theta + 3}$ (b) $\frac{2\sin\theta + 1}{5(\sin\theta + 3)}$

(c) $\frac{5(\sin\theta + 3)}{2\sin\theta + 1}$ (d) $\frac{5(2\sin\theta + 1)}{\sin\theta + 3}$

18. If $\int \frac{\cos x \, dx}{\sin^3 x(1+\sin^6 x)^{2/3}} = f(x)(1+\sin^6 x)^{1/\lambda} + C$ where c is a constant of integration, then is equal to **[JEE Main 2020]**

(a) 2 (b) $-\frac{9}{8}$ (c) – 2 (d) $\frac{9}{8}$

19. The integral $\int \frac{dx}{(x+4)^{8/7}(x-3)^{6/7}}$ is equal to (where C is a constant of integration) **[JEE Main 2020]**

(a) $-\left(\frac{x-3}{x+4}\right)^{-1/7} + C$ (b) $\frac{1}{2}\left(\frac{x-3}{x+4}\right)^{3/7} + C$

(c) $\left(\frac{x-3}{x+4}\right)^{1/7} + C$ (d) $-\frac{1}{13}\left(\frac{x-3}{x+4}\right)^{-13/7} + C$

20. If for all real triplets (a, b, c), $f(x) = a + bx + cx^2$; then $\int_0^1 f(x)dx$ is equal to **[JEE Main 2020]**

(a) $2\left\{3f(1) + 2f\left(\frac{1}{2}\right)\right\}$ (b) $\frac{1}{3}\left\{f(0) + f\left(\frac{1}{2}\right)\right\}$

(c) $\frac{1}{2}\left\{f(1) + 3f\left(\frac{1}{2}\right)\right\}$ (d) $\frac{1}{6}\left\{f(0) + f(1) + 4f\left(\frac{1}{2}\right)\right\}$

21. If $\int \frac{d\theta}{\cos^2\theta(\tan 2\theta + \sec 2\theta)} = \lambda\tan\theta + 2\log_e|f(\theta)| + C$ where C is a constant of integration, then the ordered pair $(\lambda, f(\theta))$ is equal to **[JEE Main 2020]**

(a) $(1, 1 + \tan\theta)$ (b) $(1, 1 - \tan\theta)$
(c) $(-1, 1 + \tan\theta)$ (d) $(-1, 1 - \tan\theta)$

22. $\int \frac{\sin\frac{5x}{2}}{\sin\frac{x}{2}} dx$ is equal to (where, C is a constant of integration) **[JEE Main 2019]**

(a) $2x + \sin x + 2\sin 2x + C$ (b) $x + 2\sin x + 2\sin 2x + C$
(c) $x + 2\sin x + \sin 2x + C$ (d) $2x + \sin x + \sin 2x + C$

23. If $\int \frac{dx}{x^3(1+x^6)^{2/3}} = xf(x)(1+x^6)^{\frac{1}{3}} + C$ where, C is a constant of integration, then the function $f(x)$ is equal to **[JEE Main 2019]**

(a) $-\frac{1}{6x^3}$ (b) $-\frac{1}{2x^3}$

(c) $-\frac{1}{2x^2}$ (d) $\frac{3}{x^2}$

24. The integral $\int \sec^{2/3} x \operatorname{cosec}^{4/3} x \, dx$ is equal to (here C is a constant of integration) **[JEE Main 2019]**

(a) $3\tan^{-1/3} x + C$ (b) $-3\tan^{-1/3} x + C$

(c) $-3\cot^{-1/3} x + C$ (d) $-\frac{3}{4}\tan^{-4/3} x + C$

25. If $\int e^{\sec x}(\sec x \tan x f(x) + (\sec x \tan x + \sec^2 x)) dx = e^{\sec x} f(x) + C$, then a possible choice of $f(x)$ is **[JEE Main 2019]**

(a) $x\sec x + \tan x + \frac{1}{2}$ (b) $\sec x + \tan x + \frac{1}{2}$

(c) $\sec x + x\tan x - \frac{1}{2}$ (d) $\sec x - \tan x - \frac{1}{2}$

26. If $\int \frac{dx}{(x^2 - 2x + 10)^2} = A\left(\tan^{-1}\left(\frac{x-1}{3}\right) + \frac{f(x)}{x^2 - 2x + 10}\right) + C$, where, C is a constant of integration, then **[JEE Main 2019]**

(a) $A = \frac{1}{27}$ and $f(x) = 9(x - 1)$ (b) $A = \frac{1}{81}$ and $f(x) = 3(x - 1)$

(c) $A = \frac{1}{54}$ and $f(x) = 3(x - 1)$ (d) $A = \frac{1}{54}$ and $f(x) = 9(x - 1)^2$

27. $\lim_{n\to\infty}\left(\frac{(n+1)^{1/3}}{n^{4/3}}+\frac{(n+2)^{1/3}}{n^{4/3}}+\ldots+\frac{(2n)^{1/3}}{n^{4/3}}\right)$ is equal to **[JEE Main 2019]**

(a) $\frac{4}{3}(2)^{4/3}$ (b) $\frac{3}{4}(2)^{4/3}-\frac{4}{3}$

(c) $\frac{3}{4}(2)^{4/3}-\frac{3}{4}$ (d) $\frac{4}{3}(2)^{3/4}$

28. If $\int x^5e^{-x^2}dx=g(x)e^{-x^2}+C$, where C is a constant of integration, then $g(-1)$ is equal to **[JEE Main 2019]**

(a) -1 (b) 1

(c) $-\frac{1}{2}$ (d) $-\frac{5}{2}$

29. The integral $\int\frac{2x^3-1}{x^4+x}dx$ is equal to (here C is a constant of integration) **[JEE Main 2019]**

(a) $\frac{1}{2}\log_e\frac{|x^3+1|}{x^2}+C$ (b) $\frac{1}{2}\log_e\frac{(x^3+1)^2}{|x^3|}+C$

(c) $\log_e\left|\frac{x^3+1}{x}\right|+C$ (d) $\log_e\frac{|x^3+1|}{x^2}+C$

30. Let $\alpha\in(0,\pi/2)$ be fixed. If the integral $\int\frac{\tan x+\tan\alpha}{\tan x-\tan\alpha}dx=A(x)\cos2\alpha+B(x)\sin2\alpha+C$, where C is a constant of integration, then the functions $A(x)$ and $B(x)$ are respectively **[JEE Main 2019]**

(a) $x+\alpha$ and $\log_e|\sin(x+\alpha)|$ (b) $x-\alpha$ and $\log_e|\sin(x-\alpha)|$

(c) $x-\alpha$ and $\log_e|\cos(x-\alpha)|$ (d) $x+\alpha$ and $\log_e|\sin(x-\alpha)|$

31. For $x^2\neq n\pi+1, n\in N$ (the set of natural numbers), the integral $\int x\sqrt{\frac{2\sin(x^2-1)-\sin2(x^2-1)}{2\sin(x^2-1)+\sin2(x^2-1)}}dx$ is equal to (where C is a constant of integration) **[JEE Main 2019]**

(a) $\frac{1}{2}\log_e|\sec(x^2-1)|+C$ (b) $\log_e\left|\sec\left(\frac{x^2-1}{2}\right)\right|+C$

(c) $\log_e\left|\frac{1}{2}\sec^2(x^2-1)\right|+C$ (d) $\frac{1}{2}\log_e\left|\sec^2\left(\frac{x^2-1}{2}\right)\right|+C$

32. If $f(x)=\int\frac{5x^8+7x^6}{(x^2+1+2x^7)^2}dx, (x\geq0)$, and $f(0)=0$, then the value of $f(1)$ is **[JEE Main 2019]**

(a) $-\frac{1}{2}$ (b) $-\frac{1}{4}$ (c) $\frac{1}{4}$ (d) $\frac{1}{2}$

33. Let $n\geq2$ be a natural number and $0<\theta<\frac{\pi}{2}$. Then, $\int\frac{(\sin^n\theta-\sin\theta)^{1/n}\cos\theta}{\sin^{n+1}\theta}d\theta$ is equal to (where C is a constant of integration) **[JEE Main 2019]**

(a) $\frac{n}{n^2-1}\left(1-\frac{1}{\sin^{n+1}\theta}\right)^{\frac{n+1}{n}}+C$

(b) $\frac{n}{n^2-1}\left(1+\frac{1}{\sin^{n-1}\theta}\right)^{\frac{n+1}{n}}+C$

(c) $\frac{n}{n^2-1}\left(1-\frac{1}{\sin^{n-1}\theta}\right)^{\frac{n+1}{n}}+C$

(d) $\frac{n}{n^2+1}\left(1-\frac{1}{\sin^{n-1}\theta}\right)^{\frac{n+1}{n}}+C$

34. If $\int x^5e^{-4x^3}dx=\frac{1}{48}e^{-4x^3}f(x)+C$, where C is a constant of integration, then $f(x)$ is equal to **[JEE Main 2019]**

(a) $-4x^3-1$ (b) $4x^3+1$

(c) $-2x^3-1$ (d) $-2x^3+1$

35. If $\int\frac{\sqrt{1-x^2}}{x^4}dx=A(x)(\sqrt{1-x^2})^m+C$, for a suitable chosen integer m and a function $A(x)$, where C is a constant of integration, then $(A(x))^m$ equals **[JEE Main 2019]**

(a) $\frac{1}{9x^4}$ (b) $\frac{-1}{3x^3}$

(c) $\frac{-1}{27x^9}$ (d) $\frac{1}{27x^6}$

36. If $\int\frac{x+1}{\sqrt{2x-1}}dx=f(x)\sqrt{2x-1}+C$, where C is a constant of integration, then $f(x)$ is equal to **[JEE Main 2019]**

(a) $\frac{2}{3}(x+2)$ (b) $\frac{1}{3}(x+4)$

(c) $\frac{2}{3}(x-4)$ (d) $\frac{1}{3}(x+1)$

37. The integral $\int\cos(\log_e x)dx$ is equal to (where C is a constant of integration) **[JEE Main 2019]**

(a) $\frac{x}{2}[\cos(\log_e x)+\sin(\log_e x)]+C$

(b) $x[\cos(\log_e x)+\sin(\log_e x)]+C$

(c) $x[\cos(\log_e x)-\sin(\log_e x)]+C$

(d) $\frac{x}{2}[\sin(\log_e x)-\cos(\log_e x)]+C$

38 The integral $\int\frac{3x^{13}+2x^{11}}{(2x^4+3x^2+1)^4}dx$ is equal to (where C is a constant of integration) **[JEE Main 2019]**

(a) $\frac{x^4}{6(2x^4+3x^2+1)^3}+C$ (b) $\frac{x^{12}}{6(2x^4+3x^2+1)^3}+C$

(c) $\frac{x^4}{(2x^4+3x^2+1)^3}+C$ (d) $\frac{x^{12}}{(2x^4+3x^2+1)^3}+C$

39. Let $f:R\to R$ and $g:R\to R$ be two non-constant differentiable functions. If $f'(x)=(e^{(f(x)-g(x))})g'(x)$ for all $x\in R$ and $f(1)=g(2)=1$, then which of the following statement(s) is (are) TRUE? **[JEE Advanced 2018]**

(a) $f(2)<1-\log_e 2$ (b) $f(2)>1-\log_e 2$

(c) $g(1)>1-\log_e 2$ (d) $g(1)<1-\log_e 2$

40. The integral

$$\int \frac{\sin^2 x\cos^2 x}{(\sin^5 x+\cos^3 x\sin^2 x+\sin^3 x\cos^2 x+\cos^5 x)^2}dx$$

is equal to **[JEE Main 2018]**

(a) $\frac{1}{3(1+\tan^3 x)}+C$ (b) $\frac{-1}{3(1+\tan^3 x)}+C$

(c) $\frac{1}{1+\cot^3 x}+C$ (d) $\frac{-1}{1+\cot^3 x}+C$

(where C is a constant of integration)

41. Let $f:(0,\pi)\to R$ be a twice differentiable function such that $\lim_{t\to x}\frac{f(x)\sin t-f(t)\sin x}{t-x}=\sin^2 x$ for all $x\in(0,\pi)$.

If $f\left(\frac{\pi}{6}\right)=-\frac{\pi}{12}$, then which of the following statement(s) is (are) TRUE? **[JEE Advanced 2018]**

(a) $f\left(\frac{\pi}{4}\right)=\frac{\pi}{4\sqrt{2}}$

(b) $f(x)<\frac{x^4}{6}-x^2$ for all $x\in(0,\pi)$

(c) There exists $\alpha\in(0,\pi)$ such that $f'(\alpha)=0$

(d) $f''\left(\frac{\pi}{2}\right)+f\left(\frac{\pi}{2}\right)=0$

42. Let $f:R\to R$ be a differentiable function with $f(0)=1$ and satisfying the equation $f(x+y)=f(x)f'(y)+f'(x)f(y)$ for all $x,y\in R$.

Then, the value of $\log_e(f(4))$ is .... **[JEE Advanced 2018]**

Answers

1. (c)	**2.** (3)	**3.** (15)	**4.** (7)	**5.** (16)	**6.** (5)	**7.** (a)	**8.** (4)	**9.** (6)	**10.** (b)
11. (d)	**12.** (b)	**13.** (c)	**14.** (c)	**15.** (d)	**16.** (a)	**17.** (d)	**18.** (c)	**19.** (c)	**20.** (d)
21. (c)	**22.** (c)	**23.** (b)	**24.** (b)	**25.** (b)	**26.** (c)	**27.** (c)	**28.** (d)	**29.** (c)	**30.** (b)
31. (b)	**32.** (c)	**33.** (c)	**34.** (a)	**35.** (c)	**36.** (b)	**37.** (a)	**38.** (b)	**39.** (b,c)	**40.** (b)
41. (b,c,d)	**42.** (2)								

Definite Integral

1. Let $J_{n,m}=\int_0^{1/2}\frac{x^n}{x^m-1}dx$, $\forall\, n>m$ and $n,m\in N$. Consider a matrix $A=[a_{ij}]_{3\times3}$ where $a_{ij}=\begin{cases}J_{6+i,3}-J_{i+3,3}, & i\le j\\ 0, & i>j\end{cases}$. Then, $|\text{adj}\,A^{-1}|$ is **[JEE Main 2021]**

(a) $(15)^2\times2^{42}$ (b) $(15)^2\times2^{34}$

(c) $(105)^2\times2^{38}$ (d) $(105)^2\times2^{36}$

2. The function $f(x)$, that satisfies the condition $f(x)=x+\int_0^{\pi/2}\sin x\cdot\cos y\, f(y)dy$, is **[JEE Main 2021]**

(a) $x+\frac{2}{3}(\pi-2)\sin x$ (b) $x+(\pi+2)\sin x$

(c) $x+\frac{\pi}{2}\sin x$ (d) $x+(\pi-2)\sin x$

3. Let $[t]$ denote the greatest integer $\le t$. Then the value of $8\cdot\int_{-1/2}^{1}([2x]+|x|)dx$ is **[JEE Main 2021]**

4. If $x\,\phi(x)=\int_5^x(3t^2-2\phi'(t))dt$, $x>-2$, and $\phi(0)=4$, then $\phi(2)$ is **[JEE Main 2021]**

5. If $[x]$ is the greatest integer $\le x$, then $\pi^2\int_0^2\left(\sin\frac{\pi x}{2}\right)(x-|x|)^{[x]}dx$ is equal to **[JEE Main 2021]**

(a) $2(\pi-1)$ (b) $4(\pi-1)$ (c) $4(\pi+1)$ (d) $2(\pi+1)$

6. If $U_n=\left(1+\frac{1}{n^2}\right)\left(1+\frac{2^2}{n^2}\right)^2\ldots\left(1+\frac{n^2}{n^2}\right)^n$, then $\lim_{n\to\infty}(U_n)^{\frac{-4}{n^2}}$ is equal to **[JEE Main 2021]**

(a) $e^2/16$ (b) $4/e$

(c) $16/e^2$ (d) $4/e^2$

7. $\int_6^{16}\frac{\log_e x^2}{\log_e x^2+\log_e(x^2-44x+484)}dx$ is equal to **[JEE Main 2021]**

(a) 6 (b) 8

(c) 5 (d) 10

8. The value of the integral $\int_0^1\frac{\sqrt{x}\,dx}{(1+x)(1+3x)(3+x)}$ is **[JEE Main 2021]**

(a) $\frac{\pi}{8}\left(1-\frac{\sqrt3}{2}\right)$ (b) $\frac{\pi}{4}\left(1-\frac{\sqrt3}{6}\right)$

(c) $\frac{\pi}{8}\left(1-\frac{\sqrt3}{6}\right)$ (d) $\frac{\pi}{4}\left(1-\frac{\sqrt3}{2}\right)$

9. The value of $\int_{-1/\sqrt2}^{1/\sqrt2}\left(\left(\frac{x+1}{x-1}\right)^2+\left(\frac{x-1}{x+1}\right)^2-2\right)^{1/2}dx$ is **[JEE Main 2021]**

(a) $\log_e 4$ (b) $\log_e 16$

(c) $2\log_e 16$ (d) $4\log_e(3+2\sqrt2)$

10. The value of $\lim_{n\to\infty}\frac{1}{n}\sum_{r=0}^{2n-1}\frac{n^2}{n^2+4r^2}$ is **[JEE Main 2021]**

(a) $\frac{1}{2}\tan^{-1}(2)$ (b) $\frac{1}{2}\tan^{-1}(4)$

(c) $\tan^{-1}(4)$ (d) $\frac{1}{4}\tan^{-1}(4)$

11. If the value of the integral $\int_0^5 \frac{x+[x]}{e^{x-[x]}}dx=\alpha e^{-1}+\beta$, where $\alpha,\beta\in R, 5\alpha+6\beta=0$ and $[x]$ denotes the greatest integer less than or equal to x, then the value of $(\alpha+\beta)^2$ is equal to : **[JEE Main 2021]**

(a) 100 (b) 25 (c) 16 (d) 36

12. The value of $\int_{-\pi/2}^{\pi/2}\left(\frac{1+\sin^2 x}{1+\pi^{\sin x}}\right)dx$ is **[JEE Main 2021]**

(a) $\frac{\pi}{2}$ (b) $\frac{5\pi}{4}$ (c) $\frac{3\pi}{4}$ (d) $\frac{3\pi}{2}$

13. Let the domain of the function $f(x)=\log_4[\log_5(\log_3(18x-x^2-77))]$ be (a,b). Then the value of the integral $\int_a^b\frac{\sin^3 x}{[\sin^3 x+\sin^3(a+b-x)]}dx$ is equal to .... **[JEE Main 2021]**

14. The value of $\lim_{n\to\infty}\frac{1}{n}\sum_{j=1}^{n}\frac{(2j-1)+8n}{(2j-1)+4n}$ is equal to **[JEE Main 2021]**

(a) $5+\log_e\left(\frac{3}{2}\right)$ (b) $2-\log_e\left(\frac{2}{3}\right)$

(c) $3+2\log_e\left(\frac{2}{3}\right)$ (d) $1+2\log_e\left(\frac{3}{2}\right)$

15. The value of the definite integral $\int_{-\pi/4}^{\pi/4}\frac{dx}{(1+e^{x\cos x})(\sin^4 x+\cos^4 x)}$ is equal to **[JEE Main 2021]**

(a) $-\frac{\pi}{2}$ (b) $\frac{\pi}{2\sqrt{2}}$ (c) $-\frac{\pi}{4}$ (d) $\frac{\pi}{\sqrt{2}}$

16. The value of the definite integral $\int_{\pi/24}^{5\pi/24}\frac{dx}{1+\sqrt[3]{\tan 2x}}$ is **[JEE Main 2021]**

(a) $\frac{\pi}{3}$ (b) $\frac{\pi}{6}$ (c) $\frac{\pi}{12}$ (d) $\frac{\pi}{18}$

17. The value of the integral $\int_{-1}^{1}\log(x+\sqrt{x^2+1})dx$ is **[JEE Main 2021]**

(a) 2 (b) 0 (c) -1 (d) 1

18. If $\int_0^{100\pi}\frac{\sin^2 x}{e^{\left(\frac{x}{\pi}-\left[\frac{x}{\pi}\right]\right)}}dx=\frac{\alpha\pi^3}{1+4\pi^2}, \alpha\in R$, where $[x]$ is the greatest integer less than or equal to x, then the value of α is **[JEE Main 2021]**

(a) $200(1-e^{-1})$ (b) $100(1-e)$

(c) $50(e-1)$ (d) $150(e^{-1}-1)$

19. The value of the integral $\int_{-1}^{1}\log_e(\sqrt{1-x}+\sqrt{1+x})dx$ is equal to **[JEE Main 2021]**

(a) $\frac{1}{2}\log_e 2+\frac{\pi}{4}-\frac{3}{2}$ (b) $2\log_e 2+\frac{\pi}{4}-1$

(c) $\log_e 2+\frac{\pi}{2}-1$ (d) $2\log_e 2+\frac{\pi}{2}-\frac{1}{2}$

20. Let a be a positive real number such that $\int_0^a e^{x-[x]}dx=10e-9$, where $[x]$ is the greatest integer less than or equal to x. Then, a is equal to **[JEE Main 2021]**

(a) $10-\log_e(1+e)$ (b) $10+\log_e 2$

(c) $10+\log_e 3$ (d) $10+\log_e(1+e)$

21. If $[x]$ denotes the greatest integer less than or equal to x then the value of the integral $\int_{-\frac{\pi}{2}}^{\frac{\pi}{2}}[[x]-\sin x]dx$ is equal to **[JEE Main 2021]**

(a) $-\pi$ (b) π (c) 0 (d) 1

22. If $f:R\to R$ is given by $f(x)=x+1$, then the value of $\lim_{n\to\infty}\frac{1}{n}\left[f(0)+f\left(\frac{5}{n}\right)+f\left(\frac{10}{n}\right)+....+f\left(\frac{5(n-1)}{n}\right)\right]$ is **[JEE Main 2021]**

(a) 3/2 (b) 5/2 (c) 1/2 (d) 7/2

23. Let $g(t)=\int_{-\frac{\pi}{2}}^{\frac{\pi}{2}}\cos\left(\frac{\pi}{4}t+f(x)\right)dx$, where $f(x)=\log_e(x+\sqrt{x^2+1}), x\in R$. Then, which one of the following is correct ? **[JEE Main 2021]**

(a) $g(1)=g(0)$ (b) $\sqrt{2}g(1)=g(0)$

(c) $g(1)=\sqrt{2}g(0)$ (d) $g(1)+g(0)=0$

24. Let $f(x)$ and $g(x)$ be two functions satisfying $f(x^2)+g(4-x)=4x^3$ and $g(4-x)+g(x)=0$, then the value of $\int_{-4}^{4}f(x)^2dx$ is .... **[JEE Main 2021]**

25. Let $P(x)$ be a real polynomial of degree 3 which vanishes at $x=-3$. Let $P(x)$ have local minima at $x=1$, local maxima at $x=-1$ and $\int_{-1}^{1}P(x)dx=18$, then the sum of all the coefficients of the polynomial $P(x)$ is equal to .... **[JEE Main 2021]**

26. Which of the following statements is correct for the function $g(\alpha)$ for $\alpha\in R$, such that $g(\alpha)=\int_{\pi/6}^{\pi/3}\frac{\sin^\alpha x}{\cos^\alpha x+\sin^\alpha x}dx$ **[JEE Main 2021]**

(a) $g(\alpha)$ is a strictly increasing function.

(b) $g(\alpha)$ has an inflection point at $\alpha=-\frac{1}{2}$.

(c) $g(\alpha)$ is a strictly decreasing function.

(d) $g(\alpha)$ is an even function.

27. Let $f: R \to R$ be defined as $f(x) = e^{-x} \sin x$. If $F: [0,1] \to R$ is a differentiable function, such that $F(x) = \int_0^x f(t)\,dt$, then the value of $\int_0^1 [F'(x) + f(x)] e^x \, dx$ lies in the interval **[JEE Main 2021]**

(a) $\left[\frac{327}{360}, \frac{329}{360}\right]$ (b) $\left[\frac{330}{360}, \frac{331}{360}\right]$

(c) $\left[\frac{331}{360}, \frac{334}{360}\right]$ (d) $\left[\frac{335}{360}, \frac{336}{360}\right]$

28. If the integral $\int_0^{10} \frac{[\sin 2\pi x]}{e^{x-[x]}} dx = \alpha e^{-1} + \beta e^{-\frac{1}{2}} + \gamma$, where α, β, γ are integers and $[x]$ denotes the greatest integer less than or equal to x, then the value of $\alpha + \beta + \gamma$ is equal to **[JEE Main 2021]**

(a) 0 (b) 20

(c) 25 (d) 10

29. Let $I_n = \int_1^e x^{19} (\log|x|)^n \, dx$, where $n \in N$. If $(20) I_{10} = \alpha I_9 + \beta I_8$, for natural numbers α and β, then $\alpha - \beta$ is equal to .... **[JEE Main 2021]**

30. Let $f: (0, 2) \to R$ be defined as $f(x) = \log_2 \left[1 + \tan\left(\frac{\pi x}{4}\right)\right]$.

Then, $\lim_{n\to\infty} \frac{2}{n}\left[f\left(\frac{1}{n}\right) + f\left(\frac{2}{n}\right) + \ldots + f(1)\right]$ is equal to......... . **[JEE Main 2021]**

31. If the normal to the curve $y(x) = \int_0^x (2t^2 - 15t + 10) dt$ at a point (a, b) is parallel to the line $x + 3y = -5$, $a > 1$, then the value of $|a + 6b|$ is equal to......... . **[JEE Main 2021]**

32. Let $f: R \to R$ be a continuous function such that $f(x) + f(x+1) = 2$, for all $x \in R$. If $I_1 = \int_0^8 f(x) dx$ and $I_2 = \int_{-1}^3 f(x) dx$, then the value of $I_1 + 2I_2$ is equal to......... . **[JEE Main 2021]**

33. Consider the integral, $I = \int_0^{10} \frac{[x] e^{[x]}}{e^{x-1}} dx$, where $[x]$ denotes the greatest integer less than or equal to x. Then, the value of I is equal to **[JEE Main 2021]**

(a) $9(e - 1)$ (b) $45(e + 1)$

(c) $45(e - 1)$ (d) $9(e + 1)$

34. For $x > 0$, if $f(x) = \int_1^x \frac{\log_e t}{(1+t)} dt$, then $f(e) + f\left(\frac{1}{e}\right)$ is equal to **[JEE Main 2021]**

(a) 1 (b) -1

(c) $\frac{1}{2}$ (d) 0

35. If $I_{m,n} = \int_0^1 x^{m-1} (1-x)^{n-1} dx$, for $m, n \geq 1$ and $\int_0^1 \frac{x^{m-1} + x^{n-1}}{(1+x)^{m+n}} dx = \alpha I_{m,n}, \alpha \in R$, then α equals ______ . **[JEE Main 2021]**

36. The value of $\sum_{n=1}^{100} \int_{n-1}^{n} e^{x-[x]} dx$, where $[x]$ is the greatest integer $\leq x$, is **[JEE Main 2021]**

(a) $100(e - 1)$ (b) $100(1 - e)$

(c) $100e$ (d) $100(1 + e)$

37. The value of $\int_{-\pi/2}^{\pi/2} \frac{\cos^2 x}{1 + 3^x} dx$ is **[JEE Main 2021]**

(a) $\frac{\pi}{4}$ (b) 4π (c) $\frac{\pi}{2}$ (d) 2π

38. The value of the integral $\int_0^\pi |\sin 2x| \, dx$ is .... **[JEE Main 2021]**

39. The value of $\int_{-2}^2 |3x^2 - 3x - 6| \, dx$ is .... **[JEE Main 2021]**

40. $\lim_{n\to\infty} \left[\frac{1}{n} + \frac{n}{(n+1)^2} + \frac{n}{(n+2)^2} + \ldots + \frac{n}{(2n-1)^2}\right]$ is equal to **[JEE Main 2021]**

(a) 1 (b) $\frac{1}{2}$ (c) $\frac{1}{3}$ (d) $\frac{1}{4}$

41. If $I_n = \int_{\pi/4}^{\pi/2} \cot^n x \, dx$, then **[JEE Main 2021]**

(a) $\frac{1}{I_2 + I_4}, \frac{1}{I_3 + I_5}, \frac{1}{I_4 + I_6}$ are in AP

(b) $I_2 + I_4, I_3 + I_5, I_4 + I_6$ are in AP

(c) $\frac{1}{I_2 + I_4}, \frac{1}{I_3 + I_5}, \frac{1}{I_4 + I_6}$ are in GP

(d) $I_2 + I_4, (I_3 + I_5)^2, I_4 + I_6$ are in GP

42. The value of $\int_{-1}^1 x^2 e^{[x^3]} dx$, where $[t]$ denotes the greatest integer $\leq t$, is **[JEE Main 2021]**

(a) $\frac{e-1}{3e}$ (b) $\frac{e+1}{3}$ (c) $\frac{e+1}{3e}$ (d) $\frac{1}{3e}$

43. Let $f(x)$ be a differentiable function defined on $[0, 2]$, such that $f'(x) = f'(2-x)$, for all $x \in (0, 2)$, $f(0) = 1$ and $f(2) = e^2$. Then, the value of $\int_0^2 f(x) dx$ is **[JEE Main 2021]**

(a) $1 - e^2$ (b) $1 + e^2$ (c) $2(1 - e^2)$ (d) $2(1 + e^2)$

44. The value of the integral $\int_1^3 [x^2 - 2x - 2] \, dx$, where $[x]$ denotes the greatest integer less than or equal to x, is **[JEE Main 2021]**

(a) $-\sqrt{2} - \sqrt{3} + 1$ (b) $-\sqrt{2} - \sqrt{3} - 1$

(c) -5 (d) -4

45. If $\int_{-a}^{a}(|x|+|x-2|)dx=22,(a>2)$ and $[x]$ denotes the greatest integer $\leq x$, then $\int_{a}^{-a}(x+[x])dx$ is equal to .... **[JEE Main 2021]**

46. Let $f:\left[-\frac{\pi}{2},\frac{\pi}{2}\right]\to R$ be a continuous function such that $f(0)=1$ and $\int_0^{\frac{\pi}{3}}f(t)\,dt=0$ **[JEE Advanced 2021]**

Then, which of the following statements is (are) TRUE?

(a) The equation $f(x)-3\cos 3x=0$ has at least one solution in $\left(0,\frac{\pi}{3}\right)$

(b) The equation $f(x)-3\sin 3x=-\frac{6}{\pi}$ has at least one solution in $\left(0,\frac{\pi}{3}\right)$

(c) $\lim_{x\to 0}\frac{x\int_0^x f(t)\,dt}{1-e^{x^2}}=-1$.

(d) $\lim_{x\to 0}\frac{\sin x\int_0^x f(t)\,dt}{x^2}=-1$.

Question Stem for Question Nos. 47 and 48

Question Stem

Let $f_1:(0,\infty)\to R$ and $f_2:(0,\infty)\to R$ be defined by $f_1(x)=\int_0^x\prod_{j=1}^{21}(t-j)^j\,dt,\ x>0$ and $f_2(x)=98(x-1)^{50}-600(x-1)^{49}+2450,\ x>0$, where for any positive integer n and real numbers $a_1,a_2,\ldots,a_n$, $\prod_{i=1}^{n}a_i$ denotes the product of $a_1,a_2,\ldots,a_n$. Let m_i and n_i, respectively, denote the number of points of local minima and the number of points of local maxima of function $f_i, i=1,2$ in the interval $(0,\infty)$.

47. The value of $2m_1+3n_1+m_1n_1$ is ____. **[JEE Advanced 2021]**

48. The value of $6m_2+4n_2+8m_2n_2$ is ____. **[JEE Advanced 2021]**

Question Stem for Question Nos. 49 and 50

Question Stem

Let $g_i:\left[\frac{\pi}{8},\frac{3\pi}{8}\right]\to R, i=1,2$, and $f:\left[\frac{\pi}{8},\frac{3\pi}{8}\right]\to R$ be functions such that $g_1(x)=1$, $g_2(x)=|4x-\pi|$ and $f(x)=\sin^2 x$, for all $x\in\left[\frac{\pi}{8},\frac{3\pi}{8}\right]$. Define

$$S_i=\int_{\pi/8}^{3\pi/8}f(x)\cdot g_i(x)\,dx, i=1,2$$

49. The value of $\frac{16S_1}{\pi}$ is ____. **[JEE Advanced 2021]**

50. The value of $\frac{48S_2}{\pi^2}$ is ______ . **[JEE Advanced 2021]**

51. Which of the following statements is TRUE? **[JEE Advanced 2021]**

(a) $f(\sqrt{\ln 3})+g(\sqrt{\ln 3})=\frac{1}{3}$.

(b) For every $x>1$, there exists an $\alpha\in(1,x)$ such that $\psi_1(x)=1+\alpha x$

(c) For every $x>0$, there exists a $\beta\in(0,x)$ such that $\psi_2(x)=2x(\psi_1(\beta)-1)$.

(d) f is an increasing function on the interval $\left[0,\frac{3}{2}\right]$.

52. Which of the following statements is TRUE? **[JEE Advanced 2021]**

(a) $\psi_1(x)\leq 1$, for all $x>0$

(b) $\psi_2(x)\leq 0$, for all $x>0$

(c) $f(x)\geq 1-e^{-x^2}-\frac{2}{3}x^3+\frac{2}{5}x^5$, for all $x\in\left(0,\frac{1}{2}\right)$

(d) $g(x)\leq\frac{2}{3}x^3-\frac{2}{5}x^5+\frac{1}{7}x^7$, for all $x\in\left(0,\frac{1}{2}\right)$

53. For any real number x, let $[x]$ denote the largest integer less than or equal to x. If $I=\int_0^{10}\left[\sqrt{\frac{10x}{x+1}}\right]dx$, then the value of $9I$ is ___. **[JEE Advanced 2021]**

54. The integral $\int_0^2 ||x-1|-x|\,dx$ is equal to **[JEE Main 2020]**

55. Let $[t]$ denote the greatest integer less than or equal to t. Then the value of $\int_1^2|2x-[3x]|\,dx$ is .... **[JEE Main 2020]**

56. $\int_{-\pi}^{\pi}|\pi-|x||\,dx$ is equal to **[JEE Main 2020]**

(a) $\sqrt{2}\pi^2$ (b) $2\pi^2$

(c) π^2 (d) $\frac{\pi^2}{2}$

57. If the value of the integral $\int_0^{1/2}\frac{x^2}{(1-x^2)^{3/2}}dx$ is $\frac{k}{6}$, then k is equal to **[JEE Main 2020]**

(a) $3\sqrt{2}+\pi$ (b) $2\sqrt{3}-\pi$

(c) $2\sqrt{3}+\pi$ (d) $3\sqrt{2}-\pi$

58. Let $f(x)=|x-2|$ and $g(x)=f(f(x)), x\in[0,4]$. Then $\int_0^3(g(x)-f(x))\,dx$ is equal to **[JEE Main 2020]**

(a) $\frac{3}{2}$ (b) $\frac{1}{2}$

(c) 0 (d) 1

59. Let $\{x\}$ and $[x]$ denote the fractional part of x and the greatest integer $\leq x$ respectively of a real number x. If $\int_0^n \{x\}dx, \int_0^n [x]dx$ and $10(n^2 - n), (n \in N, n > 1)$ are three consecutive terms of a GP, then n is equal to .... **[JEE Main 2020]**

60. The integral $\int_{\pi/6}^{\pi/3} \tan^3 x \cdot \sin^2 3x(2\sec^2 x \cdot \sin^2 3x + 3\tan x \cdot \sin 6x)dx$ is equal to **[JEE Main 2020]**

(a) $-\frac{1}{9}$ (b) $\frac{7}{18}$ (c) $-\frac{1}{18}$ (d) $\frac{9}{2}$

61. The value of $\int_{-\pi/2}^{\pi/2} \frac{1}{1+e^{\sin x}}dx$ is **[JEE Main 2020]**

(a) $\frac{\pi}{2}$ (b) $\frac{\pi}{4}$ (c) π (d) $\frac{3\pi}{2}$

62. If $I_1 = \int_0^1 (1-x^{50})^{100} dx$ and $I_2 = \int_0^1 (1-x^{50})^{101} dx$ such that $I_2 = \alpha I_1$, then α equals to **[JEE Main 2020]**

(a) $\frac{5049}{5050}$ (b) $\frac{5050}{5049}$ (c) $\frac{5050}{5051}$ (d) $\frac{5051}{5050}$

63. The integral $\int_1^2 e^x \cdot x^x (2 + \log_e x)dx$ equals **[JEE Main 2020]**

(a) $e(4e+1)$ (b) $4e^2 - 1$ (c) $e(4e-1)$ (d) $e(2e-1)$

64. If $f(a+b+1-x) = f(x)$, for all x, where a and b are fixed positive real numbers, then $\frac{1}{a+b}\int_a^b x(f(x)+f(x+1))dx$ is equal to **[JEE Main 2020]**

(a) $\int_{a+1}^{b+1} f(x+1)dx$ (b) $\int_{a+1}^{b+1} f(x)dx$

(c) $\int_{a-1}^{b-1} f(x+1)dx$ (d) $\int_{a-1}^{b-1} f(x)dx$

65. If θ_1 and θ_2 be respectively the smallest and the largest values of θ in $(0, 2\pi) - \{\pi\}$ which satisfy the equation, $2\cot^2\theta - \frac{5}{\sin\theta} + 4 = 0$, then $\int_{\theta_1}^{\theta_2} \cos^2 3\theta d\theta$ is equal to **[JEE Main 2020]**

(a) $\frac{\pi}{3} + \frac{1}{6}$ (b) $\frac{\pi}{3}$ (c) $\frac{2\pi}{3}$ (d) $\frac{\pi}{9}$

66. The value of α for which $4\alpha\int_{-1}^{2} e^{-\alpha|x|} dx = 5$, is **[JEE Main 2020]**

(a) $\log_e \sqrt{2}$ (b) $\log_e \left(\frac{3}{2}\right)$

(c) $\log_e 2$ (d) $\log_e \left(\frac{4}{3}\right)$

67. If $I = \int_1^2 \frac{dx}{\sqrt{2x^3 - 9x^2 + 12x + 4}}$, then **[JEE Main 2020]**

(a) $\frac{1}{6} < I^2 < \frac{1}{2}$ (b) $\frac{1}{8} < I^2 < \frac{1}{4}$

(c) $\frac{1}{9} < I^2 < \frac{1}{8}$ (d) $\frac{1}{16} < I^2 < \frac{1}{9}$

68. $\lim_{x \to 0} \frac{\int_0^x t\sin(10t)dt}{x}$ is equal to **[JEE Main 2020]**

(a) 0 (b) $\frac{1}{10}$ (c) $-\frac{1}{10}$ (d) $-\frac{1}{5}$

69. The value of $\int_0^{2\pi} \frac{x\sin^8 x}{\sin^8 x + \cos^8 x} dx$ is equal to **[JEE Main 2020]**

(a) 2π (b) 4π

(c) $2\pi^2$ (d) π^2

70. Let a function $f: [0, 5] \to \mathbb{R}$ be continuous, $f(1) = 3$ and F be defined as:

$$F(x) = \int_1^x t^2 g(t)dt, \text{ where } g(t) = \int_1^t f(u)du.$$

Then for the function F, the point $x = 1$ is **[JEE Main 2020]**

(a) not a critical point. (b) a point of inflection.

(c) a point of local maxima. (d) a point of local minima.

71. Which of the following inequalities is/are TRUE? **[JEE Advanced 2020]**

(a) $\int_0^1 x\cos x dx \geq \frac{3}{8}$ (b) $\int_0^1 x\sin x dx \geq \frac{3}{10}$

(c) $\int_0^1 x^2 \cos x dx \geq \frac{1}{2}$ (d) $\int_0^1 x^2 \sin x dx \geq \frac{2}{9}$

72. Let $f: R \to R$ be a differentiable function such that its derivative f' is continuous and $f(\pi) = -6$. If $F: [0, \pi] \to R$ is defined by $F(x) = \int_0^x f(t)dt$, and if

$$\int_0^{\pi} (f'(x) + F(x))\cos x \, dx = 2$$

then the value of $f(0)$ is .... **[JEE Advanced 2020]**

73. Let $f(x) = \int_0^x g(t)dt$, where g is a non-zero even function. If $f(x+5) = g(x)$, then $\int_0^x f(t)dt$ equals **[JEE Main 2019]**

(a) $5\int_{x+5}^{5} g(t)dt$ (b) $\int_{5}^{x+5} g(t)dt$

(c) $2\int_{5}^{x+5} g(t)dt$ (d) $\int_{x+5}^{5} g(t)dt$

74. The value of $\int_0^{\pi/2} \frac{\sin^3 x}{\sin x + \cos x} dx$ is **[JEE Main 2019]**

(a) $\frac{\pi - 1}{2}$ (b) $\frac{\pi - 2}{8}$ (c) $\frac{\pi - 1}{4}$ (d) $\frac{\pi - 2}{4}$

75. If $f: R \to R$ is a differentiable function and $f(2) = 6$, then $\lim_{x \to 2} \int_6^{f(x)} \frac{2t\,dt}{(x-2)}$ is **[JEE Main 2019]**

(a) $12f'(2)$ (b) 0 (c) $24f'(2)$ (d) $2f'(2)$

76. The value of the integral $\int_0^1 x\cot^{-1}(1-x^2+x^4)dx$ is **[JEE Main 2019]**

(a) $\frac{\pi}{4}-\frac{1}{2}\log_e 2$ (b) $\frac{\pi}{2}-\frac{1}{2}\log_e 2$

(c) $\frac{\pi}{4}-\log_e 2$ (d) $\frac{\pi}{2}-\log_e 2$

77. The value of $\int_0^{2\pi}[\sin 2x(1+\cos 3x)]\,dx$, where $[t]$ denotes the greatest integer function, is **[JEE Main 2019]**

(a) $-\pi$ (b) 2π (c) -2π (d) π

78. The integral $\int_{\pi/6}^{\pi/3}\sec^{2/3}x\,\text{cosec}^{4/3}x\,dx$ is equal to **[JEE Main 2019]**

(a) $3^{5/6}-3^{2/3}$ (b) $3^{7/6}-3^{5/6}$

(c) $3^{5/3}-3^{1/3}$ (d) $3^{4/3}-3^{1/3}$

79. If $\int_0^{\pi/2}\frac{\cot x}{\cot x+\text{cosec}\,x}dx=m(\pi+n)$, then $m\cdot n$ is equal to **[JEE Main 2019]**

(a) $-\frac{1}{2}$ (b) 1

(c) $\frac{1}{2}$ (d) -1

80. A value of α such that $\int_\alpha^{\alpha+1}\frac{dx}{(x+\alpha)(x+\alpha+1)}=\log_e\left(\frac{9}{8}\right)$ is **[JEE Main 2019]**

(a) -2 (b) $\frac{1}{2}$ (c) $-\frac{1}{2}$ (d) 2

81. The value of $\int_0^{\pi}|\cos x|^3\,dx$ is **[JEE Main 2019]**

(a) $\frac{2}{3}$ (b) $-\frac{4}{3}$ (c) 0 (d) $\frac{4}{3}$

82. If $\int_0^{\pi/3}\frac{\tan\theta}{\sqrt{2k\sec\theta}}d\theta=1-\frac{1}{\sqrt{2}},(k>0)$, then the value of k is **[JEE Main 2019]**

(a) 1 (b) $\frac{1}{2}$

(c) 2 (d) 4

83. Let $I=\int_a^b(x^4-2x^2)dx$. If I is minimum, then the ordered pair (a,b) is **[JEE Main 2019]**

(a) $(-\sqrt{2},0)$ (b) $(0,\sqrt{2})$

(c) $(\sqrt{2},-\sqrt{2})$ (d) $(-\sqrt{2},\sqrt{2})$

84. The value of $\int_{-\pi/2}^{\pi/2}\frac{dx}{[x]+[\sin x]+4}$, where $[t]$ denotes the greatest integer less than or equal to t, is **[JEE Main 2019]**

(a) $\frac{1}{12}(7\pi-5)$ (b) $\frac{1}{12}(7\pi+5)$

(c) $\frac{3}{10}(4\pi-3)$ (d) $\frac{3}{20}(4\pi-3)$

85. If $\int_0^x f(t)\,dt=x^2+\int_x^1 t^2f(t)dt$, then $f'\left(\frac{1}{2}\right)$ is **[JEE Main 2019]**

(a) $\frac{24}{25}$ (b) $\frac{18}{25}$ (c) $\frac{6}{25}$ (d) $\frac{4}{5}$

86. The value of the integral

$$\int_{-2}^{2}\frac{\sin^2 x}{\left[\frac{x}{\pi}\right]+\frac{1}{2}}dx$$

(where, $[x]$ denotes the greatest integer less than or equal to x) is **[JEE Main 2019]**

(a) $4-\sin 4$ (b) 4 (c) $\sin 4$ (d) 0

87. The integral $\int_{\pi/6}^{\pi/4}\frac{dx}{\sin 2x(\tan^5 x+\cot^5 x)}$ equals **[JEE Main 2019]**

(a) $\frac{1}{5}\left(\frac{\pi}{4}-\tan^{-1}\left(\frac{1}{3\sqrt{3}}\right)\right)$ (b) $\frac{1}{20}\tan^{-1}\left(\frac{1}{9\sqrt{3}}\right)$

(c) $\frac{1}{10}\left(\frac{\pi}{4}-\tan^{-1}\left(\frac{1}{9\sqrt{3}}\right)\right)$ (d) $\frac{\pi}{40}$

88. Let f and g be continuous functions on $[0,a]$ such that $f(x)=f(a-x)$ and $g(x)+g(a-x)=4$, then $\int_0^a f(x)g(x)\,dx$ is equal to **[JEE Main 2019]**

(a) $4\int_0^a f(x)\,dx$ (b) $\int_0^a f(x)\,dx$

(c) $2\int_0^a f(x)\,dx$ (d) $-3\int_0^a f(x)\,dx$

89. The integral $\int_1^e\left\{\left(\frac{x}{e}\right)^{2x}-\left(\frac{e}{x}\right)^x\right\}\log_e x\,dx$ is equal to **[JEE Main 2019]**

(a) $\frac{3}{2}-e-\frac{1}{2e^2}$ (b) $-\frac{1}{2}+\frac{1}{e}-\frac{1}{2e^2}$

(c) $\frac{1}{2}-e-\frac{1}{e^2}$ (d) $\frac{3}{2}-\frac{1}{e}-\frac{1}{2e^2}$

90. Let $f:R\to R$ be a continuously differentiable function such that $f(2)=6$ and $f'(2)=\frac{1}{48}$. If $\int_6^{f(x)}4t^3\,dt=(x-2)g(x)$, then $\lim_{x\to 2}g(x)$ is equal to **[JEE Main 2019]**

(a) 18 (b) 24 (c) 12 (d) 36

91. $\lim_{n\to\infty}\left(\frac{n}{n^2+1^2}+\frac{n}{n^2+2^2}+\frac{n}{n^2+3^2}+\ldots+\frac{1}{5n}\right)$ is equal to **[JEE Main 2019]**

(a) $\tan^{-1}(3)$ (b) $\tan^{-1}(2)$

(c) $\pi/4$ (d) $\pi/2$

92. If $I=\frac{2}{\pi}\int_{-\pi/4}^{\pi/4}\frac{dx}{(1+e^{\sin x})(2-\cos 2x)}$ then $27I^2$ equals .... **[JEE Advanced 2019]**

93. Let $f: R \to R$ be given by $f(x)=(x-1)(x-2)(x-5)$. Define

$$F(x)=\int_0^x f(t)dt, x>0$$

[JEE Advanced 2019]

Then which of the following options is/are correct?

(a) $F(x) \neq 0$ for all $x \in (0, 5)$
(b) F has a local maximum at $x = 2$
(c) F has two local maxima and one local minimum in $(0, \infty)$
(d) F has a local minimum at $x = 1$

94. For $a \in R, |a|>1$, let

$$\lim_{n\to\infty}\left(\frac{1+\sqrt[3]{2}+\ldots+\sqrt[3]{n}}{n^{7/3}\left(\frac{1}{(an+1)^2}+\frac{1}{(an+2)^2}+\ldots+\frac{1}{(an+n)^2}\right)}\right)=54$$

Then the possible value(s) of a is/are **[JEE Advanced 2019]**

(a) –6
(b) 7
(c) 8
(d) –9

95. The value of the integral

$$\int_0^{\pi/2}\frac{3\sqrt{\cos\theta}}{(\sqrt{\cos\theta}+\sqrt{\sin\theta})^5}d\theta \text{ equals } \ldots\ldots\ldots\ldots$$

[JEE Advanced 2019]

96. The value of $\int_{-\pi/2}^{\pi/2}\frac{\sin^2 x}{1+2^x}dx$ is **[JEE Main 2018]**

(a) $\frac{\pi}{8}$
(b) $\frac{\pi}{2}$
(c) 4π
(d) $\frac{\pi}{4}$

97. For each positive integer n, let

$$y_n=\frac{1}{n}((n+1)(n+2)\ldots(n+n))^{1/n}.$$

For $x \in R$, let $[x]$ be the greatest integer less than or equal to x. If $\lim_{n\to\infty} y_n = L$, then the value of $[L]$ is ………………. **[JEE Advanced 2018]**

98. The value of the integral $\int_0^{1/2}\frac{1+\sqrt{3}}{((x+1)^2(1-x)^6)^{1/4}}dx$ is …… **[JEE Advanced 2018]**

Answers

1. (c)	**2.** (d)	**3.** (5)	**4.** (4)	**5.** (b)	**6.** (a)	**7.** (c)	**8.** (a)	**9.** (b)	**10.** (b)
11. (b)	**12.** (c)	**13.** (1)	**14.** (d)	**15.** (b)	**16.** (c)	**17.** (b)	**18.** (a)	**19.** (c)	**20.** (b)
21. (a)	**22.** (d)	**23.** (b)	**24.** (512)	**25.** (8)	**26.** (d)	**27.** (b)	**28.** (a)	**29.** (1)	**30.** (1)
31. (406)	**32.** (16)	**33.** (c)	**34.** (c)	**35.** (1)	**36.** (a)	**37.** (a)	**38.** (2)	**39.** (19)	**40.** (b)
41. (a)	**42.** (c)	**43.** (b)	**44.** (b)	**45.** (3)	**46.** (a,b,c)	**47.** (57)	**48.** (6)	**49.** (2)	**50.** (1.5)
51. (c)	**52.** (d)	**53.** (182)	**54.** (1.5)	**55.** (1)	**56.** (c)	**57.** (b)	**58.** (d)	**59.** (21)	**60.** (c)
61. (a)	**62.** (c)	**63.** (c)	**64.** (c)	**65.** (b)	**66.** (c)	**67.** (c)	**68.** (a)	**69.** (d)	**70.** (d)
71. (a,b,d)	**72.** (4.00)	**73.** (d)	**74.** (c)	**75.** (a)	**76.** (a)	**77.** (a)	**78.** (b)	**79.** (d)	**80.** (a)
81. (d)	**82.** (c)	**83.** (d)	**84.** (d)	**85.** (a)	**86.** (d)	**87.** (c)	**88.** (c)	**89.** (a)	**90.** (a)
91. (b)	**92.** (4.0)	**93.** (a,b,d)	**94.** (c,d)	**95.** (0.5)	**96.** (d)	**97.** (1)	**98.** (2)		

Area of Bounded Regions

1. The area, enclosed by the curves $y=\sin x+\cos x$ and $y=|\cos x-\sin x|$ and the lines $x=0, x=\frac{\pi}{2}$, is **[JEE Main 2021]**

(a) $2\sqrt{2}(\sqrt{2}-1)$
(b) $2(\sqrt{2}+1)$
(c) $4(\sqrt{2}-1)$
(d) $2\sqrt{2}(\sqrt{2}+1)$

2. If the line $y=mx$ bisects the area enclosed by the lines $x=0$ and $y=0, x=\frac{3}{2}$ and the curve $y=1+4x-x^2$, then 12 m is equal to **[JEE Main 2021]**

3. The area of the region bounded by the parabola $(y-2)^2=(x-1)$, the tangent to it at the point whose ordinate is 3 and the X-axis is **[JEE Main 2021]**

(a) 9
(b) 10
(c) 4
(d) 6

4. The area of the region $S=\{(x, y): 3x^2 \leq 4y \leq 6x+24\}$ is **[JEE Main 2021]**

5. Let a and b respectively be the points of local maximum and local minimum of the function $f(x)=2x^3-3x^2-12x$. If A is the total area of the region bounded by $y=f(x)$, the X-axis and the lines $x=a$ and $x=b$, then 4A is equal to **[JEE Main 2021]**

6. If the area of the bounded region

$$R=\left\{(x, y): \max\{0, \log_e x\} \leq y \leq 2^x, \frac{1}{2} \leq x \leq 2\right\}$$

is, $\alpha(\log_e 2)^{-1}+\beta(\log_e 2)+\gamma$, then the value of $(\alpha+\beta-2\gamma)^2$ is equal to **[JEE Main 2021]**

(a) 8
(b) 2
(c) 4
(d) 1

7. The area of the region bounded by $y-x=2$ and $x^2=y$ is equal to **[JEE Main 2021]**

(a) $\frac{16}{3}$
(b) $\frac{2}{3}$
(c) $\frac{9}{2}$
(d) $\frac{4}{3}$

8. The area (in sq. units) of the region, given by the set $\{(x, y) \in R \times R \mid x \geq 0, 2x^2 \leq y \leq 4-2x\}$ is **[JEE Main 2021]**

(a) $\frac{8}{3}$ (b) $\frac{17}{3}$ (c) $\frac{13}{3}$ (d) $\frac{7}{3}$

9. The area (in square units) of the region bounded by the curves $x^2 + 2y - 1 = 0$, $y^2 + 4x - 4 = 0$ and $y^2 - 4x - 4 = 0$, in the upper half plane is .... **[JEE Main 2021]**

10. Let $g(x) = \int_0^x f(t)\,dt$, where f is continuous function in $[0, 3]$ such that $\frac{1}{3} \leq f(t) \leq 1$ for all $t \in [0, 1]$ and $0 \leq f(t) \leq \frac{1}{2}$ for all $t \in (1, 3]$. The largest possible interval in which $g(3)$ lies is **[JEE Main 2021]**

(a) $\left[-1, -\frac{1}{2}\right]$ (b) $\left[-\frac{3}{2}, -1\right]$ (c) $\left[\frac{1}{3}, 2\right]$ (d) $[1, 3]$

11. The area bounded by the curve $4y^2 = x^2(4-x)(x-2)$ is equal to **[JEE Main 2021]**

(a) $\frac{\pi}{8}$ (b) $\frac{3\pi}{8}$ (c) $\frac{3\pi}{2}$ (d) $\frac{\pi}{16}$

12. Let $f : [-3, 1] \to R$ be given as

$$f(x) = \begin{cases} \min\{(x+6), x^2\}, & -3 \leq x \leq 0 \\ \max\{\sqrt{x}, x^2\}, & 0 \leq x \leq 1 \end{cases}.$$

If the area bounded by $y = f(x)$ and X-axis is A, then the value of $6A$ is equal to .... **[JEE Main 2021]**

13. Let A_1 be the area of the region bounded by the curves $y = \sin x$, $y = \cos x$ and y-axis in the first quadrant. Also, let A_2 be the area of the region bounded by the curves $y = \sin x$, $y = \cos x$, x-axis and $x = \frac{\pi}{2}$ in the first quadrant. Then, **[JEE Main 2021]**

(a) $A_1 : A_2 = 1 : \sqrt{2}$ and $A_1 + A_2 = 1$
(b) $A_1 = A_2$ and $A_1 + A_2 = \sqrt{2}$
(c) $2A_1 = A_2$ and $A_1 + A_2 = 1 + \sqrt{2}$
(d) $A_1 : A_2 = 1 : 2$ and $A_1 + A_2 = 1$

14. The area bounded by the lines $y = ||x-1| - 2|$ is .... **[JEE Main 2021]**

15. The graphs of sine and cosine functions, intersect each other at a number of points and between two consecutive points of intersection, the two graphs enclose the same area A. Then A^4 is equal to .... **[JEE Main 2021]**

16. The area of the region

$R = \{(x, y) : 5x^2 \leq y \leq 2x^2 + 9\}$ is **[JEE Main 2021]**

(a) $11\sqrt{3}$ sq units (b) $12\sqrt{3}$ sq units
(c) $9\sqrt{3}$ sq units (d) $6\sqrt{3}$ sq units

17. If the area of the triangle formed by the positive X-axis, the normal and the tangent to the circle $(x-2)^2 + (y-3)^2 = 25$ at the point $(5, 7)$ is A, then $24A$ is equal to ... . **[JEE Main 2021]**

18. The area (in sq. units) of the part of the circle $x^2 + y^2 = 36$, which is outside the parabola $y^2 = 9x$, is **[JEE Main 2021]**

(a) $24\pi + 3\sqrt{3}$ (b) $24\pi - 3\sqrt{3}$
(c) $12\pi + 3\sqrt{3}$ $12\pi - 3\sqrt{3}$

19. The area of the region $\left\{(x, y) : 0 \leq x \leq \frac{9}{4}, 0 \leq y \leq 1, x \geq 3y, x + y \geq 2\right\}$ is **[JEE Advanced 2021]**

(a) $\frac{11}{32}$ (b) $\frac{35}{96}$ (c) $\frac{37}{96}$ (d) $\frac{13}{32}$

20. The area (in sq. units) of the region $A = \{(x, y) : |x| + |y| \leq 1, 2y^2 \geq |x|\}$ is **[JEE Main 2020]**

(a) $\frac{1}{3}$ (b) $\frac{7}{6}$ (c) $\frac{1}{6}$ (d) $\frac{5}{6}$

21. Area (in sq. units) of the region outside $\frac{|x|}{2} + \frac{|y|}{3} = 1$ and inside the ellipse $\frac{x^2}{4} + \frac{y^2}{9} = 1$ is **[JEE Main 2020]**

(a) $6(\pi - 2)$ (b) $3(\pi - 2)$ (c) $3(4 - \pi)$ (d) $6(4 - \pi)$

22. Consider region $R = \{(x, y) \in R^2 : x^2 \leq y \leq 2x\}$. If a line $y = \alpha$ divides the area of region R into two equal parts, then which of the following is true? **[JEE Main 2020]**

(a) $\alpha^3 - 6\alpha^2 + 16 = 0$ (b) $3\alpha^2 - 8\alpha^{3/2} + 8 = 0$
(c) $3\alpha^2 - 8\alpha + 8 = 0$ (d) $\alpha^3 - 6\alpha^{3/2} - 16 = 0$

23. The area (in sq. units) of the region $\{(x, y) : 0 \leq y \leq x^2 + 1, 0 \leq y \leq x + 1, \frac{1}{2} \leq x \leq 2\}$ is **[JEE Main 2020]**

(a) $\frac{23}{16}$ (b) $\frac{79}{24}$ (c) $\frac{79}{16}$ (d) $\frac{23}{6}$

24. The area (in sq. units) of the largest rectangle $ABCD$ whose vertices A and B lie on the X-axis and vertices C and D lie on the parabola, $y = x^2 - 1$ below the X-axis, is **[JEE Main 2020]**

(a) $\frac{4}{3\sqrt{3}}$ (b) $\frac{2}{3\sqrt{3}}$ (c) $\frac{1}{3\sqrt{3}}$ (d) $\frac{4}{3}$

25. The area (in sq. units) of the region $A = \{(x, y) : (x-1)[x] \leq y \leq 2\sqrt{x}, 0 \leq x \leq 2\}$, where $[t]$ denotes the greatest integer function, is **[JEE Main 2020]**

(a) $\frac{8}{3}\sqrt{2} - \frac{1}{2}$ (b) $\frac{4}{3}\sqrt{2} + 1$
(c) $\frac{8}{3}\sqrt{2} - 1$ (d) $\frac{4}{3}\sqrt{2} - \frac{1}{2}$

26. The area (in sq. units) of the region enclosed by the curves $y = x^2 - 1$ and $y = 1 - x^2$ is equal to **[JEE Main 2020]**

(a) $\frac{4}{3}$ (b) $\frac{8}{3}$ (c) $\frac{7}{2}$ (d) $\frac{16}{3}$

27. The area (in sq. units) of the region $\{(x, y) \in R^2 \mid 4x^2 \le y \le 8x + 12\}$ is **[JEE Main 2020]**

(a) $\frac{124}{3}$ (b) $\frac{125}{3}$ (c) $\frac{127}{3}$ (d) $\frac{128}{3}$

28. The area of the region, enclosed by the circle $x^2 + y^2 = 2$ which is not common to the region bounded by the parabola $y^2 = x$ and the straight line $y = x$, is **[JEE Main 2020]**

(a) $\frac{1}{3}(12\pi - 1)$ (b) $\frac{1}{6}(12\pi - 1)$
(c) $\frac{1}{6}(24\pi - 1)$ (d) $\frac{1}{3}(6\pi - 1)$

29. For $a > 0$, let the curves $C_1 : y^2 = ax$ and $C_2 : x^2 = ay$ intersect at origin O and a point P. Let the line $x = b (0 < b < a)$ intersect the chord OP and the x-axis at points Q and R, respectively. If the line $x = b$ bisects the area bounded by the curves, C_1 and C_2, and the area of $\Delta OQR = \frac{1}{2}$, then 'a' satisfies the equation **[JEE Main 2020]**

(a) $x^6 + 6x^3 - 4 = 0$ (b) $x^6 - 12x^3 + 4 = 0$
(c) $x^6 - 6x^3 + 4 = 0$ (d) $x^6 - 12x^3 - 4 = 0$

30. The area (in sq. units) of the region $\{(x, y) \in R^2 : x^2 \le y \le 3 - 2x\}$, is **[JEE Main 2020]**

(a) $\frac{31}{3}$ (b) $\frac{32}{3}$ (c) $\frac{29}{3}$ (d) $\frac{34}{3}$

31. Given, $f(x) = \begin{cases} x, & 0 \le x < \frac{1}{2} \\ \frac{1}{2}, & x = \frac{1}{2} \\ 1 - x, & \frac{1}{2} < x \le 1 \end{cases}$

and $g(x) = \left(x - \frac{1}{2}\right)^2, x \in R$. Then the area (in sq. units) of the region bounded by the curves $y = f(x)$ and $y = g(x)$ between the lines, $2x = 1$ and $2x = \sqrt{3}$, is **[JEE Main 2020]**

(a) $\frac{1}{2} + \frac{\sqrt{3}}{4}$ (b) $\frac{1}{3} + \frac{\sqrt{3}}{4}$ (c) $\frac{1}{2} - \frac{\sqrt{3}}{4}$ (d) $\frac{\sqrt{3}}{4} - \frac{1}{3}$

32. Let the functions $f : \mathbf{R} \to \mathbf{R}$ and $g : \mathbf{R} \to \mathbf{R}$ be defined by

$$f(x) = e^{x-1} - e^{-|x-1|} \text{ and } g(x) = \frac{1}{2}(e^{x-1} + e^{1-x}).$$

Then the area of the region in the first quadrant bounded by the curves $y = f(x)$, $y = g(x)$ and $x = 0$ is **[JEE Advanced 2020]**

(a) $(2 - \sqrt{3}) + \frac{1}{2}(e - e^{-1})$ (b) $(2 + \sqrt{3}) + \frac{1}{2}(e - e^{-1})$
(c) $(2 - \sqrt{3}) + \frac{1}{2}(e + e^{-1})$ (d) $(2 + \sqrt{3}) + \frac{1}{2}(e + e^{-1})$

33. The area (in sq units) of the region bounded by the curve $x^2 = 4y$ and the straight line $x = 4y - 2$ is **[JEE Main 2019]**

(a) $\frac{7}{8}$ (b) $\frac{9}{8}$ (c) $\frac{5}{4}$ (d) $\frac{3}{4}$

34. The area (in sq units) of the region $A = \{(x, y) \in R \times R \mid 0 \le x \le 3, 0 \le y \le 4, y \le x^2 + 3x\}$ is **[JEE Main 2019]**

(a) $\frac{53}{6}$ (b) 8 (c) $\frac{59}{6}$ (d) $\frac{26}{3}$

35. Let $S(\alpha) = \{(x, y) : y^2 \le x, 0 \le x \le \alpha\}$ and $A(\alpha)$ is area of the region $S(\alpha)$. If for $\lambda, 0 < \lambda < 4$, $A(\lambda) : A(4) = 2 : 5$, then λ equals **[JEE Main 2019]**

(a) $2\left(\frac{4}{25}\right)^{1/3}$ (b) $4\left(\frac{2}{5}\right)^{1/3}$ (c) $4\left(\frac{4}{25}\right)^{1/3}$ (d) $2\left(\frac{2}{5}\right)^{1/3}$

36. The area (in sq units) of the region $A = \{(x, y) : x^2 \le y \le x + 2\}$ is **[JEE Main 2019]**

(a) $\frac{13}{6}$ (b) $\frac{9}{2}$ (c) $\frac{31}{6}$ (d) $\frac{10}{3}$

37. The area (in sq units) of the region $A = \left\{(x, y) : \frac{y^2}{2} \le x \le y + 4\right\}$ is **[JEE Main 2019]**

(a) 30 (b) $\frac{53}{3}$ (c) 16 (d) 18

38. The region represented by $|x - y| \le 2$ and $|x + y| \le 2$ is bounded by a **[JEE Main 2019]**

(a) rhombus of side length 2 units
(b) rhombus of area $8\sqrt{2}$ sq units
(c) square of side length $2\sqrt{2}$ units
(d) square of area 16 sq units

39. The area (in sq units) of the region bounded by the curves $y = 2^x$ and $y = |x + 1|$, in the first quadrant is **[JEE Main 2019]**

(a) $\frac{3}{2}$ (b) $\log_e 2 + \frac{3}{2}$
(c) $\frac{1}{2}$ (d) $\frac{3}{2} - \frac{1}{\log_e 2}$

40. If the area (in sq units) of the region $\{(x, y) : y^2 \le 4x, x + y \le 1, x \ge 0, y \ge 0\}$ is $a\sqrt{2} + b$, then $a - b$ is equal to **[JEE Main 2019]**

(a) $\frac{10}{3}$ (b) 6
(c) $\frac{8}{3}$ (d) $-\frac{2}{3}$

41. If the area (in sq units) bounded by the parabola $y^2 = 4\lambda x$ and the line $y = \lambda x$, $\lambda > 0$, is $\frac{1}{9}$, then λ is equal to **[JEE Main 2019]**

(a) $2\sqrt{6}$ (b) 48 (c) 24 (d) $4\sqrt{3}$

42. The area (in sq units) bounded by the parabola $y = x^2 - 1$, the tangent at the point (2, 3) to it and the Y-axis is **[JEE Main 2019]**

(a) $\frac{8}{3}$ (b) $\frac{56}{3}$ (c) $\frac{32}{3}$ (d) $\frac{14}{3}$

43. The area of the region $A=\{(x,y); 0 \le y \le x|x|+1$ and $-1 \le x \le 1\}$ in sq. units, is **[JEE Main 2019]**

(a) 2 (b) $\frac{4}{3}$ (c) $\frac{1}{3}$ (d) $\frac{2}{3}$

44. If the area enclosed between the curves $y=kx^2$ and $x=ky^2, (k>0)$, is 1 square unit. Then, k is **[JEE Main 2019]**

(a) $\sqrt{3}$ (b) $\frac{1}{\sqrt{3}}$ (c) $\frac{2}{\sqrt{3}}$ (d) $\frac{\sqrt{3}}{2}$

45. The area (in sq units) in the first quadrant bounded by the parabola, $y=x^2+1$, the tangent to it at the point (2, 5) and the coordinate axes is **[JEE Main 2019]**

(a) $\frac{14}{3}$ (b) $\frac{187}{24}$

(c) $\frac{8}{3}$ (d) $\frac{37}{24}$

46. The area (in sq units) of the region bounded by the parabola, $y=x^2+2$ and the lines, $y=x+1, x=0$ and $x=3$, is **[JEE Main 2019]**

(a) $\frac{15}{2}$ (b) $\frac{17}{4}$ (c) $\frac{21}{2}$ (d) $\frac{15}{4}$

47. The area of the region $\{(x,y): xy \le 8, 1 \le y \le x^2\}$ is **[JEE Advanced 2019]**

(a) $8\log_e 2 - \frac{14}{3}$ (b) $8\log_e 2 - \frac{7}{3}$

(c) $16\log_e 2 - \frac{14}{3}$ (d) $16\log_e 2 - 6$

48. Let $g(x)=\cos x^2$, $f(x)=\sqrt{x}$ and $\alpha, \beta\ (\alpha<\beta)$ be the roots of the quadratic equation $18x^2-9\pi x+\pi^2=0$. Then, the area (in sq units) bounded by the curve $y=(gof)(x)$ and the lines $x=\alpha$, $x=\beta$ and $y=0$, is **[JEE Main 2018]**

(a) $\frac{1}{2}(\sqrt{3}-1)$ (b) $\frac{1}{2}(\sqrt{3}+1)$

(c) $\frac{1}{2}(\sqrt{3}-\sqrt{2})$ (d) $\frac{1}{2}(\sqrt{2}-1)$

49. A farmer F_1 has a land in the shape of a triangle with vertices at $P(0,0)$, $Q(1,1)$ and $R(2,0)$. From this land, a neighbouring farmer F_2 takes away the region which lies between the sides PQ and a curve of the form $y=x^n$ $(n>1)$. If the area of the region taken away by the farmer F_2 is exactly 30% of the area of ΔPQR, then the value of n is .... **[JEE Advanced 2018]**

Answers

1. (a)	**2.** (26)	**3.** (a)	**4.** (27)	**5.** (114)	**6.** (b)	**7.** (c)	**8.** (d)	**9.** (2)	**10.** (c)
11. (c)	**12.** (41)	**13.** (a)	**14.** (4)	**15.** (64)	**16.** (b)	**17.** (1225)	**18.** (b)	**19.** (a)	**20.** (d)
21. (a)	**22.** (b)	**23.** (b)	**24.** (a)	**25.** (a)	**26.** (b)	**27.** (d)	**28.** (b)	**29.** (b)	**30.** (b)
31. (d)	**32.** (a)	**33.** (b)	**34.** (c)	**35.** (c)	**36.** (b)	**37.** (d)	**38.** (c)	**39.** (d)	**40.** (b)
41. (c)	**42.** (a)	**43.** (a)	**44.** (b)	**45.** (d)	**46.** (a)	**47.** (c)	**48.** (a)	**49.** (4)	

Differential Equations

1. A differential equation representing the family of parabolas with axis parallel to Y-axis and whose length of latus rectum is the distance of the point (2, − 3) from the line $3x+4y=5$, is given by **[JEE Main 2021]**

(a) $10\frac{d^2y}{dx^2}=11$ (b) $11\frac{d^2x}{dy^2}+10$

(c) $10\frac{d^2x}{dy^2}=11$ (d) $11\frac{d^2y}{dx^2}=10$

2. The differential equation satisfied by the system of parabolas $y^2=4a(x+a)$ is **[JEE Main 2021]**

(a) $y\left(\frac{dy}{dx}\right)^2-2x\left(\frac{dy}{dx}\right)-y=0$ (b) $y\left(\frac{dy}{dx}\right)^2-2x\left(\frac{dy}{dx}\right)+y=0$

(c) $y\left(\frac{dy}{dx}\right)^2+2x\left(\frac{dy}{dx}\right)-y=0$ (d) $y\left(\frac{dy}{dx}\right)+2x\left(\frac{dy}{dx}\right)-y=0$

3. The difference between degree and order of a differential equation that represents the family of curves given by $y^2=a\left(x+\frac{\sqrt{a}}{2}\right), a>0$ is .... **[JEE Main 2021]**

4. Let f be a non-negative function in [0, 1] and twice differentiable in (0, 1). If $\int_0^x \sqrt{1-(f'(t))^2}\, dt = \int_0^x f(t)dt$, $0 \le x \le 1$ and $f(0)=0$, then $\lim_{x \to 0} \frac{1}{x^2}\int_0^x f(t)dt$ **[JEE Main 2021]**

(a) equals 0 (b) equals 1

(c) does not exist (d) equals 1/2

5. If $\frac{dy}{dx}=\frac{2^{x+y}-2^x}{2^y}$, $y(0)=1$, then $y(1)$ is equal to **[JEE Main 2021]**

(a) $\log_2(2+e)$ (b) $\log_2(1+e)$

(c) $\log_2(2e)$ (d) $\log_2(1+e^2)$

6. If $\frac{dy}{dx}=\frac{2^x y+2^y \cdot 2^x}{2^x+2^{x+y}\log_e 2}$, $y(0)=0$, then for $y=1$, the value of x lies in the interval **[JEE Main 2021]**

(a) (1,2) (b) $\left(\frac{1}{2}, 1\right]$

(c) (2, 3) (d) $\left(0, \frac{1}{2}\right]$

7. If $y\dfrac{dy}{dx}=x\left[\dfrac{y^2}{x^2}+\dfrac{\phi\left(\dfrac{y^2}{x^2}\right)}{\phi'\left(\dfrac{y^2}{x^2}\right)}\right], x>0$, $\phi>0$, and $y(1)=-1$, then $\phi\left(\dfrac{y^2}{4}\right)$ is equal to **[JEE Main 2021]**

(a) $4\ \phi\ (2)$ (b) $4\ \phi\ (1)$
(c) $2\ \phi\ (1)$ (d) $\phi\ (1)$

8. Let $y=y(x)$ be the solution of the differential equation $\dfrac{dy}{dx}=2(y+2\sin x-5)x-2\cos x$ such that, $y(0)=7$. Then $y(\pi)$ is equal to **[JEE Main 2021]**

(a) $2e^{\pi^2}+5$ (b) $e^{\pi^2}+5$
(c) $3e^{\pi^2}+5$ (d) $7e^{\pi^2}+5$

9. Let $y(x)$ be the solution of the differential equation $2x^2dy+(e^y-2x)dx=0, x>0$. If $y(e)=1$, then $y(1)$ is equal to **[JEE Main 2021]**

(a) 0 (b) 2
(c) $\log_e 2$ (d) $\log_e (2e)$

10. Let f be a twice differentiable function defined on R, such that $f(0)=1, f'(0)=2$ and $f'(x)\neq 0$ for all $x\in R$. If $\begin{vmatrix} f(x) & f'(x) \\ f'(x) & f''(x) \end{vmatrix}=0$, for all $x\in R$, then the value of $f(1)$ lies in the interval **[JEE Main 2021]**

(a) (9, 12) (b) (6, 9) (c) (0, 3) (d) (3, 6)

11. Let slope of the tangent line to a curve at any point $P(x, y)$ be given by $\dfrac{xy^2+y}{x}$. If the curve intersects the line $x+2y=4$ at $x=-2$, then the value of y, for which the point $(3, y)$ lies on the curve, is **[JEE Main 2021]**

(a) $\dfrac{18}{35}$ (b) $-\dfrac{4}{3}$ (c) $-\dfrac{18}{19}$ (d) $-\dfrac{18}{11}$

12. Let $y=y(x)$ be the solution of the differential equation $\dfrac{dy}{dx}=1+xe^{y-x}, -\sqrt{2}<x<\sqrt{2}$, $y(0)=0$, then the minimum value of $y(x), x\in(-\sqrt{2},\sqrt{2})$ is equal to **[JEE Main 2021]**

(a) $(2-\sqrt{3})-\log_e 2$ (b) $(2+\sqrt{3})-\log_e 2$
(c) $(1+\sqrt{3})-\log_e(\sqrt{3}-1)$ (d) $(1-\sqrt{3})-\log_e(\sqrt{3}-1)$

13. Let $y=y(x)$ be solution of the differential equation $\log_e\left(\dfrac{dy}{dx}\right)=3x+4y$, with $y(0)=0$. If $y\left(-\dfrac{2}{3}\log_e 2\right)=\alpha\log_e 2$, then the value of α is equal to **[JEE Main 2021]**

(a) $-\dfrac{1}{4}$ (b) $\dfrac{1}{4}$ (c) 2 (d) $-\dfrac{1}{2}$

14. If $y=y(x), y\in\left[0,\dfrac{\pi}{2}\right)$ is the solution of the differential equation $\sec y\dfrac{dy}{dx}-\sin(x+y)-\sin(x-y)=0$, with $y(0)=0$, then $5y'\left(\dfrac{\pi}{2}\right)$ is equal to .... **[JEE Main 2021]**

15. Let $y=y(x)$ be the solution of the differential equation $(x-x^3)dy=(y+yx^2-3x^4)dx, x>2$. If $y(3)=3$, then $y(4)$ is equal to **[JEE Main 2021]**

(a) 4 (b) 12 (c) 8 (d) 16

16. Let $y=y(x)$ be the solution of the differential equation $dy=e^{\alpha x+y}dx; \alpha\in N$. If $y(\log_e 2)=\log_e 2$ and $y(0)=\log_e\left(\dfrac{1}{2}\right)$, then the value of α is equal to .... **[JEE Main 2021]**

17 Let $y=y(x)$ be the solution of the differential equation $xdy=(y+x^3\cos x)dx$ with $y(\pi)=0$, then $y\left(\dfrac{\pi}{2}\right)$ is equal to **[JEE Main 2021]**

(a) $\dfrac{\pi^2}{4}+\dfrac{\pi}{2}$ (b) $\dfrac{\pi^2}{2}+\dfrac{\pi}{4}$ (c) $\dfrac{\pi^2}{2}-\dfrac{\pi}{4}$ (d) $\dfrac{\pi^2}{4}-\dfrac{\pi}{2}$

18. Let a curve $y=f(x)$ pass through the point $[2,(\log_e 2)^2]$ and have slope $\dfrac{2y}{x\log_e x}$ for all positive real value of x. Then the value of $f(e)$ is equal to .... **[JEE Main 2021]**

19. Let $y=y(x)$ be the solution of the differential equation $\left((x+2)e^{\left(\frac{y+1}{x+2}\right)}+(y+1)\right)dx=(x+2)dy$, $y(1)=1$. If the domain of $y=y(x)$ is an open interval α, β, then $|\alpha+\beta|$ is equal to .... **[JEE Main 2021]**

20. Let $y=y(x)$ be the solution of the differential equation $x\tan\left(\dfrac{y}{x}\right)dy=\left(y\tan\left(\dfrac{y}{x}\right)-x\right)dx, -1\le x\le 1, y\left(\dfrac{1}{2}\right)=\dfrac{\pi}{6}$. Then, the area of the region bounded by the curves $x=0$, $x=\dfrac{1}{\sqrt{2}}$ and $y=y(x)$ in the upper half plane is **[JEE Main 2021]**

(a) $\dfrac{1}{8}(\pi-1)$ (b) $\dfrac{1}{12}(\pi-3)$
(c) $\dfrac{1}{4}(\pi-2)$ (d) $\dfrac{1}{6}(\pi-1)$

21. Let $y=y(x)$ be the solution of the differential equation $e^x\sqrt{1-y^2}dx+\left(\dfrac{y}{x}\right)dy=0, y(1)=-1$. Then, the value of $[y(3)]^2$ is equal to **[JEE Main 2021]**

(a) $1-4e^3$ (b) $1-4e^6$
(c) $1+4e^3$ (d) $1+4e^6$

22. Let a curve $y=y(x)$ be given by the solution of the differential equation $\cos\left(\frac{1}{2}\cos^{-1}(e^{-x})\right)dx=\sqrt{e^{2x}-1}dy$

If it intersects Y-axis at $y=-1$ and the intersection point of the curve with X-axis is $(\alpha,0)$, then e^{α} is equal to **[JEE Main 2021]**

23. Let $y=y(x)$ be the solution of the differential equation $x dy - y dx=\sqrt{(x^2-y^2)}\,dx$, $x\geq 1$, with $y(1)=0$. If the area bounded by the line $x=1, x=e^{\pi}$, $y=0$ and $y=y(x)$ is $\alpha e^{2\pi}+\beta$, then the value of $10(\alpha+\beta)$ is equal to .... **[JEE Main 2021]**

24. Which of the following is true for $y(x)$, that satisfies the differential equation $\frac{dy}{dx}=xy-1+x-y$; $y(0)=0$ **[JEE Main 2021]**

(a) $y(1)=e^{-\frac{1}{2}}-1$ (b) $y(1)=e^{\frac{1}{2}}-e^{-\frac{1}{2}}$

(c) $y(1)=1$ (d) $y(1)=e^{\frac{1}{2}}-1$

25. Let the curve $y=y(x)$ be the solution of the differential equation $\frac{dy}{dx}=2(x+1)$. If the numerical value of area bounded by the curve $y=y(x)$ and X-axis is $\frac{4\sqrt{8}}{3}$, then the value of $y(1)$ is equal to......... . **[JEE Main 2021]**

26. Let C_1 be the curve obtained by the solution of differential equation $2xy\frac{dy}{dx}=y^2-x^2$, $x>0$. Let the curve C_2 be the solution of $\frac{2xy}{x^2-y^2}=\frac{dy}{dx}$. If both the curves pass through (1, 1), then the area enclosed by the curves C_1 and C_2 is equal to **[JEE Main 2021]**

(a) $\pi-1$ (b) $\frac{\pi}{2}-1$ (c) $\pi+1$ (d) $\frac{\pi}{4}+1$

27. Let $f(x)=\int_0^x e^t f(t)dt+e^x$ be a differentiable function for all $x\in R$. Then, $f(x)$ equals **[JEE Main 2021]**

(a) $2e^{(e^x-1)}-1$ (b) $e^{e^x}-1$

(c) $2e^{e^x}-1$ (d) $e^{(e^x-1)}$

28. The rate of growth of bacteria in a culture is proportional to the number of bacteria present and the bacteria count is 1000 at initial time $t=0$. The number of bacteria is increased by 20% in 2 h. If the population of bacteria is 2000 after $\frac{k}{\log_e(6/5)}$ h, then $\left(\frac{k}{\log_e 2}\right)^2$ is equal to **[JEE Main 2021]**

(a) 4 (b) 8 (c) 2 (d) 16

29. The population $P=P(t)$ at time t of a certain species follows the differential equation $\frac{dP}{dt}=0.5P-450$. If $P(0)=850$, then the time at which population becomes zero is **[JEE Main 2021]**

(a) $\log_e 9$ (b) $\frac{1}{2}\log_e 18$

(c) $\log_e 18$ (d) $2\log_e 18$

30. If $y=y(x)$ is the solution curve of the differential equation $x^2dy+\left(y-\frac{1}{x}\right)dx=0$; $x>0$ and $y(1)=1$, then $y\left(\frac{1}{2}\right)$ is equal to **[JEE Main 2021]**

(a) $\frac{3}{2}-\frac{1}{\sqrt{e}}$ (b) $3+\frac{1}{\sqrt{e}}$

(c) $3+e$ (d) $3-e$

31. Let us consider a curve, $y=f(x)$ passing through the point $(-2, 2)$ and the slope of the tangent to the curve at any point $(x, f(x))$ is given by $f(x)+xf'(x)=x^2$ Then **[JEE Main 2021]**

(a) $x^2+2xf(x)-12=0$ (b) $x^3+2xf(x)+12=0$

(c) $x^3-3xf(x)-4=0$ (d) $x^2+2xf(x)+4=0$

32. If the solution curve of the differential equation $(2x-10y^3)dy+ydx=0$, passes through the points $(0,1)$ and $(2,\beta)$, then β is a root of the equation **[JEE Main 2021]**

(a) $y^5-2y-2=0$ (b) $2y^5-2y-1=0$

(c) $2y^5-y^2-2=0$ (d) $y^5-y^2-1=0$

33. Let $y=y(x)$ be a solution curve of the differential equation $(y+1)\tan^2 x\,dx+\tan x, dy+y\,dx=0$, $x\in\left(0,\frac{\pi}{2}\right)$. If $\lim_{x\to 0^+} xy(x)=1$, then the value of $y\left(\frac{\pi}{4}\right)$ is **[JEE Main 2021]**

(a) $-\frac{\pi}{4}$ (b) $\frac{\pi}{4}-1$

(c) $\frac{\pi}{4}+1$ (d) $\frac{\pi}{4}$

34. Let $y=y(x)$ be solution of the following differential equation

$e^y\frac{dy}{dx}-2e^y\sin x+\sin x\cos^2 x=0$, $y\left(\frac{\pi}{2}\right)=0$. **[JEE Main 2021]**

35. Let $y=y(x)$ be the solution of the differential equation $\operatorname{cosec}^2 x\,dy+2dx=(1+y\cos 2x)\operatorname{cosec}^2 x\,dx$, with $y\left(\frac{\pi}{4}\right)=0$. Then, the value of $(y(0)+1)^2$ is equal to **[JEE Main 2021]**

(a) $e^{1/2}$ (b) $e^{-1/2}$

(c) e^{-1} (d) e

36. Let $y=y(x)$ satisfies the equation $\frac{dy}{dx}-|A|=0$, for all $x>0$, where $A=\begin{bmatrix} y & \sin x & 1 \\ 0 & -1 & 1 \\ 2 & 0 & \frac{1}{x} \end{bmatrix}$. If $y(\pi)=\pi+2$, then the value of $y\left(\frac{\pi}{2}\right)$ is **[JEE Main 2021]**

(a) $\frac{\pi}{2}+\frac{4}{\pi}$ (b) $\frac{\pi}{2}-\frac{1}{\pi}$
(c) $\frac{3\pi}{2}-\frac{1}{\pi}$ (d) $\frac{\pi}{2}-\frac{4}{\pi}$

37. Let $y=y(x)$ be the solution of the differential equation $\frac{dy}{dx}=(y+1)[(y+1)e^{x^2/2}-x], 0<x<2.1$, with $y(2)=0$. Then the value of $\frac{dy}{dx}$ at $x=1$ is equal to **[JEE Main 2021]**

(a) $\frac{-e^{3/2}}{(e^2+1)^2}$ (b) $-\frac{2e^2}{(1+e^2)^2}$
(c) $\frac{e^{5/2}}{(1+e^2)^2}$ (d) $\frac{5e^{1/2}}{(e^2+1)^2}$

38. Let $y=y(x)$ be the solution of the differential equation $\cos x(3\sin x+\cos x+3)dy=$ $[1+y\sin x(3\sin x+\cos x+3)]dx$, $0\le x\le\frac{\pi}{2}$, $y(0)=0$. Then, $y\left(\frac{\pi}{3}\right)$ is equal to **[JEE Main 2021]**

(a) $2\log_e\left(\frac{2\sqrt{3}+9}{6}\right)$ (b) $2\log_e\left(\frac{2\sqrt{3}+10}{11}\right)$
(c) $2\log_e\left(\frac{\sqrt{3}+7}{2}\right)$ (d) $2\log_e\left(\frac{3\sqrt{3}-8}{4}\right)$

39. If the curve $y=y(x)$ is the solution of the differential equation $2(x^2+x^{5/4})dy-y(x+x^{1/4})dx=2x^{9/4}\,dx, x>0$ which passes through the point $\left(1, 1-\frac{4}{3}\log_e 2\right)$, then the value of $y(16)$ is equal to **[JEE Main 2021]**

(a) $4\left(\frac{31}{3}+\frac{8}{3}\log_e 3\right)$ (b) $\left(\frac{31}{3}+\frac{8}{3}\log_e 3\right)$
(c) $4\left(\frac{31}{3}-\frac{8}{3}\log_e 3\right)$ (d) $\left(\frac{31}{3}-\frac{8}{3}\log_e 3\right)$

40. If $y=y(x)$ is the solution of the differential equation, $\frac{dy}{dx}+2y\tan x=\sin x$, $y\left(\frac{\pi}{3}\right)=0$, then the maximum value of the function $y(x)$ over R is equal to **[JEE Main 2021]**

(a) 8 (b) $\frac{1}{2}$
(c) $-\frac{15}{4}$ (d) $\frac{1}{8}$

41. If $y=y(x)$ is the solution of the differential equation $\frac{dy}{dx}+(\tan x)y=\sin x, 0\le x\le\frac{\pi}{3}$, with $y(0)=0$, then $y\left(\frac{\pi}{4}\right)$ is equal to **[JEE Main 2021]**

(a) $\frac{1}{4}\log_e 2$ (b) $\left(\frac{1}{2\sqrt{2}}\right)\log_e 2$
(c) $\log_e 2$ (d) $\frac{1}{2}\log_e 2$

42. If $y=y(x)$ is the solution of the equation $e^{\sin y}\cos y\frac{dy}{dx}+e^{\sin y}\cos x=\cos x$, $y(0)=0$, then $1+y\left(\frac{\pi}{6}\right)+\frac{\sqrt{3}}{2}y\left(\frac{\pi}{3}\right)+\frac{1}{\sqrt{2}}y\left(\frac{\pi}{4}\right)$ is .... **[JEE Main 2021]**

43. If a curve passes through the origin and the slope of the tangent to it at any point (x, y) is $\frac{x^2-4x+y+8}{x-2}$, then this curve also passes through the point **[JEE Main 2021]**

(a) (5, 4) (b) (4, 5)
(c) (4, 4) (d) (5, 5)

44. If the curve $y=y(x)$ represented by the solution of the differential equation $(2xy^2-y)dx+xdy=0$, passes through the intersection of the lines $2x-3y=1$ and $3x+2y=8$, then $|y(1)|$ is equal to .... **[JEE Main 2021]**

45. If a curve $y=f(x)$ passes through the point (1, 2) and satisfies $x\frac{dy}{dx}+y=bx^4$, then for what value of b, $\int_1^2 f(x)dx=\frac{62}{5}$? **[JEE Main 2021]**

(a) 5 (b) 10
(c) $\frac{62}{5}$ (d) $\frac{31}{5}$

46. For any real numbers α and β, let $y_{\alpha,\beta}(x), x\in R$, be the solution of the differential equation $\frac{dy}{dx}+\alpha y=xe^{\beta x}, y(1)=1$.

Let $S=\{y_{\alpha,\beta}(x):\alpha,\beta\in R\}$. Then, which of the following functions belong(s) to the set S? **[JEE Advanced 2021]**

(a) $f(x)=\frac{x^2}{2}e^{-x}+\left(e-\frac{1}{2}\right)e^{-x}$
(b) $f(x)=-\frac{x^2}{2}e^{-x}+\left(e+\frac{1}{2}\right)e^{-x}$
(c) $f(x)=\frac{e^x}{2}\left(x-\frac{1}{2}\right)+\left(e-\frac{e^2}{4}\right)e^{-x}$
(d) $f(x)=\frac{e^x}{2}\left(\frac{1}{2}-x\right)+\left(e+\frac{e^2}{4}\right)e^{-x}$

47. If $y=\left(\frac{2}{\pi}x-1\right)\text{cosec } x$ is the solution of the differential equation, $\frac{dy}{dx}+p(x)y=\frac{2}{\pi}\text{cosec } x, 0<x<\frac{\pi}{2}$, then the function $p(x)$ is equal to **[JEE Main 2020]**

(a) $\cot x$ (b) $\text{cosec } x$
(c) $\sec x$ (d) $\tan x$

48. The differential equation of the family of curves, $x^2=4b(y+b), b\in R$, is **[JEE Main 2020]**

(a) $xy''=y'$ (b) $x(y')^2=x+2yy'$
(c) $x(y')^2=x-2yy'$ (d) $x(y')^2=2yy'-x$

49. Let $y=y(x)$ be the solution of the differential equation, $\frac{2+\sin x}{y+1}\cdot\frac{dy}{dx}=-\cos x, y>0, y(0)=1$.
If $y(\pi)=a$ and $\frac{dy}{dx}$ at $x=\pi$ is b, then the ordered pair (a,b) is equal to **[JEE Main 2020]**

(a) (1, 1) (b) $\left(2,\frac{3}{2}\right)$
(c) (1, −1) (d) (2, 1)

50. If a curve $y=f(x)$, passing through the point (1, 2), is the solution of the differential equation, $2x^2dy=(2xy+y^2)dx$, then $f\left(\frac{1}{2}\right)$ is equal to **[JEE Main 2020]**

(a) $\frac{1}{1+\log_e 2}$ (b) $\frac{1}{1-\log_e 2}$
(c) $1+\log_e 2$ (d) $\frac{-1}{1+\log_e 2}$

51. The solution curve of the differential equation, $(1+e^{-x})(1+y^2)\frac{dy}{dx}=y^2$, which passes through the point (0, 1) is **[JEE Main 2020]**

(a) $y^2+1=y\left(\log_e\left(\frac{1+e^{-x}}{2}\right)+2\right)$

(b) $y^2+1=y\left(\log_e\left(\frac{1+e^{x}}{2}\right)+2\right)$

(c) $y^2=1+y\log_e\left(\frac{1+e^{x}}{2}\right)$

(d) $y^2=1+y\log_e\left(\frac{1+e^{-x}}{2}\right)$

52. If $x^3dy+xy\,dx=x^2dy+2y\,dx$; $y(2)=e$ and $x>1$, then $y(4)$ is equal to **[JEE Main 2020]**

(a) $\frac{\sqrt{e}}{2}$ (b) $\frac{3}{2}+\sqrt{e}$
(c) $\frac{3}{2}\sqrt{e}$ (d) $\frac{1}{2}+\sqrt{e}$

53. The solution of the differential equation $\frac{dy}{dx}-\frac{y+3x}{\log_e(y+3x)}+3=0$ is (where C is a constant of integration) **[JEE Main 2020]**

(a) $x-\log_e(y+3x)=C$ (b) $y+3x-\frac{1}{2}(\log_e x)^2=C$
(c) $x-2\log_e(y+3x)=C$ (d) $x-\frac{1}{2}(\log_e(y+3x))^2=C$

54. If $y=y(x)$ is the solution of the differential equation $\frac{5+e^x}{2+y}\cdot\frac{dy}{dx}+e^x=0$ satisfying $y(0)=1$, then a value of $y(\log_e 13)$ is **[JEE Main 2020]**

(a) 0 (b) −1
(c) 1 (d) 2

55. The general solution of the differential equation $\sqrt{1+x^2+y^2+x^2y^2}+xy\frac{dy}{dx}=0$ is (where C is a constant of integration) **[JEE Main 2020]**

(a) $\sqrt{1+y^2}+\sqrt{1+x^2}=\frac{1}{2}\log_e\left(\frac{\sqrt{1+x^2}+1}{\sqrt{1+x^2}-1}\right)+C$

(b) $\sqrt{1+y^2}-\sqrt{1+x^2}=\frac{1}{2}\log_e\left(\frac{\sqrt{1+x^2}+1}{\sqrt{1+x^2}-1}\right)+C$

(c) $\sqrt{1+y^2}+\sqrt{1+x^2}=\frac{1}{2}\log_e\left(\frac{\sqrt{1+x^2}-1}{\sqrt{1+x^2}+1}\right)+C$

(d) $\sqrt{1+y^2}-\sqrt{1+x^2}=\frac{1}{2}\log_e\left(\frac{\sqrt{1+x^2}-1}{\sqrt{1+x^2}+1}\right)+C$

56. If $y=y(x)$ is the solution of the differential eq., $e^y\left(\frac{dy}{dx}-1\right)=e^x$ such that $y(0)=0$, then $y(1)$ is equal to **[JEE Main 2020]**

(a) $2+\log_e 2$ (b) $2e$
(c) $1+\log_e 2$ (d) $\log_e 2$

57. Let $y=y(x)$ be a solution of the differential equation, $\sqrt{1-x^2}\frac{dy}{dx}+\sqrt{1-y^2}=0, |x|<1$. If $y\left(\frac{1}{2}\right)=\frac{\sqrt{3}}{2}$, then $y\left(\frac{-1}{\sqrt{2}}\right)$ is equal to **[JEE Main 2020]**

(a) $\frac{\sqrt{3}}{2}$ (b) $-\frac{\sqrt{3}}{2}$
(c) $-\frac{1}{\sqrt{2}}$ (d) $\frac{1}{\sqrt{2}}$

58. If $\frac{dy}{dx}=\frac{xy}{x^2+y^2}$; $y(1)=1$; then a value of x satisfying $y(x)=e$ is **[JEE Main 2020]**

(a) $\frac{1}{2}\sqrt{3}e$ (b) $\sqrt{3}e$
(c) $\sqrt{2}\,e$ (d) $\frac{e}{\sqrt{2}}$

59. Let $y = y(x)$ be the solution of the differential equation, $xy' - y = x^2(x\cos x + \sin x), x > 0$. If $y(\pi) = \pi$, then $y''\left(\frac{\pi}{2}\right) + y\left(\frac{\pi}{2}\right)$ is equal to **[JEE Main 2020]**

(a) $2 + \frac{\pi}{2} + \frac{\pi^2}{4}$ (b) $1 + \frac{\pi}{2}$

(c) $1 + \frac{\pi}{2} + \frac{\pi^2}{4}$ (d) $2 + \frac{\pi}{2}$

60. Let $y = y(x)$ be the solution of the differential equation $\cos x \frac{dy}{dx} + 2y\sin x = \sin 2x, x \in \left(0, \frac{\pi}{2}\right)$. If $y\left(\frac{\pi}{3}\right) = 0$, then $y\left(\frac{\pi}{4}\right)$ is equal to **[JEE Main 2020]**

(a) $2 - \sqrt{2}$ (b) $2 + \sqrt{2}$ (c) $\sqrt{2} - 2$ (d) $\frac{1}{\sqrt{2}} - 1$

61. Let $y = y(x)$ be the solution curve of the differential equation, $(y^2 - x)\frac{dy}{dx} = 1$, satisfying $y(0) = 1$. This curve intersects the x-axis at a point whose abscissa is **[JEE Main 2020]**

(a) 2 (b) $2 - e$

(c) $-e$ (d) $2 + e$

62. If for $x \geq 0$, $y = y(x)$ is the solution of the differential equation, $(x+1)dy = ((x+1)^2 + y - 3)dx$, $y(2) = 0$, then $y(3)$ is equal to...... . **[JEE Main 2020]**

63. Let b be a nonzero real number. Suppose $f : \mathbf{R} \to \mathbf{R}$ is a differentiable function such that $f(0) = 1$. If the derivative f' of f satisfies the equation

$$f'(x) = \frac{f(x)}{b^2 + x^2}$$

for all $x \in R$, then which of the following statements is/are TRUE? **[JEE Advanced 2020]**

(a) If $b > 0$, then f is an increasing function
(b) If $b < 0$, then f is a decreasing function
(c) $f(x)f(-x) = 1$ for all $x \in \mathrm{R}$
(d) $f(x) - f(-x) = 0$ for all $x \in \mathrm{R}$

64. Given that the slope of the tangent to a curve $y = y(x)$ at any point (x, y) is $\frac{2y}{x^2}$. If the curve passes through the centre of the circle $x^2 + y^2 - 2x - 2y = 0$, then its equation is **[JEE Main 2019]**

(a) $x^2 \log_e |y| = -2(x-1)$ (b) $x\log_e |y| = x - 1$

(c) $x\log_e |y| = 2(x-1)$ (d) $x\log_e |y| = -2(x-1)$

65. Let f be a differentiable function such that $f(1) = 2$ and $f'(x) = f(x)$ for all $x \in R$. If $h(x) = f(f(x))$, then $h'(1)$ is equal to **[JEE Main 2019]**

(a) $4e^2$ (b) $4e$ (c) $2e$ (d) $2e^2$

66. Let $f : [0, 1] \to R$ be such that $f(xy) = f(x).f(y)$, for all $x, y \in [0, 1]$ and $f(0) \neq 0$. If $y = y(x)$ satisfies the differential equation, $\frac{dy}{dx} = f(x)$ with $y(0) = 1$, then $y\left(\frac{1}{4}\right) + y\left(\frac{3}{4}\right)$ is equal to **[JEE Main 2019]**

(a) 5 (b) 3
(c) 2 (d) 4

67. The curve amongst the family of curves represented by the differential equation, $(x^2 - y^2)dx + 2xydy = 0$, which passes through (1, 1), is **[JEE Main 2019]**

(a) a circle with centre on the **Y**-axis
(b) a circle with centre on the **X**-axis
(c) an ellipse with major axis along the **Y**-axis
(d) a hyperbola with transverse axis along the **X**-axis.

68. The solution of the differential equation, $\frac{dy}{dx} = (x-y)^2$, when $y(1) = 1$, is **[JEE Main 2019]**

(a) $\log_e \left|\frac{2-y}{2-x}\right| = 2(y-1)$

(b) $-\log_e \left|\frac{1+x-y}{1-x+y}\right| = x + y - 2$

(c) $\log_e \left|\frac{2-x}{2-y}\right| = x - y$

(d) $-\log_e \left|\frac{1-x+y}{1+x-y}\right| = 2(x-1)$

69. The solution of the differential equation $x\frac{dy}{dx} + 2y = x^2 (x \neq 0)$ with $y(1) = 1$, is **[JEE Main 2019]**

(a) $y = \frac{x^2}{4} + \frac{3}{4x^2}$ (b) $y = \frac{x^3}{5} + \frac{1}{5x^2}$

(c) $y = \frac{3}{4}x^2 + \frac{1}{4x^2}$ (d) $y = \frac{4}{5}x^3 + \frac{1}{5x^2}$

70. If $y = y(x)$ is the solution of the differential equation $\frac{dy}{dx} = (\tan x - y)\sec^2 x$, $x \in \left(-\frac{\pi}{2}, \frac{\pi}{2}\right)$, such that $y(0) = 0$, then $y\left(-\frac{\pi}{4}\right)$ is equal to **[JEE Main 2019]**

(a) $\frac{1}{e} - 2$ (b) $\frac{1}{2} - e$

(c) $2 + \frac{1}{e}$ (d) $e - 2$

71. Let $y = y(x)$ be the solution of the differential equation, $\frac{dy}{dx} + y\tan x = 2x + x^2 \tan x$, $x \in \left(-\frac{\pi}{2}, \frac{\pi}{2}\right)$, such that $y(0) = 1$. Then **[JEE Main 2019]**

(a) $y'\left(\frac{\pi}{4}\right) - y'\left(-\frac{\pi}{4}\right) = \pi - \sqrt{2}$

(b) $y'\left(\frac{\pi}{4}\right) + y'\left(-\frac{\pi}{4}\right) = -\sqrt{2}$

(c) $y\left(\frac{\pi}{4}\right)+y\left(-\frac{\pi}{4}\right)=\frac{\pi^2}{2}+2$

(d) $y\left(\frac{\pi}{4}\right)-y\left(-\frac{\pi}{4}\right)=\sqrt{2}$

72. If $\cos x\frac{dy}{dx}-y\sin x=6x,\left(0<x<\frac{\pi}{2}\right)$ and $y\left(\frac{\pi}{3}\right)=0$, then $y\left(\frac{\pi}{6}\right)$ is equal to **[JEE Main 2019]**

(a) $\frac{\pi^2}{2\sqrt{3}}$ (b) $-\frac{\pi^2}{2\sqrt{3}}$

(c) $-\frac{\pi^2}{4\sqrt{3}}$ (d) $-\frac{\pi^2}{2}$

73. Let f be a differentiable function such that $f'(x)=7-\frac{3}{4}\frac{f(x)}{x},(x>0)$ and $f(1)\neq 4$. Then, $\lim_{x\to 0^+} xf\left(\frac{1}{x}\right)$ **[JEE Main 2019]**

(a) does not exist (b) exists and equals $\frac{4}{7}$

(c) exists and equals 0 (d) exists and equals 4

74. Let $y=y(x)$ be the solution of the differential equation, $(x^2+1)^2\frac{dy}{dx}+2x(x^2+1)y=1$ such that $y(0)=0$. If $\sqrt{a}\,y(1)=\frac{\pi}{32}$, then the value of '$a$' is **[JEE Main 2019]**

(a) $\frac{1}{4}$ (b) $\frac{1}{2}$

(c) 1 (d) $\frac{1}{16}$

75. Consider the differential equation, $y^2dx+\left(x-\frac{1}{y}\right)dy=0$. If value of y is 1 when $x=1$, then the value of x for which $y=2$, is **[JEE Main 2019]**

(a) $\frac{5}{2}+\frac{1}{\sqrt{e}}$ (b) $\frac{3}{2}-\frac{1}{\sqrt{e}}$

(c) $\frac{1}{2}+\frac{1}{\sqrt{e}}$ (d) $\frac{3}{2}-\sqrt{e}$

76. If $y=y(x)$ is the solution of the differential equation, $x\frac{dy}{dx}+2y=x^2$ satisfying $y(1)=1$, then $y\left(\frac{1}{2}\right)$ is equal to **[JEE Main 2019]**

(a) $\frac{13}{16}$ (b) $\frac{1}{4}$

(c) $\frac{49}{16}$ (d) $\frac{7}{64}$

77. If $\frac{dy}{dx}+\frac{3}{\cos^2 x}y=\frac{1}{\cos^2 x},x\in\left(\frac{-\pi}{3},\frac{\pi}{3}\right)$ and $y\left(\frac{\pi}{4}\right)=\frac{4}{3}$, then $y\left(-\frac{\pi}{4}\right)$ equals **[JEE Main 2019]**

(a) $\frac{1}{3}+e^6$ (b) $-\frac{4}{3}$

(c) $\frac{1}{3}+e^3$ (d) $\frac{1}{3}$

78. If $y(x)$ is the solution of the differential equation $\frac{dy}{dx}+\left(\frac{2x+1}{x}\right)y=e^{-2x}$, $x>0$, where $y(1)=\frac{1}{2}e^{-2}$, then **[JEE Main 2019]**

(a) $y(x)$ is decreasing in $\left(\frac{1}{2},1\right)$ (b) $y(x)$ is decreasing in (0, 1)

(c) $y(\log_e 2)=\log_e 4$ (d) $y(\log_e 2)=\frac{\log_e 2}{4}$

79. If a curve passes through the point $(1,-2)$ and has slope of the tangent at any point (x,y) on it as $\frac{x^2-2y}{x}$, then the curve also passes through the point **[JEE Main 2019]**

(a) $(\sqrt{3},0)$ (b) $(-1,2)$

(c) $(-\sqrt{2},1)$ (d) $(3,0)$

80. Let $y=y(x)$ be the solution of the differential equation, $x\frac{dy}{dx}+y=x\log_e x,(x>1)$. If $2y(2)=\log_e 4-1$, then $y(e)$ is equal to **[JEE Main 2019]**

(a) $-\frac{e}{2}$ (b) $-\frac{e^2}{2}$

(c) $\frac{e}{4}$ (d) $\frac{e^2}{4}$

81. Let Γ denote a curve $y=y(x)$ which is in the first quadrant and let the point (1, 0) lie on it. Let the tangent to Γ at a point P intersect the y-axis at Y_P. If PY_P has length 1 for each point P on Γ, then which of the following options is/are correct? **[JEE Advanced 2019]**

(a) $xy'+\sqrt{1-x^2}=0$

(b) $xy'-\sqrt{1-x^2}=0$

(c) $y=\log_e\left(\frac{1+\sqrt{1-x^2}}{x}\right)-\sqrt{1-x^2}$

(d) $y=-\log_e\left(\frac{1+\sqrt{1-x^2}}{x}\right)+\sqrt{1-x^2}$

82. Let $y=y(x)$ be the solution of the differential equation $\sin x\frac{dy}{dx}+y\cos x=4x$, $x\in(0,\pi)$. If $y\left(\frac{\pi}{2}\right)=0$, then $y\left(\frac{\pi}{6}\right)$ is equal to **[JEE Main 2018]**

(a) $\frac{4}{9\sqrt{3}}\pi^2$ (b) $\frac{-8}{9\sqrt{3}}\pi^2$

(c) $-\frac{8}{9}\pi^2$ (d) $-\frac{4}{9}\pi^2$

83. Let $f:[0,\infty)\to R$ be a continuous function such that $f(x)=1-2x+\int_0^x e^{x-t}f(t)\,dt$ for all $x\in[0,\infty)$. Then, which of the following statement(s) is (are) TRUE? **[JEE Advanced 2018]**

(a) The curve $y=f(x)$ passes through the point (1, 2)

(b) The curve $y=f(x)$ passes through the point (2, – 1)

(c) The area of the region $\{(x, y)\in[0, 1]\times R : f(x)\le y\le\sqrt{1-x^2}\}$ is $\dfrac{\pi-2}{4}$

(d) The area of the region $\{(x, y)\in[0, 1]\times R : f(x)\le y\le\sqrt{1-x^2}\}$ is $\dfrac{\pi-1}{4}$

84. Let $f:R\to R$ be a differentiable function with $f(0)=0$. If $y=f(x)$ satisfies the differential equation $\dfrac{dy}{dx}=(2+5y)(5y-2)$, then the value of $\lim_{x\to-\infty} f(x)$ is .... **[JEE Advanced 2018]**

Answers

1. (d)	**2.** (c)	**3.** (2)	**4.** (d)	**5.** (b)	**6.** (a)	**7.** (b)	**8.** (a)	**9.** (c)	**10.** (b)
11. (c)	**12.** (d)	**13.** (a)	**14.** (2)	**15.** (b)	**16.** (2)	**17.** (a)	**18.** (1)	**19.** (4)	**20.** (a)
21. (b)	**22.** (2)	**23.** (4)	**24.** (a)	**25.** (2)	**26.** (b)	**27.** (a)	**28.** (a)	**29.** (d)	**30.** (d)
31. (c)	**32.** (d)	**33.** (d)	**34.** (4)	**35.** (c)	**36.** (a)	**37.** (a)	**38.** (b)	**39.** (c)	**40.** (d)
41. (b)	**42.** (1)	**43.** (d)	**44.** (1)	**45.** (b)	**46.** (a,c)	**47.** (a)	**48.** (b)	**49.** (a)	**50.** (a)
51. (c)	**52.** (c)	**53.** (d)	**54.** (b)	**55.** (a)	**56.** (c)	**57.** (d)	**58.** (b)	**59.** (d)	**60.** (c)
61. (b)	**62.** (3)	**63.** (a,c)	**64.** (c)	**65.** (b)	**66.** (b)	**67.** (b)	**68.** (d)	**69.** (a)	**70.** (d)
71. (a)	**72.** (b)	**73.** (d)	**74.** (d)	**75.** (b)	**76.** (c)	**77.** (a)	**78.** (a)	**79.** (a)	**80.** (c)
81. (a,c)	**82.** (c)	**83.** (b,c)	**84.** (0.4)						

For Solutions
Scan the QR Code